TREES AND SHRUBS
HARDY IN THE BRITISH ISLES

TREES AND SHRUBS HARDY IN THE BRITISH ISLES

BY W. J. BEAN, C.V.O., I.S.O., V.M.H.

FORMERLY CURATOR, ROYAL BOTANIC GARDENS, KEW
VEITCH MEMORIAL MEDALLIST, (1922 AND 1934)

VOL. II

LONDON
JOHN MURRAY, ALBEMARLE STREET, W.

First Edition (2 vols) . . . 1914
Third Volume (*First Edition*) . . 1933
Seventh Edition
Volume I 1950
Volumes II and III . . . 1951

MADE AND PRINTED IN GREAT BRITAIN BY
OLIVER AND BOYD LTD. AND PUBLISHED BY
JOHN MURRAY (PUBLISHERS) LTD.

CONTENTS

VOLUME II

PLATES

The names of the trees and shrubs illustrated in their place in the text are printed in SMALL CAPITALS in the INDEXES

VOLUME II

Following page 636

PART II (*continued*)

DESCRIPTIVE LIST OF GENERA AND SPECIES

FABIANA. SOLANACEÆ

A genus of some twenty-five species of heath-like shrubs all natives of South America, especially of Chile. It was named after a Spanish archbishop, F. Fabiano, who studied botany. The parts of the flower are in fives.

F. IMBRICATA, *Ruiz and Pavon.* SOLANACEÆ

An evergreen shrub of heath-like appearance, ultimately reaching 6 to 8 ft. in diameter and in height; erect in habit when young, ultimately spreading. Branches downy, long, and tapered, densely furnished with short, slender twigs, from $\frac{1}{2}$ to 2 ins. long. These twigs are themselves completely covered with tiny, pointed, three-angled leaves, $\frac{1}{12}$ in. long, and, in June, are each terminated by a solitary pure white flower. Corolla $\frac{5}{8}$ to $\frac{3}{4}$ in. long, tubular, but narrowing towards the base, with the rounded shallow lobes at the apex reflexed; calyx bell-shaped, $\frac{1}{12}$ in. long. Fruit a dry capsule $\frac{1}{4}$ in. long splitting downwards into two halves from the top to the calyx persisting at the base.

Native of Chile; introduced in 1838. This beautiful shrub is unfortunately rather tender, and at Kew, although it occasionally survives the winter, has never been a success fully in the open. In milder and more upland localities it is a shrub of great beauty, flowering freely and transforming each branch into a slender raceme of blossom. It likes a light soil, and can be increased easily by late summer cuttings in gentle heat.

F. VIOLACEA, *Hort*

(F. imbricata Comber's variety)

The first and only mention of this name that I can find is in *The Floricultural Cabinet* for 1854, p. 211, where occurs the following note:—

> "As hardy as the pretty, hardy F. imbricata, which has tube-shaped heath-like white flowers, very neat and pretty. The new plant is like the old one excepting the flowers being of a *violet* colour; very handsome."

I assume that the shrub there referred to is the same as that introduced by H. F. Comber during his Andean expedition, 1925-7, which is now growing in a good many gardens and which was shown at Westminster so finely in blossom by Lord Swaythling, from Townhill Park, Southampton, at the Amateurs' Show, 28th June 1932, when it was awarded a First-Class Certificate. It has been generally regarded as a form of F. imbricata, but in its present state is certainly very distinct in habit and leaf as well as in flower-colour. It may at once be distinguished by its much more spreading habit, due to the branches springing at almost right angles from older ones. Plants 2 or 3 ft. high will be quite as wide as they are tall. In the commonly cultivated type of F. imbricata, on the other hand, the branches are attached at an angle of 45° or less, and the plant is erect and slender. The leaves of Comber's plant also are only half the length of those of the other and are more closely appressed.

With regard to colour of blossom, the shrub seems to be variable. On Lord Swaythling's plant the flowers were pale mauve; Comber in his field note describes them as being hare-bell blue. Mr Clarence Elliott, who found the shrub near Bulnes in S. Chile 10 to 12 ft. high, describes the flowers as a good blue-lilac. Judging by plants at Kew, this new-comer is hardier and freer-growing than the old F. imbricata.

FABIANA IMBRICATA (see p. 1)

FAGUS. BEECH. CUPULIFERÆ

The beeches of the southern hemisphere are now generally regarded as forming a genus by themselves, and are here treated as such (see NOTHOFAGUS). The true beeches are confined to the northern hemisphere, where they are found on all three continents. They form a very homogeneous group of usually large trees with smooth grey trunks; about seven species are usually recognised. Of these, F. orientalis from Asia Minor, the Caucasus, etc., and F. Sieboldii from Japan are very near F. sylvatica, both being distinguished by leaflike appendages at the base of the husk. F. orientalis is further distinguished by large, more or less obovate leaves.

They are deciduous, with large, flat, alternate, parallel-ribbed leaves. Flowers unisexual; the males crowded and numerous on slender-stalked, globose heads; each flower consisting of a four- to six-lobed calyx, surrounding a cluster of eight to twelve stamens. Female flowers two or three in a cluster; the fruit a triangular nut with sharp edges, two nuts being entirely or partially enclosed in a four-lobed, woody husk (involucre).

All the beeches are quite hardy and thrive in a loamy soil, especially if situated on a limestone foundation. They should be increased by seeds, but the varieties distinguished by coloured foliage or by peculiarities of growth have to be grafted in spring.

F. ENGLERIANA, *Seemen*. ENGLER'S BEECH

(F. sylvatica chinensis, *Franchet*)

A deciduous tree usually 20 to 50 (rarely 70) ft. high, nearly always in a wild state divided at the base into many stems; young shoots glabrous. Leaves ovate to oval, usually widest below the middle, rounded or broadly wedge-shaped at the base, pointed, the margins wavy; 2 to 4 ins. long, 1 to 2 ins. wide; rather glaucous when quite young, at first silky-hairy beneath, otherwise glabrous; veins in ten to fourteen pairs; stalk slender, ¼ to ½ in. long. Husk ½ to ⅝ in. long, covered with downy, often spoon-shaped bracts; the stalk slender, glabrous, 1½ to 2½ ins. long. Nut about as long as the husk.

Native of Central China; discovered by Henry, introduced by Wilson to the Arnold Arboretum in 1907 and thence to Kew in 1911 (No. 703). It is quite hardy and grows satisfactorily, if not very quickly, in this country. Its distinctive characters are the long slender stalk of the husk, combined with the glabrous leaves (except when young). F. japonica, its nearest ally, is well distinguished by the nuts being twice as long as the husk and consequently exposed. Wilson observes of F. Engleriana that, as seen in China, its many stems diverge somewhat and never attain to any great thickness.

F. GRANDIFOLIA, *Ehrhart*

(F. americana, *Sweet*; F. ferruginea, *Aiton*)

A deciduous tree, 70 to 80 ft. high, occasionally more, with a thin, smooth, grey bark; spreading by means of root suckers, so that one tree will form of itself a colony of stems; young shoots at first clothed with long hairs, which soon fall away. Leaves ovate or oval, 2 to 5 ins. long, ¾ to 2½ ins. wide, taper-pointed, usually wedge-shaped at the base, coarsely toothed, at first clothed with silky hairs, but soon dark green and quite glabrous above except along the midrib; paler below, and with tufts of hairs in the vein-axils and along the midrib; stalk ¼ in. or rather more long; veins usually eleven to fifteen pairs. Fruits about ¾ in. long; the three-angled nuts enclosed by a downy, prickly husk, the prickles much recurved.

Native of eastern N. America; introduced in 1766. The American beech, like so many other trees of its region, has never been much of a success in Britain. It is easily distinguished from F. sylvatica by the suckering habit, the narrower, more pointed, regularly toothed leaves, with more numerous veins.

F. JAPONICA, *Maximowicz*. JAPANESE BEECH

Little is known of this beech in this country, and so far as I am aware, it was not introduced in a living state until 1907, when it was sent to Kew by Prof. Sargent. In 1910, the Japanese authorities of the Shepherd's Bush Exhibition of that year brought over a few small trees. It is a deciduous tree up to 70 or 80 ft. high, often, it is said, a bush; the quite young shoots are furnished with silky hairs. Leaves oval to ovate, sometimes rather diamond-shaped, tapered at both ends, but more abruptly towards the base; 2 to 4½ ins. long, 1 to 1¾ ins. wide; wavy at the margin, rather glaucous beneath; although silky at first, the leaf becomes glabrous by autumn; stalk ½ to ⅝ in. long; veins nine to thirteen. Male flowers on a slender stalk 1½ to 2½ ins. long. Nuts triangular, ½ in. long, ¼ in. wide; the lobes of the husk little more than half as long as the nut, downy, and covered with short stiff spines; the stalk slender, 1 to 1½ ins. long. Its most distinctive characters appear to be the relative shortness of the husk to the nut, the long fruit-stalk, and the shallow undulations of the leaf-margin.

F. LONGIPETIOLATA, *Seemen*

(F. sylvatica longipes, *Oliver*; F. sinensis, *Oliver*)

A deciduous tree up to 80 ft. high, with pale grey bark and glabrous young shoots. Leaves ovate (sometimes narrowly so) broadly wedge-shaped, rarely rounded at the base, gradually tapered to a point, sharply but shallowly toothed or merely wavy at the margin; 2½ to 5½ ins. long, 1½ to 2¾ ins. wide; dark bright green above, rather glaucous and covered with fine down beneath; veins in nine to thirteen pairs; leaf-stalk ½ to 1⅛ ins. long. Husk up to 1 in. long, covered with slender, curled bristles; its stalk 1½ to 2 ins. long, downy near the husk only.

Native of Central and W. China; discovered by Henry; introduced in 1911. Wilson observes that, whilst at its best it is a stately tree which resembles F. Sieboldii in general appearance, it is usually rather small. Its leaves in size and shape resemble those of the American F. grandifolia, but the leaf-stalk is much longer. This length of leaf-stalk combined with the closely downy undersurface of the leaves, their ovate shape, and the long slender stalk of the husk make the species very distinct.

FAGUS LUCIDA, *Rehder and Wilson*, was discovered in Hupeh, China, by Henry about 1887 and twenty years later by Wilson; plants introduced by the latter in 1911 are in cultivation. He found it a tree from 20 to 30 ft. high, with a "broad, flattened or rounded crown." The leaves are very distinct. They are ovate, 2 to 4 ins. long, 1 to 2¼ ins. wide, glossy green on both surfaces, the veins running out from the undulated margins to form small but distinct teeth.

F. ORIENTALIS, *Lipsky*. ORIENTAL BEECH

(F. sylvatica macrophylla, *De Candolle*; F. Winkleriana, *Koidzumi*)

A deciduous tree sometimes 100 ft. or more high in a wild state; young shoots silky-hairy. Leaves obovate or rather rhomboidal in outline, usually broadest above the middle, mostly broadly wedge-shaped, sometimes rounded at the base, shortly pointed; margins wavy, not toothed; 2½ to 4½ ins. long, half as much wide; silky-hairy on the midrib and veins beneath; veins in seven to ten pairs; stalk ¼ to ½ in. long, silky-hairy. Husk ⅞ in. long, obovoid, downy and covered with bristles, some of which near the base are spoon-shaped; stalk up to 1¼ ins. long, downy.

Native of E. Europe and Asia Minor, where it takes the place of common beech, to which it is closely akin. The common beech has none of the spoon-shaped appendages seen on the husks of F. orientalis and its leaves are as a rule smaller and usually have small teeth on the margin. Dr Turrill of Kew, who has travelled extensively in Bulgaria, tells me that the two species meet in the south-eastern Rhodopes, near Daridere, F. sylvatica being abundant on the higher hills, F. orientalis in the lowlands; also that the trunk is of an even paler grey than that of F. sylvatica. F. orientalis was introduced to Kew from Leningrad in 1910 and is quite hardy.

F. SIEBOLDII, *Endlicher*. SIEBOLD'S BEECH

(F. sylvatica Sieboldii, *Maximowicz*)

A deciduous tree, 100 ft. high, very closely allied to F. sylvatica. Leaves ovate to rhomboidal, the base tapered, rounded or slightly heart-shaped, the apex pointed; 2 to 4 ins. long, 1 to 2¼ ins. wide; margins wavy, edged with fine hairs; silky hairy on the veins beneath; stalk ¼ to ⅜ in. long; veins in seven to ten pairs. Nut triangular, $\frac{5}{8}$ in. long; the husk hard and woody, downy, furnished with long bristles, those near the base enlarged into linear or spathulate appendages $\frac{1}{2}$ in. long; fruit-stalks stout, thick, and about $\frac{1}{2}$ in. long.

Native of Japan, where it forms considerable forests. The tree itself and its timber are similar in most respects to the British tree. Botanically, it differs chiefly in the leaflike appendages attached to the base of the husk; the latter also is more truncate, and less tapered at the base than in F. sylvatica.

F. SYLVATICA, *Linnæus*. COMMON BEECH

(Plates 1 and 2)

A deciduous tree up to 100 ft. high, occasionally almost 150 ft., with a smooth grey trunk, sometimes of enormous thickness—6 to 8 ft. through; young shoots at first silky hairy, soon becoming glabrous. Leaves oval, inclined to ovate, pointed, unequally rounded at the base, ordinarily 2 to $3\frac{1}{2}$ ins. long, $1\frac{1}{2}$ to $2\frac{1}{2}$ ins. wide, but as much as 5 ins. by 3 ins.; obscurely toothed or merely unevenly undulated at the margin; midrib and veins hairy, especially beneath; stalk downy, $\frac{1}{4}$ to $\frac{1}{2}$ in. long. Nut triangular, $\frac{5}{8}$ in. long, usually a pair enclosed in a hard, woody, pear-shaped, four-lobed husk, covered with bristles and $\frac{3}{4}$ to 1 in. long, solitary on an erect downy stalk about as long as itself. Veins of leaf in five to nine pairs.

Native of Europe, and indigenous to England. Few trees are more pleasing than a well-grown beech, either in the wide, spreading form it takes when growing in an isolated position, or when, in close association with others of its kind, and drawn up by them, it forms a tall, smooth, column-like trunk. The largest of the former kind in Britain is the famous beech at Newbattle Abbey, 100 ft. high, 130 ft. in diameter, the trunk 21 ft. in girth. Of the latter the finest was in Ashridge Park, Bucks, known as the "Queen Beech"—130 to 140 ft. high. The young foliage of the beech is one of the most beautiful objects in nature in May—a tender shimmering green of a shade not quite matched by any other tree. The beech has produced many varieties, some of which have first been noticed in gardens, others in a wild state. The following is a selection of the more important:—

Var. CONGLOMERATA.—A dwarf bush of rounded form, leaves small, contorted.

Var. CRISTATA, *Loddiges*.—Leaves very shortly stalked, coarsely triangular-toothed, apex decurved.

Var. CUPREA, *Loddiges*. Copper Beech.—This probably originated as a seedling from the purple beech (var. purpurea). Its leaves are paler than in that variety, and of a coppery red.

Var. FASTIGIATA. Dawyck Beech.—A tree of fastigiate habit first noticed in the grounds of the late Mr F. R. S. Balfour of Dawyck; it may be similar to one called PYRAMIDALIS by Petzold in 1864.

Var. GRANDIDENTATA.—Leaves coarsely toothed; branches slender.

Var. HETEROPHYLLA, *Loudon*. Fern-leaved Beech.—Of all the forms of beech marked by differences in shape of leaf, this is the handsomest. In this variety the leaf assumes various shapes; sometimes it is long and narrow (4 ins. long by $\frac{1}{4}$ in. wide), sometimes deeply and pinnately lobed, some of the lobes penetrating to the midrib; between these two, numerous intermediate shapes occur, often on the same branch. Unlike many of the varieties of beech with curious foliage, this makes a fine shapely tree, and it is a distinct ornament to any garden. There is a fine specimen in Mr Hamilton Buchanan's garden at Leny, near Callander, N.B., which is over 60 ft. high, and whose trunk is over 7 ft. in girth. Others are at Devonhurst House, Chiswick, and in the nursery at Knap Hill. The forms called asplenifolia, incisa, laciniata, and salicifolia belong here.

Var. MACROPHYLLA (latifolia).—Some of the beeches are remarkable for large leaves, and the one long known in gardens under both these names is a striking form; its leaves are usually 3 to 5 ins. long, 2 to 3½ ins. wide. In 1898, the King of Denmark's gardener sent to Kew a variety that had been called "Prince George of Crete." This is the biggest-leaved beech I have seen, some leaves being 7 ins. long, 5½ ins. wide.

Var. PENDULA. Weeping Beech.—There are several types of weeping beech. The one best known under the name pendula is not a high tree, but sends out its great arms in a horizontal or drooping direction; from these the smaller branches depend almost vertically, the whole making a tent-like mass. Var. MILTONENSIS is a weeping beech which originated at Milton Park, Northamptonshire; the trunk of this form is erect, the branches horizontal and pendulous. Var. BORNYENSIS has a somewhat similar habit, but the side branches are more pendulous. Var. PAGNYENSIS, found originally in the forest of Pagny (Meurthe-et-Moselle), forms a spreading head of drooping branches, the whole tree of umbrella-like shape. Var. REMILLYENSIS and var. TORTUOSA are of the same class.

Var. PURPUREA, *Aiton*. Purple Beech.—Leaves deep purple when mature; of a beautiful pale red in spring. This is by far the most popular of the varieties of beech. It is not of garden origin, but appears to have been observed growing naturally in at least three places, viz.:—in the Hanleiter Forest, near Sonderhausen, in Thuringia; in the Darney Forest in the Vosges; and in the village of Buchs, in the canton of Zurich, Switzerland. The last is the oldest recorded site of the purple beech, three trees there being mentioned in a work dated 1680. They were the survivors of a group originally of five, which, according to legend, had sprung up on the spot where five brothers had killed each other. Most of the trees in cultivation are considered to have sprung from the Hanleiter tree. The purple beech comes partially true from seed, and some deeper or brighter coloured forms have in this way been obtained, such as nigra, atropurpurea, purpurea major p. nova, "Swat Magret," etc. The majority of the seedlings, however, are either the ordinary green type, or but faintly coloured.

Var. PURPUREA PENDULA.—A weeping purple beech.

Var. QUERCIFOLIA. Oak-leaved Beech.—Leaves narrowly ovate; deeply, irregularly, sometimes doubly toothed. I have seen a shoot of var. heterophylla growing on a tree of this variety.

Var. ROTUNDIFOLIA.—Perhaps the daintiest of beech varieties; leaves round, with a slightly heart-shaped base; ½ to 1¼ ins. diameter, very closely set on the branches. It appears to have originated at Brookwood, Knap Hill, Woking, whence a specimen was sent to Kew by Major McNair in 1872. The habit is slender and erect.

Var. VARIEGATA.—There are several variegated beeches, the commonest being striped with white (argenteo-variegata). A yellow striped one is aureo-variegata. In var. TRICOLOR the leaves are purplish, edged and striped with rose and pinkish white; this is very pretty when the leaves are young.

Var. ZLATIA, *Späth*. Golden Beech.—Leaves yellow when young, but of a shade not deep enough to be termed "golden"; when mature they scarcely differ from those of ordinary beech.

The timber of beech makes an excellent fuel, but is not highly valued for constructive purposes, especially in the open air. For articles in domestic use and kept under cover it is useful, being hard and close in texture. The most important industry connected with beech timber is that of chair-making in the High Wycombe district of Buckinghamshire.

Much alarm has in recent years been felt in regard to the effects on British beechwoods of the "Beech Coccus" (Cryptococcus fagi). This insect surrounds itself with a white cottony substance, and sometimes infests trunks and limbs so badly as to resemble drifts of snow. As a result of its attacks the complete doom of the beech in this country has been foretold. These fears are much exaggerated; and an investigation made at Kew into the matter did not reveal the death of a single tree that could indubitably be traced to this insect. (See *Kew Bulletin*, 1911, p. 332.)

FALLUGIA PARADOXA, *Endlicher*. ROSACEÆ

(Bot. Mag., t. 6660)

A slender deciduous shrub, 4 to 8 ft. high, much branched below, more thinly above; branchlets white, covered with down. Leaves produced in clusters closely and alternately along the twigs, $\frac{1}{2}$ to $\frac{2}{3}$ in. long, $\frac{1}{3}$ in. wide, cut usually into three or five (occasionally seven) narrow-linear lobes, recurved at the edges and $\frac{1}{12}$ in. wide; dark green above, paler below, and covered all over with pale down. Flowers produced either singly or a few together on a raceme $1\frac{1}{4}$ to 4 ins. long, from the end of the shoot or from the leaf-axils near the end. Each flower is 1 to $1\frac{1}{4}$ ins. across, petals white; calyx $\frac{1}{4}$ in. diameter, downy, with five ovate, pointed lobes; and five small bracts alternating with them. The heads of fruits are very handsome, each carpel being terminated by a slender style 1 in. to $1\frac{1}{2}$ ins. long, clothed with silky hairs, the whole forming a dense feathery mass, $1\frac{1}{2}$ ins. across. Flowers in July.

Native of New Mexico, Utah, and Nevada; introduced in 1877. This interesting and beautiful shrub is very rare in cultivation, and likely to remain so. Coming from the dry, sun-baked hills of the south-western United States, it finds in the English climate conditions almost the opposite of its native surroundings. It would probably be best suited on a warm slope in the Isles of Scilly. Elsewhere it will thrive best in well-drained soil at the base of a sunny wall.

FATSHEDERA LIZEI, *Guillaumin*. ARALIACEÆ

(Bot. Mag., t. 9402)

An evergreen shrub of loose free growth, with stout young shoots that are $\frac{3}{8}$ in. or more in diameter, downy at first and thickly furnished with warts. Leaves from 4 to 10 ins. across, scarcely so much long, of leathery texture; dark glittering green, five-lobed in palmate fashion, the lobes reaching one-third or halfway to the base; stalk terete, about as long as the blade, often purplish. Flowers produced in October and November in a terminal panicle, 8 to 10 ins. long and 4 ins. wide, made up of numerous hemispherical umbels. Each umbel is 1 in. in diameter and carries from one dozen to three dozen flowers which, individually, are $\frac{1}{4}$ in. wide; petals five, ovate, pale green, finally much decurved; stamens five, white. The centre of the flower is occupied by a large green disk, in the centre of which the pistils are set. Flower-stalks thinly covered with loose branching down. Fruit not seen but probably black if ever developed.

This interesting plant is a hybrid raised in 1910 by Messrs Lizé Frères, nurserymen, of Nantes, by crossing Fatsia japonica Moseri with the pollen of Irish ivy (Hedera hibernica). Some doubt has been expressed as to the authenticity of this origin, but Mr Guillaumin states (*Revue Horticole*, 1924, p. 180) that " Messrs Lizé's plant, showing morphological and anatomical characters of both Hedera and Fatsia, also intermediate ones, appears to be truly a hybrid between the two genera. The constant sterility of the stamens supports this opinion." Its general appearance certainly suggests this parentage, as also does its mode of growth, for although Fatsia japonica is a very sturdy shrub, this hybrid has inherited enough of the scandent nature of the ivy to render the support of a stake necessary to keep it upright. It is a handsome evergreen, grows vigorously and, judging by its parentage, should prove useful for shady situations and for town gardens. It has been cultivated at Kew for some years and has never suffered from cold; both its parents are indeed very hardy. The flowers, however, come so late in the season that often they do not open. It is very easily increased by cuttings and quite possibly may become popular for furnishing very shady places where flowering shrubs will not succeed. Repeated pruning in its young state would probably give it a bushy shape.

FATSIA JAPONICA, *Decaisne and Planchon.* ARALIACEÆ

(Aralia japonica, *Thunberg*)

An evergreen shrub or small tree, oftenest a spreading bush from 6 to 15 ft. high. Stems very thick, not much branched, unarmed, marked with large scars left by fallen leaves. Leaves leathery, varying in size according to the size and vigour of the plant, ordinarily 12 to 16 ins. across; palmate, with a broad heart-shaped base and usually nine lobes, the lobes reaching more than half-way to the base, ovate, coarsely and bluntly toothed except towards the base, where the opening between the lobes is wide and rounded; stalk round, stout, smooth, often 1 ft. or more long. The upper surface is dark shining green, the lower one paler, both quite glabrous. Flowers milky white, produced in the autumn on large branching panicles of globose heads, each head 2 to 3 ins. wide; stalks white like the flowers. Fruits black, pea-shaped.

Native of Japan; introduced in 1838. This very handsome shrub, which bears about the largest leaves of any hardy evergreen, is well known as a plant grown in pots for house decoration. It is not so well known that it succeeds very well out-of-doors, and often makes a striking display in October, provided it is given a sheltered, semi-shaded spot. Plants near London, 8 ft. high, have been outside and unprotected for the last twenty years. It is well worth growing for its bold and striking foliage. Propagated by cuttings put singly in pots, and plunged in mild bottom heat any time after the wood is fairly firm. Var. VARIEGATA has large blotches of white towards the end of the lobes.

FEIJOA SELLOWIANA, *Berg*. MYRTACEÆ

(Bot. Mag., t. 7620; Orthostemon Sellowianus, *Berg*)

An evergreen shrub or small tree of bushy habit; young shoots, buds and undersurface of the leaves clothed with a whitish felt. Leaves opposite, oval or ovate, toothless, blunt at the apex, tapered or rounded at the base; 1 to 3 ins. long, ¾ to 1½ ins. wide; dark lustrous green and glabrous above except when quite young; whitish, felted and conspicuously veined beneath; stalk ¼ in., or less, long, felted. Flowers solitary, produced in July from the lowermost leaf-axils of the current year's shoots, usually two or four of them on each shoot; each flower is 1¼ to 1¾ ins. wide and borne on a felted stalk 1 to 1½ ins. long. Sepals four, roundish-oblong, ⅜ in. long, felted outside, reflexed. Petals four, broadly oval, concave, finally reflexed, red in the centre, whitish at the margin. Stamens very numerous, erect, ¾ to 1 in. long, rich crimson. Fruit an egg-shaped berry up to 2 ins. long, with the remains of the calyx at the top, said to have a pleasant, rich, aromatic flavour. Fruits were produced in this country during the hot dry year of 1921.

Native of S. Brazil and Uruguay; discovered in 1819 by a German collector named Sellow, after whom it was named. The generic name commemorates Don Feijo, a botanist of San Sebastian. This shrub is not hardy fully in the open air at Kew, but grows and flowers well on a south wall there. The flowers are beautiful and richly coloured, especially the brush of long, erect, crimson stamens which constitute the conspicuous feature of the blossom. It grows well in light loamy soil and should have full sunlight. It can be increased by cuttings placed in heat in July or August. Considering the length of time it has been known, this fine shrub has been rather surprisingly neglected in British gardens. It is 20 ft. high at Trewidden in Cornwall.

FENDLERA RUPICOLA, *A. Gray*. SAXIFRAGACEÆ

(Bot. Mag., t. 7924)

A deciduous shrub, 3 to 6 ft. high, of somewhat thin, straggling habit under cultivation, and with ribbed, downy young shoots. Leaves opposite, lanceolate on the sterile branches; ½ to 1¼ ins. long, ¼ to ½ in. wide; prominently three-nerved, rough with stiff, short bristles above, hairy beneath, almost without stalks. On the flowering twigs the leaves are much smaller, linear, clustered on short twigs. Flowers white or faintly rose-tinted, ¾ to 1¼ ins. across, usually solitary, sometimes in threes, produced during May and June on short twigs springing from the wood of the previous year; petals four, contracted at the base into a distinct claw, hairy outside; calyx downy, with four narrow, ovate lobes; seed-vessel conical, ½ in. long, with the calyx persisting at the base.

Native of the south-western United States; introduced to Europe about 1879. This shrub—one of the most beautiful of its own region—is too much of a sun-lover to be seen at its best in our climate. It comes from the sunburnt slopes of the mountainous regions of Texas, Arizona, etc., where it is a sturdy, rigid-branched shrub, and produces a great wealth of rosy-tinted flowers, which are said to give it the appearance of a peach-tree, although the four petals and opposite leaves, of course, proclaim a different affinity. I have seen it very fine in continental gardens. In Britain it needs the sunniest position that can be given it against a wall. Mr E. A. Bowles, of Waltham Cross, is very successful with it. Propagated by cuttings of rather soft wood in gentle heat.

FICUS CARICA, *Linnæus*. FIG. URTICACEÆ

A deciduous tree, forming in the south of Europe and in the East a short, rugged trunk, 2 to 3 ft. in diameter, and a low, spreading head of branches; in Britain it is mostly a shrub. Leaves alternate, three- or five-lobed, 4 to 8 ins. or even more in length and width; heart-shaped at the base, varying much in the depth of the lobes, which themselves are blunt or rounded at the end, and usually scalloped into broad rounded teeth; both surfaces, but especially the upper one, rough to the touch, with short stiff hairs; stalk 1 to 4 ins. long. Flowers produced on the inner surface of a roundish, pear-shaped receptacle, nearly closed at the top, which afterwards develops into the succulent sweet fruit we know as the fig. The leaves have a very characteristic odour.

Native of W. Asia, and the eastern Mediterranean region, cultivated in the south and west of Europe, even in Britain, from early times. The cultivation of the fig in this country for its fruits does not come within the province of this book. Except in the mild parts of the south and west, where its fruits ripen in the open air, it needs more or less the protection of glass, or at least of a south wall. In the open at Kew the fig gets to be a shrub 6 to 10 ft. high, according to the mildness or otherwise of successive winters. The severest frosts cut it to the ground, whence strong young shoots spring up the following summer. Only once or twice in twenty years has it borne palatable fruit. On the whole, unless wall protection can be given, the fig is not worth growing in ou average climate except for its interest and associations.

The plants cultivated in gardens are exclusively females, which have the power, like the cucumber, to develop fruit without being fertilised. The fertilisation of the wild fig, through the agency of two generations yearly of an insect (Blastophaga), is one of the most remarkable instances known of the interrelation of insect and plant life for their mutual benefit. The cultivated fig in the south of Europe is fertilised through the agency of the same insect, but the pollen is taken from a (functionally) male form of the fig known as the Caprifig. (See *Gardeners' Chronicle*, 14th Oct. 1911, p. 267.)

F. STIPULATA. *Thunberg*

(Bot. Mag., t. 6657; F. repens, *Hort.*)

An evergreen climber clinging to walls, etc., in the same way as ivy; juvenile shoots thin, wiry, bristly, sending out aerial roots from the joints. Leaves of the juvenile (better known) state alternate, closely set in two opposite rows; obliquely heart-shaped, pointed; $\frac{3}{4}$ to $1\frac{1}{4}$ ins. long, two-thirds as wide; dull green, usually glabrous; stalk very short. Leaves of the adult or fruit-bearing state remarkably different; they are more leathery, ovate, with a heart-shaped base, pointed; $1\frac{1}{2}$ to $3\frac{1}{2}$ ins. long, half as much wide; bright dark green above, paler and beautifully net-veined (especially as seen through a lens) beneath; stalk hairy, about $\frac{1}{2}$ in. long. Fruit of the ordinary fig shape, although more tapered at the end than in the common fig; $2\frac{1}{2}$ ins. long, $1\frac{1}{2}$ ins. wide at the terminal part, tapering thence to the stalk which is $\frac{1}{2}$ in. long; in colour it is at first green, then bright orange, ultimately tinged with reddish purple and decorative.

Native of China and Japan; introduced in 1771. This fig is well known in its juvenile state as a climber in conservatories and cool greenhouses, whose walls it will closely cover with its abundant leafage. The adult stage is reached as a rule only after the plant has grown 10 or 12 ft. high and got beyond its support. It then develops thick, non-clinging young shoots bearing the very different leaves described above. Although one may occasionally see plants growing into the open air through ventilators of greenhouses and surviving the winter, I did not realise how hardy it really is until the late Mr W. Robinson of Gravetye told me that he had seen it growing on the walls of Knapp Castle, near Horsham, covering up much of the front to 40 ft. high. It has been growing there for over thirty years. It also climbs on St Matthew's Church, Chelston, near Torquay.

Var. MINIMA. *Hort.*—A form which has very small leaves in the juvenile state.

FITZROYA PATAGONICA, *Hooker fil.* PATAGONIAN CYPRESS. CONIFERÆ

(Bot. Mag., t. 4616; F. cupressoides, *Johnston*)

A unisexual, rarely bisexual evergreen tree, from 50 to 80 ft. high in a wild state, forming in cultivation in this country a widely pyramidal small tree of dense habit, the terminal portions of the branches slender and pendulous. Leaves linear or slightly obovate, $\frac{1}{8}$ to $\frac{1}{4}$ in. long, arranged in pairs or in whorls of threes, often thickened and keeled beneath; sometimes rounded, sometimes tapered to a bluntish apex, spreading, dark green, with two bands of stomata on both surfaces. Cones globose, $\frac{1}{3}$ in. wide, with few scales.

Native of the mountains of W. Patagonia and S. Chile; discovered in 1834 by Capt. Fitzroy, commander of the "Beagle"; introduced for Messrs Veitch by W. Lobb in 1849. It is an interesting and elegant small tree or shrub, but is only at home in the mildest parts of our islands, such as Fota, near Cork, Pencarrow in Cornwall, in the west of Scotland, etc. There are two specimens at Kew, one 8 ft. and the other 14 ft. high, which came through the severe winter of 1946-47 but they are, of course, in very sheltered positions. In young plants the leaves are larger, flatter, and more spreading than in adult ones. Female trees bear cones freely, in even a small state, but they are usually infertile.

A second species, F. ARCHERI, *Bentham* (Diselma Archeri, *Hooker fil.*), is found in Tasmania, but it is more tender than the South American species.

FOKIENIA HODGINSII, *Henry and Thomas*. CONIFERÆ

(Cupressus Hodginsii, Dunn)

An evergreen tree ultimately 40 to 50 ft. high, with a trunk up to 3 ft. in girth, without down in all its parts. The ultimate branchlets are arranged in one plane to form tripinnate, frond-like sprays. The leaves are in fours but amalgamated and flattened (as in Libocedrus), with only the four points free; the two side ones are longest and have slender points and a white streak of stomata at the back; the back and front ones are shorter and more abruptly pointed. Each quartette of leaves is $\frac{1}{3}$ in. long on young trees, becoming shorter on older ones until, on flowering shoots, they become only $\frac{1}{10}$ in. long and quite blunt. Cones ripening the second year, globose, about 1 in. long, with twelve to sixteen scales which are wedge-shaped or club-shaped, with a small boss in the sunken centre of the top. Seeds (two to each scale) have two very unequal wings.

Native of the province of Fokien, China; discovered about 1904 by Capt. A. Hodgins. A new genus was made for this interesting conifer by Prof. A. Henry and Mr Thomas in the *Gardeners' Chronicle* for 4th February 1911. As is there pointed out, it is intermediate in its characters between the Chamæcyparis or flat-leaved section of Cupressus and Libocedrus. The cones resemble those of Cupressus in having table-shaped scales, but it resembles Libocedrus in the unequal wings of the seeds and in foliage. To Libocedrus macrolepis especially it is closely alike in foliage. It was introduced to cultivation by Admiral Clinton-Baker, who sent two plants to his brother's collection at Bayfordbury, Herts, in 1909. It is still very rare and only likely to be hardy in the milder counties.

FONTANESIA. OLEACEÆ

A genus named in honour of R. L. Desfontaines, a French savant born in 1750, in Brittany; died in Paris, 1833. It is composed of two deciduous shrubs, or as some authorities hold, but one, closely allied to the ashes, but with simple opposite leaves. Flowers numerous, small and greenish; petals four; stamens two. Fruit a thin, flat capsule whose two cells are surrounded by a wing. These shrubs have about the same value in gardens as the privet, being easily cultivated in any soil of moderate quality, and readily propagated by late summer cuttings.

F. FORTUNEI, *Carrière*

(F. phillyreoides sinensis, *Debeaux*)

A deciduous shrub, 10 to 15 ft. high in gardens, but said to become a tree 30 to 40 ft. high in China; young branchlets angular, glabrous. Leaves lanceolate, long-pointed, 1 to $4\frac{1}{2}$ ins. long, $\frac{1}{3}$ to 1 in. wide, entire, bright green, and quite glabrous. Flowers greenish white, produced in terminal, slender panicles 1 to 2 ins. long, and in axillary shorter ones; each flower $\frac{1}{6}$ in. long. Fruit a flat oblong disk, $\frac{3}{8}$ in. long, with winged margins, notched at the apex.

Native of China; found by Fortune in 1845, and later by several other collectors, near Shanghai. It is very closely allied to the following better known species from Asia Minor, of which, by some authors, it is considered merely a variety. The most obvious distinctions are the larger more uniformly lance-shaped leaves (often oval or oblong in the other), and the more slender, elongated panicles. In a note by Commander W. Perry preserved in the Kew Herbarium, it is stated that the Chinese make fences round their compounds with branches of this tree interlaced. These take root and form a graceful hedge.

F. PHILLYREOIDES, *Labillardière*

A privet-like, deciduous shrub, 6 to 10 ft. high, forming a great number of slender twigs, angular and glabrous when young. Leaves ovate-lanceolate, oval, or oblong; $\frac{1}{2}$ to $2\frac{1}{2}$ ins. long, $\frac{1}{4}$ to $\frac{5}{8}$ in. wide; usually with a tapering point, entire, glabrous. Flowers about $\frac{1}{8}$ in. long, greenish white, very numerous on terminal panicles $\frac{1}{2}$ to 1 in. long, supplemented by smaller clusters in the leaf-axils, produced during June on leafy twigs. A prominent feature of the flower is the protruded stamens. Fruit a flat disk, roundish or oblong, two-seeded, and surrounded by a membranous wing; $\frac{1}{4}$ to $\frac{3}{8}$ in. long.

Native of the Orient (Cilicia, Syria, etc.); introduced in 1787. This shrub retains its leaves long in the autumn. It is perfectly hardy and flowers copiously, and has about the same decorative value as the privet.

Var. NANA.—A form of more compact habit and slower growth.

FORESTIERA. OLEACEÆ

A group of New World shrubs, of which three species are occasionally cultivated in botanical collections. They have some affinity with the olive. Leaves deciduous, opposite; flowers small, greenish, without petals, unisexual; the sexes often on separate plants. The fruit, which is oblong or egg-shaped and pulpy, I have never seen produced in this country, and the flowers but rarely. Even in their absence the first two species described below are easily distinguished from each other by the short-stalked, downy leaves of ligustrina; and the long, narrow, much tapered, smooth leaves of acuminata. They grow in any ordinary soil, and are easily propagated by late summer cuttings. The genus has also been known as "Adelia." The name here adopted was given in honour of Charles Le-Forestier, a French physician and naturalist.

F. ACUMINATA, *Poiret*. SWAMP PRIVET

(Adelia acuminata, *Michaux*; Borya acuminata, *Willdenow*)

A deciduous shrub, usually 4 to 8 ft. high, or a small tree, sometimes 20 to 30 ft. high in a wild state, of spreading habit; branches slender, the short ones occasionally spine-tipped. Leaves lanceolate or oval-lanceolate, $1\frac{1}{2}$ to $2\frac{1}{2}$ ins. long, $\frac{1}{2}$ to $\frac{3}{4}$ in. wide at the middle, tapering gradually to both ends; shallowly toothed from the middle to the apex; stalk $\frac{1}{4}$ to $\frac{1}{2}$ in. long. Male flowers clustered in small stalkless tufts; female ones on branched stalks; both minute, greenish, and of no beauty. Fruit cylindrical, pointed, $\frac{1}{2}$ in. long, purple.

Native of the S.E. United States; introduced in 1812. A shrub of botanical interest only, and privet-like appearance.

F. LIGUSTRINA, *Poiret*

(Adelia ligustrina, *Michaux* ; Borya ligustrina, *Willdenow*)

A deciduous shrub, up to 10 ft. in height, forming a wide bush with slender branches, downy when young, often becoming spine-tipped. Leaves oval or slightly obovate, $\frac{3}{4}$ to 1$\frac{3}{4}$ ins. long, $\frac{1}{4}$ to $\frac{3}{4}$ in. wide ; tapered at both ends, shallowly toothed all round except near the base ; dull green and glabrous above, paler and downy beneath ; stalks $\frac{1}{4}$ in. or less long. Flowers green, inconspicuous, produced from the twigs of the preceding year ; the males in dense stalkless clusters ; females fewer, on short spurs. Fruit $\frac{1}{4}$ in. long, egg-shaped, blue-black.

Native of the S.E. United States ; introduced in 1812. Of no garden value.

F. NEO-MEXICANA, *Gray*

(Adelia neo-mexicana, *O. Kuntze*)

A deciduous shrub 6 to 9 ft. high, of spreading habit ; young shoots glabrous. Leaves opposite, obovate, oval, or oblanceolate, faintly toothed or entire, mostly rounded or bluntish at the apex, tapered at the base ; $\frac{1}{2}$ to 1$\frac{3}{4}$ ins. long, $\frac{1}{4}$ to 1 in. wide, quite glabrous ; stalk $\frac{1}{8}$ to $\frac{1}{4}$ in. long. Flowers unisexual, clustered at the joints, small and inconspicuous. Fruits black, covered with blue bloom, egg-shaped, scarcely $\frac{1}{4}$ in. long, each on a slender stalk $\frac{1}{8}$ to $\frac{1}{4}$ in. long.

Native of the S.W. United States ; introduced to Kew in 1925, but known to American botanists long before. F. acuminata is easily distinguished from neo-mexicana by its slenderly pointed, longer leaves and larger cylindrical fruits. The latter is quite hardy and grows well in this country, but its chief attraction is in the fruits, for whose copious development our climate probably is not sunny enough.

FORSYTHIA. OLEACEÆ

This genus, consisting, so far as is known at present, of six or seven species of deciduous shrubs, commemorates Wm. Forsyth, once superintendent of the Royal Gardens at Kensington (1737-1804). They are allied to the lilacs and jasmines, having opposite, trifoliate or simple leaves, angular stems, and yellow flowers produced in spring on short stalks from the joints of the previous year's wood. Calyx four-lobed, green ; corolla also four-lobed, the lobes uniting at the base into a short tube ; stamens two, styles either long or short, both long-styled and short-styled forms belonging to each species. Two or three species are Chinese ; one East European.

All are very easily cultivated ; they are gross feeders, and like a rich, deep, loamy soil. Propagated very easily by cuttings made of half-ripened shoots. F. viridissima needs no pruning, nor does F. intermedia, but F. suspensa Fortunei, may if desired be cut hard back every spring as soon as the flowers are past. There are some worthless variegated forsythias that need no detailed mention.

F. EUROPÆA, *Degen and Baldacci*. ALBANIAN FORSYTHIA

(Bot. Mag., t. 8039)

A deciduous shrub, of erect habit, from 3 to 6 ft. high ; young wood not downy, but dotted with lenticels. Leaves ovate, 2 to 3 ins. long, $\frac{3}{4}$ to 1$\frac{1}{2}$ ins. wide ; of firm texture, glabrous sometimes sharply and unequally toothed, but usually entire; pointed at the apex, rounded at the base; stalk $\frac{1}{6}$ to $\frac{1}{4}$ in. long. Flowers yellow, produced in March from the buds of the previous year's growth, mostly singly, occasionally in pairs. Corolla $1\frac{1}{4}$ ins. diameter, with four narrow-oblong divisions. Calyx-lobes ovate, green, $\frac{1}{6}$ in. long.

Native of Albania, discovered by Dr A. Baldacchi in 1897, and first introduced by him to this country by means of seeds sent to Kew in 1899. Some doubt has been expressed as to its being truly native of Europe, as its fellow species are only found in the Far East; but from the wild nature of the country in which it was found, and the fact that several cases of analogous distribution in other genera exist, this does not seem justified. It is allied to F. viridissima, but differs in the ovate leaves (widest near the base), and by a lanky habit which makes it more ungainly. It is the least ornamental of forsythias, but of geographical interest.

F. INTERMEDIA, *Zabel* (Plate 3)

This is supposed, and no doubt justly, to be a hybrid between F. suspensa and F. viridissima. It opens its blossoms immediately after F. suspensa, and before the other parent. Its branching, too, is intermediate, and rather like that of the erect form of suspensa. Leaves occasionally trifoliolate, but mostly intermediate between the simple leaves of both parents; more tapering at the base than in F. suspensa. Flowers as in suspensa, to which this beautiful shrub is in no way inferior in beauty. It is not so good for covering arbours, etc., but is more suitable for grouping on lawns. The three following forms of this hybrid have been named by a German botanist, and distinguished as follows:—

Var. DENSIFLORA, *Koehne*.—Flowers densely crowded on the shoots; a very distinct form; style longer than stamens.

Var. SPECTABILIS, *Koehne*.—A seedling form, with larger, deeper yellow, and more abundant flowers; style shorter than stamens. In many respects the most beautiful of forsythias.

Var. VITELLINA, *Koehne*.—Of erect, strong habit; flowers rich dark yellow; style longer than stamens.

F. GIRALDIANA, *Lingelsheim*

(Bot. Mag., t. 9662)

A deciduous shrub up to 15 ft. high, branches gracefully spreading; young shoots slender, soon glabrous, black-purple on the upper side; pith lamellate. Leaves 2 to 4 ins. long, $\frac{3}{4}$ to $1\frac{3}{4}$ ins. wide, narrowly ovate-lanceolate, tapered to rounded at the base, tapered at the apex to a long slender point, glabrous above, slightly hairy on the veins beneath; stalk $\frac{1}{6}$ to $\frac{1}{2}$ in. long, slightly hairy. Flowers solitary, soft yellow, the short stalks covered with persistent bud-scales; corolla 1 to $1\frac{1}{2}$ ins. across with a short tube and four oblong-lanceolate, pointed lobes; stamens yellow.

Native of Kansu, China, first collected by Reginald Farrer in 1914. Like all the forsythias it is handsome in flower and of easy cultivation and although not the best of its kind is of value as the earliest species to come into bloom (the first week in March). Its distinguishing marks—in combination—are its lamellate pith, its entire leaves and its early flowering.

F. OVATA, *Nakai*

(Bot. Mag., t. 9437)

A deciduous shrub ultimately 6 ft. high, of bushy habit; young shoots glabrous, pale greyish brown, sprinkled with small dark lenticels; pith chambered. Leaves opposite, roundish ovate, with a short slender point and a rounded or slightly heart-shaped base; coarsely toothed to nearly entire; 2 to 3½ ins. long, 1¼ to 2½ ins. wide; glabrous on both surfaces; stalk ¼ to ½ in. long. Flowers opening in March, bright yellow, the four-lobed corolla ⅝ to ¾ in. wide; calyx-lobes ciliate. The flowers are solitary, two at each joint, often produced on short spur-like shoots on one- or two-year-old wood. Seed vessel ½ in. long, ovoid, but drawn out to a slender apex before splitting into two parts.

Native of Korea; described and named by the Japanese botanist, Nakai, in the *Japanese Botanical Magazine* for 1917, p. 104. It was collected by Wilson and introduced to cultivation the following year under his number 10456. It is very readily distinguished from the older forsythias by the broad leaves which have conspicuous teeth, often ⅛ to ¼ in. wide. It is usually in bloom in early March if the weather be mild—and is quite a promising shrub although scarcely equal to the finest of the older kinds in beauty, its flowers being smaller. In habit it is dwarfer and compact.

The late Mr F. N. Meyer collected a forsythia very similar to this in the broad shape and coarse toothing of the leaves in the province of Shantung, China, during 1907; Rehder has named it F. SUSPENSA LATIFOLIA.

F. SUSPENSA, *Vahl*. GOLDEN BELL

(Bot. Mag., t. 4995)

A deciduous shrub of rambling habit, which, if trained on a wall will grow 30 ft. high, but in the open, and unsupported, forms a mass of interlacing, often pendulous branches, 8 or 10 ft. high; young branches glabrous. Leaves mostly simple, 2 to 4 ins. long, 1 to 2 ins. wide; but occasionally on strong shoots trifoliolate, three-lobed, or two-lobed; coarsely toothed, pointed; the simple leaves are rounded or broadly wedge-shaped at the base; the leaflets tapering there; stalk about ½ in. long. Flowers golden yellow, produced one to as many as six in a cluster from the buds of last year's wood in late March and early April, lasting a month in beauty; each flower 1 to 1¼ ins. across. Calyx-lobes oblong-lanceolate, ¼ in. long.

Native of China, but introduced from Japanese gardens to Holland in 1833, and thence, nearly twenty years later, to England. It and F. intermedia are the finest of early, yellow-flowering shrubs. In gardens it is represented by two distinct forms, viz., FORTUNEI, a shrub of stiffer growth, with erect or arching (not so pendulous) shoots; and SIEBOLDII, a form with slender pendent shoots which reach the ground and take root. There are, however, plants in cultivation which it is difficult to assign to either. Forsythia suspensa may be used in a variety of ways; the slender creeping form (Sieboldii) is useful for covering a steep slope, and for using as a climber on house fronts, arbours, etc. The stiffer one (Fortunei) is the best for massing on a lawn. It may, if desired, be pruned hard back every spring as soon as the flowers are over. Treated in this way, healthy plants will make shoots 4 to 6 ft. long in a season, furnished the following spring from end to end with golden yellow blossom.

A form with lemon-yellow flowers has recently been introduced from Central China by Wilson. It has shorter and comparatively broader petals. There is another with dark purplish young shoots.

The following varieties are of later introduction:—

F. SUSPENSA ATROCAULIS, *Rehder*.—Discovered by Wilson in 1907 in Western Hupeh under his No. 637. It has much the same lax habit as the var. Sieboldii but is distinct in the young shoots being of a dark purplish hue as indicated by the varietal name, also in the corolla lobes being as much as ½ in. wide, more rounded at the end, and of a paler shade of yellow. A fine and distinct variety. Var. DECIPIENS, *Koehne*.—First noticed in Späth's nursery, near Berlin, about 1905. Its flowers are of a dark yellow and its growth strong, but its chief distinctive character is in the length of the flower-stalks which are occasionally close on 1 in. long, according to Koehne—an author, however, whose species and varieties have frequently been based on unreliable characters. Var. PUBESCENS, *Rehder*.—Young shoots and leaves downy and purplish.

The late Mr F. N. Meyer collected a forsythia resembling F. OVATA in the broad shape and coarse toothing of the leaves in the province of Shantung, China, during 1907. Dr Rehder has named it F. SUSPENSA LATIFOLIA.

F. VIRIDISSIMA, *Lindley*

(Bot. Mag., t. 4587)

A deciduous or partially evergreen shrub, 5 to 8 ft. high, with stiff, erect

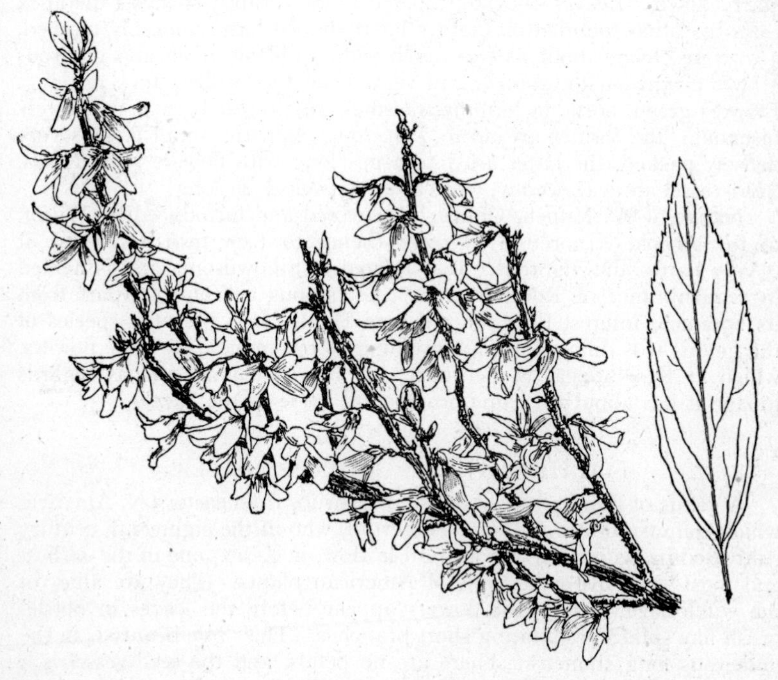

FORSYTHIA VIRIDISSIMA

glabrous branches. Leaves lance-shaped, 3 to 6 ins. long, ¾ to 1½ ins. wide, tapering at both ends, but more slenderly towards the pointed apex, toothed on the upper half, or quite entire; stalk ¼ to ½ in. long. Flowers bright yellow, 1¼ ins. across, the four corolla lobes narrow-oblong, ½ in. long. Calyx-lobes convex, ovate, ⅛ in. long.

Native of China; introduced by Fortune in 1844. Although this species is not so wonderful a garden shrub as F. suspensa, it is a very handsome and useful one. It flowers one or two weeks later, usually in April, and is sturdy enough to hold its branches erect. It is distinguished from both its fellow species, F. europæa and F. suspensa, by the shape of its leaves.

F. VIRIDISSIMA KOREANA, *Rehder*.—Differs from the type in its "more spreading habit, larger and brighter coloured flowers, longer and narrower sepals" (Rehder). Introduced from Korea to the Arnold Arboretum by Wilson in 1917 and to Kew in 1925. It is considered to be an improvement on the type.

It may be mentioned that the shoots of F. suspensa are hollow, with pith only at the joints; in F. viridissima the pith is separated into thin disks (lamellate) all along the shoots.

FORTUNEARIA SINENSIS, *Rehder and Wilson*.
HAMAMELIDACEÆ

A monotypic, deciduous shrub of strong spreading growth, ultimately 20 to 25 ft. high; young shoots, leaf-stalks and flower-stalks covered with starry down. Leaves obovate, tapered more abruptly towards the apex than the often rounded or slightly heart-shaped base, unevenly toothed, 3 to 6 ins. long, about half as much wide; dullish green and glabrous above, downy on the midrib and veins beneath; stalk $\frac{1}{8}$ to $\frac{1}{3}$ in. long. Flowers green, borne in terminal racemes either entirely male or entirely bisexual; the former are up to $\frac{3}{4}$ in. long, with the small flowers very densely packed, the latter are 1 to 2 ins. long with flowers $\frac{1}{6}$ in. across. Seed-vessel an oval, woody, two-valved capsule $\frac{1}{2}$ in. long.

Native of W. Hupeh, China; discovered and introduced by Wilson to the Arnold Arboretum in 1907, thence to Kew in 1910, where it is very hardy and vigorous. It is related to Sinowilsonia and is named in remembrance of Robt. Fortune, the famous collector. Apart from its botanical interest (like Sinowilsonia Henryi it is the only species of the genus) it is difficult to find anything to recommend it. The flowers, which at Kew appear in February, are inconspicuous, and as regards foliage it has about the same ornamental value as the hazel.

FOTHERGILLA. HAMAMELIDACEÆ

A genus of four species of deciduous shrubs from eastern N. America, which commemorates Dr John Fothergill, who in the eighteenth century cultivated in his garden at Stratford-le-Bow, in Essex, one of the earliest and most extensive collections of American plants. They are allies of the witch-hazels, and their flowers appear before the leaves in bottle-brush like spikes terminating short branches. Their sole beauty is in the numerous long stamens. There are no petals, and the seed-vessel is a downy, hard-shelled capsule, opening at the top and containing two seeds.

F. GARDENI, *Murray*

(F. alnifolia, *Linnæus fil.*, Bot. Mag., t. 1341; F. carolina, *Britton*)

A deciduous shrub of thin habit, rarely more than 2 or 3 ft. high, with slender, crooked, often rather weak and spreading branches; young twigs covered with white, stellate hairs. Leaves oval or obovate, 1 to $2\frac{1}{2}$ ins. long,

3/4 to 1 3/4 ins. wide; heart-shaped, rounded or tapering at the base, with several large unequal teeth above the middle, downy, and green or whitish beneath; stalk 1/4 in. long, downy. Flowers in cylindrical terminal spikes, consisting chiefly of a mass, 1 to 1 1/2 ins. long, and about 1 in. through, of white stamens with yellow anthers; petals none.

Native of the south-eastern United States; first discovered by Dr Garden of Charlestown, U.S.A., and introduced in 1765. It flowers on the naked branches in April and May, and is then very pretty and fragrant. Although hardy, this shrub is not robust. It does not like a heavy soil so much as one of peat and sandy loam combined. The leaf is variable in shape, on account of which attempts have been made to differentiate two or three varieties such as OBTUSA (Bot. Mag., 1341), with obovate bluntish leaves; and ACUTA, with ovate, pointed leaves. The foliage often turns a beautiful crimson before falling. This species differs from the following in its much smaller stature, and in the inflorescence being from half to two-thirds as wide.

F. MAJOR, *Loddiges*

(F. alnifolia major, Bot. Mag., t. 1342)

A deciduous shrub, ultimately 6 to 10 ft. high, forming a rounded bush with mostly erect stems; young branchlets covered with stellate, whitish hairs. Leaves roundish oval or broadly ovate, 2 to 4 ins. long, and from two-thirds to nearly as wide, with a few teeth above the middle, or almost entire; upper

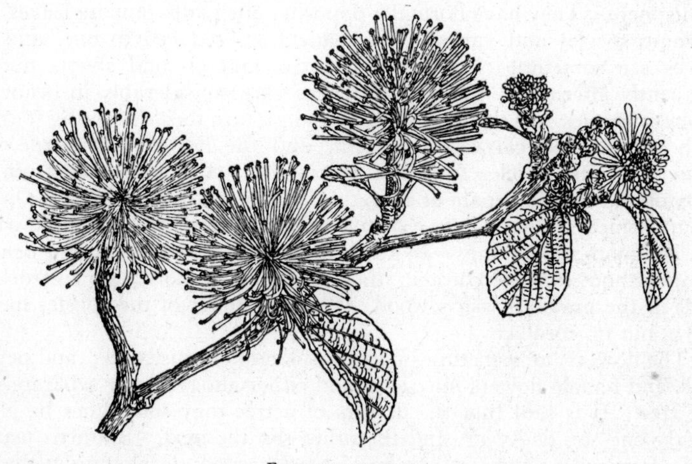

FOTHERGILLA MAJOR

surface dark glossy green becoming almost or quite glabrous, lower one glaucous, with stellate hairs, especially on the midrib and veins; stalk downy, about 1/3 in. long. Flowers numerous, in an erect, cylindrical spike, 1 to 2 ins. long, terminating short lateral twigs; the inflorescence owes its beauty to the numerous clustered stamens, which have pinkish white stalks 3/4 in. long, and yellow anthers; petals none. The seed-vessel is a downy, woody capsule 1/2 in. long, splitting at the top.

Native of the Allegheny Mountains from Virginia to S. Carolina; grown in English gardens in 1780, but apparently long lost to cultivation until reintroduced to Kew from the Arnold Arboretum in 1902. It is a most charming shrub, especially to those who love out-of-the-way species. It succeeds extremely well in a mixture of peat and sandy loam, producing its fragrant spikes profusely in May. The leaves turn orange-yellow before falling. It strikes root freely from cuttings of fairly firm wood in gentle heat, and is quite hardy. Certainly it is in every way superior to the commoner F. Gardeni, and it is strange that it was so long lost to gardens.

F. MONTICOLA, *Ashe*

A deciduous shrub up to 6 ft. high, in habit more open and spreading than F. major. Leaves 2 to 4 ins. long, roundish to obovate, usually cordate at the base, sparsely toothed, thinly downy beneath often on the veins only and pale green there (not glaucous as in F. major); stalk $\frac{1}{3}$ to $\frac{2}{3}$ in. long. In the flowers there is little difference from F. major; as in that species they are erect spikes of white stamens 1 to 2 ins. long; although somewhat wider.

Native of the S.E. United States from N. Carolina to Alabama; introduced to Europe by Mr Hesse of Weener, Hanover, and to England in 1910. It is as ornamental a shrub as F. major and grows equally well. The leaves fade off to red in autumn.

FRAXINUS. ASH. OLEACEÆ

A group of some sixty species of deciduous trees and a few shrubs, all except three found in the temperate latitudes of the northern hemisphere. They have normally opposite, unequally pinnate leaves, but in some species and varieties the leaflets are reduced to one, and the leaves are sometimes in whorls of three, and on odd shoots not infrequently alternate. The inflorescences vary considerably in beauty in different species. In the most ornamental groups, the "flowering" ashes, both corolla and calyx are present, and the flowers are borne very numerously in panicles from the end of the young shoot and from the axils of the terminal pair of leaves. This is the manna ash or ORNUS group, sometimes made into a distinct genus. In another group to which our common ash belongs—FRAXINASTER—the flowers have no beauty, being without calyx or corolla; they are borne in short panicles from the buds of the previous year's wood. The remainder of the species have a calyx, but no corolla.

The flowers are sometimes perfect, sometimes unisexual; and perfect male and female flowers may be found either altogether or separately on one tree. It is said that the flowers of a tree may sometimes be all or mostly one sex one year, and the other sex the next. Stamens usually two. Fruit one- or two-celled, one- or two-seeded, developing at the end a long, flattened wing or membrane, usually from $\frac{3}{4}$ to $1\frac{1}{2}$ ins. long and $\frac{1}{4}$ to $\frac{1}{3}$ in. wide. Many of the species hereinafter described do not flower in this country, and even those that do, like the common ash, do not carry crops of fruit every year. From all its allies in gardens, except Jasminum and one species of Syringa, Fraxinus is distinguished by its pinnate leaves.

In gardens and parks, the ashes are welcome for their stately form and fine pinnate foliage. Some of them, like excelsior and americana, yield an admirable timber. They are frequently found in nature on a limestone formation, and should be especially noted by those whose ground is so situated. For the rest, they are gross feeders, and like a good loamy soil and abundant moisture. They should always, if possible, be raised from seed, which may be sown in cold frames or shallow boxes, and thinly covered with soil. Grafting for the weeping, coloured, and other garden varieties has, perforce, to be resorted to, but the stock should always be of the species to which the variety belongs. The ashes produce a very fibrous and extensive root system, which renders their transplanting safe and easy. The only species at all unsatisfactory in cultivation are those like nigra and mandshurica, which, being excited into growth by unseasonable warmth early in the year, are almost invariably cut back by later frost. Some species, like dipetala, need rather more warmth than our climate affords. But given a good soil, and not too exposed a position, the ashes generally are satisfactory.

The following is a selection of the more desirable species :—

For timber.—Excelsior, americana.

For beauty of foliage and habit.—Angustifolia, americana, biltmoreana, oregona, pennsylvanica, excelsior, ex. var. heterophylla, ex. var. pendula.

For flower.—Ornus, Mariesii.

For interest.—Spæthiana, anomala.

For small gardens.—Bungeana, dimorpha, excelsior var. globosa.

F. AMERICANA, *Linnæus*. WHITE ASH

A fine timber tree up to 120 ft. high in a wild state, with a trunk 5 or 6 ft. in thickness ; young shoots glabrous, dark polished green or brownish, becoming grey the second year. Leaves 8 to 15 ins. long ; leaflets seven or nine (sometimes five), oblong-lanceolate or oval, stalked ; ordinarily 4 to 6 ins. long (on vigorous young trees 7 or 8 ins.), 1 to 3 ins. wide ; rounded or tapered at the base, long and slender-pointed, entire or the terminal part toothed ; dark green and glabrous above, whitish and downy along the midrib and veins beneath. Common stalk yellowish white, glabrous, round, with a scarcely perceptible groove on the upper side ; stalk of lateral leaflets about ⅓ in. long, of the terminal one ½ to 1 in. long. Flowers without petals, produced on the previous year's growth. Fruit 1 to 2 ins. long, ¼ in. wide ; the body roundish.

Native of eastern N. America ; introduced in 1724. This handsome and striking ash is one of the best of American deciduous trees in this country, being quick-growing and producing timber of similar quality to that of our native species, much esteemed for making oars. There are trees over 80 ft. high at Kew. Whilst there is nothing to show that it is superior to our native ash, it would be worth planting in quantity under forest conditions as an experiment. It appears to grow more quickly in a small state. The distinguishing characters of this ash as compared with other American species of the same character are : its round main leaf-stalk, the white under-surface of the stalked leaflets, and the glabrous, dark, young shoots. (Compare with F. texensis and F. biltmoreana, its nearest allies.)

Var. ACUMINATA, *Wesmael*.—Leaflets almost without down beneath, bright green above, and nearly or quite entire.

Var. JUGLANDIFOLIA, *Rehder*.—This striking variety has leaflets as much as 9 ins. long, by 3 ins. wide, not conspicuously toothed at the upper half, densely pubescent over the whole under-surface, but not on the main leaf-stalk or young shoots.

Var. MICROCARPA, *Gray.*—Fruit about ½ in. long; common in the south-eastern United States.

F. ANGUSTIFOLIA, *Vahl.* NARROW-LEAVED ASH

(F. numidica, *Dippel*)

A tree 60 to 80 ft., occasionally 90 ft. high; young shoots and leaves perfectly glabrous. Leaves 6 to 10 ins. long; leaflets seven to thirteen, lanceolate, 1 to 3 ins. long, ⅓ to ¾ in. wide, sharply and rather coarsely or even jaggedly toothed except towards the narrowly tapered base; apex long-pointed; dark glossy green above. The terminal leaflet is the only one that has a stalk (¼ to ⅓ in. long); main-stalk with two wings on the upper side forming a groove that is open from the base to the lowest pair of leaflets, but beyond them closed, except where the leaflets are attached. Flowers produced from the joints of the previous year's wood, and with neither calyx nor corolla. Fruits 1 to 1¼ ins. long.

Native of S. Europe and N. Africa. The most distinctive character of the species is the entire absence of down, differing in this respect from its near ally F. oxycarpa. It is an elegant tree, allied botanically to the common ash.

Var. LENTISCIFOLIA, *Henry.*—Leaflets more spreading (in the typical form they point forwards) and set further apart on the main-stalk, making the leaf sometimes 10 ins. or more long, and the tree very graceful. A form with more slender, pendulous branches is distinguished as PENDULA.

Nearly allied to, and perhaps scarcely specifically distinct from F. angustifolia, is

F. OXYCARPA, *Willdenow* (F. oxyphylla, *Bieberstein*).—Its leaves have the same number of leaflets, mostly of the same shape and size, but they are always downy about the midrib and lower veins. Fruits more tapered at the base. The species has a more Eastern natural habitat than F. angustifolia, reaching to Persia, the Caucasus, and Asia Minor.

F. ANOMALA, *Torrey.* UTAH ASH

A tree 18 to 20 ft. high, with glabrous, square, slightly winged, slender, young shoots. Leaves simple (rarely with two or three leaflets), ovate, sometimes roundish or obovate, tapered at the base, bluntish or pointed at the apex, inconspicuously toothed; 1 to 2½ ins. long, ¾ to 1¾ ins. wide; grey-green, glabrous on both surfaces; stalk ½ to 1 in. long. It flowers on the previous year's growths, and the fruits (not seen in this country) are ⅔ in. long, obovate or oval.

Native of Colorado, Utah, and Nevada; said by Sargent to be not rare. Introduced in 1893 to Kew, where it forms a lax-branched, small tree, quite distinct from every other cultivated ash in the combination of square stems and simple leaves, but only worth growing as a curiosity.

F. BERLANDIERIANA, *De Candolle*

A tree up to 30 ft. high, with quite glabrous, round branchlets. Leaflets usually five, deep lustrous green above, paler beneath; the terminal one obovate, 2½ to 4 ins. long, 1½ to 2½ ins. wide; the lateral ones more oval and smaller, all coarsely toothed above the middle, soon quite glabrous; midrib prominent below, the side ribs connected by conspicuous netted veins; main leaf-stalk grooved. Fruit 1 to 1½ ins. long; often three-winged (Sargent).

Native of Texas and Mexico; introduced to Kew under the name of F. coriacea in 1897. (The true F. coriacea, *S. Watson*, according to Sargent, has the shoots tomentose when they appear, remaining downy for one or two years.) As seen at Kew, F. Berlandieriana is a pleasing small tree of free growth, and distinct in the deep glossy green, glabrous leaves and branchlets; in these respects it resembles F. lanceolata, but is smaller in all its parts.

F. BILTMOREANA, *Beadle*. BILTMORE ASH

As lately as 1898, this ash was distinguished from F. americana and named by Mr Beadle. No doubt it exists in some gardens, looked upon as ordinary white ash. There is one on the hill at Kew crowned by the Temple of Æolus, which is over 80 ft. high and more than 8 ft. in girth. It is close to a true white ash of about the same size, which Mr Elwes regards as the largest in England. The chief distinction of the Biltmore from the white ash resides in its densely downy young shoots, the down persisting for two years; the white under-surface of the leaflets and their common stalk are similarly downy. On the old tree at Kew the largest leaflets are 6 ins. long by 3 ins. wide, and the entire leaf up to 20 ins. long. The trunk is similar to that of F. americana, but the first year wood is dull grey (not green or brown as in americana), nor does it acquire during the second season the pale, polished surface of the white ash. In other respects it resembles that species, especially its var. juglandifolia, but the wing of the fruit is not extended down the body so much. In its downy shoots it resembles F. pennsylvanica, but that species has the leaflets green beneath and the main leaf-stalk more distinctly grooved. Elwes figures a handsome tree at Fawley Court, Oxfordshire, 68 ft. high.

F. BRACTEATA, *Hemsley*

(F. Griffithii, *C. B. Clarke*)

A deciduous tree of the Ornus group, 40 ft. high; young shoots glabrous, four-angled, bright green. Leaves variable in size; on young trees 6 to 12 ins. long. Leaflets five to eleven, ovate, wedge-shaped or rounded at the base, tapered at the apex to a bluntish point, very variable in size; ordinarily 1 to 3 ins. long (but sometimes 5 ins.), about half as wide; not toothed, deep polished green, perfectly glabrous, and with impressed veins above; paler and glabrous beneath. The main leaf-stalk has an even, well-defined groove above; terminal leaflet long-stalked, the others shortly so. Panicles terminal, also borne in the upper leaf-axils; downy, pyramidal, 3 to 6 ins. long, with a pair of small oblong bracts at the base of each subdivision. The flowers are probably white, but have not yet been seen in this country. Fruit 1 to 1¼ ins. long, $\frac{1}{12}$ in. wide.

Native of Hupeh, China; discovered by Henry in 1887; introduced by Wilson for Messrs Veitch in 1900. It is a distinct ash in its square branchlets and glabrous, shining, entire leaflets, the largest of which resemble the leaf of Ligustrum lucidum. A promising species, whose hardiness, however, has scarcely yet been put to the test.

F. BUNGEANA, *De Candolle*

A shrub or small tree up to 15 ft. high; twigs minutely downy. Leaves of thin texture, 4 to 6 ins. long; leaflets five or seven, stalked, unequal-sided, oval and obovate; 1 to 2 ins. long, ½ to 1 in. wide; tapered at the base, with abrupt slender points, round-toothed except towards the base, quite glabrous. Main leaf-stalk minutely downy, with a narrow groove on the upper side; stalk of leaflets ⅛ to ¼ in. long, minutely downy. Flowers (with petals) produced in terminal panicles; fruit a little over 1 in. long, ⅕ in. wide.

Native of N. China; introduced in 1881 to the Arnold Arboretum, Mass., where I have seen healthy bushes 4 or 5 ft. high and through. The true plant is little known in Britain, although many ashes under the name have been introduced, which have turned out to be chinensis or other species. It belongs to the Ornus group, and is very distinct from the only other shrubby ashes in cultivation—the tiny leaved dimorpha and xanthoxyloides. Bunge's ash is one of the few whose twigs and leaf-stalks are downy, whilst the leaf-blades are glabrous.

F. DIPPELIANA, *Lingelsheim*, as sold by Späth of Berlin, is apparently a form of F. Bungeana, or very closely allied to it, the leaves perhaps broader (up to 1½ ins. wide) and shorter pointed.

F. CAROLINIANA, *Miller*. SWAMP ASH

A tree rarely more than 40 ft. high; young shoots glabrous, brown. Leaves 5 to 12 ins. long; leaflets five or seven, stalked, oval, 2 to 4 ins. long, 1¼ to 2 ins. wide (terminal one larger and up to 6 ins. long, sometimes obovate), mostly tapered, sometimes rounded at the base, pointed, sharply toothed; dark green and glabrous above; pale duller green beneath, with white hairs along the sides of the midrib and lower veins. Main leaf-stalk round, with a slight groove on the upper side; stalks of side leaflets up to ½ in. long, that of terminal one up to 1 in. long. Flowers without petals, produced in short panicles on the shoots of the preceding year. Fruit described by Sargent as elliptical or obovate, up to 2 ins. long, frequently three-winged, ½ to ¾ in. wide.

Native of the south-eastern United States; introduced in 1783, but extremely rare. Trees which in vegetative characters appear to be true, and which were received from the United States as F. caroliniana, are in the collection at Kew; but one would scarcely expect the tree to be hardy in this country, as it comes from the coast region of the Atlantic and Gulf States, and reaches even to Cuba.

F. CHINENSIS, *Roxburgh*

A tree up to 50 ft. with stout, greyish, glabrous young shoots, and grey buds. Leaflets usually seven, sometimes nine, variable in shape and size; terminal (and largest) one oval or obovate, 3 to 5½ ins. long, 2 to 3 ins. wide, its stalk ¾ to 1¼ ins. long; the pairs towards the base smaller, oval, the lowest pair 1½ to 3 ins. long, sometimes roundish oval; all shallowly round-toothed, stalked; dark dull green above, pale beneath, with dense brown down at the sides of the midrib and base of the veins only. Common stalk with a continuous open channel on the upper side with tufts of down where the leaflets are attached. Flowers and fruit not seen in this country; the latter described by Henry as about 1½ ins. long, ¼ in. wide, oblanceolate, and either rounded or pointed at the apex.

Native of China; introduced under the name of "Bungeana" in 1891. It has been also wrongly named "F. obovata" in gardens. Young trees are striking in the large size of their leaflets. Henry says this is one of the trees on which the wax insect lives.

F. DIMORPHA, *Cosson and Durieu*. ALGERIAN ASH

A deciduous bush or a small tree, 20 ft. or more high; branchlets glabrous, purplish on the upper side. Leaves 1½ to 3 ins. long, composed of five to eleven (mostly seven or nine) leaflets, which are ovate, ⅜ to 1⅛ ins. long, ⅙ to ½ in. wide; rather prominently toothed, scarcely stalked; glabrous, except for a tuft of down at the base of the midrib beneath; the main leaf-stalk is slightly winged between each pair of leaflets. Flowers produced from the axils of the previous year's wood. Fruits 1½ ins. long, ¼ in. wide.

Var. DUMOSA, *Carrière*.—A purely shrubby variety, forming a dense rounded bush with interlacing branches. Leaves uniformly smaller than in the type, and only ¼ to ⅝ in. long.

Native of N. Africa, in the mountains of Algeria and Morocco. It is rare in gardens, but very distinct among cultivated ashes, and worth growing for its dwarf habit and minute leaflets. Var. dumosa makes a neat and pleasing bush and is sometimes regarded as a variety of the following:—

F. XANTHOXYLOIDES, *Wallich*, is very closely allied and very similar to F. dimorpha, but differs in having the branchlets covered with a dense but extremely minute dark down; the leaves and leaf-stalks have a scattered but longer down. It is a native of the north-western Himalaya, Afghanistan, etc. Bushes at Kew raised from seed sent from India do not appear to be quite so hardy as F. dimorpha.

F. DIPETALA, *Hooker and Arnott*. FRINGE-FLOWERED ASH

A shrub 10 to 12 ft. high, or occasionally a small tree; young shoots four-sided and four-winged, slightly warted, not downy. Leaves 2 to 5 ins. long; leaflets commonly five, but varying from three to nine; obovate or oval, tapered at the base, rounded or hardly pointed at the apex; ½ to 1¼ ins. long, toothed except at the lowest third; quite glabrous on both surfaces. Main leaf-stalk glabrous, grooved above; the terminal leaflet rather long-stalked, the uppermost pair stalkless, those below more or less stalked. Flowers creamy white, ⅓ in. long, produced from the joints of the previous year's growth in panicles 2 to 4 ins. long. Fruits about 1 in. long, ¼ in. wide, with a notched tip.

Native of California, where it was discovered in 1830 by David Douglas; but not introduced, so far I am aware, until 1879, when Prof. Sargent sent it to Kew. There is now a small tree there about 14 ft. high, which does not flower, and is sometimes injured at the tips by frost. It appears to be one of the most ornamental of ashes in flower, but needs a rather warmer climate than near London. It should be tried in the south-west. Its four-angled stems, glabrous leaves, and the production of flowers on the old wood, distinguish it well among the ashes with petalled flowers.

F. ELONZA, *Dippel*

A small, elegant tree with glabrous, grey-green young shoots furnished with whitish warts; buds dark brown, scurfy. Leaves up to 10 or 11 ins. long, with nine to thirteen leaflets, which are ovate, oval or lance-shaped, broadly tapered at the base, shortly pointed, sharply toothed; 1 to 3 ins. long, ½ to 1 in. wide; stalkless, dark dull green, and glabrous above, with brownish down densely tufted near the base of the midrib beneath. The main leaf-stalk is whitish beneath, downy in places, winged on the upper side, the wings erect and forming a narrow groove. Flowers and fruit not seen. This ash is of uncertain origin, and is supposed to be a hybrid, probably with F. oxycarpa as one parent. It has been cultivated in England since 1878.

F. EXCELSIOR, *Linnæus*. COMMON ASH

One of the largest of European deciduous trees, reaching in favoured sites from 100 to 140 ft. in height; bark of the trunk pale, fissured; young wood grey, glabrous; buds black. Leaves 10 to 12 ins. long; leaflets most frequently nine or eleven, sometimes less or more; oblong lance-shaped, tapered at the base, slender-pointed, toothed; 2 to 4½ ins. long, 1 to 1⅓ ins. wide; dark green and glabrous above, paler beneath, and with fluffy brown down at the sides of the lower part of the midrib. Main leaf-stalk usually more or less downy, the wings on the upper side meeting and forming a sharp angle. The terminal leaflet is stalked, the lateral ones scarcely so. Flowers produced from the joints of the previous year's wood in short, dense panicles in April. Fruits (commonly called "keys") pendent in large bunches, each fruit about 1½ ins. long, ¼ to ⅓ in. wide.

Native of Europe, including Britain and the Caucasus. It is one of the most valuable of all our timber trees, yielding a whitish wood of great toughness and durability. Elwes considered it at the present time the most economically valuable of British timber trees. For some purposes, especially in coachbuilding and implement-making, it has no rival either native or foreign. An isolated ash of goodly size makes a tree of great beauty and dignity, forming a shapely, oval, or rounded head of branches. It likes a deep, moist, loamy soil, and thrives well on calcareous formations. In some parts of the north of England, on the east side of the Plain of York for instance, it is a common hedgerow tree, almost as common as the elm is in the south. In such positions, especially where the adjoining fields are arable, it is not an unmixed blessing, being one of the grossest of feeders. Both in nature and in gardens the common ash has produced a large number of varieties. A considerable number of those that have received names must be considered worthless from any point of view, and the following list only includes the more distinct or the more ornamental:—

Var. ANGUSTIFOLIA, *Schelle*.—Leaflets as a rule not more than ⅝ in. wide. It is apt to be confused with F. oxycarpa, but is distinguished by its black bud and the longer stalk of the terminal leaflet.

Var. ASPLENIFOLIA.—Leaflets only ⅛ to ¼ in. wide—a monstrosity merely.

Var. AUREA.—Young shoots yellow; older bark yellowish, especially noticeable in winter.

Var. AUREA PENDULA.—Young shoots yellow, branches weeping and forming a flat, umbrella-shaped head.

Var. CONCAVIFOLIA.—Leaflets small, boat-shaped.

Var. CRISPA (syn. atrovirens).—A deformed, stunted bush with leaves 2 or 3 ins. long, the leaflets much curved.

Var. FOLIIS ARGENTEIS.—Leaflets bordered with white; often deformed.

Var. GLOBOSA.—A dwarf rounded bush, densely branched. Vars. NANA and MYRTIFOLIA are much the same.

Var. GLOMERATA, *Simon-Louis*.—Leaflets as many as fifteen closely set on the common stalk, comparatively short and broad; some of them 3 ins. long and 2 ins. broad, stout in texture, basal pair of leaflets close to the branch; all somewhat hooded and puckered. Very distinct.

Var. HETEROPHYLLA. One-leaved Ash.—In this remarkable variety the terminal leaflet only, or occasionally one or two more, is developed. In other respects it is the same as the common ash. Its one leaflet is oval or ovate, long-stalked, toothed, and variable in size, usually 3 to 6 ins. long, 1¼ to 2½ ins. wide, but often proportionately broader or shorter. I have measured it as much as 8 ins. long and 5 ins. wide. This variety has arisen independently in many places, both cultivated and wild, and varies considerably. It is also known as integrifolia, monophylla, and simplicifolia.

Var. HETEROPHYLLA LACINIATA.—Leaves jaggedly and coarsely toothed.

Var. HETEROPHYLLA PENDULA.—All the branches weeping; this and the preceding varieties have leaves as in heterophylla.

Var. MONSTROSA.—Branchlets often fasciated; leaves often alternate.

Var. PENDULA, *Aiton*. Weeping Ash.—There are various forms of weeping ash. The commonest has all its branches weeping, forming a spreading, umbrella-like head. The most remarkable example is in the Earl of Harrington's garden at Elvaston, and is 98 ft. high, with streamer branches reaching to within 20 ft. of the ground. Var. PENDULA WENTWORTHII, Wentworth Weeping Ash, has an erect trunk and leading shoot, but the branches are very pendulous. It thus makes a tall, slender pyramid or spire. (See also vars. aurea pendula and heterophylla pendula.)

Var. SCOLOPENDRIFOLIA.—Leaflets narrow, often curled and deformed, narrower than in the type. Not free-growing.

Var. TRANSONI.—Leaves yellow.

Var. VERTICILLATA.—Leaves occasionally in threes instead of the usual pairs, but in this, as in some other abnormal forms of common ash, the leaves are frequently alternate.

F. FLORIBUNDA, *Wallich*. HIMALAYAN ASH

In 1876 the late Sir George King, then of the Calcutta Botanic Gardens, sent seeds of this fine ash to Kew. Of the trees raised one survived until 1915 after being cut to the ground in the winter of 1880-81. There is, however, another specimen at Kew, now about 8 ft. high and 5 ins. in girth. It is apparently perfectly hardy but its rate of growth with us is not such as to recommend it for general cultivation, except in the milder counties. It is one of the Ornus group, and in the north-western Himalaya, where it is native, reaches 80 to 100 ft. in height. Its branches are without down, and its leaves 10 to 15 ins. long. Leaflets usually seven or nine, oblong (terminal one obovate), tapered at both ends; 3 to 6 ins. long, 1 to 2½ ins. wide; sharply toothed, glabrous above, downy beneath, chiefly on the midrib and veins. Main-stalk grooved, stalk of leaflets ¼ to ½ in. long. Flowers white, in large terminal panicles. It resembles some of the big-leaved forms of F. Ornus, but the leaflets are normally much larger, more prominently ribbed beneath, and longer pointed. I have not seen it in flower, but the blossoms appear in panicles. Introduced first, Loudon says, in 1822, but killed in the winter of 1836-7.

F. HOLOTRICHA, *Koehne*

A small tree, with the young branchlets, leaf-stalks, and both surfaces of the leaves clothed with a dense soft down. Leaflets nine to thirteen on each leaf, of pretty even size, lanceolate, tapered at the base, sharply and slenderly toothed, margins hairy; 1¾ to 2¾ ins. long, ¼ to ½ in. wide; dull green on both surfaces. Common stalk pale beneath, shallowly grooved above. The entire leaf is 6 to 10 ins. long, the terminal leaflet usually stalked, the others nearly or quite stalkless.

Native of the eastern Balkan Peninsula, first noticed in cultivation in several parts of Germany. It has flowered there and belongs to the common ash group. When in leaf it is very distinct among the ashes with nine to thirteen leaflets, in the dense down which covers all the younger parts. Introduced from Späth's nursery, Berlin, in 1909, and thriving well in cultivation.

F. LANCEOLATA, *Borkhausen*. GREEN ASH

(F. viridis, *Michaux*)

Nearly allied to F. pennsylvanica, the red ash, of which some authorities regard it as a variety, this species is most readily distinguished by its bright green, glabrous young shoots, and by its narrower, slightly stalked, more sharply and conspicuously toothed leaflets, which are 3 to 6 ins. long, lance-shaped, green on both surfaces, glabrous above except along the midrib, and downy at the sides of the midrib beneath ; main-stalk only slightly grooved. It is a tree rarely more than 60 ft. high, according to Sargent, and is most abundant in the south Central United States. It has long been cultivated in Europe, and is fairly common in gardens, but some forms approach F. pennsylvanica.

Var. ALBO-MARGINATUS.—This is a variegated form with white margins to the leaflets. Usually found in gardens as a variety of americana (or " alba "), it is, like typical lanceolata, distinguished by the leaves being pale bright green (not whitish) beneath, by their much shorter stalks, and the distinct groove along the main-stalk. The young branchlet, however, is more or less downy, and thus shows some affinity with pennsylvanica.

F. LONGICUSPIS, *Siebold and Zuccarini*. JAPANESE FLOWERING ASH

A slender tree, 20 to 30, sometimes 50 ft. high in Japan, belonging to the Ornus or " flowering " group ; young shoots glabrous, grey. Leaves ordinarily 4 to 6 ins. long ; leaflets usually five (rarely seven), which are 1½ to 4 ins. long, ¾ to 1½ ins. wide, ovate to obovate, tapered at the base, the apex abruptly contracted into a slender point, toothed, glabrous above, downy only at the sides of the midrib near the base beneath. The terminal leaflet, which is the largest, has a stalk ½ to ¾ in. long, the uppermost pair are stalkless, the lower pair or pairs shortly stalked ; common stalk grooved on the upper side. Flowers white, in terminal and axillary panicles 3 to 5 ins. long, produced in June. Introduced from Japan in 1894, but rare in cultivation. It is the Japanese representative of F. Ornus, differing most obviously in the few leaflets. According to Sargent, it changes in autumn to a conspicuous purple colour.

F. MANDSHURICA, *Ruprecht*. MANCHURIAN ASH

A fine tree, often 100 ft. high ; young shoots glabrous, greyish. Leaves 8 to 15 ins. long ; leaflets stalkless, or nearly so, usually nine or eleven, sometimes seven or thirteen ; oval or oblong-lanceolate, 2 to 4½ ins. long, 1 to 2 ins. wide ; tapered to the base, slender-pointed, sharply (occasionally doubly) toothed ; dull green and with scattered bristles above, paler beneath, and more conspicuously bristly, especially on the midrib and veins. Main leaf-stalk winged above, the two wings forming a deep groove with tufts of brown down where the leaflets join.

Native of Japan and the adjacent parts of the Asiatic mainland ; introduced to Kew from St Petersburg in 1882. It is one of the greatest failures among ashes on account of its suspectibility to injury by spring frost. Its broadly winged fruits, which Sargent says are borne on the previous year's wood in great clusters, have not been produced in Britain. It is a valuable tree in the Far East, and attains to noble dimensions there. The leaf is distinct in the conspicuous sunken veins above, correspondingly prominent beneath. Closely allied to F. nigra.

F. MARIESII, *Hooker fil*. MARIES' ASH

A small deciduous tree, forming a rounded, bushy head of branches, and apparently unlikely to be more than 15 to 20 ft. high ; branchlets and buds greyish, downy. Leaves 3 to 7 ins. long, with three or five leaflets attached to the upper third of the main leaf-stalk, which is scurfy and purplish on the upper side, and has a swollen, dark purple base. Leaflets oval or ovate, 1 to 3½ ins. long, ½ to 1¾ ins. wide; the apex abruptly tapered, the base rounded or wedge-shaped; shallowly toothed or almost entire; dull green, glabrous; stalks of side leaflets $\frac{1}{10}$ to ¼ in. long, that of the terminal leaflet up to ¾ in. long; all purple at the base. Flowers creamy white, in axillary and terminal

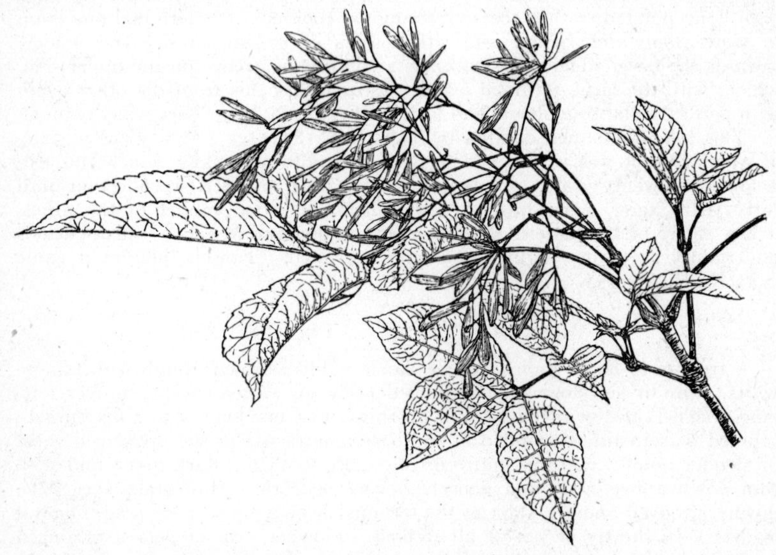

FRAXINUS MARIESII (in fruit)

panicles 3 to 6 ins. long; produced in June. Fruits ½ to 1¼ ins. long, ⅛ to ¼ in. wide; very handsome in July, when they become deep purple.

Native of Central China; introduced by Maries for Messrs Veitch in 1878. Of the flowering ashes (Ornus group) this is, I consider, the most ornamental, being very pretty both in flower and fruit. Being of slow growth and never of large size, it is admirable for small gardens.

F. NIGRA, *Marshall*. BLACK ASH

(F. sambucifolia, *Lamarck*)

A native of eastern N. America, whence it was introduced to England in 1800, this ash has never been a success, and appears to be unworthy of cultivation. It is a tree 80 to 90 ft. high in a wild state, and grows in damp situations; young shoots glabrous. Leaflets seven to eleven, oblong or oblong lance-shaped, slender-pointed, 3 to 5 ins. long, 1 to 2 ins. wide; glabrous on both surfaces except for reddish down along the side of the midrib and veins, beneath which it is densest towards the base, and extends round the main-stalk. All the leaflets except the terminal ones are stalkless—even more distinctly so than in F. mandshurica. In many of its characters the black ash is similar to F. mandshurica; the leaflets, however, are much less tapered or even rounded at the base, and the marginal teeth are shallow and quite inconspicuous. It has little interest or value in gardens.

F. OBLIQUA, *Tausch*

(F. Willdenowiana, *Koehne*; F. rotundifolia, *Hort.*, not *Lamarck*)

A small tree free from down in all parts, forming a rounded, dense head of branches; young shoots with small white warts. Leaves often in threes, 9 to 12 ins. long; leaflets usually nine or eleven, sometimes seven, scarcely stalked, ovate-lanceolate, 2 to 3½ ins. long, ¾ to 1 in. wide; tapered at the base, long-pointed, rather coarsely triangular-toothed; the terminal one is up to 5 ins. long and 1½ ins. wide, the others decreasing in size successively towards the base. The main-stalk has a continuous groove on the upper side, which, with the large terminal leaflet, distinguishes this from the other ashes with perfectly glabrous shoots and leaves. Fruit 1 in. long, ⅓ in. wide, pointed.

This ash was named obliqua by Tausch in 1834 (see *Flora*, xvii., p. 521), at which time it was in cultivation as F. rotundifolia, a name which clung to it for over seventy years, for plants so-called were in the Kew collection until forty years ago. According to Lingelsheim, a monographer of the ashes, it is a native of the eastern Mediterranean region and W. Asia, but a curious uncertainty as to its origin has always prevailed. Tausch thought it came from North America.

F. OREGONA, *Nuttall*. OREGON ASH

A tree up to 80 ft. high; young shoots reddish brown, rough with minute warts, more or less downy, sometimes densely so. Leaves 6 ins. to over 1 ft. long; leaflets five or seven, oval or oblong, 2 to 5 ins. long, 1 to 2 ins. broad; tapered or sometimes rounded at the base, contracted at the apex to a short or slender point; margins entire or obscurely toothed; dark green and with thin down above, pale and densely downy beneath. Main-stalk very pale, downy, grooved above; stalk of the terminal leaflets up to 1 in. long; lateral leaflets very shortly or not at all stalked. Flowers without petals, produced on the previous year's shoots. Fruit 1¼ to 2 ins. long, ⅓ in. wide towards the apex.

Native of western N. America, where it is a valuable timber tree. It was discovered by Douglas in 1825, but does not seem to have been introduced until many years after. It was in cultivation at Kew about eighty years ago, and trees up to 50 ft. high are very healthy and handsome. The finest tree known to Mr Elwes was at Nuneham, and about 65 ft. high. It is distinguished among ashes that, like itself, have all the young vegetative parts downy, by the large size of the stalkless or nearly stalkless, scarcely toothed side leaflets.

Var. PULVERULENTA, *Hort.*—Leaflets specked with grey. A tree at Kew is very vigorous, but this marking spoils rather than improves it.

F. ORNUS, *Linnæus*, MANNA ASH (Plate 4)

(Ornus europæa, *Persoon*)

A deciduous, very leafy tree, from 50 to 65 ft. high, forming a dense rounded head of branches; buds rough, grey; young shoots ordinarily without down. Leaves 5 or 8 ins. long, with five to nine leaflets which are ovate or oblong (the terminal one obovate), 2 to 4 ins. long, ¾ to 1¾ ins. wide; more or less tapered at the base, abruptly pointed at the apex, shallowly round-toothed; dull green and glabrous above; the base of the midrib beneath and the stalk downy. Main-stalk grooved above, furnished with brownish down where the leaflets are attached. Flowers whitish, very abundantly produced in May in terminal and axillary panicles 3 or 4 ins. long, along with the leaves of the new shoots; petals linear, ¼ in. long. Fruit about 1 in. long.

Var. LATIFOLIA, *Aiton.*—Leaves broader than those of the type and roundish oval in outline.

Var. VARIEGATA.—Leaves speckled with yellow; a form to be avoided.

Native of S. Europe and Asia Minor; cultivated since early in the eighteenth century, if not before; now one of the best known of exotic trees. It is a handsome tree with very luxuriant leafage, and decidedly ornamental in flower, although the blossom has a faint, not agreeable odour. Manna sugar is obtained from the stems by incision.

F. PAXIANA, *Lingelsheim*

(Bot. Mag., t. 9024; F. densiflora, *Lingelsheim*)

A deciduous tree 40 to 60 ft. high, with a trunk 3 to 4 ft. in girth; terminal winter buds very large, covered with brown down; young shoots glabrous. Leaves pinnate, 10 to 13 ins. long, consisting of seven or nine leaflets which are lanceolate, broadly wedge-shaped or rounded at the base, slenderly pointed, toothed, 3½ to 6 ins. long, 1 to 2 ins. wide; glabrous on both surfaces; stalk absent or up to ¼ in. long. Flowers white, produced during May and June in panicles 8 to 10 ins. wide, not so much long, at the end of leafy shoots; flower-stalks glabrous; petals oblong, rounded at the end, ⅛ in. long; calyx $\frac{1}{16}$ in. long, bell-shaped, toothed. Wings of the fruit truncheon-shaped in outline, 1 to 1¼ ins. long, $\frac{3}{16}$ in. wide, rounded at the end.

Native of Hupeh and Szechuen, China; introduced by Wilson in 1901. In a young state it is distinct in its stiff young shoots and especially for its large, downy winter-buds, clasped at the base by two thick scales. It belongs to the flowering (or Ornus) group of ashes. The base of the leaf-stalk is sometimes much enlarged after the fashion of F. Spaethiana and F. platypoda, the former of which can always be distinguished from it by having the lowest pair of leaflets very much smaller than all the others. It is hardy at Kew, but cannot be included amongst the best ashes there owing to its liability to injury by spring frosts. In localities where it escapes these it promises to be a handsome flowering ash, as it is, indeed, at Headfort in Co. Meath. It has ripened seed there.

F. PENNSYLVANICA, *Marshall.* RED ASH

(F. pubescens, *Lamarck*)

A tree 40 to 60 ft., sometimes more, high; young shoots clothed with a dense pale down. Leaves up to 1 ft. long; leaflets seven or nine, oblong lanceolate or narrowly oval, 3 to 6 ins. long, 1 to 2 ins. wide, broadly tapered at the base, long and slenderly pointed, rather obscurely toothed, or entire, especially at the lower half; dull green on both surfaces, and nearly or quite glabrous above, except along the sunken midrib which sometimes is downy; covered beneath with a pale down. The leaflets, especially the lower ones, are stalked, the stalks grooved and downy, as is also the common stalk. Male and female flowers occur on separate trees, and are produced on the old wood just below the new shoot. Fruit 1 to 2 ins. long.

Native of eastern N. America; introduced in 1783, often known under the name " F. pubescens " given to it by Lamarck in 1786, a year later than the accepted name. As common in gardens as F. americana, the red ash is not so effective and large a tree, although it grows quickly when young. From that species it is of course easily distinguished by its downy shoots and green under-side of the leaves. F. pennsylvanica exists in several forms in cultivation, some of which it is not easy to differentiate from F. lanceolata. F. GLABRA, *Koehne*, is an instance, regarded as a hybrid between the two.

Var. AUCUBÆFOLIA, *Rehder*.—Leaflets mottled with yellow. This variety in some of its characters is intermediate between pennsylvanica and lanceolata; the leaves are far from being as downy as the former, but the shoots are quite downy. A handsome variegated tree.

F. PLATYPODA, *Oliver*

(Hooker's Icones Plantarum, t. 1929)

A deciduous tree ultimately 60 to 70 ft. high; young shoots glabrous. Leaves 6 to 10 ins. long, made up of seven to eleven leaflets which are oval-oblong or lanceolate, finely toothed, slender-pointed, tapered at the base; 2 to 4 ins. long, ½ to 1¼ ins. wide; greyish green and glabrous above, with conspicuous down beneath towards the base of the midrib; stalk of leaflets very short and downy except that of the terminal one which is up to ½ in. long; main-stalk conspicuously dilated at the base and downy there. Panicles 4 to 6 ins. long. Fruits ("keys") oblong but tapered towards each end, especially towards the slender point, about 2 ins. long, ⅜ in. wide.

Native of Hupeh and Szechuen, China; discovered by Henry about 1887; introduced by Wilson in 1909. The chief distinguishing character of this ash is the broadened, enlarged base of the leaf-stalk. F. Paxiana and F. Spaethiana have the same peculiarity, but neither of them has the conspicuous patch of down near the base of the leaflets and both have the keys broadening towards the apex. There seems to be some doubt as to its place in the genus. Lingelsheim, Rehder, and Schneider put it with the Fraxinaster group, but Stapf observes that the material at Kew proves it to be of the Ornus or "flowering" group. The difficulty seems to arise from the absence of flowering specimens. I am not quite sure that the true thing is in cultivation in this country. Certainly some of the plants raised from Wilson's seed (No. 4423), which was supposed to be platypoda, are really Paxiana.

F. POTAMOPHILA, *Herder*

A small tree up to 30 or 35 ft. high, with green shoots; free from down in all its parts. Leaves 4 to 12 ins. long; leaflets stalked, usually nine or eleven, sometimes seven or thirteen; 1 to 3 ins. long, ¾ to 1½ ins. broad; tapered at the base, triangular toothed, pointed, dull green. Main leaf-stalks whitish beneath, with a broad, shallow groove above; stalks of the leaflets ¼ to ½ in. long, except the terminal one, which is ¾ to 1 in. long. Flowers and fruit not seen.

Native of Turkestan and other parts of W. Asia; introduced to Kew by way of St Petersburg Botanic Garden in 1891. It is an elegant small tree, very rare in cultivation, but quite distinct among ashes with the same number of leaflets, in their being conspicuously stalked, and, together with the young shoot, quite glabrous.

F. PUBINERVIS, *Blume*

A deciduous tree 45 ft. or more high; young shoots glabrous. Leaves up to 1 ft. or more long, with the main-stalk grooved on the upper side and made up of five to eleven leaflets which are narrowly ovate to oblong, long-pointed, broadly wedge-shaped or almost rounded at the base, toothed; 2 to 5 ins. long, 1 to 2 ins. wide; dark green and glabrous above, hairy close along the midrib and base of the chief veins beneath; shortly stalked. Fruits oblanceolate, tapering from near the end (which is often notched) to the base; 1¼ to 1¾ ins. long, $\frac{3}{16}$ to $\frac{5}{16}$ in. wide.

Native of Japan; introduced about 1900. It is quite hardy and grows well. It belongs to the Ornus or "flowering" ash group and is one of those that have the lowest pair of leaflets distinctly smaller than the others. This together with the grooved main-stalk of the leaf, and the fringe of down along the midrib, supply its chief distinctive features. Wilson during his expedition to Korea in 1917 seems to have found it on Quelpaert Island. It is perfectly hardy.

F. QUADRANGULATA, *Michaux*. BLUE ASH

A tree 60 to 70, occasionally over 100 ft. high; branchlets square and distinctly four-winged, not downy; bark of the trunk covered with loose plates. Leaves 7 to 14 ins. long, with five to eleven leaflets, which are ovate to lanceolate, 3 to 5 ins. long, 1 to 2 ins. wide; rounded or broadly wedge-shaped and unequal at the base, tapering at the apex to a long, slender point, sharply toothed; yellowish green and glabrous above, paler and downy beneath, especially about the midrib and veins. Common stalk minutely downy, and grooved on the upper side; stalks of leaflets $\frac{1}{8}$ to $\frac{1}{4}$ in. long. Flowers in short panicles from the previous year's wood; fruit $1\frac{1}{2}$ ins. long, $\frac{5}{16}$ in. wide, oblong, with a notch at the apex.

Native of the south-eastern and Central United States; introduced in 1823. It produces a valuable timber in the United States, but does not seem to have ever attained any great size in this country, although small trees at Kew are healthy and handsome. It is readily distinguished from all ashes with the same number of leaflets by its square, winged branchlets, except F. bracteata, and that has untoothed leaflets, and belongs to the Ornus group.

F. RHYNCOPHYLLA, *Hance*

(Garden and Forest, 1893, fig. 70; F. chinensis rhyncophylla, *Hemsley*)

A deciduous tree up to 80 ft. high in a wild state; young shoots glabrous, yellowish. Leaves mostly 6 to 12 ins. long, with five leaflets which are oblong, ovate, or obovate, shortly and slenderly pointed, wedge-shaped or rounded at the base, coarsely round-toothed; terminal leaflet 3 to 7 ins. long, 1 to 3 ins. wide, with a stalk up to 1 in. long, the other two pairs successively smaller and very shortly-stalked; dark green and glabrous above, with a fringe of down on the midrib and lower veins beneath; main-stalk slightly grooved, with tufts of down where the leaflets are attached. Flowers produced at the end of leafy shoots in June on panicles 3 to 6 ins. long; they have a calyx but no petals. Fruits oblanceolate, $1\frac{1}{2}$ ins. long, $\frac{3}{16}$ in. wide.

Native of Korea, China, and Japan; introduced from Pekin to the Arnold Arboretum in 1881. It is quite hardy and grows well in this country, being notable amongst the ashes for the large size of its leaflets, the terminal one especially. It is one of the Ornus group but belongs to the sub-section Ornaster, the flowers of which have a calyx but no corolla. It is closely related to F. chinensis, a very variable species to which some authors attach it as a variety. It is well distinguished from it by the number of leaflets being only five, F. chinensis having mostly seven or nine.

F. ROTUNDIFOLIA, *Miller*

(F. oxycarpa parvifolia, *Boissier*; F. parvifolia, *Lamarck*)

A small tree with green, glabrous young shoots and black buds. Leaves 5 to 8 ins. long, with seven to thirteen stalkless leaflets, which are oval or ovate, 1 to 2 ins. long, $\frac{1}{2}$ to 1 in. wide; tapered at both ends, sharply toothed except at the base; dull green and glabrous above, downy along the midrib beneath.

Main leaf-stalk whitish beneath, hairy and winged on the upper side, the two wings being closed except at the base and where the leaflets are attached.

Native of S. Europe and Asia Minor; introduced, according to Loudon, in 1822. Some authorities regard this ash as a variety of F. oxycarpa (see under F. angustifolia), but it differs so markedly in the shape and length of the leaflets and by their being so much more closely set on the main-stalk that it seems better to retain it. At the same time the distinctions between it, angustifolia, and oxycarpa as a species do not appear capable of very clear definition.

Var. NANA.—A dwarf form with smaller leaflets averaging 1 in. long, $\frac{1}{2}$ to $\frac{5}{8}$ in. wide, with a patch of down near the base. A healthy bush at Kew thirty years old is only 5 ft. high.

F. SPÆTHIANA, *Lingelsheim*. SPÄTH'S ASH

(F. serratifolia, *Hort.*; F. Sieboldiana, *Dippel*, not *Blume*)

A small or medium-sized tree of vigorous growth; young shoots shining, grey, stout, glabrous. Leaves up to $1\frac{1}{2}$ ft. long, with seven or nine (sometimes five) leaflets, which are oblong or narrowly obovate, the largest 8 to 9 ins. long, $2\frac{1}{2}$ to 3 ins. wide, but extremely variable in size according to the vigour of the shoot, the smallest being 2 to 4 ins. long, $\frac{3}{4}$ to $1\frac{1}{2}$ ins. wide; they are stalkless, markedly unequal at the base, long-pointed, coarsely round-toothed; glabrous above, pale beneath and slightly downy about the base of the midrib and lower veins. The common stalk is glabrous, crooked on big leaves, slightly grooved on the upper side, with the bases dark brown, very much swollen, and clasping the shoots; the lowest pair of leaflets is much the smallest. Flowers in terminal panicles. Fruit $1\frac{1}{2}$ ins. long, $\frac{1}{3}$ in. wide towards the apex, where it is broadest.

Native of Japan, belonging to the Ornus group; introduced over sixty years ago. Its leaves and leaflets are of remarkable dimensions on vigorous plants, but its most distinctive character is furnished by the enormous bases of the leaf-stalk. The whole tree has a yellowish tinge; worth cultivating as a striking and remarkable ash.

F. SYRIACA, *Boissier*. SYRIAN ASH

A deciduous tree, small in cultivation, and of slow growth; young branches without down, those of a year or two old usually packed closely with protuberances, which are the seats of the fallen leaves and buds. Leaves quite glabrous, normally in whorls of three, and densely crowded, but on free-growing shoots often alternate and well apart. Leaflets one to five (usually three), lance-shaped, tapered at the base; 1 to 4 ins. long, $\frac{1}{3}$ to $1\frac{1}{4}$ ins. wide; coarsely and sharply toothed, glossy dark green. The whole leaf is from 4 to 8 ins. long, the main-stalk and midribs whitish beneath, the former grooved above. Flowers produced in short racemes on the wood of the previous year. Fruit narrowly obovate, 1 to $1\frac{1}{2}$ ins. long, $\frac{1}{3}$ in. wide.

Native of Syria and Afghanistan and the country between. It does not, so far as I have observed, possess any recommendation for gardens, but is very distinct in the remarkably crowded leaves, and in the conspicuous protuberances on the younger branches. It has been cultivated under the wrong name of "F. Sogdiana."

F. TEXENSIS, *Sargent*. TEXAN ASH

A tree rarely 50 ft. high in nature; young shoots stout, glabrous, deep brown. Leaves on young trees 6 to 15 ins. long. Leaflets five or seven, oval or ovate (terminal one sometimes obovate), rounded or tapered, and often very unequal at the base, pointed at the apex in young plants, sometimes rounded in adult ones; coarsely but shallowly round-toothed, dark green and glabrous above, grey-white beneath, and at first downy, with the midrib and chief veins permanently beset with white hairs. The leaflets of adult trees are described by Sargent as 2 to 2½ ins. long by 1 to 2 ins. wide, but on trees at Kew twelve years old they are as much as 6½ ins. long by 3 ins. wide. Common stalk round except for a flattening at the top; stalk of leaflets up to ½ in. long. The fruit resembles that of F. americana but is only ½ to 1 in. long.

Native of limestone districts in Texas; discovered by Dr Bigelow in 1852; introduced to Kew in 1901. It is closely allied to F. americana, but has broader, more shortly pointed leaflets, commonly only five to each leaf. Young trees are vigorous, and particularly notable for their large deep green leaflets.

F. TOMENTOSA, *Michaux fil.* PUMPKIN ASH

(F. profunda, *Britton*; F. Michauxii, *Britton*)

A deciduous tree 50 to occasionally well over 100 ft. high; young shoots, leaf-stalks and flower-stalks conspicuously downy. Leaves 10 to 18 ins. long, composed of usually seven, sometimes nine, leaflets which are oblong-lanceolate or ovate, rounded or broadly wedge-shaped at the base, slender-pointed, inconspicuously or not at all toothed; 3 to 9 ins. long, 1½ to 3½ ins. wide; nearly glabrous above but softly downy beneath, especially near the midrib and veins; stalk of lower leaflets up to ¼ in. long; main-stalk round, not winged. Flowers produced during April on slender axillary panicles up to 5 ins. long, the most noticeable feature of which are the cup-shaped calyces, ⅛ in. long and unusually large for an ash. Fruit 2½ ins. long, ⅜ in. wide, often notched at the end. The flowers have no petals.

Native of the E. United States from New York to Florida; introduced to Kew from the Arnold Arboretum in 1912. This fine tree is most closely akin to the red ash, but it has larger "keys" and leaflets, is more conspicuously downy, and the calyx, as noted above, is larger. The popular name of "pumpkin ash" is said to have been given to the tree because it is "swell-butted," which means, presumably, that adult trees show pumpkin-shaped swellings near the base of the trunk. Trees 20 ft. high are at Kew.

F. VELTHEIMI, *Dieck*

(F. angustifolia monophylla, *Henry*)

A bushy habited tree very similar in form and arrangement of leaf to the one-leaved form of common ash, but easily distinguished from it by the leaves being quite glabrous beneath, and narrower. Leaflets usually solitary, sometimes in twos or threes, in which case the terminal one is always much larger than the lateral ones; lanceolate, 2 to 5 ins. long, ¾ to 1½ ins. wide; tapered towards both ends, the margins set with coarse, sharp, outstanding teeth; dark lustrous green above, quite glabrous on both surfaces. Lateral leaflets, when present, ¾ to 2½ ins. long, ¼ to ¾ in. wide. Stalk 1 to 2½ ins. long. It is no doubt a monophyllous variety of angustifolia. It has been in cultivation at Kew under other names for forty years at least, and makes a distinct and curious as well as an attractive tree.

F. VELUTINA, *Torrey*. ARIZONA ASH

(F. pistaciæfolia, *Torrey*)

A tree 30 to 40 ft. high, with a slender trunk; young shoots slender, and, like the leaf-stalks and leaflets, densely clothed with a velvety down. Leaves 4 to 6 ins. long, with five or seven leaflets which are lanceolate or narrowly oval, tapered at the base, long-pointed, 1½ to 2½ ins. long, ½ to ¾ in. wide (terminal one often larger, obovate, up to 3½ ins. long), the upper part bluntly and unevenly toothed, edged with fine hairs; dull greyish green. Common stalk with an open groove on the upper side: leaflets usually stalkless, the basal pair and terminal one occasionally stalked. Flower panicles downy. Fruit ½ to ⅔ in. long with an oblong-obovate to elliptic wing shorter than the body.

Native of S.W. United States and Mexico; introduced in 1891 to Kew, where it makes a neat, elegant, very leafy tree, distinct because of the grey down with which all the young parts are covered, combined with stalkless leaflets. F. holotricha and F. oregona have the same combination of characters, but in the former the leaflets are up to thirteen in number, and in oregona they are much larger.

FREMONTIA CALIFORNICA, *Torrey*. STERCULIACEÆ

(Bot. Mag., t. 5591)

A deciduous or half-evergreen, small tree, 15 to 30 ft. high, with soft and very downy twigs. Leaves alternate, 2 to 4 ins. long, 1½ to 3 ins.

FREMONTIA CALIFORNICA

wide; variable in outline, with usually three to seven lobes or large teeth, but sometimes almost entire; upper surface dull green, specked with star-shaped hairs when young, lower surface felted with brown-white, similar hairs. Flowers 2 to 2½ ins. across, produced singly on short stalks. There are no petals, the bright golden calyx being the conspicuous part of the flower; it is at first widely cup-shaped, has five roundish divisions, and is densely downy outside and very hairy in the centre inside. Stamens united in a short column, dividing at the top into five radiating arms ⅜ in. long. Ovary conical, with a slender style.

Discovered in California by Col. Frémont, after whom it is named, in 1846; this plant first flowered in England, at Chiswick, in 1854. It was again introduced from the Sierra Nevada by William Lobb in 1853, since when it has existed in numerous gardens in the milder parts of the kingdom. It is not hardy in the open at Kew, but a fine plant 10 ft. high grew in one of the bays outside the Temperate House, and flowered finely for several years. It was not trained, and took the form of a small tree. Although it survived the winter of 1908-9, and blossomed well the summer following, it has since died. The tree, in fact, is not long-lived, and although plants occasionally survive twenty or twenty-five years, growing and flowering admirably to the very last season, they are always liable to sudden collapse and death. Usually the plant is given a place on a wall, which would scarcely appear to be necessary in the milder parts. It flowers from May to July.

The fremontia produces plenty of its black seeds, which furnish the best and simplest means of increase. So averse is it to root disturbance, that young plants should be grown in pots until planted in their permanent places. It likes a well-drained, sandy loam.

F. MEXICANA, *Macbride*. STERCULIACEÆ

(Bot. Mag., t. 9269; Gardeners' Chronicle, 12th May 1928, fig. 158; Fremontodendron mexicana, *Davidson*)

An evergreen or partially evergreen shrub or small tree 10 to 20 ft. high; young shoots densely covered with pale brown, stellate down. Leaves variable in shape, mostly five-lobed, about 3 ins. wide, covered with the same down as the young shoots, dull green; stalk as long as the blade. Flowers orange yellow, without petals, their beauty consisting in the calyx which is 2½ to 4 ins. wide, with five deep rounded lobes. Stamens united at the base into a short column with five radiating arms at the top. Seed vessel conical, containing numerous black seeds.

Native of Lower California, originally discovered by Miss K. O. Sessions near Encenado; introduced in 1926. In general appearance and flower structure it bears a close resemblance to F. californica, but so far as can be judged from young plants the leaves are more densely downy, the flowers are larger and of a more orange shade, and the plant certainly is not so hardy. At Kew, even against a south wall, it was killed during the winters of 1927-8 and 1928-9. Seedlings grow much more quickly than those of F. californica and will reach 5 or 6 ft. in height in one season, continuing to flower from the leaf-axils from July to September. At its best it would appear to be handsomer than F. californica and in the milder counties may supplant it, but elsewhere it is too tender to affect the popularity of the older species. It flowers freely when a few months old.

FREYLINIA CESTROIDES, *Colla*. SCROPHULARIACEÆ

(F. lanceolata, *G. Don*; Capraria lanceolata, *Linnæus fil.*)

An evergreen shrub of dense, very leafy habit, 12 ft. or more high; young shoots slightly hairy, angled. Leaves opposite, linear, tapering towards both ends, slender-pointed; 2 to 5 ins. long, $\frac{1}{8}$ to $\frac{3}{8}$ in. wide; dark rather bright green on both surfaces, perfectly glabrous; midrib prominent beneath; scarcely stalked. Flowers sweetly scented, produced in a slender terminal panicle 2 to 4 ins. long, also from the axils of the terminal leaves, the whole forming at its best a compound pyramidal panicle 10 to 12 ins. high. Corolla $\frac{1}{2}$ in. long, tubular, $\frac{1}{8}$ to $\frac{1}{4}$ in. wide, with five small rounded lobes; yellow or creamy-white outside, richer yellow within and hairy in the throat; lobes often tipped with pink. Calyx $\frac{1}{12}$ in. long, deeply five-lobed. Stamens normally four, occasionally five; included in the corolla, to the inside of which they are attached.

Native of S. Africa; introduced in 1774. Usually grown in greenhouses and too tender for our average climate, this is hardy in the Isle of Wight and in the southern maritime counties. A very healthy specimen is in the garden of Ryde House, near Ryde. It is luxuriantly leafy, 10 ft. high, and I saw it in flower there in November 1921. A plant also flowered with Mrs Charles Williams at Greenway, S. Devon, the following month. The flowers are richly fragrant and the shrub is elegant in growth. It is evidently a lover of heat and sunshine, which probably explains its flowering after the hot summer of 1921. It blossoms wonderfully in Algiers. The best place for it with us would be against a warm south wall. It is related to Phygelius capensis.

FUCHSIA. ONAGRACEÆ

In the milder parts of the British Isles like Cornwall, S.W. Ireland, Isle of Wight, Isle of Man, etc., fuchsias make some of the most brilliant features of the late summer and autumn garden, growing into trees 10 ft. or more high, with trunks 6 ins. or more through. In colder, more northerly, and inland localities, they may still be grown in the open air, although they can scarcely be termed hardy shrubs, seeing that they are killed to the ground almost invariably. Yet even at Kew, groups of several sorts of fuchsias make very pleasing displays of colour from July onwards. Shoots spring up freely from the old stools, and attain a length of 3 to 5 ft. during the growing season, continuing to flower as they lengthen until the frosts come. The flower-buds add much to the beauty of the plants. A little brushwood or rough litter may be laid over the stools in very severe frost. Fuchsias like a well-drained, loamy soil, and can be increased with the greatest ease by means of soft-wood cuttings struck in heat.

As to the leading features of the genus, the leaves are opposite or whorled (rarely alternate), and deciduous; the flowers are pendulous, and produced singly on their stalks from the leaf-axils, or crowded in a terminal cluster; the calyx is tubular at the base, separating into four-pointed segments; the petals are four, springing from the end of the calyx-tube; the stamens eight; the fruit a juicy, four-sided berry, with rounded corners. Natives of S. America, Mexico, and New Zealand.

F. EXCORTICATA, *Linnæus fil*

(Bot. Reg., t. 857)

A deciduous shrub or small tree, up to 40 ft. high in a wild state, the trunk 6 to 18 ins. in diameter, with a thin, loose, peeling bark; young shoots glabrous. Leaves alternate, ovate, ovate-lanceolate or oval, tapered or rounded at the base, pointed, slightly or not at all toothed; 1½ to 4 ins. long, ½ to 1½ ins. wide; dark green and glabrous above, very pale or whitish beneath and downy along the midrib; stalk ⅓ to 1 in. long. Flowers of the ordinary fuchsia shape, pendulous, solitary in the leaf-axils, ¾ to 1¼ ins. long. Calyx-tube swollen at the base, then, after forming a neck, developing a funnel-shaped tube, finally dividing into four spreading awl-shaped lobes ⅓ in. long, the colour greenish, greenish-purple or dull red. Petals four, small, showing their pointed purplish tips between the lobes of the calyx. Stamens eight, very variable in length. Fruit ½ in. long, purplish black, juicy.

Native of New Zealand; introduced about 1820. It is very distinct among fuchsias by reason of its alternate leaves. It cannot be compared with the S. American species in beauty of blossom, but it is interesting in its peeling bark. It succeeds in many of the gardens of Cornwall and Devon, and Col. F. Stern grows it in his chalk garden at Highdown, near Worthing, where it flowers from May onwards. The finest plant I ever saw, however, was in Mr M'Douall's garden at Logan, in Wigtownshire, which in 1931 was 15 ft. high and 20 ft. in diameter.

The following descriptive list of a few sorts is by no means exhaustive, but will serve to draw attention to the outdoor possibilities of a genus of shrubs which must, on the whole, be regarded as greenhouse rather than hardy:—

F. COLENSOI, *Hooker fil.*, is another closely related, New Zealand species with alternate leaves very pale beneath, but it is a low rambling shrub with long, straggling, procumbent branches; young shoots very slender. Leaves roundish ovate, or heart-shaped, ½ to 1½ ins. long. Flowers very like those of F. excorticata, pendulous.

F. CONICA, *Lindley*.—A stiff-habited shrub with short-jointed, red shoots. Leaves broadly ovate or oval, mostly 1 to 1½ ins. long. Flowers slender, red and purple; calyx ½ in. long, with sepals ⅞ in. long and ⅛ in. wide; petals narrowly obovate. Distinct in the combination of small leaves and long flowers. Native of Chile.

F. CORALLINA, *Hort.* (syn. F. exoniensis).—Branches reddish purple when young. Leaves often in threes, 1½ to 4 ins. long, ½ to 2 ins. wide; dark green suffused with red-purple, especially the stalk, midrib, and veins. Calyx 1¼ to 1½ ins. long, with rich scarlet-red sepals ¼ in. wide; petals purple, obovate; stamens red, standing out ¾ in. beyond the petals. A selected form or hybrid of F. macrostemma.

F. GLOBOSA, *Lindley* (Bot. Reg., t. 1556).—A sturdy bush with ovate leaves 1 to 2 ins. long, glossy beneath. Calyx 1 in. long, rich red, with a short tube and sepals ¾ in. long, ¼ in. wide; petals rich purple, broadly obovate, ⅝ in. wide. This is distinguished by its stout buds and the comparative broadness and shortness of the floral parts.

F. GRACILIS, *Hort.* (Bot. Reg., t. 847).—A form of the macrostemma group, with smaller leaves proportionately longer-stalked than those of corallina. Flowers red and purple; calyx ¾ in. long, sepals ⅙ in. wide; stalk very slender, 1½ to 2 ins. long. A very elegant shrub, of which several minor forms with colloquial names are grown.

F. MACROSTEMMA, *Ruiz and Pavon*.—A South American species, introduced early in the nineteenth century. It probably includes all the foregoing sorts, being distinguished by a rich scarlet calyx, purple petals, much protruded stamens, and still more protruded style. Leaves mostly in threes at each joint. Figured in *Bot. Mag.*, t. 97, as coccinea (not of *Aiton*).

F. PARVIFLORA, *Lindley* (Bot. Reg., t. 1048), is a native of Mexico, introduced by the Horticultural Society in 1824 to the Chiswick garden, where it flowered two years later. It grew in a sheltered nook in Dame Alice Godman's garden at South Lodge, near Horsham, where it was a small-leaved prostrate shrub with small flowers each on a slender, downy stalk $\frac{1}{4}$ to $\frac{1}{2}$ in. long. Calyx tube $\frac{1}{3}$ to $\frac{1}{2}$ in. long, pink; petals purple. The leaves are opposite, oval or obovate, $\frac{1}{2}$ to $1\frac{1}{4}$ ins. long, slenderly stalked, the young shoots downy, and the flowers pendulous. In most gardens it will need winter shelter.

F. PROCUMBENS, *R. Cunningham* (Bot. Mag., t. 6139; syn. F. Kirkii, *Hooker fil.*), is the third New Zealand species. It is a perfectly prostrate creeping shrub with very slender wiry stems and alternate, roundish ovate, or almost orbicular leaves, mostly heart-shaped at the base, sometimes obscurely toothed, $\frac{1}{4}$ to $\frac{3}{4}$ in. long. Flowers erect, solitary in the leaf-axils, $\frac{1}{2}$ to $\frac{3}{4}$ in. long, without petals, opening from July onwards. Calyx-tube pale orange yellow, the four ovate lobes $\frac{1}{4}$ in. long, at first spreading then reflexed back to the tube, mostly purple but green at the base; anthers blue. Fruit flesh pink, $\frac{3}{4}$ in. long, oval. Distinct from all other fuchsias in its erect flowers. Discovered in 1834; introduced about twenty years later.

F. PUMILA, *Hort.*—A dainty little shrub of dwarf, compact, rounded habit; leaves $\frac{1}{3}$ to $\frac{3}{4}$ in. long, $\frac{1}{8}$ to $\frac{1}{3}$ in. wide, lanceolate; stalks, midrib, and veins red (like the young wood). Flowers on slender red stalks 1 in. long; calyx red, petals purple, the whole flower $\frac{3}{4}$ in. long.

F. RICCARTONI, *Hort.*—Considered to be one of the hardiest of fuchsias. It has the same colouring as the preceding, but the flower-buds are unusually stout, and the floral parts short and broad. Sepals $\frac{1}{2}$ in. long, $\frac{1}{4}$ in. wide; calyx-tube scarcely $\frac{1}{4}$ in. long. Leaves ovate-lanceolate, with a purplish tinge.

GARRYA. CORNACEÆ

A genus of evergreen, unisexual shrubs or small trees, with opposite leaves and flowers produced in greyish catkins. With the exception of G. elliptica, they have not much value in the majority of gardens, being more or less tender, and with little flower beauty. In the colder parts of our islands all the following will need protection, but in the south of England G. elliptica and G. Thureti are hardy in selected positions. Increased by cuttings of half-woody twigs in gentle heat. The genus was named by Douglas, in honour of Mr Garry of the Hudson's Bay Co., who helped him in his plant-collecting expeditions in western N. America. Garrya is a somewhat anomalous genus usually placed with the cornels, but by some authorities kept apart in a separate natural order—Garryaceæ, of which it is the only genus.

G. ELLIPTICA, *Douglas*

(Bot. Reg., t. 1686)

An evergreen shrub, or even a small tree, of vigorous, rapid growth and bushy habit, growing 6 to 12 ft. high in this country (16 ft. in the milder parts); young wood downy. Leaves oval to roundish; $1\frac{1}{2}$ to 3 ins. long, half, or more than half, as wide; more or less rounded at each end, the apex terminating in a short, abrupt tip; dark shining green above, grey-woolly beneath; margins wavy, but not toothed; stalk stout, woolly, $\frac{1}{4}$ in. long. Flowers densely crowded on slender pendent catkins 3 to 6 ins. long in cold districts, but 1 ft. or more long in warm ones, produced in a cluster towards the end of the shoot and in the leaf-axils near. Bracts silky in the male plant, cup-shaped, enclosing the base of the stamens; in the female plant longer and narrower. Fruit globular-ovoid, silky, with a thin, brittle shell, enclosing two seeds embedded in a dark red juice.

Native of California and Oregon; introduced by Douglas in 1828. For Garrya elliptica to be seen at its best, one must visit the gardens of Cornwall,

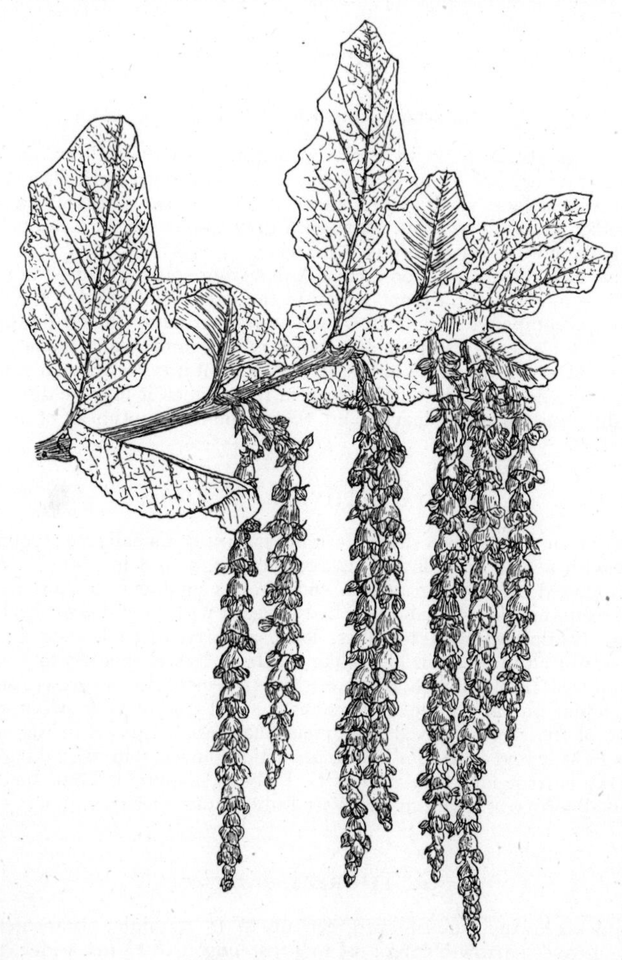

Garrya elliptica (male plant)

Devon, and similar places. It becomes there 16 ft. high, and as much through, and bears male catkins up to 12 ins. long. It is at its best from November to February, and at that season no evergreen shrub, perhaps, is more attractive than is this when laden with a great crop of silvery grey catkins. Near London, although not so satisfactory as in the south-west, it is an excellent evergreen if a suitable spot be chosen. It does not need a rich soil nor abundant moisture, and the best possible position for it is a sunny, rather dry bank sloping south or west, and protected by other vegetation on the north and east sides. It is a bad shrub to transplant, and should be grown in a pot until given a permanent place. The male plant, which we figure, is much the more ornamental, the catkins of the female being only 1½ to 4 ins. long. Cuttings of both strike root freely if taken in late summer and given a little heat. In very cold districts this Garrya will need wall protection. The down beneath the leaf is curly.

G. FREMONTII *Torrey*

(Gardeners' Chronicle, 1881, i., fig. 83)

An evergreen shrub up to 12 ft. in height. Leaves leathery, dark glossy green, obovate or oval, 1½ to 3 ins. long, tapering at both ends, with appressed hairs on both surfaces when young, afterwards glabrous. Catkins in a terminal cluster, each catkin 2 to 4 ins. long, with grey woolly bracts. Fruits globose, at first hairy, ultimately glabrous, ¼ in. wide.

Native of California, Oregon, etc. A flowering spray is figured in the place cited above, taken from a plant grown in the gardens of Gordon Castle, N.B. From the accompanying note it would appear to have proved hardier there than G. elliptica, both species being grown on the same wall. Some years ago I saw it in Messrs Dickson's nursery at Chester, but it is very rare in cultivation. It has not the fine qualities of G. elliptica, from which it may be distinguished by its differently shaped leaves and the ultimate smoothness of its foliage and fruit.

G. MACROPHYLLA, *Bentham*

A very robust evergreen shrub, forming naturally a small tree; young wood covered with a pale grey down. Leaves oblong, 5 to 8 ins. long, 2 to 4 ins. wide; rounded or tapering at both ends; apex ending in a short tip; dark glossy green and glabrous above, felted beneath with grey down; stalk ½ to 1 in. long. Male catkins 1 to 3 ins. long, axillary, often branched; female flowers produced in the axils of leaflike bracts on lateral shoots 3 to 5 ins. long.

Introduced from Mexico in 1846. This species can be grown on a wall near London, but in Guernsey it makes a small tree of very striking aspect. It is one of the largest leaved evergreens that can be grown in the open air. Flowers in May and June, but has no attractions apart from its striking foliage. This shrub is frequently met with as G. Fadyeni, a quite different species with much smaller leaves, found in the West Indies, and not hardy.

G. THURETI, *Carrière*

A quick-growing, robust evergreen up to 15 ft. high; branchlets stout, downy. Leaves narrow-oblong; 2½ to 4 ins. long, 1 to 1¼ ins. wide; tapering equally to both ends, the apex ending in a short, abrupt tip; upper surface becoming glabrous and glossy, lower one covered with a greyish down; stalk ½ in. long. Catkins more or less erect, greyish, terminal and axillary, 1½ to 3 ins. long, with the bracts in pairs at ⅓ in. apart, ovate-lanceolate, pointed, and very hairy.

A hybrid raised about 1862 at Antibes by M. Gustave Thuret, who crossed G. Fadyeni with the pollen of G. elliptica. This shrub is interesting but of little ornament. At Kew it is 12 ft. high, and as hardy as the pollen parent. Where the winters are not severe it forms a large, vigorous bush, but is disfigured by exceptionally severe frost. It blossoms in June.

GAULTHERIA. ERICACEÆ

An extensive genus of evergreen shrubs, most abundant in America; found also in the Himalaya, China, Malay Archipelago, and Australasia, but absent from Europe. The few species cultivated out-of-doors in Britain are shrubs of tufted habit, spreading by means of underground suckers. Leaves mostly alternate. Corolla of the pitcher- or bell-shape characteristic of the heaths and their allies; calyx five-lobed or toothed, persistent, becoming in many species fleshy and coloured like the fruit to which it adheres. Stamens ten. Fruit consisting of five cells, many-seeded, enclosed by the fleshy, persistent calyx.

In outward appearance Gaultheria is often very similar to Vaccinium, especially in leaf. I do not know of any easily discernible character to distinguish them in that respect. In flower, however, they are easily distinguished by the relative positions of corolla and ovary. In Vaccinium the calyx and corolla are uppermost, and the remnants of the calyx are usually present on the top of the fruit; in Gaultheria the ovary is uppermost and (with the exception of two or three species from New Zealand) the fruit becomes enclosed by the calyx-lobes which enlarge upwards and become fleshy.

The New Zealand members of this genus evidently hybridise considerably in their native state. The late Sir Arthur W. Hill of Kew collected specimens there which showed several gradations between antipoda and oppositifolia, between antipoda and perplexa, and between oppositifolia and perplexa. G. rupestris, a species rare in cultivation, is united to oppositifolia and perplexa by intermediate states.

The Gaultherias are peat, moisture, and often shade loving plants. The best of them in gardens is G. Shallon, which, planted in shady spots and not disturbed, will make very luxuriant and handsome low thickets of great density. It will grow quite well in ordinary soil. The generic name commemorates Dr Gaulthier, an eighteenth-century botanist and physician of Canada.

G. ANTIPODA, *Forster*

An evergreen shrub, said to vary in a wild state from a prostrate plant a few inches high on mountain sites, to an erect shrub 2 to 4 ft. high in lowland ones; young shoots usually bristly and downy. Leaves oval, orbicular or obovate, toothed, 1/3 to 2/3 in. long, thick and leathery, strongly veined, glabrous, dark green; stalk very short, bristly. Flowers solitary in the terminal leaf-axils. Corolla white, 1/8 in. long, cylindrical; borne on a downy flower-stalk about as long as itself. Calyx-lobes ovate-oblong, pointed, usually enlarging at the fruiting stage and becoming fleshy and enclosing the seed-vessel, the whole a white or red berry-like fruit about 1/2 in. across. Sometimes, as in the nearly allied G. perplexa, the calyx-lobes remain dry and unchanged; both states may be found on the same branch.

Native of New Zealand in the North and South Islands from sea-level to 4000 ft. altitude; introduced in 1820. It is a variable shrub, especially in habit and size of leaf; the latter, on young plants raised from seed, remain for some years about 1/4 in. or less in length. A curiosity, suitable for rock garden cultivation in the milder counties. Another New Zealand species of the same group as antipoda and perplexa is

G. DEPRESSA, *Hooker fil.*—It is always low and prostrate and has orbicular or oval leaves ⅛ to ⅓ in. long, sparsely toothed. The flowers are small, solitary in the terminal leaf-axils. Fruit very large for this plant, being up to ⅜ in. wide, fleshy, globose, white or red. It differs from antipoda chiefly in habit and the smaller leaves. (Syn. G. antipoda depressa, *Hooker fil.*)

G. CODONANTHA, *Airy-Shaw*

(Gardeners' Chronicle, 9th Dec. 1933, fig. 182)

A large, bushy, evergreen shrub up to 8 ft. high, with long graceful shoots, bristly when young. Leaves alternate, distichous, ovate to ovate-lanceolate, acuminate, cordate at the base, from 2½ to 7 ins. long, 1 to 5 ins. wide, with two thin marginal veins and two stouter ones running out with the midrib to the point; beautifully net-veined between and covered with short brown hairs beneath; stalk very short. Flowers in very shortly stalked, axillary clusters; corolla wavy white, often banded with red when fully open, ¾ in. wide, cup-shaped, opening successively; calyx triangularly five-lobed.

Native of Assam, very striking and handsome, found at about 5000 ft. altitudes by Kingdon Ward in 1928 and introduced under his number 8024. It flowered at Exbury in November 1933 and was given an Award of Merit at Vincent Square the same month. It is only likely to be hardy in our mildest counties. The flowers are unusually large for the genus.

G. CUNEATA, *Bean*

(Bot. Mag., t. 8829; G. pyroloides var. cuneata, *Rehder and Wilson*)

A low evergreen shrub 1 to 1½ ft. high, of close compact habit; young shoots very downy. Leaves of firm, leathery texture, obovate, oblanceolate, or narrowly oval, pointed, wedge-shaped at the base, shallowly toothed; ½ to 1⅛ ins. long, ¼ to ½ in. wide; dark glossy green and glabrous above, paler and dotted with dark glands beneath; stalk $\frac{1}{16}$ in. long. Flowers produced from June onwards in a cluster of axillary racemes, each 1 to 1½ ins. long, near the end of the twigs; main flower-stalk minutely downy. Corolla white, nodding, urn-shaped, ¼ in. long, with five small recurved lobes. Stamens ten, enclosed within the corolla, their stalks downy. Calyx whitish, five-lobed, the lobes triangular, $\frac{1}{12}$ in. long, ciliate; ovary silky. Fruit a downy capsule, enclosed except at the top by the calyx, which becomes snow-white and fleshy as in most gaultherias, the whole berry-like, globose, and ⅜ in. wide. Seeds numerous, shining, brown.

Native of W. Szechuen, China; introduced in 1909 by Wilson, who found it "quite common on humus-clad rocks in moist woods." It differs from G. Miqueliana (*q.v.*) and pyroloides in the silky ovary and downy fruit; the latter, however, is hidden by the white fleshy calyx. The white "berries" are ripe from August onwards and give the plant an interesting appearance. In November 1928 I noticed it in Mr Armytage Moore's garden at Rowallane, Co. Down, still bearing a great crop of them. It is very hardy and makes a pretty, dwarf ground cover.

G. FORRESTII, *Diels*

(Gardeners' Chronicle, 8th Oct. 1927, fig. 128)

An evergreen shrub, 1 to 5 ft. high; young shoots furnished with scattered bristles pointing forwards. Leaves leathery, oblong, narrowly oval or oblanceolate, pointed, tapered at the base, shallowly toothed; 1½ to 3 ins. long, ½ to 1½ ins. wide; dark bright green above, paler beneath and at first sprinkled with bristles, which fall and leave dark brown spots; stalk about $\frac{1}{8}$ in. long. Racemes slender, 1 to 2 ins. long, produced from the axils of the leaves in spring over the whole length of the previous season's shoots; main flower-stalk angular, downy, white. Corolla rather globose, $\frac{1}{5}$ in. wide, waxy white; calyx-lobes ovate, minutely ciliate. Fruits egg-shaped to globose, $\frac{1}{4}$ to $\frac{3}{8}$ in. long, the colour described by Forrest as "light China to Prussian blue," each on its stalk about $\frac{1}{8}$ in. long.

Native of Yunnan, China; discovered by Forrest in 1906 at altitudes of 10,000 to 20,000 ft. on the eastern flank of the Tali Range. The flowers are fragrant and the whiteness of the main and secondary flower-stalks adds to the beauty of the plant. It is in cultivation, seems to be fairly hardy, and should make an attractive addition to peat-loving evergreens, but chiefly in regard to its flowers. Mr Hanger of the R.H.S. gardens at Wisley considers it the best of the gaultherias in that respect, but poor (in this country) in regard to its fruits.

G. FRAGRANTISSIMA, *Wallich*

(Bot. Mag., t. 5984; G. ovalifolia, *Wallich*)

A large evergreen shrub or small tree; young shoots angled (even triangular), not downy. Leaves leathery, ovate, narrowly oval, pointed, tapered at the base, toothed; $1\frac{1}{2}$ to 4 ins. long, $\frac{3}{4}$ to 2 ins. wide; glabrous or nearly so, bright green above, freely sprinkled with dark brown dots beneath (the remnants of bristles); stalk $\frac{1}{12}$ to $\frac{1}{6}$ in. long. Racemes 1 to 3 ins. long, produced from the leaf-axils in April from the shoots made the previous year; main-stalk angled, downy. Flowers drooping, fragrant, closely packed on the raceme. Corolla ovoid to bell-shaped, scarcely $\frac{1}{4}$ in. long, greenish yellow or whitish, glabrous or nearly so outside; calyx five-lobed to half its depth. Fruit surrounded, as it usually is in this genus, by the enlarged fleshy calyx which is a beautiful dark blue; each one is borne on a stalk $\frac{1}{12}$ to $\frac{1}{6}$ in. long and downy like the main-stalk.

Native of the mountains of India, where it is widely spread; also of Ceylon; introduced about 1850, but described originally by Wallich in the *Asiatic Researches* in 1818. It succeeds well in the open air in Cornwall and similar places, and survives out-of-doors at Kew, but it really needs greenhouse treatment in many parts of the country. It is most nearly related to G. Forrestii but is a much more vigorous plant.

G. HISPIDA, *R. Brown*

(Gardeners' Chronicle, 13th Aug. 1927, fig. 53)

An evergreen shrub 2 to 3 ft., occasionally 6 to 7 ft., high; young shoots, the midrib of the leaves and the flower-stalks freely furnished with bristles and down. Leaves leathery, oblong or narrowly oval-lanceolate, very shortly stalked, minutely toothed, tapered at both ends, the apex with a short mucro; 1 to $2\frac{1}{4}$ ins. long, $\frac{1}{4}$ to $\frac{3}{4}$ in. wide; dark dull green and glabrous above. Flowers in terminal panicles (made up partly of axillary racemes) 1 to 3 ins. long. Corolla broadly urn-shaped, $\frac{1}{6}$ in. long, white; calyx-lobes triangular-ovate at first, afterwards enlarging, becoming succulent and berry-like, snow-white, enclosing the seed-vessel and forming a flattened, globose fruit $\frac{3}{8}$ to $\frac{1}{2}$ in. wide.

Native of the Australian Alps (Victoria) at altitudes of 4000 to 6000 ft., also of Tasmania up to 4000 ft. Whilst it survives even hardish winters at Kew and passes through mild ones uninjured, it really requires a warmer locality to do itself justice. The late Lord Wakehurst showed a charming plant from his garden in Sussex at Westminster in August 1927, well furnished with its white fruits. The late Mr Vicary Gibbs re-introduced it from Tasmania shortly before his death.

G. HOOKERI, *Clarke*

(Gardeners' Chronicle, 23rd Oct. 1943, fig. 77)

An evergreen shrub 3 to 6 ft. high; young shoots bristly. Leaves about 2 ins. long, oval-lanceolate, rounded at the base, the apex pointed (often abruptly), shallowly toothed, dotted and bristly beneath; stalk very short. Racemes downy, 1 to 2 ins. long with the flowers very shortly stalked and set rather closely. Corolla tubular and rather lily-of-the-valley like, white, $\frac{1}{5}$ in. long. Fruit globose, $\frac{1}{5}$ in. wide, purplish blue, covered with bloom.

Native of the Sikkim Himalaya up to 11,000 ft. altitude. It was in cultivation in 1933, probably before. Lord Aberconway obtained an Award of Merit for it on 21st September 1943, when he showed it in fruit at Vincent Square, Westminster.

G. LAXIFLORA, *Diels*

An evergreen shrub 3 to 6 ft. high; young shoots and leaves not downy. Leaves ovate-lanceolate, rounded or slightly heart-shaped at the base, tapered to a very slender, slightly curved apex, finely and regularly toothed; 2 to $4\frac{1}{2}$ ins. long, $\frac{1}{2}$ to $1\frac{3}{4}$ ins. wide; dark glossy green; prominently net-veined; of stiff, rather hard texture; stalk $\frac{1}{8}$ to $\frac{1}{4}$ in. long. Flowers produced in slender axillary racemes 2 to 3 ins. long, carrying twelve to twenty or more blossoms, white or yellowish, the broadly bell-shaped corolla $\frac{1}{8}$ in. long; anthers yellow; ovary shaggy. Fruit globose, $\frac{1}{4}$ in. wide, purplish black, ripe in August.

Native of Yunnan, China. Cultivated at Edinburgh and raised there, no doubt, from seeds collected by Forrest, who describes the bark, foliage, and all parts of the plant as strongly aromatic with a pungent pleasant odour, and the flowers as being fragrant. It makes graceful shoots 1 to 2 ft. long in a season and the racemes spring from the leaf-axils of the terminal half during the following May.

G. MIQUELIANA, *Takeda*

(Bot. Mag., t. 9629; G. pyroloides, *Miquel*, partly)

An evergreen shrub 8 to 12 ins. high; young shoots at first downy becoming glabrous. Leaves oval, toothed, tapered about equally at both ends; $\frac{1}{2}$ to $1\frac{1}{4}$ ins. long, $\frac{3}{8}$ to $\frac{3}{4}$ in. wide; glabrous, distinctly net-veined beneath, dark green above. Flowers drooping, solitary to as many as six on racemes 1 to 2 ins. long; main flower-stalk downy. Corolla rather globose, $\frac{1}{4}$ in. wide, white, with small triangular teeth at the mouth; ovary glabrous. Calyx-lobes triangular at first, ciliate, afterwards enlarging and enclosing the seed-vessel, forming a berry-like fruit $\frac{3}{8}$ in. wide, globose, white or pink, edible.

Native of Japan and a handsome small evergreen both as regards flowers and fruits. It is quite hardy and flowers in June. It is most nearly related to the G. cuneata previously described—a white-fruited Chinese species but with a downy ovary and narrower obovate leaves. It may be noted that the names pyroloides and pyrolæfolia are much confused. The former was originally given by Miquel to the white-fruited species from Japan just described; but unfortunately he united with it what has been known as pyrolæfolia, a

Himalayan species with blue-black fruits, thereby causing the confusion. The name "pyrolæfolia" has been suppressed and the Japanese shrub has been called G. Miqueliana as given above. G. pyroloides (*q.v.*) differs from both cuneata and Miqueliana in having the leaves clustered near the end of the twigs.

G. NUMMULARIOIDES, *G. Don*

A dwarf evergreen shrub, 4 to 6 ins. high, forming dense tufts, and spreading by underground shoots; stems slender and wiry, covered with bristles, and bearing over their whole length leaves ¼ in. apart in two opposite rows. Leaves leathery, heart-shaped, becoming smaller towards the tip of the shoot; ¼ to ⅝ in. long, about the same wide; the lower surface and the margins are bristly; the upper side is dark dull green and wrinkled, the lower one very pale polished green; stalk ⅛ in. or less long. Flowers produced singly in the leaf-axils from the under-side during August; corolla egg-shaped, white or tinged with pink, scarcely ¼ in. long.

Native of the Himalaya; long cultivated, but still rare in gardens. It makes charming dense tufts of foliage and stems, but needs some shelter. Plants which grew in the open in the rock garden at Kew, and which had not suffered from cold since the frosts of 1895, were killed by the severe winter of 1946-47. Its roundish leaves, closely and regularly set in two rows, and gradually decreasing in size towards the end of the shoot, with the slender, conspicuously bristly stems, render it quite distinct from any other plant in cultivation. Increased by cuttings.

G. OPPOSITIFOLIA, *Hooker fil.*

A very leafy evergreen shrub of sturdy, bushy, much branched habit, up to 8 ft. high in a wild state; young shoots mostly glabrous, but with scattered bristles sometimes. Leaves opposite, stalkless, ovate, heart-shaped or oblong-ovate, toothed, the base often overlapping the stem; 1 to 2 ins. long, ¾ to 1½ ins. wide; dark glossy green and glabrous above, pale, strongly net-veined and occasionally with scattered bristles beneath. Flowers borne very numerously in terminal panicles as much as 4 ins. wide and long; flower-stalks glabrous. Corolla bell-shaped, white, about ⅙ in. long; calyx-lobes narrow triangular, glabrous, dry, and never apparently becoming fleshy and enlarged, as is usual in this genus.

Native of New Zealand in the mountains of the North Island up to 3000 ft. It flowers with us in May and June. The species is very distinct in the opposite leaves, being the only one of the genus with that character known to me, but at the upper part of the branches towards the flower-panicle there are sometimes three in a whorl. It is the most ornamental of the gaultherias in New Zealand in regard to its flowers and comparable in this respect with the better Chinese and Himalayan species. In 1931 there was a bush 3 ft. high and 4 ft. wide at Wakehurst in Sussex, which flowered beautifully every year.

G. FAGIFOLIA, *Hooker fil.*, is near the above, having its white flowers in racemes up to 2 ins. long. The leaves, however, are alternate and usually ½ to 1 in. long. The calyx-lobes do not enlarge nor become succulent. New Zealand. It is succeeding well with Mr J. B. Stevenson at Tower Court, Ascot. It may be a hybrid between G. oppositifolia and G. antipoda.

G. OVATIFOLIA, *A. Gray*

A low evergreen shrub of spreading or trailing habit from 8 to 12 ins. high, the branches erect, sparingly furnished with comparatively long hairs. Leaves broadly ovate, pointed at the apex, rounded or slightly heart-shaped at the base, very shallowly toothed of hard rather leathery texture and arranged regularly on the shoots about $\frac{1}{4}$ in. apart; $\frac{3}{4}$ to $1\frac{1}{2}$ ins. long, $\frac{1}{2}$ to $1\frac{1}{4}$ in. wide; dark glossy green and wrinkled above, margins of young leaves hairy; stalk $\frac{1}{16}$ to $\frac{1}{12}$ in. long, hairy. Flowers solitary in the leaf-axils, each on a stalk $\frac{1}{12}$ in. long. Corolla white or pinkish, bell-shaped, $\frac{1}{5}$ in. long, with five small teeth at the mouth. Calyx five-lobed, bristly, the lobes about half as long as the tubular part. Fruit scarlet, $\frac{1}{4}$ in. wide, globose, described as very spicy and delicious.

Native of W. North America in the Cascade Mountains, Oregon, northwards to British Columbia, including Vancouver Island. It is not common in cultivation but it is in the Leonardslee collection and used to be grown by Mr Murray Hornibrook in Queen's County, Ireland. (The name must not be confused with G. ovalifolia, a synonym of G. fragrantissima.)

G. HUMIFUSA, Rydberg (syn. G. myrsinites, *Hooker*), is nearly akin to G. ovatifolia, but is of neater, closer, more tufted habit and about 4 ins. high. The leaves are about half the size; fruit smaller but also scarlet. It is quite hardy and has been known for over one hundred years. Suitable for the rock garden. Native of western N. America.

G. PERPLEXA, *T. Kirk*

An evergreen shrub sometimes prostrate, sometimes 1 to 3 ft. high, the branches wiry, flexuous and often interlaced. Leaves linear, pointed, $\frac{1}{4}$ to $\frac{1}{2}$ in. long, $\frac{1}{16}$ in. wide, often recurved, inconspicuously bristle-toothed, quite glabrous, very shortly stalked. Flowers solitary in the leaf-axils towards the end of the shoot, each on a glabrous stalk $\frac{1}{12}$ to $\frac{1}{6}$ in. long; corolla white, urn-shaped, $\frac{1}{8}$ in. long; calyx-lobes linear-lanceolate, minutely downy on the margins. The seed-vessel is usually enclosed in the enlarged succulent calyx, as occurs in this genus generally, the whole forming a rosy red, berry-like fruit $\frac{1}{2}$ in. across; but frequently the calyx remains dry and unenlarged.

Native of the North and South Islands, New Zealand, where it has a wide range of habitats, but is commonest at elevations of 1500 to 3000 ft.; first discovered about 1847. It is a curious shrub of no great beauty, being remarkable for the often intricate interlacing of the slender branches and the small narrow leaves which are distinct from those of any other species in cultivation. It is grown under glass at Kew, but it is in the Rectory Garden at Ludgvan, near Penzance, and it is in the open air at Wakehurst in Sussex. It flowers in May in England. Suitable for the rock garden in the milder counties.

G. PROCUMBENS, *Linnæus*. CREEPING WINTERGREEN

(Bot Mag., t. 1966)

A low, tufted evergreen shrub, growing 2 to 6 ins. high, spreading by creeping roots, from which it sends up slender stems naked except at the top, where they carry a cluster of about four leaves; stems at first downy, afterwards glabrous and glossy. Leaves dark glossy green, thick and leathery, quite glabrous, obovate or oval, $\frac{3}{4}$ to $1\frac{1}{2}$ ins. long, $\frac{1}{2}$ to $\frac{7}{8}$ in. wide; faintly toothed, the teeth often bristle-tipped; they have a strong aromatic odour and taste like that of birch, and turn reddish as winter approaches; stalk $\frac{1}{6}$ in. long. Flowers produced in July and August, singly in the leaf-axils and at the top of the stem. Corolla ovoid-cylindrical, $\frac{1}{4}$ in. long, nodding, pinkish white; calyx-lobes broadly ovate, edged with tiny hairs; flower-stalk downy, $\frac{1}{4}$ in. long, decurved. Fruit bright red, globose, $\frac{1}{3}$ in. wide, with a pleasant, rather inspid taste.

Native of eastern N. America; introduced in 1762. It has there a variety of popular names such as "box-berry," "creeping wintergreen," and, because of the fondness of partridges for the berries, "partridge-berry." An oil is extracted from it which possesses stimulating and tonic properties, but is now largely adulterated with birch-oil. As a garden plant it is very pleasing for the cheerful dark green of its lustrous leaves, forming neat close tufts. It makes a pleasing undergrowth or furnishing beneath thin deciduous shrubs. Owing to the leaves in a great measure hiding the drooping flowers and fruit, its attractiveness is almost wholly in the habit and foliage.

G. PYROLOIDES, *Miquel, emend. Takeda*

(G. pyrolæfolia, *Hook. f. ex C.B.Cl.*)

An evergreen shrub of close tufted habit, 4 to 8 ins. high; young shoots slightly downy. Leaves clustered towards the end of the twig, obovate to roundish, wedge-shaped at the base, rounded or blunt at the apex, toothed except towards the base, $\frac{5}{8}$ to $1\frac{1}{2}$ ins. long, $\frac{3}{8}$ to 1 in. wide; glabrous except for scattered bristles beneath; stalk $\frac{1}{12}$ in. or less long. Flowers produced in May and June, two to five on a downy raceme up to 1 in. long; corolla egg-shaped, $\frac{1}{5}$ in. long, white or pink, with small teeth at the orifice; calyx-lobes small triangular; ovary glabrous. Fruit $\frac{1}{4}$ in. wide, globose-ovoid, blue-black.

Native of the Himalaya; found by Hooker in Sikkim in 1849. In 1922 it was collected during the Mt. Everest expedition at 13,500 ft. altitude. In places it forms a dense ground cover in the way of the North American G. procumbens. It is related to G. cuneata described above, which is, however, well distinguished by its white fruits, its downy ovary, and by the oval or narrowly obovate leaves which are distributed all along the downy young shoots. (See also G. Miqueliana.)

G. SHALLON, *Pursh*. SALAL, SHALLON

(Bot. Mag., t. 2843)

An evergreen shrub, 2 to 6 ft. high, forming a dense thicket of stems, and spreading by means of underground suckers; young branches reddish and bristly, becoming rough with age. Leaves leathery, broadly ovate, the base rounded or heart-shaped, the apex always sharply pointed; evenly and finely bristle-toothed; $1\frac{1}{2}$ to 4 ins. long, $\frac{3}{4}$ to $2\frac{1}{2}$ ins. wide; stalk reddish, hairy, $\frac{1}{8}$ to $\frac{1}{4}$ in. long. Flowers produced during May and June in viscid, glandular racemes $1\frac{1}{2}$ to 5 ins. long, at the end of the previous year's shoots, and in the axils of several terminal leaves; each flower produced from the axil of a hooded, ovate bract, $\frac{1}{4}$ in. long. Corolla pinkish white, egg-shaped, downy, $\frac{3}{8}$ in. long, five-toothed at the mouth; calyx white, its lobes triangular, downy, pressed to the corolla. Fruit a juicy, top-shaped, hairy berry, dark purple, $\frac{3}{8}$ in. wide, carrying many tiny seeds, and pleasantly flavoured; the bracts adhere at the base.

Native of western N. America; introduced by Douglas in 1826. This useful and handsome shrub is one of the best we have for forming a dense evergreen thicket in moist, shady spots. It can be propagated by seeds, which it ripens in great numbers, also by division of the old plants, but to do the latter advantageously it is necessary to plant the pieces in a few inches of sandy soil on a hot-bed. Broken up and planted in the open ground the pieces take long to recover. It may be recommended as cover for game.

G. SINENSIS, *Anthony*

A compact, matted, evergreen shrub up to 12 ins. or more high and more in width; young shoots slender, reddish, hairy. Leaves dense, $\frac{2}{8}$ to $\frac{3}{8}$ in. long, half as much wide, obovate to oblanceolate, scarcely stalked, apex mucronulate, base cuneate, very shallowly toothed, dark shining green. Flowers axillary, solitary; corolla white, urn-shaped. Fruit bright blue, globose to fig-shaped, $\frac{1}{2}$ in. wide. According to the catalogue of Mr Marchant of Wimborne there are forms with pink and white fruits.

Native of Yunnan, China, discovered in August 1914 at 12-13,000 ft. altitudes by Forrest; later by Kingdon Ward, one of whose introduced plants, then in flower, was given an Award of Merit at Vincent Square on 25th April 1939. It is an admirable hardy rock garden shrub.

G. TETRAMERA, *W. W. Smith*

(Bot. Mag., t. 9618)

An evergreen shrub, 2 ft. and upwards high, usually more in width; young shoots bristly. Leaves leathery, obovate to oblanceolate and roundish, 1 to 2 ins. long, about half as wide, rounded to pointed at the apex, rounded to cuneate at the base, shallowly toothed, glabrous above, sparsely bristly below; stalk short. Flowers fragrant, crowded in axillary racemes about 1 in. long; corolla greenish white, ovoid, nearly closed at the mouth where are four or five tiny revolute lobes. Fruit brilliant violet-blue or china blue, globose, $\frac{1}{4}$ in. wide.

Native of S.W. China, discovered and collected several times by Forrest in 1912, in one instance at 13,000 ft. altitude. It should, therefore, be fairly hardy but will, no doubt, succeed best in the south and west. I have for instance seen it very attractively in fruit at Exbury on the Solent.

G. TRICHOPHYLLA, *Royle*

(Bot. Mag., t. 7635)

A low evergreen shrub of densely tufted habit, 3 to 6 ins. high, spreading by means of underground shoots; stems wiry and slender, bristly, furnished with twelve or more leaves to the inch. Leaves stalkless, narrow-oblong; $\frac{1}{4}$ in. long, $\frac{1}{10}$ to $\frac{1}{8}$ in. wide; glabrous on both surfaces, but bristly on the margins, glossy dark green above, pale beneath. Flowers solitary in the leaf-axils; corolla pink, $\frac{1}{6}$ in. long and wide, bell-shaped. Fruit blue.

Native of Himalaya up to 13,000 ft.; introduced to Kew in 1897, where it has, up to the present, proved fairly hardy in ordinarily sheltered places. It is a dainty plant suitable for the rock garden, and pleasing for the bright green of its foliage and neat habit. Propagated by cuttings and division.

G. VEITCHIANA, *Craib*

(Bot. Mag., t. 9174)

A low evergreen shrub forming a dense, rounded tuft, and spreading by underground stems; branchlets clothed with minute down, with which are intermixed long bristles. Leaves of hard texture, $1\frac{1}{2}$ to $3\frac{1}{2}$ ins. long, half as wide; oblong or slightly obovate, rounded or broadly tapered at the base, abruptly narrowed at the apex to a short glandular tip; shallowly toothed, the teeth often bristle-tipped; upper surface much wrinkled, dark glossy green, conspicuously net-veined, without down; lower surface at first furnished with bristles which partially fall away, leaving it harsh to the touch; stalk $\frac{1}{12}$ to

$\frac{1}{8}$ in. long. Flowers densely packed in axillary racemes, 1 in. or more long, white. Corolla $\frac{1}{6}$ in. long, nodding, narrowed from the base to the mouth; calyx-lobes lanceolate; main-stalk downy, each flower produced in the axil of an ovate, membranous, more or less ciliated bract $\frac{1}{4}$ in. long; the short glabrous flower-stalk is also furnished with bracts partially hiding the flower. Fruit indigo-blue, about the size of a small pea.

Native of Hupeh, China; introduced by Wilson about 1907, and a very

GAULTHERIA VEITCHIANA

distinct, neat evergreen, thriving well in peat and much moisture. Allied to the Himalayan G. Hookeri.

G. WARDII, *Marquand and Shaw*

(Bot. Mag., t. 9516)

An evergreen shrub of low spreading growth 3 or 4 ft. high; young shoots covered with pale brown bristles. Leaves almost stalkless, of hard leathery texture, elliptic-lanceolate, slenderly pointed, rounded at the base, margins recurved; 1 to $3\frac{1}{2}$ ins. long, $\frac{1}{2}$ to $1\frac{1}{4}$ ins. wide, at first bristly, finally glabrous above and with conspicuously sunken, netted veins; thickly bristly beneath. Racemes produced from the axils of the terminal leaves of the previous season's growths, about $\frac{1}{2}$ in. long, with the six to ten flowers closely packed. Calyx deeply five-lobed, the lobes ovate-lanceolate, $\frac{1}{6}$ in. long, hairy outside; corolla white, $\frac{1}{5}$ in. wide, only slightly exceeding the calyx-lobes, pitcher-shaped; ovary downy. The floral bracts (which are narrowly obovate) and the flower-stalks are downy and bristly.

Native of S.E. Tibet, discovered on "dry pine-clad slopes amongst bracken, etc." by Kingdon Ward in 1924. It is interesting botanically in the calyx remaining dry and membranous and never becoming fleshy and fruit-enclosing, as is almost invariably the case in this genus. Apart from that, the two most marked characters of the plant are its general bristliness and the deeply sunken veins of the leaf. The plants in cultivation bear Kingdon Ward's number, 7134, for which he supplied the following field note:—"Flowers snow-white, in masses. Berries blue with white bloom; undershrub growing on sunny boulder slopes, in thickets." It appears to be quite hardy at Kew, but has grown much more vigorously at Exbury, near the Solent, where it flowers regularly in May or June and ripens its milky blue fruits by September.

GAULTHETTYA WISLEYENSIS, *Rehder*

(Journ. Royal Hort. Society, 1939, fig. 16)

This is a bigeneric hybrid raised (or first came into public notice) in the Horticultural Society's gardens at Wisley. (The name "Gaulnettya" has also been used for it.) Its parents are presumed to be Gaultheria Shallon and Pernettya mucronata. Several hybrids between these two genera of natural origin have been found in New Zealand. A special interest of the Wisley hybrid is that it unites a Californian shrub with a very dissimilar South American one.

G. wisleyensis is an evergreen, bushy shrub 3 ft. or more high, young shoots downy. Leaves oval to ovate, 1½ to 2½ ins. long, tapered at both ends or rounded at the base, shallowly toothed, leathery, soon nearly or quite glabrous. Flowers pearl-white, borne in downy, glandular clusters of terminal and axillary racemes near the end of the shoots, each 1½ to 2½ ins. long, carrying six to fifteen flowers and opening in May and June. Mr Marchant compares them in general appearance to lily-of-the-valley blossoms. Fruit globose, ¼ in. wide, purple-black, very abundantly produced. This shrub, attractive both in flower and fruit, was given an Award of Merit at Vincent Square, 20th June 1939.

GAYLUSSACIA. HUCKLEBERRY. VACCINIACEÆ

This genus contains some forty to fifty species which belong exclusively to the New World, the greater proportion being found in S. America. About half a dozen species are in cultivation, all from eastern N. America, and, with the exception of G. brachycera, deciduous shrubs. The leaves are alternate, not toothed except in brachycera, and often resin-dotted. The corolla resembles that of Vaccinium, to which genus Gaylussacia is closely allied. The fruit is berry-like, outwardly similar to that of Vaccinium, but markedly different in containing ten cells and ten nutlets, instead of the four or five cells and numerous minute seeds of Vaccinium. The genus commemorates J. L. Gay-Lussac, the French chemist (1778-1850). Cultivation the same as for Vaccinium; but these shrubs have obtained little attention in gardens. Some of the species yield in a wild state large crops of edible fruits in N. America, but have no value in that respect with us.

G. BACCATA., *K. Koch.* BLACK HUCKLEBERRY

(G. resinosa, *Torrey and Gray*)

A deciduous, much-branched shrub, 1 to 3 ft. high, the young wood minutely downy and viscid. Leaves obovate or oval, mostly bluntish at the apex; 1 to 2¼ ins. long, ½ to ¾ in. wide; deep green above, paler yellowish and clammy with numerous resin-dots beneath. Flowers produced in May in drooping racemes 1 in. or less long, carrying six to eight flowers, each on a thin stalk $\frac{1}{8}$ to $\frac{1}{4}$ in. long. Corolla conical, $\frac{1}{5}$ in. long, narrowed towards the mouth, dull red. Berry $\frac{1}{4}$ to $\frac{1}{3}$ in. diameter, globose, shining black, without bloom.

Native of eastern N. America; introduced in 1772. In the United States it is considered the best of the huckleberries for eating, although said to vary very much in quality in different localities. It is distinguishable from the other deciduous huckleberries by the abundant resinous secretion on twig, leaf, flower-stalk, etc.

Var. LEUCOCARPA.—Fruits whitish.

GAYLUSSACIA DUMOSA

G. BRACHYCERA, *A. Gray*. BOX HUCKLEBERRY

(Vaccinium buxifolium, *Salisbury*, Bot. Mag., t. 928)

A dwarf evergreen shrub, 6 to 12 ins. high; young stems angled, glabrous or minutely downy. Leaves thick, leathery, oval to ovate, toothed, $\frac{1}{3}$ to 1 in. long, about half as wide, dark glossy green above, paler below, glabrous, very shortly stalked. Flowers produced in May and June in short axillary racemes near the end of the shoot, each flower on a very short stalk. Corolla cylindrical, but contracted at the mouth, $\frac{1}{4}$ in. long, white, faintly striped with red. Berries not seen; described as blue.

Native of the eastern United States, on the mountains and hills from Virginia northwards to Pennsylvania; originally introduced in 1796. It was subsequently quite lost to cultivation, but through the agency of the Arnold Arboretum, Mass., has been restored to gardens. It is still a very rare plant, but one of the daintiest of evergreens, forming low, neat patches, resembling to some extent Vaccinium Vitis-idæa minor.

G. DUMOSA, *Torrey and Gray*. DWARF HUCKLEBERRY

(Vaccinium dumosum, *Andrews*, Bot. Mag., t. 1106)

A deciduous shrub, 1 to 2 ft., or sometimes twice as much high, spreading by underground stems, the young twigs furnished with gland-tipped hairs. Leaves narrowly oval or obovate, pointed, $\frac{3}{4}$ to $1\frac{1}{2}$ ins. long, $\frac{1}{4}$ to $\frac{5}{8}$ in. wide; deep shining green, more or less glandular downy on both surfaces and at the edges, not toothed; stalk very short. Flowers produced in June on short downy racemes furnished with oval, persistent, leaf-like bracts ¼ in. or more long, from the axils of which the flowers spring. Corolla bell-shaped, ⅓ in. long and wide, pure waxy white, nodding; calyx with downy triangular lobes. Berries globose, black, ¼ to ⅓ in. wide, downy; not much valued for eating.

Native of eastern N. America from Newfoundland to Florida, never far from the coast, and said to prefer sandy soil; introduced in 1774. It is a handsome shrub both in flower and fruit, and differs from the other deciduous species in cultivation by the large, white, open bell-shaped flowers.

G. FRONDOSA, *Torrey and Gray*. DANGLEBERRY

(Vaccinium frondosum, *Linnæus*; V. venustum, *Aiton*)

A deciduous shrub, 3 to 6 ft. high, with slender, divergent branches; young wood glabrous or nearly so. Leaves obovate or oval, rounded or notched at the apex; 1 to 2½ ins. long, ½ to 1¼ ins. wide; bright green and glabrous above, rather glaucous, downy, and sprinkled with resin-dots beneath. Flowers produced in June and July on loose, slender racemes 1½ to 3 ins. long, each flower on a threadlike, pendulous stalk ⅓ to 1 in. long. Corolla roundish bell-shaped, scarcely ⅕ in. long, purplish green; calyx-lobes glabrous, triangular. Berry blue, ⅓ in. or more wide, globose, very palatable.

Native of the eastern United States; introduced in 1761. This is one of the handsomest of the gaylussacias, and is distinct in the long-stalked flowers and lax racemes, and the bluntish leaves. The popular name refers to the loosely hanging berries; they are not freely developed in this country.

G. URSINA, *Torrey and Gray*. BEAR HUCKLEBERRY

(Vaccinium ursinum, *Curtis*)

A deciduous shrub of loose branching habit, 2 to 5 ft. high; young twigs slightly downy. Leaves obovate or oval, pointed, tapering or rounded at the base; 1½ to 4 ins. long, ¾ to 1½ ins. wide; green and more or less downy on both sides, thin. Flowers produced during June in racemes 1 to 2 ins. long, each of the six to ten flowers being borne on a slender stalk about ½ in. long. Corolla roundish, bell-shaped, dull white or reddish, ⅕ in. long, lobes recurved. Berry shining black, globose, ⅓ to ½ in. diameter.

Native of the south-eastern United States, and especially on the mountains of N. Carolina, whence it was introduced to Kew in 1891. It is most nearly allied to G. frondosa, differing in the pointed, thinner leaves, green on both sides, and in having a black fruit, but resembling that species in the loose sparsely flowered racemes. The fruit is described as insipid.

GENISTA. BROOM. LEGUMINOSÆ

A large genus of shrubs, mostly deciduous, but sometimes acquiring the character of an evergreen from the colour of the young branches. They vary from dwarf and prostrate plants a few inches high to tall ones with a stature of over 20 ft. In a wild state they are found almost exclusively in Europe, but a few reach the western borders of Asia and the southern shores of the Mediterranean. With but one exception among cultivated hardy species (G. monosperma, with white flowers), the blossom is of some shade of yellow, and all have the pea-flower (or papilionaceous) form. The leaves are simple or trifoliolate, often so small and few as to be negligible; in these cases the work usually done by leaves devolves upon the green branches.

As garden shrubs some of the genistas, such as ætnensis, hispanica, cinerea, glabrescens, pilosa, and virgata, are in the very front rank, and are all worth growing. They are easily accommodated and do not require a rich or manured soil. A sunny position (for most of them are essentially sun-lovers) and a well-drained, light loam suits them best. Whenever possible, genistas should be raised from seed, as plants so obtained are usually healthier and longer-lived than cuttings. Still cuttings are frequently employed. They are taken in late July or August, and dibbled in very sandy soil in frames, usually pushing roots the following spring. The taller species are all improved by shortening back several times in the young state to induce a bushy habit. They transplant badly after a few years, and should be given permanent quarters early, or else grown in pots. (See also Cytisus.)

A considerable number of tender or half-hardy species have been, and continue to be, introduced from the south of Europe and the islands of the Mediterranean. Many of them can be cultivated in the Scilly Isles, but they are of no use for the ordinary climate of Great Britain. The species dealt with in the following pages include all in cultivation that are really hardy. As a rough guide to their identification they may be arranged as follows:—

1. Leaves and branches opposite

Horrida, radiata.

2. Leaves alternate, simple

Ætnensis, anxantica, aspathaloides, cinerea, monosperma (flowers white), ovata januensis, pilosa, tinctoria, virgata.

3. Leaves alternate, trifoliolate

Glabrescens, nyssana, ephedroides.

4. Leaves alternate; branches spiny

Anglica, dalmatica, germanica, hispanica, falcata.

5. Branches winged

Sagittalis, delphinensis.

G. ÆTNENSIS, *De Candolle*. Etna Broom

(Garden, 4th March 1893; Spartium ætnense, *Bivona*, Bot. Mag., t. 2674)

A tall shrub up to 15 or 20 ft. high, occasionally even more, with a main stem 6 to 12 ins. thick, and assuming the form of a small tree of erect, sparse habit, with very little foliage, but numerous slender, bright green, rushlike branches, which are pendulous when young. Leaves very few and scarcely noticeable, being narrow, linear, and $\frac{1}{4}$ to $\frac{1}{2}$ in. long. Flowers produced in July, scattered singly on the shoots of the year towards the end, each $\frac{1}{2}$ in. or so across, the petals golden yellow, the calyx green, angular-toothed, bell-shaped. Seed-pod $\frac{1}{2}$ in. long, ending in a sharp, decurved point and carrying two or three seeds.

Native of Sardinia and Sicily, and found on the slopes of Mount Etna at altitudes of 3000 to 6000 ft. It flowers during July and early August, when few hardy shrubs are in bloom; being of great beauty then, this broom is one of the most valuable of all its kind. Its tall habit makes it useful for planting at the back of shrubberies, where it can overtop without unduly shading other things. Although practically devoid of foliage, the bright green young branchlets give the plant almost the quality of an evergreen. It always makes a conspicuous feature in the grounds at Kew in July. It is a very hardy shrub, one of the largest and oldest specimens in the country, being in the gardens at Howick in Northumberland.

G. ANGLICA, *Linnæus*. NEEDLE FURZE, PETTY WHIN

A deciduous, more or less prostrate shrub, 1 to 2 ft. high. Branches slender, interlaced, very spiny; spines numerous, $\frac{1}{4}$ to $\frac{3}{4}$ in. long. Leaves simple, glabrous, ovate-lanceolate, pointed, about $\frac{1}{4}$ in. long. Flowers yellow, $\frac{1}{2}$ in. long, crowded on short racemes terminating leafy twigs. Seed-pod $\frac{1}{2}$ in. long.

Widely distributed over Western Europe, and frequent on moors and wild places in Great Britain. Although pretty when in flower, it is not one of the most attractive of genistas. The spines are really modified branches, and may often be seen bearing leaves. The species resembles G. germanica, but is distinguished by its glabrous leaves and branchlets.

Var. SUBINERMIS, *Legrande*.—A form nearly or quite without spines. It has recently been found in the Lake district.

G. ANXANTICA, *Tenore*. NEAPOLITAN BROOM

(G. tinctoria anxantica, *Fiori*)

A dwarf deciduous shrub of diffuse habit, very nearly allied to G. tinctoria, and of a similar type of growth. Leaves oval, sometimes broadly so. Racemes terminal; flowers yellow, $\frac{2}{3}$ in. long; pods quite glabrous.

Native of the country round Naples. It is one of the group of which G. tinctoria is the central and typical species, and is scarcely specifically distinct from it. It differs chiefly in being wholly free from down, and in its considerably larger flowers. It is appropriate for the rockery. It should be mentioned that the name "anxantica" is given to other genistas, and even to species of Cytisus, especially to C. purgans, to which, of course, the true plant bears no resemblance.

G. ASPATHALOIDES, *Poiret*

(G. Lobelii, *De Candolle*)

A deciduous dwarf or prostrate shrub reaching when old 6 to 10 ins. in height, usually dwarfer; young shoots downy, distinctly grooved, becoming spine-tipped with age. Leaves alternate, simple, very tiny (about $\frac{1}{4}$ in. long), linear, hairy, soon falling. Flowers $\frac{3}{8}$ in. long, pale yellow, solitary in the terminal leaf-axils or in clusters of two to four, each on a downy stalk $\frac{1}{8}$ to $\frac{1}{4}$ in. long. Corolla of the normal broom-flower shape. Calyx downy, $\frac{3}{16}$ in. long, with narrowly triangular lobes. Pod $\frac{5}{8}$ in. long, $\frac{1}{8}$ in. wide, pointed, downy. Blossoms in June.

Native of S.W. Europe, N. Africa, Corsica, Sardinia, Sicily, etc. This interesting dwarf shrub is charming for a sunny spot in the rock garden. A plant has been growing at Kew for many years and has proved perfectly hardy there. Planted above a stone, it has fallen over it and forms a pendulous mass of spine-tipped twigs 18 ins. in diameter and about 3 ins. in thickness. It needs the sunniest possible position. G. horrida has similar spine-tipped twigs, but its leaves are opposite, and Erinacea pungens, similarly spiny, has purplish-blue flowers. The plant was originally found in Barbary about 1786 by Poiret, the French botanist and traveller (1760-1834). G. Lobelii has been considered a variety of this species, but there seems to be no distinct dividing line between the two.

G. CINEREA, *De Candolle*

(Bot. Mag., t. 8086)

A deciduous shrub, 8 to 10 ft. high, with long, slender, scourge-like branches, grooved and clothed with fine silky hairs when young. Leaves grey green, simple, stalkless, narrowly lanceolate, pointed, about ½ in. long, ⅛ in. wide, covered with silky hairs beneath. Flowers in short clusters, usually two to four in each, bright yellow, ½ in. long; standard petal roundish with a notch at the top, about ½ in. long. Calyx ⅙ in. long, silky. Pod very silky, ½ to ⅔ in. long, containing two to five seeds. Blossoms June and July.

Native of S.W. Europe, especially of Spain, where it grows on the Sierra Nevada up to an altitude of 6000 ft. It is one of the showiest and most desirable of genistas, and although cultivated at Kew for over sixty years is still quite rare in gardens. It is useful in flowering after the majority of the brooms are past. Very similar in leaf and flower to G. virgata, it may be distinguished by longer, more slender branchlets and less twiggy habit when old, and in its flowers being mostly produced in small lateral clusters instead of racemes.

G. DALMATICA, *Bartling*. DALMATIAN BROOM

(Bot. Mag., t. 8075. G. Silvestris *Scop.* var. pungens *Vis.*)

A dwarf deciduous shrub, forming a neat dense tuft, 4 to 6 ins. high, ultimately 1 ft. or more through; branches thin, angular, very hairy and spiny. Spines stiff and sharp, being really the terminations of curious pinnately divided branchlets. Leaves simple, mostly confined to the base of the shoot; thin, linear, pointed, about ⅓ in. long, hairy. Racemes terminal, 1 to 1½ ins. long, erect, densely set with golden yellow flowers. Flowers ⅓ in. long; standard petal broadly ovate; calyx with five slender awl-shaped lobes, hairy. Pod round and flat, ½ in. long, ripening usually but one seed. Blossoms in June and July. The plant in general suggests a miniature G. hispanica.

Native of Dalmatia, Herzegovina, etc., where it forms part of the underwood of pine forests, and generally affects dry situations. Introduced to Kew in 1893, it has proved a delightful plant. It may be used for furnishing shelves in the rock garden, and it provides a pleasing undergrowth for groups of thinly planted taller shrubs, provided the shade is not too dense. At flowering time the tufts are entirely hidden by the closely packed, golden yellow racemes. The flowering shoots die back considerably during winter, springing up from the base in spring. Propagation is best effected by means of cuttings placed under a bell-glass in an unheated frame in August.

G. DELPHINENSIS, *Villars*

(Journ. Royal Hort. Society, 1942, fig. 29)

A prostrate, dwarf, scarcely woody shrub only a few inches high, its young shoots very crooked, zig-zagged, winged (like G. sagittalis on a small scale), the wings silky-hairy beneath. Leaves few and ¼ in. or less long, appressed-silky beneath, ovate, oval. Flowers bright yellow, borne at and near the end of the shoots in June in axillary and terminal clusters of three or more but, often singly or in pairs; calyx silky. Pods $\frac{1}{2}$ to $\frac{3}{4}$ in. long, $\frac{3}{16}$ in. wide, appressed-silky, abruptly pointed, carrying three to six seeds.

Native of S. France, where it reaches the Pyrenees, mostly in rocky calcareous sites where it flowers from June to August. A very distinct and interesting as well as a pretty, dwarf plant for the rock garden or alpine house. The flowers individually are amongst the largest in the genus. It was excellently grown by the late Mr Fred Stoker in Essex.

G. EPHEDROIDES, *De Candolle*

A deciduous shrub of erect habit, much branched, up to 3 or 4 ft. high; young shoots very slender, finely grooved, downy at first. Leaves very sparse, each made up of three linear leaflets $\frac{1}{4}$ in. long, soon dropping; those towards the end of the shoot simple, grey, downy. Flowers yellow, solitary, fragrant, borne alternately on the shoot mostly towards the top, $\frac{3}{8}$ in. long; they are of the ordinary broom-flower shape. The calyx has two large triangular teeth and three small ones. Pod $\frac{1}{4}$ to $\frac{1}{3}$ in. long, oval, ending in a curved beak, downy, carrying one to three seeds. Seeds black, shining. Flowers in May and June.

Native of Sardinia, Corsica, and Sicily, often near the sea coast. It bears some resemblance to Ephedra distachya in habit and this suggested the specific name. It appears to be nearest to G. radiata, but that species has its flowers in a terminal head. It is one of a goodly number of brooms that have practically no foliage, the normal functions of which are performed by the green stems. It is a rather tender shrub and needs a sunny, sheltered nook.

G. FALCATA, *Brotero*

A very spiny, gorse-like shrub, the young shoots very stiff, more or less hairy, ribbed, the spines mostly three-pronged or branched, $\frac{1}{2}$ to 2 ins. long, downy. Leaves quite small, narrowly obovate to oval, stalkless, $\frac{1}{6}$ to $\frac{1}{2}$ in. long, $\frac{1}{12}$ to $\frac{1}{4}$ in. wide, ciliate. Flowers yellow, $\frac{1}{3}$ to $\frac{1}{4}$ in. long, solitary in the axils of the spines or a few in short clusters, very copiously produced and sometimes collectively forming very handsome, woody, columnar panicles over 1 ft. long. Pod $\frac{3}{4}$ in. long, $\frac{3}{16}$ in. wide, glabrous.

Native of Portugal, where it blossoms in April and May.

G. FLORIDA, *Linnæus*

A deciduous shrub 2 to 3 ft. high; shoots erect, crowded, distinctly grooved, downy. Leaves $\frac{1}{4}$ to $\frac{1}{2}$ in. long, $\frac{1}{8}$ in. or less wide, linear-oblong to obovate, silky-hairy especially beneath. Flowers yellow, $\frac{1}{2}$ in. long, borne towards the top of the shoots, making racemes or leafy panicles 1 to 3 ins. long; calyx $\frac{3}{16}$ in. long, silky-hairy, the lobes linear-lanceolate. Pods two- or three-seeded.

Native of Spain and Morocco in mountainous regions.

G. GERMANICA, *Linnæus*

A deciduous shrub about 2 ft. high, with spiny, hairy shoots; spines mostly branched, $\frac{1}{2}$ to $\frac{3}{4}$ in. long. Leaves ovate-lanceolate, $\frac{1}{2}$ to $\frac{3}{4}$ in. long, $\frac{1}{8}$ to $\frac{1}{4}$ in. wide, hairy especially about the margins, dark green. Racemes 1 to 2 ins. long, terminating leafy, spineless shoots. Flowers yellow, $\frac{1}{3}$ to $\frac{1}{2}$ in. long; standard petal reflexed. Pod $\frac{1}{2}$ in. long, hairy. Blossoms in June.

Native of Central and W. Europe, where it is widely distributed. Its nearest ally is G. anglica, but it is well distinguished by its hairy shoots and leaves and sturdier habit. It is apt to grow rank, and become rather ragged in rich garden soil; a sunny, rather dry position suits it best.

G. GLABRESCENS, *Briquet*

(Bot. Mag., t. 8201 ; Cytisus glabrescens, *Sartorelli*)

A low, deciduous shrub of dense habit, up to 3 ft. high, with angled branchlets. Leaves trifoliolate with leaf-stalks ½ to 1 in. long ; leaflets stalkless or nearly so, obovate or oblong, ¼ to ½ in. long, clothed with silky hairs beneath. Flowers produced from the joints of the previous year's shoots, one to four, or occasionally more, at each joint ; yellow. Each flower is about ½ in. long, on a hairy stalk of equal length. Pods 1 to 1½ ins. long, ¼ in. wide, glabrous.

Native of Central Europe, on the Lepontine Alps at considerable altitudes. This delightful shrub, which forms a neat, compact mass of branches, was introduced to Kew in 1896. It flowers in May, when the plant is almost hidden by blossom. It is worth a place in the rock garden, or wherever dainty plants can be accommodated without danger of being smothered by stronger-growing neighbours. It has usually been grown under the name of Cytisus glabrescens, but Mr John Briquet, a close student of this group, puts it in Genista. It is also known as Cytisus emeriflorus.

GENISTA GLABRESCENS

G. HISPANICA, *Linnæus*. SPANISH GORSE

(Bot. Mag., t. 8528)

A deciduous shrub, usually from 1 to 1½ ft. (sometimes 2½ ft.) high, forming dense, cushion-like masses ; branches interlacing, spiny and hairy, the spines much branched, ¾ to 1 in. long, each subdivision needle-pointed. Leaves confined to the flowering twigs, linear-lanceolate, about ⅓ in. long, $\frac{1}{16}$ to ⅛ in. wide ; hairy beneath. Flowers as many as twelve in a rounded head or cluster 1 in. or so across, terminating short, erect, leafy, hairy shoots ; each flower is ⅓ in. long, rich golden yellow. Pod flattish oval, carrying one to four seeds.

Native of S.W. Europe ; introduced in 1759. It flowers in the latter half of May and in June, and produces at that time a more gorgeous display of golden yellow blossom than probably any other dwarf shrub. Healthy plants are completely covered with bloom, and when they have been planted to cover a breadth of 10 ft. or so, produce a most brilliant colour effect. On shelves or small plateaux of the rock garden single plants are very charming. Although its leaves are deciduous, this shrub gives an evergreen effect through the deep green of its crowded twigs and spines. As with others of the spiny group of genistas, it is not advisable to give it rich or manured soil, otherwise it is apt to grow rank and soft, and during winter the younger parts are apt to die in patches and spoil the next crop of flowers. A soil of moderate quality, and especially a well-drained, sunny position, suits it best. It can be propagated by seeds and by August cuttings. One of the most indispensable shrubs in the south of England.

G. HORRIDA, *De Candolle*

A dwarf, flat-topped, very spiny shrub of close, tufted habit; stems grooved, opposite, rigid, ending in a sharp spine, and more or less clothed with short silky hairs. Leaves opposite, minute, trifoliolate, composed of three linear leaflets ¼ in. or so long, covered with silky hairs. Flowers ¼ in. long, produced in small terminal heads, three to eight together, standing just clear of the branches; yellow. Calyx, flower-stalk, and pod hairy.

GENISTA HISPANICA (see p. 59).

Native of S.W. Europe; introduced in 1821. Although hardy enough, it does not always flower freely, and is not much grown. Our climate apparently is not sunny enough to develop its full beauty. On the mountains of Central Spain, at elevations of 3000 to 5000 ft., it is crowded with its short heads of yellow blossom every July. It is one of the interesting groups of genistas with opposite leaves and branches, and does not appear likely to become more than 1½ to 2½ ft. high. The whole plant has a silvery grey hue, and forms a dense, cushion-like mass.

G. JANUENSIS, *Viviani*. GENOA BROOM

(G. genuensis, *Persoon*; G. triangularis, *Willdenow*; G. scariosa, *Viviani*, Loddiges Bot. Cabinet, t. 1135; G. triquetra, *Waldstein*—not *L'Héritier*)

A low, procumbent, deciduous shrub a few inches high, the spreading triangular stems without down, but with thin transparent wings. From the stems arise erect flowering twigs 1 to 3 ins. long, bearing a single flower in each of the four to ten terminal leaf-axils. Leaves linear-lanceolate to narrowly ovate, glabrous, pointed or bluntish, $\frac{1}{4}$ to 1 in. long, $\frac{1}{16}$ to $\frac{3}{16}$ in. wide, dark green with thin transparent margins. Flowers clear bright yellow; standard petal, roundish ovate, $\frac{1}{4}$ in. wide; keel and wing petals about as long. Pod 1 in. long, $\frac{3}{16}$ in. wide, glabrous, containing four to seven seeds.

Native of Central and S.E. Europe; introduced long ago and cultivated at Kew in 1850. It has probably been out of cultivation for some time and personally I had not seen it until the Chelsea Show of May 1932, when a group of young plants in a pan were shown by Mr G. P. Baker of Sevenoaks, charmingly in flower, under the name "G. triquetra." It was originally named in 1802 from a plant found on the island of Palmaria, near Spezia in Italy, but it is also widely spread on the mainland. It is essentially a plant for a ledge in the rock garden, where it will spread 2 to 3 ft. wide. The distinctive characters are (in combination) its prostrate habit, triangular stems, simple leaves, axillary blossoms, and its entirely glabrous parts.

The name "triquetra" was given to this broom by Waldstein and Kitaibel in 1805, but as it had already been used by L'Héritier in 1784 for a quite different shrub with trifoliate leaves, it has no standing. The true G. TRIQUETRA, *L' Héritier*, is figured in the *Botanical Magazine*, t. 314, and is said by Aiton to have been cultivated in England by a Mr Ord as long ago as 1770. I saw a broom under the name in the Glasnevin Botanic Garden in 1897, but it seems now to be very rare. It does not appear to exist in a wild state and it has been suggested that it is a hybrid between Cytisus monspessulanus and Genista tinctoria.

G. LYDIA, *Boissier*

(G. spathulata, *Spach*)

A deciduous shrub about 2 ft. high, of lax, pendulous growth; young shoots slender, five-angled, glabrous, green. Leaves linear, pointed, glabrous; $\frac{3}{8}$ in. long, $\frac{1}{16}$ in. wide; set about half an inch apart. Flowers produced three or four together towards the end of short lateral twigs in May and June, bright yellow, $\frac{3}{8}$ in. long, standard petal $\frac{1}{4}$ in. wide; calyx glabrous, $\frac{1}{12}$ in. long, tubular, with five narrowly triangular, pointed, erect lobes. Pod about 1 in. long with a short bristle at the end, containing two to four seeds.

Native of E. Europe (Macedonia, Transylvania, Hungary, etc.). Dr W. B. Turrill of Kew found it in Bulgaria on limestone rocks above Bačkova in 1926. This pretty broom is very little known in gardens, but is a charming shrub for the rock garden. At Kew it passed through the winter of 1928-9 without injury in a sheltered spot although otherwise unprotected and flowered profusely the following June. It has succeeded well also at Aldenham, an even colder locality.

G. MONOSPERMA, *Lamarck*

(Retama monosperma, *Boissier*)

A straggling, unarmed shrub, 2 to 4 ft. high in this country, but more than twice as high in its native state; branches very slender, pendent, and rush-like, grooved, covered with short, silky hairs when young. Leaves few and inconspicuous, $\frac{1}{4}$ to $\frac{3}{4}$ in. long, linear. Racemes short, silky, distributed along the branches; $\frac{1}{2}$ to $1\frac{1}{2}$ ins. long, carrying from five to fifteen blossoms. Flowers milky white and delightfully fragrant, $\frac{1}{2}$ in. long; the petals covered with silky hairs, the calyx dark, and contrasting with the petals. Pod oval, $\frac{1}{2}$ in. long, containing mostly one (but sometimes two) black-brown seeds.

Native of S. Europe and N. Africa; introduced, according to Aiton, in 1690, but always very rare because of its tenderness. In the Scilly Isles it thrives admirably, but near London it needs the protection of a sunny, sheltered wall, such as that outside a hothouse. The soil must be lightish and well drained. In its native country the thin flexible branches are used for tying—in the same way as willows are here.

G. NYSSANA, *Petrovič*. NISSA BROOM

A deciduous, erect shrub of sparse habit, thickly covered with soft hairs in all its parts—branches, leaves, flowers, and pods. Branches leafy, but little forked, slender, erect, slightly furrowed. Leaves trifoliolate; leaflets linear, pointed, $\frac{1}{2}$ to $\frac{3}{4}$ in. long, $\frac{1}{8}$ in. or less wide, margins slightly decurved. Flowers yellow, $\frac{1}{2}$ in. long, in slender terminal racemes 4 to 6 ins. long, each flower produced in the axil of a trifoliolate, leaflike bract, which becomes smaller towards the apex of the inflorescence. The growth of the year, including branch and raceme, will measure from 12 to 18 ins. in length. Pod short, thick, ovate, pointed, carrying one or two seeds.

Native of Servia, Albania, Macedonia, etc.; introduced to Kew in 1899. It has proved quite hardy, and is most distinct in its dense covering of short soft hairs. The specific name refers to Nissa in Serbia, one of its habitats.

G. OVATA, *Waldstein and Kitaibel*

(G. tinctoria ovata, *Schultze*)

A deciduous shrub, 2 to 4 ft. high, with erect, slightly grooved, shaggy young shoots. Leaves ovate or narrow oblong, the largest $1\frac{1}{2}$ ins. long and 1 in. wide, hairy at the margins and beneath. Flowers borne in short, dense racemes $1\frac{1}{2}$ to 2 ins. long; yellow, each flower $\frac{1}{2}$ to $\frac{3}{4}$ in. long. Pod hairy.

Native of Central and S. Europe. Usually regarded as a species, this is closely allied to G. tinctoria, differing chiefly in its much broader leaves, and its conspicuously hairy stems, pods, etc. The true plant is rarely seen, the one commonly grown under the name being one of the numerous forms of G. tinctoria elatior.

G. PATULA. *M. Bieberstein*

(Gardeners' Chronicle, 17th Nov. 1934, fig. 141)

A deciduous, thin-foliaged shrub of spreading habit, 6 to 10 ins. high, up to 1 ft. or more across; young shoots very slender, strongly grooved, glabrous. Leaves simple, linear to linear-lanceolate, slender-pointed, very variable in size but mostly $\frac{1}{3}$ to 1 in. long, by $\frac{1}{20}$ to $\frac{1}{8}$ in. wide; some, however, are $\frac{3}{4}$ to 2 ins. long and $\frac{1}{12}$ to $\frac{3}{16}$ in. wide, glabrous. Flowers solitary, axillary, bright golden yellow, $\frac{3}{8}$ in. long, crowded to form spikes a few inches long, terminating the shoots; opening in May and June.

Native of limestone cliffs near Trebizond, up to 3000 ft. altitude, where it was collected by Mr E. K. Balls in May 1934, and noted by him as happiest in hot sunny crevices. Very distinct for its thin narrow foliage.

G. PILOSA, *Linnæus*

A deciduous shrub growing 1 to $1\frac{1}{2}$ ft. high, procumbent when young, afterwards forming a low, tangled mass of slender, twiggy shoots. Leaves distributed along the branchlets of the year, but gathered in clusters on the year-old shoots; they are simple, $\frac{1}{4}$ to $\frac{1}{2}$ in. long, narrowly obovate, the margins folded upwards, and the lower surface covered with closely pressed, silvery hairs. Flowers bright yellow, produced singly or in pairs (but each on its own short stalk) from the leaf-axils, the whole forming a crowded raceme 2 to 6 ins. long. When in blossom the whole plant becomes a mass of bright yellow. Pods ¾ to 1 in. long, narrow, silky on the surface, two- to six-seeded.

This pretty broom is spread widely over the southern half of Europe, and is also a native of gravelly heaths, etc., in the south and south-west of Britain. It is valuable for forming a dense covering for the ground, even for plots planted with groups of taller shrubs or trees, provided of course it is not unduly shaded. It is also useful for the rock garden, and for covering dry, sunny banks.

G. RADIATA, *Scopoli*

(Cytisus radiatus, *Koch* ; Enantiosparton radiatum, *Koch*)

A rounded, bushy shrub, 3 ft. high, with deciduous leaves, but evergreen from the colour of the shoots. Branches opposite, distinctly grooved, slender, occasionally spine-tipped, very distinctly jointed. Leaves opposite, trifoliolate, stalkless, consisting of three narrowly linear leaflets ¼ to ½ in. long, silky. The flowers are in a terminal head of about six blossoms and about 1 in. across ; each flower is ½ in. long, deep yellow ; petals and calyx silky. Pods silky, ovate, tapering at the end to a sharp curved point, usually one-seeded.

Native of Central and S. Europe ; introduced from Italy in 1758. This interesting and distinct shrub, peculiar for its thicket of slender branchlets, mostly thinner than a knitting needle, is not very common, but sometimes makes a good display of bloom in June. It is of interest botanically in being one of the few genistas with opposite branches and leaves. In general appearance it bears some resemblance to the shrubby horsetails (Ephedra).

G. SAGITTALIS, *Linnæus*

A prostrate shrub, under 1 ft. in height, and evergreen from the character of its green, foliaceous, winged branches. Stems with a slender, woody core, but edged on each side with a membranous wing, sometimes continuous up the stem, sometimes interrupted at the joints, the stem thus becoming flat and nearly ¼ in. wide. Leaves few and scattered, oval or ovate, ½ to ¾ in. long, hairy. Raceme erect, terminal, cylindrical, 1 to 1½ ins. long, hairy. Flowers closely packed, each ½ in. long, yellow, the petals expanding but little ; calyx hairy. Pods ¾ in. long, silky four- to six-seeded. Blossoms in June.

Native of Central and S.E. Europe, frequently inhabiting upland pastures. It is very hardy, and thrives well in gardens, where it attracts notice for its pretty flowers and unusual stems. It may be used as an edging for borders, or grown in patches in the front of shrubberies.

G. SERICEA, *Wulfen*

A deciduous shrub of low, tufted growth, usually under 1 ft. in height, and consisting of a cluster of short, erect growths ; young shoots finely silky-hairy. Leaves simple, linear to narrowly oblong, tapered towards both ends ; mostly ⅓ to ¾ in. long, about ⅛ in. wide ; glabrous above, clothed beneath with silky hairs. Flowers yellow, about ½ in. long, borne in terminal clusters of three to five, opening in late May or June ; they are of the typical broom-flower shape. Petals, calyx, and seed-pod silky-hairy ; pod about ¾ in. long.

Native of Dalmatia, Istria, Tyrol, etc., found in calcareous soil often on stony mountainous sites. It is common on Monte Spaccato, near Trieste. Though known to botanists since the eighteenth century, it has been little cultivated and I had not seen it alive until 1925, when it was obtained for Kew from Trieste. It is essentially a plant for a sunny ledge in the rock garden, a spot for which its low, tufted, compact habit fits it admirably.

G. SILVESTRIS, *Scopoli*

An erect, deciduous shrub with very slender, angular stems slightly appressed-downy at first, often crowded, more or less spiny. Leaves mostly linear to narrowly lanceolate, $\frac{1}{3}$ to $\frac{3}{4}$ in. long, $\frac{1}{20}$ to $\frac{1}{12}$ in. wide, soon glabrous. Flowers yellow, closely set in terminal erect racemes 1 to 4 ins. long, opening in May and June; corolla $\frac{3}{8}$ in. long, slender; calyx silky-hairy, its lobes subulate. Pod ovoid, usually one-seeded.

S.E. Europe; introduced in 1818. A handsome, free-flowering, quite hardy shrub.

For var. pungens, *Visiani*, see G. dalmatica.

G. SPHÆROCARPA, *Boissier*

A deciduous shrub, 3 to 4 ft. high (or more in cultivation); stems erect, slender, ribbed, mostly glabrous, pale green. Leaves simple, stalkless, very small and downy beneath, only present on young plants and soon falling, leaving the plant leafless for the greater part of its career. Flowers yellow, $\frac{1}{8}$ to $\frac{1}{6}$ in. long, crowded and set alternately in two rows on axillary racemes $\frac{1}{2}$ to $1\frac{1}{2}$ ins. long, borne mostly singly or in pairs; calyx and corolla glabrous; pod globose, $\frac{1}{2}$ in. wide, carrying usually one kidney-shaped seed.

Native of N. Africa and Spain, cultivated in the Jardin du Roi, Paris, in 1780. Interesting for its very numerous tiny blossoms open in May and June and its curious, globose pods.

G. TINCTORIA, *Linnæus*. DYER'S GREENWEED

In its modern acceptation, this name may be taken to cover a group of allied forms put under one variable species. Plants have been received at Kew under perhaps a score of different specific names; they differ in certain characters of more or less importance, but still bear a striking resemblance to each other. It has been found impossible to fix on permanent characters that would clearly differentiate them, and they have, in consequence, been all included under G. tinctoria. Many are minor forms of the tall, erect dyer's greenweed (G. elatior, *Koch*). Others are distinguished by characters defined below.

G. TINCTORIA (type).—A low, often semi-prostrate shrub with creeping roots, usually only a few inches high in a wild state, but up to 2 ft. under cultivation. Stems more or less grooved, clothed with simple, dark green leaves that are linear-lanceolate, $\frac{1}{2}$ to 1 in. long, hairy on the margins. Racemes erect, terminal, each 1 to 3 ins. long, produced on the shoots of the year from June to September. Owing to the branching of the stems near the top under cultivation, a crowd of racemes is often produced, forming one large panicle. Flowers $\frac{1}{2}$ to $\frac{3}{4}$ in. long, yellow, without hairs; pod $\frac{1}{2}$ to $\frac{3}{4}$ in. long, glabrous, carrying eight to twelve seeds.

This typical form is common in the British Isles, especially in poor grassland, and dry gravelly soils. It is also spread over Europe, and reaches Siberia. Under cultivation it is a pretty plant and flowers freely, but is not so attractive as its variety PLENA, which is also a dwarf, semi-prostrate shrub, but owing to the more numerous petals more brilliant in colour. This is, indeed, one of the best of all dwarf yellow-flowered shrubs. Seeds and cuttings can be employed to increase the typical form, but the double-flowered one, being sterile, can only be propagated by cuttings. In former times this genista was of some value as the source of a yellow dye.

Although known as "greenweed," the colour derived from it was a bright yellow, and it was only by afterwards dipping the yellow yarn or cloth into a blue solution of woad (*Isatis*) that the green tint was obtained. This was the process by which was obtained the once celebrated "Kendal green," so-called from the town of Kendal in Westmoreland, in the vicinity of which the plant was abundant, and where also the process was first introduced by Flemish emigrants in the reign of Edward III.—*Treasury of Botany*, vol. i., p. 526.

Var. ELATIOR, *Schultze* (G. elatior, *W. D. Koch*).—In its morphological characters this resembles ordinary G. tinctoria, but is an altogether stronger-growing, bigger shrub. It is of quite erect habit, 3 to 5 ft. high; leaves up to 1½ ins. or more long, and ¼ to ½ in. wide. Flowers individually no larger than in the cultivated type, but they are borne in large panicles sometimes 12 to 18 ins. high. Several minor forms, varying in size and shape of leaf, are included under this.

Var. HIRSUTA, *De Candolle.*—Habit approaching the type, but with twigs and leaves hairy.

Var. MANTICA, *Fiori* (G. mantica, *Pollini*).—Of medium height, with downy leaves, stems, and pods; young wood purplish; calyx reddish. This distinct variety flowers earlier than the ordinary tinctoria.

(Var. OVATA, *Schultze*, see G. ovata.)

G. VILLARSII, *Clementi*

(G. Villarsiana, *Jordan*; G. pulchella, *Visiani*)

In a wild state this is often found in arid mountainous places and is there a pigmy bush a few inches high, consisting of a thick, short main-stem and a gnarled, twisted mass of short twigs. In places more favourable to its growth it will make shoots one to three inches long in a season, but it is always dwarf; young shoots grey, downy, grooved. Leaves linear, hairy on both surfaces, ¼ in. or so long. Flowers yellow, solitary in the terminal leaf-axils of the shoot, ⅓ in. long, of the usual broom-flower shape; calyx very hairy, with triangular pointed lobes; petals hairy; pod ½ in. long, very hairy.

Native of Dalmatia, Istria, S.E. France. This is another of the dwarf Alpine brooms very suitable for growing on a sunny shelf in the rock garden. It is perfectly hardy at Kew. In its frequently starved, wild condition, the twigs occasionally become rather spine-tipped, but this tendency disappears under the softer conditions of cultivation. Flowers in May.

G. VIRGATA, *De Candolle.* MADEIRA BROOM

(Bot. Reg., vol. 30, t. 11)

A deciduous shrub of bushy habit when old, up to 12 ft. high, and as much or more through; young branches grooved. Leaves simple, grey-green, with little or no stalk, about ½ in. long, ⅛ in. wide; silky beneath, edges slightly decurved. Racemes 1 to 2 ins. long, terminating short shoots of the year, very abundant. Flowers bright yellow, ½ in. long, standard petal roundish, about ½ in. across. Calyx clothed with silky hairs. Pod 1 in. long, very silky, carrying three to five seeds. Flowers in June and July, and intermittently until October.

Native of Madeira, and one of the few shrubs from that island that are really hardy with us. It was brought home from Madeira by Francis Masson in 1777, on his return from the Cape of Good Hope, where he had for five years been collecting plants for Kew. It has naturalised itself in several parts of the Kew woods, and is never injured in the least by frost, but until quite recently it was scarcely known in gardens. Flowering in June and July when shrubs generally are going out of flower, and thriving quite well in semi-shaded positions in thin woodland, it is an exceptionally valuable broom, especially as it will thrive in rough grass which gets no more attention than an annual mowing. It resembles G. cinerea previously described (*q.v.*), and the two probably are geographical forms of one species.

GENISTA VIRGATA

GINKGO BILOBA, *Linnæus*. MAIDENHAIR TREE. GINKGOACEÆ (Plate 5)

(Salisburia adiantifolia, *Smith*)

A deciduous tree, over 100 ft. high, unisexual, not resinous, usually of somewhat, pyramidal habit (the male at least); trunk often branching low, and forming several erect main branches; secondary branches spreading, pendulous at the ends. Branchlets of two kinds: (1) short, stout spurs, which increase very slowly in length and bear the leaves at the tip; (2) long, free-growing shoots with the leaves alternate. Trees in a stunted or unhealthy state produce only the first type of shoot, and will remain practically stationary for many years. Leaves long-stalked, fan-shaped, tapering from the irregularly jagged, often notched apex to the wedge-shaped base; up to 3 ins. deep, about 2 to 3 ins. wide; not downy, yellowish dull green, the veins all running lengthwise, and repeatedly forking as the leaf broadens towards the end; stalk slender, 1½ to 3½ ins. long. Flowers borne on the short shoots, the males in cylindrical, short-stalked catkins about 1 in. long, consisting of green stamens only;

the females on a stalk 1½ to 2 ins. long, ultimately developing a yellowish green plum-like fruit 1 to 1½ ins. long, surrounded by a malodorous, fleshy layer.

The ginkgo is probably a native of China, but it does not appear to have been found indubitably wild. It is certainly not indigenous to Japan, as is often stated, although it was introduced from there to Europe about 1730, and to England twenty-eight years later. It is undoubtedly one of the most distinct and beautiful of all deciduous trees, the leaves being quite unlike those of any other. The popular name refers to their similarity in shape to the pinnules of the maidenhair fern (*Adiantum*).

Most of the large trees in the British Isles are males, but a female tree recently found in Bath bears fruit abundantly, and female shoots grafted on the fine male tree at Kew produce fruits annually. The female tree has been supposed to be less erect in habit than the male, or to have even pendulous branches. Two fine female trees in the botanic garden at Vienna, which I saw in 1908, have that character. Whilst the fleshy part of the fruit has a rancid, evil odour, the kernel of the nut is well flavoured, and esteemed by the Japanese. The Ginkgo is best raised from seed, and it requires a deep good soil; when young it is often extremely slow of growth, and although very hardy, is no doubt better suited in climates with a hotter summer than ours. Good seeds are now produced by S. European trees, and offer the best means of propagation.

This tree is the only species of its genus, and stands well apart from all the rest of the Coniferæ. It has usually been regarded as a very distinct member of the Yew family (Taxaceæ), but recent investigators place it in a separate natural order (Ginkgoaceæ). It is well represented in a fossil state, and is the last representative of a race of trees that in earlier stages of the world's history filled an important place in its vegetation. Mr E. H. Wilson stated that the two sexes of this tree do not differ in habit.

Var. AUREA is described as having bright yellow leaves, but I have not seen it. Var. FASTIGIATA is an erect-branched, more slender tree. Var. LACINIATA has large deeply cut leaves. Var. PENDULA may be the tree which has been supposed to be female. Var. VARIEGATA has leaves patched with yellow.

GLEDITSCHIA. HONEY LOCUST. LEGUMINOSÆ

(Sometimes spelt Gleditsia)

A small group of pod-bearing, deciduous trees named in honour of Gottlieb Gleditsch, a German professor of botany, who flourished in the eighteenth century, and was a friend of Linnæus. They are natives of eastern N. America, China, Japan, and Persia. The leaves are beautifully subdivided into numerous leaflets, pinnately or bipinnately arranged, and the trunks and branches of most species are more or less formidably armed with simple or branched spines. These characters of leaf and stem combined distinguish Gleditschia as a genus from all other hardy trees. No gleditschia has any beauty of blossom, the flowers being small, green, and borne in racemes a few inches long. They are sometimes perfect, sometimes unisexual, and differ from most of the Leguminosæ we are familiar with in the open air in the petals being uniform, and with no resemblance to the pea-shaped blossom so characteristic of the family. The seeds are produced in pods, varying in length from 1 to 2 ins. (in G. aquatica) to 18 ins. long (in G. triacanthos). In all except G. aquatica and G. texana the pods contain pulp and numerous seeds, which, however, they do not release, as most of the family do, by splitting. They often become spirally twisted before falling. The species best worth growing are G. triacanthos and G. caspica, both striking and ornamental-foliaged trees, very interesting on account of their huge spines.

Gleditschias should be raised from seed. They are rather tender in a young state, owing to the habit of growing late in the season, so that the succulent tips are cut back in winter. After a few years the hardier species lose this defect. They like a good loamy soil and a sunny position, thriving better in the south of England, where the summers are hotter, than in the north; still better in France and Italy. Besides the species to which notice is given below, the following is in cultivation.

G. DELAVAYI, *Franchet.*—Introduced by Wilson from Yunnan, China, in 1900, this appears to be more tender, at least when young, than any other species in cultivation. It is well distinguished even in a young state by its downy shoots, all the others being glabrous. In the young state the leaflets are small, and as many as three dozen to a simply pinnate leaf, but in adult trees they become much reduced in number. Pods up to 20 ins. long, twisted.

G. AQUATICA, *Marshall.* WATER LOCUST

(G. inermis, *Miller*; G. monosperma, *Walter*)

A tree described by Sargent as 50 to 60 ft. high, with a trunk 2 to 2½ ft. in diameter, but in this country inclined to be shrubby, and to form several stems; spines ultimately about 4 ins. long, branched; young shoots not downy, but marked with conspicuous lenticels. Leaves up to 8 ins. long, simply or doubly pinnate; leaflets of the pinnate leaf (or of each division of the bipinnate ones) twelve to twenty-four. Each leaflet is lanceolate-oblong; 1 to 1½ ins. long, ¼ to ½ in. wide; rounded, bluntish, or somewhat pointed at the apex; margins wavy; glossy and glabrous except for the down on the short stalk of the leaflet, on the upper side of the main-stalk, and scattered hairs on the margins of the leaflets. Flowers borne on slender racemes 3 or 4 ins. long. Pod obliquely diamond-shaped, 1¾ ins. long, nearly 1 in. wide, not pulpy inside; seeds solitary (rarely two).

Native of the south-eastern United States; introduced in 1723, according to Aiton, but now extremely rare. It is hardy at Kew, but grows slowly. Its small, one-seeded pod well distinguishes it, but I do not know that this has been borne in cultivation here.

G. CASPICA, *Desfontaines.* CASPIAN LOCUST

A tree 30 to 40 ft. high, its trunk excessively armed with formidable, branching, slightly flattened spines, 6 ins. or more long; young shoots smooth. Leaves 6 to 10 ins. long, simply or doubly pinnate. Leaflets up to twenty on the pinnate leaves, or on each division of the doubly pinnate ones; ovate to oval, 1 to 2 ins. long, ⅜ to ¾ in. wide; rounded and with a minute bristle-like tip at the apex, very shallowly round-toothed. The midribs and main leaf-stalk on the upper side, as well as the very short stalk of the leaflet, are downy; the leaf otherwise is glabrous and shining green. Flowers green, almost stalkless, densely arranged on downy racemes, 2 to 4 ins. long. Pod scimitar-shaped, usually about 8 ins. long, 1 to 1¼ ins. wide.

Native of N. Persia, in the neighbourhood of the Caspian Sea; introduced, according to Loudon, in 1822. It is a sturdy tree with much larger leaflets than G. triacanthos, and is remarkable for the size and number of spines on the trunk, which is, indeed, the most formidably armed among cultivated trees. The species is well worth growing on that account. The leaflets are not so large in this country as on trees grown on the Continent. At Vienna I have seen them as much as 2½ ins. long, by over 1 in. wide. It is much confused with, and usually grown as G. sinensis, a confusion which apparently existed in Loudon's time.

G. JAPONICA, *Miquel.* JAPANESE LOCUST (Plate 6)

(G horrida, *Willdenow*)

A tree 60 to 70 ft. high, the trunk and branches very formidably armed with branched spines; young shoots on plants at Kew dark purplish brown, smooth and shining. Leaves simply or doubly pinnate, 8 to 12 ins. long, each leaf or leaf-section carrying fourteen to twenty-four leaflets. Leaflets ovate to lanceolate, often unequal at each side the midrib, blunt to pointed at the apex, margins entire; main-stalk, midrib, and stalk of leaflets downy. In Japanese fruit-bearing specimens the leaflets are ¾ to 1½ ins. long, ¼ to ½ in. wide, but in small cultivated trees they are only ⅓ to ⅝ in. long. Pod 8 to 10 ins. long, 1 to 1¼ ins. wide; scimitar-shaped, ultimately twisted.

Native of Japan; introduced to Kew in 1894, where young trees raised from seed supplied by Boehmer are quite hardy, although slow-growing. In their young state, the small leaflets give them a very different aspect to native specimens, but they are unsurpassed among hardy trees in their fern-like elegance. The species appears to be allied to G. caspica, under which by one authority it has been placed. The pulp in the pods, as in G. sinensis, is saponaceous, and is used by the Japanese for washing cloth.

G. MACRACANTHA, *Desfontaines*

A deciduous tree 50 to 60 ft. high, the trunk armed with great, branched, very stiff spines; shoots glabrous, ribbed, more or less warted. Leaves simply pinnate; leaflets six to twelve, ovate oblong sometimes inclined to obovate, 1 to 3½ ins. long, ½ to 1½ ins. wide, shallowly toothed, glabrous except on the main and individual very short stalks. Flowers in downy, stalked, simple, slender racemes 3 to 6 ins. long. Pod 6 to 13 ins. long, about 1½ ins. wide, blackish and long-persistent.

Native of Central China and said to have been in cultivation since 1800. A tree bearing its large pods was growing in the Montpelier Botanic Garden in 1889, and another is in the Jardin des Plantes at Paris.

G. SINENSIS, *Lamarck.* CHINESE HONEY LOCUST

A deciduous tree up to 40 or 45 ft. high in nature, armed with often branched spines several inches long; young shoots glabrous or soon becoming so. Leaves pinnate, 5 to 8 ins. long, composed of eight to fourteen (sometimes more) leaflets which are ovate, ovate-lanceolate, blunt or pointed, obliquely tapered at the base, margins slightly wavy; $1\frac{1}{4}$ to 3 ins. long, $\frac{5}{8}$ to $1\frac{1}{8}$ ins. wide; downy on the midrib above, soon glabrous elsewhere, net-veined beneath, stalks and main-stalk downy. Flowers greenish white, in pendulous downy racemes $2\frac{1}{2}$ to $3\frac{1}{2}$ ins. long, each flower $\frac{1}{4}$ in. wide on a downy stalk about $\frac{1}{8}$ in. long. Pod 5 to 10 ins. long, $\frac{3}{4}$ to $1\frac{1}{4}$ ins. wide, scarcely curved, dark purplish brown, flat.

Native of China; described and named by Lamarck in 1786 from a tree growing at Versailles. This honey-locust, according to Henry, occurs wild on the mountains near Pekin, but there are plants at Kew raised from Wilson's seeds (No. 1214) collected in 1908 in Szechuen and distributed under this name. It would seem, therefore, if this identification be correct, to have a wide distribution in China. The young shoots of Wilson's 1214 are quite downy. The old trees in France and Italy came from eastern China. The flowers have no beauty.

G. TEXANA, *Sargent*

(Sargent, Silva of N. America, Vol. xiii., p. 13)

A deciduous tree up to 120 ft. high with smooth, pale bark; young shoots glabrous, branches spineless. Leaves 4 to 8 in. long, the main-stalk at first hairy, pinnate or bipinnate, with six or seven pairs of pinnae, each carrying six to sixteen pairs of leaflets which are oblong-ovate, $\frac{1}{2}$ to 1 in. long, very shallowly toothed, apex rounded, scarcely stalked, dark shining green. Flowers in glabrous racemes 3 or 4 ins. long, the males dark, orange-yellow. Pod flat, 4 to 5 ins. long, 1 to $1\frac{1}{4}$ ins. wide, dark chestnut-brown without pulp.

A natural hybrid between G. triacanthos and G. aquatica, found only in a grove on the bottom lands near Brazoria in Texas, first noted in 1892; introduced to cultivation in 1900. In foliage it is like G. triacanthos but differs in having no spines; from G. aquatica it differs by its many-seeded pods.

G. TRIACANTHOS, *Linnæus*. HONEY LOCUST

A tree reaching in a wild state 140 ft. in height, with a trunk up to 5 or 6 ft. in diameter, both it and the branches more or less armed with stout, sharp spines 3 to 12 ins. long, and branched. Young shoots slightly downy at the base only; spines when present on them simple or three-forked. Leaves 4 to 8 ins. long, either simply or doubly pinnate, the latter confined to vigorous leading shoots; the leaves of the short, flowering twigs are invariably simply pinnate. Leaflets on each pinnate leaf (or section of bipinnate one) fourteen to thirty-two; $\frac{1}{2}$ to $1\frac{1}{2}$ ins. long, $\frac{3}{16}$ to $\frac{5}{8}$ in. wide; oblong-lanceolate, mostly rounded at the apex, wavy or shallowly toothed at the margin, glossy dark green; both surfaces at first downy. Male flowers green, crowded on downy, often clustered racemes about 2 ins. long; female racemes few-flowered. Fruit more or less scimitar-shaped, 1 to $1\frac{1}{2}$ ft. long, 1 to $1\frac{1}{2}$ ins. wide, dark shining brown.

Native of Central N. America; introduced in 1700. The honey locust is the best of the genus in this country, and deserves to be more commonly planted than it is, not only for its interest but for the beautiful fern-like foliage, which turns a clear bright yellow in autumn. The spines are not so formidably developed in this country as on the Continent, nor do they develop in woods or shady spots like they do in places fully exposed. It only occasionally bears fruit with us, never with the freedom and regularity seen in more sunny climates like the south of France. A tree well-laden with dry pods rattling with every fitful movement of the air, makes rather a weird sound in the dusk. Perhaps the finest tree in the country is at Kew, now 60 ft. high and 5 ft. 10 ins. in girth of trunk. The popular name refers to the likeness of the tree in foliage to the locust (Robinia), and to the thick, succulent, sweetish pulp in which the seeds are set.

Var. BUJOTII, *Rehder*.—A very elegant, pendulous tree; branches and branchlets very slender; leaflets narrower than in the type, often mottled with white. There is a fine tree of this variety at the entrance to the park at Segrez in France.

Var. INERMIS.—Some trees appear never to bear thorns, and have been distinguished by this name; but unarmed plants are said to occur among batches of seedlings raised from thorn-bearing trees.

Var. NANA.—A dwarf, sturdy bush or small tree; leaflets comparatively short and broad.

GLOBULARIA CORDIFOLIA, *Linnæus*. GLOBULARIACEÆ

(Sweet's Flower Garden, vol. i., t. 34)

An evergreen prostrate shrub forming tufts or mats 2 to 4 ins. high, the root-stock and lower parts woody; young shoots glabrous, purplish, often creeping. Leaves alternate, wedge-shaped, once or twice notched at the broad rounded apex, tapered gradually to the base; $\frac{3}{4}$ to $1\frac{1}{2}$ ins. long (including the long, slender stalk), $\frac{1}{8}$ to $\frac{3}{8}$ in. wide; margins towards the apex often wavy or faintly crenulate. Flowers blue, closely packed in a hemispherical head $\frac{1}{2}$ to $\frac{3}{4}$ in. wide, borne at the top of an erect glabrous stalk $1\frac{1}{2}$ to 4 ins. high. Corolla two-lipped, the upper lip two-lobed, the lower one three-lobed, all the lobes linear; calyx five-lobed, hairy, the lobes awl-shaped. Stamens four, conspicuously exposed.

Native of the Alps, Tyrol, and mountains of S. Europe, usually in rocky places and in limestone districts; cultivated in England in 1633, according to Aiton. It flowers in July and August and is worth a place in the rock garden for its neat close habit and its pretty heads of blue flowers with prominently outstanding stamens. Increased by division or by cuttings.

GLYPTOSTROBUS PENSILIS, *K. Koch*. CONIFERÆ

(G. heterophyllus, *Endlicher*)

The Chinese swamp cypress is a small deciduous tree with glabrous young shoots. As in the nearly related Taxodiums the young shoots are of two kinds: 1. persistent and bearing axillary buds; 2. deciduous and without any buds. The former, which are usually terminal, bear the leaves spirally round the twig; the latter bear the leaves distichously (that is, arranged in two opposite rows) and they fall off it in autumn, carrying the leaves with them. The leaves also are of two kinds: those on the budless, deciduous twigs are linear, $\frac{1}{3}$ to $\frac{1}{2}$ in. long, $\frac{1}{20}$ in. wide, pointed or bluntish; those on cone-bearing twigs short, scale-like, $\frac{1}{12}$ to $\frac{1}{8}$ in. long. There are also others of intermediate size. Cones obovoid or pear-shaped, $\frac{3}{4}$ to 1 in. long, $\frac{3}{8}$ to $\frac{1}{2}$ in. wide towards the top.

Known only as a cultivated tree chiefly in the province of Canton in S. China, where it is found on the banks of water. It is believed to have died out in a wild state. The twigs and leaf arrangement very much resemble those of the American swamp cypress. It is not hardy at Kew, but plants grown in pots under glass are very charming for many weeks in autumn and early winter for the soft glowing red of the fading leaves. It can be grown outside in mild southern and western gardens. In Capt. E. de Rothschild's garden at Exbury in Hampshire there is a healthy plant about 15 ft. high. According to Henry, the Chinese peasants plant it on the north side of their villages to bring luck to the home, and amongst the rice fields to increase the crop.

GORDONIA ALTAMAHA, *Sargent*. THEACEÆ

(G. pubescens, *L'Heritier*; Franklinia Altamaha, *Marshall*)

A deciduous tree, 15 to 30 ft. high; branchlets covered with a close down. Leaves alternate, obovate-oblong, 4 to 6 ins. long, 1½ to 2 ins. wide; tapering gradually at the base to a short stalk, toothed towards the apex; dark shining green above, paler, and covered with a close down beneath. Flowers 2 to 3 ins. or more across, white, on stout, very short stalks, produced singly from the leaf-axils near the end of the shoots; sepals roundish, ½ in. across, downy on the outside; petals obovate, round-toothed at the end, downy on the outside. Fruit globular ¾ in. wide.

Originally found in 1770 by John Bartram, on the banks of the Altamaha River, in Georgia, U.S.A., and introduced to England four years later, this rare and beautiful tree has not, according to Sargent, been seen in a wild state since 1790, and is now only known as a cultivated plant. It appears to be too tender to thrive anywhere except in our milder counties. It has on more than one occasion been tried at Kew out-of-doors, but has only survived a few years. It is well worth trying where the conditions are more favourable, both for the beauty of its flowers during late summer and for the fine scarlet of its dying foliage. The soil and conditions that suit the Himalayan rhododendrons ought to suit it. It was 8 ft. high at Tower Court, Ascot, in May 1943.

G. LASIANTHUS, *Ellis*, the Loblolly bay, is an allied species of great beauty also, but even more tender than the above. It is an evergreen tree sometimes 70 ft. high, with white flowers 2½ to 3 ins. across, on stalks about as much long. Found in moist situations in the south-eastern United States (Georgia, Florida, etc.). It should be grown as advised for G. Altamaha, but with even more regard to shelter and warmth. At Kew it is grown in a cold house.

The generic name commemorates Alexander Gordon, a nurseryman at Mile End at the time of its introduction.

G. AXILLARIS, *Szyszylowicz* (Plate 7)

(G. anomala, *Sprenger*; Polyspora axillaris, *Sweet*, Bot. Mag., t. 4019)

An evergreen shrub or small tree; young shoots smooth, grey. Leaves shortly stalked, stout, very leathery, oblanceolate to oblong, tapered more gradually towards the base than to the often blunt apex, shallowly-toothed towards the end only; 2½ to 7½ ins. long, ¾ to 2½ ins. wide; glabrous and dark glossy green. Flowers creamy white, 3 to 6 ins. wide, solitary on very short stalks produced from the terminal part of the shoot. Petals five or six, $1\frac{1}{2}$ ins. wide, deeply notched; stamens very numerous; anthers yellow. Fruit erect, oblong, $1\frac{1}{4}$ to $1\frac{1}{2}$ ins. long, $\frac{5}{8}$ in. wide, hard and woody, the hardened sepals persisting below.

Native of China and Formosa; first named "Camellia axillaris" by Ker in 1818, and figured under that name in the *Botanical Magazine*, t. 2047, the following year. So poor was this figure that another plate in the same periodical was allotted to the species in 1843. It has been cultivated in a cool greenhouse at Kew for many years, but in Cornwall and other places is grown in the open air. In flower it resembles a single white camellia and at its best is very beautiful. Both Wilson and Forrest have found it plentifully in western China. It likes a soil free from calcareous matter. Its flowering season is an intermittent one extending from November to May.

It has been confused with the N. American G. Lasianthus, an evergreen tree with similar foliage, but very easily distinguished by the flowers being borne on stalks about 3 ins. long.

GRABOWSKIA BOERHAAVIFOLIA, *Schlechtendal*. SOLANACEÆ

(Bot. Reg., t. 1985; Lycium boerhaavifolium, *Linnæus*)

A deciduous shrub, 6 to 10 ft. high, of loose, spreading habit; young branches glabrous, armed with sharp spines which are $\frac{1}{4}$ in. long the first year, but grow longer. Leaves alternate, grey, fleshy; roundish, widely ovate or obovate; 1 to $1\frac{1}{2}$ ins. long, $\frac{3}{4}$ to $1\frac{1}{4}$ ins. wide; wavy at the margin, tapering at the base, glabrous; stalk $\frac{1}{4}$ in. or less long. Flowers $\frac{2}{5}$ in. long and wide, produced in May, sometimes singly on a short stalk in the leaf-axils, sometimes in terminal or axillary racemes 1 in. long; corolla pale blue, tubular at the base, spreading to five reflexed lobes; calyx $\frac{1}{6}$ in. long, bell-shaped, with five angular teeth.

Native of Brazil and Peru; introduced in 1780, but rarely seen. Near London it requires the protection of a south wall. The foliage resembles that of Atriplex Halimus, and the flowers are like those of Lycium chinense. It has been associated with the Lyciums, but differs in the fruit, which we rarely or never see. Named in honour of Dr Grabowski, a Silesian botanist of the eighteenth century. It has little more than botanical interest.

GREVILLEA. PROTEACEÆ

The species described below are the hardiest members of the remarkable order of plants to which they belong, which, in a wild state, is confined to the southern hemisphere. In Grevillea, the flowers have no petals, the calyx is more or less deeply four-divided, bearing the anthers at the concave apex of each division. All the species are somewhat tender. Propagated by half-ripened shoots taken about July, and placed in a frame with a little bottom heat. They enjoy a proportion of peat in the soil.

This genus was named by Robert Brown in honour of Charles Francis Greville (1749-1809), once a Vice-President of the Royal Society, to whom the botanists of his period were "indebted for the introduction and cultivation of many rare and interesting plants."

G. ACANTHIFOLIA, *A. Cunningham*

(Bot. Mag., t. 2807)

An evergreen plant several feet high; young shoots slightly angular and glabrous except for a few whitish hairs at first. Leaves 2 to 3 ins. long, 1 to 1¼ ins. wide, bipinnately lobed, the five or six primary lobes ½ to ¾ in. long, reaching nearly to the midrib, again cut into three triangular lobes, each lobe ending in a stiff spine; dark dull green and glabrous except for a few pale hairs when young similar to those on the shoot; stalk ¼ to ½ in. long. Inflorescence terminal or axillary, 1½ to 3 ins. long, with the closely packed flowers all on one side. Flowers dull pink, each about ½ in. long except for the long, strongly curved glabrous style so characteristic of the grevilleas, which stands out ⅝ in. beyond the rest of the flower; they have no petals and the calyx is four-lobed, rather bellied below, the lobed part strongly curved. A feature of the inflorescence is the dense furnishing of silky white hairs that cover the flower-stalk, ovary, and calyx.

Native of the Blue Mountains, New South Wales, where it was found by Allan Cunningham in 1817 and introduced soon after. It is evidently hardier than is generally supposed for it was grown out-of-doors by Lt.-Col. Messel at Nymans, near Handcross in Sussex, for a good many years until it perished in the winter of 1928-9. It flowers in May, and whilst the blossom is more curious than attractive, the much-divided, stiff, prickly foliage makes it a distinct and handsome evergreen.

G. ALPINA, *Lindley*

(G. alpestris, *Meissner*; Bot. Mag., t. 5007)

An evergreen shrub usually dwarf and under 2 ft. high in gardens, of bushy rounded shape; young shoots clothed with spreading hairs. Leaves set on the twigs several to the inch, narrowly oblong or oval, blunt-ended, ⅓ to 1 in. long, $\frac{1}{12}$ to ¼ in. wide, but made narrower by their recurved margins; dark green, downy, minutely warted above; silky-hairy beneath, stalkless. Flowers produced about five together in terminal clusters, the perianth (calyx) about ½ in. long, curved, swollen at the base, red at the lower part, yellow upwards, downy. A conspicuous part of the flower is the stout downy style with its knob-like stigma standing out ¼ in. beyond the calyx and of a similar colour.

Native of South Australia in mountainous districts; first flowered in this country apparently by Messrs Rollison of Tooting in May 1857. It is very frequently shown at the Royal Horticultural Society's meetings in spring, grown in pots. Although in a climate like that of Kew its tenure as an outdoor shrub is insecure and often short, it is about as hardy as G. sulphurea, and (say) thirty miles south of London, is well worth growing in a sunny sheltered spot in the rock garden. It blooms freely and over a long season, but the red of the flowers is not particularly bright.

G. ROSMARINIFOLIA, *A. Cunningham*

(Bot. Mag., t. 5971)

An evergreen shrub of loose, graceful habit, 6 or 7 ft. high, with slender, downy branches. Leaves alternate, closely set on the branches, very like those of rosemary; 1 to 2 ins. long, averaging ⅛ in. wide; stalkless, pointed, dark grey-green and rough above, covered beneath with closely pressed silvery hairs. Flowers deep rosy red, densely arranged in terminal racemes, each flower 1 in. or less long, on a glabrous stalk ¼ in. long. Calyx silky inside, scarcely ½ in. long. with hooked divisions, two long and two short, in the apex of each of which is enclosed an anther; styles about ¾ in. long, red.

Native of N.S. Wales; discovered by Allan Cunningham in 1822. Near London this shrub will only survive mild winters, but it succeeds and flowers well in the Grayswood Hill garden, Haslemere. In Cornwall it is quite at home, and makes fine bushes 6 or 7 ft. high, and twice or thrice as much wide.

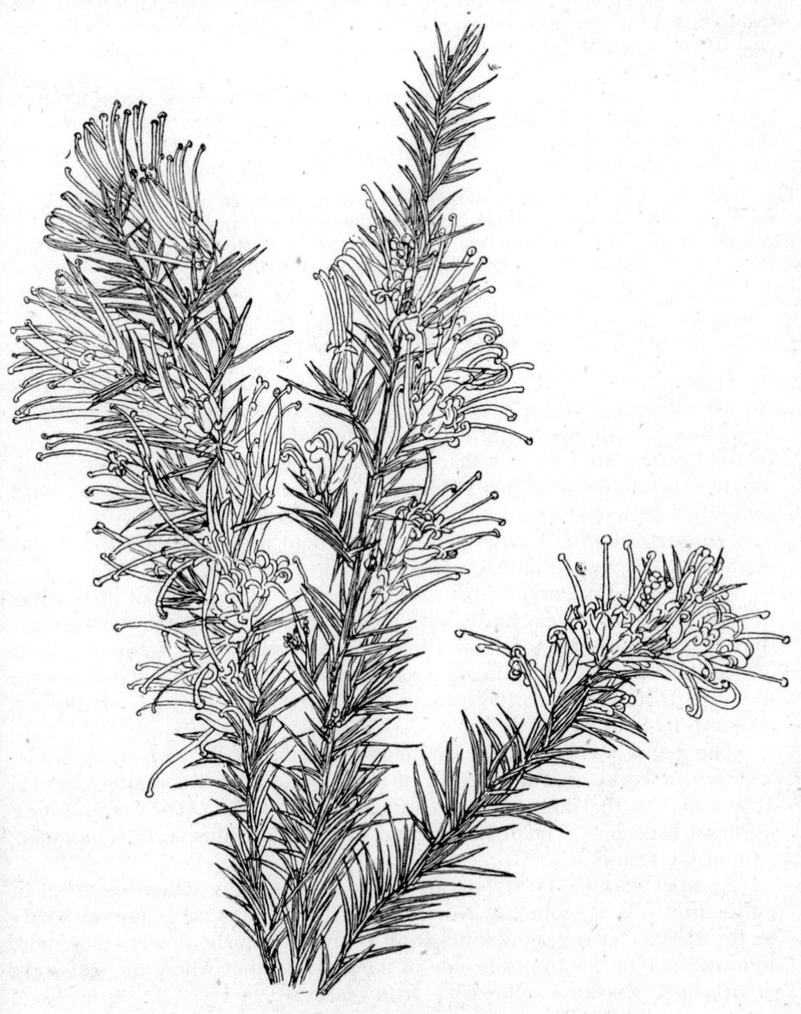

GREVILLEA SULPHUREA

G. SULPHUREA, *A. Cunningham*

(G. juniperina sulphurea, *Bentham*)

An evergreen bush of sturdy habit, probably 6 ft. high ultimately; young shoots very downy. Leaves linear or needle-like; $\frac{1}{2}$ to 1 in. long, $\frac{1}{16}$ to $\frac{1}{12}$ in. wide, made narrower by the curling back of the margins; prickly pointed, pale beneath; glabrous except for a few appressed hairs beneath when young; produced in alternate, closely set tufts. Flowers pale yellow, produced during May and June at the end of short lateral twigs in a short raceme (almost an umbel) of a dozen or more blossoms. The calyx is a slender tube ½ in. long, covered with silky hairs, and slit deeply on one side; the inch-long style protrudes through the slit, and the concave, dilated ends of the four divisions of the calyx are curled back, each enclosing a stalkless anther. Seed-vessel a dry, spindle-shaped pod ½ in. long, with the erect style still attached at the end.

Native of N.S. Wales. This interesting and pretty shrub is the hardiest of grevilleas, but is not really hardy except against a warm, sheltered wall in the London district. It is admirably adapted for Cornwall and other mild counties, and I have seen it growing and flowering well at Haslemere.

The following species are mentioned by Mr E. Thurston as being cultivated in the open air in Cornwall in addition to those described in this work:—G. asplenifolia, *Knight*, at Trebah; G. oleoides, *Sieber*, at Ludgvan Rectory; G. ornithopoda, *Meissner*, at Trewidden; G. Preissei, *Meissner*, at Trebah; G. thyrsoidea, *Meissner*, at Bosahan.

GREWIA PARVIFLORA, *Bunge*. TILIACEÆ

A deciduous shrub, 6 to 8 ft. high, with the young shoots and leaves furnished with starlike down. Leaves alternate, ovate, or sometimes three-lobed; rounded, slightly heart-shaped, or tapered at the base, pointed at the apex, 2 to 5 ins. long, half to two-thirds as wide; rough to the touch above, downy beneath. Flowers creamy yellow, with numerous yellow stamens; about ½ in. across; produced during July and August, in small axillary umbels of about six flowers on the shoots of the year. Fruit roundish, orange or red, ¼ in. wide.

Native of China and Korea; introduced in 1888. It is of little value in gardens, and not very hardy with us, probably needing a hotter summer than ours. The finest specimen I have seen in Europe was in the collection of the late Mr de Vilmorin, at Les Barres in France. When I saw it, it was 7 ft. high and 10 ft. through, flowering freely in July. It flowers a month later in England.

The genus was named by Linnæus in honour of Dr Nehemiah Grew, who wrote works on the anatomy of plants, and died in London in 1712. It is allied to the limes, but is confined to Asia and Africa, containing numerous species. The inner bark has the tough fibrous nature characteristic of the family.

Another species, G. OPPOSITIFOLIA, *Roxburgh*, is sometimes seen in cultivation. It is from the North-West Himalaya, and is not so hardy as the above. It is very distinct from it, in bearing the flowers in a short inflorescence on the opposite side of the shoot to that where the leaf-stalk is attached. Flowers yellowish; fruit black.

GRINDELIA CHILOËNSIS, *Cabrera*

(Bot. Mag., t. 9471; G. speciosa, *Lindley and Paxton*)

An evergreen shrub of bushy shape 2 to 3 ft. high and as much or more wide, with thick stems woody at the base which produce annually stout, erect, semi-herbaceous shoots, sticky to the touch, scurfy, and densely clothed with leaves over their whole length. Leaves linear-oblong to oblanceolate, pointed, tapering at the base, the margins set with coarse outstanding teeth; shortly or not at all stalked; 2 to 4½ ins. long, ⅓ to ¾ in. wide; grey green, sticky when young, ultimately thickly sprinkled with small circular patches of dried gum. Flower-heads produced during the summer singly from the end of the shoot on a stout erect stalk up to 12 or 15 ins. long; they are about 3 ins. wide, both the ray- and disk-florets of a rich bright yellow; ray-florets pointed, about 1 in. long, ⅛ to 3/16 in. wide. Bracts of the involucre awl-shaped to narrowly triangular, ⅜ to ½ in. long.

Native of Argentina. It seems originally to have been introduced by Mr H. Wooler of Upper Tulse Hill, about 1850, seeds having been sent to him by his son, who found it just above high-water mark at a place called New Bay on the coast of Patagonia. In 1911 it was flowered at The Elms, Yalding, Kent, by Capt. S. G. Reid. The plants at present in cultivation were raised from seed collected in 1925-6 by H. F. Comber. There is a fine plant in Col. Stern's garden at Highdown, near Worthing, which flowers more or less continuously from May to October. It is also grown at Kew, and by Lt.-Col. Messel at Nymans, in all places hardy but more truly shrubby in the warmer places. Mr Wooler, its first cultivator, was quite successful with it over ninety years ago. According to Lindley and Paxton, who figure it in their *Flower Garden*, iii., p. 119, he had thirty to forty flower-heads open on his plant at one time. An interesting character of the plant is the coating of pale gum which covers the top of the flower-head whilst it is in the bud state and must keep out wet. The flowers are not very agreeably scented but the young shoots have a pleasant and slightly aromatic fragrance.

GRISELINIA. CORNACEÆ

A small genus of trees and shrubs, native of New Zealand and Chile. Two species are found in the former country, both of which are cultivated out-of-doors in the milder parts of the British Isles. They are somewhat tender, especially G. lucida, but where they thrive make handsome evergreens. Male and female flowers are produced on different plants; they are quite small, dull coloured, and of no ornament. The attractions of both species are in their shapely habit and shining foliage.

G. LITTORALIS, *Raoul*

A large evergreen shrub or small tree, of rounded habit, at present up to 10 or 25 ft. high in Britain, but twice as high in a wild state. Leaves leathery, oval or ovate, 1 to 3 ins. long, half to two-thirds as wide, of a shining yellowish green, glabrous, the apex blunt, the base unequal-sided; stalk ½ to ¾ in. long. Flowers yellowish green, small, produced during May in axillary racemes or panicles 1 to 2 ins. long. The female plant produces panicles of green oblong fruits, ¼ in. long.

Native of New Zealand up to 3500 ft. altitude; cultivated in Kew since the middle of last century, but only hardy there in mild winters. All the plants outside were killed in the winter of 1908-9. In milder and especially maritime localities this shrub makes an excellent evergreen, and has been strongly recommended for forming hedges and wind breaks. It is rarely seen in fruit in this country, owing probably to the male plant being more propagated than the female. But in the garden of Mr Charles Hamilton at Hamwood, Co. Meath, where a tree of each sex is grown, the female bears abundant crops of berries containing fertile seeds which spring up about the grounds. It strikes very readily from cuttings of half-ripened wood placed in gentle heat, or of somewhat harder wood under handlights. There is a tree over 20 ft. high at Kilmacurragh, Co. Wicklow.

G. LUCIDA, *Forster*

A robust evergreen shrub or small tree, up to 8 or 10 ft. high in Britain. Leaves leathery, thick, glossy, rather pale green, oblong or broadly ovate, 4 to 7 ins. long, 2 to 3½ ins. wide; glabrous on both sides, markedly unequal at the base, stalk 1 to 1½ ins. long. Flowers small, green, in axillary panicles; female ones without petals. Fruit ⅓ in. long, purple.

Native of New Zealand, and only hardy in Cornwall and similar localities. At Kew it will not survive permanently even against a wall. It is, therefore, not so useful a shrub as G. littoralis, although from the larger size of its leaves it is a more striking one. Propagated by grafting on littoralis

Var. MACROPHYLLA, *Hooker fil.* (G. macrophylla of gardens), is a larger leaved, more robust form.

GUEVINA AVELLANA, *Molina*. PROTEACEÆ

(Bot. Mag., t. 9161)

An evergreen tree 30 to 40 ft. high, densely and luxuriantly leafy; young shoots stout, clothed thickly with a soft brown down as are the leaf-stalks also. Leaves pinnate or doubly pinnate; from 6 to 16 ins. long, 4 to 10 ins. wide; the primary divisions three to fifteen, each consisting of one to five leaflets. The number of leaflets on one leaf may vary from three to over thirty and individually they vary much in size. On young vigorous plants the largest leaflets are as much as 7½ ins. long and 3 ins. wide; the smallest less than 1 in. long. They are usually ovate to triangular in outline, sharply toothed, rounded or truncate at the base, pointed at the apex, leathery in texture, and of the richest lustrous green. Racemes produced in the leaf-axils during August, 4 ins. long, carrying twenty to twenty-five pairs of usually ivory-white flowers with very narrow recurved sepals, beyond which the stamens project half an inch; style ⅓ in. long, curved, hairy at the base. Fruit a hard nut the size of a small acorn, turning red, then purple, finally black. Seeds edible.

Native of Chile; introduced in 1826. It is not really hardy at Kew, and although it survives normal winters in a sheltered spot, it is not worth struggling with out-of-doors. But in Devonshire and Cornwall it is very fine. The best tree I have seen is one at Trewidden, near Penzance, which when I saw it in 1930 was 35 ft. high and 13 ft. in diameter at the base—a pyramidal tree of great beauty. In regard to foliage alone it would be difficult to find an evergreen of its type more handsome. "Guevina" is an adaptation of the Chilean name for the tree. Ripe fruits have been developed at Rostrevor, Co. Down, and the seeds found to be palatable. The flowers vary in colour from pure white to yellowish or greenish white, occasionally tinged with red.

GYMNOCLADUS. LEGUMINOSÆ

A genus consisting of two deciduous, pod-bearing trees, one native of N. America, the other of China, and most nearly related among hardy trees to Gleditschia. They have doubly pinnate leaves, flowers in racemes or panicles, and large thick pods; the flowers are regular, being composed of five equal-sized petals, and a tubular, five-lobed calyx, with no indication of the pea-flower shape so common in this family. The American species is perfectly hardy in the south of England, but grows extremely slowly, and rarely flowers. It likes a rich loamy soil. The Chinese tree, G. CHINENSIS, *Baillon*, is 40 ft. high, with leaves 1 to 3 ft. long, each of the pinnæ consisting of twenty to twenty-four oblong leaflets, $\frac{3}{4}$ to $1\frac{1}{2}$ ins. long, silky beneath. Flowers, lilac-purple, both perfect and unisexual, borne on the same tree, in downy racemes. Pod 4 ins. long, $1\frac{1}{2}$ ins. wide. Native of China, and said by Henry to be rather rare. Introduced to Kew in 1888, but not hardy there, and only likely to succeed in the mildest parts of the kingdom.

In both species propagation must be effected by means of imported seeds.

G. CANADENSIS, *Lamarck*. KENTUCKY COFFEE

(G. dioica, *Koch*)

A deciduous tree up to 110 ft. high, with a trunk 6 to 10 ft. in girth, usually branching low down, and forming a narrow, rounded head. Branchlets downy when young, light grey, marked by numerous small scars. Leaves up to 3 ft. long and 2 ft. wide; bipinnate, the two lowest pairs of pinnæ being simple leaflets, but the upper ones composed of four to seven pairs of leaflets. The leaflets are ovate, $1\frac{1}{2}$ to $2\frac{1}{2}$ ins. long (the two lowest pairs considerably larger); grey-green and hairy beneath, principally on the veins and midrib. The tree is diœcious, the panicles of the female tree being 8 to 12 ins. long, 3 to 4 ins. wide, narrowly pyramidal; flowers downy, $\frac{3}{4}$ to 1 in. long; petals greenish white, calyx not quite so long as the petals, tubular at the base, with five linear teeth. In the male tree the inflorescence is about one-third the length of the females. Pod 6 to 10 ins. long, $1\frac{1}{2}$ to 2 ins. wide.

Native of the eastern and Central United States; cultivated in England before the middle of the eighteenth century. In its foliage it is perhaps the most beautiful of all hardy trees. It evidently needs more summer heat than it gets here, for there are fine specimens both in France and Germany suggesting in their leafless state the habit and branching of the horse chestnut. In autumn a curious effect is produced by the leaflets falling off and leaving the naked common stalk on the branches for some time. In winter, young trees have a very distinct and rather gaunt appearance, the branches being few, thick, and rough. The finest tree in England appears to be at Claremont, which is 60 ft. high and 7 ft. in girth of trunk, and flowers frequently. The common name is said to have originated through the people of Kentucky and Tennessee at one time roasting and grinding the seeds to make a beverage like coffee.

Var. VARIEGATA.—Leaves slightly marked with white spots; apparently of little value in this country.

HALESIA. SNOWDROP TREES. STYRACACEÆ

In British gardens the snowdrop trees are almost exclusively represented by the beautiful H. carolina; but a second species, H. diptera, is sometimes seen; whilst a third, H. PARVIFLORA, *Michaux*, a native of S. Georgia and Florida, is not known in cultivation, and but little in a wild state. The leading characteristics of the genus are the pendulous snowdrop-like flowers, produced in clusters on the previous year's wood, and the winged fruits. Leaves alternate, deciduous, the down with which they and other young parts are more or less furnished being stellate. The genus was named in honour of Dr Stephen Hales, a learned author, who was born at Bekesbourne, in Kent, in 1671, and died at Teddington in 1761. The halesias like a moist, well-drained, loamy soil, and thrive best in a sheltered, sunny position. Propagation is by seeds and layers. All three species are native of the south-eastern United States.

Pterostyrax (*q.v.*) is a small group of North Asiatic trees and shrubs, sometimes united with Halesia, but very well marked by differences pointed out in the notes on the genus. From the also nearly allied Styrax, Halesia differs in the winged fruits and inferior ovary.

H. CAROLINA, *Linnæus*. SNOWDROP or SILVER-BELL TREE (Plate 8)

(H. tetraptera, *Ellis*)

A deciduous tree, 20 to 30 ft. high in this country; said to be occasionally twice as high in its native places, with a trunk 3 ft. in thickness. With us it is

HALESIA CAROLINA

of spreading habit, often a shrub; young shoots at first clothed with stellate down. Leaves oval to obovate, wedge-shaped or rounded at the base, abruptly taper-pointed, minutely toothed; 2 to 5 ins. long, $\frac{3}{4}$ to $2\frac{1}{2}$ ins. wide, thickly covered beneath with grey stellate down, less so above; stalk $\frac{1}{4}$ to $\frac{3}{8}$ in. long, downy. Flowers produced in May on slender, downy, pendulous stalks $\frac{1}{2}$ to 1 in. long, in clusters of three to five from the joints of the naked, year-old wood. Corolla white, bell-shaped, $\frac{1}{2}$ to $\frac{3}{4}$ in. long and wide, shallowly four-lobed. Fruit somewhat pear-shaped, but with four prominent wings running lengthwise and an awl-shaped termination; altogether about $1\frac{1}{2}$ ins. long.

Native of the south-eastern United States; introduced by Mr J. E. Ellis in 1756. It is undoubtedly one of the most beautiful flowering trees introduced to this country from N. America; yet it is by no means abundantly planted.

Var. GLABRESCENS, *Perkins* (H. parviflora, *Hort.*, not *Michaux*), differs from the type in the oblong oval leaves proportionately narrower (three or four times as long as wide), soon quite glabrous beneath. Flowers smaller, fruits more narrowly four-winged; the whole plant less downy.

Var. MEEHANI, *Perkins*, was raised from seed in Meehan's nursery, Germantown, Philadelphia. It differs from ordinary H. carolina in its smaller, shorter-stalked flowers; the corolla is more cup-shaped; leaves thicker and more coarsely wrinkled. May be a hybrid.

Var. STENOCARPA, *Koch*.—A fine form or hybrid with deeply lobed corolla. Perhaps a hybrid between this species and H. diptera.

H. DIPTERA, *Ellis*

A deciduous shrub, 8 to 15 ft. high (occasionally a small tree twice as high in a wild state); young branches stellately downy at first. Leaves oval or obovate, 3 to 5½ ins. long, 1½ to 3 ins. wide; minutely and rather distantly toothed, abruptly pointed, wedge-shaped or rounded at the base; downy on both sides on first opening, but soon almost glabrous except on the midrib and veins beneath; stalk ½ to ¾ in. long. Flowers pendulous, produced in May in clusters or short racemes from the joints of the year-old wood; stalks ½ to ¾ in. long, slender, downy. Corolla bell-shaped, ¾ in. long, deeply four-lobed, white; calyx very downy; stamens hairy. Fruit oblong, 1½ to 2 ins. long, ¾ in. wide, with two longitudinal wings ¼ to ⅜ in. wide, ending in a short spike.

Native of the south-eastern United States; introduced in 1758. This is far from being as good a garden shrub as H. carolina; it is less hardy and is shy-flowering. It grows well, and is over 12 ft. high at Kew, but never flowers as it does in France, especially south of Paris. Easily distinguished from H. carolina by the two-winged fruit, and larger broader leaves.

H. MONTICOLA, *Sargent* (Plate 9)

(H. carolina monticola, *Rehder*)

This, the "Mountain Snowdrop tree," is a deciduous tree often 80 to 100 ft. high in a wild state, with a trunk 3 ft. in diameter and free of branches for more than half its height. It grows at altitudes of not less than 3000 ft. on the mountains of the S.E. United States where, according to Sargent, it is an important timber tree. Botanically it is evidently very nearly related to the well-known snowdrop-tree, H. carolina, differing in its larger flowers, larger fruit, and of course in size, for H. carolina rarely attains more than one-third its stature and is indeed more usually a shrub with us than even a small tree. H. monticola is distinct also in its bark, which separates from the trunk in large, loose, plate-like scales, whereas the main stem of H. carolina has a close bark with only small appressed scales. The flowers are in clusters of two to five, each ¾ to 1 in. long, pure white; the four-winged fruits are up to 2 ins. long. Leaves scarcely different from those of H. carolina in shape, size or downiness.

H. monticola is probably the hardier of the two, and has proved to be a valuable flowering tree in N. America, as it grows rapidly and begins to blossom there when about 12 ft. high. Sargent observes that it is the best halesia for the gardens of the N.E. United States. It is in cultivation in this country and blossoms in May.

Var. ROSEA, *Sargent*, has flowers of a pale rose colour.

HALIMIOCISTUS SAHUCII, *Janchen*. CISTACEÆ

A natural bigeneric hybrid between Helianthemum umbellatum and Cistus salvifolius found wild in France. It was introduced and cultivated first by Sir Oscar Warburg in his garden at Boidier near Epsom about

1929. Being very attractive and satisfactorily hardy, it has become pretty well known in gardens. It is an evergreen shrub, 15 to 18 ins. high of spreading but close growth, with linear to linear-oblanceolate leaves, $\frac{1}{3}$ to $1\frac{1}{2}$ ins. long and $\frac{1}{12}$ to $\frac{3}{16}$ in. wide, hairy especially beneath. Flowers white, up to $1\frac{1}{8}$ ins. across, opening in June and borne in abundance.

H. WINTONENSIS, *O. Warburg*

(Cistus wintonensis, *Hillier*)

This is a hybrid raised in Messrs Hillier's nursery at Winchester and it originated probably from Helianthemum lasianthum crossed with Cistus salvifolius. It is an evergreen shrub of bushy, rather spreading habit and $1\frac{1}{2}$ to 2 ft. high. The young shoots are covered with a soft white wool as are also the leaves, both becoming a dull green later. Leaves elliptic-lanceolate, pointed, tapered at the base, rather prominently three-nerved, $\frac{3}{4}$ to 2 ins. long, scarcely stalked. Flowers 2 ins. wide, the five petals white, broadly wedge-shaped, each having a crimson-maroon blotch towards the base, which gives the flower a striking zone of colour, the actual base being marked with a bright yellow, triangular patch. These successive zones of white, crimson and yellow give the blossom a beauty as unusual as it is conspicuous. This hybrid is of especial interest as uniting in itself two distinct although closely related genera. It is admirable for a sunny, rather dry spot in the rock garden or elsewhere, but has not, I fear, a very strong constitution. The flowers often keep open well on in the afternoon. It is scarcely hardy enough to withstand a severe winter except in the milder counties, but survives our ordinary winters near London. It flowers in May and June.

HALIMODENDRON ARGENTEUM, *De Candolle*

SALT TREE. LEGUMINOSÆ

(Halodendron, *Voss*; Robinia halodendron, *L'Heritier*, Bot. Mag., t. 1016)

A deciduous shrub, naturally 4 to 6 ft. high, with very spiny, spreading, somewhat angular branches, greyish, and covered with a fine down when young. Leaves pinnate, composed usually of two pairs of leaflets, the common stalk ending in a stiff spine, which remains after the fall of the leaflets. The latter are $\frac{3}{4}$ to $1\frac{1}{2}$ ins. long, $\frac{1}{8}$ to $\frac{1}{4}$ in. wide; oblanceolate, stalkless, tapering to the base, and covered with a minute, grey down. Flowers two to four together on racemes 2 ins. long, produced from short leafy spurs on the old wood; each flower $\frac{5}{8}$ in. long, with pale purplish pink petals and a bell-shaped, five-toothed, downy calyx. Pod $\frac{1}{2}$ to 1 in. long, $\frac{1}{4}$ to $\frac{1}{2}$ in. wide, inflated, produced on a stalk protruding beyond the persistent calyx.

Native of Siberia; introduced by Dr Wm. Pitcairn in 1779. Owing to its susceptibility to damp when grown on its own roots (which makes it difficult to raise from seed in this country), this shrub should be grafted on Caragana arborescens, to which it is nearly allied. Standards 4 to 5 ft. high should be chosen so as to display the very graceful habit of the plant. In this way it forms a small round-headed tree whose lower branches are pendent. It flowers in June and July, and very freely on well-ripened wood. At such times its elegance of growth, its abundant flowers, and its handsome grey foliage render it very attractive.

Var. PURPUREUM, *Zabel*, has deeper rosy purple flowers.

HALIMIUM. CISTACEÆ

A genus of about seven species closely related to Helianthemum, to which they have been united. They differ from that genus in having a very short, straight style and three or five sepals, whereas Helianthemum has an elongated style, curved or bent at the base and always five sepals. They require the same cultural conditions.

H. ALYSSOIDES, *K. Koch*

(Helianthemum alyssoides, *Ventenat*)

A shrub about 2 ft. high, but twice as much in diameter, forming a low mound of tangled, slender, spreading branches, densely clothed with grey, partly starry down. Leaves narrowly obovate or oblong to ovate-lanceolate, mostly tapered at the base, rounded or blunt at the apex; $\frac{1}{3}$ to $1\frac{1}{4}$ ins. long, $\frac{1}{8}$ to $\frac{1}{2}$ in. wide; grey with a dense down. Flowers in a branched, terminal hairy corymb; each flower $1\frac{1}{2}$ to $1\frac{3}{4}$ ins. diameter, bright yellow, unblotched. Sepals three, ovate, pointed, very hairy, $\frac{1}{3}$ in. long; flower-stalk thickening upwards.

Native of Spain and Portugal; flowering from May onwards. It is allied to H. formosum, but differs in not having the long silky hairs characteristic of that species mixed with the short close down, also by the unspotted petals.

H. HALIMIFOLIUM, *Willkomm and Lange*

(Helianthemum halimifolium, *Willdenow*)

A shrub 2 to 3 ft. high in the open, twice as high against a wall; branches erect, scaly, downy and white when young, becoming smoother afterwards. Leaves narrowly obovate or oblong, the lower ones only short-stalked, $\frac{3}{4}$ to 2 ins. long, $\frac{1}{8}$ to $\frac{1}{2}$ in. wide; tapered and three-nerved at the base; they are white with scaly down when young, becoming dull grey-green with age. Flowers bright yellow, $1\frac{1}{2}$ ins. across, with a small spot at the base of each petal; produced in erect, comparatively few-flowered panicles 6 ins. or more high; petals inversely heart-shaped; sepals three to five, the two outer small ones often missing, the inner ones ovate. In wild specimens the sepals are densely covered with scales as well as somewhat downy, but in cultivated plants they are frequently almost smooth.

Native of Portugal, Spain, and the Mediterranean region, some of its forms being found in N. Africa; cultivated in England since the middle of the seventeenth century. Belonging to the same group as H. formosum, it is distinguished by its tall, slender flower-stems, and its scaly or glabrous, never densely silky calyx.

H. LASIANTHUM, *K. Koch*

(Helianthemum lasianthum, *Persoon*)

A low shrub with wide-spreading branches, growing 2 to 3 ft. high, but more in width, the young shoots erect, the whole plant grey with short down intermixed with which are numerous whitish, stellate or long simple hairs. Leaves oblong, oval or obovate; $\frac{1}{2}$ to $1\frac{1}{2}$ ins. long, $\frac{1}{4}$ to $\frac{1}{2}$ in. wide; three-nerved at the narrowed base, the apex rounded or abruptly pointed. Flowers borne at the end of short side twigs, clustered, but appearing successively; each flower $1\frac{1}{2}$ ins. in diameter, bright rich yellow, each petal with a conspicuous brownish purple blotch near, but not reaching to the base. Sepals three, ovate, taper-pointed, very hairy.

Native of Central and S. Portugal; introduced in 1780; perhaps the most beautiful of all the sun roses we cultivate. It is perfectly hardy, and I have never seen it permanently injured by frost—even 30° to 32°. It is admirable for

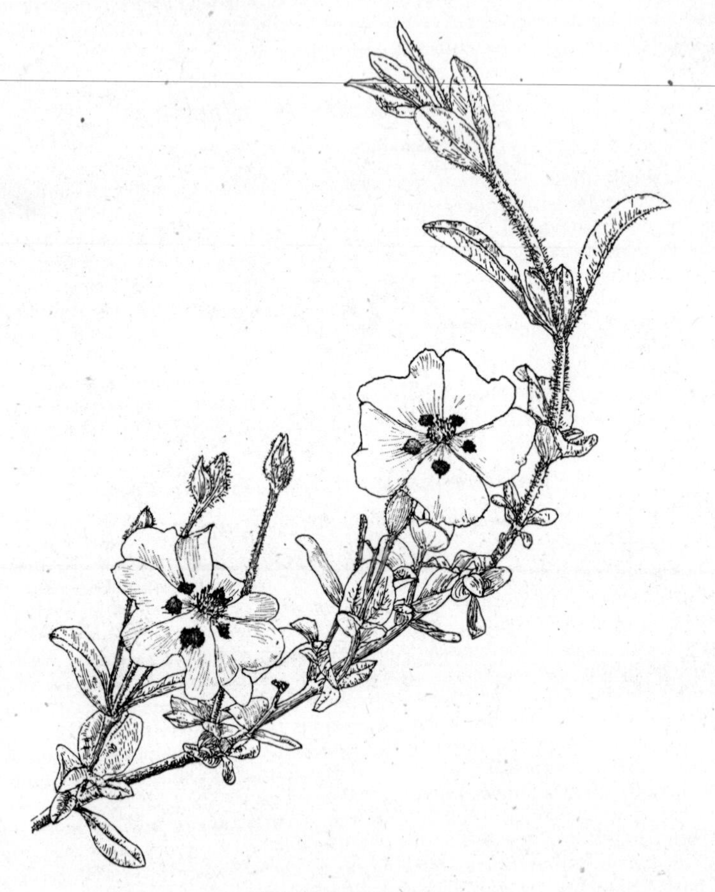

HALIMIUM LASIANTHUM

covering a dry sunny bank, and remains well furnished with foliage through the winter. It commences to flower in May.

Var. CONCOLOR, flowers without the basal blotch on each petal.

H. OCYMOIDES, *Willkomm and Lange*

(Helianthemum ocymoides, *Persoon*)

An erect shrub, 2 to 3 ft. high; young shoots clothed with a dense white down, with which are mixed long silky hairs. Leaves narrowly obovate or oblong, three-nerved, and tapered at the base, mostly pointed at the apex;

$\frac{1}{2}$ to 1 in. long, $\frac{1}{8}$ to $\frac{1}{4}$ in. wide; covered with a close, white down when young, becoming green with age. Panicles erect, but loose and comparatively few-flowered, 3 to 9 ins. high, sparsely hairy; flower-stalks slender. Flowers rich yellow, 1 to $1\frac{1}{4}$ ins. across, petals triangular, with a black and purple blotch at the base of each. Sepals three, oval-lanceolate, sparsely hairy, or glabrous and glossy.

Native of Portugal and Spain; introduced in 1880. It is a very pretty species, noteworthy for the golden yellow of its flowers and the deeply coloured blotch. It is hardy except in severe winters. It most resembles H. alyssoides and H. halimifolium, but from the former differs in the blotched petals, and glabrous or nearly glabrous sepals. It is never scaly, as in H. halimifolium, and the petal blotch is much deeper; both, however, have the same marked difference in colour between the young and old leaves.

H. UMBELLATUM, *Spach*

(Bot. Mag., t. 9141; Helianthemum umbellatum, *Miller*)

An evergreen bush of erect, open habit, about 18 ins. high, with the general aspect of a small rosemary; young branches viscid and downy. Leaves linear, viscid when young; stalkless, $\frac{1}{2}$ to $1\frac{1}{4}$ ins. long, $\frac{1}{12}$ to $\frac{1}{8}$ in. wide; dark glossy green above, white with down beneath. Racemes erect, 4 to 6 ins. high, with the flowers arranged at intervals in whorls, and terminating in a six- or eight-flowered umbel at the top. Flowers white, $\frac{3}{4}$ in. across, the petals inversely heart-shaped, with a yellow stain near the base. Sepals three, ovate, more or less hairy.

Native of the Mediterranean region; introduced in 1731. This is a distinct and very pretty shrub, more resembling a rosemary in foliage than the common run of sun roses.

Var. SYRIACUM, *Willkomm* (Helianthemum syriacum, *Boissier*), is a curious dwarf, semi-prostrate variety, rising only a few inches from the ground. Flowers usually two or three in an inflorescence, pale yellow or yellowish white.

HAMAMELIS. WITCH-HAZELS. HAMAMELIDACEÆ

A remarkable and beautiful genus of small trees and shrubs, consisting of four or five species. They are distinguished very readily from all other hardy shrubs by the thin, narrow, yellow petals, sometimes $\frac{3}{4}$ in. long, and only $\frac{1}{16}$ to $\frac{1}{12}$ in. wide. The leaves are alternate, and much resemble those of our native hazel. This resemblance led the early settlers in N. America to use branches of H. virginiana as divining-rods—as hazel twigs were (and still are) at home; to its supposed magic property it owes its popular name. The parts of the flower are in four.

The witch-hazels like a good, but not very heavy loam, and are benefited in a young or not well-rooted state if peat and leaf-soil are added. When established this is not necessary. The quaint habit of the species is one of their charms, but without interfering with this it is worth while to train up a leading shoot to obtain height, especially if the plants, as they often do, assume and retain a low, sprawling mode of growth. The Asiatic species graft easily on H. virginiana. It is best to establish a quantity of seedlings of the latter in pots, and put on the scions about the beginning of April, they should then be placed in gentle heat. Seeds, it must be remembered, frequently take two years to germinate.

HALIMIUM UMBELLATUM (see p. 85)

H. JAPONICA, *Siebold and Zuccarini*.
JAPANESE WITCH-HAZEL

(Bot. Mag., t. 6659)

A deciduous, spreading shrub or small tree, often sparsely branched; the quite young twigs furnished with stellate hairs. Leaves oval, ovate or obovate, 2 to 3½ ins. long, 1¼ to 2½ ins. wide, with wavy margins, base unequal and sometimes slightly heart-shaped; the five to eight pairs of parallel veins run forward at an acute angle from the midrib; lower surface densely covered when young with down which mostly falls away by autumn; stalk $\frac{1}{4}$ to $\frac{3}{4}$ in. long, downy. Flowers yellow, slightly scented, produced a few together in globose heads during January and February on the then leafless twigs made the previous summer; petals $\frac{2}{3}$ in. long, very narrow, strap-shaped, and much crumpled; bracts reddish, downy outside.

Native of Japan. This is one of the most beautiful of winter or early spring-flowering shrubs. It flowers freely, and its thin wrinkled petals make a very pretty picture at the inclement season when they appear, especially if the shrub has a dark background of evergreens. The species is a somewhat variable one, the shrub grown in gardens as H. japonica, is a flattish, wide-spreading shrub, and the plants called "arborea" and "Zuccariniana" in gardens are only forms of it.

Var. ARBOREA (H. arborea, *Masters*) differs from ordinary japonica in being of more gaunt, treelike form, and 15 to 20 ft. high, in the deeper yellow of the petals, and in the calyx having a deep claret shade. It perhaps flowers at an earlier date. Introduced from Japan by Siebold in 1862. Bot. Mag., t. 6659.

Var. ZUCCARINIANA is also treelike, but its flowers, instead of being of the golden yellow of H. arborea, are of a pale lemon yellow, and the calyx is green. But both are mere seminal variations, and both, to be obtained true, must be propagated by grafting on seedlings of either themselves or H. virginiana. Seeds cannot be relied on to come true, those of arborea will often produce H. japonica; as a large experimenter in the raising of the Japanese witch-hazels has expressed it to me, "you sow seeds and may get anything." The flower-buds of these witch-hazels are already formed on short stalks in the leaf-axils by July, six or perhaps eight months before they expand.

Var. FLAVO-PURPURASCENS, *Rehder*.—This witch-hazel was shown in flower as "H. japonica rubra" at one of the early spring shows of the Royal Horticultural Society in 1919, which was the first time I had seen it. It differs from ordinary H. japonica in the petals being suffused with dull red, giving them a rather indeterminate hue; the calyx is dark purple inside. It appears to be wild in several provinces of Japan: Oshima, Musashi, Mutsu, etc., having been collected in the last-named as long ago as 1880. To my taste, the red suffusion in the petals rather spoils, than improves, the clear yellow of the type. It was described as a new species by Mr Makino in the *Tokyo Botanical Magazine* for 1913, under the name H. incarnata. Whilst it does not seem likely that the world contains another hamamelis that would be as distinct from mollis and japonica as they are from each other, probably slightly varying forms of H. japonica will continue to appear.

H. MOLLIS, *Oliver*. CHINESE WITCH-HAZEL

(Bot. Mag., t. 7884)

A deciduous shrub or small tree, with stout, zigzag, spreading branches, very downy when young. Leaves roundish or very broadly obovate, shortly and abruptly pointed, heart-shaped, but unequal-sided at the base, 3 to 5 ins. long, three-fourths as broad, widely and shallowly toothed, covered beneath with clustered (stellate) hairs; stalk $\frac{1}{4}$ in. long, stout and downy. Flowers rich golden yellow, very fragrant, produced in stalkless, crowded clusters from December to February on the twigs of the previous summer's growth; petals strap-shaped, about $\frac{5}{8}$ in. long, not wavy as in japonica; calyx-lobes rich red-brown, hairy outside, glabrous within. Seeds jet black.

Native of China; first discovered and introduced about 1879, by Maries, from the district of Kiu-kiang, near the Yangtze-kiang River. Afterwards it was found much farther west by Henry and Wilson. This is undoubtedly the finest of all known witch-hazels, both as regards flower and foliage; and because of the early date at which it flowers (it is often in full bloom on New Year's Day), it has made a very precious addition to the garden flora. It is rather curious that it remained in the Coombe Wood nursery for twenty years, regarded merely as a superior form of japonica. It can be propagated easily by grafting on the Virginian witch-hazel.

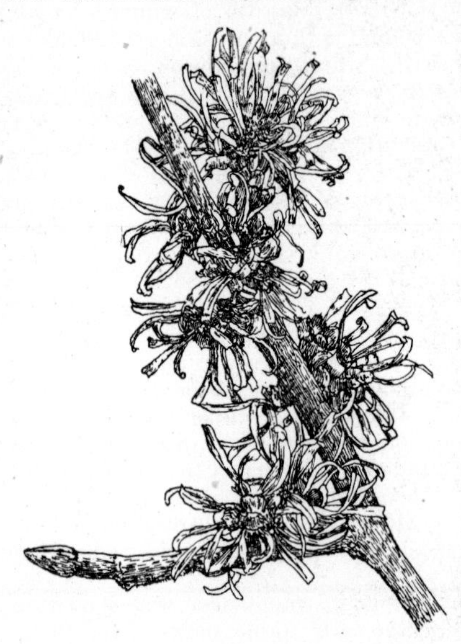

HAMAMELIS MOLLIS

H. VERNALIS, *Sargent*

Professor Sargent (*Trees and Shrubs*, ii. p. 137, t. 156) figured and described this as a new species in 1913. It is closely allied to H. virginiana, but is a native of Missouri, Arkansas, and Louisiana, and resembles the Asiatic species in flowering on the leafless wood from January to March. It differs from H. virginiana also in the following respects: the inner surface of the calyx-lobes is red, and it has the habit of spreading by suckers or under-ground stems. The leaves are of a paler duller green. A plant introduced to Kew in 1910 bore a few flowers in January 1912. It grows naturally on gravelly, often inundated banks of streams, and was collected by Engelmann in Missouri as long ago as 1845. The flowers have a pungent, not very agreeable odour. (Bot. Mag., t. 8573.)

H. VIRGINIANA, *Linnæus*. VIRGINIAN WITCH-HAZEL

(Bot. Mag., t. 6684)

A small deciduous tree, 20 or even 30 ft. high in a wild state, often a shrub of bushy habit; with a short thick trunk and crooked, wide-spreading branches; young shoots at first downy. Leaves broadly ovate to obovate, 3 to 5 ins. long, 2 to 3½ ins. wide; unequal at the base, unevenly and coarsely round-toothed, especially on the upper part; glabrous or nearly so above, downy with stellate hairs on the midrib and veins beneath; stalk downy, ¼ to ½ in. long. Flowers golden yellow, opening in September and continuing until November, produced two to four together in a cluster at the end of a stalk ¼ in. long; petals ½ to ⅝ in. long, narrowly strap-shaped, crumpled; calyx with four short, broadly ovate, hairy lobes, yellowish brown inside.

Native of eastern N. America from Nova Scotia to the mountains of the Carolinas and Tennessee; introduced in 1736. This interesting shrub or tree, although so long an inhabitant of our gardens, is not very common nowadays, being eclipsed by the newer, winter-flowering, Asiatic species. The beauty of this witch-hazel is sometimes decreased by its being in full leaf at flowering time, so that the blossoms, closely tucked to the twigs, have little chance to show themselves, especially as the leaves turn yellow also before falling. The fruits—woody, nutlike bodies ½ in. long, bursting at the top—do not ripen and discharge their seeds until twelve months after the time of flowering. Various popular remedies are made from extracts and decoctions of the bark and leaves.

Var. PALLIDA.—A distinctly paler yellow form exhibited at Vincent Square on 12th January 1932 from the Royal Horticultural Society's Gardens at Wisley.

HARTIA. TERNSTRŒMIACEÆ

This genus, of which only one species has so far been described, is named in honour of Sir Robert Hart, for many years Inspector-General of the Chinese Maritime Customs. Of the genera better known in gardens, it is most closely related to Stewartia, from which it is distinguished "by the more extensive cohesion of the stamens and by its more numerous seeds."

H. SINENSIS, *Dunn*

(Hooker's Icones Plantarum, t. 2727)

An evergreen shrub or tree from 20 to 50 ft. high, its young shoots silky-hairy at first, becoming glabrous and afterwards brown or greyish. Leaves alternate, 3 to 5 ins. long, 1 to 2 ins. wide, elliptical inclined to ovate or obovate, pointed, more or less rounded at the base, toothed, each tooth tipped with a dark gland; dark glossy green and glabrous above; paler, conspicuously veined and at first silky-hairy beneath (chiefly on the midrib), becoming nearly or quite glabrous; stalk up to ¾ in. long, hairy, winged. Flowers white, 1 to 1½ ins. wide, produced singly in early summer from axillary buds on short leafy shoots, each on a stout stalk ¼ to ½ in. long. Petals five, roundish ovate with jagged margins. Calyx-lobes ovate, silky. Fruit conical, woody, ¾ in. long. Stamens very numerous, united at the base to form a short tube; anthers golden yellow.

Discovered in Yunnan, China, by Henry; introduced by Forrest who found it west of Tengyueh in June 1912 and several times later; it occurs at altitudes of 5000 to 9000 ft. The flowers resemble those of the tea-plant (Camellia Thea) to which it is closely akin, and it may prove to possess about the same degree of hardiness. It is growing vigorously in Cornwall and Dorset and may have flowered there. It has blossomed at Exbury, Hants, where Capt. de Rothschild has it in a cool house. It is a handsome-leaved evergreen and some of Forrest's wild specimens show that it is capable of bearing abundant crops of blossom.

HEDERA HELIX, *Linnæus*. COMMON IVY. ARALIACEÆ

An evergreen climber, with a strong, rather acrid odour when crushed, attaching itself to trees, buildings, etc., by means of rootlike growths from the stem, or, where such support is absent, creeping over the ground; young shoots clothed with minute stellate hairs. Leaves alternate, thick, leathery, very dark glossy green, broadly ovate or somewhat triangular, those of the climbing shoots with three or five deep or shallow lobes and stalks of varying length. The starry hairs in typical H. Helix have five to eight "rays." The ivy never flowers on the creeping or climbing shoots, but produces bushy branches, mostly when it has reached the top of its support; these have no aerial roots, and their leaves are never lobed, but are wavy in outline or entire at the margin, and more narrowly ovate. Flowers produced in October, in a terminal cluster of globose umbels, yellowish green. Berries dull inky black, globose, about ¼ in. across, containing two to five seeds.

Native of Europe, found almost everywhere in Britain, especially in shady spots, its natural habitat being the forest, where it can climb trees. The ivy, however, is very adaptable, and can be grown in almost any situation. No introduced evergreen climber can rival it for covering old trees, buildings, etc. Many think that serious damage is done to trees by allowing ivy to climb over them, but this, in my belief, only occurs when the ivy has reached the leafy shoots; so long as the ivy is confined to the trunk and larger branches no harm, I think, is done. At any rate, I know trees in perfect health which have supported ivy for sixty years. An ivy-laden tree is one of the most beautiful objects of the winter landscape. On houses ivy is rather beneficial than otherwise, keeping them dry and warm.

Ivy is propagated with the greatest ease by means of cuttings which may be given gentle heat if it is desirable to get them to root quickly, or dibbled thickly under handlights or even in the open air. The more delicate highly coloured varieties are sometimes grafted on the common ivy, but need constant watching to prevent the stock over-running the scion. One of the most useful purposes to which ivy can be put is as a ground-covering under trees where no grass will grow. It is also very useful for covering iron-rail fencing, or posts and chains. As regards its use on buildings it is capable of attaining at least 100 ft. in height. Leaves of ivy are eaten by horses, cattle, and sheep apparently with relish and without evil results.

The number of varieties into which the common ivy has sported is legion; a great number have been given Latin names, cumbersome and unnecessary, for they often differ from each other but little, and are very apt with age (the coloured ones especially) to revert to the green type. The older botanists made all the hardy ivies varieties of H. Helix, but for garden purposes at least this is an undesirable arrangement, necessitating an unwieldy nomenclature. The following is a representative selection of what may be regarded as forms of H. Helix; others are treated here as species. It may be mentioned that when cuttings of the bushy, flowering state of the ivy are rooted, the plants retain that adult habit, and become sturdy, rounded bushes that flower freely. The varietal name " arborescens " is then added to the specific name, or to that of any of the following varieties, to distinguish them from the climbing condition. They are commonly termed " tree " ivies.

Var. ARBORESCENS. Common Tree Ivy.—The flowering shoots of common ivy grown from cuttings, as just described; there are both silver and golden variegated forms of it.

Var. CAVENDISHII.—A striking variety, whose rather small, angularly lobed leaves are edged with creamy white.

Var. CHRYSOPHYLLA.—Leaves variegated with patches of yellow, or wholly yellow, or wholly green. Rather handsome when seen in good condition.

Var. CONGLOMERATA.—A dwarfed, very slow-growing form, the leaves small and crowded.

Var. DELTOIDEA.—Leaves very distinct in shape, triangular in main outline, with rounded corners and two deep basal lobes, the inner edges of which overlap. Of stiff habit, and assuming a bronzy tint in autumn.

Var. LOBATA MAJOR.—Leaves five-lobed, chiefly distinguished by the very large, narrowly ovate, pointed middle lobe.

Var. MARGINATA.—This name has been given to a set of small-leaved forms, all of which have white or creamy white margins, except MARGINATA RUBRA, in which the margins become red in autumn.

Var. MIMINA.—The smallest of all ivies. Leaves closely set on the shoot; ½ to 1 in. across, three-lobed, the lobes triangular.

Var. OVATA.—A very distinct form, the leaves ovate, pointed, rounded at the base, rich green and entire, or very slightly lobed even in the climbing state.

Var. PEDATA.—Leaves small, very deeply three- or five-lobed, the lobes narrow-lanceolate, and usually from ⅛ to ¼ in. wide; dark green with whitish veins.

Var. SAGITTÆFOLIA.—Leaves arrow-head shaped; in the way of deltoidea, but with sharp instead of rounded points, the basal lobes very deep.

H. CANARIENSIS, *Willdenow*

(H. algeriensis, *Hort.*; H. maderensis, *Hort.*)

Leaf large, leathery, somewhat shallowly three- or five-lobed in the climbing state, 2 to 6 (or even 8) ins. across, heart-shaped at the base; in the flowering state entire and rounded or tapered at the base. Fruit black, as in H. Helix, from which species this differs among other respects in the starry, composite hairs of the young shoots and inflorescence, having thirteen to fifteen rays instead of five to eight, as in H. Helix. The true canariensis is quite distinct from H. hibernica, with which it has been associated; it is sometimes known in gardens as "canariensis nova." Native of Canary Islands and N. Africa.

Var. AZORICA.—A vigorous variety, with leaves 3 to 6 ins. across, vivid green, five- or seven-lobed; lobes ovate, blunt-pointed. The quite young wood and leaves are covered with a thick tawny felt. Introduced from St Michael, in the Azores, by the late firm of Osborn of Fulham.

H. CHRYSOCARPA, *Walsh*

(H. poetarum, *Bertolini*)

Fruits yellow. Leaves of the climbing state triangular or broadly ovate with a heart-shaped base, shallowly lobed or entire; those of the fruiting state small, often diamond-shaped, and not lobed.

Native of S. Europe from Italy to Greece.

H. CINEREA, *Hibberd*. HIMALAYAN IVY

(H. Helix himalaica)

A well-marked species found in various parts of the Himalaya. Leaves triangular-ovate to ovate-lanceolate, taper-pointed, 2 to 4½ ins. long, 1 to 2½ ins. wide; often with two lobes near the base, and several large bluntish teeth upwards. This ivy has a distinct grey tinge, the veins still paler grey, and the leaves are longer in proportion to their breadth than other ivies. Fruit yellow or red. Rather more tender than H. Helix, but does well on a wall. In the fruiting state the leaves are entire, ovate-lanceolate, half to two-thirds as wide as they are long, tapered at the base; sometimes unequal-sided.

H. COLCHICA, *Koch*. PERSIAN IVY

(H. Rœgneriana, *Hort.*; H. amurensis, *Hort.*)

Leaves ovate or heart-shaped, entire or slightly lobed, 3 to 7 ins. across, as much as 10 ins. long; younger parts sometimes purplish tinted. Young shoots clothed with yellowish, scalelike, starry down. This ivy is extremely distinct from our native species, and is a native of the south side of the Caucasus range and of N. Persia. In none of its forms does it ever become so deeply lobed as H. Helix does, although in var. DENTATA the margins have frequently a few distant teeth. The finest form of H. colchica is commonly known as "H. amurensis," but I can find no authority for the name. There is no ivy from the Amoor region in the Kew Herbarium. H. colchica is the most striking of all ivies, and climbs rapidly when once established. The "tree" form makes a striking evergreen bush with uniformly ovate leaves.

H. HIBERNICA, *Kirchner*. IRISH IVY

Leaves black green, 3 to 6 ins. across, with usually five triangular lobes. A strong-growing vigorous ivy useful for ground-cover beneath trees, etc. It is often called canariensis in gardens, but that species has a paler green, more leathery leaf. The "tree" form makes a handsome bush. There are both yellow and white variegated forms of this species, which is not quite so hardy as H. Helix; said to be found wild in Ireland and the west of Scotland.

Var. MACULATA (H. latimaculata).—A form of hibernica with leaves three- or five-lobed, blotched and streaked with creamy white.

H. RHOMBEA, *Siebold*. JAPANESE IVY

A Japanese ivy of rather delicate growth, but quite hardy; the leaves are triangular to ovate, often heart-shaped at the base, usually slightly three-lobed; very dark green. One form, known in gardens as H. japonica variegata, has a thin marginal line of white.

HEDYSARUM MULTIJUGUM, *Maximowicz*. LEGUMINOSÆ

A deciduous shrub, 3 to 5 ft. high, of somewhat sparse, gaunt habit; young branches erect, zigzag in growth, covered with fine down. Leaves 4 to 6 ins. long, alternate, pinnate. Leaflets seventeen to forty-one, $\frac{1}{4}$ to $\frac{3}{4}$ in. long, $\frac{1}{8}$ to $\frac{1}{3}$ in. wide; ovate, oblong, oval or obovate, pointed; glabrous above, minutely downy beneath. Racemes axillary, erect, long-stalked, 6 to 12 ins. long, produced from the axil of each leaf as the shoot develops. Flowers pea-shaped, rosy magenta, $\frac{3}{4}$ in. long, arranged on the upper two-thirds of the raceme on very short stalks; standard petal $\frac{1}{2}$ in. or a little more across, with a patch of yellow at the base. Calyx $\frac{1}{4}$ in. long, split either above or below. Pod flat, almost circular, rough, containing usually one seed.

Native of Mongolia, where it is said to inhabit dry regions. It thrives very well in a sunny position planted in sandy loam, and flowers on the shoots of the year from June to September. Seeds are produced in sunny seasons, but they are uncertain. It is usually propagated by layering, also by cuttings. To correct the rather ungainly habit of this shrub after a few years, we find it a good plan to peg down the branches;

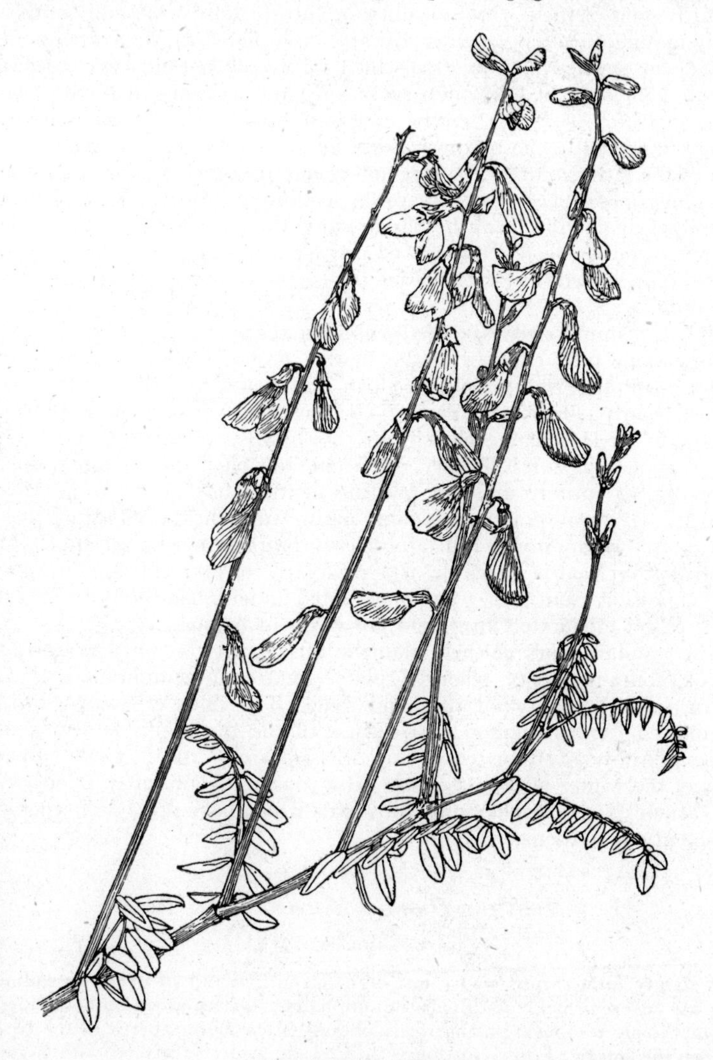

HEDYSARUM MULTIJUGUM

this causes them to break into new growth at the base. The magenta shade in the flower is objectionable to some people, but the shrub is useful in being late flowering and showy.

Var. APICULATUM, *Sprague*.—Leaflets seventeen to twenty-seven, minutely pointed. Bot. Mag., t. 8091.

HELIANTHEMUM. Sun Rose. CISTACEÆ

Only a small proportion of the total number of species of sun roses are hardy, and of these, three shrubby or sub-shrubby ones, and another of only annual duration, occur in Britain. Besides them, there are about half a dozen species in cultivation which survive all but our very hardest winters. They are of low, often spreading and procumbent habit; the leaves opposite, evergreen, entire. Flowers rose-like, terminal, solitary to many-flowered in the inflorescence. Petals five; sepals three or five, when of the latter number the two outer ones are much smaller than the three inner ones. Seed-vessel a capsule opening in three valves. (Herein is the chief distinction from the nearly allied Cistus, which has a capsule with five or ten valves.) Natives of Europe and Asia Minor. The genus is also represented in N. America by species now separated under Halimium.

Helianthemums need above all things a sunny spot. They are best on some slope fully exposed to the south. Essentially sun-lovers, their flowers open sluggishly or not at all in dull weather, and their time of greatest beauty is in the forenoon. The flowers never last longer than a day, and in the H. Chamæcistus group they mostly close up at noon. The flowers appear in extraordinary profusion, but each day's crop is succeeded by an entirely different one the next. They flower from May onwards. Any soil of an open, loamy nature suits them; in nature they often occur on limestone. All are of easy propagation by cuttings. If a mild bottom heat is available, it is preferable to take cuttings in quite a soft condition; but if they are to be rooted under a handlight they must be left to get moderately firm, and put in about August.

The standard work on these plants in this country is *Sweet's Cistineæ*, a book containing 112 coloured plates of Helianthemum and allied genera, published between 1825 and 1830. The value of Sweet's work is impaired by his method of treating all the mere garden forms as species. Many of these have since disappeared. In fact, the great frosts of the winter of 1837-8 destroyed a considerable number of species and varieties of Helianthemum and Cistus which have not again secured a place in our gardens.

H. alpestre, *Dunal*. Alpine Sun Rose

(Sweet's Cistineæ, t. 2)

A dainty little shrub, 3 to 5 ins. high, forming a tuft of dense spreading branches covered thickly with pale, minute hairs. Leaves green on both sides, oval-lanceolate to obovate or narrowly oblong, often more tapered at the base than at the apex; $\frac{1}{4}$ to $\frac{1}{2}$ in. long, $\frac{1}{12}$ to $\frac{1}{6}$ in. wide, furnished with a few comparatively long hairs, especially on the margins. Flowers produced in June and July in a loose terminal raceme, three to five together; each flower $\frac{1}{2}$ to $\frac{3}{4}$ in. diameter, bright yellow, unblotched, borne on a slender, downy stalk. Sepals five, hairy; the three inner ones oval and about half as long as the petals, the two outer ones linear, much smaller. Stipules absent.

Native of the mountains of Central Europe at 6000 to 7000 ft. altitude, of the Caucasus, and Asia Minor; introduced in 1818. This pretty little plant, although now rare, has existed at Kew and in the Vicarage garden at Bitton for many years. It is quite hardy, and admirable for the rock garden.

H. APENNINUM, *De Candolle*

(Sweet's Cistineæ, t. 62 ; H. polifolium, *Persoon*)

A low, spreading, much-branched shrub up to 18 ins. high, the stems and leaves thickly clothed above and below with a close, white, stellate down, giving the whole plant a mealy appearance. Leaves linear-oblong or linear, the margins much recurved, ½ to 1 in. long, ⅛ to ⅕ in. wide ; bluntish or pointed. Racemes terminal, producing numerous flowers in succession. Flowers pure white, 1 in. or rather more across, nodding in the bud state, but becoming erect at expansion. Petals obovate, slightly toothed at the end. Sepals five, the two outer ones linear, very small ; the three inner ones ovate, twice as long as the others, all white with down.

Native of Europe and Asia Minor ; found in a few places in S.W. England, such as the Brent Downs in Somersetshire, and at Torquay and Babbicombe in Devonshire, usually on limestone. It is, of course, quite hardy, and so nearly allied to H. Chamæcistus that some botanists regard it as a variety. It is distinct enough, however, for garden purposes, in its less spreading habit, its white foliage and flowers, and by the smaller, bodkin-shaped stipules. There are hybrids between the two, *e.g.* H. CONFUSUM (Sweet's Cistineæ, t. 91), with white flowers, but broader leaves and longer stipules than ordinary polifolium.

Var. RHODANTHUM (Sweet's Cistineæ, t. 7).—Flowers reddish ; leaves not so much recurved as in the type.

H. CANUM, *Baumgarten*

(H. vineale, *Persoon*)

A dwarf shrub, forming a compact tuft rarely more than 6 ins. high, but 1 ft. or more in diameter ; young stems and leaves covered with a short down and a few hairs. Leaves hairy and green above, grey beneath with down, ovate-oblong, ¼ to ¾ in. long. Flowers in terminal racemes, sometimes a panicle, usually of three to six blooms, each ½ in. across, bright yellow, unblotched. Sepals five, hairy, the two outer ones very small ; stipules absent. Seed-vessel thickly hairy.

Native of Europe, and found in a few stations in the British Isles, mostly on limestone, in the west of England and the west of Ireland. It is hardy, and makes a pleasing little tuft for the rock garden when covered with its brightly coloured flowers. From the other British species it is not only distinct in its small, compact habit ; it differs also in having no stipules. With the species cultivated in gardens it is only likely to be confused with H. alpestre, which has also no stipules, but whose leaves are green on both surfaces. Botanists also rely on the longer, oval and pointed flower-buds of H. alpestre as a distinction from the globose ones of the present species.

H. CHAMÆCISTUS, *Miller*

(H. variabile, *Spach* ; H. vulgare, *Gaertner*)

A low semi-shrubby plant, covering ground over 2 or 3 ft. across, but scarcely rising more than 1 ft. above it ; the older stems prostrate, the young flowering ones erect, somewhat hairy. Leaves flat, variable in size and shape, usually oblong, sometimes approaching ovate or lanceolate ; ¾ to 2 ins. long, ⅛ to ½ in. wide, sometimes green on both sides, but usually grey or white with stellate down beneath, and more or less bristly hairy above; stalk $\frac{1}{8}$ to $\frac{3}{16}$ in. long; stipules lance-shaped, longer than the leaf-stalk. Racemes terminal, with many but successively developed flowers. Flower-stalks decurved, erect only when the flower is expanded. Flowers yellow, about 1 in. across. Sepals five, the two outer ones small, fringed with hairs; three inner ones ovate, with three or four prominent hairy ribs.

Native of Europe, where it is widely spread, including the British Isles. This is probably the hardiest of all the sun roses, and is well known in gardens by the numerous, highly coloured, sometimes double-flowered varieties which have sprung from it, making brilliant displays from May to July. It is sometimes found with rosy flowers in a wild state. Some of the best cultivated forms are unnamed, and have been raised in the ordinary way from seed. Others have been given popular names; two of the best being "Fireball," bright scarlet-red, and "the Bride," pure white. Robert Sweet, in his book on the Cistus family, published 1825-1830, figured and described numerous varieties under Latin names. Some of these have been lost, but of those that survive a selection is here given. It is, however, in the power of anyone to obtain as good or better forms by raising seedlings themselves. In all its forms H. Chamaecistus is only a morning bloomer, the flowers closing soon after midday—the bright red "Fireball" is one of the latest to keep open. In spite of this defect they are worthy of more extended cultivation, for they bear an amazing profusion of blossom lasting over several weeks.

Var. CROCATUM (Sweet's Cistineæ, t. 92).—Leaves green and hairy on both sides; flowers saffron coloured.

Var. CUPREUM (Sweet's Cistineæ, t. 58).—Leaves green both sides; flowers copper-coloured; there is a double-flowered form of this.

Var. DIVERSIFOLIUM MULTIPLEX (Sweet's Cistineæ, t. 98).—Leaves green above, whitish beneath, flowers double, dark red.

Var. MUTABILE (Sweet's Cistineæ, t. 106).—Leaves green above, grey beneath; flowers pale rose.

Var. ROSEUM (Sweet's Cistineæ, t. 55).—Leaves green above, grey-white beneath; flowers rather paler than those of var. mutabile.

Var. STRAMINEUM (Sweet's Cistineæ, t. 93).—Leaves green above, whitish beneath; flowers sulphur-yellow, with a darker yellow patch at the base of each petal.

Var. SURREJANUM (H. surrejanum, *Miller*, Sweet's Cistineæ, t. 28).—This curious variety is said to have first been found near Croydon in Surrey. It is distinguished from the type by the narrow petals being deeply notched at the end; they are linear-lanceolate, about $\frac{1}{8}$ in. wide, $\frac{3}{8}$ in. long, yellow. This variety has little beauty and is really a deformity.

Var. VENUSTUM (Sweet's Cistineæ, t. 10).—Leaves lustrous green above, whitish beneath; flowers rich crimson, with a yellow spot at the base. Some of these varieties are probably hybrids with H. glaucum.

Cultivators may easily get new and, it may be, superior varieties by raising plants from their own seed.

H. GLAUCUM, *Persoon*

Closely akin to H. Chamæcistus is a group of sun roses with shorter and comparatively broader leaves, light green with down above, white beneath. They are distinguished from H. Chamæcistus in having stellate down on both surfaces of the leaves. To this group the sun rose known in gardens as H. CROCEUM belongs (Sweet's Cistineæ, t. 53). The habit is the same as that of H. Chamæcistus, but it is very distinct in summer in the almost white foliage, with which the rich yellow flowers are in admirable contrast. Its proper name is H. GLAUCUM CROCEUM, *Boissier*. Native of S. and S.W. Europe. Many of the garden varieties (see under *Chamæcistus*) are hybrids, or perhaps forms of this species, more especially those whitish on the upper surface.

H. LUNULATUM, *Lamarck*

A dwarf, cushion-like, evergreen sub-shrub 4 to 8 ins. high; young shoots covered with a close down and sprinkled with hairs. Leaves elliptic-oblong to obovate, tapered at the base, rounded or obtuse at the apex; $\frac{1}{3}$ to $\frac{5}{8}$ in. long, $\frac{1}{8}$ to $\frac{3}{16}$ in. wide; dull green and glabrous above, furnished beneath with starry hairs and long simple ones; margins hairy; stalk $\frac{1}{12}$ in. or less long. Flowers $\frac{1}{2}$ in. wide, opening during June and July, usually singly, at the end of the young shoots; petals bright yellow, roundish, with a crescent-shaped stain at the base; flower-stalk $\frac{1}{2}$ to 1 in. long, downy like the young shoots.

Native of the Alpine regions of Italy, often on limestone. This is a neat little plant, forming a gay patch of colour in midsummer. Suitable for a sunny spot in the rock-garden. Easily propagated by soft cuttings in gentle heat.

HELICHRYSUM. COMPOSITÆ

A large genus of shrubs and herbs of varying type and aspect, most abundant in Australasia and South Africa; leaves entire and mostly alternate. The generic limits have been undecided and the three species here described are often grown under the name OZOTHAMNUS.

H. ANTENNARIUM, *Mueller*

(Ozothamnus Antennaria, *Hooker fil.*; Bot. Mag., t. 9152)

An evergreen shrub of bushy, densely leafy growth, 3 or 4 ft. high; young shoots minutely downy at first. Leaves narrowly obovate, $\frac{1}{2}$ to $1\frac{1}{4}$ ins. long, rounded or notched at the apex, tapered to the base, soon glabrous, very dark green above, greyish beneath; stalk about $\frac{1}{3}$ in. long. Flower-heads white, about $\frac{1}{6}$ in. wide, densely clustered in terminal corymbs which are rounded and 1 to 2 ins. across, opening in June.

Native of Tasmania, where it is fairly common, especially on the mountains of the south and east. Originally discovered by Gunn in 1835, it was introduced to Kew about 1880 (or probably before). It is hardy enough there to succeed in one of the nooks of the Temperate House wall, where it has flowered freely and attractively every summer over a lengthy period.

H. ROSMARINIFOLIUM, *De Candolle*

(Ozothamnus rosmarinifolius, *De Candolle*)

An evergreen shrub, 6 to 9 ft. high, with ribbed, glutinous young branches. Leaves alternate, closely set on the branches; $\frac{1}{2}$ to $1\frac{1}{2}$ ins. long, $\frac{1}{12}$ in. or less wide; linear, glabrous, dark green and rather glutinous above, pale beneath; margins recurved. Flower-heads snow-white, crowded, about $\frac{1}{6}$ in. diameter, produced from June to August at the end of short side shoots in rounded corymbs $\frac{1}{2}$ to $\frac{3}{4}$ in. across.

Native of Tasmania and Victoria, and hardy only in the warmer counties. At Kew it needs the protection of a wall. Where it thrives, this is undoubtedly one of the most beautiful shrubs introduced from Tasmania. About midsummer every little twig is terminated by its cluster of blossoms, which as a whole almost hide the plant in a snow-white sheet. It is popularly known as "snow in summer." The flowers are practically everlasting; I have specimens collected, dried, and pressed over thirty years ago, which are still pure white. For room decoration long sprays should be cut, hung upside down in a place as free as possible from dust, and allowed to become dry and rigid. After a few weeks they may be taken down and arranged in the ordinary way in vases, where the flowers will remain white and beautiful for many months, no water of course being needed.

Of other species in cultivation, H. GLOMERATUM, *Hooker fil.*, is a curious evergreen shrub up to 8 ft. high, with long, slender, thong-like shoots covered with white down, and sparse roundish leaves ¼ to 1¼ ins. long, also covered with white down beneath. Flower-heads in small, short-stalked, axillary or terminal, globose clusters, ½ in. diameter. Scarcely so hardy as H. rosmarinifolium, and of little merit. Native of New Zealand.

H. SELAGO, *Bentham and Hooker* .

An evergreen shrub much branched and 6 to 15 ins. high; young branchlets arching or pendulous, about $\frac{1}{12}$ in. thick, with a cypress-like appearance due to the leaves being closely appressed to the stem. Leaves overlapping, ovate to triangular, $\frac{1}{10}$ to ⅛ in. long, pointed or bluntish, dark polished green and convex outside, covered inside with a white wool which shows slightly at the edges and at the base of the leaves. With age they become markedly keeled or ridged at the back. Flower-heads produced singly at the end of the shoot, stalkless, the chief feature being the bracts of the involucre which are linear-oblong, $\frac{3}{16}$ in. long, dull white or yellowish, and with membranous tips.

Native of New Zealand, where it occurs in mountainous districts of the South Island up to 4500 ft. altitude. I have not seen it in flower, but perhaps its chief claim to notice is in its curious cypress-like growth and the outlining of each leaf when young with a thin fringe of white wool escaped from the otherwise hidden inner surface. Considering the latitudes and altitudes at which it occurs wild it should be hardy. The late Lord Wakehurst found it to grow well in his rock garden at Wakehurst, in Sussex, and it was from his plant that the above description was made. It is, however, variable. The New Zealand specimens preserved at Kew show that. One of them has shoots fully $\frac{3}{16}$ in. thick and they vary also in the amount of wool they display. *See* also Ozothamnus.

HELWINGIA JAPONICA, *Dietrich.* CORNACEÆ

(H. ruscifolia, *Willdenow*)

A deciduous shrub, 3 to 5 ft. high, with glabrous twigs. Leaves simple, alternate, ovate, tapering at both ends, long-pointed, 1½ to 3 ins. long, ½ to 1¼ ins. wide; with fine, rather bristle-like teeth on the margins, quite glabrous and bright green on both surfaces; stalk ½ to 1 in. long; stipules hair-like. Flowers unisexual, very small, pale green or greenish white; females produced singly or in threes on the midrib about the centre of the upper surface of the leaf; males more numerous; they are stalkless, and of no beauty. Fruit ¼ in. long, roundish oval.

Native of Japan; introduced to Europe by Siebold in 1830. It has not the least merit as an ornamental shrub, although the foliage in a milder climate is larger and perhaps more striking than as here described; but it is a plant of singular botanical interest. The morphological explanation of the anomalous position of the flowers in the middle of the leaf (for no true leaf ever produces flowers) is that the flower-stalk in reality originates in the axil of the leaf, but is united from end to end with the stalk and midrib. This shrub is hardy at Kew, and is propagated by cuttings of young wood.

HETEROMELES ARBUTIFOLIA, *Roemer*. TOLLON. ROSACEÆ

(Photinia arbutifolia, *Lindley*; Bot. Reg., t. 491)

An evergreen tree, occasionally 30 ft. high, or in cultivation more often a shrub, with downy young bark. Leaves stiff and leathery, 2 to 4 ins. long, ¾ to 1½ ins. wide; oblong, lanceolate or obovate, tapering at the base to a thick downy stalk ½ to ¾ in. long; the margins set with stiff teeth, each tipped with a small black gland. Flowers produced very numerously in a large, flattish panicle, composed of corymbose clusters terminating the shoot, and in the axils of the uppermost leaves. Each flower is from ¼ to ⅜ in. diameter; petals pure white; calyx with short, glabrous, triangular lobes. Fruit about the size of holly berries, bright red, tasting like common haws.

Native of California; introduced by Menzies in 1796. It is a handsome evergreen, unfortunately not hardy at Kew, but thrives well in the Grayswood Hill garden at Haslemere, where I have seen it in flower in August; also in Lord Annesley's garden at Castlewellan, Co. Down. Sargent states that the fruit-covered branches are gathered in large quantities in California, and used as we use holly for Christmas decorations. It may be grown on a wall, but is, of course, at its best in the open where the climate is suitable. It is the only species of the genus, and is very closely allied to Photinia, but differs in having only ten stamens to each flower.

HIBISCUS SYRIACUS, *Linnæus*. MALVACEÆ

(Bot. Mag., t. 83; Althæa frutex, *Hort.*)

A deciduous shrub, with rather erect branches but bushy habit, up to 10 ft. and more high. Leaves variable in size, ordinarily from 2 to 4 ins. long, with stalks ¼ to 1 in. long; of ovate outline, more or less distinctly three-lobed and coarsely toothed, glabrous except for an occasional bristle on the veins. Flowers produced singly on short stalks from the leaf-axils towards the end of the branch. Each flower is from 2½ to 4 ins. across, with five free petals forming a trumpet mouth. The colour is exceedingly variable in the numerous forms of this shrub, some being white, others red, violet, purple, or striped; whilst others again have double or semi-double flowers. Commences to bloom in August.

The date of the introduction of this shrub to Britain is not known, but as it was included by Gerard among the garden shrubs of his time, it has been cultivated here for probably 350 years. In early times it was known as the "Syrian Ketmie," and in the specific name Linnæus suggested that it was from Syria, but it has never been found truly wild except in India and China. In Syria, as in more western countries, it exists as a cultivated plant only. It is perfectly hardy in most parts of Britain, but owing to its late-flowering habit, it is often necessary in the north to treat it as a wall plant in order that its flowers may develop under more favourable conditions. In the south, where the cold rains do not come so early, it can be grown quite in the open, and there is no shrub more beautiful during September, especially if that month be hot and sunny. In selecting a place for it, shady and ill-drained spots should be avoided. Any soil of moderate or good quality suits it. It can be propagated by cuttings or by layers, and rare sorts may be grafted on common ones. Plants growing too large for their places may be pruned back in early April. One of the common features of the gardens at Versailles are large bushes of this hibiscus, cut hard back annually into formal shape. Both in France and in Italy it flowers with greater profusion and regularity than under our uncertain skies. There is a tree in the Padua Botanic Gardens 20 ft. high. A great number of varieties have been raised and named, and the following list must only be regarded as a selection of a representative few of approved merit. On the whole, single-flowered ones are to be preferred.

Admiral Dewey.—Pure white; double.
Cæleste.—Purplish blue; single.
Grandiflorus superbus.—Rosy; single.
Hamabo.—Pale blush, with a large crimson blotch at the base of each petal; single, one of the best. (The plant cultivated under this name is not the H. Hamabo of *Siebold*, Flora Japonica, t. 93.)
La Reine.—Rose coloured; single.
Monstrosus.—White with dark purple centre; single.
Pulcherrimus.—Pink and white; double.
Puniceus.—Red; double.
Rubis.—Ruby-coloured; single.
Souvenir de Chas. Lebreton.—Lilac purple; double.
Totus albus.—Pure and wholly white; single.
Variegatus.—Foliage white-variegated; flowers double, purple.

HIPPOPHAË. ELÆAGNACEÆ

Two species of deciduous, willow-like trees and shrubs found in Europe and the temperate regions of Asia. Flowers unisexual, the sexes on different trees, inconspicuous and of no beauty. Leaves alternate, scaly beneath. Fruit an orange-coloured or yellow, roundish, juicy berry. The genus is allied only to Elæagnus and Shepherdia; Elæagnus differs in its bisexual flowers and scaly, silvery fruits; and Shepherdia has opposite leaves. (For cultivation, see H. rhamnoides.)

H. RHAMNOIDES, *Linnæus*. SEA BUCKTHORN

(Bot. Mag., t. 8016)

A deciduous shrub, sometimes a tree 30 to 40 ft. high, the whole of the younger parts of the plant covered with silvery grey scales; twigs stiff, frequently spine-tipped. Leaves scarcely stalked, linear, 1 to 3 ins. long,

$\frac{1}{8}$ to $\frac{1}{4}$ in. wide; tapered at both ends, upper surface dark greyish green, and not so scaly as the silvery grey under-surface. Flowers very small, produced in April along the twigs of the previous year in short axillary clusters; each flower solitary in the axil of a deciduous bract. Fruit an orange-coloured berry, between globose and egg-shaped, $\frac{1}{4}$ to $\frac{3}{8}$ in. long, shortly stalked; in colour by September.

Native of Europe (including Britain) and temperate Asia. With its narrow, silvery leaves and brightly coloured berries clustered thickly on the branches from autumn until February, the sea buckthorn stands out remarkably distinct from all others in our gardens. Its beauty is so striking that it ought to be indispensable to every garden where winter effects are desired. Whilst it is, as the popular name suggests, frequently found on sea-shores, it thrives perfectly well in inland districts. At Kew it succeeds admirably at the margin of water, and in the ordinary soil of the gardens. It is not generally known that the plants are unisexual, so that the female one alone bears fruit, and then only if a male plant be growing near enough for the flowers to become pollinated. It is best grown in groups of about six females to one male. The pollen is carried by wind. Solitary female plants can be fertilised by hand, which is best done by waiting until the pollen of the male plant is ripe—shown by the little shower of yellow dust when the branch is tapped—and then cutting off a branch and shaking it over the female plant. It would be a useful thing if nurserymen who stock this shrub would graft a piece of male on female plants. Perhaps no other fruiting shrub is so attractive as this for so long a time. However pressed by hunger, birds will not eat the berries, which are filled with an intensely acid, yellowish juice.

Propagation may be effected by seeds or by layers. The latter is the simpler way of obtaining plants whose sex is known. There appears to be no way of distinguishing seedlings until they flower.

H. SALICIFOLIA, *Don*

A deciduous, somewhat spiny tree, 30 to 40 ft. high, with a coarse bark cut into longitudinal flakes; young shoots covered with brownish down as well as scales. Leaves linear-oblong, 1 to 3 ins. long, $\frac{1}{4}$ to $\frac{1}{2}$ in. wide, dull green (not silvery) above, the lower surface covered with a greyish white felt; midrib brown; stalk $\frac{1}{8}$ to $\frac{1}{4}$ in. long. Flowers as in H. rhamnoides. Berries pale yellow.

Native of the Himalaya up to 10,000 ft. altitude, and perfectly hardy at Kew, where there is a tree 40 ft. high, with the head of branches 30 ft. through and the trunk 4 ft. 9 ins. in girth; the twigs pendulous. This tree bears fruit, but does not compare with H. rhamnoides in beauty. It is easily distinguished by its broader, not silvery leaves, felted rather than scaly beneath, and by the paler, less brilliantly coloured fruit. Introduced in 1822.

HOHERIA POPULNEA, *Cunningham*. MALVACEÆ

(Gardeners' Chronicle, 23rd Nov. 1901)

An evergreen shrub or small tree, 10 to 30 ft. high, glabrous except on the young shoots, flower-stalks, and calyx, which are more or less pubescent. According to Cheeseman's *Flora of New Zealand*, it is a most variable species. He distinguishes three varieties, viz., vulgaris, lanceolata, and angustifolia, the first of which is the one cultivated here, and apparently the most handsome. Its leaves are 3 to 5 ins. long, $1\frac{1}{2}$ to $2\frac{1}{2}$ ins. wide; ovate, firm in texture, edged with large, sharply pointed unequal teeth. Flowers abundant, pure white, opening in September in clusters from the leaf-axils, each flower ¾ to 1 in. across, with spreading, narrowly oblong petals and numerous stamens. Fruit a cluster of five winged capsules.

Native of New Zealand. Although this beautiful tree may have been in cultivation much earlier, it only sprang into notice about the beginning of this century, when it flowered at the Trinity College Botanic Garden, Dublin, and was figured in the place above quoted. It is grown out-of-doors in Cornwall and most of the milder counties. It likes a rich loamy soil, and is increased by cuttings. Hoheria is closely allied to Plagianthus, but differs in having its carpels winged at the back, and keeping closed when ripe. Some years ago I noted a tree at Wisley, then about six years old and 10 ft. high, growing in a sheltered spot in the Wild Garden. It was quite healthy and set with flower-buds then —in July.

Vars. ANGUSTIFOLIA and LANCEOLATA are distinguished by their smaller, narrower leaves; those of the former are usually only 1 to 2 ins. long.

HOLBOELLIA. LARDIZABALACEÆ

A genus of five species of evergreen climbers native of China and the Himalaya named after F. L. Holboell, once superintendent of the Botanic Garden at Copenhagen.

H. CORIACEA, *Diels*

A vigorous evergreen climber growing, according to Wilson, 20 ft. high in nature, but apparently capable of becoming much taller under cultivation; young shoots twining, ribbed, purplish, and, like the leaves and flower-stalks, quite glabrous. Leaves composed of three leaflets borne on a common stalk 1½ to 3½ ins. long, each leaflet having its own stalk ¼ to 1 in. long. Leaflets 2½ to 6 ins. long, 1 to 3 ins. wide, the middle one the largest and longest-stalked, oval or oblong inclined to obovate and usually widest towards the pointed apex, rounded at the base; side leaflets ovate to lanceolate; all three dark glossy green, leathery, and conspicuously veined beneath. Male flowers scarcely ½ in. long; petals erect, in white, oblong, ⅛ in. wide; stamens with pale purple stalks scarcely longer than the anthers. The male flowers are produced in a group of corymbs at the end of the previous year's growth or in the leaf-axils, the whole making a cluster of blossom 3 ins. long and 4 ins. wide. Female flowers produced in corymbs of usually three or four blooms from the axils of the lower leaves of the young shoots. They are rather larger than the males and appear on a main-stalk up to 5 or 6 ins. long; petals fleshy, much paler than the males, greenish white tinged with purple; styles three, erect, cylindrical ¼ in. long. The fleshy fruit is purple, 1¾ to 2¼ ins. or even more long, nearly 1 in. wide. Seeds jet black.

Native of Hupeh, China; introduced by Wilson in 1907. It is quite hardy and is vigorous enough to climb into and over a small tree. The description given above was made from a plant which first flowered at Kew in April and May 1921. Messrs Rehder and Wilson observe that it is closely related to H. latifolia, a species easily distinguished from it by often having five or even more leaflets to one leaf; also more tender. H. coriacea is an interesting addition to the somewhat meagre number of really hardy evergreen climbers.

H. LATIFOLIA, *Wallich*

(Stauntonia latifolia, *Wallich*)

An evergreen twining shrub with compound leaves, consisting of three, five or seven radiating leaflets, which are glabrous, obovate, acuminate, of leathery texture, dark glossy green, 2 to 7 ins. long, one-third as wide, borne on a main-stalk 2 to 6 ins. long, themselves with stalks 1 in. or more long. Flowers borne on short corymbs in the leaf-axils, very fragrant, unisexual, with both sexes often on the same corymb. Sepals six, greenish white in the male, narrow-oblong, about ½ in. long; in the females larger, purplish; petals six, minute. Fruit irregular-oblong, sausage-shaped, 2 to 3 ins. long, containing numerous seeds.

Native of the Himalaya, where the fruits are eaten by the natives. A luxuriant climber, which thrives exceedingly well in the south-western counties, but in cold localities requires greenhouse protection to be seen at its best. The flower should be fertilised by hand.

HOVENIA DULCIS, *Thunberg*. RHAMNACEÆ

(Bot. Mag., t. 2360)

A deciduous tree 30 ft. high (much more in a wild state); twigs downy when young. Leaves alternate, oval or heart-shaped; from 4 to 7 ins. long, 3 to 6 ins. wide; taper-pointed, coarsely and unequally toothed, downy beneath, especially on the veins. Flowers in terminal and axillary forked clusters 2 to 3 ins. across; the individual flower ¼ in. or so wide, yellow. Flower-stalks swelling unevenly after the decay of the flower into a fleshy, contorted mass, red, and sweet to the taste. They are chewed by the Japanese and Chinese. Fruit about the size of a pea, containing three seeds, and often partially embedded in the fleshy stalks.

Native of China, but now cultivated extensively in Japan and N. India. This curious tree is fairly hardy at Kew, where it forms a rather ungainly shrub with erect branches, growing very vigorously in the summer, but cut back more or less in winter.

HUDSONIA ERICOIDES, *Linnæus*. BEACH HEATHER. CISTACEÆ

Hudsonia is a genus of three species exclusively North American, and allied to Cistus and Helianthemum, which it resembles in the fleeting nature of its blossom. Its always yellow flowers and three-valved seed-vessel distinguishes it from Cistus, and from both it differs markedly in the heathlike habit. Named in honour of Wm. Hudson, an English botanist of the eighteenth century.

H. ericoides is a low, bushy, evergreen shrub of heathlike aspect, rarely more than 6 or 8 ins. high. Leaves grey-green, awl-shaped; ¼ to ⅓ in. long, erect and overlapping but not pressed to the stem, hairy. Flowers bright yellow, ⅓ in. across, produced during May singly on very slender, silky stalks about ½ in. long, crowded at the upper parts of the branches; petals five, soon falling; sepals three, silky.

Native of eastern N. America, in dry sandy soil near the coast, from Newfoundland to N. Carolina; introduced in 1805, but always rare owing to the difficulty in cultivation. The late Sir John Ross of Bladensburg, who, so far as I know, is the only one who has had any success with it, told me that it did best planted in a made bed consisting of peat at the bottom, and about 6 ins. of sand at the top. So far as winter cold is concerned, it must be hardy anywhere in Britain, considering the high latitudes it reaches in a wild state. But even in American gardens it is not easy to establish. It may be recommended to those knight-errants in gardening who delight in mastering difficult subjects. It probably needs a sandy, well-drained, slightly saline soil, with full sunshine.

HYDRANGEA. SAXIFRAGACEÆ

A group of Asiatic and North American deciduous shrubs, sometimes treelike, sometimes climbing, with the leaves opposite or in threes, and large terminal corymbs or panicles of flowers. A peculiarity of Hydrangea, shared among hardy shrubs by Viburnum and the rare Schizophragma, is the production in most of the species of large, showy, sterile flowers and small fertile ones on the same inflorescence. The sterile flower has no stamens or seed-bearing parts, but consists merely of three to six flat, spreading sepals with some remnants of petals in the centre. The functions of these flowers are no doubt advertisement and the attraction of insects for purposes of fertilisation. The perfect or fertile flowers are quite small and very numerous, the sepals and petals four or five, the stamens eight or ten. Seed-vessel a small capsule, with the styles and calyx adhering, many-seeded. The sterile flowers are usually confined to the margin of the inflorescence, but some species have nothing but fertile flowers. In gardens the most popular hydrangeas are those culture-forms which have none but sterile flowers.

The stronger-growing species like paniculata and Bretschneideri require a rich loamy soil to bring out their best qualities. The hortensis section do not appear to be very particular as to soil or position. Most of the genus are easily increased by cuttings made of moderately ripe summer wood, placed in gentle heat. H. quercifolia is better layered. The following species should be pruned back every spring:—arborescens, cinerea, paniculata, radiata. The question of blue-flowered hydrangeas is alluded to under H. hortensis; several Asiatic species vary from blue to pink.

Among the species not given detailed mention below are:—

H. HIRTA, *Siebold*.—A low shrub with very coarsely toothed leaves somewhat bristly on both sides, and corymbs 2 to 3 ins. across, of none but small fertile flowers. Native of Japan. I have seen it from Mr T. Smith's nursery at Newry but it has little garden value.

H. VIRENS, *Siebold*.—Branches slender, pendulous, bearing small lanceolate or oval leaves, and, at the end of short axillary, shoots, small corymbs 1 to 3 ins across, with often only one to three large sterile blossoms, which are whitish and ¾ to 1½ ins. wide. Native of Japan, and of elegant habit, but only suitable for the milder parts of these islands. Cultivated by Sir John Ross of Bladensburg, at Rostrevor, Co. Down.

H. ANOMALA, *D. Don*

(H. altissima, *Wallich*)

A deciduous climber, up to 40 ft. or more high, attaching itself to tree trunks by aerial roots in a wild state; young shoots either hairy or glabrous; the bark of the older branches peeling off in large, thin, brown flakes. Leaves ovate or oval, 3 to 5 ins. long (more in mild climates) half to three-fourths as wide; rounded at the base, pointed, regularly triangular- or roundish-toothed; glabrous on both sides except for tufts of down in the vein-axils beneath; stalk at first hairy, 1 to 3 ins. long. Corymbs 6 to 8 ins. across, with a few white sterile flowers at the margins, each ⅔ to 1½ ins. in diameter; the small perfect flowers are yellowish white; stamens ten (often more). Blossoms in June.

Native of the Himalaya and China; introduced in 1839. It is nearly allied to H. petiolaris, but differs in having fewer stamens, not so flat an inflorescence, and usually more coarsely toothed leaves. It is not so hardy probably as H. petiolaris, although it grows well outside on a wall at Kew. Both these species are distinguished by the petals of the fertile flowers cohering into, and falling away in, one cap-like piece.

H. ARBORESCENS, *Linnæus*

A deciduous shrub of somewhat loose habit, 4 to 10 ft. high; young shoots rather downy at first, becoming glabrous. Leaves broadly ovate, oval or roundish; 3 to 7 ins. long, 2 to 6 ins. wide; pointed at the apex, rounded or heart-shaped at the base, coarsely toothed; upper surface bright dark green, lower one paler; both glabrous, or with down only on the veins or in the vein-axils beneath; stalk 1 to 3 ins. long. Corymbs flattish, much branched, usually 4 to 6 ins. across, with few or no large sterile flowers. Fertile flowers dull white, very small and crowded; flower-stalks downy. Seed-vessels eight-ribbed, with calyx adhering at the top.

Native of the eastern United States, from the State of New York southwards; introduced by Peter Collinson in 1736. A vigorous and hardy species, which flowers freely in July and August, but is not particularly attractive. It is allied to H. radiata, differing chiefly in the nearly glabrous leaves.

Var. GRANDIFLORA, *Rehder*.—A very beautiful form, in which all the flowers are of the large sterile type and pure white. It appeared in this country in 1907, but I was informed by Prof. Sargent that it was found wild in the mountains of Pennsylvania fifty or more years ago. It is quite hardy, and showy enough to be regarded as an admirable substitute for H. hortensis in the colder parts of the country. It blooms from July to September, and is probably the best hydrangea to cultivate out-of-doors near London and in places with a similar climate. Its one defect is that its flower-heads are often so heavy that the stalk is not stout enough to hold them upright.

H. BRETSCHNEIDERI, *Dippel* (Plate 10)

(H. pekinensis, *Hort.*; H. vestita pubescens, *Maximowicz*)

A deciduous shrub, 8 to 10 ft. high, forming a sturdy bush, old bark peeling; young branches glabrous. Leaves oblong to ovate, 3 to 5 ins. long, 1 to 2¼ ins. wide; rounded or wedge-shaped at the base, slender pointed, regularly toothed; dull and glabrous above, hairy on the veins and sometimes over the whole surface beneath. Corymbs flattened, 4 to 6 ins. across, with a considerable number of large sterile flowers at the margins; these are ¾ to 1¼ ins.

across, the three or four sepals rounded or obovate, white, afterwards rosy. The small, perfect flowers are dull white; flower-stalks clothed with erect bristly down. The seed-vessels are egg-shaped, the persistent calyx forming a raised band round the middle.

Native of China; introduced from the mountains about Pekin in 1882, by Dr Bretschneider. Planted in a sunny position in good soil, this makes a really handsome shrub, flowering in June and July, perfectly hardy and always vigorous.

H. CINEREA, *Small*

A species intermediate between H. arborescens, whose leaves are almost glabrous, and H. radiata, which has them clothed beneath with a close, snowy-white felt. In H. cinerea the leaves are covered beneath with a dense greyish down. The corymbs have few large sterile flowers or none.

Found wild in mountainous parts of the south-eastern United States. A variety, STERILIS, *Rehder*, in which nearly all the flowers are of the large sterile type, is described as having originated in Ohio, U.S.A., and was introduced in 1910, but I have not seen it flower in cultivation. There has long been in cultivation a hydrangea intermediate between H. radiata and H. arborescens, which has been regarded as a hybrid between the two. It is known as H. canescens, *Kirchner*, and H. arborescens canescens, *Nicholson*, but I do not know how it differs from the species named as above by Dr Small.

H. DAVIDII, *Franchet*

A deciduous shrub up to 6 or 7 ft. high; young shoots downy, slender. Leaves oblong-lanceolate, tapered towards both ends but more especially towards the long, slender, curved apex, fairly regularly and conspicuously toothed; 3 to 7 ins. long, 1 to 2½ ins. wide; upper surface pale green, with scattered hairs; lower surface conspicuously downy on the midrib and in a less degree on the veins; stalk ½ to 1 in. long. Inflorescence a loose corymb 5 to 10 ins. wide; the small fertile flowers are pale blue; sterile flowers white, 1 to 2 ins. across, the (normally) four sepals rounded ovate; flower-stalks downy. The seed-vessel has the calyx-tube reaching to about its middle.

Native of W. China; introduced in 1908. The inflorescence as a rule has no single main-stalk, but its main sections spring directly from where the uppermost pair of leaves are attached to the stem. It is a quite handsome species and flowers in June and July, the large white sterile flowers contrasting with the inner blue fertile ones. Discovered in Mupin by the Abbé David in 1869; described and named by Franchet in 1885.

H. HETEROMALLA, *Don*

(H. vestita, *Wallich*)

A deciduous shrub, often a small tree in its native places. Leaves oval to narrowly ovate-lanceolate; 3 to 8 ins. long, 1½ to 3 ins. wide; tapered at both ends or sometimes rounded at the base, finely toothed; glabrous except for some appressed hairs above, covered with a close white down beneath; stalk ¾ to 1¾ ins. long. Corymbs 4 to 7 ins. across, somewhat thin; the large, white sterile flowers at the margin ¾ to 1¼ ins. diameter; flower-stalks with erect bristly down. Seed-vessels surmounted by the thickened bases of the two or three styles, and with the calyx persisting as a ring about the middle. Flowers in July and August.

Native of the Himalaya; introduced in 1821. The distinguishing characters of this species are the very downy, whitish under-surface of the leaves, the thickened bases of the persistent styles at the top of the fruit, and the position of the calyx about the middle. It has been much confused with H. Bretschneideri, which is never so downy beneath the leaf, and has a more tapered apex to the fruit. It is also allied to

H. ASPERA, *Don*, a Himalayan and Chinese species having oblong, finely toothed leaves covered with a dense coat of pale down. But the fruit of H. aspera is cup-shaped, the bases of the usually three styles persisting at the top are not thickened, and the calyx band is quite at the top. Also, the bluish sepals of the sterile flowers are frequently toothed, which they never appear to be in H. heteromalla.

Neither H. heteromalla nor H. aspera is so hardy and useful a shrub in gardens as H. Bretschneideri; they are now rarely seen. Forms of both have been introduced by Wilson from Central and Western China in recent years, which will probably be hardier than the Himalayan types previously known. H. aspera was very ornamental at Coombe Wood, the corymbs 4 to 6 ins. across, the sterile flowers of a beautiful blue or lavender shade. Wilson also found a completely sterile form of H. aspera (var. STERILIS), with a ball of pinkish flowers 4 to 5 ins. across—very handsome (Wilson, 1473A, Packang, C. China.)

H. HORTENSIS, *Smith*

(Bot. Mag., t. 438; H. Hortensia, *Siebold*; H. macrophylla, *De Candolle*; Hortensia opuloides, *Lamarck*)

A deciduous shrub up to 8 ft. high and 12 ft. or more in diameter, forming a dense, leafy, hemispherical bush furnished to the ground; glabrous in almost every part except the flower-stalks and vein-axils beneath the leaves. Leaves ovate or oval, tapered at the base, pointed at the apex, toothed; varying much in size, often 6 to 8 ins. long, on vigorous branches; strongly ribbed, pale bright green; stalk $\frac{1}{4}$ to 1 in. long. Corymbs usually about 6 ins. across, but considerably more in specimens subjected to special cultivation, rounded and with all or nearly all the flowers sterile, pink or blue.

Introduced from China to Kew, in 1789, by Sir Joseph Banks. This shrub has for centuries been a popular garden plant in China and Japan. It is probably only truly wild in China, and in that state of course the larger proportion of the flowers are of the small, fertile kind, as in other wild species, but I do not know that the genuine wild type is in gardens.

Near London the common hydrangea is not genuinely hardy; that is to say it is rarely a success grown fully in the open with neither shade nor shelter. In my experience, under these conditions, it is cut back to ground level in all but mild winters. But it is a distinctly shade-loving shrub and if given shade and shelter it will often flower beautifully except after the hardest winters. I have seen it also growing and flowering well on the north side of a building in the Kew district. In the milder counties, especially Devon and Cornwall, it is one of the most gorgeous of outdoor shrubs and brightens the gardens in late summer and autumn more and longer than perhaps any other.

Var. MARIESII, introduced from Japan in 1879, has the marginal flowers only sterile; they are remarkably large, often over 3 ins. across and of a delicate mauve-pink (see *The Garden*, 1898, p. 390, plate 1196).

Var. NIGRA, *Nicholson* (syns. H. cyanoclada, *Hort.*; H. mandschurica, *Hort.*)—Young stems dark purple, almost black; flowers bright rose-coloured, and all or nearly all sterile.

These two varieties are similar to the common hydrangea in leaf and habit, and neither is any hardier; but the three following, although commonly placed under H. hortensis as varieties, are very distinct and hardier. They also flower from side buds of the previous year's growths, and the crop of flowers is not therefore dependent on the fate of the terminal bud. As the type from which they spring is spontaneous in Japan, it appears to deserve specific distinction from H. hortensis. They can be recognised out of flower by the dull leaves.

H. ACUMINATA, *Siebold* (H. hortensis acuminata, *A. Gray*).—Leaves ovate, long pointed, dull green, with appressed, bristly hairs on both sides, especially beneath. Flowers sterile only on the margin of the corymb, their sepals ovate to oval, 1 to 1½ ins. long, blue or pink.

H. JAPONICA, *Siebold* (H. hortensis var. Lindleyi).—Of the same type as acuminata, of which it is no doubt a form, having dull dark green, ovate, oval or slightly obovate, coarsely toothed leaves, tapered at the points and with curly hairs on the midrib and chief veins below; more or less downy beneath. Flowers sterile only at the margin of the corymb, white and rosy pink; the small central ones deeper mauve-pink.

H. STELLATA, *Siebold*.—Leaves smaller than in the two preceding, but also dull green, hairy on both sides, coarsely toothed, especially towards the apex. Flowers pinkish, rosy or white, with numerous small, narrowly oval sepals; sometimes called "flore pleno" on that account. There are numerous other varieties, but they belong to the greenhouse rather than the outdoor garden.

A curious circumstance in connection with the flowering of Hydrangea hortensis is the changing of the colour from pink to blue and *vice versa*, although pink is, apparently, the normal colour. In some places the flowers are uniformly and regularly blue, in others they never become that colour, and plants that have for years borne blue flowers will produce pink ones when they are removed to places where the flowers usually come pink. No satisfactory explanation has been yet offered for this peculiarity, although it appears almost certain that it is due to the presence in the soil of some ingredient of a ferruginous nature. But alum applied as a weak solution to plants in pots is also said to induce blueness. Iron filings mixed with the soil are also relied on for the same purpose. A preparation called "Cyanol" is successfully used. It is difficult to explain why, as sometimes happens, pink and blue flowers are borne on the same plant at the same time.

The name of this shrub has caused some confusion owing to its having been called now H. hortensis, now H. Hortensia; the older and proper name is no doubt "hortensis," given to the plant in 1792 by Sir James E. Smith (*Icon. Pict.*, t. 12). "Hortensia" was originally applied to this shrub as a generic name (H. opuloides, *Lamarck*) in 1789. Latterly, further name-hunting has revealed a fourth name, viz. "H. macrophylla," attributed to De Candolle and now adopted by Dr Rehder. With regard to the supposed connection between this shrub and Queen Hortense, the following extract from *L'Inventaire des Cultures de Trianon*, p. 29, a book by Le Comte Jaubert published in Paris in 1876, will be of interest:—

> It is generally believed that the Hortensia bears the name of Queen Hortense daughter of the Empress Josephine, and for this reason it was used sometimes under the Second Empire as a political emblem. This is a serious error. This plant was dedicated to Madame Hortense Lepaute, wife of a celebrated clockmaker of Paris and a friend of the botanist [Commerson].

H. HYPOGLAUCA, *Rehder*

A deciduous shrub up to 9 ft. high, with smooth purplish-brown shoots Leaves ovate to ovate-oblong, with a short slender point and rounded base finely toothed; 2½ to 4½ ins. long, 1 to 2½ ins. wide; dullish green above, pale and rather glaucous beneath, glabrous except for bristles on the midrib and veins, especially beneath; stalk $\frac{1}{2}$ to $1\frac{1}{4}$ ins. long. Flowers in rounded or flattish cymes 5 or 6 ins. wide terminating the current year's shoots and expanding in June. Sterile flowers 1 to $1\frac{1}{4}$ ins. wide, consisting of four white oval sepals; they occur only on the outskirts of the inflorescence. Fertile flowers about $\frac{1}{4}$ in. wide, white; styles three; flower-stalks bristly.

Native of W. Hupeh, China; discovered by Henry near Ichang and later by Wilson in 1901. It is allied to H. xanthoneura, which is very distinct in its proportionately narrower leaves, more tapered at the base and green beneath; also in the more abundant and conspicuous down on the midrib and veins beneath.

H. INTEGERRIMA, *Engler*

(H. scandens, *Poeppig*—not of *Seringe* nor *Maximowicz*; Cornidia integerrima, *Hooker*)

An evergreen climbing shrub growing wild on tall trees and on rocks; young shoots clad with starry down and in the climbing state adhering by aerial roots. Leaves entire, stout and leathery, elliptic or slightly obovate in the adult state, pointed, tapered to cordate at the base; 2 to 6 ins. long and 1 to 3 ins. wide; distinctly net-veined, dark green and glabrous; stalk from $\frac{1}{4}$ to $1\frac{3}{4}$ ins. long. Curious small pits often occur in the vein-axils beneath. In the juvenile plants in cultivation the leaves are less than 2 ins. long, heart-shaped at the base, and with stalks $\frac{1}{4}$ in. or less long. Inflorescence terminal and axillary, sometimes a columnar panicle as much as 6 ins. long and $3\frac{1}{2}$ ins. wide, sometimes smaller and more rounded, but always made up of numerous small corymbs. Most of the flowers are of the small fertile type, but a few of the large, creamy-white, sterile type, 1 to $1\frac{1}{4}$ ins. across, are occasionally produced. I have not found the colour of the fertile flowers recorded, but presumably the yellow anthers constitute their main feature. In their bud state the segments of the panicle are enclosed by large pale bracts and in that state are globose and $\frac{1}{2}$ in. or more wide. Seed capsules vase-shaped, $\frac{1}{8}$ in. wide, with the styles persisting at the hollowed apex.

Although the first description of this climber appeared in 1830 in De Candolle's *Prodromus*, vol. iv., p. 666, it was not, I believe, introduced to cultivation until H. F. Comber sent home seeds during his Chilean journey, 1925-7. Poeppig's name "scandens" has often been given to it, but this specific name had previously been used for the Japanese H. virens by the younger Linnæus in 1781. It is growing in Col. Messel's garden at Nymans, Sussex, where plants have developed the climbing state. There it has hitherto proved quite hardy. As in H. petiolaris (the H. scandens of Maximowicz) the climbing shoots with aerial roots are sterile, flowers being produced only on growths of a bushy nature. It is native of various parts of Chile up to 3000 ft. altitude; the late Mr H. J. Elwes collected it in the Chillan Valley. Its climbing habit, associated with toothless leaves, distinguishes it among all cultivated hydrangeas. If it can be established in cultivation it may make a useful addition to hardy, self-clinging, evergreen climbers, which are very scarce. Mr Clarence Elliott informs me that he saw it as much as 50 ft. high.

H. INVOLUCRATA, *Siebold*

A deciduous, semi-shrubby plant, often less than $1\frac{1}{2}$ ft. high, but much higher in milder climates; young shoots, leaves, flower-stalks, and ovary covered with bristly, pale down. Leaves ovate-oblong, rounded or tapered at the base, slender-pointed, margined with numerous fine, bristle-like teeth; 3 to 6 ins. long, 1 to $2\frac{1}{2}$ ins. wide; roughened, especially above; stalk $\frac{1}{4}$ to 1 in. long. Corymb 3 to 5 ins. across, enclosed in the bud state by about six large broadly ovate bracts, the largest about 1 in. long, covered with a felt of appressed whitish down. Sterile flowers at the margin of the corymb, ¾ to 1 in. across, the three to five sepals white or blue-white, slightly downy. Small fertile flowers blue. Blossoms from August to October.

Native of Japan. The distinguishing feature of this species is the whorl of bracts (involucre) at the base of the inflorescence, which persists through the flowering. It is very pretty when in bloom, the blue (sometimes rosy lilac) fertile flowers making an effective contrast with the large sterile whitish ones. Unfortunately it is not very hardy, and is often killed back more or less in winter, the flowers being borne on the new shoots which spring from the base. It thrives well in the west country.

H. LONGIPES, *Franchet*

A shrub of spreading habit, 6 to 8 ft. high; young shoots more or less covered at first with loose down. Leaves rough to the touch, roundish ovate, with a heart-shaped or rounded base, and an abrupt, slender point; 3 to 7 ins. long, one-half as much or more wide; sharply and prominently toothed, both surfaces, but especially the lower one, covered with short flattened bristles; stalks slender, bristly when young, and from half to fully as long as the blade. Corymbs flattish, 4 to 6 ins. across, the sterile flowers ¾ to 1½ ins. across, white. Fertile flowers small, white; flower-stalks bristly. Seed-vessel roundish, glabrous, with the calyx at the top.

Native of Central and W. China; introduced by Wilson for Messrs Veitch in 1901. It is a lax-habited shrub, with remarkably long-stalked leaves like those of petiolaris. It was first described by Franchet in 1885, and by a curious coincidence Mr Hemsley described it again as a new species two years later, adopting the same name.

H. PANICULATA, *Siebold*

(Flora Japonica, t. 61)

A deciduous shrub, sometimes tree-like, and 12 to 20 ft. high; young shoots at first downy, becoming glabrous. Leaves often in threes, oval or ovate, tapered at both ends, or rounded at the base, toothed; 3 to 6 ins. long, 1½ to 3 ins. wide; with scattered, flat, bristly hairs above, and pale bristles on the veins beneath; stalk ½ to 1 in. long. Panicles pyramidal, varying in size according to the strength of the shoot, usually 6 to 8 ins. long, two-thirds as wide at the base. Outermost flowers sterile, ¾ to 1¼ ins. wide, white changing to purple-pink; the small fertile flowers yellowish white; flower-stalks downy. Blooms in August and September.

Native of Japan, where it is sometimes a tree 25 ft. high, also of China. From all other cultivated hydrangeas except H. quercifolia this is distinguished by the shape of its inflorescence. It is a hardy and very ornamental shrub.

Var. GRANDIFLORA, *Siebold*.—A form introduced from Japan about 1870, in which all, or nearly all, the flowers are sterile and large, forming a closely packed pyramid of blossom at first white then purplish pink, finally brown. This variety is undoubtedly the most showy of hydrangeas in localities where H. hortensis cannot be grown. To obtain it at its best it should be planted in good loamy soil, rich, but not too stiff. The shoots should be pruned back in spring before growth recommences, and after the young shoots are a few inches long the weakest should be removed. If very large panicles are desired the shoots may be reduced to six or ten on plants 1 to 2 ft. high—more for larger plants. A mulching of rotted manure should be given when growth is well started. Such treatment will produce panicles 18 ins. high, and 12 ins. through at the base. The typical form may be treated in the same way. To many people's taste these monstrous panicles may be objectionable, and to my mind a bush moderately thinned, or not at all, is more elegant and pleasing. Hard pruning and thinning tends to shorten the life of these plants.

Var. PRÆCOX, *Rehder*.—This flowers six weeks in advance of the type, at least in the United States, where I have seen it in bloom in the second week in July.

H. PETIOLARIS, *Siebold and Zuccarini* (Plate 11)

(Bot. Mag., t. 6788; H. scandens, *Maximowicz*)

A deciduous climber, reaching in Japan to the tops of trees 60 to 80 ft. high, and attaching itself closely to the trunks and limbs by means of aerial roots;

HYDRANGEA PETIOLARIS

young stems glabrous or hairy, older ones with peeling brown bark. Leaves roundish ovate, straight or heart-shaped at the base, and with short, tapered points; regularly, sharply, and finely toothed; 1½ to 4½ ins. long, two-thirds to nearly as wide; dark bright green and glabrous above, paler and often with tufts of down in the vein-axils beneath; stalk varying in length from ¼ to 4 ins. Corymbs expanding in June, flat, from 6 to 10 ins. across, with large white sterile flowers on the margins, 1 to 1¾ ins. across, and on stalks 1 to 1½ ins. long; the small fertile ones with which the centre is filled being a duller white; stamens fifteen to twenty-two; flower-stalks downy.

Native of Japan; introduced in 1878. This climber ascends trees, walls, or whatever support it has, in much the same way as ivy does. It grows vigorously, and flowers well on a wall, but a more effective way of growing it is as a bush in the open, for it is very hardy. A few plants may be put round the base of an upturned tree-stump, boulder, or even a mound, which they will soon climb over and cover. After that, the mass assumes a low, spreading, bushlike form, light and elegant in appearance, and very striking when in flower. This hydrangea is in gardens often called "Schizophragma hydrangeoides," a name that belongs to an allied but quite distinct climber. In place of the three- to six-parted sterile blossom of the present species, the sterile flower of the Schizophragma consists of a single ovate sepal, 1 to 1½ ins. long.

H. QUERCIFOLIA, *Bartram*

(Bot. Mag., t. 975)

A deciduous shrub, up to 6 or more ft. high in a wild state, rarely seen more than half as high in this country; young shoots thick and stout, woolly. Leaves broadly oval or broadly ovate, sometimes roundish in general outline, but five- or seven-lobed, after the fashion of the large-leaved American red oaks like Quercus rubra; minutely toothed, 3 to 8 ins. long, two-thirds to fully as wide; dark dull green and glabrous above, downy beneath; stalk 1 to 2½ ins. long. Panicle erect, 4 to 10 ins. high, round-topped, pyramidal. Outer flowers sterile, 1 to 1½ ins. diameter, white, changing with age to a purplish shade. Fertile flowers very numerous, crowded, ⅛ in. diameter; petals five, oblong. Flower-stalks furnished with loose hairs. Blossoms from June to September.

Native of the south-eastern United States; introduced in 1803. From all the cultivated hydrangeas this is readily distinguished by its large scalloped leaves. It is very handsome both in foliage and flower, but is unfortunately slightly tender. It suffers at Kew, but in such gardens as that at Bitton Vicarage, or Mrs Chambers' at Haslemere, where the conditions are rather more favourable, it thrives remarkably well. It is quite uncommon, and deserves a sheltered position. Propagated by layering. A broader-leaved and superior form is sometimes distinguished as "H. platanifolia."

H. RADIATA, *Walter*

(H. nivea, *Michaux*)

A deciduous shrub, 3 to 6 ft. high; young branches soon becoming glabrous. Leaves ovate or oval, 2 to 6 ins. long, 1 to 3 ins. wide; tapered or rounded at the base, taper-pointed, toothed; upper surface dark green, downy along the veins; lower one covered with a close snow-white felt; stalk 1 to 2 ins. long. Corymbs rounded, 4 to 8 ins. across, always with a few large, sterile, long-stalked flowers at the margin, which are 1 to 1¼ ins. across, and white. Fertile flowers very small and numerous, white. Seed-vessels shaped like those of a poppy, with the calyx adhering at the top. Blossoms in July.

Native of N. and S. Carolina; introduced in 1786. The vividly white under-surface of the leaf distinguishes this hydrangea from all others in cultivation, and gives it a peculiar interest. It is allied to H. arborescens, with which H. cinerea forms a connecting link.

H. ROBUSTA, *Hooker fil. and Thomson*

(H. cyanema, *Nuttall*; Bot. Mag., t. 5038)

A deciduous shrub of spreading habit 8 to 15 ft. high; young shoots more or less downy. Leaves ovate or oval, rounded or often heart-shaped at the base, shortly pointed, conspicuously and jaggedly toothed; 5 to 11 ins. long,

3 to 7½ ins. wide; rough with scattered hairs above, bristly downy beneath; stalk 1 to 4 ins. long. Inflorescence nearly 1 ft. wide. Sterile flowers white, from 1 to 2¼ ins. wide, consisting of three to five ovate, orbicular, or obovate sepals that are always toothed, sometimes jaggedly so. Fertile flowers blue. Calyx-tube as long as the seed-vessel.

Native of the Himalaya in Sikkim and Bhotan. As it is found at elevations of 5000 to 8000 ft., it is only likely to be hardy in our warmer maritime counties, but it should certainly be tried there as, both in leaf and inflorescence, it is one of the most striking of hydrangeas. The figure in the *Botanical Magazine* quoted above appeared in 1858 when it flowered at Kew, having no doubt been raised from seed sent home by Joseph Hooker a few years previously. It has since been re-introduced.

H. SARGENTIANA, *Rehder*

(Bot. Mag., t. 8447)

A deciduous shrub of gaunt habit, up to 10 ft. high; young shoots very stout, ribbed, and thickly clothed with stiff transparent bristles and small erect hairs, giving the shoot a remarkable, somewhat mossy aspect. Leaves ovate, with a rounded base, 4 to 5 ins. long, 2 to 3 ins. wide on the flowering shoots; but broadly ovate, with a heart-shaped base, 6 to 10 ins. long by 4 to 7 ins. wide on the sterile shoots, deep dull green, and covered with minute hairs above; pale, bristly, and prominently net-veined beneath; stalk 1 to 4½ ins. long, bristly and downy. Flowers produced in July and August in a flattish corymb 6 to 9 ins. across, with sterile flowers 1¼ ins. across, pinkish white, confined to the outside; fertile flowers deep rosy lilac; flower-stalks downy, the main ones bristly also.

Native of China (W. Hupeh); discovered by Wilson, and introduced for Harvard University by him in 1908. Very distinct on account of its bristly character. It is rather tender. First flowered at Kew in July 1911.

H. SERRATA, *De Candolle*

(H. cyanea, *Hort.*; H. Thunbergii, *Siebold*)

This is probably no more than a distinct variety belonging to the group of dull, green-leaved hydrangeas to which H. acuminata and H. stellata belong, which are usually placed as varieties of H. hortensis (*q.v.*). As represented in gardens it is a small, neat, deciduous shrub, usually 2 to 3 ft. in height, the young stems smooth and very dark, ultimately almost black. Leaves oval or ovate-oblong, tapered about equally towards both ends, toothed at the terminal part only; 1½ to 3½ ins. long, ⅝ to 1½ ins. wide; dull green and with appressed hairs above, paler and glabrous beneath except for occasional tufts of down in the vein-axils. Corymbs 2 to 4 ins. across, the sterile flowers ½ to ¾ in. across, the sepals overlapping, broader than long, blue or pink, often with a shallow notch at the apex; flower-stalks downy. Native of Japan and hardier than H. hortensis, but liable to be injured in hard winters. A dainty shrub, flowering in July and August.

H. STRIGOSA, *Rehder*

(Bot. Mag., t. 9324)

A deciduous shrub of erect growth, up to 9 ft. high, the young shoots covered with grey, appressed, forward-pointing bristles and often somewhat four-sided. Leaves lanceolate to lanceolate-oblong, with a long slender point and tapered base, finely toothed; 3 to 8 ins. long, ¾ to 2¼ ins. wide; furnished thinly with pale appressed bristles on the upper surface and much more densely beneath, especially on the midrib and veins; stalk $\frac{1}{2}$ to $1\frac{1}{4}$ ins. long. Flowers in corymbs terminating the leafy growths of the year and 7 or 8 ins. wide. Sterile flowers 1 to $1\frac{1}{4}$ ins. wide on slender stalks, the four sepals obovate, often toothed, pale purplish blue or white. Fertile flowers small, white;

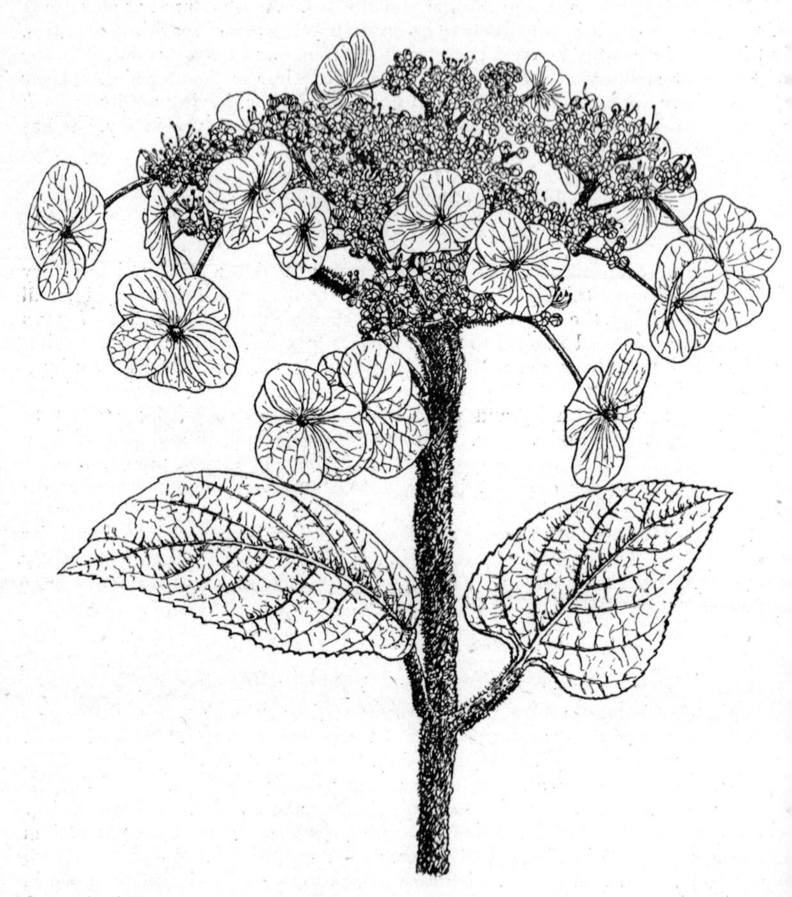

HYDRANGEA SARGENTIANA

flower-stalks densely bristly. Seed-vessels hemispherical, flat-topped, ribbed, $\frac{1}{8}$ in. wide.

Native of W. Hupeh, China; found in 1901 by Wilson and previously by Henry. It is most closely allied to H. aspera, but that species as represented by Nepal specimens has a more woolly pubescence, not wholly bristle-like and appressed as in H. strigosa. Probably, however, there is no genuine persistent character to separate them. I saw H. strigosa in flower during early June 1931 at Edinburgh. It had had winter protection there, but it is hardy in the milder parts of the south and west. At Wakehurst in Sussex it grows luxuriantly, but at Kew is frequently killed back to ground level in winter.

H. VILLOSA, *Rehder*

A deciduous shrub up to 9 ft. high; young shoots hairy, angular. Leaves narrowly oval to oblong-lanceolate, long and slenderly pointed, wedge-shaped at the base, edged with fine but unequal teeth; 4 to 9 ins. long, 1½ to 3 ins. wide; upper surface dull green and furnished with short bristles that make it rough to the touch; lower surface clothed with a grey softer down; stalk 1 to 2 ins. long. Cymes terminal on the leafy shoots of the year and in the axils of the upper leaves, 6 ins. across, flattish. Sterile flowers few, 1 to 1½ ins. wide, pale blue, borne on long slender stalks, the four sepals obovate and toothed except near the base; fertile flowers ⅙ to ¼ in. wide; petals oblong-ovate; styles two. All the flower-stalks are clothed with pale hairs. Seed-vessel hemispherical, ⅛ in. wide.

Native of W. Szechuen, China; discovered and introduced by Wilson in 1908-9. It first flowered at Kew in October 1915, but a month or two earlier is its normal time. It is rather remarkable for the size of its leaves, and the blue flowers with toothed sepals are pretty. It is related to H. strigosa but the appressed bristles of that species distinguish it. It is also close to H. aspera.

H. XANTHONEURA, *Diels*

A deciduous shrub, 8 to 15 ft., of loose, thin habit, sending out long slender branches, which are furnished with a few bristly hairs when young, slightly warted. Leaves in pairs or threes, ovate or oval, with a short, slender point and rounded base, sharply toothed, 3 to 6 ins. long, 1¼ to 2½ ins. wide, dark green and glabrous above, pale beneath with whitish appressed hairs on the midrib and chief veins; stalk ½ to 1¾ ins. long, slightly bristly. Inflorescence a flattish, corymbose panicle, 5 or 6 ins. across, margined with creamy white, sterile flowers 1¼ to 2 ins. across. Perfect flowers ¼ in. across, dull white; calyx-lobes broadly triangular.

Native of Central China; introduced for Messrs Veitch by Wilson about 1904. It is a shrub of elegant and distinct habit, and with considerable beauty in flower. It has some affinity with H. Bretschneideri. This description was made from a plant that flowered at Coombe Wood in June 1911.

HYMENANTHERA. VIOLACEÆ

A genus of some four or five species of shrubs or small trees, evergreen or nearly so. Leaves alternate, small; flowers also small, with the sepals and petals in fives; stamens also five, cohering to form a tube; fruit a berry.

H. ANGUSTIFOLIA, *R. Brown*

An evergreen (or, at Kew, partly deciduous) shrub of erect, slender shape; young shoots finely downy, afterwards warted. Leaves quite glabrous, linear-oblanceolate; $\frac{1}{12}$ to ⅙ in. wide, ½ to 1¼ ins. long; usually quite toothless, dark green, turning purplish in winter. Flowers yellowish, ¼ in. wide, the five petals recurved, solitary or in pairs, produced from the leaf-axils. Anthers five, almost stalkless, arranged on the inner wall of a staminal tube, which narrows towards, and is fringed at, the top. Calyx $\frac{1}{12}$ in. long, with five ovate lobes, green. Fruit a fleshy berry, globose, ⅓ in. long, white with purple markings.

Native of Tasmania, where it grows on the summits of the Western Mountains at 3000 to 4000 ft. altitude. It may be, as stated by F. von Mueller, a variety of H. dentata, but that is a native of New South Wales and Victoria and has much larger, conspicuously toothed leaves, whilst angustifolia is confined to Tasmania and is distinguished by its small, narrow, toothless leaves. It is evidently quite hardy at Kew, where it was 5 ft. high after being planted out some ten years. The flowers are often unisexual, the anthers being small in the female ones, the pistil very small in the male ones. Cheeseman gives a description of a hymenanthera under Mueller's name in his *Manual of the New Zealand Flora*, but thinks there can be little doubt that it will prove to be distinct from the Australian one.

H. OBOVATA, *T. Kirk*, a New Zealand species, was 6 ft. high at Wakehurst in Sussex in 1933. It grows up to 12 ft. high, its leaves obovate, narrowed at the base to a short stalk, 1 to 2 ins. long, mostly entire. Fruit purplish. These two hymenantheras are curious shrubby members of the violet family, their affinity to the other members being shown by the aggregation of the anthers into the urn-shaped tube mentioned above.

H. CRASSIFOLIA, *Hooker fil.*

(Bot. Mag., t. 9426)

A low, semi-evergreen shrub of dense, rounded habit, 3 to 6 ft. high, twice as much in diameter in this country, with stiff, flat-growing branches, covered when young with a short pubescence. Leaves obovate, entire, rounded or slightly notched at the apex, ½ to 1 in. long; glabrous, firm, and thick in texture, densely crowded and alternate on the branches. Flowers almost stalkless, very small (⅛ in. wide), borne in leaf-axils, with five brownish, reflexed petals of no beauty, and five stamens. Berry almost globular, about ¼ in. diameter, white often stained with purple.

Native of New Zealand; first seen in this country about 1875. It is a shrub of great botanical interest in being related to the violet and pansy, and although with not the least beauty of flower, is very attractive in autumn when laden with its abundant pure white berries. It is quite hardy at Kew. One of the finest specimens in the British Isles is in the Glasnevin Botanic Garden, 6 ft. high and 12 to 15 ft. diameter. It retains some of its leaves through the winter, but can scarcely be called evergreen. Propagated by cuttings or by seeds.

H. CHATHAMICA, *T. Kirk*, also from New Zealand, is genuinely evergreen, and has lanceolate leaves 3 to 4 ins. long, toothed and prominently veined. Hardy only in the milder parts of Ireland, Cornwall, etc.

HYPERICUM. HYPERICACEÆ

A large and well-marked genus, composed mainly of herbaceous plants, but comprising also some twenty or more shrubby and sub-shrubby ones, hardy in this country, and of considerable beauty. The leading characteristics of these species are the five sepals and petals, and the three to five styles of the flower; the capsular fruit usually more or less cone-shaped; and the invariably opposite or whorled leaves, often dotted with pellucid glands. They rarely grow more than 4 or 5 ft. high in this country, and most of them retain more or less foliage in mild winters; in severe ones they are deciduous. The stems of some of the species here described are only half woody, and naturally die back some distance every winter. Although the flowers are always yellow in these shrubby species, there is considerable variety among them either in size or depth of shade. The plants themselves vary much in foliage and general aspect.

In gardens, perhaps the chief value of the hypericums is in their habit of flowering during late summer and autumn, when comparatively few shrubs remain in bloom. Planted in groups, as the hardier species should always be, they also give during a large part of the year healthy masses of deep green or blue-green foliage. They are of the simplest culture, and all of them like a well-drained loamy soil and abundant moisture. Many of them produce seeds, and none, so far as I am aware, will not increase easily by cuttings. These should be taken off in August, dibbled in pots of sandy soil, and placed in gentle heat. Species like H. calycinum and inodorum, that produce creeping rootstocks, are very easily increased by division.

H. ADPRESSUM, *Bartram*

A deciduous shrub, woody and creeping at the base, sending up shoots 12 to 20 ins. high, scarcely branched. Leaves stalkless, narrowly oblong to narrowly lanceolate, 1 to 2¼ ins. long, ⅛ to ⅜ in. wide, pointed, tapered to a stalkless base. Flowers yellow, about ½ in. wide, borne in terminal rounded clusters, branching but compact and 2 ins. across, opening in July and August; sepals lanceolate to ovate-lanceolate, ⅕ in. long.

Native of eastern N. America from Massachusetts to Georgia and Louisiana and quite hardy. It is often found wild in damp situations. Introduced in 1888.

H. ÆGYPTICUM, *Linnæus*

(Bot. Mag., t. 6481)

A dwarf, evergreen shrub, 1 ft. or more high, with round stems. Leaves crowded, ovate or obovate, pointed, ⅛ to ⅓ in. long, greyish green. Flowers solitary at the end of short twigs, pale golden yellow; petals erect rather than spreading, ¼ in. long; sepals oblong, erect, half as long as the petals.

Native of the Mediterranean coasts and islands, but not of Egypt; said to have been introduced in 1787, but now rarely seen. The reason of this, no doubt, is its tenderness; it can only be grown permanently either in our mildest districts or with winter protection. This is unfortunate, for it is one of the daintiest and prettiest of its genus. It flowers in August.

H. ANDROSÆMUM, *Linnæus*. TUTSAN

(Androsæmum officinale, *Allioni*)

A half-woody shrub of vigorous bushy habit, 2 to 3 ft. high, with angled or slightly winged stems branching towards the top, and bearing flowers on each branchlet. Leaves slightly aromatic, the largest among hardy hypericums, and sometimes 3½ to 4 ins. long, 2 to 2¼ ins. wide; ovate, blunt at the apex, cordate at the base, and stalkless. Flowers three to nine together in cymose clusters at the end of the main-stalk and lateral branches; each flower about ¾ in. across, light yellow; styles three; calyx nearly as wide as the corolla. Fruit a three-celled, berry-like capsule, nearly globose, and about the size of a pea, turning first purple, finally almost black, filled when ripe with a wine-coloured juice.

Native of Europe; rare in Britain, but sometimes found wild in the south of England and west of Scotland. Although of no great beauty in regard to flower, this species is handsome in its healthy, robust appearance, fine big leaves, and dark fruits. The name "Tutsan" is a corruption of *toute-saine* (heal-all), and refers to the many curative properties the plant was once supposed to possess. It is one of the best things for furnishing rather shaded places, and flowers from June until September.

H. ASCYRON, *Linnæus*

A semi-herbaceous species, scarcely woody enough to be termed a shrub, sending up from the ground every year annual stems from 2 to 5 ft. high. Leaves narrowly oblong, 1½ to 4 ins. long, rounded at the tip, the base clasping the stem. Flowers 2 ins. across, yellow; petals broad at the apex, narrowing to a claw at the base.

Native of N. America and N. Asia, and of little merit for gardens. Its habit is coarse and ungainly, and the lower leaves of the stem die early. Flowers in July and August.

In the *Botanical Magazine*, t. 8557, however, is figured a superior form which Dr Rehder has named VILMORINII. It was obtained for Kew from Mr Maurice de Vilmorin and was raised from seed collected in Korea. The flowers are over 3 ins. across, making noble, terminal clusters up to 8 ins. in diameter—an immense improvement on the ordinary type.

H. BALEARICUM, *Linnæus*

(Bot. Mag., t. 137)

A remarkably distinct species of close, shrubby habit and about 2 ft. high, the stems winged and more or less warted. Leaves ¼ to ½ in. long, ovate or oblong, rounded at the tip; the lower side covered with curious wart-like lumps with a corresponding depression on the upper side; the margin entire, but very wavy or wrinkled. Flowers yellow, terminal and solitary, 1½ ins. wide, fragrant; petals narrow and fragile; stamens ½ in. long.

Native of the Balearic Isles; introduced to Britain from Majorca in 1714. This curious plant, quite different in its warted leaves from all other cultivated hypericums, is, unfortunately, not hardy except in the warmer parts of the country. It flowers from June to September.

H. BUCKLEYI, *Curtis*

(Garden and Forest, 1891, fig. 91)

A dwarf, deciduous, semi-woody plant forming a dense rounded tuft of slender, angled stems, 6 to 12 ins. high. Leaves ¼ to 1 in. long, oblong or obovate, rounded at the apex, tapered at the base. Flowers one or three at the end of the shoot, bright yellow, ½ to 1 in. diameter; petals narrowly obovate; sepals leaflike, spreading in the fruiting stage.

This charming little shrub is one of the rarest of N. American plants, being confined in a wild state to a few mountain tops in N. Carolina and Georgia. It was introduced to Kew in 1893, but had been discovered fifty years before. Of too fragile and delicate a nature to hold its own in an ordinary shrubbery, it is on the other hand admirably adapted for some nook of the rock garden, where it makes gay patches in July. It produces abundant seed. Under cultivation its leaves and flowers are considerably larger than in wild examples, and its dainty character is apt to be spoilt by too rich a soil. (See *densiflorum*.) I saw a charming tuft at Borde Hill in July 1939, 4 ft. across and in full flower.

H. CALYCINUM, *Linnæus*. ROSE OF SHARON, AARON'S BEARD

(Bot. Mag., t. 146)

A low, nearly evergreen shrub, with a creeping root-stalk and erect, obscurely angled, unbranched stems, 12 to 18 ins. high. Leaves rich bright green, ovate oblong, 2 to 3 ins. long, slightly odorous, with little or no stalk. Flowers solitary, rarely in pairs, at the top of the stem, 3 to 4 ins. across, bright yellow; petals obovate; sepals green, roundish, ¾ in. long; stamens in five bundles, yellow, ¾ to 1 in. long, very numerous; styles five.

Native of the Orient. Introduced in the latter part of the seventeenth century, this has proved so well adapted to our climate as to have become naturalised in some parts of the country. On the whole, it is the most useful and not far from the most beautiful of hypericums, admirable for making a dense carpet on the ground in half-shaded places beneath trees, etc., where most shrubs would not thrive, flowering from the end of June to September. In hard winters it loses much of its foliage, and in any case, if a clean level growth is desired, it is best to cut the old stems down to the ground just as the new growths are pushing from the base in spring. Propagated with the greatest ease by dividing up the plants.

H. CHINENSE, *Linnæus*

(Bot. Mag., t. 334)

A tender, quite woody species only hardy in the milder parts of the kingdom, growing about 2 ft. high; stems round. It has evergreen, narrow-oblong leaves, stalkless, 1½ to 3½ ins. long, ½ to 1 in. wide. Flowers either solitary or in terminal cymes of three to seven, bright yellow, 1½ to 2½ ins. across; stamens in five bundles, some as long as the petals; styles united to form one slender tapering column ½ to ¾ in. long, divided at the top into five radiating stigmas.

Native of China; introduced in 1753; often used as a greenhouse plant, but I have seen it thriving out-of-doors in the Grayswood Hill garden, near Haslemere, flowering in September. Worth trying in the south and west.

H. CORIS, *Linnæus*

(Bot. Mag., t. 6563)

An evergreen, semi-shrubby plant, erect and 6 to 15 ins. high, or sometimes procumbent; stems round, very slender and clustered, glabrous. Leaves in whorls of four to six, linear, ⅓ to 1 in. long, $\frac{1}{16}$ in. or less wide, stalkless, revolute, blunt; midrib prominent beneath. Flowers borne in axillary clusters of three to five, forming terminal panicles 2 to 5 ins. long. Corolla ¾ in. wide, glowing yellow; petals ovate-oblong; sepals linear-oblong, about ⅕ in. long, margined with dark glands; stamens in three bundles. Blossoms in June and July.

Native of Central and S.E. Europe, cultivated in 1640. It is related to H. empetrifolium, which has angled stems and fewer, usually three, leaves in a whorl.

H. DENSIFLORUM, *Pursh*

(Garden and Forest, 1890, fig. 67)

An evergreen shrub, 2 to 4 ft. high (6 ft. in its native state); branches erect, two-angled. Leaves 1 to 2 ins. long, usually less than ¼ in. wide, linear-lanceolate, recurved at the edges. Flowers very numerous, in compact cymose panicles; each flower ½ in. across. Fruit three-celled, slender, ¼ in. long, subtended by the five oval-oblong, spreading sepals.

Native of the pine-barrens from New Jersey to Florida, and Kentucky west to Arkansas and Texas. It is a near ally of the commoner H. prolificum, but is smaller in flower and narrower in leaf; its fruit also is more slender. Some botanists have regarded them as forms of one species. The following arrangement will help towards the identification of the rather confused American species:—

FRUIT THREE-CELLED; STYLES THREE; FLOWERS STALKLESS

1. *Frondosum.*—Flowers 1½ ins. across.

FRUIT THREE- SOMETIMES FOUR-CELLED; STYLES THREE; FLOWERS STALKED

2. *Galioides.*—Leaves very narrow (see desc.); sepals linear.
3. *Buckleyi.*—Habit dwarf, compact; flowers up to 1 in. wide.
4. *Prolificum.*—Habit tall, erect; flowers 1 in. across.
5. *Densiflorum.*—Habit tall, erect; flowers ½ in. across.

FRUIT FIVE-CELLED; STYLES FIVE

6. *Lobocarpum.*—Habit tall, erect; flowers ⅖ to ⅗ in. wide; leaves green.
7. *Kalmianum.*—Dwarfer; flowers ⅗ to 1 in. wide; leaves glaucous.

All these species have free stamens, being thereby distinguished from the Asiatic species, which have them in bundles, usually five bundles to each flower.

H. ELATUM, *Aiton*

(H. grandifolium, *Choisy*; H. multiflorum, *Hort.*)

A sub-evergreen shrub, up to 5 ft. high, with slightly angled, branching stems. Leaves aromatic when crushed, deep green, 1½ to 3 ins. long, ovate, blunt or rounded at the tip. Flowers borne in abundant cymes at the ends of the shoots and in the axils of the terminal leaves, one to three flowers in each final subdivision of the inflorescence; each flower yellow, 1 in. across, with three long styles; sepals ovate, reflexed in fruit. Fruit dark brown, at first rather pulpy like that of H. Androsæmum, but longer and more tapered at the top.

Native of the Canary Islands, but now naturalised in some of the milder parts of the British Isles, *e.g.*, the counties of Cornwall, Argyll, Perth, and Down. It is sometimes confounded with H. Androsæmum, but is amply distinguished by the aromatic, smaller foliage, the tapering fruit, and especially the much longer styles. (See also H. hircinum.)

H. EMPETRIFOLIUM, *Willdenow*

(Bot. Mag., t. 6764)

A dwarf evergreen shrub, up to 12 or 15 ins. high, with slender, erect, angled branches. Leaves produced occasionally in pairs, but usually three at each joint; ¼ to ½ in. long, linear, with the margins curled under; stalkless. Flowers in an erect panicle, producing three cymes in each tier; each flower ½ to ⅔ in. across, pale golden yellow; sepals small, oblong, with black glands on the margin. Fruit a three-celled capsule ¼ in. long, with the spreading sepals attached at the base.

Native of Greece and the islands of the Grecian Archipelago; introduced to the Hammersmith nursery of Messrs Lee in 1788. It is a rather tender plant, and will survive only our mildest winters without protection. But for the warmer counties few more charming dwarf shrubs could be found. Even in cooler districts it is well worth the little protection it requires. Flowers from late July to September.

H. FRONDOSUM, *Michaux*

(H. aureum, *Bartram*, Bot. Mag., t. 8498)

A deciduous, much-branched shrub of rounded habit, about 4 ft. high, often rising on a single stem from which the lower branches have fallen, thus giving it the aspect of a miniature tree; the older branches covered with a greyish brown, peeling bark; young shoots two-winged. Leaves blue-green, oblong, 1 to 2 ins. long, with a minute, abrupt point, and numerous transparent glands. Flowers in clusters terminating the shoot and its upper branches, orange yellow, 1½ ins. across, the stamens forming a dense bush ¾ in. across. The fruit is a three-celled, broad-based cone ½ in. high, with the very large, leaflike, unequal sepals at the base.

Discovered by Bartram in 1776 "upon the steep dry banks of the Patse-Lega Creek, a branch of the Flint River," Georgia, this hypericum, despite its great beauty, does not appear to have reached this country until late in the nineteenth century. Healthy plants flower and set their fruit in extraordinary abundance, and it is wise to remove the latter except such as may be required for seed. It appears to prefer rocky places in its native home, and is often found on the cliffs of river-courses where it gets some shade. It is wild in several of the south-eastern United States, and is the handsomest of all the American species. (See *densiflorum*.)

H. GALIOIDES, *Lamarck*

(Garden and Forest, 1897, fig. 55)

An evergreen bush, 2 to 3 ft. high, of broad, compact habit, and with round stems, much branched towards the top. Leaves from ¾ to 2 ins. long, ⅙ in. or less wide; dark green dotted with pellucid glands; margins recurved. Flowers ½ to ¾ in. across, yellow, borne in cymes both terminal and axillary on the many branchlets, and thus transforming the end of each branch into a large panicle of flowers 6 to 10 ins. long and 3 to 4 ins. wide; sepals and petals narrow. Styles and cells of seed-vessel three; calyx linear, as long as the fruit.

Native of the eastern United States from Delaware to Florida; introduced to the Jardin des Plantes at Paris about 1790, but almost lost sight of until 1897, when it was reintroduced to Kew from the Arnold Arboretum. It commences to flower in July and continues until October. Its very narrow leaves and terete stems distinguish it among allied species. (See *densiflorum*.)

H. HIRCINUM, *Linnæus*

An almost evergreen, semi-woody plant, usually 2 to 3 ft., sometimes 4 ft. high, with erect, two-angled stems much branched towards the top. Leaves with a goat-like odour when crushed, ovate, stalkless, 1 to 2½ ins. long. Cymes terminating the stem and its numerous branches; on strong shoots borne in the leaf-axils also. Flowers 1½ ins. across, bright yellow, stamens ¾ to 1¼ ins. long; styles three, rather shorter than the stamens. Fruit three-celled, ¼ in. long, tapered.

Native of the middle and southern latitudes of Europe and the Mediterranean region; introduced in 1640. It is now established in some parts of Britain, an escape from gardens. The only hypericum with which it is likely to be confused is H. elatum, but besides its distinctive odour H. hircinum has longer stamens and styles, smaller leaves, later flowers, and the sepals fall away from the fruit. It flowers from early August to October. A very hardy, handsome plant.

Var. MINOR, *Lavallée*.—Of dwarf, compact, and more rounded habit, about 1 ft. high; leaves smaller. Very dainty.

H. HOOKERIANUM, *Wight and Arnott*

(H. oblongifolium, *Hooker*; Bot. Mag., t. 4949)

A tall, erect species, 3 to 5 ft. high in cultivation, 8 ft. high in nature; evergreen or partly deciduous according to the locality and winter; branchlets not angled. Leaves 1 to 3 ins. long, ½ to 1½ ins. wide; ovate, round or pointed at the tip. Flowers in a terminal cymose cluster, six or more together; each flower (of which there is usually but one at a time open) 2 ins. across, rather cup-shaped owing to the concave shape of the full, broad, overlapping petals. Stamens in five bundles.

Native of the Sikkim Himalaya and the mountains of Assam; originally introduced to cultivation by Thomas Lobb, from near Mufflong, in Assam. It is the handsomest and most vigorous of the North Indian species, hardier than patulum, but liking a sheltered place. It flowers from early August to October. It is apt to become gaunt in habit, and naked at the base with age, and should be renewed from seed when that condition arrives. From its two allies, patulum and lysimachioides, it differs in the branchlets being terete, especially just beneath the inflorescence.

H. INODORUM, *Willdenow*

An elegant shrub, 3 to 4 ft. high, evergreen, with long, slender, usually unbranched stems compressed or slightly two-winged towards the top, and luxuriantly leafy (the leaf-pairs from ¼ to 1 in. apart). Leaves oblong or ovate, 1 to 2 ins. long, dull dark green, rounded at the apex, inodorous. Flowers small compared with the size of the plant, and wanting in beauty; often solitary at the end of the shoot, but on strong shoots produced in small terminal clusters; they are ¾ or 1 in. across, with narrow, fragile petals, linear sepals, and three styles; stamens longer than petals.

Native of E. Europe and the Caucasus. In its graceful arching habit and strong vigorous growth this species is attractive, but it is one of the most disappointing in its flowers, which appear a few at a time from July to September. It has a creeping root stalk, and eventually forms a large dense thicket; it is thus easily increased by division.

H. KALMIANUM, *Linnæus*

(Garden and Forest, 1890, fig. 24; Bot. Mag., t. 8491)

An evergreen bush, 2 to 3 ft. high, with four-angled branches. Leaves glaucous green, 1 to 2 ins. long, ⅛ to ⅓ in. wide; narrow-oblong or oblanceolate, dotted with transparent glands. Flowers produced in small cymes at the end of the branch and in the axils of the terminal leaves; ¾ to 1 in. across, bright yellow; sepals ¼ to ⅓ in. long. Fruit ovate, five-celled.

Native of eastern N. America, where it is confined to the cliffs of rivers and lakes from the Falls of Niagara northwards; said now to have become rather rare. It is named after Peter Kalm, the famous Swedish naturalist and traveller who discovered it in 1750. Nine years later it was introduced to England, but appears to have disappeared from cultivation for a long period, the plants so-called being always H. prolificum. In 1911, the late Mr Dunbar of the Parks Department, Rochester, N.Y., sent seeds of the true plant to Kew. H. prolificum has narrower petals and not so handsome a flower.

H. KOUYTCHENSE, *Léveillé*

(Bot. Mag., t. 9345)

A deciduous or more or less evergreen shrub, 2 to 4 ft. high, of rounded shape, wholly glabrous. Leaves 1 to 3 ins. long, $\frac{1}{4}$ to $1\frac{1}{4}$ ins. wide, ovate to narrowly oval, pointed, tapered to rounded at the base, scarcely stalked, rather glaucous beneath, with a sprinkling of translucent dots there. Flowers often three in terminal clusters, sometimes solitary, up to $2\frac{1}{4}$ ins. across; petals rich yellow, about 1 in. long by $\frac{5}{8}$ in. wide, obovate-oblong, more or less toothed, not touching; sepals ovate-lanceolate, slender-pointed, $\frac{3}{8}$ in. long.

Native of W. China; introduced in 1907 by E. H. Wilson, who found it in Eastern Szechuen, but it had been discovered two years previously in Kweichou by the French traveller Émile Bodinier. It is nearly akin to H. patulum and is equally beautiful, but like that species it is not entirely hardy. Blossoms from June onwards.

H. LESCHENAULTII, *Choisy*

(Bot. Mag., t. 9160; H. triflorum, *Blume*)

A shrub, evergreen in mild climates, lax in growth, free from down in leaf and stem, ordinarily 4 to 8 ft. high; branches slender, reddish brown. Leaves stalkless, firm in texture, ovate-oblong, bluntish at the end, rounded at the base; $1\frac{1}{2}$ to $2\frac{1}{2}$ ins. long, $\frac{3}{4}$ to $1\frac{1}{8}$ ins. wide; dark, slightly glaucous green above, more definitely glaucous and thickly sprinkled with translucent dots beneath. Flowers rich yellow, $2\frac{1}{2}$ to 3 ins. wide, produced singly or in threes (sometimes in sevens) at the end of the shoot. Petals 1 in. wide, rather concave, roundish obovate, slightly overlapping. Sepals $\frac{1}{3}$ to $\frac{5}{8}$ in. long, narrowly to broadly ovate-lanceolate or oblanceolate. Stamens yellow, $\frac{1}{3}$ in. long, very numerous, arranged in five bundles. Ovary conical, tapering upwards to the five recurved styles. Seed-vessel $\frac{4}{5}$ in. long.

Native of Java and other parts of Malaya; discovered on the Javan mountains by Leschenault about 1805. The date of its introduction is not definitely known, but it was flowering in Mr Riall's garden at Old Conna Hill, Co. Wicklow, in July 1882. So far as I have seen it is, in combined size and richness of colouring, the finest flowered of all hypericums. It is closely related to H. Hookerianum and H. patulum, but according to Dr Stapf is distinguished from them by its "very variable but always herbaceous and spreading calyces with their acute or acuminate, often unequal sepals and the rather large, long-tapering, conical capsules" (*Botanical Magazine*, *loc. cit. supra*). It is not quite hardy at Kew, where it is grown in a practically unheated house, making shoots half to fully a yard long in a season, attaining a height of 12 ft. or more and flowering during the summer and autumn months. I saw it very fine in Mr Armytage-Moore's garden at Rowallane, Co. Down, one autumn day some years ago, growing fully in the open and flowering freely.

H. LOBOCARPUM, *Gattinger*

(Garden and Forest, 1897, fig. 57)

A free-growing shrub, 3 to 6 ft. high, with erect, angled branches. Leaves narrowly oblong or oblanceolate, 1 to 2½ ins. long, scarcely stalked, margins decurved. Flowers in dense cymes forming large leafy panicles; yellow, about ½ in. across; sepals about ⅛ in. long, styles five; fruit five-celled. Blossoms in August and September.

Native of the south-eastern United States in N. Carolina and Tennessee; introduced in 1898. It has very much the aspect of prolificum, but differs in its five-celled fruit. (See *densiflorum*.)

H. LYSIMACHIOIDES, *Wallich*

An evergreen or semi-evergreen shrub up to 4 ft. in height, but cut to the ground at Kew in severe winters and not likely to grow so high; branchlets angled. Leaves ovate, pointed, ¾ to 1½ ins. long, glaucous beneath. Flowers in terminal cymes, each flower 1 to 1½ ins. wide; petals bright golden yellow; sepals ⅓ in. long, linear-lanceolate; stamens very numerous, in five bundles.

Native of the west Himalaya; introduced to France in 1894 by Mr Maurice de Vilmorin, and to England ten years later. At Bitton, near Bristol, it thrives admirably, forming a graceful bush 3 or 4 ft. high, and flowering abundantly. It is nearly allied to H. patulum, but differs in its narrow sepals and smaller flowers.

H. MOSERIANUM, *André*

(Garden, 17th Dec. 1898—coloured plate)

A hybrid between H. patulum and H. calycinum, raised in Mr Moser's nursery at Versailles about 1887. It is a dwarf plant of tufted habit, sending up arching, reddish shoots each year 1 to 1½ ft. long. Leaves intermediate between those of the parents and up to 2 ins. long, ovate, rather glaucous beneath. Flowers from one to five in a cluster at the end of the shoot, but not more than one of each cluster opens simultaneously; each flower 2 to 2½ ins. across, with broad, overlapping, golden yellow petals. Stamens in five bundles.

This is one of the most attractive of the hypericums, whose only fault is that it is frequently killed back in winter, and when planted in a group, leaves the ground bare until the young growths push again, which is not until May. It is hardier than H. patulum, although it has inherited the cymose inflorescence of that species, and thus a great flower beauty. A bed at Kew stood unchanged for twenty years, only protected by dry leaves during hard frost. It flowers from July up to October.

Var. TRICOLOR.—Leaves edged with rose-colour and white. This appeared as a sport on typical H. Moserianum in 1891, but is too delicate to be of much value in the open air except in favoured spots.

H. NUDIFLORUM, *Michaux*

A deciduous shrub or sub-shrub up to 3 or 4 ft., stems square, glabrous, slender, erect. Leaves oval-oblong, 1 to 2¼ ins. long, ¼ to ¾ in. wide, apex rounded, base tapered, thin in texture, glabrous, scarcely stalked. Flowers bright-yellow, ½ to ¾ in. wide, borne dichotomously on terminal and axillary cymes 4 or 5 ins. across; sepals ⅙ in. long, oval-oblong; fruit conical, ¼ in. long, pointed. Blossoms in July and August.

Native of the S.E. United States from N. Carolina to Florida and quite hardy. The inflorescence usually stands out leafless and clearly above the foliage and is interesting for its successive branching into two ("dichotomy").

H. OLYMPICUM, *Linnæus*

A deciduous, glabrous sub-shrub with a procumbent rootstock, sending up shoots 6 to 15 ins. high, or tufted; stems mostly unbranched, slightly two-edged. Leaves narrowly oval or oblong, $\frac{1}{3}$ to $1\frac{1}{4}$ ins. long, $\frac{1}{12}$ to $\frac{1}{4}$ in. wide, pointed, stalkless, grey-green. Flowers bright yellow, $1\frac{1}{2}$ to 2 ins. across, borne in terminal clusters of up to five, ovate to obovate, $\frac{1}{2}$ to $\frac{5}{8}$ in. wide, opening from midsummer onwards; stamens in three groups.

Native of S.E. Europe and W. Asia, cultivated in the Chelsea Botanic Garden as early as 1706. An attractive species when in flower but should be given a warm sheltered corner.

Var. LATIFOLIUM, Bot. Mag., t. 1867, is a form with larger leaves $\frac{5}{8}$ in. wide.

H. PATULUM, *Thunberg*

(Bot. Mag., t. 5693)

A dwarf shrub in this country, but said to grow as much as 6 ft. high in Japan and the Himalaya. Leaves 1 to $2\frac{1}{2}$ ins. long, ovate, deep green above, glaucous beneath. Flowers 2 ins. across, borne in a cyme at the end of the shoot; petals bright golden yellow, overlapping, roundish; sepals broadly ovate, $\frac{1}{3}$ in. long. Stamens in five bundles.

Introduced to Kew from Japan by Oldham in 1862; a native also of China and the Himalaya. The type is not absolutely hardy, and almost always has its stems cut back to ground-level during the winter. These spring up again the following season from 1 to 2 ft. high, and flower from July to October. After a few years the shoots are apt to become more and more weakly and it becomes necessary to renew the stock from cuttings. The only species with which it can be confounded are: H. Hookerianum, from which it differs in the branchlets being two-edged, especially just beneath the flowers; H. lysimachioides, which has narrow, linear-lanceolate sepals; and H. uralum, with flowers half the size.

Var. HENRYI.—A much more robust plant than the type, surviving hard winters uninjured. Leaves larger, thicker in texture; inflorescence larger, and stems stouter. This fine variety, superior to the type in every way, and one of the best of hypericums, was introduced to Kew from China in 1898, by Prof. Henry. In general appearance it resembles H. Hookerianum, but has the two-edged branchlets of patulum.

Var. FORRESTII, *Chittenden*, is a very fine form introduced from the Lichiang Range by Forrest. Its flowers are fully 2 ins. wide and very freely produced. It very much resembles var. Henryi, and I do not know that it differs from it in any important botanical character, but it is considered to be the better shrub. In some gardens the leaves change to a good red in autumn.

H. PROLIFICUM, *Linnæus*

(Garden and Forest, 1890, fig. 66)

A stout, erect-growing evergreen bush, 3 to 5 ft. high, the growths of the year but little branched, two-edged especially towards the top. Leaves dark, shining green, narrow-oblong, tapering to a short stalk; $1\frac{1}{2}$ to $2\frac{1}{2}$ ins. long, to $\frac{1}{2}$ in. wide, dotted with numerous transparent glands. Flowers in terminal clusters and in the leaf-axils near the end of the shoot; each flower about 1 in. across, bright yellow. Fruits three-celled.

Native of the eastern and central United States; introduced about the middle of the eighteenth century. Under cultivation it is the healthiest and most vigorous of the American species, although not so handsome in flower as H. frondosum. It bears enormous crops of fruit. Allied to H. densiflorum, it differs in its larger leaves and flowers; and from H. Kalmianum and H. lobocarpum (which have five-celled fruits) its three-celled ones distinguish it. Commencing to flower in July, it continues for six or eight weeks. (See *densiflorum*.)

H. REPTANS, *Hooker fil. and Thomson*

A low, prostrate, self-rooting shrub a few inches high, often tufted; stems very slender, almost thread-like, two-edged, glabrous. Leaves $\frac{1}{4}$ to $\frac{1}{2}$ in. long, oval-oblong, apex blunt, usually crowded $\frac{1}{8}$ to $\frac{1}{3}$ in. apart on the stem. Flowers terminal, solitary, golden yellow, $1\frac{3}{4}$ ins. across; petals obovate; sepals about $\frac{1}{2}$ in. long, oval, blunt; capsule globose, $\frac{1}{2}$ in. wide.

Native of the Himalaya at from 9000 to 11,000 ft., cultivated by the late Mr G. F. Wilson in 1881. A charming rock garden plant, quite hardy.

H. RHODOPEUM, *Frivaldsky*

(Gardeners' Chronicle, 24th Sept. 1932, p. 224)

An evergreen sub-shrub of tufted habit, producing dense rounded clusters, 12 ins. or more across, with erect or procumbent, slender, hairy, terete stems 3 to 6 ins. long, springing from a woody rootstock. Leaves in decussate pairs, rather crowded, stalkless, $\frac{1}{4}$ to $\frac{5}{8}$ in. long, oval, apex rounded, hairy on both surfaces. Flowers bright yellow, 1 to $1\frac{1}{2}$ ins. across, springing from the terminal leaf axils in clusters of three or four; petals oblong, $\frac{1}{8}$ to $\frac{1}{4}$ in. wide; stamens very numerous, about $\frac{1}{4}$ in. long.

Native of S.E. Europe, very profuse flowering and attractive in May. Suitable for the rock garden.

H. URALUM, *Don*

(Bot. Mag., t. 2375; H. patulum uralum, *Koehne*)

A semi-evergreen shrub, 2 to 3 ft. high, with slightly two-edged, much-branched stems. Leaves ovate or oval, 1 to $1\frac{1}{2}$ ins. long, dull green above, glaucous green beneath; with a faint orange-like aroma when crushed. Flowers produced during August and September in terminal cymes of three to fifteen flowers, each flower 1 in. across, golden yellow; petals round, concave, overlapping; sepals roundish oval, green, $\frac{3}{16}$ in. long; stamens in five bundles, styles five; fruit five-celled.

Native of Nepal; introduced in 1820. The specific name has nothing to do with the Ural Mountains; it is an adaptation of the Nepalese name for this shrub, "Urala swa." Nearly allied to H. patulum, it is a much freer-growing shrub, with thinner leaves and a hardier constitution, but it is not so handsome in flower.

HYSSOPUS OFFICINALIS, *Linnæus*. HYSSOP. LABIATÆ

A low, partially evergreen, aromatic bush, quite woody at the base $1\frac{1}{2}$ to 2 ft. high; shoots erect, green, square, covered when young with minute down. Leaves opposite, linear or narrowly oval, $\frac{1}{3}$ to $1\frac{1}{2}$ ins long $\frac{1}{61}$ to $\frac{1}{4}$ in. wide; tapered at both ends, very minutely toothed, or roughened at the edges, rich green, glandular-punctate on both surfaces. Flowers produced in close, axillary whorls on the shoots of the year, forming a terminal panicle, and commencing to open about midsummer and continuing until September. From six to twelve or more flowers appear in each whorl, and they of a bluish purple shade in the type, about $\frac{1}{2}$ in. long, two-lipped. The leaves and young shoots have a pleasant mint-like scent.

Native of S. Europe, in the Mediterranean region, and W. Asia. Cultivated as a medicinal herb in England since 1548, probably long before. An infusion of hyssop is an old-fashioned remedy for removing phlegm. It is an easily cultivated plant requiring a warm, light soil, and is easily increased by cuttings during the summer and autumn. There is a white-flowered variety, ALBUS, and one with red flowers, RUBER.

IBERIS. CANDYTUFT. CRUCIFERÆ

The majority of the species in this well-known genus are herbaceous, often annuals, but the following species are perennial and sufficiently woody to claim notice here. The most characteristic features of the genus are, firstly, the inflorescence, which is a flattish raceme often elongated by the time the seed is formed, and, secondly, the petals; of these there are (as always in this Natural Order) four to each flower, the two outermost ones of which are distinctly larger than the two inner ones, especially on the flowers at the edge of the inflorescence. They like a sunny position, a well-drained soil, and are easily propagated by late summer cuttings.

I. GIBRALTARICA, *Linnæus*. GIBRALTAR CANDYTUFT

(Bot. Mag., t. 124)

An evergreen, flat-topped, half-woody plant up to 12 ins. high or sometimes more, and in favourable localities as much as 2 or 3 ft. in diameter. Leaves linear-obovate, $\frac{3}{4}$ to 2 ins. long, $\frac{1}{4}$ to $\frac{1}{2}$ in. wide; rounded at the apex and usually although often inconspicuously toothed on the terminal half, gradually tapered towards the base, glabrous. On the flower-stems the leaves decrease in size, finally becoming linear and about $\frac{1}{8}$ in. wide. Flower-stems 6 to 8 ins. long, often branched towards the top. Flowers crowded in flattish umbel-like clusters 2 to 3 ins. wide; white or reddish lilac, or both, with the paler ones in the centre. The two outer petals are much larger than the two inner ones and those of the outermost flowers may be $\frac{1}{2}$ to $\frac{3}{4}$ in. long. The flat seed-pod is about $\frac{3}{8}$ in. long, notched at the top.

Native of S. Spain and Morocco, its best-known habitat being the Rock of Gibraltar, from which it takes its specific name; introduced in 1732. It grows in crevices and holes in the face of the cliffs, where to all appearance there is no soil. The true plant is not common, although other species often may be seen under this name. It is very suitable for sunny gardens on the south coast, planted in full sun in a light soil with which stones or rubble has been freely mixed. In colder parts it survives only mild or moderately severe winters. It blossoms from May to July. From the other species it can be distinguished by its usually branched flower-stems, usually toothed leaves, and more highly coloured flowers.

I. SEMPERFLORENS, *Linnæus*

An evergreen shrub up to 2 ft. high of bushy shape, free from down. Leaves narrowly obovate, rounded at the apex, tapered to the base, $\frac{3}{4}$ to $2\frac{1}{2}$ ins. long, $\frac{1}{4}$ to $\frac{1}{2}$ in. wide; dark dull green, not toothed. Flowers white or tinged with pink, fragrant, produced in crowded, flattish racemes 1 to 2 ins. long and wide. Seed pod $\frac{3}{8}$ in. wide, $\frac{1}{4}$ in. long, very slightly notched at the apex.

Native of S. Italy and Sicily, often in calcareous soil; introduced in 1679. In shape and size of leaf it resembles I. gibraltarica, but the latter is well distinguished by its toothed foliage, also by the more distinctly notched seed pod. I. semperflorens is the tenderest of these shrubby candytufts. Suitable for sunny places on the south coast. Its flowering season is from November to April.

I. SEMPERVIRENS, *Linnæus*

An evergreen sub-shrub 6 to 12 ins. high, of spreading habit, free from down; stems slender, thickly furnished with linear or oblanceolate leaves which are $\frac{1}{2}$ to 2 ins. long, $\frac{1}{8}$ to $\frac{3}{16}$ in. wide; blunt or rounded at the apex, not toothed. Flowers white, produced from April to June in racemes at first flattish and 1 to $1\frac{1}{2}$ ins. wide, but elongating later; main flower-stalk 2 to 4 ins. long with the flowers at the terminal half. Seed-pod roundish or obcordate, $\frac{1}{4}$ in. wide, notched at the top.

Native of S. Europe and W. Asia; introduced in 1731 and for very many years a favourite in gardens and the commonest of these sub-shrubby candytufts. It is very hardy and covers itself every spring with a sheet of white flowers. It is well distinguished from the two preceding species by its narrow leaves.

Var. GARREXIANA, *Nicholson*, has still narrower leaves often pointed at the apex; inflorescence more slender.

Other species grown in gardens are:—I. SAXATILIS, *Linnæus*, a dwarf plant 3 to ins. high with hairy shoots and linear leaves $\frac{3}{8}$ to 1 in. long, edged with hairs, and white flowers in clusters 1 in. wide; admirable for rock gardens. I. TENOREANA, *De Candolle*, 4 to 8 ins. high, shoots hairy; leaves obovate to narrowly oblong, round-ended, $\frac{1}{2}$ to $1\frac{1}{2}$ ins. long, edged with fine hairs; flowers white or pinkish in flattish clusters 1 to 2 ins. wide. Both are native of S. Europe and are distinct from the preceding species in their hairy shoots and leaves.

IDESIA POLYCARPA, *Maximowicz*. FLACOURTIACEÆ

(Bot. Mag., t. 6794; Polycarpa Maximowiczii, *Linden*)

The genus Idesia consists, so far as is at present known, of this species, a medium-sized, deciduous tree, and commemorates E. I. Ides, a Dutchman who travelled in China early in the eighteenth century. The branches of I. polycarpa usually grow out from the trunk horizontally, and the younger ones have a large core of pith. Leaves dark green and quite glabrous above, glaucous beneath, and hairy at the base where the main veins join the stalk; heart-shaped, contracted at the apex to a short point, rather distantly toothed, and ordinarily about 6 ins. long by 5 ins. wide, but occasionally half as large again; leaf-stalk usually three-fourths as long as the leaf. Flowers fragrant, yellow-green, without petals, in terminal panicles; unisexual, and produced on different trees. Male panicles 5 or 6 ins. long, each flower $\frac{1}{3}$ in. across, the usually five sepals covered, like the flower-stalks, with a short brownish down; stamens numerous. Female flowers smaller, and in a longer, looser panicle than the males, with similar but smaller sepals, and a prominent globular ovary. Fruits hanging like a bunch of small grapes, each berry about the size of a pea, globular, containing numerous seeds lying in pulp; at first green, the berries become dark brown, finally a deep red.

This interesting tree was first made known to Europeans by R. Oldham, the Kew collector, who found it in Japan in 1862-3; it is a

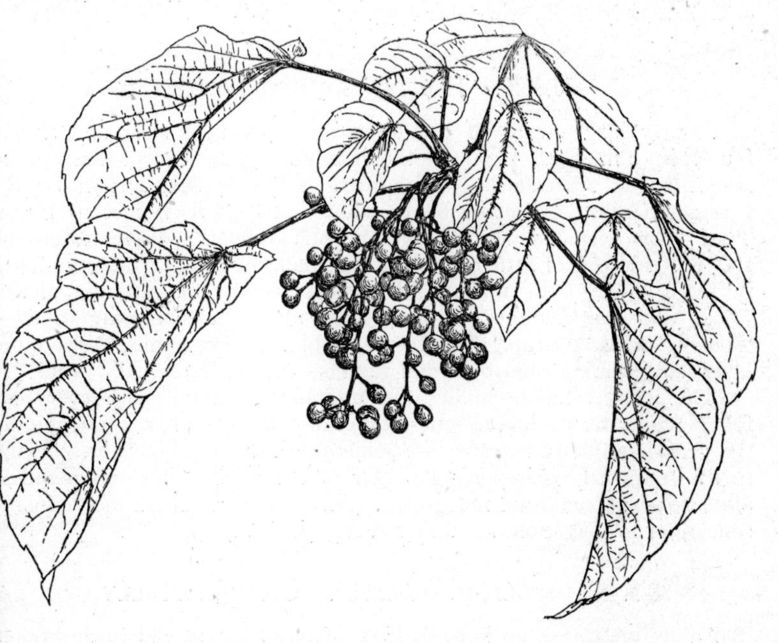

IDESIA POLYCARPA in fruit

native also of China. Soon after, it was introduced to Europe by way of St Petersburg, and was already in the famous arboretum at Segrez in 1869. In general appearance it suggests a Catalpa, but the leaves are thicker and not so large. It grows very well in a loamy soil, and is hardy at Kew, where it flowers in June and July and produces fruit annually. As a flowering tree it has no claims to notice, but the fruits make it interesting, and, if the autumn be fine enough to enable them to reach their final stage of colouring, distinct and handsome. Seeds ripen on the Continent, whence they can be obtained, and germinate freely. They afford a better means of increase than cuttings. There is a tree 40 ft. high at Trewithen in Cornwall.

Var. VESTITA, *Diels*.—Differs from the type chiefly by the undersurface of the leaves being densely downy. Wilson found it in Western Szechuen, China, at elevations of over 8000 ft. as a tree 20 to 50 ft. high with a trunk 1 ft. in diameter. The flowers are yellow as in the type; fruit described as brick red. The species varies considerably in the size and shape of its leaves, but this variety is well distinguished by its downy leaves which are almost felted when young. Introduced in 1908. Forrest sent home seeds of it and the typical form as well. Col. Stern raised the variety vestita from Farrer's seeds also, but I have not seen it in fruit. Farrer describes it as "a beautiful and graceful tree, with abundant long and loose panicles of rich scarlet berries." During the warm, dry summer of 1934 the typical I. polycarpa produced fine crops of red berries. It was especially good at Wakehurst, and specimens grown in the garden there were given an Award of Merit by the Royal Horticultural Society on 6th November 1934.

ILEX. HOLLY. AQUIFOLIACEÆ

A very large genus of deciduous and evergreen trees and shrubs found in almost all parts of the habitable globe except western N. America and Australasia. In gardens they are best known by the evergreen group, especially by I. Aquifolium and its numerous forms. They have very frequently angular young shoots; leaves alternate, stalked. Flowers of little or no beauty, small, often dull white, produced in the leaf-axils, the males and females usually on separate plants. Petals and stamens four to six. Fruit although commonly called a "berry," really a drupe, usually red or black, with a thin, fleshy outer layer, surrounding one to several nutlets—generally termed "seeds."

The most valuable hollies are undoubtedly those with evergreen foliage, but the deciduous ones, especially those earlier known under the generic name of PRINOS, are sometimes handsome in fruit. Owing to the frequently unisexual character of the plants, these often fail to appear if both sexes are not grown. All the species like a moist, loamy soil. (For propagation, see under *I. Aquifolium*.)

I. AQUIFOLIUM, *Linnæus*. COMMON HOLLY

An evergreen tree, up to 80 ft. high, of very leafy, much-branched habit, forming naturally a dense pyramidal mass; branchlets often clothed more or less with minute dark down. Leaves glossy dark green, 1 to 3 ins. long, $\frac{3}{4}$ to $2\frac{1}{2}$ ins. wide; very variable in size, outline, and toothing. Ordinary seed-raised young trees have very wavy leaves with large, triangular, outstanding teeth $\frac{1}{2}$ in. long; but as they increase in height the leaves of the upper branches become less spiny, until finally the tops of good-sized trees will be found almost wholly furnished with quite entire leaves. The spines are no doubt a means of protection against browsing animals, and are no longer needed when the trees become tall. But even very large trees retain their spininess on the lower branches. Flowers small, dull white, short-stalked, fragrant, produced during May and June, clustered in the leaf-axils. Berries round, red, $\frac{1}{4}$ in. diameter, containing two to four nutlets. The common holly may be either male, female, or bisexual.

Native of Europe (including Britain, where it is found wild in all parts except the north-east of Scotland) and W. Asia. The common holly is on the whole the most useful of evergreen trees and shrubs. For providing shelter nothing else equals it, because of its habit of keeping dense near the ground; and during the dark months a holly tree well laden with its bright red fruit is one of the handsomest and most cheerful objects our winter landscape provides. It makes the best of all evergreen hedges.

The holly does not transplant well, and unless it be removed with a con-
iderable amount of soil attached to its roots, this operation can only be done
afely either about the end of September or in May, when root-activity has
ommenced. If the roots have been injured in transplanting, it is a good
lan to reduce proportionately the top growth by as much as one-half (see
hapter on Transplanting). The common holly should be raised from seed.
Being slow of germination it is advisable, as with Cratægus, to mix the berries
rith sand or fine earth in a heap, which should be exposed for a year to all
reathers and turned occasionally. This rots the outer covering and allows
he two to four nuts or seeds each fruit contains to separate. They are then
own (soil and seed together) shallowly. The varieties do not come true from
eed, and have to be propagated by cuttings or by grafting. Cuttings are best
nade of thin side twigs about 4 ins. long, with a heel attached, and placed in
nild heat. They will also take root under a handlight out-of-doors, but are
lower. Grafting is done in spring on the seedlings of the type.

Cultivated, as it has been, for hundreds of years in Britain, the common
olly has sported into an enormous number of varieties, most of them hand-
ome, some curious, and a few worthless. An unfortunate practice, commenced
ong ago when they were few in number, has obtained of giving them
umbersome Latin names when colloquial ones would have served quite as
vell. A representative selection of these varieties is given below.

There is in Europe a well-marked group of evergreen hollies of which
. Aquifolium may be taken as the type, which includes also I. Perado,
. platyphylla, and its variety balearica. The origin of many garden hollies
s not known or recorded, but it appears certain that some of the European
hollies mentioned, chiefly perhaps the Balearic one, have been concerned in
he production of the great race of garden varieties known to-day. Those
vith large, flattish, often less spiny and less glossy leaves show most strongly
he influence of the Balearic holly: those with smaller, very polished,
undulated leaves have inherited a greater proportion of characters from I.
Aquifolium, or, like the variegated sorts, are branch sports from it.

It may be remarked that all variegated hollies whose variegation is in the
centre of the leaf have a strong tendency to "run out," that is, to revert to the
green sorts from which they originally sprang, and it is necessary to cut out
he green twigs as they appear. The marginally variegated ones do not show
uch a tendency.

Var. ALTACLARENSIS. Highclere Holly.—Leaves dark, slightly glossy
green, up to 4½ ins. long, 3 ins. wide; bark purplish; spines variable. One
of the big-leaved group; male. The holly called "nobilis" scarcely differs
rom this.

Var. ARGENTEA MARGINATA. Silver-leaved.—Leaves up to 3 ins. long
and 2 ins. wide, dark green in the centre with a silvery margin. There are
about half a score forms included under this variety, all with white leaf margins,
amongst them :—A. MARGINATA ERECTA, centre of leaf mottled green; and
A. MARGINATA PENDULA (Perry's weeping), branches pendulous.

Var. ARGENTEA MEDIO-PICTA. Silver Milkmaid.—Leaves dark green, with
a large blotch of creamy white in the centre. Male and female.

Var. ARGENTEA REGINA. Silver Queen.—The best white variegated sort;
young wood purplish, the variegation clear and broad. A male.

Var. AUREA MARGINATA. Gold-leaved.—This variety, like the "Silver-
leaved," includes some half a score forms; they are all distinguished by the
leaves having an unequal margin of yellow.

Var. AUREA MEDIO-PICTA. Golden Milkmaid.—A fine variety, the leaves
very wavy at the margin, and the centre golden, with only a thin irregular
margin of green. Male and female.

Var. AUREA PENDULA. Golden weeping.—A pendulous variety with purple bark, the dark green centre of the leaf surrounded by a margin of gold.

Var. AUREA REGINA. Golden Queen.—Probably the finest of all variegated golden hollies. Leaves up to 3½ ins. long, 2¼ ins. wide, margined with deep yellow; some leaves wholly yellow. Male.

Var. CAMELLIÆFOLIA.—One of the very finest of green hollies. Leaves dark burnished green, oblong, the largest 5 ins. long and 2 ins. wide, mostly without spines, but sometimes with one to eight spines. Female.

Var. CHINENSIS, *Loesener*.—A wild Chinese form of I. Aquifolium introduced by Wilson in 1901, and later. Leaves ovate-lanceolate, 3 to 4½ ins. long, 1½ ins. wide, very spiny. Distinct from common holly in the long narrow leaves.

Var. CRASSIFOLIA. Leather-leaf Holly.—An extraordinary variety, with thick, purple young branches. Leaves 1½ to 2 ins. long, ¾ to ⅞ in. wide, very thick and leathery, the triangular spines ⅙ to ¼ in. long. It has no beauty, but is remarkably curious. Female.

Var. CRISPA. Screw-leaved.—Bark purple. Leaves spirally twisted and contorted, some having several spines, but mostly with few or none. One of the least ornamental. Var. CRISPA PICTA, is a form of it, blotched with yellow in the centre. Male.

Var. DONNINGTONENSIS. Donnington Holly.—An elegant variety with purple bark, glossy, dark purplish green narrow-oblong leaves, with a lance-shaped apex, 2 ins. long, ½ to ¾ in. wide, with a few large spines or none. Male.

Var. FEROX. Hedgehog Holly.—Bark purple. Leaves small, and besides having the usual marginal spines, armed with curious clusters or bands of them on the surface; male. Var. FEROX ARGENTEA is similar, but the spines and margin are white. Var. FEROX AUREA, leaves with the spines and margin green, the centre yellow.

Var. FISHERI. Fisher's Holly.—A fine green-leaved form; largest leaves 4 ins. long by 2¾ ins. wide; formidably armed with large spines. Male.

Var. FLAVESCENS. Moonlight Holly.—Leaves as in common holly, but suffused with yellow, especially when young. Female.

Var. FRUCTU LUTEO.—Yellow-fruited. Most of the red-berried species of Ilex have yellow-fruited varieties. This does not differ from the type, except in this respect. Female.

Var. HANDSWORTH NEW SILVER.—One of the best of the white-margined hollies; bark purple; leaves up to 3½ ins. long, very dark green, the margin clear white, and armed with large spines. Female.

Var. HASTATA (kewensis).—A curious green-leaved variety of no beauty; bark purple; leaves ½ to 1½ ins. long, narrow, the basal part armed with disproportionately large spines.

Var. HODGINSII.—One of the hybrids between Aquifolium and perhaps balearica. Leaves roundish ovate, dull dark green, up to 4 ins. long. A very striking green, berry-bearing variety of vigorous habit.

Var. LATISPINA.—Bark purple; leaves green, ovate, 2 to 3 ins. long, marked by a long, slender, deflexed point, and one or more irregularly-placed, slender spines on the margin, ¼ to ¾ in. long; very distinct.

Var. LAWSONIANA.—Leaves dullish green, up to 3½ ins. long, ovate or oval, rather spiny, the centre marked with a large irregular blotch of yellow. A striking holly, but very apt to revert to the green form, known as HENDERSONI.

Var. MARNOCKII.—A fine holly in the way of camelliæfolia, but with proportionately broader leaves, somewhat twisted, entire or armed with large spines. Female.

Var. MONSTROSA.—Resembling latispina, with the apex and spines of the same character, but with more of the latter—often four or five down each side.

Var. MUNDYI.—A vigorous, striking variety belonging to the hybrid group, showing platyphylla or balearica influence. Largest leaves 4 ins. by $2\frac{1}{2}$ ins. wide, dullish green, oval or roundish oval; the margins set regularly with short, slender spines, the surface rugose. Male.

Var. MYRTIFOLIA.—Leaves small, mostly about $1\frac{1}{2}$ ins. long by $\frac{1}{2}$ to $\frac{5}{8}$ in. wide, well armed with slender spines; sometimes larger and less spiny.

Var. OVATA.—A very distinct and pleasing sort; bark purple. Leaves especially thick and leathery, dark glossy green, $1\frac{1}{2}$ to $2\frac{1}{2}$ ins. long, ovate, very regularly armed on the margin with short outstanding spines. Male.

Var. PENDULA. Weeping.—Like the common holly, but with rather stiffly arching and pendulous branches. A striking lawn tree. (For the variegated "Perry's weeping," see *argentea marginata*.)

Var. RECURVA.—A dwarf kind with small, very spiny leaves, dark green, ovate, 1 to $1\frac{3}{4}$ ins. long, the midrib much decurved, the blade also twisted. Male.

Var. SCOTICA.—A very distinct sort, with lustrous deep green oval leaves up to 3 ins. long, remarkable for the entire absence of marginal spines; the apex is sometimes spine-tipped, usually blunt. Female.

Var. SCOTICA AUREA.—Has a central blotch of yellow; a sport from the above; raised by Paul of Cheshunt.

Var. SHEPHERDII.—A fine holly in the way of Hodginsii, but with bright green leaves, the largest of which are 4 ins. long, $2\frac{1}{2}$ ins. wide.

Var. SMITHII.—Of the same type as donningtonensis, but without the intense purple bark and purple tinge in the leaves of that variety. Male.

Var. WATERERIANA. Waterer's Holly.—A dwarf compact kind usually wider than high, and dense in habit. Leaves often quite without marginal spines or only a few; dark green with a rich yellow border. Male.

Var. WILSONI.—One of the finest of the platyphylla or balearica hybrids. Leaves only slightly glossy, up to 5 ins. long by nearly 3 ins. wide, well armed at the edges with spines $\frac{1}{4}$ in. long. Female.

I. CILIOSPINOSA, *Loesener*

An evergreen shrub up to 12 or 15 ft. high; young shoots covered with short down. Leaves leathery, ovate to oval, slender-pointed, spine-tipped, rounded to wedge-shaped at the base, spiny toothed; 1 to 2 ins. long, $\frac{1}{2}$ to 1 in. wide; dark dull green above, pale below, quite glabrous. Berry egg-shaped, $\frac{1}{4}$ in. long, red, containing two stones; the berry is usually solitary in the axil of the leaves on a stalk $\frac{1}{8}$ in. long.

Native of W. Szechuen, China; discovered by Wilson in 1904, introduced in 1908. This is a neat, small-leaved holly, erect and slender in a small state, and appears to be quite hardy at Kew. The specific name refers to the rather numerous, slender, forward-pointing teeth of the leaves, which are not particularly distinctive in this respect. It is considered to be related to the Himalayan I. dipyrena but is well distinguished by its much smaller stature, smaller, darker green leaves and round (not angular) shoots.

I. CORNUTA, *Lindley*. HORNED HOLLY

(Bot. Mag., t. 5059)

An evergreen shrub, 8 to 10 ft. perhaps more high; of bushy, dense, rounded habit, and usually wider than high; young shoots glabrous, pale, and somewhat angular the first year. Leaves leathery, dark glossy green, $1\frac{1}{2}$ to 4 ins. long, 1 to 3 ins. wide ; of variable shape, but usually more or less rectangular, often comparable in outline to a flying bat, with four large spines at the corners representing the outstretched limbs ; there is, in addition, always a terminal spine usually much decurved, and frequently one or two pairs of smaller spines at the sides. The number of spines therefore varies from five to nine, and they are rigid and needle-pointed ; but on the upper branches of old specimens the spines are fewer or absent, as in the common holly ; stalk $\frac{1}{6}$ in. or less long. Flowers small, dull white, produced in axillary clusters in April. Fruit round, red, larger than in common holly, borne on a stalk $\frac{1}{3}$ to $\frac{5}{8}$ in. long.

Native of China ; found by Fortune near Shanghai, and sent by him to Messrs Standish of Bagshot in 1846. It is still a rather uncommon plant, although quite hardy in the London district. Of comparatively slow growth, and of neat compact habit, it is suitable for positions where many evergreens would soon become too large. Its distinct and handsome foliage also makes it interesting, but it bears fruit only shyly.

I. CRENATA, *Thunberg*. JAPANESE HOLLY (Plate 12)

An evergreen shrub, usually 5 to 9 ft. high, or a small tree of very dense, rigid, compact habit ; young shoots angular, and covered with minute dark down. Leaves crowded, oblong-lanceolate, $\frac{1}{2}$ to $\frac{3}{4}$ in. long, $\frac{1}{8}$ to $\frac{1}{4}$ in. wide ; tapered at the base to a short stalk, sharply pointed and with a few incurved teeth at the margins ; glossy green, and of hard texture. Flowers dull white ; fruit black.

Native of Japan ; introduced to Europe about 1864. It is not easy to ascertain what is the typical form of this holly, but the one above described is what is commonly regarded as such—very distinct in its close habit and small leaves, and rarely more than 3 or 4 ft. high. But the two following are very distinct hollies from Japan also attributed to this species.

Var. MAJOR (syn. elliptica).—A small tree, occasionally 20 ft. high, with box-like, oval leaves, $\frac{1}{2}$ to $1\frac{1}{4}$ ins. long, $\frac{1}{4}$ to $\frac{5}{8}$ in. wide, minutely round-toothed. Fruit black, round, $\frac{1}{4}$ in. diameter, on stalks $\frac{1}{4}$ in. or less long. By some this is regarded as Thunberg's type.

Var. MARIESII (Ilex Mariesii, *Veitch*).—Whilst var. major represents one extreme of this variable species, var. Mariesii represents the other. It is a very stiff-habited, extraordinarily dwarf holly, with stunted twigs hidden by orbicular or broadly ovate leaves about $\frac{1}{4}$ in. wide, sometimes entire, sometimes with a pair of shallow teeth near the apex. Fruits black, on stalks $\frac{1}{12}$ in. long. Interesting for the rock garden as a pigmy. Introduced for Messrs Veitch by Maries about 1879. It only grows part of an inch a year. Perhaps a distinct species.

Var. VARIEGATA.—A form with leaves of the same shape and size as the type, but spotted or blotched with yellow, sometimes wholly of that colour.

Ilex crenata in all its forms is a popular shrub in Japan. It is used largely for clipping into fantastic shapes, also as a dwarf hedge. I have been told by a traveller that so dense and hard are some of these flat-topped hedges there, that a man can walk along the top of them. It can be increased by cuttings, and is quite hardy.

I. DECIDUA, *Walter*

(I. prinoides, *Aiton*)

A deciduous shrub, usually 5 to 10 ft. high, occasionally a small tree up to 30 ft. in the southern parts of its habitat ; shoots glabrous and covered with a grey bark. Leaves oval or narrowly obovate, tapered at both ends, often blunt at the apex, shallowly round-toothed ; 1 to $2\frac{1}{2}$ ins. long, $\frac{1}{3}$ to $\frac{3}{4}$ in. wide ;

of firm texture, glabrous except along the midrib ; stalk downy, $\frac{1}{6}$ to $\frac{1}{3}$ in. long. The leaves are often crowded on short lateral spurs. Male flowers on slender stalks $\frac{1}{2}$ in. long ; females on shorter ones. Fruits round, orange to scarlet, $\frac{1}{4}$ in. diameter.

Native of the south-eastern United States ; introduced in 1760. It occasionally bears a good crop of its berries, which are very persistent on the branches. The branches do not break into leaf until May, and the fruits formed the previous autumn are then still remaining. From the red-fruited I. verticillata and I. lævigata, this differs in having the nutlets many-ribbed ; in the others they are smooth. Its habit of producing short spurs crowded with leaves and flowers also gives it a distinct aspect.

I. DIPYRENA, *Wallich*. HIMALAYAN HOLLY

An evergreen tree, ultimately 40 ft. or more high, the angular young shoots and winter buds minutely downy. Leaves oblong or narrowly oval, tapered at the base, slenderly pointed and spine-tipped, 2 to 5 ins. long, $\frac{5}{8}$ to $1\frac{1}{2}$ ins. wide ; dull, opaque green, leathery ; stalk $\frac{1}{4}$ in. or less long. Like the common holly it is very spiny on the margins when young, but as the plant attains maturity the spines become fewer and finer, and ultimately the leaves of the upper branches become entire. Flowers very numerous, in dense round clusters in the leaf-axils. Fruits oval, red, large for a holly, commonly two-seeded.

Native of the Himalaya. Whilst inferior to the common holly as an ornamental evergreen, both in the lack of lustre on the foliage, and as rarely bearing fruit, this species is interesting and worth growing for its distinctness. There is an example at Kew 30 ft. high and 17 ft. through, which makes a handsome specimen. I have never known this tree injured ; even the great frosts of February 1895 did not affect it. But in a young state the species is susceptible to intense cold, and the Kew tree was killed back to ground-level in 1867.

I. BEANII, *Rehder* (I. dipyrena elliptica, *Dallimore* ; I. elliptica of our previous editions).—Although commonly regarded as a form of the common holly, this is, no doubt, a hybrid between it and I. dipyrena, which in general appearance it closely approaches, the leaves being a dull green, although shorter and comparatively broader.

I. FARGESII, *Franchet*. FARGES' HOLLY

An evergreen small tree, up to 15 or 20 ft. high, quite devoid of down in all its parts. Leaves narrow-oblong or narrowly oblanceolate, 2 to 5 ins. long, $\frac{3}{8}$ to $1\frac{1}{8}$ in. wide ; slenderly tapered and entire towards the base, more abruptly tapered towards the apex, where are a few incurved teeth ; dull green ; stalk $\frac{1}{3}$ to $\frac{1}{2}$ in. long, reddish. Fruit red, globose, often in threes or fours in the leaf-axils, $\frac{1}{4}$ in. diameter ; stalk $\frac{1}{6}$ in. long, reddish.

Native of W. China, in the province of Szechuen ; introduced by Wilson for Messrs Veitch in 1900. It is not a species of great promise as an ornamental evergreen except in the milder counties, but is remarkably distinct in its long, narrow, opaque leaves. On young plants they are more toothed towards the base than in adult ones.

I. GENICULATA, *Maximowicz*

A deciduous unisexual shrub 5 to 8 ft. high ; young shoots angular, free from down. Leaves ovate to oval-lanceolate, toothed, with a long slender point and a rounded or broadly wedge-shaped base ; $1\frac{1}{2}$ to $2\frac{1}{2}$ ins. long, $\frac{3}{4}$ to $1\frac{1}{4}$ ins. wide ; downy only on the midrib and chief veins beneath ; stalk $\frac{1}{8}$ to $\frac{3}{8}$ in. long.

Fruit globose, cinnabar-red, ¼ in. wide, usually solitary on a very slender, purple-brown, pendulous, glabrous stalk ¾ to 1½ ins. long.

Native of the mountains of Central Japan where, according to Wilson, it is everywhere rare. He writes: "The first wild bush of this holly I had ever seen was about 6 ft. high and as much in diameter, bearing thousands of its brilliantly coloured fruits suspended from slender stalks. I thought I had never seen, in fruit, a shrub so lovely." It has been growing in the Arnold Arboretum, Mass., since 1894 and succeeds admirably there. It was added to the Kew collection in 1926, but apparently had not previously been in cultivation in this country. It belongs to the Prinos or deciduous group of hollies, which includes I. verticillata and I. serrata (Sieboldii), but is distinct from all cultivated species in the length of its fruit-stalks. The specific name refers to a curious joint or "knee" on the terminal half of these stalks, which marks the place whence abortive flowers have fallen. When these remain on and develop, as they occasionally do, there may be three fruits on a stalk.

I. GLABRA, *A. Gray.* INKBERRY

(Prinos glaber, *Linnæus*)

An evergreen shrub, 3 to 7 ft. high, with erect branches, densely leafy; young shoots angular, minutely downy. Leaves narrowly obovate to oblanceolate, entire, or with a few obscure teeth near the apex; ¾ to 1¾ ins. long, ⅓ to ⅝ in. wide; dark green above, paler beneath, glossy and glabrous on both surfaces; stalk ⅛ to ¼ in. long. Male flowers borne three or more together on a slender stalk; females solitary; both very small. Fruit round, black, ¼ in. diameter.

Native of eastern N. America; introduced in 1759. Emerson says this shrub is occasionally found 8 or 9 ft. high, but it is very slow-growing, and plants I know to be forty years old are only 3 or 4 ft. high. It is a neat-habited evergreen, quite unarmed, but of no particular merit, and rather like a phillyrea.

I. INSIGNIS, *Hooker fil.*

It is unfortunate that this splendid holly can only be grown in the milder parts of the British Isles. At Kew it has to be given the protection of a cool greenhouse. It is a small evergreen tree without any down; branchlets stout, silvery grey, lustrous. Leaves oblong, inclined to ovate; 5 to 9 ins. long, 2 to 2½ ins. wide; slender-pointed, tapered at the base, armed at the edges with small spine-tipped teeth; dark dull green; midrib pale green, prominent; stalk ¾ to 1 in. long, purplish. Fruit bright red, roundish oval, ⅖ in. long, scarcely stalked.

Native of Sikkim at 6000 to 8000 ft. In a small or seedling state it is quite distinct, the leaf-margins being wavy and formidably armed with numerous spiny teeth ¼ to ⅓ in. long, pointing different ways.

I. INTEGRA, *Thunberg*

(Othera japonica, *Hort.*)

An evergreen tree, 30 to 40 ft. high in Japan, about half as high at present in this country; pyramidal when young; young shoots angled, glabrous. Leaves obovate or oval, 1½ to 4 ins. long, ¾ to 1¼ ins. wide, tapered more gradually to the stalk and to the blunt apex; margin quite devoid of teeth or spines; dark glossy green; stalk ¼ to ½ in. long. Fruit deep red, globose, nearly ½ in. diameter.

Native of China, Japan, and Korea; introduced in 1864. This is distinct from the large-leaved hollies in the entire absence of spines on the leaves of either old or young plants. It is a handsome evergreen, slightly tender when raised from seed the first one or two winters, but perfectly hardy afterwards. Specimens that bear fruit are at Osborne, Isle of Wight; Abbotsbury, in Dorset; Enys, in Cornwall; and, no doubt, in other places also.

I. LÆVIGATA, *A. Gray*. SMOOTH WINTERBERRY

(Prinos lævigatus, *Pursh*)

A deciduous shrub, 6 to 8 ft. high; young shoots glabrous. Leaves narrowly oval, obovate or lanceolate, tapered at both ends; $1\frac{1}{2}$ to $2\frac{1}{2}$ ins. long, $\frac{1}{2}$ to $\frac{3}{4}$ in. wide; finely pointed, obscurely toothed, pale green and glossy on both surfaces, and glabrous except sometimes for a little down along the veins beneath; stalk $\frac{1}{4}$ in. or less long. Male flowers on slender stalks $\frac{1}{3}$ to $\frac{3}{4}$ in. long; female ones on very short stalks; calyx glabrous. Fruit orange-red, $\frac{1}{3}$ in. diameter, solitary.

Native of the eastern United States; introduced in 1812. This is not so well known in gardens as I. verticillata, nor is it perhaps so ornamental with us. It is closely allied to that species, under the notice of which some distinctions are pointed out. It may be added here that the leaf-stalks are generally shorter and the fruits larger in I. lævigata. Both species affect low, wet situations in a wild state.

Var. HERVEYI, *Robinson*.—Fruits yellow.

I. LATIFOLIA, *Thunberg*. TARAJO

(Bot. Mag., t. 5597)

An evergreen tree, occasionally 50 to 60 ft. high in Japan, rarely more than 20 ft. high in this country; young shoots very stout, $\frac{1}{3}$ in. diameter, angular, not downy. Leaves very thick, dark lustrous green, oblong; 4 to 8 ins. long, $1\frac{1}{2}$ to 3 ins. wide; tapered about equally at both ends, the marginal teeth shallow and not spiny; the under-surface is rather yellow; stalk $\frac{1}{2}$ to 1 in. long. Fruit red, globose, $\frac{1}{3}$ in. diameter, crowded in considerable numbers on short axillary racemes.

Native of Japan; introduced to Europe by Siebold in 1840. Although this species is hardy at Kew it does not succeed very well. But a few miles to the south it thrives admirably in favourable situations; there are fine specimens at Claremont and at Leonardslee, and no doubt still larger ones in Devon and Cornwall; at Chaddlewood, Plympton, it is over 20 ft. high. Sargent regarded it as the handsomest broad-leaved evergreen of Japan.

I. MACROCARPA, *Oliver*

(Hooker's Icones Plantarum, t. 1787)

This is a native of Szechuen and Hupeh in China, and was introduced by Wilson during his third expedition to China in the autumn of 1907, when collecting for Harvard University. It is a tree up to 50 ft. high, deciduous; its branchlets and leaves perfectly glabrous on cultivated plants. Leaves oval to ovate, $2\frac{1}{2}$ to 4 ins. long, $1\frac{1}{4}$ to 2 ins. wide; broadly wedge-shaped at the base, shortly acuminate, finely and shallowly toothed, dark green above, glossy green beneath. These characters are taken from plants raised from seed in the spring of 1908. In wild specimens the leaves are larger; the flowers are described as appearing one to seven together, and the fruit is $\frac{3}{5}$ in. diameter, black. It appears to be quite hardy, and grows vigorously.

I. MONTANA, *A. Gray*

(I. monticola, *A. Gray*; I. dubia monticola, *Loesener*)

A deciduous shrub (sometimes a tree in a wild state), with glabrous young stems. Leaves ovate to oval, with a long, tapering, lanceolate point, and a wedge-shaped base, sharply toothed; 2 to 5 ins. long, ¾ to 2¼ ins. wide; pale green, glabrous, or downy only on the midrib and veins; stalk slender, ¼ to ⅝ in. long. Flowers white, the males crowded at the end of short spur-like branches, or in the leaf-axils of the previous year's growth, along with two or three leaves; the females short-stalked, fewer, often solitary. Fruit globose, bright orange red, ⅖ in. across, borne on stalks about ¼ in. long.

Native of the eastern United States from New York State southwards. It is allied to I. decidua, having the fruits red, the seeds many-ribbed at the back, and leaves often clustered on short spurs, but I. decidua has round-toothed leaves usually widest above the middle, and blunt at the apex. Introduced to Kew from N. Carolina in 1899, but possibly in cultivation earlier.

I. OPACA, *Aiton.* AMERICAN HOLLY

An evergreen tree, sometimes 40 to 50 ft. high in a wild state, with a trunk 6 to 9 ft. in girth, resembling the common holly in habit; young shoots minutely downy. Leaves dull green above, yellow-green beneath, oval, tapered more abruptly at the base than at the spine-tipped apex; 1½ to 3½ ins. long, half as wide; the margins armed with broad, spine-tipped teeth, which tend to disappear from the uppermost leaves of adult specimens; stalk grooved, ¼ to ½ in. long, minutely downy. Male flowers in three- to nine-flowered, slender-stalked cymes; females usually solitary; all small, dull white; calyx-lobes edged with minute hairs. Fruit red, round, ¼ in. diameter, on a stalk about as long.

Native of the eastern and central United States; introduced in 1744. In gardens this species is only likely to be confused with the Himalayan I. dipyrena, which has similarly opaque, evergreen foliage, but that species has longer narrow leaves with shorter stalks, and much shorter-stalked, more congested flower-clusters. The fruit also is larger. I. opaca sometimes bears fruit very freely in this country, and is then ornamental, but it is never so attractive as our common native species. The largest specimen I know is at Kew, 25 ft. high, two-thirds as wide.

Var. XANTHOCARPA, *Rehder.*—Fruits yellow; has been found wild in Massachusetts. Introduced in 1901.

I. PEDUNCULOSA, *Miquel*

An evergreen shrub, or a tree up to 20 or 30 ft. high; young shoots glabrous. Leaves unarmed, ovate or oval, tapering or rounded at the base, slender pointed, margins entire; 1½ to 3 ins. long, ¾ to 1¼ ins. wide; dark glossy green and glabrous; stalk ½ to ¾ in. long. The chief peculiarity of this holly is the length of the fruit-stalk, which is 1 to 1½ ins. long, so that the bright red fruits, each ¼ in. across, stand out conspicuously.

Native of Japan; introduced by Sargent in 1893. Hardy.

Var. CONTINENTALIS, *Loesener.*—Introduced by Wilson to the Coombe Wood nursery from Hupeh, China, in 1901 and 1907, this differs from the Japanese type in having leaves up to 4 or 5 ins. long, and a minutely ciliate calyx. It is apparently quite hardy. There is a line of minute down on the midrib above, and the young plants at Coombe Wood had the leaves inconspicuously toothed—perhaps a juvenile character only.

I. Perado, *Aiton*

(Loddiges' Botanical Cabinet, t. 549)

An evergreen tree, hardy in the warmer parts of the kingdom, with deep green leathery leaves of variable shape, oval, ovate or obovate; 3 to 5 ins. long, 1½ to 2½ ins. wide; sometimes entire, sometimes with spiny teeth, the apex often blunt or rounded. Berries deep red, roundish oval, ⅓ in. in diameter, on stalks about as much long, crowded in the leaf-axils.

Native of the Canary Islands and the Azores; cultivated in Britain since 1760. It thrives very well in the Isle of Wight and in Ireland, and no doubt elsewhere, but like I. platyphylla is confounded with I. Aquifolium. It may have hybridised with that species, and thus become a parent of some of the large-leaved, less spiny garden hollies. It differs from I. Aquifolium in the distinctly winged leaf-stalk, at each side of which beneath there is a groove. The spines also are much shorter.

I. Pernyi, *Franchet*

An evergreen small tree, occasionally 20 to 30 ft. high in a wild state, more often a shrub half as high; branches stiff, densely furnished with leaves, and clothed with a short dense pubescence when young. Leaves squarish at the base, with a long triangular apex and two large spines, and often a smaller one, at each side; ⅝ to 2 ins. long, ⅜ to 1 in. wide; dark glossy green, leathery; stalk 1/12 in. long, at first downy like the young shoot. Flowers pale yellow, produced in minute axillary clusters, the sepals roundish and edged with minute hairs. Fruit stalkless or nearly so, red, roundish oblong, ¼ in. diameter.

Native of Central and W. China; discovered in 1858 by the Abbé Perny; introduced by Wilson for Messrs Veitch in 1900. It appears to be widely spread and common in certain parts of China. It bears most resemblance to I. cornuta, but its smaller leaves, with the apices much more elongated, and its downy shoots distinguish it. Its habit, in a young state at least, is slenderly pyramidal and very shapely, and altogether it is a charming addition to dwarf, slow-growing evergreens. Paul Perny, after whom it is named, was a courageous French missionary who worked in the province of Kiuchu between 1850 and 1860. He was the first naturalist who explored that province, which he is said to have originally entered in the guise of a Chinese beggar.

Var. Veitchii, *Hort.*, has larger and especially broader leaves.

I. platyphylla, *Webb and Berthelot.*
Canary Island Holly

An evergreen tree, 30 or more ft. high, of densely leafy, bushy habit, young shoots miuntely scurfy or downy. Leaves broadly oval, very stiff and leathery, rounded or tapered at the base, usually pointed and spine-tipped at the apex, 3 to 6 ins. long, 2 to 3½ ins. wide; the margins set with short spines, irregular in number and size, often entire; stalk ½ in. long, covered with scurfy down. Fruits deep red, ⅖ in. diameter, on stalks ⅓ in. long.

Native of the Canary Islands, cultivated in Britain since 1760. From I. Aquifolium it is not very easy to distinguish this species in words, although it is distinct enough in general appearance. Its leaves are larger and duller, the teeth are smaller, the leaf-stalk flatter and the blade less undulated at the margin. It is pretty certain that either it or balearica, a geographical variety mentioned below, share in a greater or less degree the percentage of many garden hollies, especially those with big, flattish, rather dull-surfaced leaves. The true platyphylla of Webb (different from the holly so called in gardens) is probably tender.

Var. BALEARICA (I. balearica, *Desfontaines*).—Leaves ovate or oval, 2 to 3½ ins. long, 1 to 2 ins. wide, stout and dark green; spines usually few and irregular or absent. Female plant in gardens. Native of the Balearic Islands and S. Spain.

Var. MADERENSIS.—Leaves ovate or oval, 2½ to 3½ ins. long, bright green, the margins uniformly spiny, the spines pointing forwards. Very close to balearica. A variegated holly known as MADERENSIS VARIEGATA, with an irregular yellow blotch in the centre, is probably a hybrid in whose origin I. Aquifolium has a share, as indicated by the large spines and wavy margin.

Var. NIGRESCENS.—A fine dark green variety, the largest leaves of which are 4 ins. long by 2¾ ins. wide, ovate, sparsely and irregularly spiny. A male.

I. RUGOSA, *Fr. Schmidt*

A low evergreen shrub of spreading, sometimes prostrate habit; young shoots not downy, angled. Leaves narrowly oval or oblong, tapered about equally to each end, blunt or rounded at the apex, shallowly round-toothed; ¾ to 2 in . long, ⅜ to ¾ in. wide; dark bright green and wrinkled above, paler and conspicuously veined beneath, not downy; stalk ⅛ in. long. Flowers shortly stalked; males six or eight, females one or two in the leaf-axils. Fruit often solitary, roundish ovoid, about ¼ in. wide, red, ripe in September.

Native of Japan and Saghalin; originally described and named in 1868; introduced to cultivation in 1895, but very rare in this country. It is very distinct among cultivated hollies in its lax growth (making slender shoots up to 1 ft. long in a season) and especially in the wrinkled surface of its leaves. It is very hardy in the Arnold Arboretum and ought to be quite hardy with us, but shrubs from its native regions are often excited into growth too early in spring and suffer from late frosts in consequence.

I. SERRATA, *Thunberg*

(I. Sieboldii, *Miquel*)

A deciduous shrub, up to 12 or 15 ft. high, with spreading branches; young shoots angled, zigzag, minutely downy. Leaves oval and ovate to somewhat obovate; tapered at both ends, usually more slenderly at the apex; finely toothed, 1 to 3 ins. long, ⅓ to 1 in. wide; dull green above, and soft with minute down when young, becoming glabrous later; covered with a more conspicuous, persistent down and prominently veined beneath; stalk ⅓ in. or less long, downy. Flowers inconspicuous in axillary clusters. Fruit red, globose, ⅙ in. diameter.

Native of Japan; apparently introduced for the first time in 1893 to Kew from Yokohama, but known in the United States since about 1866. It is quite hardy, and bears good crops of fruit. It has very much the aspect of the North American I. verticillata, but is not so ornamental, the fruits being smaller and scarcely so bright; its leaves are also more finely toothed. Sargent observes that the leafless branches are sold in immense quantities in Tokyo for house decoration; for this purpose they are admirably suited, as the berries hang on and retain their colour a long time.

Var. LEUCOCARPA.—Fruits white; leaves shorter and broader. Introduced in 1893.

I. VERTICILLATA, *A. Gray*. BLACK ALDER. WINTERBERRY

(Bot. Mag., t. 8832; Prinos verticillatus, *Linnæus*)

A deciduous shrub, 6 to 10 ft. high, of spreading habit; young shoots glabrous. Leaves oval, obovate, or lanceolate, tapered at both ends; 1½ to 3 ins. long, ½ to 1 in. wide; shallowly and often doubly toothed; glabrous above, downy beneath, especially on the midrib and veins; stalk ¼ to ½ in. long. Male flowers in clusters of six or more in the leaf-axils; female ones fewer. Calyx edged with small hairs. Fruits often solitary or in pairs, bright red (or, in var. CHRYSOCARPA, *Robinson*, yellow), ¼ in. diameter, round.

Native of eastern N. America; introduced in 1736. This is the most ornamental of the American deciduous hollies, and is frequently very showy in autumn with the glossy scarlet berries, which are in full colour before the leaves fall. The only species with which it is likely to be confused is I. lævigata (*q.v.*), a species which has also red fruits and is deciduous. It differs from this by its glabrous or nearly glabrous leaves; its long, slender-stalked male flowers; its calyx margins not being hairy; and by its solitary fruits. I. verticillata is somewhat variable, and American botanists distinguish the following varieties:—

Var. CYCLOPHYLLA, *Robinson*.—Leaves small, roundish, rather clustered at the end of the twig, finely downy on the veins beneath.

Var. PADIFOLIA (Prinos padifolius, *Willdenow*).—Leaves downy all over the lower surface.

Var. TENUIFOLIA (Prinos tenuifolius, *Torrey*).—Leaves thinner and less downy than in the type. Female flowers more often solitary.

I. VOMITORIA, *Aiton*. CASSENA

(I. Cassine, *Walter*, not *Linnæus*)

An evergreen shrub, sometimes a small tree, 15 to 20 ft. high; young shoots rigid, spreading, covered with a minute down. Leaves glabrous, glossy dark green, narrowly oval or inclined to ovate, tapered at the base, bluntish at the apex, the margin shallowly and remotely toothed; ½ to 1½ ins. long, ¼ to ¾ in. wide; stalk $\frac{1}{12}$ to ⅛ in. long, downy like the young wood. Flowers produced in axillary clusters on the year-old wood, the males numerous and on stalks ⅛ in. long; females solitary or in pairs. Fruit scarlet, round, ⅕ in. diameter.

Native of the south-eastern United States; introduced in 1700. A neat evergreen shrub something like a phillyrea in appearance, but incapable of withstanding our hardest winters.

I. YUNNANENSIS, *Franchet*

An evergreen shrub, ultimately 10 to 12 ft. high, with bright green branchlets covered with outstanding down which persists two years. Leaves of a beautiful brownish red when quite young, becoming glossy green with age, ovate, rounded at the base, acutely pointed, round-toothed, ¾ to 1⅛ ins. long, rather more than half as wide. Fruit about ¼ in. diameter, red.

Native of W. China; introduced by Wilson about 1901, and since cultivated in the Coombe Wood nursery. It has not yet flowered under cultivation, but is worth growing as a neat, cheerful-looking evergreen. It was first discovered by Delavay, afterwards by Henry. It is allied to I. crenata, but the leaves are more leathery, the branches more downy, and the fruit red.

Var. GENTILIS, *Loesener*.—Leaves and shoots often nearly or quite glabrous.

ILLICIUM. ANISE TREES. MAGNOLIACEÆ

A small genus of evergreen shrubs or small trees allied to Magnolia, with an agreeable aromatic odour resembling that of aniseed. Leaves alternate, entire. Fruit starlike, the carpels being borne round a central axis. Two species are grown out-of-doors in the British Isles, one from the S.E. United States, the other from China and Japan. Both are rather tender. They prefer a partially peaty soil, especially until well-established, and can best be propagated by layers.

I. ANISATUM, *Linnæus*

(I. religiosum, *Siebold*; Bot. Mag., t. 3965)

A shrub or small tree, the young branches of which are glabrous, green spotted with brown. Leaves 2 to 4 ins. long, ¾ to 1 in. wide, narrowly oval, blunt at the apex, tapering at the base to a short thick stalk. Flowers about 1 in. across, shortly stalked, clustered in the leaf-axils, not fragrant. Petals narrow, numerous (up to thirty), pale greenish yellow.

Native of Japan and Formosa; introduced in 1790. Flowers from March to May. Hardy in Cornwall, Scilly, the south of Ireland, etc., this, near London, is suitable for a wall or specially sheltered spot. The leaves and wood have a strong aromatic and agreeable fragrance. This shrub was long thought to be the "star anise" of the Japanese and Chinese, but that tree is really quite a different species, now known as I. VERUM. (See J. D. Hooker in *Bot. Mag.*, t. 7005.) I. anisatum thrives well at Leonardslee.

I. FLORIDANUM, *Ellis*. POISON BAY

(Bot. Mag., t. 439)

A shrub 6 to 8 ft. high, of compact, much-branched habit. Leaves 3 or 4 ins. long, lance-shaped to narrowly oval, tapered at both ends, entire, leathery, glabrous. Flowers borne in May and June singly near the end of the shoots, each one composed of from twenty to thirty strap-shaped, pointed petals, ¾ to 1 in. long, maroon-purple. Fruit a little over 1 in. wide.

Native of the southern United States; first found by Bartram in W. Florida in 1766, and introduced to England five years later. A small specimen lived outside for a long time without protection in the Coombe Wood nursery, where it stood on a sunny slope, but as a rule near London it requires the shelter of a wall or some winter covering. It is really best adapted for Cornwall and places with a similar climate. The whole plant is permeated with an agreeable aromatic fragrance.

INDIGOFERA. LEGUMINOSÆ

A large genus of herbs and shrubs, notable in containing the indigo plant (I. tinctoria). Of the shrubby species a few may be grown out-of-doors in Britain, but the shoots in our climate, although woody, are usually of only annual duration, unless given the protection of a wall. Leaves pinnate; flowers pea-shaped, and produced in axillary racemes. Pod long and narrow.

The eight species here included are all handsome plants, requiring a good, but not a heavy, loamy soil, and a sunny position. They are increased by cuttings made of half-ripened shoots placed in a close, slightly heated frame. The cuttings should be kept under glass the first winter, remaining in their pots until spring.

I. AMBLYANTHA, *Craib*

A deciduous shrub 5 or 6 ft. high ; young shoots furnished with appressed whitish hairs. Leaves pinnate, 4 to 5 ins. long, composed of seven to eleven leaflets. Leaflets narrowly oval, tapered towards both ends, the apex terminated by a short mucro ; $\frac{1}{2}$ to $1\frac{1}{4}$ ins. long, $\frac{1}{6}$ to $\frac{2}{3}$ in. wide ; the terminal one the largest ; there are pale appressed hairs on both surfaces, more abundant beneath ; stalk $\frac{1}{16}$ in. long. Racemes 3 to $4\frac{1}{2}$ ins. long, slender, erect, produced continuously from the leaf-axils from June until October. Flowers arranged closely on the raceme (ten or so to the inch) each $\frac{1}{4}$ in. long, varying in colour from pale rose to deep pink. Calyx green, hairy, $\frac{1}{8}$ in. long, with awl-shaped lobes of unequal length ; flower-stalk $\frac{1}{6}$ in. long. Pod 1 to $1\frac{3}{4}$ ins. long, $\frac{1}{8}$ in. wide, covered with close down. The flower approximates a pea-flower or broom-flower in structure.

Native of China. Plants at Kew obtained from Messrs Veitch in 1913 were introduced by Purdom from Kansu. Wilson found it previously in W. Hupeh, where it is abundant, and it was originally named from specimens collected by him in that province in June 1907. It is quite a pretty shrub, flowering over a long period when shrubs in bloom are not plentiful. It seems to be hardier than most of the indigoferas and its stems survive winters of at least moderate severity.

I. DECORA, *Lindley*

(Bot. Mag., t. 5063 ; I. incarnata, *Nakai*)

A low deciduous shrub, 1 to 2 ft. high, perhaps more in mild districts. Stems reddish brown, slender, bearing pinnate leaves 4 to 6 ins. long at intervals of 1 to $1\frac{1}{2}$ ins. Leaflets in three and a half to six and a half pairs on each leaf ; 1 to $2\frac{1}{2}$ ins. long, $\frac{1}{2}$ to 1 in. wide ; ovate-lanceolate to oval, with a short, abrupt, bristle-like tip ; glabrous above, furnished beneath with fine hairs attached by the centre. Racemes 6 ins. long, produced in the leaf-axils, twenty to forty flowers on each. Flowers $\frac{5}{8}$ to $\frac{3}{4}$ in. long, each borne on a slender stalk $\frac{1}{4}$ in. long, the oblong standard petal white, lined with pale crimson towards the base ; wing-petals pink. Calyx with broadly triangular lobes.

Native of China and perhaps Japan ; introduced about 1845 by Fortune, who found it growing in the gardens of Shanghai. It is a charming dwarf shrub, flowering freely in July and August, its shoots being mostly cut back to the ground in winter. It is not adapted for rough treatment, and should be given a front place in the shrubbery, or even a place in the rock garden.

I. DIELSIANA, *Craib*

A deciduous shrub 3 to 5 ft. high, of thin diffuse habit ; young shoots angular, thinly furnished at first with pale appressed hairs, afterwards nearly or quite glabrous. Leaves $2\frac{1}{2}$ to 5 ins. long, made up of seven to eleven leaflets which are oval-oblong or obovate, rounded or tapered at the base, rounded at the apex, with a minute prolongation of the midrib there ; $\frac{1}{3}$ to $\frac{7}{8}$ in. long, $\frac{1}{4}$ to $\frac{3}{8}$ in. wide ; pale beneath, with appressed hairs on both surfaces. Racemes sub-erect, up to 5 or 6 ins. long, slender, densely set with blossom. Flowers of an approximately pea-flower shape, nearly ½ in. long, pale rose ; calyx silky, ⅛ in. long, with awl-shaped lobes ; petals downy.

INDIGOFERA DECORA (see p. 143)

Native of Yunnan, China, at 7000 to 8000 ft. altitude ; discovered by Forrest on the eastern flank of the Tali Range in 1906. It has succeeded very well at Kew, commencing to blossom in June and continuing to September by racemes successively produced in the leaf-axils.

I. Gerardiana, *Baker*

(I. Dosua, *Lindley*, in Bot. Reg. 28, t. 57, not *Hamilton*)

A deciduous shrub with downy, slightly-ribbed branches. At Kew, where it is almost invariably cut back to the ground each winter, it sends up a dense thicket of erect, scarcely branched shoots 2 to 4 ft. high, clothed from top to bottom with leaves. Where the climate is milder the shoots survive, and it then becomes a much-branched shrub, perhaps 6 or 8 ft. high. On a wall at Kew it is 10 ft. high. Leaves pinnate, 2 to 4 ins. long, composed of six to ten pairs of leaflets and an odd one; leaflets $\frac{3}{8}$ to $\frac{5}{8}$ in. long, obovate or oval, clothed with grey appressed hairs on both sides, the apex notched or rounded and having a short bristle-like tip. Racemes produced from the leaf-axils in succession from below upwards, on the terminal part of the shoot. They are 3 to 5 ins. long, bearing short-stalked, pea-shaped flowers $\frac{1}{2}$ in. long, rosy purple, two dozen or more on each raceme. Calyx downy, with lance-shaped lobes. Pod deflexed when ripe, $1\frac{1}{2}$ to 2 ins. long, $\frac{1}{8}$ in. wide, cylindric, six- to ten-seeded.

Native of the north-western Himalaya. Commencing to blossom about the end of June, and continuing until the end of September, having also foliage of great beauty and luxuriance, this is one of the most ornamental of late-flowering shrubs. It has the disadvantage of starting late into growth, and it is not until June that the stools become well furnished. For this reason it is not suitable for planting alone in masses. It likes abundant sunshine, and does not flower so freely in dull seasons.

I. hebepetala, *Bentham*

(Bot. Mag., t. 8208)

A deciduous shrub, growing about 4 ft. high at Kew, but considerably taller where it is not cut back during winter; stems glabrous, except when quite young. Leaves pinnate, 7 to 9 ins. long, with usually seven to nine (occasionally eleven) leaflets, which are oblong, broadly oval or slightly ovate, short-stalked; 1 to $2\frac{1}{2}$ ins. long, half as much wide; rounded or notched at the apex, glabrous above, the appressed hairs beneath attached by their middle. Racemes 3 to 9 ins. long, produced from the leaf-axils of the terminal part of the shoot, and developing in succession as it lengthens. Flowers closely set, twenty to sixty on one raceme, each $\frac{1}{2}$ to $\frac{5}{8}$ in. long, the standard petal crimson, wing and keel petals rose-coloured. Pod $1\frac{1}{2}$ to 2 ins. long, cylindric, glabrous, carrying eight to ten seeds.

Native of the north-western Himalaya, where it is widely spread at altitudes of 6000 to 8000 ft. It is strange that so handsome a shrub should be so little known in gardens. The date of its introduction is not recorded, but it has been cultivated at Kew since 1881, when it came with a collection of plants bequeathed by Mr J. C. Joad, a well-known amateur of his time. It produces its richly coloured racemes during August and September. In the open ground its stems rarely survive the winter, and are generally cut back to the old woody stool, a new crop springing up in early summer.

I. Kirilowii, *Maximowicz*

A shrub or sub-shrub, with erect stems, which are slightly hairy when very young, soon glabrous and somewhat angular. Leaves pinnate, 4 to 6 ins. long, composed of usually seven to eleven leaflets which vary in shape from roundish to broadly oval, obovate, or rhomboidal, $\frac{1}{2}$ to $1\frac{1}{4}$ ins. long, wedge-shaped or rounded at the base, tapered at the apex, and terminated by a fine bristle-like elongation of the midrib; bright green above, both surfaces furnished with pale flattened hairs. Racemes erect, about 5 ins. long, the flowers crowded on the upper half; rose-coloured, ¾ in. long; calyx slightly hairy, and with sharp, unequal, lance-shaped lobes. Pod 1½ to 2 ins. long, ⅙ in. wide.

Native of N. China, Manchuria, and Korea; not very common in cultivation. It is allied to I. decora, but is distinguished by the shorter, broader leaves hairy on both sides. The calyx teeth of I. decora are also shorter and broadly triangular and the flowers paler coloured.

I. PENDULA, *Franchet*

(Bot. Mag., t. 8745)

A deciduous shrub of spreading habit, ultimately 8 to 10 ft. high; young shoots furnished with pale hairs flattened to the bark. Leaves pinnate, 8 to 10 ins. long. Leaflets nineteen to twenty-seven to each leaf, oblong to oval, rounded at the apex, where is a short prolongation of the midrib, rounded or tapered at the base; ¾ to 1¼ ins. long, about ½ in. wide; soon glabrous above, furnished beneath with appressed pale hairs. Racemes quite pendulous and very slender, the largest 1½ ft. long, produced during August and September from the leaf-axils of the current year's shoots. Flowers of nearly the common broom shape, very numerous, opening successively from the base onwards, each ⅓ to ½ in. long; petals rosy purple, downy outside; calyx downy, with awl-shaped lobes; flower-stalk very short. Pod 2 ins. long.

Native of Yunnan, China; discovered by Delavay in 1887; introduced by Forrest in 1914. This species is remarkable for the great length and slenderness of its racemes which develop successively along the shoots. At Kew, hard frosts kill it back to the ground, but it springs up again, and as the flowers come on the leafy shoots of the year its blossom is not lost thereby.

I. POTANINII, *Craib*

A deciduous shrub of lax habit 4 ft. or more high; young shoots at first clothed with appressed down. Leaves pinnate, 3 to 6 ins. long, composed of five to nine leaflets; main-stalk downy. Leaflets oval, ovate, or oblong, bluntish at the apex with a short mucro there, tapered or almost rounded at the base; ½ to 1¼ ins. long, ⅛ to ½ in. wide; with appressed hairs on both surfaces; shortly stalked. Flowers rosy pink, ⅜ in. long, of pea-flower shape, produced from June onwards on axillary racemes 2 to 5 ins. long. Calyx hairy, $\frac{1}{10}$ in. long, with five narrow awl-shaped lobes. Seed-pod 1 to 1¼ ins. long.

Native of Kansu; discovered by Potanin, the Russian traveller, in 1885; introduced by W. Purdom to the Arnold Arboretum (No. 539*a*) in 1911, also by Farrer to England later. It is a free-flowering hardy shrub, producing its blossom successively for two or three months. Seeds are now offered in trade catalogues.

ITEA. SAXIFRAGACEÆ

A small genus of deciduous and evergreen small trees or shrubs, one species native of N. America, the others of E. Asia. It belongs to the Escallonia group of Saxifragaceæ, and has alternate leaves, five-parted flowers, but differs from Escallonia itself in the narrow petals, and all other allied hardy shrubs like Philadelphus, Deutzia, Hydrangea, etc., by its alternate leaves. The only genuinely hardy species is I. virginica.

I. ILICIFOLIA, *Oliver*

An evergreen shrub of bushy habit, said to attain a height of 18 ft. occasionally in a wild state, and already 6 to 12 ft. high in this country; stems quite glabrous. Leaves holly-like but thinner, broadly oval, 2 to 4 ins. long, 1½ to 2¾ ins. wide, the apex short-pointed; dark glossy green above, paler below, both surfaces glabrous, except for tufts of hair in the axils of the chief veins beneath; margins armed with stiff spiny teeth; stalk ¼ to ½ in. long. Racemes pendulous, arching, 6 to 12 ins. long, ½ in. wide, crowded with greenish white flowers; petals narrow, ⅙ in. long. Blossoms in August.

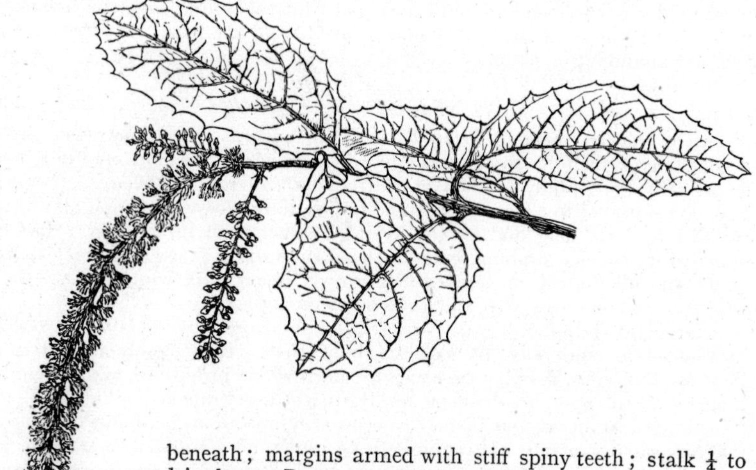

ITEA ILICIFOLIA

Native of W. China; discovered by Henry, and first raised from seeds sent by him to the late Lord Kesteven, with whom it flowered at Casewick in 1895. It is not hardy at Kew except against a wall, but is very suitable for the rather warmer parts of the British Isles. At Borde Hill, Sussex, there is a bush about 12 ft. high and as much wide, in perfect health. Its foliage is handsome and its racemes elegant. Easily increased by cuttings of moderately ripened shoots.

I. VIRGINICA, *Linnæus* (Plate 13)

(Bot. Mag. t. 2409)

A deciduous shrub, 3 to 5 ft. high, with erect, glabrous clustered stems, branched only towards the top. Leaves narrowly oval or oblong, tapering at both ends, 1½ to 3½ ins. long, ¾ to 1¼ ins. wide; bright green and glabrous above, paler and slightly hairy beneath, chiefly on the midrib and veins; margins set with fine, regular teeth; stalk ⅛ to ¼ in. long, downy, grooved on the upper side. Flowers fragrant, creamy white, ⅓ to ½ in. across, produced very close together on slender, erect, cylindrical, downy racemes 3 to 6 ins. long and about ⅝ in. through, terminating short, leafy twigs; each flower is on a downy stalk, ⅛ in. long. Petals narrow, ¼ in. long; calyx downy, with five linear, pointed lobes half as long as the petals. Seed-vessels brown, dry, ¼ in. long, downy.

Native of the eastern United States, usually affecting moist places; introduced in 1744. This is a pretty shrub, and useful in flowering during July. The leaves often remain on the plant until December. It sends up its erect, slender stems one summer, which branch copiously near the top the next, each twig producing a raceme at the end. It may be increased by means of cuttings made of moderately ripened wood in July or August, and given gentle heat; but for ordinary garden purposes division of the old plants is quicker and usually sufficient. Pruning should consist of entirely removing sufficient of the older stems to afford light and space for the young ones, by means of which the plant is continually renewing itself from the base. It loves a good soil and abundant moisture

I. YUNNANENSIS, *Franchet*

An evergreen shrub 6 to 10 ft. high, in general appearance very much resembling I. ilicifolia in the holly-like leaves, which are not, on the whole, so strongly and spinily toothed or so frequently of rounded shape; they are 2 to 4 ins. long, 1¼ to 2 ins. wide; spine-tipped, dark glossy green and glabrous; stalk, ¼ to ⅝ in. long and on the average longer than in ilicifolia. Flowers crowded on slender, arching, cylindrical racemes up to 7 ins. long, each flower (stalk and all) only ¼ in. long with narrowly linear, dull white petals. In a wild state it flowers in May and June, later in cultivation.

Native of Yunnan, China; originally discovered by Delavay in 1883; introduced to cultivation by Forrest about 1918. It is closely related to I. ilicifolia, but on the average the leaves are narrower in proportion to their length, longer-stalked and less conspicuously toothed. Franchet alludes to the "included" stamens, but in both species they appear to be about as long as the very narrow petals. It requires to be grown on a south wall at Kew. It does not promise to be any improvement on I. ilicifolia, especially as one sees the latter at Borde Hill, Sussex, laden every summer with graceful blossom.

IVA ORARIA, *Bartlett*. MARSH ELDER. COMPOSITÆ

(I. frutescens, *Hort.*)

A sub-shrub with stems somewhat fleshy, 3 to 10 ft. high, branched at the upper parts; shoots minutely downy. Leaves nearly stalkless, oblong-lanceolate, pointed, rather strongly toothed, cuneate, 4 to 6 ins. long, 1 to 2 ins. wide, three-veined, being reduced in size upwards until, in the flowering parts, they become small and linear. Inflorescence terminal, more or less pyramidal; flower-heads greenish white, ⅙ in. wide, hemispheric, axillary, each consisting of staminate and a few pistillate flowers and beset by four or five broadly ovate bracts.

A native of the S. United States; introduced in 1711. It is mostly found growing in salt marshes and muddy sea-shores, and although quite hardy has little to recommend it for gardens.

JAMESIA AMERICANA, *Torrey and Gray*. SAXIFRAGACEÆ

(Bot. Mag., t. 6142)

A deciduous shrub, 4 to 7 ft. high, of bushy, rounded habit, and usually more in diameter than it is high; branches stout, stiff, very pithy, covered with a bright brown, downy bark, which afterwards peels off in papery flakes. Leaves opposite; on the barren shoots ovate, 1 to 3 ins. long, $\frac{3}{4}$ to 2 ins. wide; coarsely and regularly toothed, with scattered, flattened hairs above; downy, almost felted beneath; on the flowering twigs the leaves are much smaller, and often of more oval outline; stalks

JAMESIA AMERICANA

downy, $\frac{1}{4}$ to $\frac{3}{4}$ in. long. Flowers slightly fragrant, pure white, $\frac{1}{2}$ in. across, produced during May in erect, terminal pyramidal panicles 1 to $2\frac{1}{2}$ ins. long and broad; petals five, oblong; calyx woolly, with five-pointed ovate lobes; stamens ten.

Native of western N. America; introduced to Kew in 1862. This interesting and pretty shrub was first found in 1820 by Dr Edwin James, after whom it was named; he was then acting as botanist and historian to Major Long's Expedition to the Rocky Mountains. It can be propagated by cuttings, and, given a sunny position, and an open, not too rich soil, thrives excellently. It is the only species of the genus. Var. ROSEA, *Purpus*, found in S. Nevada, I have not seen. Flowers pink.

JASMINUM. JASMINE. OLEACEÆ

Of the large number of species belonging to this genus (about 200) only about a dozen are cultivated permanently in the open air in Britain. They are either climbers or shrubs of loose, spreading habit, and are either evergreen or deciduous; leaves alternate or opposite, trifoliolate or pinnate. Flowers yellow or white, rarely red, usually fragrant; corolla with a slender, tapering tube, expanding at the mouth into normally five (sometimes more) spreading lobes. Stamens two. The berry-like fruits are normally twin, but frequently only one develops.

Provided the climatic conditions are suitable, the jasmines are easily cultivated; they like a good loamy soil and a sunny position. All are easily increased by cuttings of moderately ripened wood. Nudiflorum, officinale, and floridum are seen at their best on walls; primulinum will in most places need winter protection.

J. BEESIANUM, *Forrest and Diels*

(Bot. Mag., t. 9097)

A deciduous climber 10 ft. or more high; shoots minutely downy when young especially at the joints, slender, grooved. Leaves opposite, ovate to lanceolate, $1\frac{1}{4}$ to 2 ins. long, $\frac{1}{3}$ to $\frac{3}{4}$ in. wide, dark green above, greyish green beneath with short down on both sides, at least when young; stalk $\frac{1}{8}$ in. or less long. Flowers usually in threes produced in the terminal leaf-axils of short, leafy twigs. Each flower is $\frac{3}{8}$ to $\frac{1}{2}$ in. wide, rose to carmine (also, according to Wilson, rarely pale rose to white); the corolla is tubular at the base, hairy in the throat, spreading at the mouth into usually six rounded lobes, fragrant. Fruit a rather flattened, globose berry, black, $\frac{1}{2}$ in. wide.

Native of Szechuen and Yunnan, China; introduced by Forrest in 1906 for the firm of Bees Ltd. I have never seen it noticeably attractive in flower, but it produces large crops of shining black berries which give a fine effect and remain on the branches well into winter. It has been very finely shown at Vincent Square from the Cambridge Botanic Garden. Quite hardy.

J. FARRERI, *Gilmour*. FARRER'S JASMINE

(Bot. Mag., t. 9351)

A wide-spreading evergreen shrub 6 or 8 ft. high, of luxuriantly leafy habit; young shoots angled, at first downy and purplish, then green. Leaves alternate, 2 to 5 ins. long, made up of three leaflets which are ovate-lanceolate, slender-pointed, rounded, or (the side ones) obliquely tapered at the base; the terminal leaflet is up to 4 ins. long and $\frac{3}{4}$ to $1\frac{5}{8}$ ins. wide, stalked; the side ones are much smaller and stalkless; in both the upper surface is dull and at first purplish green, wrinkled, slightly downy when young; undersurface downy, especially on the midrib and veins; main leaf-stalk $\frac{1}{2}$ to 1 in. long purplish, downy. Flowers bright yellow, not fragrant, produced in May and

June (and less abundantly later) as many as a dozen together in terminal cymes. Corolla ¾ in. long, ⅝ in. wide, its lobes ovate. Calyx funnel-shaped, downy, the five triangular teeth shorter than the tube, hairy; the whole calyx is about one-sixth the length of the corolla.

In the original issue of the third volume this jasmine appeared as "J. Giraldii," under which name it has been cultivated in gardens. Mr J. S. L. Gilmour has, however, found that, although closely akin, it is distinct from that species (see *Bot. Mag.*, *loc. cit.*). It was discovered in Upper Burma and introduced to cultivation by Farrer in 1919. The description given above was made from a fine bush growing in Col. Stern's garden at Highdown, near Worthing, which, in 1931, was about 6 ft. high and flowers very freely every May and June. It is related to J. revolutum, but differs in its downy character and almost invariably trifoliolate leaves. Quite evergreen at Highdown. It should be hardy in all but the most inclement parts of Britain.

J. FLORIDUM, *Bunge*

(Bot. Mag., t. 6719)

A nearly evergreen shrub of rambling habit; branches angled, glabrous. Leaves alternate; mostly composed of three leaflets, but occasionally five, never apparently more. Leaflets oval, sometimes obovate or ovate, ½ to 1½ ins. long, ¼ to ⅝ in. wide, pointed, glabrous. Flowers yellow, in terminal cymose clusters, usually produced from July onwards; corolla ½ to ¾ in. long, the lobes five, pointed. Calyx-lobes five, about ⅛ in. long, awl-shaped. Fruit about the size of a small pea, black.

Native of China; cultivated in that country and Japan; introduced by the Earl of Ilchester about the middle of last century. It was originally discovered in North China, but Henry found it frequently in Central China, about Ichang. It is closely akin to J. revolutum, having alternate leaves and yellow flowers, but differs in the longer, more slender calyx-lobes, and in never having more than five leaflets to one leaf. It has long been grown on a wall at Kew, but is not so hardy as J. revolutum.

J. FRUTICANS, *Linnæus*

(Bot. Mag., t. 461)

A semi-evergreen shrub, producing a dense mass of slender, erect stems from 3 to 5 ft. high, but thrice as much against a wall; young shoots angular, glabrous. Leaves alternate; composed of three leaflets on a common stalk about ⅙ in. long, or of one leaflet only. Leaflets narrow-oblong or linear-obovate, ¼ to ¾ in. long, one-third as much wide; tapering at the base, more rounded at the apex, deep green, glabrous on both surfaces, but edged with minute hairs. On strong sucker shoots, the leaflets are occasionally twice as large. Flowers yellow, produced from June onwards, usually in threes or fives at the end of short twigs. Corolla ⅝ in. long and wide; calyx bell-shaped, with five slender lobes. Fruit globose, shining black, the size of a pea.

Native of S. Europe, N. Africa, and Asia Minor; cultivated since the middle of the sixteenth century, perhaps before. The largest plant I have seen is growing on a house front between Kew Bridge and the entrance to Kew Gardens; it covers the wall up to 10 or 15 ft. high. On the hills above Hyères, I have seen it growing abundantly and quite handsome in the fall of the year by reason of the crop of shining black berries. There the shrubs are mostly 1½ to 3 ft. high. In hot seasons it fruits freely in England.

J. NUDIFLORUM, *Lindley*

(Bot. Mag., t. 4649; J. Sieboldianum, *Blume*)

A deciduous shrub of rambling habit, growing 12 to 15 ft. high against a wall, with long, slender, pendulous, glabrous, four-angled branchlets. Leaves opposite, composed of three leaflets borne on a common stalk about ¼ in. long. Leaflets oval-oblong, ½ to 1¼ ins. long, one-third to half as wide, tapered at both ends, deep lustrous green, not toothed, but furnished at the margin when young with tiny hairs. Flowers bright yellow, ¾ to 1 in. diameter, produced from November to February; they are solitary on stalks ¼ in. long, clothed with several small, narrow, green bracts. Corolla tubular at the base and nearly 1 in. long, spreading into six divisions. Calyx-lobes six, linear, pointed.

Native of China; introduced by Fortune for the Horticultural Society in 1844. A very hardy plant, of great value in gardens because of its habit of flowering during the very darkest months. No plant does so much to lighten up in midwinter dull suburban streets of London, and the fact that it will thrive in such places adds much to its worth. It blossoms best against a sunny wall, but, after warm summers especially, flowers very freely in the open ground. A pleasing arrangement is to plant it in association with Berberis Aquifolium, against whose purplish winter-shade of leaf the leafless flower-laden sprays of this jasmine are peculiarly bright and effective.

Var. AUREUM has leaflets blotched with yellow.

J. OFFICINALE, *Linnæus*. COMMON JASMINE

(Bot. Mag., t. 31)

A deciduous, or nearly deciduous, climbing shrub, making shoots 6 ft. or more long in one season, and ultimately, if carefully trained, reaching 40 ft. in height; young shoots very slender, angled, glabrous or soon becoming so. Leaves opposite, pinnate, composed of five, seven, or nine leaflets, which are ½ to 2½ ins. long, ⅙ to 1 in. wide; slightly downy at or about the margin, the terminal one much the largest and stalked; side one stalkless. Flowers white, deliciously fragrant, produced from June until October in a terminal cluster of cymes, each cyme with three or five blossoms. Corolla ⅞ in. long and about the same across the four or five spreading lobes. Calyx-lobes almost thread-like, ⅓ in. long; flower-stalk about 1 in. long. Fruit not regularly or freely produced, black, ⅓ in. long, solitary or twin.

Var. AFFINE (J. affine, *Carrière*).—A form with larger pink flowers and broader calyx-lobes. (Bot. Reg. xxxi., t. 26.)

Var. AUREUM.—Leaflets rather handsomely blotched with yellow, but it is scarcely as hardy as the green type. Loudon mentions a double-flowered variety, but this I have not seen.

Native of Persia, N.W. India, China. The common jasmine (or jessamine) has been cultivated from time immemorial in Britain, and its fragrance and beauty have given it a place in English gardens as secure as that of the lilac or lavender. In the north it is hardy only against a wall or on a roof, but in the south it grows well in the open, where if supported in the early stages and pruned back every spring it will make a self-supporting bush. But perhaps its charm is greatest when allowed to form a loose tangle on a house front, as one may often see it in cottage gardens between London and the south coast. Even in winter the tangle of young stems has a cheerful green effect. A popular perfume is extracted from the flowers.

J. PARKERI, *Dunn*. PARKER'S JASMINE

An evergreen shrub from 6 to 12 ins. high, of tufted habit; young shoots grooved, very minutely downy, becoming glabrous. Leaves alternate, pinnate, ½ to 1 in. long, made up of three or five leaflets. Leaflets oval or ovate, pointed, tapered at the base, not toothed, stalkless, ⅛ to ⅜ in. long. Flowers yellow, solitary, terminal or produced from the leaf-axils. Corolla-tube slender, ½ to ¾ in. long, ½ in. across the six spreading lobes. Calyx cup-shaped, scarcely ⅛ in. long, minutely downy, five-ribbed and with five awl-shaped lobes. Fruit ⅙ in. wide, two-lobed, globose, greenish white, translucent.

Native of the Chambra State, N.W. India; discovered by Mr R. N. Parker in 1919, introduced in 1923. Mr Parker observes that it flowers in June (as it does also with us) and grows on rocks or hot, dry banks. Except when trailing over a rock it is never more than 12 ins. high. It is a curious little jasmine, often forming in a wild state a ball of densely packed twigs a few inches wide. Under cultivation, with better soil, it grows more freely, and makes a charming little shrub for the Alpine garden. Quite hardy at Kew. Its dwarf habit and solitary flowers make it very distinct.

J. POLYANTHUM, *Franchet*

(Revue Horticole, 1891, fig. 69; Bot. Mag., t. 9545)

An evergreen climber growing 6 to 10 ft. high; young shoots slightly warted, not downy. Leaves opposite, 3 to 5 ins. long, pinnate, composed mostly of five or seven leaflets, the lowest pair rather near the stem. The side leaflets are ovate, ½ to 1½ ins. long, very shortly stalked; the terminal one lanceolate, 1½ to 3 ins. long, more slenderly pointed; all are of thin texture, quite glabrous except for a tuft of down at the vein-axils beneath, obliquely rounded or cordate at the base. Panicles axillary, many-flowered, 2 to 4 ins. long, glabrous. Flowers very fragrant, white inside, rose-coloured outside; the slender tube of the corolla ¾ in. long, spreading at the mouth into five obovate lobes, giving it a diameter of ¾ in. Calyx ⅛ in. long with five erect, awl-shaped teeth nearly as long as the tube.

Native of Yunnan, China; discovered in 1883 by Père Delavay. Forrest found it flowering between May and August 1906 in the Tali valley and along the eastern flank of the Tali Range up to 8000 ft. altitude. Presumably the plants in cultivation were introduced by him. As the specific name implies, it is free-flowering, and the rosy colouring outside the corolla is unusual in the hardier jasmines. It must have wall protection in a climate like that of Kew and is no doubt better suited for the south and west. Sometimes thirty to forty flowers are borne on a single panicle.

J. PRIMULINUM, *Hemsley* (Plate 14)

(Bot. Mag., t. 7981; J. Mesnyi, *Hance*)

An evergreen, rambling shrub, probably 6 to 10 ft. high, forming a dense interlacing mass of branches; young stems four-angled, glabrous. Leaves opposite; composed of three leaflets borne on a common stalk about ⅓ in. long. Leaflets lance-shaped or narrowly oval, 1 to 3 ins. long, ⅓ to ¾ in. wide, short-stalked (the side ones smaller), dark glossy green. Flowers 1½ to 1¾ ins. diameter, bright yellow, produced in spring and summer, solitary on stalks ½ to 1½ ins. long, and furnished with tiny, green, leaflike bracts. Corolla often semi-double, composed of from six to ten divisions, each ⅓ to ½ in. wide, rounded at the end. Calyx-lobes usually five or six, narrow, pointed, ¼ in. long, glabrous or minutely ciliate.

Native of W. China; introduced by Wilson for Messrs Veitch in 1900. As the plant had never been found bearing seed, the collector was obliged to send home living plants by an overland route to Hong-Kong, and thence to England. This jessamine is certainly the most striking of all those that can be grown out-of-doors anywhere in this country, but it is only likely to thrive in the very mildest spots. At Kew, even against a wall, it succumbs to severe frost. The best method of cultivating it is, apparently, to grow it in pots out-of-doors, exposed to full sunshine and generously treated at the root, then to house it and keep it as dry as possible without losing its foliage during the winter. It then makes a fine display in spring. It appears to have found acceptable conditions in middle and south Italy, where I have seen it profusely in flower. It is closely allied to J. nudiflorum in all essential characters, but is much larger in all its parts.

J. REVOLUTUM, *Sims*

(Bot. Mag., t. 1731; Bot. Reg., t. 178)

A nearly evergreen shrub, not climbing, but of lax, spreading habit; stems not downy, slightly angular, the stoutest among cultivated jasmines. Leaves alternate, composed of usually three or five, sometimes seven leaflets, which are oval or ovate, tapered to both ends, the side ones $\frac{3}{4}$ to $1\frac{1}{2}$ ins. long, the terminal one up to 2 ins. or more long, and $1\frac{1}{4}$ ins. wide; all of a dull, very dark green above, paler and brighter green beneath; stalk of terminal leaflet up to $\frac{1}{2}$ in. long; of the others, very short or absent. Flowers yellow, fragrant, produced in terminal corymbs of six, twelve, or more together. On very vigorous shoots the terminal inflorescence is augmented by two or three axillary ones, making the whole cluster forty- to fifty-flowered, and about 5 ins. across. Corolla $\frac{3}{4}$ to 1 in. across; calyx-lobes about one-third as long as the cup, triangular.

Native of Afghanistan and the north-west Himalaya. It varies somewhat in size of leaf, and the jasmines known in gardens as J. Reevesii and J. triumphans are this species. It is nearly allied to J. Wallichianum (*q.v.*), and like it is sometimes cut back in winter, but as it flowers from June onwards on the shoots of the year this is not of much consequence. Still, a sheltered spot should be given to it. Belonging to the same group of alternate-leaved jasmines with very short calyx-lobes is J. HUMILE, *Linnæus*, a native of S.E. Europe. It is a dwarf plant with nearly always ternate leaves, and two to six flowers on a stalk. It was cultivated by Tradescant in 1656, but being rather tender, and not so ornamental as either revolutum or Wallichianum, has probably disappeared from cultivation. It used to be known as "Italian jasmine" (Bot. Reg., t. 350).

J. STEPHANENSE, *Lemoine*

A hybrid between J. Beesianum and J. officinale, raised by Messrs Lemoine and Son of Nancy, about 1918. It is a vigorous climber with slender, glabrous, angled young shoots. The leaves vary from the simple ovate-lanceolate ones of J. Beesianum to the pinnate ones of J. officinale, but the leaflets rarely, if ever, number more than five to each leaf, the terminal leaflet the largest; they are dull green above, slightly downy beneath; stalk $\frac{1}{4}$ to $\frac{1}{2}$ in. long. Flowers borne in terminal clusters, fragrant, soft pale pink. The slender tube of the corolla is about $\frac{1}{2}$ in. long and the flower is about the same in width across the rounded, auricled lobes. The bell-shaped base of the calyx is $\frac{1}{8}$ in. long, downy, with erect awl-shaped lobes of about the same length.

At Kew this jasmine flowers in June and July. It is attractive enough to have been given an Award of Merit at Vincent Square, 6th July 1937.

J. Wallichianum, *Lindley*

(Bot. Reg., t. 1409)

A nearly evergreen shrub, with slender, angled, glabrous branchlets. Leaves alternate, composed of seven to thirteen leaflets which are lanceolate to ovate, taper-pointed, $\frac{1}{2}$ to $1\frac{1}{2}$ ins. long, $\frac{1}{4}$ in. or more wide; the terminal one much the longest and largest, dark green; both blade and stalk sometimes more or less downy. Flowers yellow, $\frac{5}{8}$ in. long, $\frac{1}{2}$ in. across the rounded, spreading lobes; produced in a cluster at and near the end of the shoot, solitary on the stalk, or often in triplets. Calyx-lobes about one-third as long as the cup, triangular, downy. (Syn. J. humile glabrum.)

Native of Nepal; introduced about 1812. It is most nearly akin to J. revolutum, differing in the greater number and smaller size of the leaflets, in the few flowers on the cyme, and in being less robust. Both these species differ from the two other alternate-leaved jasmines in the very short, comparatively broad calyx-lobes.

JUBÆA spectabilis, *Humboldt, Bonpland and Kunth.* Wine Palm. Palmaceæ

(Gardeners' Chronicle, 2nd Nov. 1895, figs. 89, 90)

A tall evergreen tree, with a trunk 40 to 60 ft. high and 15 ft. in girth, the stem naked up to the leaves, but covered with small cracks running lengthwise. Leaves pinnate, up to 15 ft. long in adult specimens, the upper ones more or less erect, the lower ones horizontal; leaflets ("pinnæ") 1 to 2 ft. long; the whole forming a dense hemispherical head of foliage. On young plants, of course, the leaves are much smaller and only 3 or 4 ft. long; they become larger as the tree grows older, and reach their maximum size just before the trunk commences to form and grow in height.

Native of Chile, where, up to early in the nineteenth century, it was very plentiful. Darwin, in his *Voyage of the Beagle* (p. 312), records that on one estate alone it numbered hundreds of thousands. That was early in the nineteenth century; now it is comparatively rare, having been cut down for the sake of its sugary sap which, when concentrated by boiling, acquires a treacle-like consistency and taste. It seems that the sap can only be acquired by felling the palm and collecting it at the upper end of the trunk, from which it continues to flow for a considerable time. A large tree will in the end yield as much as 90 gallons. The boiled sap is known to the Chileans as "palm honey" and is much esteemed by them.

There is a magnificent example of this palm in the Temperate House at Kew, its trunk 10 ft. in girth and some 45 ft. high, the spread of its foliage 30 ft. Mr E. Thurston does not record the species in his *Trees and Shrubs of Cornwall*, but I believe there are many places where it would succeed in that county. Mr L. de Rothschild had it in the open air for several winters at Exbury, Hants. The late Mr Irwin Lynch, who left Kew in 1879, records in the *Journal of the Royal Horticultural Society*, vol. xxxviii., p. 202, that a fine specimen once existed near the principal entrance to the gardens from Kew Green. It had disappeared before I entered Kew in 1883, and subsequent attempts to grow it in the open air have failed. Magnificent trees may be seen in several gardens on the shores of Lake Como.

JUGLANS. Walnut. JUGLANDACEÆ

The walnuts, of which eight or nine species are in cultivation, are deciduous trees, or occasionally shrubs, with pinnate leaves aromatically scented. Flowers unisexual, both sexes on the same plant; the male flowers very numerous in slender, pendulous catkins, with many stamens produced in the axil of a lobed scale; female flowers few. The male catkins (rather elegant in the Asiatic species) are borne towards the end of the previous year's shoots; the nut-bearing spike terminates the young shoot of the current season. Fruit a hard-shelled nut, surrounded by a thin or fleshy husk. The cultivated species are from Europe, N. Asia, and N. America, but two or three species of which little is known are found in S. America. The only other genus of trees with which Juglans is likely to be confused is Carya (the hickories), but among other differences, Juglans is distinguished by the pith of the young shoots being in thin transverse plates, thus dividing the hollow portion of the shoot into a series of chambers, and by the unbranched male catkins. In Carya the pith is continuous, and the male catkins three-branched.

In gardens, Juglans is seldom represented except by the common walnut, grown for its nuts, and by the black walnut, grown for its stately form and noble foliage. The striking group of North Asiatic species—cordiformis, cathayensis, stenocarpa, etc.—is scarcely known, yet in a young state their leaves are 2 to 3 ft. long. Hopes have been entertained that the same group may prove of value for their edible nuts, which they bear, many together, in clusters, but I do not think that they, or any other species except the common one, will ever be worth growing for the fruit. J. nigra and J. regia both yield a valuable timber, but the former never appears to have been given a fair trial under favourable conditions as a forest tree in Britain.

Walnuts should always, if possible, be grown from seed, and as they bear transplanting badly, should be given permanent places early. The nuts should be sown as soon as ripe, and not allowed to become dry. All the species like a deep loamy soil. The named varieties of common walnut are propagated by grafting on the type. Some of the species are tender in a young state and apt to be cut by late frost, thus rendering them bushy-topped. It is, in consequence, sometimes necessary to tie up a shoot to form a new leader. The walnut flowers have no colour beauty, and are fertilised by wind; hybrids have been obtained from species growing near to each other. The following have been named:—

J. ALATA, *Carrière* (J. cinerea regia).—Young wood downy. Leaflets usually nine, resembling those of J. regia, but slightly toothed; downy beneath.

J. PYRIFORMIS, *Carrière* (J. nigra regia).—Leaves of nine to thirteen leaflets, finely toothed, smooth beneath, and generally intermediate between the parents; fruit more resembling that of J. regia. (Syn. J. intermedia.)

J. VILMORINIANA, *Carrière* (J. nigra x regia).—Foliage as in J. pyriformis, but the fruit more resembling that of J. nigra. The original of this hybrid is now a noble tree in Mr de Vilmorin's garden at Verrières-le-Buisson, near Paris. It was planted where it stands, in 1816, to commemorate the birth of an eldest son in the de Vilmorin family, and when I saw it some years ago it was over 90 ft. high, and 10 ft. in girth of trunk.

J. CALIFORNICA, *S. Watson*

Under this name two trees, now considered distinct enough to rank as full species, were included by S. Watson. The true J. californica is a large shrub or small, round-headed tree whose leaves are made up of eleven to fifteen leaflets each 1 to $2\frac{1}{2}$ ins. long, $\frac{1}{3}$ to $\frac{3}{4}$ in. wide, and glabrous. Fruit globose, $\frac{1}{3}$ to $\frac{3}{4}$ in. wide, enclosing a nut deeply grooved lengthwise. Coming from S. California it is not hardy with us.

The other, J. HINDSII, *Rehder* (J. californica Hindsii, *Jepson*, is a native of N. California and is a tree 50 to 70 ft. high (occasionally more) with fifteen to nineteen leaflets to each leaf. The entire leaf is 9 to 12 ins. long, the leaflets 2 to 4 ins. long, $\frac{3}{4}$ to 1 in. wide, coarsely toothed; downy on the midrib and veins beneath. Young shoots and leafstalks very downy. Fruit globose, downy, 1 to 2 ins. wide; nut, thick-shelled, shallowly-grooved.

J. Hindsii was introduced to Kew in 1926 and is hardy there. It is related to J. rupestris which differs in having even more (up to twenty-three) leaflets, narrower and more finely toothed. It is much planted in Californian towns as a street tree.

J. CATHAYENSIS, *Dode*

A tree up to 70 ft. high, with thick young shoots covered the first year with very viscid, gland-tipped hairs, as are also the main-stalks of the leaves, the fruits, and fruit-stalks. Leaves 2 to 3 ft. long, with eleven to seventeen leaflets, which are ovate-oblong, 3 to 6 (occasionally 8) ins. long, half as wide; obliquely rounded or heart-shaped at the base, taper-pointed, finely toothed, dark green and downy above, paler and with starry down beneath; midribs with gland-tipped hairs like those of the main leaf-stalk. Male flowers in pendulous, cylindrical catkins 9 to 15 ins. long. Fruits clustered at the end of a stout stalk about 6 ins. long, egg-shaped, $1\frac{1}{2}$ to $1\frac{3}{4}$ ins. long, pointed. Nut of similar shape, sharply pointed, six- to eight-angled, the angles spiny-toothed; rind $\frac{1}{8}$ to $\frac{1}{6}$ in. thick.

Native of Central and W. China, where it is common. Introduced by Wilson in 1903 to the Coombe Wood nursery, where young trees 8 or 10 ft. high have borne fruits. Owing to the thickness of the shell, the nuts are of small value for eating, although the kernel is of good flavour. It is a promising, fine-foliaged tree of the same type as J. mandshurica; they differ chiefly in the fruit, but the present species is a better grower.

J. CINEREA, *Linnæus*. BUTTER-NUT

A tree 50 to 60, rarely 100 ft. high, usually forming a wide-spreading head of branches; young wood covered with a dense, rusty brown, clammy felt, which partly falls away by the end of the season. Leaves 10 to 20 ins. long, composed of seven to nineteen leaflets, which are 2 to 5 ins. long, $\frac{3}{4}$ to $2\frac{1}{4}$ ins. wide; oblong lance-shaped, taper-pointed, obliquely rounded at the base, finely and regularly toothed; upper surface at first hairy, especially on the midrib; lower surface covered with soft, star-shaped hairs; common-stalk thickly furnished with gland-tipped, sticky hairs. Male flowers in catkins 2 to 4 ins. long. Fruits three to five in a drooping cluster, each tapering to a point at the top, rounded at the base, $1\frac{1}{2}$ to $2\frac{1}{2}$ ins. long, covered with sticky hairs. Nut 1 to $1\frac{1}{2}$ ins. long, with a short point; kernel sweet, oily.

Native of eastern N. America; introduced early in the seventeenth century. Although so long cultivated, this tree is comparatively rare in Britain, and is evidently not so well adapted for our climate as the black walnut, rarely bearing fruit. As a small tree it is quite handsome, but grows slowly. According to Elwes, the largest tree in the country, at Coolhurst,

Horsham, is a little over 50 ft. high. From J. nigra it differs in its pointed,

JUGLANS CORDIFORMIS (see p. 159)

more numerous fruits, its more downy leaves, and by a transverse tuft of down between the scar left by each fallen leaf and the bud above it.

J. CORDIFORMIS, *Maximowicz*

A tree up to 50 ft. high; young shoots stout, covered with brownish glandular hairs. Leaves as in J. mandshurica and Sieboldiana, except that the leaflets are somewhat more distinctly heart-shaped at the base, but not enough to afford a reliable means of distinction. Male catkins often 1 ft. in length. Fruit globose, 1½ ins. diameter, produced in dense clusters of ten or more. Nut 1¼ ins. long, very distinct in shape; it has a broad, rounded, heart-shaped base, and a slender pointed apex, and is much flattened.

Native of Japan, but apparently uncommon in a wild state. Although scarcely distinguishable from its allies, J. Sieboldiana and J. mandshurica, in growth, it is very distinct from them in the shape of the nuts, which are offered for sale in the markets of Japanese towns. In my experience this is the best grower of this group of walnuts. A tree at Kew about thirty years old is 30 ft. high, and produces both male and female inflorescence freely. The former are very striking, although yellowish green. Nuts 1¼ ins. long form on this tree and occasionally mature. It is one of the most attractive of pinnate-leaved trees.

J. MANDSHURICA, *Maximowicz*

A tree 50 to 70 ft. high; young shoots very stout, and like the common stalk of the leaf, clothed with brown, glandular hairs. Leaves 1½ to 2 ft. (in vigorous young trees 3 ft.) long, composed of eleven to nineteen leaflets, which are oblong, taper-pointed, finely toothed, obliquely rounded or slightly heart-shaped at the base; 3 to 7 ins. long, 1¼ to 2½ ins. wide. When young, both surfaces are furnished, the lower one especially, with starry tufts of down, much of which afterwards falls away from the upper side. Male catkins 4 to 10 ins. long, slender, pendulous. Fruits clustered several on a stalk, roundish ovoid, 1¾ ins. long, covered with sticky down. Nut deeply pitted and grooved, 1½ ins. long, abruptly pointed at the top.

Native of Manchuria, especially in the regions of the Amur and Ussuri rivers, and of N. China; first introduced by Maximowicz to St Petersburg. As a young tree it is, like J. cordiformis and J. Sieboldiana, remarkably striking in the size of its leaves. It is closely allied to the latter, but in my experience does not succeed so well; botanically, the chief difference is in the form of the nuts, and the leaves of J. mandshurica are distinctly more slenderly pointed.

J. NIGRA, *Linnæus*. BLACK WALNUT

A tree 80 to over 100 ft. high, with a wide-spreading head and a tall dark trunk, with deeply furrowed bark; young shoots downy. Leaves 1 to 2 ft. long, composed of eleven to twenty-three leaflets, the terminal odd one often absent. Leaflets fragrant when rubbed; 2 to 5 ins. long, ¾ to 2 ins. wide; ovate or oblong lance-shaped, obliquely rounded at the base, long and taper-pointed, unevenly toothed, glossy and glabrous above except when quite young, downy beneath; common stalk minutely downy. Male catkins 2 to 4 ins. long. Fruit globose or slightly tapered at the base, solitary on the stalk or in pairs, 1½ to 2 ins. thick, not downy. Nut 1 to 1½ ins. across, broader than long.

Native of the eastern and central United States; introduced early in the seventeenth century. Next to the common walnut this is the best known in the genus. Its nuts are of no value as food, but it is a more ornamental tree than J. regia, thriving almost as well in this country as in any of its native haunts. Trees over 100 ft. exist; the largest I have seen stands in Marble Hill Park, a magnificent tree with a trunk 5 yds. in girth. As a young tree the black walnut is particularly handsome, with its shapely pyramidal habit and large pinnate leaves. One of the most valuable of the world's timber trees, it is now becoming rare in a wild state.

Var. ALBURYENSIS, *Jackson*, an interesting variation from the type, grows at Albury Park, near Guildford; this bears its fruits in clusters like J. cinerea, sometimes as many as six together, and it is also distinct in its pendulous branches.

J. REGIA, *Linnæus*. COMMON WALNUT

A tree 60 to 100 ft. high, with a rounded, spreading head of branches; the bark of the upper branches smooth and ash-coloured; young shoots without down. Leaves somewhat acrid-scented when rubbed, usually 8 to 12 ins. long, on vigorous young growths 18 ins.; composed mostly of five or seven, sometimes nine, rarely eleven or thirteen leaflets. These are oval or ovate, shortly pointed, margins entire; terminal leaflet the largest, 3 to 6 ins. long, the basal pair less than half the length and width; both surfaces glabrous except for small tufts of hair in the vein-axils beneath. Male catkins 2 to 4 ins. long. Fruit green, glabrous, 1½ to 2 ins. across.

Native of E. Europe and Asia Minor to Afghanistan. The date of its introduction is not known, but it has existed in this country for many centuries. As an ornamental tree the common walnut is not so striking as several other species. It is chiefly grown for its nuts and for its soft, unripe fruits, which are made into a pickle. Its timber is a very valuable one, being perhaps the best obtainable for gunstocks. It is also largely used for furniture and veneering. Numerous varieties of the walnut have sprung up in cultivation:—

Var. BARTERIANA.—Nuts almond-shaped.

Var. HETEROPHYLLA.—Leaflets long, narrow, irregularly lobed.

Var. LACINIATA.—Leaflets very handsomely cut into deep narrow lobes. A handsome foliage tree, superior to var. heterophylla.

Var. MAXIMA (macrocarpa). Bannut or Clawnut.—Nuts about twice the ordinary size, but not good keepers. Probably the same as the "Noyer à bijoux" of the French, so-called because of the large shells being often mounted as jewel boxes.

Var. MONOPHYLLA, *De Candolle*.—Leaflets reduced in number to a large terminal one and a pair of small ones, the latter often absent.

Var. PENDULA.—Branches stiffly pendulous.

Var. PRÆPARTURIENS.—A dwarf bushy form, fruiting when quite young; known in orchards as "Prolific."

Var. RACEMOSA, *Duhamel*.—Fruits in clusters of ten to fifteen; known in orchards as "Cluster."

Var. RUBRA.—Flesh of the kernel red, the skin blood-red; found wild in Styria, and said to come true from seed.

Of the above the only one notable as an ornamental tree is var. laciniata. Other varieties are cultivated for the qualities of their fruit, such as "Highflyer," "Meylanaise," "Mayette," "Noix St Jean," "Parisienne"; but a consideration of them is outside the scope of this work. A curious variety known as "thin-shelled" (to the French as "à coque tendre"), has shells so thin that they are easily pierced by birds; in some districts it is valueless on that account.

J. RUPESTRIS, *Engelmann*. TEXAN WALNUT

A small tree, often semi-shrubby; young shoots covered with short yellowish down. Leaves 6 to 12 ins. long; leaflets thirteen to over twenty, lance-shaped or narrowly ovate; 1 to 3 ins. long, ¼ to ¾ in. wide; long and taper-pointed, finely toothed, obliquely rounded at the base; when young both surfaces are covered with minute down, which mostly falls away except on the midrib and chief veins; common stalk downy like the young shoots. Male catkins slender, 2 to 4 ins. long. Fruit globose, ½ to 1 in. diameter, covered with a thin, smooth husk. Nut deeply grooved. Native of Central and W. Texas.

Var. MAJOR, *Torrey*.—A tree 50 ft. high, with larger, fewer, more downy and more coarsely toothed leaflets (up to 6 ins. long); fruit 1½ ins. diameter, clothed with brownish red down. Native of New Mexico, Arizona, etc.

The typical J. rupestris, discovered in West Texas in 1835, was sent to Kew by Prof. Sargent in 1881, and again in 1894. It is a handsome bushy tree, quite distinct from all other cultivated walnuts in its small, narrow, thin leaflets. The var. major has a more western habitat, and is of less interesting, coarser appearance; it sometimes ranks as a species, J. major, *Heller*.

J. SIEBOLDIANA, *Maximowicz*

A tree over 50 ft. high, with stout young shoots clothed, like the common stalk of the leaf, with glandular hairs. Leaves 1½ to 2 (occasionally 3) ft. long, composed of eleven to seventeen leaflets, which are oblong, taper-pointed, finely toothed, obliquely rounded or slightly heart-shaped at the base; 3 to 7 ins. long, 1½ to 2 ins. wide; downy on both surfaces, especially beneath. Male catkins slender, up to 1 ft. long. Fruits clustered on long racemes, roundish ovoid, 2 ins. long, covered with sticky down. Nut about 1¼ ins. long, rounded at the base, pointed at the top, nearly glabrous, but with a prominent ridge at the union of the two halves.

Native of Japan; introduced to Europe about 1860, by Siebold. It is abundant in the forests of Japan, and its nuts are valued as food there. In Britain it gives no promise of bearing fruit to any advantage, and in spite of the considerable period that has elapsed since its introduction, there appears to be no large specimen in the country. It appears to differ from mandshurica chiefly in the apex of the leaflet being more abruptly tapered and shorter-pointed, and in the prominent ridge and smoother surface of the nut.

J. STENOCARPA, *Maximowicz*

Little is known of this walnut, but it is akin to J. mandshurica and Sieboldiana, differing, however, in the following respects: the terminal leaflet is obovate, and thus very distinct in shape from the side leaflets, which are oblong; there is no patch of down above the scar left by the fallen leaf, as in the mandshurica group. The species was discovered in Manchuria by Maximowicz, who described the nuts as cylindrical or oblong-oval, with a long tapering apex. J. stenocarpa has been grown on the Continent as J. macrophylla, an appropriate name, for I have a leaf 2 ft. 8 ins. long, with only eleven leaflets, the terminal one 8 ins. long by 5 ins. wide; the largest side ones 7½ ins. long by 3 ins. wide.

JUNIPERUS. JUNIPER. CONIFERÆ

The junipers are spread widely over the temperate and sub-tropical regions of the northern hemisphere, the hardy spe ciescoming from China and Japan, N. America, Europe, and N. Africa. The only species native of the British Isles is J. communis, which is not uncommon on chalk hills. They are evergreen, and range from trees up to 100 ft. high down to low, spreading, or prostrate shrubs. The bark is usually thin, and often peels off in long strips. Leaves of two types: (1) awl-shaped, and from $\frac{1}{8}$ to $\frac{7}{8}$ in. long, borne in whorls of threes or in pairs; (2) small, scale-like, and rarely more than $\frac{1}{16}$ in. long, arranged oppositely in pairs and closely appressed to the branchlet. The first kind is found on the juvenile plants of all species; and several species, notably those of the communis group, retain it permanently. But other species, namely, those of the Sabina group, including virginiana and chinensis, as they get older, develop more and more of the minute scale-like type of leaf which is essentially characteristic of the adult plant. A number of species, long after they have reached the fruit-bearing stage, continue to produce the juvenile as well as the adult type. This peculiarity is, however, apparently more characteristic of cultivated than of wild specimens. The flowers are unisexual, and most frequently the two sexes occur on separate trees, sometimes on one. The male flowers are small, erect, columnar or egg-shaped bodies, composed of ovate or shield-like scales, overlapping each other and each carrying anthers at the base. The fruit is composed of usually three to six coalescent, fleshy scales, forming a berry that carries one to six seeds. It is this fruit that distinguishes the junipers from the tree cypresses, which they much resemble in foliage. Without fruit, the junipers can usually be recognised by a peculiar, aromatic, somewhat pungent odour, especially strongly developed in the savin.

Junipers like a well-drained, loamy soil, and are essentially lime-lovers, all the cultivated species except J. horizontalis being found commonly, although not invariably, on a limestone formation. This gives the genus a special value in chalky districts, where the impossibility of growing satisfactorily most of the heath family somewhat limits the number of evergreens available. Many of the species take two years to ripen their fruit, and the seeds will often lie dormant a year. Their germination may sometimes be hastened by plunging them in boiling water from three to six seconds, but this should only be regarded as an experiment, and tried with a portion of the seeds. All junipers can be increased by cuttings, a method especially suitable for the shrubby sorts.

The species most to be recommended are:—

Tall.—Virginiana, chinensis, excelsa, drupacea, and communis var. fastigiata.

Shrubby.—Sabina and its varieties, procumbens, communis, and communis var. compressa.

J. Cedrus, *Webb and Berthelot.* Mountain Cedar

Of this interesting tree very few specimens are said now to remain in a wild state, mostly in almost inaccessible places in the Canary Islands. Unfortunately it is only likely to be permanently hardy in the south-western counties, but it should certainly be tried there. Its leaves are in whorls of threes, set closely on three-cornered branchlets; they are uniformly awl-shaped, $\frac{1}{3}$ to $\frac{5}{8}$ in. long, $\frac{1}{16}$ to $\frac{1}{12}$ in. wide; very concave, and with two glaucous, stomatic bands above. Berries globose, $\frac{1}{3}$ in. wide. The wood of this tree is very pleasantly perfumed, and was highly valued by the Guanches of Teneriffe for making mummy cases. Dr Perez of Orotava has done much to revive an interest in this remarkable juniper, some specimens of which he says have trunks a yard or more in diameter. It is one of the communis group, and differs from that species and J. rigida by having two distinct glaucous lines on the upper side of the leaf, separated by the midrib.

In the Mediterranean region occurs another juniper, J. OXYCEDRUS,

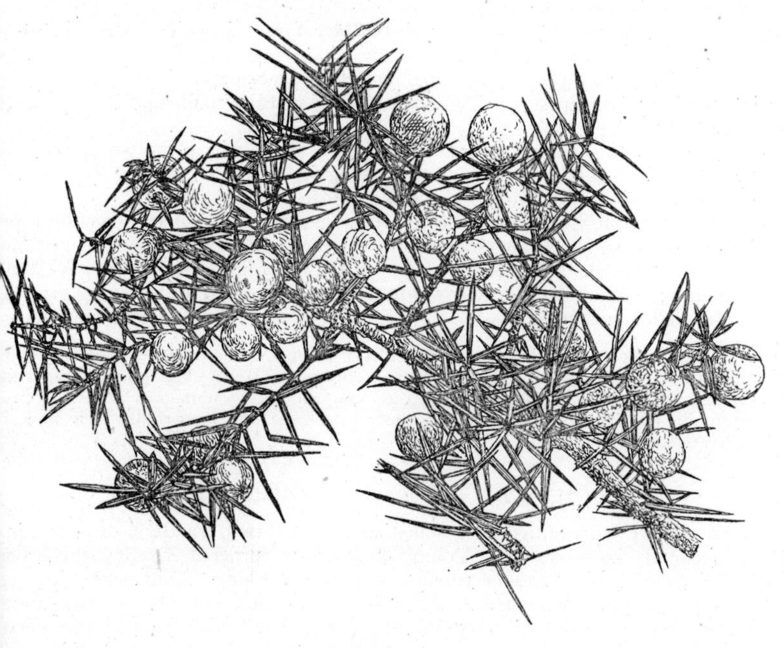

JUNIPERUS OXYCEDRUS

Linnæus, which appears to be only a geographical form of J. Cedrus, somewhat hardier, but now very rarely seen in this country and needing a warmer climate. It thrives very well on the Riviera, where I have seen good specimens at the Villa Thuret, Antibes. Elwes mentions a tree 35 ft. high near Montpellier. Fruits up to $\frac{1}{2}$ in. diameter, dark brown with more or less glaucous bloom. Leaves stouter than in J. Cedrus.

J. CHINENSIS, *Linnæus*. CHINESE JUNIPER

A tree up to 60 ft. high; young shoots terete. Leaves of two types that are nearly always found on the same tree, viz., juvenile awl-shaped ones, and small, scale-like, adult ones. The former are $\frac{1}{4}$ to $\frac{1}{3}$ in. long, sharply and stiffly pointed, arranged either in threes or oppositely in pairs, with two glaucous lines on the upper surface, green elsewhere. Scale-like leaves usually in pairs, rarely in threes, closely flattened to the branchlet, $\frac{1}{16}$ in. long, blunt at the apex. The plants are unisexual, and the male flowers, very freely borne in early spring, are yellow and pretty. Fruits about $\frac{1}{4}$ in. diameter, roundish or rather top-shaped, whitish with bloom when ripe; seeds two or three.

Native of Japan, Mongolia, and China; introduced to Kew in 1804 by W. Kerr. This juniper and J. virginiana are the commonest and best of tree-like junipers for gardens. It is perfectly hardy. From J. virginiana it differs in its blunt, scale-like leaves, and in the awl-shaped ones being frequently in whorls of threes. As a rule both juvenile and adult leaves occur on the same tree, but occasionally specimens of good age have nothing but juvenile foliage. There are male trees at Kew which bear flowers in the axils of leaves of the awl-shaped, juvenile type.

Var. ALBO-VARIEGATA.—A well-marked form in which a considerable portion of the younger growth is wholly creamy white, the rest wholly green. Introduced from Japan by Fortune, one of whose original plants used to grow in the Knap Hill nursery. This variety is of sturdier habit and dwarfer than the type.

Var. AUREA. Young's Golden Juniper.—The whole of the young parts of this plant are golden yellow, very striking in summer. Raised in Young's nursery at Milford, in Surrey; of rather dense, slender form.

Var. JAPONICA.—A dwarf shrub with foliage mostly of the juvenile type. It is represented in gardens by two sub-varieties, viz., japonica AUREA, with all the young growths of a golden yellow, habit spreading, producing a few long branches; and japonica AUREO-VARIEGATA with portions of the young growths golden-yellow, also dwarf.

J. SPHŒRICA, *Lindley*.—Trees under cultivation by this name do not appear to differ from J. chinensis. The true plant, according to Henry, has much larger fruits ($\frac{7}{10}$ in. diameter) spherical, not glaucous, and containing numerous seeds. It was originally discovered by Fortune in 1846, in China, and is probably not now in cultivation.

J. COMMUNIS, *Linnæus*. COMMON JUNIPER

A shrub of spreading habit, sometimes a small tree, usually 6 to 12 ft. high (occasionally 20 to 40 ft.). Young shoots three-cornered, bearing the leaves in whorls of three. Leaves spreading, $\frac{1}{4}$ to $\frac{5}{8}$ in. long, $\frac{1}{16}$ in. wide; always awl-shaped and terminated by a needle-like point, concave on the upper surface, with one comparatively broad glaucous band of stomata up the centre divided sometimes by a green line towards the base; beneath, the leaf is green and keeled. Fruit globose or rather oval, about $\frac{1}{4}$ in. diameter, black covered with a blue bloom, and containing two or three seeds embedded in resinous mealy pulp, ripening the second or third year.

Native of Europe from the mountains of the south to Russia and Norway, reaching eastwards to the Himalaya and Kamtschatka. It is widely spread in Britain, and is also found in both eastern and western N. America. The common juniper is essentially a shrub of limestone hills, and in elevated gardens on that formation, it and its varieties are some of the most satisfactory and pleasing of evergreens. It is not uncommon as a tree in Scandinavia but grows so slowly when it has reached that state that scarcely any difference is perceptible in one man's recollection. It is best raised from seeds, which frequently lie dormant a year. The berries were once used as a diuretic in medicine, and are still employed to flavour gin. In Norway a kind of beer is made from them.

There are several named varieties, both wild and of garden origin:—

Var. AUREA.—Young shoots and young leaves yellow.

Var. COMPRESSA.—A slender, cone-shaped shrub of minute dimensions with branches and leaves so dense as to form a rigid mass, the leaves very short. This remarkable shrub is the daintiest of conifers, and probably the slowest growing of them. Plants twenty years of age will often not have reached $1\frac{1}{2}$ ft. in height. It is sometimes called the Irish juniper (hibernica) but that name, I think, properly belongs to var. fastigiata (*q.v.*).

Var. ECHINIFORMIS. Hedgehog Juniper.—Of dwarf, globose habit.

Var. FASTIGIATA (syns. var. hibernica; var. suecica). Irish Juniper.—A slender, perfectly columnar tree with short leaves, very striking when in good health. The best specimens I have seen are in Scotland. There is one at Abercairney over 20 ft. high and 3 ft. in diameter, and another at Scone Palace. The tree is extremely effective in formal arrangements. It is found wild in Norway, Sweden, etc.

Var. HEMISPHERICA.—A dwarf, globose variety, said to grow wild on Mount Etna and other mountainous parts of S.E. Europe.

Var. NANA (syn. alpina).—A dwarf, alpine form, growing about 1 ft. high, with a stunted habit, short branches, and small fruit. Its dwarfness is apparently due merely to climate conditions, as both it and an intermediate form (INTERMEDIA) are said to revert to ordinary communis under lowland conditions. It is found wild in the Tyrol, etc., and similar forms occur in N. America, which have been called CANADENSIS.

J. CONFERTA, *Parlatore*

(Wilson's Conifers of Japan, t. 59; J. litoralis, *Maximowicz*)

An evergreen prostrate shrub with angular young shoots densely clothed with leaves. Leaves in whorls of three, awl-shaped, $\frac{1}{4}$ to $\frac{5}{8}$ in. long, $\frac{1}{16}$ in. or less wide; very sharply pointed, pale glossy green and keeled beneath, grooved above with one broad glaucous line of stomata along the middle. Fruit globose, $\frac{1}{4}$ to $\frac{1}{2}$ in. wide, black covered with glaucous bloom and containing three ovoid, triangular seeds.

Native of the sea-coasts of Japan, especially on the sand dunes of Hakodate Bay in Yezo, where it was discovered by Maximowicz in 1861. Introduced by Wilson in 1914. It is now cultivated in several gardens in Britain and promises to succeed well. It should be a useful plant for growing near the sea and for forming a low ground cover. Botanically it is most closely allied to J. rigida, especially in the grooved leaves with one stomatic stripe above and in the three-seeded fruit, but that species is a small tree with much more thinly disposed leaves. In habit J. conferta more resembles J. procumbens, a species well distinguished by the green midrib dividing the stomatic upper surface into two stripes. J. procumbens has been grown erroneously under the name of "J. litoralis," which is really a synonym of J. conferta. Young plants of J. conferta have their leaves much less densely set on the branchlets than adult ones. A plant at Borde Hill, Sussex, shows its prostrate character very well.

J. COXII, *A. B. Jackson*

This fine juniper was found by Messrs E. H. M. Cox and R. Farrer in Upper Burma in 1920 and was introduced by them, but it had been discovered some six years previously by Kingdon Ward. It is an evergreen tree 80 to 100 ft. high with a single erect stem and graceful weeping branches, and Mr Cox estimates that the girth of the largest tree is 30 ft. or more. The habit is narrowly pyramidal, the branchlets slender and rich dark green; the leaves are $\frac{1}{4}$ to $\frac{1}{2}$ in. long, $\frac{1}{16}$ in. or less wide, borne in threes, prickly pointed, with the two longitudinal strips of stomata on the upper side yellowish rather than glaucous and divided by a green median line. Fruits egg-shaped, $\frac{3}{8}$ in. long, dark purplish brown, and each contains one seed only.

Up to the publication of Mr Jackson's name in the *New Flora and Silva*, vol. v., p. 31, in October 1932, there was a disposition amongst botanists to regard this tree as a variety of J. recurva. But I think its enormous size and single stem (J. recurva is always more or less branched at the base), its very pendulous habit, and its longer, more outstanding leaves set further apart, amply justify its ranking as a species.

Farrer describes this tree as growing always at altitudes of over 10,000 ft. in a region " where the summer is wet and sunless, the winters of Alpine cold, and the springs late, ungenial and chilly." This species is quite hardy at Kew, but it succeeds better in the warmer, softer counties of the south and west. In the woods at Exbury, near the Solent, it is growing extremely well and has borne fruit there. There seems to be no reason why it should not develop in such places not only into the finest of all junipers (which it is naturally) but into one of the most beautiful of all conifers. According to Farrer the wood is " close and fine in grain, immortal, and of the most delicious fragrance, either fresh or burned." It is probably to its " immortal " quality that is due the love of the Chinese for this wood for coffin-making. The prices they are willing to pay for it make it one of the most costly of timbers.

J. DRUPACEA, *Labillardière*. SYRIAN JUNIPER

(Arceuthos drupacea, *Antoine*)

A unisexual tree of pyramidal or columnar shape, 30 to 40 ft. high in cultivation, 60 ft. high in nature; young shoots three-cornered, and bearing the leaves in spreading whorls of three. Leaves uniformly awl-shaped, sharply and stiffly pointed, $\frac{1}{2}$ to $\frac{7}{8}$ in. long, $\frac{1}{12}$ to $\frac{1}{8}$ in. wide at the base; upper surface slightly concave, marked with two dull glaucous bands of stomata separated by a narrow green midrib; margins also green. The under-surface is wholly green, and has the midrib rather prominent. Fruit globose, $\frac{3}{4}$ to 1 in. wide, brown with a glaucous covering.

Native of the mountains of Greece, Asia Minor, and Syria; introduced about the middle of last century. It thrives better than most junipers at Kew, and from its beauty and the distinctness of its shape, is well worth cultivation. It is easily distinguished by the size of its leaves, which (like the fruits) are the largest found among junipers. It differs from other species in the leaf-bases being attached to the stem, and extending downward to the next whorl (decurrent). No fruits appear to have been developed in this country.

J. EXCELSA, *Bieberstein*

A tree 30 to 40 ft. high in cultivation, twice or thrice as high in nature; bark brown, peeling off in strips; branchlets very slender. Leaves of both adult and juvenile forms, the latter awl-shaped, in pairs or in threes, $\frac{1}{8}$ to $\frac{1}{4}$ in. long, sharply pointed. Adult leaves scale-like, in pairs, closely appressed to the branchlets, ovate, $\frac{1}{24}$ in. long, thickened towards the pointed apex, which is incurved; there is a glandular hollow towards the base. Male and female flowers on the same or separate plants. Fruit globose, $\frac{1}{3}$ in. diameter, dark brown covered with a blue bloom, containing four to six seeds.

Native of S.E. Europe, Asia Minor, and the Caucasus. It is an elegant, narrowly pyramidal tree in cultivation, and thrives very well. The typical form seems to lose its juvenile foliage, but in the handsomer var. PERKINSII, well marked by its glaucous hue, the leaves are wholly of a semi-juvenile or intermediate type, half or less than half of the length of the true juvenile ones, but quite distinct from the true adult, scale-like leaves. They are from $\frac{1}{16}$ to $\frac{1}{8}$

in. long, in pairs or in threes, awl-shaped and spreading. From J. virginiana, chinensis, and Sabina this species is distinguished by having twice or thrice as many seeds in each fruit.

Var. STRICTA has the same type of foliage as var. Perkinsii, but is not so glaucous.

J. FLACCIDA, *Schlechtendal*

But little need be said of this juniper, which is a native of the Chisos mountains of Texas and of N.E. Mexico. It was introduced from the latter country by Hartweg in 1838, but owing to its tenderness has never been common. There is a notable tree at Bicton in Devonshire which Elwes estimated to be about 40 ft. high in 1906. I have also seen it in the garden at Villa Thuret, near Antibes, and in the Hanbury garden at La Mortola. It is also growing in the Botanic Gardens of Genoa and Naples.

It is a tree of distinct habit, producing long, weeping, graceful branches; young shoots very thin and slender. Adult leaves in opposite, decussate pairs, narrowly lanceolate, appressed to the twigs at the base, slightly spreading at the end, sharply pointed, $\frac{1}{12}$ to $\frac{1}{10}$ in. long. Juvenile leaves often in threes, sometimes in pairs, awl-shaped, $\frac{1}{4}$ in. long, spine-tipped. Berries up to $\frac{1}{2}$ in. wide, angular-globose, reddish brown, covered at first with glaucous bloom, carrying six to twelve seeds. Both kinds of leaves are borne on cone-bearing shoots of the Bicton tree. This juniper is well worth growing in gardens with a climate similar to that of Bicton.

J. FORMOSANA, *Hayata*

(J. taxifolia, *Masters*—not *Hooker*)

In a few gardens in Britain, notably at Eastnor Castle and Bicton, there grows a juniper usually known as "oblonga pendula" or "communis pendula." It is the J. formosana described in 1908 by Hayata, the Japanese botanist, which had previously been confused with the J. taxifolia, *Hooker*. It was introduced by Fortune from China, where it is a tree 40 ft. high, probably between 1843 and 1845, and was put in commerce a few years later by Knight and Perry of Chelsea as J. oblonga pendula. It is an elegant tree, with the ends of the branches pendulous. Branchlets very slender and lax, three-cornered, bearing the narrowly awl-shaped leaves in whorls of three, the whorls $\frac{1}{6}$ to $\frac{1}{3}$ in. apart. Leaves $\frac{1}{3}$ to $\frac{5}{8}$ in. long, finely pointed, spreading, glacuous on the upper side, with a fine green line up the centre; lower side wholly green, keeled. Fruit globose, $\frac{1}{3}$ in. across, reddish brown, containing three seeds. It much resembles J. rigida in habit and leaf, but that species is well distinguished by the groove that traverses the centre of the upper surface of the leaf, which has, moreover, no green line dividing the glaucous band into two parts.

J. HORIZONTALIS, *Moench*. CREEPING JUNIPER

On the shores of the Great Lakes and other parts of eastern N. America there is found a low, prostrate juniper which is very closely akin to J. Sabina. It is known by various names, chiefly as J. Sabina prostrata, but also as J. prostrata and J. procumbens (which last name belongs rightly to a Japanese species), also as J. hudsonica, *Loddiges*. It is, no doubt, entitled to rank as a species and is treated as such by American botanists under the name J. horizontalis, the "Waukegan juniper." Its adult scale-like leaves are sharply pointed and in pairs. Fruit about $\frac{1}{3}$ in. diameter, on recurved stalks, pale blue, with usually two or three seeds. The whole plant has a glaucous-blue colour; it is, perhaps, the bluest of junipers and very noticeable although not common in gardens. It does not occur on limestone.

J. MACROCARPA, *Sibthorp*. LARGE-BERRIED JUNIPER

(J. neaboriensis, *Lawson*; J. Oxycedrus macrocarpa, *Ascherson*)

A small tree up to 12 or 15 ft. high or a shrub of pyramidal shape; young shoots triangular in cross section. Leaves in threes spreading horizontally, awl-shaped, ½ to 1 in. long, about $\frac{1}{12}$ in. wide, sharply pointed; upper surface with two glaucous-grey bands of stomata between the green margins and the midrib. Berries globose, ⅓ to ½ in. wide, blue-white at first, afterwards purplish brown.

Native of the Mediterranean region from Spain to Syria and said to occur also in Bulgaria. If the latter statement be true, the species should be fairly hardy. Plants under the name and of dense pyramidal habit have been healthy out-of-doors at Kew since 1918; they are correct as regards foliage, but not having yet borne fruit one cannot be certain they are true. Gordon avers it is "quite hardy and one of the finest." Introduced in 1838, now very rare. It is closely related to J. Oxycedrus, which has smaller, less glaucous berries, shorter leaves tapering from the middle (not from the base as in macrocarpa).

J. OCCIDENTALIS, *Hooker*. WESTERN JUNIPER

(J. pyriformis, *Lindley*)

A round-headed tree up to 45 ft. (rarely 60 ft.) high, or a shrub; its trunk occasionally 2 to 3 ft. in diameter. Young shoots $\frac{1}{16}$ to $\frac{1}{12}$ in. thick with the scale-like, grey-green, overlapping leaves closely pressed to the stem, and arranged in threes; the exposed part is diamond-shaped, $\frac{1}{16}$ in. long, bluntish, with a conspicuous gland on the back. The leaves on juvenile shoots are awl-shaped, sharply pointed, keeled at the back, ⅛ in. long, sometimes in pairs. Berries subglobose to egg-shaped, ¼ to ⅓ in. long, covered with a glaucous bloom carrying two or three seeds.

Native of N.W. America from the State of Washington and British Columbia to California; first collected by Douglas about 1829. It has always been very rare in cultivation although, as it has been found up to elevations of 10,000 ft., it should be hardy enough. Douglas found trees 50 to 60 ft. high with clean erect trunks. The late Mr F. R. S. Balfour introduced it to his collection at Dawyck, near Peebles, some years ago.

J. PACHYPHLÆA, *Torrey*. CHEQUER-BARKED JUNIPER

A tree 50 to 60 ft. high, with a very distinct bark that cracks up into curious small squares. Leaves of two kinds, awl-shaped and scale-like, with intermediate states; the former ⅛ to ¼ in. long, very sharply pointed, mostly in threes, whitish on the upper side, glaucous beneath; the scale-like ones in pairs or in threes, closely flattened to the branchlet, $\frac{1}{16}$ in. long, ovate, pointed, with the points incurved. Under a strongish glass minute teeth can be seen on the margin, and there is a resin-gland on the back. Fruits ripening the second year, globose or slightly longer than broad, ½ in. long, covered with blue bloom.

Native of dry mountain-sides in the south-western United States. It has been cultivated at Kew since about 1873, but is still scarcely 20 ft. high. Our climate is scarcely sunny and hot enough for it. The specimen at Kew, however, shows the curious chequered bark which is the most distinctive feature of this juniper. A fine specimen in the Jesup collection of timbers at the Natural History Museum of New York shows this character remarkably well. J. pachyphylœa is very pretty in the silvery young growth of the juvenile form, and is now offered for sale by nurserymen.

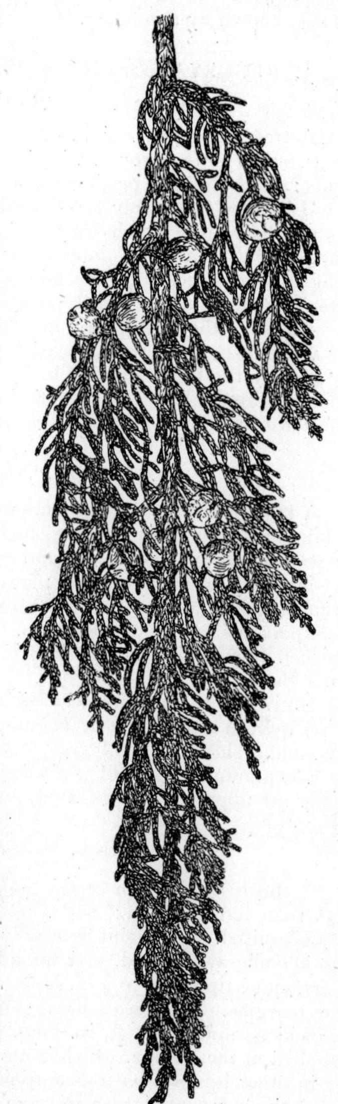

JUNIPERUS PHŒNICEA

J. PHŒNICEA, *Linnæus*

Although trees and shrubs bearing this name are occasionally to be met with in gardens, it would seem that the true plant is now rare, and only to be found in the warmer parts of the country. It is a native of S. Europe, N. Africa, and the Canary Islands, and according to Aiton, was introduced in 1683. The adult leaves are in pairs or in threes, scale-like, $\frac{1}{25}$ in. long, very closely arranged and appressed to the branchlet; the juvenile leaves (few or absent in old trees) are needle-like and in whorls of threes. Fruit variable, but mostly globose, about $\frac{1}{3}$ in. diameter, dark reddish or yellowish brown, without bloom, containing three to nine seeds.

Var. TURBINATA.—Fruits egg-shaped, sometimes top-shaped, as compared with the usually spherical ones of the type.

J. PROCUMBENS, *Siebold and Zuccarini*

A low, spreading shrub of sturdy habit, $1\frac{1}{2}$ to 2 ft. high, and densely furnished with stiff branchlets. Leaves $\frac{1}{4}$ to $\frac{1}{3}$ in. long, always awl-shaped, and in threes, ending in a sharp, stiff point; concave on the upper side and glaucous, but with a distinct green midrib and margins; lower side bright green, with a groove near the base. The leaves point forward, and are somewhat incurved towards the tip.

Native of Japan; described by Siebold in 1844, about which time it was in cultivation as J. squamata at Kew. It appears afterwards to have almost disappeared from cultivation, but was reintroduced in 1893. There is a very fine example in the Vicarage Garden at Bitton, 4 or 5 yds. across and about 18 ins. high. It is allied to J. squamata, but is a more vigorous and hardy shrub, its foliage larger, stiffer, and more spiny at the tip. No dwarf juniper, indeed, is handsomer than this, or makes a more striking low, dense covering for the ground. It never appears to have borne fruit in cultivation, but strikes root readily from cuttings. It must not be confused with a prostrate form of J. Sabina found in N. America, which is also known by this name.

J. RECURVA, *Buchanan-Hamilton*. HIMALAYAN JUNIPER (Plate 15)

A tree 30 to 40 ft. high, or a shrub, usually broadly pyramidal in shape, and clothed to the ground with branches, which are curved downwards at the ends; bark brown, peeling off in thin flakes. Leaves in whorls of threes, $\frac{1}{8}$ to $\frac{1}{4}$ in. long, uniformly awl-shaped, all pointing forwards and rather appressed to the branchlet which they completely hide; upper (inner) surface very concave and glaucous; outer surface dull green changing to brown before the leaf falls, grooved along the middle. Fruit egg-shaped, $\frac{3}{8}$ in. long, brown the first year, ripening to a dark purple the second; one-seeded.

Native of the Himalaya; introduced in 1830. A graceful tree and distinct, its value in gardens is decreased by the dull colour of the foliage, giving very frequently the impression of bad health. Male and female flowers occur on the same tree, It has lived out-of-doors at Kew for many years, but requires the warmer, moister conditions of such places as Cornwall to show it at its best.

J. RIGIDA, *Siebold and Zuccarini*

A tree sometimes 20 ft. or more high, of elegant form, the branches being pendulous at the ends; young shoots glabrous, triangular. Leaves triangular in section, always needle-like and very slender, $\frac{1}{3}$ to $\frac{3}{4}$ in. long, and produced in spreading whorls of threes; very sharply pointed. The upper surface is deeply grooved and has one glaucous band of stomatic lines along the middle; elsewhere the leaf is bright green. Fruit $\frac{1}{4}$ in. or more wide, at first broadly conical, then globose, dark brown, ripening the second year. Seeds one to three in each berry.

Native of Japan; introduced by John Gould Veitch in 1861. It thrives very well in the southern counties of England, making a small, broadly pyramidal shrub or small tree, but is not very common. Most closely allied to J. communis, it is still very distinct in its narrower, longer leaves grooved along the upper side, and thinner, more elegant habit.

J. SABINA, *Linnæus*. COMMON SAVIN

A shrub reaching in certain conditions 10 to 15 ft. in height, but usually less than half as high; the whole plant emitting a strong, aromatic odour when bruised. The habit is usually stiff and spreading. Leaves of two types: the juvenile awl-shaped, and the adult scale-like. Juvenile leaves in opposite pairs, spine-tipped, $\frac{1}{8}$ to $\frac{1}{6}$ in. long, the concave upper side glaucous, except on the margins. The scale-like, genuinely adult leaves are on very slender branchlets, and about $\frac{1}{20}$ in. long, green, bluntish at the apex, thickened and rounded at the outside, which is marked about the centre with a sunken gland. As in other junipers with dimorphic foliage, there is an intermediate state in which the leaves are larger and more pointed than the fully adult ones. Plants either uni- or bi-sexual. Fruit globose or broadly top-shaped, $\frac{1}{5}$ to $\frac{1}{4}$ in. diameter, dark brown, ultimately covered with a blue bloom, and containing usually two seeds.

Native of the mountains of Central and S. Europe, and chiefly, but not invariably, found on limestone. It was cultivated in England in the first half of the sixteenth century. It is one of the handsomest and most useful of dwarf evergreens, especially for elevated and chalky districts, being easily increased by cuttings.

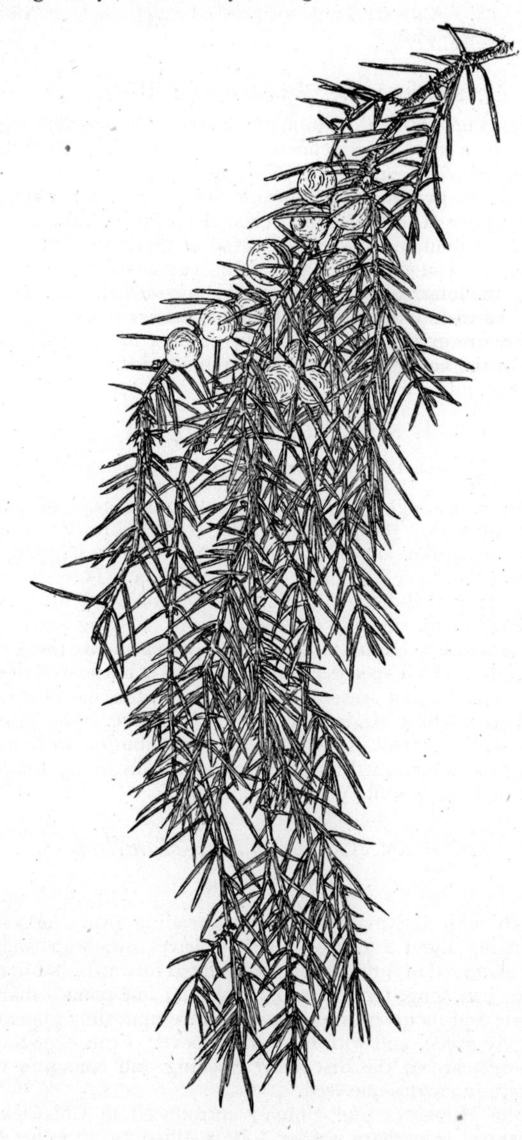

JUNIPERUS RIGIDA (see p. 170)

Var. HUMILIS, *Endlicher*. Carpet Juniper.—A low shrub of spreading habit, $1\frac{1}{2}$ to 2 ft. high, with both types of foliage.

Var. TAMARISCIFOLIA, *Aiton*. Spanish Savin.—A shrub of spreading habit like the preceding, but taller; leaves of the two types, the juveniles often in threes.

Var. VARIEGATA.—A dwarf shrub with close branches whose younger parts are tipped with creamy white.

J. SALTUARIA, *Rehder and Wilson*

Not much is known of this juniper in this country although it was discovered by Wilson in N.W. Szechuen, China, in 1904, and found again by Purdom in Kansu seven years later. Wilson described it as a shapely tree 10 to 48 ft. high, of pyramidal shape and dense, erect branching. Leaves scale-like, closely pressed to the stem, "clear deep green," about $\frac{1}{12}$ in. long, the exposed portion diamond-shaped, incurved at the bluntish tip and with a gland at the base. The tree is bi-sexual, its egg-shaped or nearly globose berries about $\frac{1}{5}$ in. long, black, shining and one-seeded. It appears to be most nearly related to J. Wallichiana, which has berries twice as long. Wilson records that there are extensive woods of this juniper in the neighbourhood of Sungpan, most of the houses of which city are built of it. It has recently been introduced to England.

J. SCOPULORUM, *Sargent*

(Garden and Forest, 1897, fig. 54; J. virginiana scopulorum, *Jones*)

A tree up to 40 ft. high, forming a round-topped head of branches, its trunk often dividing near the ground; bark reddish brown; young shoots slender. Leaves scale-like, closely pressed to the stem, overlapping, arranged in pairs and altogether very like those of J. virginiana. There is on the back of each leaf a usually well-defined gland. Berry globose, $\frac{1}{4}$ in. wide, covered with a bright blue bloom, ripening the second year, carrying one or two seeds.

Native of the western United States, where it represents the J. virginiana of the eastern States. That species is closely akin to it but is well distinguished by ripening its seeds the first season. J. scopulorum, too, has only six stamens to each male flower, whilst virginiana has ten to twelve. The former, which was made a species by Sargent in 1897, is quite hardy, but owing to its similarity with virginiana has not obtained much notice from cultivators, and although it was introduced in 1839, is quite uncommon to-day.

J. SQUAMATA, *Buchanan-Hamilton*

(J. densa, *Gordon*)

A low shrub with the main branches spreading over the ground, and the branchlets rising about 2 ft. above them. Leaves always awl-shaped (never scale-like), and arranged in threes; they are pointed forwards, but not appressed to the stem, $\frac{1}{8}$ to $\frac{1}{6}$ in. long, terminated by a slender fine point; margins green on the upper side and incurved, the concave centre uniformly glaucous; lower side of leaf wholly green, and with a central groove. Fruit egg-shaped, about $\frac{1}{3}$ in. long, reddish brown the first year, ripening and changing to purplish black the second; it carries one seed.

Native of the Himalaya and China; introduced to Chiswick from the former about 1836, or perhaps earlier. It is allied to J. recurva, which it resembles in its uniform foliage, and the purple-black, one-seeded berries. The leaves, however, are broader, shorter, and more conspicuously glaucous, and the habit and general aspect very different. There is a good specimen at Bayfordbury from which the above description was made, which makes a handsome low shrub, very dense and leafy in growth.

Var. FARGESII is a very distinct variety and was introduced by Wilson from Szechuen, W. China, in 1908. It is a tree usually from 15 to 40 ft. high, but in *The Garden* for 8th March 1924, Wilson figures a tree 85 ft. high which he saw in China. It differs from the type in the spreading branches, in the leaves being longer (1/4 to 1/3 in.) and narrower; also in the smaller berries 1/4 in. or less long. It is in cultivation at Kew and Bedgebury. As in the type, the berry carries one seed. It seems on the whole distinct enough to rank as a species.

J. SQUAMATA WILSONII, *Rehder*, is a shrub up to 6 ft. high of very dense habit, the shoots recurved at the tips and crowded with leaves that are about 1/6 in. long and broader than in the type. Discovered and introduced by Wilson in 1909.

Var. MEYERI, *Rehder*.—Erect shrub of dense habit; leaves very glaucous beneath, 1/3 in. long. Given an Award of Merit at Vincent Square, 19th May 1931.

J. THURIFERA, *Linnæus*. INCENSE JUNIPER

A tree 30 to 40 ft. high in a wild state; narrowly pyramidal in cultivation. Leaves of two sorts, viz., awl-shaped and scale-like; the former sharply pointed, 1/8 to 1/6 in. long, arranged in opposite pairs in four superposed rows, the upper surface having two glaucous lines separated by a green one; scale-like leaves 1/20 to 1/16 in. long, pointed, and with a hollow at the back. Intermediate forms occur. Fruit 1/4 to 1/3 in. diameter, roundish, covered with glaucous bloom when ripe.

Native of S.W. Europe and N. Africa; long introduced, but rare. It is fairly hardy at Kew, and is now about 30 ft. high, most of its foliage being of the juvenile or intermediate kind. Its young shoots are nevertheless occasionally much cut by severe winters, as they were in that of 1908-9. The trees are unisexual.

J. VIRGINIANA, *Linnæus*. RED CEDAR

A tree usually 40 to 50, occasionally 60 to 100 ft. high; the bark peeling off in long loose strips. It is pyramidal when young, becoming more round-topped with age. Leaves of both awl-shaped (juvenile), and scale-like (adult) forms on the same tree. The former, arranged in pairs, are 1/8 to 1/4 in. long, pointed, concave inside and glaucous except on the margins, grey-green and convex outside, pointing forward. Scale-leaves 1/16 in. long, ovate, pointed (sometimes slenderly), thickened and convex outside, overlapping. Young specimens have none other than the awl-shaped type of leaf; as they grow older, branches of scale-like leaves appear until, in the adult state, the tree bears scarcely any other, and it is on these that the fruits are borne; fruits, however, are sometimes to be seen on branches bearing an intermediate type of leaf. Male and female flowers are usually separated on different trees, but occasionally appear on the same. Fruits roundish, 1/4 in. long, scarcely so wide, covered with a blue glaucous bloom, carrying one or two seeds.

Native of the eastern and Central United States and eastern Canada; introduced about the middle of the seventeenth century. This juniper is by far the commonest and largest of the arborescent species cultivated in gardens. The largest I have seen is at Arley Castle in Shropshire, nearly 70 ft. high and 5 ft. in girth of trunk, but according to Elwes there is one at Pains Hill, 13 ft. 9 ins. in girth. It likes a well-drained loamy soil, is perfectly hardy, and altogether one of the best thriving of eastern N. American trees in this country, especially on chalky soils. From the next most common of tree-like junipers, J. chinensis, this in all its forms is best distinguished by its awl-shaped leaves being nearly always in pairs, and by its scale-like leaves being always pointed. Small plants are like J. Sabina, but that is to be distinguished by its peculiar rank smell when crushed.

Under cultivation J. virginiana has produced a good number of varieties owing to its variability when raised from seed. Of these varieties the following are the most distinct :—

Var. AUREO-VARIEGATA.—A proportion of the young shoots are yellow, sometimes wholly, sometimes the tips only. Vars. AUREO-SPICA and ELEGANTISSIMA are improved forms of this.

Var. BEDFORDIANA (syn. J. Gossaintheana, *Loddiges*).—A tree of columnar form, with long slender branches, pendulous at the ends. The habit is elegant, and the leaves never appear to assume the quite short scale-like form, but remain either in the juvenile or intermediate states. More tender than the type, and possibly belonging really to J. barbadensis, a sub-tropical representative of J. virginiana found in the southern United States and West Indies.

Var. DUMOSA.—Of close, rounded form, always dwarf; leaves bright green. COMPACTA and HUMILIS are the same or similar.

Var. GLAUCA (syn. argentea).—Leaves silvery grey during the spring and summer, changing to green.

Var. PENDULA.—Various pendulous forms are known, the best being a female one of the typical colour, the branches of which are horizontal, the tips pendulous; PENDULA VIRIDIS has bright green foliage.

Var. SCHOTTI, *Gordon* (syn. viridis).—Leaves bright green, habit compact, pyramidal.

Var. TRIPARTITA.—A bush of spreading habit and low growth.

J. WALLICHIANA, *Hooker fil.* BLACK JUNIPER

(J. pseudo-sabina, *Hooker fil.*, not *Fischer*)

A tree 60 ft. high in Sikkim, according to Brandis, with spreading branches. Leaves of two types—(1) juvenile, in whorls of threes, $\frac{1}{8}$ to $\frac{1}{4}$ in. long, sharply pointed, pointing forwards, concave and very glaucous above, green and keeled below, all very closely set upon the branchlet, with the stalk extending down and attached to it (decurrent); and (2) adult leaves $\frac{1}{16}$ in. long, scale-like, arranged in opposite pairs overlapping each other and appressed to the branchlet, pointed with the points incurved, grooved outside, bright green. Male and female flowers on separate trees. Fruits egg-shaped, tapered at the top, $\frac{1}{4}$ to $\frac{1}{2}$ in. long, at first dark brown, blue when ripe, one-seeded.

Native of the Himalaya up to 15,000 ft. elevation; introduced by Sir Joseph Hooker in 1849 to Kew, where there is a healthy tree about 20 ft. high. This bears both types of foliage. A healthy specimen at Leonardslee has mostly the juvenile type, but bore fruit in 1911, and one at Kew bears male flowers.

The true J. PSEUDO-SABINA, *Fischer*, is an allied species, but shrubby, and has the scale-like leaves blunt or rounded at the end; the fruits are like those of Wallichiana in being one-seeded, but more globose and smaller. Native of Siberia, probably not in cultivation.

KADSURA JAPONICA, *Jussieu*. MAGNOLIACEÆ

This is the only hardy member of a small genus belonging to the Magnolia family, and closely related to the schizandras, but differing from them in having the fruits arranged in a globose head instead of an elongated spike. K. japonica is a climbing, evergreen shrub up to 12 ft., with slender, twining branches. Leaves oval or lanceolate, slender-pointed, dark green, 2 to 4 ins. long, 1¼ to 1¾ ins. wide; quite glabrous and remotely toothed. Flower solitary on a slender stalk 1 to 1½ ins. long, and borne singly in the leaf-axils of the current season's growth from June until autumn; the corolla yellowish white, ¾ in. across, composed of six to nine fleshy petals. Berries scarlet, clustered in a globose head 1 to 1¼ ins. wide.

Native of Japan; introduced in 1860. This interesting and uncommon twiner is not particularly hardy in the open, and should be given the shelter of a wall. It can be increased by cuttings of half-ripened wood put in gentle heat.

Var. VARIEGATA.—Leaves with an irregular border of creamy white.

KALMIA. ERICACEÆ

A small group of shrubs, mostly evergreen, native of eastern N. America, and named by Linnæus in honour of Peter Kalm, one of his pupils, and the author of a famous eighteenth-century book of North American travel. They are all handsome plants, especially K. latifolia and K. polifolia, with the leaves in some species alternate, in others opposite or in threes. Flowers five-parted, flattish, open, and produced in showy clusters. They show an interesting mechanism to secure fertilisation. There are ten stamens, which on first expanding are bent back so that the anthers are held in little cavities in the corolla. The "knee" formed by the stalk of the stamen is sensitive, and when the pollen is ripe, if it be touched, the anther is released with a jerk, sending a little dust of pollen in the direction of the stigma, or over the insect whose movements set it in motion. The fruit is a globose capsule, five-celled and many-seeded. The foliage of kalmias is mostly considered poisonous to animals that graze on it. K. angustifolia is on this account known as "lamb-kill" in the United States.

Kalmias like a peaty soil and cool, permanently moist conditions at the root. They are best propagated by seed, which should be sown as advised for rhododendrons, and afterwards pricked off in boxes. K. polifolia may be increased by cuttings of moderately ripened growths in July and August.

K. ANGUSTIFOLIA, *Linnæus*. SHEEP LAUREL

(Bot. Mag., t. 331)

An evergreen shrub, varying considerably in height and habit. The largest form is 2 to 4 ft. high, and of thin, open growth; the smallest a dwarf, tufted plant 6 ins. or so high; young wood slightly downy. Leaves in pairs or in threes, oval or ovate; ¾ to 2 ins. long, ¼ to ¾ in. wide; glabrous and bright green above, paler or semi-glaucous beneath; stalk ⅙ to ⅓ in. long. Flowers produced in June, densely packed in rounded clusters 2 ins. across at the termination of the previous year's growth. Corolla saucer-shaped, ⅓ in. across, deep rosy red; lobes five, shallowly triangular. Calyx and flower-stalk downy.

Native of eastern N. America; introduced in 1736, and the commonest of kalmias in gardens. It spreads by sucker growths at the base, and the dwarfer forms are dainty shrubs. Propagated by seed or by pulling old plants apart in spring. Several minor forms have been given names referring to differences in habit, shape of leaf, and colour of flower, such as: NANA (syn. pumila),

KALMIA CUNEATA (see p. 177)

dwarf; OVATA, leaves ovate, broader; ROSEA, flowers rose-coloured; RUBRA, flowers deeper red than ordinary. The specific name "angustifolia" has no significance except in relation to K. latifolia.

K. CAROLINA, *Small*, is a near ally of K. angustifolia, kept apart from it on the strength of its permanently downy leaves and style. Flowers pink or purple. Native of the S.E. United States from Virginia to S. Carolina. Introduced 1906.

K. CUNEATA, *Michaux*

(Bot. Mag., t. 8319)

A deciduous, sometimes partially evergreen shrub, 3 to 4 ft. high, of thin, erect, gaunt habit; young shoots reddish, glandular-hairy. Leaves alternate, nearly or quite stalkless, obovate or narrowly oval; $\frac{3}{4}$ to 2 ins. long, $\frac{1}{5}$ to $\frac{1}{2}$ in. wide, always narrowed towards the base, but pointed or rounded at the apex; glabrous and dark green above, paler and with scattered gland-tipped hairs beneath. Flowers produced in June and July at the end of the previous year's growth in a series of clusters (fascicles), each consisting of two to six blossoms. Corolla white, $\frac{1}{2}$ to $\frac{5}{8}$ in. across, cup-shaped; lobes shallow, rounded. Calyx-lobes $\frac{1}{8}$ in. long, ovate, green, glabrous; flower-stalks thread-like, $\frac{3}{4}$ to $1\frac{1}{4}$ ins. long, beset with a few scattered hairs.

Native of the Carolinas, south-eastern United States; discovered by Michaux, and introduced to Britain in 1820, but for many years quite lost to cultivation, until reintroduced to Kew in 1904. It is a distinct species, but has a somewhat inelegant habit owing to its sparse branching. It loses all or nearly all its leaves in severe weather, and is, perhaps, seen to best advantage planted thinly with an undergrowth of some dwarf peat-loving evergreen like Leiophyllum or Bruckenthalia.

K. HIRSUTA, *Walter.*

(Bot. Mag., t. 138)

This, the "hairy Kalmia," is an evergreen shrub 1 to 2 ft. high, with very bristly slender young shoots. Leaves alternate, very shortly stalked, oval or oblong, pointed, tapered at the base; $\frac{1}{4}$ to $\frac{1}{2}$ in. long, $\frac{1}{12}$ to $\frac{1}{4}$ in. wide; bright green, bristly like the young shoots. Flowers solitary in the leaf-axils, $\frac{1}{2}$ in. wide, each borne on a slender bristly stalk; corolla pink, flattish, saucer-shaped; sepals linear-lanceolate, pointed, $\frac{1}{4}$ in. long, bristly, persisting after the corolla has fallen.

Native of the S.E. United States from Virginia to Florida, where it flowers in June; introduced from Carolina in 1790 by Mr Watson, "nurseryman of Islington." It was figured during the following year in the *Botanical Magazine*, but has never secured a firm footing in English gardens, being too tender for all but our mildest counties. It is very distinct in its bristliness, and in habit and size of leaf rather resembles Daböecia cantabrica. I have not seen it in flower, but pictures show that it has considerable beauty. The corolla has the typical flat, round shape, and it has, like the other species, little pockets towards which the stamens are bent back and in which the anthers are retained. It would be interesting to try this species again in some of the warm south coast gardens.

K. LATIFOLIA, *Linnæus.* CALICO BUSH

(Bot. Mag., t. 175; K. lucida, *Hort.*)

A large, robust, evergreen shrub with rather the aspect of a rhododendron when not in flower, a single plant sometimes forming a dense thicket 10 ft. high, and 15 ft. through; young shoots slightly downy. Leaves alternate, leathery, glabrous, rich glossy green, oval; 2 to 5 ins. long, $\frac{3}{4}$ to $1\frac{1}{2}$ ins. wide; tapering at both ends, often in a cluster at the end of the twig; stalk $\frac{1}{4}$ to 1 in. long. Flowers crowded in several flattish or rounded clusters, terminating the growth of the previous year, and collectively 3 or 4 ins. across. Corolla saucer-shaped, $\frac{3}{4}$ to 1 in. across, varying in colour from white or pale blush to deep rose, with five triangular blunt lobes. Stamens white, with brown anthers. Calyx-lobes ovate, $\frac{1}{10}$ in. long, covered with viscous hairs like the flower-stalk, which is slender, and $\frac{3}{4}$ to $1\frac{1}{4}$ ins. long. The flowers vary much in depth of shade, size, and density in the truss.

Native of eastern N. America; introduced in 1734, and probably the

KALMIA LATIFOLIA MYRTIFOLIA

most beautiful evergreen shrub obtained from that region. There are bushes of the dimensions given above in the south of England, but generally the species has not been planted so extensively as it deserves. It is said sometimes to be over 30 ft. high in a wild state. A great breadth of it in the Arnold Arboretum, near Boston, U.S.A., 200 to 300 yards long, provides every June one of the public flower feasts of that city. I have also seen it wild on the

New Hampshire Hills, where it grows in woods, but is seen at its best on grass and juniper covered hills sprinkled in groups, or as isolated bushes, generally 4 to 6 ft. high.

Var. MYRTIFOLIA *Jäger* (K. myrtifolia, *Andrè*), is a dwarf bush usually 2 to 4 ft. high, the largest leaves about 2 ins. long. It is a pretty, neat bush, useful in places where the type is too large.

Var. POLYPETALA, *Nicholson*.—A form in which the corolla lobes are divided almost to the base. It was found near South Deerfield, Mass., and is merely a curiosity of no merit.

Var. RUBRA, *K. Koch*.—Flowers deep pink.

KALMIA POLIFOLIA

K. POLIFOLIA, *Wangenheim*

(K. glauca, *Aiton*; Bot. Mag., t. 177)

An evergreen shrub, 1 to 2 ft. high, of rather thin, erect, bifurcating habit, but bushy; young shoots two-edged, covered with a fine down at first. Leaves opposite in pairs, or in threes; narrowly oblong or ovate; $\frac{3}{4}$ to $1\frac{1}{2}$ ins. long, $\frac{1}{8}$ to $\frac{3}{8}$ in. wide; recurved at the margins, tapering at both ends; dark lustrous green above, and glabrous except on the midrib; lower surface glaucous white; stalk $\frac{1}{12}$ in. long, appressed to the stem. Flowers in a terminal, flattish cluster, 1 or $1\frac{1}{2}$ ins. across; produced late in April. Corolla saucer-shaped, about $\frac{1}{2}$ in. across, with five broad, shallow lobes, of a beautiful pale purplish rose; stamens of the same colour, but with brown anthers. Calyx-lobes $\frac{1}{8}$ in. long, oblong; flower-stalks glabrous, very slender.

Native of eastern N. America; introduced in 1767. Naturally a swamp plant, it likes a cool, moist soil. Under the drier conditions usually given it under cultivation it is a sturdier, more erect shrub than it appears to be in nature, where it is described as straggling. It is very hardy, and one of the brightest of spring-flowering shrubs of its colour. Useful for forcing early into bloom for conservatories.

KALMIOPSIS LEACHIANA, *Rehder*. ERICACEÆ

(Gardeners' Chronicle, 10th May, 1941, fig. 90)

An evergreen shrub 6 to 12 ins. high, of compact, tufted habit; young shoots minutely downy. Leaves $\frac{1}{4}$ to $\frac{3}{4}$ in. long, about half as wide, oval or slightly obovate, pointed, cuneate at the base, dark green and densely dotted with glistening, sunken glands beneath. Flowers axillary and terminal, each on a slender, glandular, hairy stalk $\frac{1}{2}$ to $\frac{3}{4}$ in. long, forming erect clusters of about ten, 1 to 2 ins. long. Corolla open bell-shaped, $\frac{1}{2}$ to $\frac{5}{8}$ in. wide, rosy red tinged purple, five-lobed; calyx also five-lobed, the lobes $\frac{1}{8}$ in. long, pointed, rosy; stamens ten, packed in the mouth of the corolla, the base of each fringed with hairs.

Native of the Siskiyou Mts. of Oregon; discovered in 1930. I saw it very charmingly in flower in Mr Musgrave's garden at Hascombe, near Godalming, in May 1939. It was also shown in a pot and covered with blossom at the Alpine Garden Society's Show in April 1941, by the late Mr Guiseppi and awarded the Farrer Memorial Medal as the best plant of its class shown. It makes an admirable rock garden shrub, very distinct from Kalmia in its glandular parts and in the absence of little pouches in the corolla. According to Dr Rehder there is some danger of its becoming extinct in a wild state owing to its very limited distribution.

KERRIA JAPONICA, *De Candolle*. ROSACEÆ

(Bot. Reg., t. 1873)

A deciduous shrub of bushy form, 4 to 6 ft. high, branches and twigs slender, supple, quite glabrous and glossy, forming a dense interlacing mass. Leaves alternate, $1\frac{1}{2}$ to 4 ins. long, ovate-lanceolate, parallel-veined, the base rounded, the point long and tapering, glabrous above, hairy (especially on the veins) beneath; the margins doubly toothed. The leaves are much larger on the barren shoots of the year than on the flowering twigs. Flowers yellow, solitary at the end of short leafy twigs springing from the previous year's shoots; $1\frac{1}{4}$ to $1\frac{3}{4}$ ins. across; petals normally five, obovate; calyx green. $\frac{1}{2}$ in. across, with five oblong lobes. Stamens numerous, yellow. Fruit not often produced in this country, but as seen on wild specimens, is a cluster of two or three nut-like bodies about the size of peppercorns, enveloped in the persistent calyx. Flowers in April and May.

Var. AUREA VARIEGATA has yellow-margined leaves.

Var. PLENA (Corchorus japonicus, *Hort.*), Bot. Mag., t. 1296.—A double-flowered variety much commoner in gardens than the type, and remarkably distinct in growth, the branches being stouter, more erect, and the shrub of a gaunt and rather lanky habit, showing none of the dense twiggy character of the type. The flower is a rounded mass of bright yellow petals, 1½ to 2 ins. across. It is as hardy as the type, but is often given wall protection. In the vicarage garden at Bitton it is 12 ft. high.

Var. VARIEGATA, *Zabel.*—Like the type in habit, but scarcely so vigorous; its leaves are deeply and irregularly margined with white. It flowers more or less during the whole summer, but is scarcely so hardy as the type.

KERRIA JAPONICA

The Kerria has long been cultivated in Japan, and its existence there was known as long ago as 1700, but the double-flowered form (the first introduced) did not reach England until 1804, when it was introduced to Kew by Wm. Kerr, a plant collector sent out from that establishment the previous year to China. As the reproductive parts were wanting, its botanical affinities could only be surmised, and it was called "Corchorus japonicus," a name which still clings to it in establishments somewhat behind the times. Corchorus is a genus allied to the lindens. When the single-flowered typical plant was introduced in 1834 by Mr Reeves, and blossomed two or three years later, it was seen to belong to the rose family, and was then named Kerria by De Candolle. This species, the only one of its genus known, is a native of China, and is only naturalised or cultivated in Japan. It was collected in flower and fruit by Wilson in W. Hupeh, China, in 1900, and earlier by Henry.

The typical Kerria is a beautiful shrub when in flower, and quite hardy, thriving in good loamy soil. It is easily increased by moderately soft cuttings placed in brisk bottom heat. The variegated form likes a sheltered spot. All the kerrias are benefited by an occasional thinning out of old stems.

KETELEERIA FORTUNEI, *Carrière*. CONIFERÆ

(Abies Fortunei, *Murray*; Gardeners' Chronicle, 1884, i., figs. 64-7)

An evergreen tree, probably 100 ft. high, with horizontal branches; young shoots furnished with scurf which soon falls away leaving them smooth; winter buds small, the basal scales with long, free, linear points. Leaves linear, 1 to 1½ ins. long, $\frac{1}{12}$ to $\frac{1}{5}$ in. wide; flat, pointed, broadest near the base, where they are abruptly narrowed to a short stalk; shining green on both sides, with twelve to sixteen stomatic lines beneath, forming a pale, faintly defined band each side the midrib, which is quite prominent on both surfaces. The leaves are arranged like those of many silver firs, being attached spirally, but twisted at the base so as to bring them into two opposite spreading sets; they persist five or more years. Cones (only known from imported specimens) erect, cylindrical, 4 to 6 ins. long, stalked, and described as purple.

Native of China; introduced by Fortune in 1844, and extremely rare in cultivation. The finest tree in Europe was in Messrs Rovelli's nursery at Pallanza, in Italy. I saw this tree in May 1912, when Mr Rovelli told me it was 85 ft. high: its trunk was 2 ft. 9 ins. in diameter; many old cones were scattered beneath. It is scarcely hardy enough to thrive in the average climate of the British Isles, but would no doubt succeed well in Cornwall, S.W. Ireland, and such-like places. A small plant in the tree nursery at Kew was practically stationary in size for several years, although it withstood hard frosts with impunity. Fortune described the tree as having the appearance of a cedar of Lebanon; the Pallanza tree, comparatively young, had very much the aspect of a silver fir. Keteleeria is most nearly allied to Abies, but is very distinct in the male catkins being borne in umbels and in the persisting cone bracts.

K. DAVIDIANA, *Franchet*, is another species native of W. China. It was introduced to Kew by Henry in 1889, and Wilson found it and introduced it again in 1908. The young shoots differ from those of K. Fortunei in remaining downy for two years or more. According to Wilson's specimens of adult plants, the leaves of cone-bearing or adult branches differ from those of K. Fortunei in becoming blunt and conspicuously notched at the apex, and in having the midrib sunken above. The cone-scales are also more reflexed at the margin. Wilson found cones 8 ins. long. A healthy plant at Kew is 6 ft. high.

KOELREUTERIA. SAPINDACEÆ

A genus of five species of deciduous trees, natives of eastern Asia. They have alternate, pinnate or bipinnate leaves and flowers in large terminal panicles; calyx unequally five-lobed; petals four; fruit bladder-like. Named after J. G. Koelreuter, a professor of botany at Karlsruhe, 1733-1806.

K. APICULATA, *Rehder and Wilson*

(Gardeners' Chronicle, 17th Oct., 1925, fig. 123)

A deciduous tree, 15 to 40 ft. high, with a trunk 1 to 3 ft. in girth; young shoots at first minutely downy. Leaves doubly pinnate, with five to nine primary divisions, the basal ones of which carry as many as nine or eleven leaflets, the others bearing fewer successively towards the terminal one, which consists of a single leaflet. The entire leaf is 7 to 18 ins. long, two-thirds as wide. Leaflets arranged alternately on the stalks, mostly ovate in main outline, but conspicuously lobed and toothed, the lobes and apex either tapered or rounded, the base tapering to a short stalk; ¾ to 1½ ins. long, except the deeply lobed terminal one which is much larger; upper surface almost glabrous except on the midrib and veins; lower one downy and with tufts in the vein-axils. Flowers ½ in. long, bright yellow, borne in erect terminal panicles 6 to 12 ins. long and nearly as wide. Seed-vessel conical, bladder-like, 2 ins. long, 1½ ins. wide, with a rounded base and rounded apex, dark brick red. Seeds shining dark brown, ¼ in. long, nearly globose.

Native of W. Szechuen, China; introduced to the Coombe Wood Nursery in 1904. It flowered first at Kew in August 1921, and has ripened seed from which young plants have been raised. It is readily distinguished from K. paniculata by its usually doubly pinnate leaves, more numerous leaflets downy beneath, and less sharply pointed capsules. Wilson describes it as a low tree with a wide spreading head and relatively thick trunk. It is quite hardy at Kew, and apparently flowers more freely than paniculata; both should be given as sunny positions as possible. It is quite attractive in the fruiting state. The Chinese use the flowers for making a yellow dye.

K. BIPINNATA, *Franchet*, another Chinese species, is not hardy here nor in Paris, although it has been tried several times. It differs from K. paniculata in its leaves being invariably doubly, sometimes trebly, pinnate, in its more regularly and less coarsely toothed leaflets, and the rounder, broader valves of the fruit.

K. PANICULATA, *Laxmann*

A deciduous tree, up to 30 to 60 ft. high, with soft, pithy wood and rather gaunt habit in a young state, becoming more compact with age; young shoots minutely downy. Leaves alternate, pinnate, sometimes partially bipinnate; the nine to fifteen leaflets ovate, short-stalked or stalkless, coarsely and irregularly toothed, downy beneath. The entire leaf is from 6 to 18 ins., or even more, in length, and the separate leaflets from 1 to 4 ins. long, the larger ones often pinnately lobed at the base. Flowers in a large, terminal, pyramidal panicle, sometimes over 12 ins. long, made up of a series of elongated, slender racemes, carrying numerous short-stalked, yellow flowers, each about ½ in. wide; petals four; stamens eight, downy. Fruit a conical, inflated, three-valved capsule, 1½ to 2 ins. long; seeds about the size of peas, dark brown.

Native of China; introduced to England in 1763, and said to have first been cultivated at Croome, in Worcestershire. It is quite hardy and very handsome, flowering in July and August. When seen at its best the tree is a mass of deep yellow flowers, and these are succeeded by the striking bladder-like fruits. It loves the sun, and I have never seen it quite so fine in this country as it is in Central France. Its handsome leaves turn bright yellow in autumn. It likes a good loamy soil. The seeds afford the best means of propagation, and are obtainable from French nurserymen. Failing them, root-cuttings may be used. The tree is probably not long-lived, and is rather subject to the attacks of coral-spot fungus. One of the finest specimens in this country is in the nursery at Knap Hill. It is 40 ft. high, its trunk 6 ft. in girth, and its head of branches 105 ft. in circumference.

KOELREUTERIA PANICULATA

KOLKWITZIA AMABILIS, *Graebner*. CAPRIFOLIACEÆ

(Bot. Mag., t. 8563)

A deciduous bush, up to 12 ft. high, of twiggy habit; young shoots at first hairy, then rough. Leaves opposite, broadly ovate, long-pointed, rounded at the base, shallowly and remotely toothed; 1 to 3 ins. long, $\frac{3}{4}$

o 2 ins. wide, dark dull green and sparsely hairy above; paler, prominently net-veined and bristly on the veins beneath; ciliate; chief veins three or four each side the midrib; stalk bristly, $\frac{1}{12}$ to $\frac{1}{8}$ in. long. Flowers twin, produced during May and June in corymbs 2 to 3 ins. across, terminating short lateral twigs. Corolla bell-shaped, $\frac{5}{8}$ in. long and the same in width at the mouth, where are five roundish, spreading lobes;

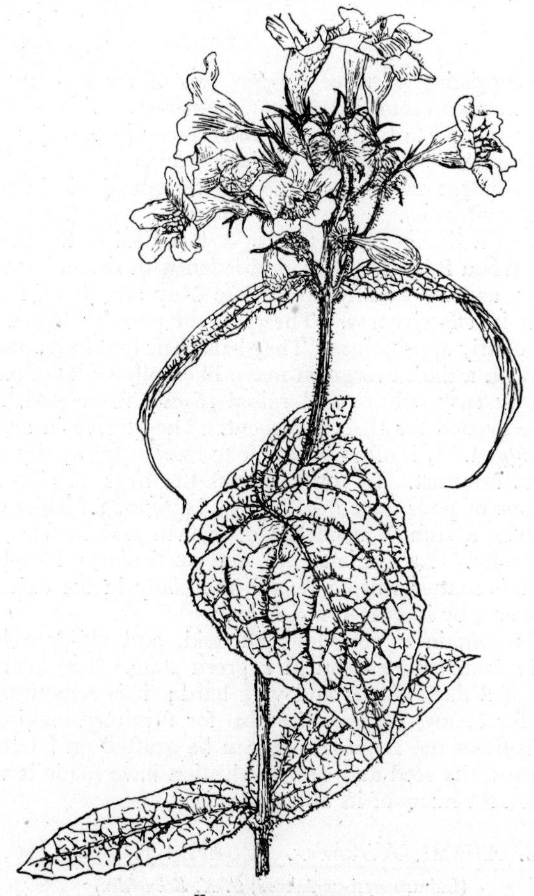

KOLKWITZIA AMABILIS

pink with yellow in the throat, hairy. Calyx $\frac{1}{2}$ in. across, with five or six very narrow, radiating lobes, hairy; flower-stalk $\frac{1}{3}$ to $\frac{5}{8}$ in. long, slender, hairy. Stamens four. Fruit egg-shaped, $\frac{1}{4}$ in. long, covered with brown bristles $\frac{1}{8}$ in. long. A curious feature is the persistent elongated calyx standing out beyond the fruit.

Native of the province of Hupeh, China, on the watershed of the Han and Yangtse rivers, where it occurs among rocks at 9000 to 10,000 ft.; introduced by Wilson for Messrs Veitch in 1901, and cultivated in the nursery at Coombe Wood, where it first flowered under cultivation in June 1910. The flowers of this rare and remarkable shrub resemble those of Abelia, but its remarkable, hairy calyx and fruit are very different. I have not seen this shrub finer anywhere than at Borde Hill, Sussex, in the garden of Col. Stephenson Clarke, where, in a position fully exposed to the south it is 11 or 12 ft. high and flowers profusely in June.

LABURNUM. LEGUMINOSÆ

A genus consisting of three species, two of them small trees, one shrubby, together with some hybrids and numerous varieties. Laburnum is very closely related to Cytisus, differing chiefly in the structure of the seed. The leaves are composed of three leaflets, and the flowers are produced in pendent racemes on the arborescent species, and in erect ones on the shrubby one.

Few trees of a similar character are so beautiful as the two common laburnums. When fully in flower, and laden with streaming racemes of golden colour, as they usually are in late May and June, nothing can surpass them in effectiveness. The German popular name, "Golden Rain," is peculiarly appropriate. They look their best in a group of three to six trees, with a dark evergreen mass, like holly or holm oak, behind them. Of very easy culture and raised readily from seed, no special directions are needed for their treatment. They thrive in any soil that is not waterlogged. It is often advisable to remove the seed-pods as soon as the flowers are past. In some seasons the trees develop and ripen enormous crops of pods, and this, besides being of no value or beauty, is apt to induce a stunted condition of growth and reduce succeeding crops of blossom. Laburnums are not particularly long-lived, and attention to this matter will be repaid, especially in the case of valued or fine specimens, by increased longevity.

The seeds contain a poisonous alkaloid, and children have been known to die from eating them in a green state. The heart-wood of the trunk is of a dark colour and very hard; it is sometimes used as a substitute for ebony, occasionally also for furniture making. Many trees and shrubs of the Leguminosæ can be grafted on laburnum, and the abundance of its seed and easy cultivation have made it very much used as a stock for many of its allies.

L. ADAMI, *Kirchner*. PURPLE LABURNUM

(Laburnocytisus Adami, *C. K. Schneider*)

A deciduous tree with the habit and aspect of L. anagyroides, up to 25 ft. high; leaflets oval or obovate, 1½ to 2½ ins. long. Racemes 5 to 7 ins. long; flowers yellowish suffused with purple, of the same shape and character as those of L. anagyroides, but, like the leaflets, smaller. The leaves and young shoots differ in being nearly or quite glabrous.

Although much inferior to either of the common laburnums in beauty, there is no more interesting tree in our gardens than this. It appeared in the nursery of Mr Jean Louis Adam, at Vitry, near Paris, in 1825. According to Adam's account, he had grafted the dwarf purple broom (Cytisus purpureus) on a common laburnum, and on the grafted plant a branch appeared with purplish yellow flowers intermediate in hue between those of scion and stock—L. Adami, in fact, as we know it to-day. A few years after L. Adami had been put into commerce, a further remarkable phenomenon was observed in connection with this tree. It was found that it had a tendency to "sport" back more or less to both the parent types. This character it has maintained ever since, and to-day almost every specimen of Laburnum Adami shows on its branches, not only the hybrid itself but pieces of pure L. anagyroides and pure Cytisus purpureus that have sprung spontaneously from its tissues. All three flower together, the curious tufts of the cytisus suggesting witches' brooms. Many authorities have in times past doubted the possibility of a hybrid being produced by grafting, but the correctness of Adam's account has latterly been proved by Prof. Winkler of Tubingen, who has produced graft hybrids between the tomato and black nightshade. Further, a similar instance has been brought to light of graft hybrids between medlar and hawthorn (see Cratægomespilus). These graft hybrids have been termed "chimæras," because there seems to be a mixture of the parents in their tissues, rather than a genuine and entire fusion. The outer tissues are often found under the microscope to resemble those of one parent, the inner ones those of the other.

L. ALPINUM, *Berchtold and Presl.* SCOTCH LABURNUM (Plate 16)

A deciduous tree, 20 ft. (rarely 30 ft.) high, with usually a short, sturdy trunk. Leaves trifoliolate, with a stalk 1 to 2 ins. long; leaflets oval or obovate, 2 to 4 ins. long, deep green, not so downy beneath as in L. anagyroides. Racemes pendulous, slender, 10 to 15 ins. long, carrying numerous golden yellow flowers, each $\frac{3}{4}$ in. long on a thin stalk $\frac{1}{4}$ to $\frac{1}{2}$ in. long; both the flower-stalks and the main-stalk of the raceme are glabrous or thinly downy. Seed-pods 2 to 3 ins. long, flat, with the upper seam (suture) distinctly winged and forming a knife-like edge.

Native of Central and S. Europe; cultivated in the British Isles for at least three hundred years, probably much longer, but not a native. It was long confused with the common laburnum until its distinctness was noted by Miller in his Dictionary. It differs in the following characters: leaflets larger and less hairy; racemes longer, and opening two to three weeks later (early June); upper seam of pod flattened out into a thin edge in place of the thickened one of L. anagyroides. L. alpinum is undoubtedly the superior species for gardens.

Var. AUTUMNALE.—Usually bears a small second crop of blossom in autumn.

Var. GRANDIFLORUM.—Leaflets broader; flowers larger, racemes longer. Var. MACROSTACHYS is perhaps the same.

Var. PENDULUM.—Branches weeping.

Var. PILOSUM.—Racemes longer, under-side of leaflet furnished with scattered hairs.

An old variety commonly known as "Latest and Longest" is still one of the best of laburnums.

L. ANAGYROIDES, *Medicus.* COMMON LABURNUM
(L. vulgare, *Presl.*)

A deciduous tree, 20 to 30 ft. (rarely more) high, often branching close to the ground and forming a wide-spreading, bushy tree. Leaves trifoliolate, with a stalk 2 to 3 ins. long; leaflets oval or slightly obovate, $1\frac{1}{2}$ to 3 ins. long, downy beneath. Racemes pendulous, cylindrical, 6 to 10 ins. long, downy. Flowers golden yellow, $\frac{3}{4}$ in. long, each borne on a thin, downy stalk $\frac{1}{4}$ to $\frac{1}{2}$ in. long. Seed-pod 2 to 3 ins. long, the upper seam or suture thickened and keeled, but not winged as in L. alpinum. It blooms from the third week of May into June.

Native of Central and S. Europe, long cultivated in, but not a native of Britain. It was probably one of the earliest ornamental plants introduced to this country, as its great beauty would attract early travellers, and the seed could be easily obtained and transported. No foreign tree is better adapted to our climate. The differences between it and L. alpinum are indicated under that species.

Var. ALSCHINGERI, *C. K. Schneider*.—A wild variety which is found in East Europe, and differs chiefly from the type in the calyx being distinctly two-lipped, the lower lip the longer; the leaflets are more silky-hairy and grey-blue beneath. Var. JACQUINIANUM is similar.

Var. AUREUM.—Leaves golden yellow; one of the prettiest of golden-leaved trees. It affords one of the commonest instances showing the influence of scion on stock, for on grafted trees yellow-leaved shoots frequently appear considerably beneath the point of union. (Syn. chrysophyllum.)

Var. AUTUMNALE, flowers a second time in autumn.

Var. CARLIERI.—Leaflets smaller; racemes thinner; flowers more distinctly spotted. Said to be a hybrid between L. anagyroides and Cytisus nigricans, which is extremely doubtful.

Var. INVOLUTUM (syn. bullatum).—Leaves curled. A curiosity merely.

Var. PENDULUM.—Branchlets slender and weeping; very graceful in habit.

Var. QUERCIFOLIUM.—Leaflets curiously lobed after the fashion of an oak leaf, the main leaf-stalk being sometimes winged. The leaf is occasionally five-parted (quinquefoliolate). A very distinct and rather handsome form.

Var. SEMPERFLORENS.—Flowers a second time in late summer.

Var. SESSILIFOLIUM.—Leaves crowded, almost stalkless, their bases thus being brought close to the branchlet. A curiosity of no garden value, the branches having a stiff, stunted appearance; not free-flowering.

Two hybrids at least, produced by natural agencies, between anagyroides and alpinum are cultivated. They are L. PARKSII and L. WATERI, both beautiful trees, the latter especially; they show botanical characters intermediate between the parents, but L. Watereri has retained the full length of raceme of L. alpinum. The laburnums known as INTERMEDIUM and VOSSII are of the same origin.

L. CARAMANICUM, *Bentham and Hooker*

(Bot. Mag., t. 7898)

Although described as a small tree in its native country, this species has not yet, in Great Britain, got beyond the dimensions of a shrub 3 to 6 ft. high. It is deciduous, and has a thin habit, making long, straight, erect shoots, which towards the end of the summer produce near the top a number of short, stiff twigs, each terminated by a raceme of flowers. Leaves grey-green, trifoliolate, short-stalked; leaflets almost stalkless, obovate, with a short abrupt point, from $\frac{1}{4}$ to $\frac{3}{4}$ in. long, the side ones the smaller. Racemes terminal, erect, 3 to 7 ins. long. Flowers golden yellow, $\frac{3}{4}$ in. long; the stalk slender, $\frac{1}{4}$ in. long, with a small bract about the middle; standard petal roundish, $\frac{1}{2}$ in. diameter. Seed-pod 2 to 3 ins. long, $\frac{1}{2}$ in. wide, flat, the upper seam distinctly winged, developing one to four seeds.

Native of Greece and Asia Minor; introduced about 1879, but still very uncommon. It has lived outside at Kew for a good many years, but the shoots are cut back severely every winter. Owing to its flowering late in the season on the shoots of the year, this does not affect its blossoming, although the plants increase slowly in size. To be seen at its best, no doubt, it needs a hotter, sunnier climate than ours. It flowers too late to ripen seed with certainty, but they do occasionally ripen, as in 1911. Cuttings taken in August will strike root in gentle heat.

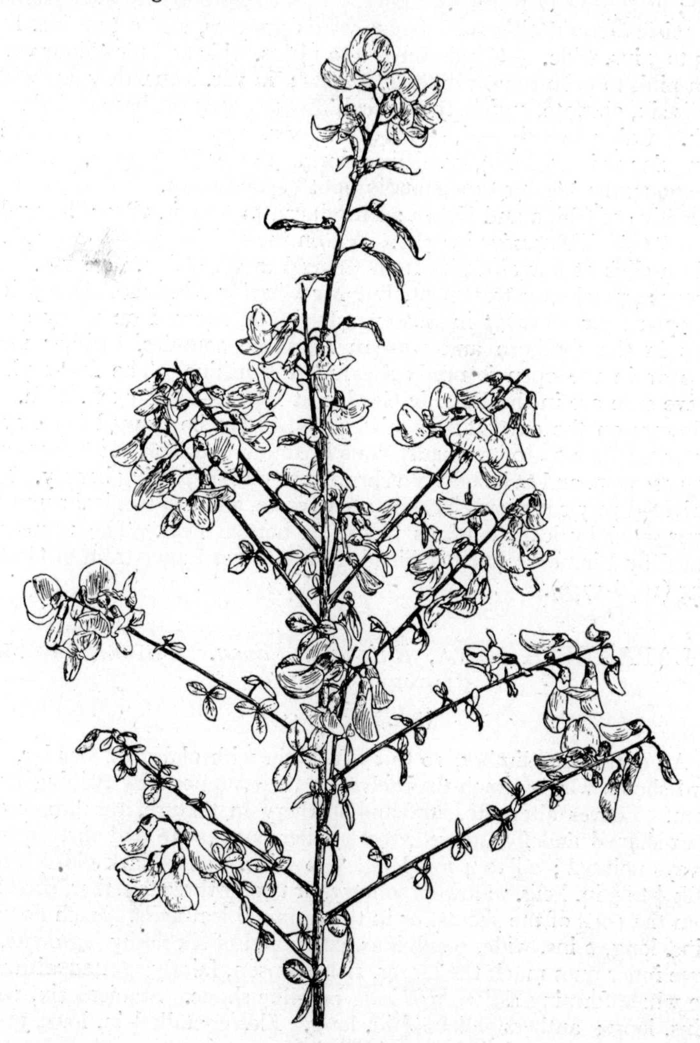

LABURNUM CARAMANICUM

LAGERSTRŒMIA INDICA, *Linnæus*. CRAPE MYRTLE
LYTHRACEÆ (Plate 17)

(Bot. Mag., t. 405)

A deciduous tree 20 to 30 ft. high, or a shrub, the bark of the trunk and older branches grey and smooth; young shoots glabrous, four-angled. Leaves opposite, alternate or in whorls of three, privet-like, mostly obovate, not toothed, glabrous; 1 to 2½ ins. long, ¾ to 1½ ins. wide; very shortly stalked. Flowers produced from July to September in panicles terminating the current year's growths, and 6 to 8 ins. long by 3 to 5 ins. wide. Each flower is 1 to 1½ ins. wide and the colour varies from pink to deep red on different plants; in var. ALBA they are white. Petals six, obovate, curiously crinkled, contracted at the base to a slender stalk. Calyx bell-shaped, ⅓ to ½ in. long, green, glabrous, with six triangular pointed lobes, persisting during the fruiting stage. Stamens numerous, the slender style standing out beyond them.

Native of China and Korea; introduced to Kew in 1759; figured in the *Botanical Magazine* in 1798. Wilson found it in open grassy places and on cliffs at low altitudes from Central to W. China. Near London it needs greenhouse treatment, but Mr Charles Nix has flowered it in the open near Crawley in Sussex. It should succeed on many sunny walls in the southern and western maritime counties. Either under glass or in the open it needs the fullest sunshine. The finest plants I have seen are in the Botanic Garden at Padua—trees 25 ft. high. As it flowers on the current season's shoots, it can be pruned back every winter, as appears to be usually done in Italian gardens. It flowers over a long season, and at its best is a shrub or tree of surpassing beauty. Now cultivated very commonly in sunny temperate, and sub-tropical countries. Propagated by leafy cuttings placed in bottom heat. The genus was named by Linnæus after his friend, Magnus von Lagerström of Gottenburg (1696-1759).

LAPAGERIA ROSEA, *Ruiz and Pavon*. CHILEAN BELL FLOWER. LILIACEÆ

(Bot. Mag., t. 4447)

An evergreen climber, 10 to 15 ft. high, with glabrous, slender, stiff, hard shoots which attach themselves to their supports by twining round them. Leaves alternate, stiff and leathery in texture, the larger ones heart-shaped and five-nerved, the smaller ones ovate and three-nerved, always pointed; 1¼ to 4 ins. long, ¾ to 3 ins. wide; dark glossy green, stalk ¼ to ⅜ in. long. Flowers solitary, or two or three together, produced from the ends of the shoots, or in the terminal leaf-axils. Each flower is 3 ins. long, 2 ins. wide, pendulous, composed of six fleshy segments, the three inner ones much the larger, rich crimson, faintly spotted with rose, the whole forming a flower of long bell-like shape. Stamens six, white, 2 ins. long; anthers yellow, ¼ in. long. Flower-stalk ½ in. long, mostly covered with clasping bracts. Fruit an ovoid-oblong berry, rather three-sided, 2 ins. long, 1 in. wide, tapering towards the apex, with numerous seeds embedded in its pulp.

Native of Chile; introduced to Kew in 1847, ever since which date it has been prized as one of the most beautiful-flowered of greenhouse climbers. In later times it has been much grown on shady walls in Cornwall, Devon, and similar climates. It has also been successfully grown and flowered in the Edinburgh Botanic Garden on a south wall shaded by a high building. It is one of the remarkable woody climbers belonging to the lily family, and has a rambling root system from which it sends up new shoots. The whole plant at maturity is curiously stiff in texture and, apart from the flowers, in no way attractive. It does not like fierce sunshine, loves abundant moisture and a peaty sandy soil. It flowers over most of the summer and autumn months. Propagated by seeds or layers. The flowers vary in size and depth of colouring, and several forms have been named, the best of which is SUPERBA.

Var. ALBIFLORA (syn. L. alba) has pure white exquisitely beautiful flowers and was introduced by Richard Pearce in 1860. It cannot be relied on to come true from seeds. (*Bot. Mag.*, t. 4892.) The genus, of which this is the only species known, was named in honour of the Empress Josephine, whose maiden name was "de la Pagerie."

Dr Wilfrid Fox, whilst travelling in Chile in 1932, found a form of Lapageria growing wild whose flowers were white striped lengthwise with crimson.

LARDIZABALA BITERNATA, *Ruiz and Pavon*.
LARDIZABALACEÆ

(Bot. Mag., t. 4501)

A vigorous evergreen climber, with ternate, biternate, and triternate leaves. The three, six, or nine leaflets are of hard texture, each 2 to 4 ins. long, the middle one of each trio the largest. They vary much in outline, but are mostly ovate, the lateral ones more or less oblique, and often sessile; margins shallowly crenate, with here and there a sharply pointed tooth; leaf-stalks covered with short brown hairs. Flowers unisexual; males $\frac{3}{4}$ in. across, produced in drooping spikes 3 to 4 ins. long from the leaf axils; the sepals form the most effective part of the flower, being broadly ovate, fleshy and dark chocolate purple; petals small, narrow, white and mealy. Female flowers on slender stalks 1 in. long, solitary in the leaf-axils; rather larger than the male. Fruit sausage-shaped, 2 to 3 ins. long; seeds flattened and about the size of small peas.

Native of Chile; introduced in 1844, it flowered in the Exeter nursery five years later. Seen in flower, it is very striking. The fruit is sweet, pulpy, and edible, and is said to be sold in the markets of Chile. This climber is essentially one for the milder parts of the kingdom. It is too tender to be satisfactory even on a wall at Kew.

LARIX. LARCH. CONIFERÆ

Amongst the comparatively few deciduous conifers, the larches stand out as peculiarly well-marked and distinct. They are all trees of timber-producing size, forming an erect, tapering trunk, carrying usually a cone-shaped head of horizontal branches upturned at the ends, and often ultimately pendulous spray. As in the cedars, the branchlets are of two kinds: (1) elongated slender ones, growing from a few inches to 2 ft. or more yearly, and bearing the leaves singly and spirally; and (2) short, spur-like ones which lengthen a minute fraction of an inch annually, and bear numerous (20 to 40) leaves crowded in a terminal tuft. Leaves linear or needle-like, falling in autumn. Flowers unisexual, both sexes appearing on the one tree. Males globose to cylindrical, made up of numerous yellow-anthered, short-stalked stamens. Females erect, globose, usually red, developing into a cone composed of thin, concave, rounded, very persistent, woody scales; bracts either protruded or included. Seeds in pairs on each scale, winged, ripening and falling the first autumn. Of its nearest allies, with a similar leaf arrangement, Pseudolarix differs in the much larger, more woody cone-scales falling away early from the central axis; Cedrus is, of course, evergreen, and its cones much larger.

The larches are widely spread over the cool parts of the northern hemisphere, often in mountainous regions. They like a fairly good loamy soil, and an abundant rainfall. One species, L. americana, succeeds in damp spots, but the rest like a well-drained site. They should always, if possible, be raised from seeds, which should be sown evenly and thinly, and slightly covered with soil—the common larch out-of-doors, usually in raised beds not more than 4 ft. wide to facilitate weeding, the rarer ones in unheated frames for better protection. They may be planted out permanently at $1\frac{1}{2}$ ft. high and upwards. Rarer sorts can be grafted in spring on seedlings of the common larch.

Larches are very liable to be infested with a white woolly insect (*Chermes abietis*), commonly known as "larch blight." This insect passes part of its existence on spruce. It is thought that the punctures caused by it afford one means by which the spores of the fungoid parasite, *Dasyscypha calycina*, effects its entry. This fungus, commonly known as "larch canker" or "larch blister," has done very much damage to larch plantations during recent decades. The "blight" is best attacked by spraying with paraffin emulsion, especially in spring; the "canker," with Bordeaux mixture. But such measures can of course only be adopted for comparatively small garden specimens. The canker is as yet only seriously affecting the common larch (*q.v.*).

L. AMERICANA, *Michaux*. TAMARACK

(L. laricina, *Koch*; L. microcarpa, *Desfontaines*)

A tree 50 to 80 ft. high, with a trunk sometimes nearly 2 ft. in diameter; young shoots often glaucous, turning yellowish brown, never downy. Leaves three-sided, $\frac{3}{4}$ to $1\frac{1}{4}$ ins. long, very slender, bluntish. Cones egg-shaped, $\frac{1}{3}$ to $\frac{2}{3}$ in. long, $\frac{1}{4}$ to $\frac{1}{2}$ in. wide; scales enclosing the bracts.

Native of eastern N. America, from Newfoundland and Labrador south to Virginia, and west to the Rocky Mountains. It is distinguished from all other cultivated larches by its small cones. Introduced, according to Aiton, in 1760, it has never been much cultivated, owing, no doubt, to the greater beauty and economic value of the European larch, but as it thrives in places too damp for the latter (occupying swampy ground in some of its native haunts), it is worth trying in such positions. There are trees about 70 ft. high at Arley Castle, near Bewdley, and elsewhere. Some confusion exists in gardens between this species and L. dahurica, both having been called "L. pendula," and the latter having at one time been regarded as E. American. L. americana is easily distinguished by its shorter leaves and smaller cones.

L. EUROLEPIS, *A. Henry*. DUNKELD LARCH

(L. Henryana, *Rehder*)

A hybrid between L. europæa, the common larch, and L. leptolepis, the apanese one, first raised about 1900 at Dunkeld in Perthshire, where considerble plantations of it are growing. The year-old shoots resemble those of ommon larch in their yellowish colour but show the influence of leptolepis being sometimes slightly downy, also in the bracts of the young cones being eflexed, this latter character being one of the best distinctive features of the apanese species. The adult cones take after common larch in being conical, their yellowish stalks, and in the bracts being occasionally exposed. I have een plantations at Dunkeld and Blair-Atholl which are notable for their vigour nd cleanliness. Up to the present I believe they have escaped infestation by ither insects or fungi. Trees in favourable situations should in time attain tatures of 80 ft. or more. According to the late Prof. Henry, hybrid seedlings ave repeatedly been obtained from ten trees of L. leptolepis at Dunkeld that ere raised from Japanese seed sown in 1884. They are evidently fertilised y pollen wafted on to them when in flower from numerous common larches rowing near.

L. eurolepis promises to be a useful addition to timber trees, especially if rst crosses can continue to be raised. The value of the second generation rees is not yet conclusively ascertained, but it is probable that, as with L. endula, they will not possess the vigour of first generation trees.

L. EUROPÆA, *De Candolle*. COMMON LARCH

(L. decidua, *Miller*)

A tree reaching 100 to 140 ft. in height in this country, with an erect, apering trunk, 2 to 5 ft. thick, clothed with fissured, scaling bark; branchlets ale yellowish grey, not downy. Leaves light green, $\frac{3}{4}$ to $1\frac{1}{2}$ ins. long, linear, vith the midrib raised beneath, and with two to four lines of stomata at each ide of it. Female flowers red, $\frac{1}{2}$ in. long, egg-shaped. Cones at first reddish, ltimately 1 to $1\frac{1}{2}$ ins. long, $\frac{3}{4}$ to 1 in. wide at the base, tapering slightly towards he top; scales rounded, downy at the base outside.

Native of N. and Central Europe, mostly in mountainous regions; ntroduced early in the seventeenth century, but first brought into notice as a orest tree in the British Isles by the third and fourth Dukes of Atholl, 100 o 150 years later. Two of the oldest, or perhaps the very oldest larches in he British Isles are standing near the old cathedral at Dunkeld, planted there n 1738. No tree ever introduced to Britain has proved of so much value, or een so extensively planted. For many years its economic importance has xceeded that of any other tree—even the oak. About the middle of last entury it began to be noticeably attacked by a fungoid parasite, known as he "larch blister" or "larch canker." This is *Dasyscypha calycina*, and its irulence has increased, so that many plantations have been partially or vholly destroyed. Larches growing in damp, lowland sites, or in pure stands, re more liable to disease than those growing on bleak hill-sides, or mixed vith broad-leaved trees.

As a garden tree the larch has much to recommend it; in habit it is ingularly beautiful when grown as an isolated specimen, the horizontal or pwardly curved branches being furnished with pendulous branchlets. It ttains to an imposing height; its trunk is handsomely coloured, and no tree xceeds it in the beauty and soft tenderness of the young green foliage.

Two weeping forms are in cultivation :—

Var. PENDULA.—A tree with an erect trunk and horizontal branches, b with the pendulous character of the branchlets extremely developed.

Var. PENDULINA.—Wholly pendulous, the tree forming an umbrella-shape head of branches and branchlets without a leader.

L. SIBIRICA, *Ledebour* (L. europæa sibirica, *Loudon*). Siberian Larch.—Althoug closely related to the common larch, this may be distinguished by the earlier grow in spring, the longer, more slender leaves, and in the more concave scales of the con It appears to have no value in this country. Its early growth renders it very subje to injury by late spring frosts. I have only seen plants a few feet high.

L. GRIFFITHIANA, *Carrière*. HIMALAYAN LARCH

(Bot. Mag., t. 8181)

So far as the British Isles are concerned, this larch is only likely to con under the notice of those whose gardens are in the milder countie Introduced first by Sir Joseph Hooker, in 1848, and by others subsequentl very few trees now exist in the country, and of them the best are at Coldrenic in Cornwall, and Strete Raleigh, in Devon. In the former place a tree (se *Gardeners' Chronicle*, 2nd Mar. 1907, fig. 56) has attained about as high stature as it does in Sikkim, being nearly 60 ft. high. From other larch L. Griffithiana is well distinguished by the large size of its purplish cones, whic are 2½ to 3 ins. long, 1 to 1¼ ins. diameter, cylindrical, slightly tapering towar the top ; scales roundish obovate, straight cut across the top, downy outside bracts yellowish, longer than the scales, the awl-like apex much reflexe at least when young. The tree has much the habit of common larch, but th branchlets are more markedly pendulous. The young shoots are downy, an the leaves 1 to 1¼ ins. long. They are very subject to the attacks of the whi woolly larch blight, and an occasional spraying with paraffin emulsion durin the summer may be necessary to keep the trees in health whilst young.

Native of Nepal, Sikkim, and Bhotan.

L. KURILENSIS, *Mayr*. KURILE LARCH

(L. dahurica japonica, *Maximowicz*)

A tree up to 70 ft. high, forming a stout trunk 2 to 2½ ft. in diameter young shoots very downy and dark brown, the down persisting the secon season. Leaves ½ to 1 in. long, rounded at the end, very broad in proportio to their length, of a glaucous green, and with two conspicuous stomat bands beneath. Cones about ¾ in. long, oval-cylindrical, the scales with thi slightly bevelled, not reflexed, margins, indented about the middle.

Native of the Kurile Islands, especially on the main island (Iturup It was at first regarded as a variety of L. dahurica, from which its broad leaves and persistently downy and much darker coloured young shoots we distinguish it. It was introduced to Kew in 1897, from Japan. It is at prese remarkable there, chiefly for its curious, thin, lanky aspect, due to the scarcit of the elongated branches as compared with the short spur-like ones. This probably due to want of vigour, but it is still one of the least promising of larche probably needing colder winters and later springs than obtain in S. England.

L. LEPTOLEPIS, *Endlicher*. JAPANESE LARCH

(Gardeners' Chronicle, 1883, i., fig. 13 ; L. Kaempferi, *Sargent*)

A tree 80 to 100 ft. high, with a trunk 3 to 4 ft. thick, and (in the ope a wide-spreading head of branches ; bark scaling, showing a pale grey-brow surface beneath ; young shoots glabrous to downy, rich reddish brown the firs winter. Leaves $1\frac{1}{4}$ to $1\frac{5}{8}$ ins. long, $\frac{1}{16}$ to $\frac{1}{12}$ in. wide; rather glaucous, flat above, ridged beneath, and with two bands of stomatic lines there. Cones somewhat globose, and broader in proportion to their length than those of any other larch, being about 1 in. wide and long; also very distinct in the thin, rounded scales being markedly curved back when ripe.

Native of Japan; introduced in 1861 by John Gould Veitch. A good deal of attention has lately been given to this tree as one likely to take the place of the common larch in places where that tree, through the attacks

LARIX LEPTOLEPIS

of larch canker, has ceased to be profitable. Hitherto the Japanese larch has been almost, although not wholly, immune from the attacks of larch canker, but it is well known that newly introduced trees are not so liable to disease as those softened by long cultivation, and the great proportion of planted trees are quite young. It is certainly worth extensive trial under forest conditions. At Dunkeld and Blair Atholl, in Perthshire, both classic sites in regard to larch planting, I saw very promising plantations some years ago. It is never likely to rival the European one in size. In the garden it is worth growing as an isolated specimen or in a small group, being very distinct from the common larch in the greater thickness and proportionate length of the branches, and in the broader cones and leaves.

L. OCCIDENTALIS, *Nuttall*. WEST AMERICAN LARCH

(Bot. Mag., t. 8253)

A tree 100 to 200 ft. high, with a narrow, pyramidal head, and a trunk sometimes 6 to 8 ft. in diameter; bark scaling. On some of the young trees at Kew the young shoots are glabrous, on others downy. Leaves $1\frac{1}{4}$ to $1\frac{3}{4}$ ins. long, scarcely distinguishable from those of common larch. Cones oblong to egg-shaped, about $1\frac{1}{2}$ ins. long, $\frac{3}{4}$ in. wide; the scales thin, rounded, slightly reflexed at the margin. The cone is rendered very distinct by the conspicuous tongue-like apex of the bracts protruding horizontally $\frac{1}{4}$ in. or more beyond the scales.

Native of western N. America, from British Columbia southwards. In N. Montana, in the neighbourhood of Flat Head Lake, it is, according to Sargent, sometimes 250 ft. high. It is, therefore, the most magnificent of all larches, and as it produces a fine timber it deserves a thorough trial under forest conditions in this country. It was introduced to Kew in 1881 by Prof. Sargent, and trees there are now over 60 ft. high, with shapely trunks and short branches, in general appearance very like the common larches close by, except for the prominent bracts of the cones alluded to above and the more slender habit. For many years these were the only trees in the country, but a considerable quantity of seed has lately been imported from which thousands of thriving young trees have been raised. Inhabiting the same geographical region as L. occidentalis is

L. LYALLII, *Parlatore.* Lyall's Larch.—This is a tree 40 to 50, occasionally 80 ft. in height. Its cones resemble those of L. occidentalis in having conspicuously protruded bracts, but it is quite distinct in other respects. The young wood is densely woolly, almost felted, the leaves four-sided, cones up to 2 ins. long, with the scales distinctly fringed, pink when young. A few small plants have been introduced, but they have a miserable appearance, and the species does not give any promise as yet of succeeding in the British Isles. Native of China.

L. PENDULA, *Salisbury*

(L. americana pendula, *Loudon* ; L. dahurica, *A. Henry*, not *Turczaninow*)

A presumed chance hybrid between L. americana and L. europæa which was first noticed in Peter Collinson's garden at Peckham and afterwards taken by him to Mill Hill where he went to reside in 1740. For a long time it was thought to have been introduced from America but this has never been confirmed and, unless it was afterwards completely destroyed in its wild state there by early settlers, is indeed unlikely. Its vigour and fertility are commented on by early writers and a good many seedlings raised from it became distributed through the country. Henry did not think that they have retained the vigour of the original, but there are, nevertheless, trees in this country between 70 and 90 feet high. The finest is a tree of the latter height at Woburn with a trunk about 8 ft. in girth.

Following Henry (*Trees of Great Britain and Ireland*, vol. ii., p. 378), I used the name " L. dahurica " for this tree in early editions, and the description there given was mostly based on a tree at Kew which proved to be L. pendula after having for many years been labelled " L. dahurica." Prof. Henry first broached the idea of its hybrid origin in the *Gardeners' Chronicle*, 18th Sept. 1915, p. 178. This theory seems to be pretty generally accepted although, according to Aiton, L. americana was not introduced until 1760 or twenty years after L. pendula existed in Collinson's garden at Mill Hill. Full reliance, however, must not be placed on Aiton's statements in regard to the dates he gives for the introduction of plants. No doubt his statements were based on the best knowledge available for him, but in the case of a tree like the American larch, widely spread in nature and easily transmitted by means of seed, it might very well have been introduced at a much earlier date than he knew of.

The young shoots of L. pendula are pink when young, changing to yellowish, not downy. Leaves very much the same as those of common larch. Cones ⅝ to 1½ ins. long, ½ to 1 in. wide, ovoid-conic ; cone scales brown, downy at the base, with usually bevelled margins ; bract usually concealed.

L. DAHURICA, *Turczaninow.*—The true Dahurian larch is scarcely known in this country, where it grows so badly as not to be worth cultivation. At home it is a large tree up to 80 or sometimes 100 ft. high. The young shoots are usually downy; the egg-shaped cones ¾ to 1 in. long. There are two big old trees in the Moscow Botanic Garden. Native of E. Siberia ; introduced in 1827. Closely related to it is

L. OLGENSIS, *A. Henry*, which was originally described in the *Gardeners' Chronicle*, 27th Feb. 1915. It is chiefly remarkable for the dense covering of reddish hairs that clothe the young twigs. Cones ¾ to 1 in. long. It was collected in 1860 on the shores of Olga Bay in E. Siberia, about 120 miles to the north-east of Vladivostock. Seeds were introduced a few years ago and young plants are at Bedgebury in Kent, but they are not succeeding well.

L. Potanini, *Batalin*. Western Chinese Larch

(Bot. Mag., t. 9338; L. chinensis, *Beissner*; L. thibetica, *Franchet*)

A tree 60 to 70, sometimes 100 ft. high; young shoots yellowish and slightly downy. Leaves 1 in. long, pointed, somewhat four-sided through the prominence of the midrib above and below. Cones egg-shaped, about 1½ ins. long, ¾ to 1 in. wide, rounded at the top; scales rounded, downy outside; bracts protruded.

Native of W. China; introduced for Messrs Veitch by Wilson from the neighbourhood of Tatien-lu in 1904. The leaves have a strong, aromatic, and distinctive odour when crushed. Judging by a figure of the tree as it grows in China (see *Kew Bulletin*, 1910, p. 174), it has much the general aspect of the common larch. Wilson says it yields the most valuable timber in W. China. It differs from all other larches except L. Lyallii in the leaves being ridged on both surfaces, and from that species in the only slightly downy young twigs.

L. Principis Rupprechtii, *Mayr*. Prince Rupprecht's Larch

(L. dahurica Principis Rupprechtii, *Rehder and Wilson*.)

A deciduous tree 80 to 100 ft. high, found by H. Mayr in 1903, at Wutai in the province of Shansi, N. China. Forests of it were afterwards found to exist by Purdom and the American collector Meyer, on the slopes of Wutai mountain. Young plants were introduced to Kew from the Arnold Arboretum in 1916 which grew well and by 1930 were 20 to 30 ft. high. Their young shoots are reddish brown, not downy. A remarkable feature of the young trees at Kew is the size of the leaves on the long shoots (not on the spur-like ones) which are often 2 to 4 ins. long. This is, no doubt, a juvenile character merely, as Mayr figures them only 1 to 1¾ ins. long. Cones as figured by Mayr 1¾ ins. long, 1⅛ ins. wide, their scales erect, thin, finely toothed, not downy, the bracts showing mostly or only at the base of the cone. Specimens in the Herbarium at Kew, collected in Korea by Wilson in 1918, are very distinct in their much smaller cones, which are only ¾ to 1⅛ ins. long, in this respect approaching those of L. dahurica, of which species Rehder and Wilson have connected this larch as a variety. Besides N. China and Korea, they give Manchuria and Amurland as other habitats. Cones produced on the trees at Kew resemble those of the Korean trees in size.

LAURELIA serrata, *Philippi*. Monimiaceæ

(Bot. Mag., t. 8279; L. aromatica, *Masters*, not *Poiret*)

An evergreen tree with square, downy young stems. Leaves leathery, opposite, narrowly oval, 2½ to 5 ins. long, 1 to 2½ ins. wide; tapered at both ends, coarsely toothed, dark glossy green and glabrous on both surfaces, except for a few centrally attached, flattened hairs beneath; stalk ¼ in. long, downy. When crushed the leaf has a pleasant, spicy, aromatic fragrance, similar to that of bay laurel. The flowers are packed in short racemes in the leaf-axils, small and very numerous, yellowish green. The most remarkable feature of the plant are the seeds, which, when they escape from the capsules, are seen to be furnished with a tuft of long fine brown hairs which enable them to travel long distances on the wind.

Native of Chile. Of this interesting and peculiar tree there are examples in the milder parts of Ireland and in Cornwall. It is only hardy in such places. It flowered in the garden at Kilmacurragh in April 1904. A tree at Penjerrick, near Falmouth, is about 50 ft. high.

LAURUS. LAURACEÆ

Two species of evergreen trees or shrubs with entire, glabrous leaves, aromatic when crushed. Flowers with the sexes on different plants and borne in small, axillary, almost stalkless clusters; sepals four; stamens usually twelve. Fruit a black berry. The name is an old Latin one.

L. CANARIENSIS, *Webb and Berthelot*. CANARY ISLAND LAUREL

An evergreen tree up to 60 ft. high in a wild state, with a trunk 2 to 3 ft. in diameter; young shoots dark purplish brown, downy, giving off a pleasant aromatic fragrance like that of the common bay laurel when crushed. Leaves similarly aromatic, alternate, firm and leathery, ovate or oval, abruptly pointed or with a short slender point, wedge-shaped to rounded at the base; 2½ to 5 ins. long, 2 to 3 ins. wide; lustrous dark green and glabrous above; pale, dull, conspicuously veined and more or less hairy especially on the midrib beneath; stalk ¼ to ½ in. long. Flowers ⅜ in. wide, pale greenish yellow, produced in April on short, downy-stalked umbels in the axils of the leaves of the previous summer. The perianth has four segments with down on the back; stamens usually sixteen to twenty. Fruit egg-shaped, ½ in. long, each borne on a stout stalk ¼ in. long.

Native of the Canary Islands and the Azores. This fine evergreen is hardy in the southern and western maritime counties and in localities with a similar climate. It is cultivated at Lanarth in Cornwall and at Abbotsbury in Dorset. The tree is unisexual, the male flowers with their numerous stamens being the more ornamental. On large old trees the leaves appear to be comparatively narrower, longer and more lanceolate in outline than in the younger cultivated ones. This species differs from L. nobilis, a much hardier one, in its leaves being much larger and in its twigs being downy.

L. NOBILIS, *Linnæus*. BAY LAUREL

An evergreen, aromatic tree or shrub, 20 to 40 ft., sometimes 60 ft. high, usually of dense pyramidal shape, and formed of a cluster of erect, much-branched stems; young shoots and leaves glabrous. Leaves alternate, narrowly oval or ovate, 1½ to 4 ins. long, ½ to 1½ ins. wide; usually about equally tapered to each end, of firm texture, dark glossy green, often with wavy margins; stalk ⅛ to ⅓ in. long. Flowers greenish yellow, small, very shortly stalked, produced in small umbels in the uppermost leaf-axils; the sexes on different trees. Fruit globose or slightly oval, shining, black, ½ in. long.

Native of the Mediterranean region; cultivated in Britain since the sixteenth century, probably before. It is quite hardy at Kew, although occasionally browned by hard winters. This is the true "laurel" of the ancients, and the one whose leaves were used to make crowns for triumphant heroes, and the fruiting sprays to make wreaths for distinguished poets (poets laureate). It is interesting to note in the latter connection that the term "bachelor" as applied to the recipient of degrees, has been derived through the French *bachelier* from "baccalaureus," *i.e.* laurel-berry. Nowadays the leaves are put to a more prosaic use, and are commonly used for flavouring milk puddings. It has no relationship with common or cherry laurel (see Prunus Laurocerasus), or with the Alexandrian laurel (see Danaë Laurus).

The bay laurel bears clipping well, and is very largely grown in tubs and pots on the Continent as formal standards or pyramids for the decoration of entrances to mansions, hotels, etc. Perhaps the finest bay laurels in the kingdom are at Margam Park, Glamorgan. Even in 1837 there was one 60 ft. high. At Abbazia, on the East Istrian Coast, and at Fiume, across the Bay of Quarnero, I have seen beautiful woods of primeval bay laurel; in these places, growing on rocky sites, they form thickets of slender stems 50 ft. high.

Var. ANGUSTIFOLIA (syn. salicifolia).—The species shows some variation in shape of leaf; of several forms this is the most distinct. The leaves are 1½ to 3½ ins. long, but only ¼ to ⅞ in. wide.

Var. UNDULATA.—Leaf-margins conspicuously wavy.

LAVANDULA. LAVENDER. LABIATÆ

A genus of about twenty species of shrubs, sub-shrubs, and herbaceous perennials. Leaves opposite, entire, toothed or lobed; flowers of some shade of blue running to some shade of violet or lilac, borne in erect, glandular spikes; corolla and calyx tubular. Natives of the Mediterranean region, the Canaries, and India.

L. DENTATA, *Linnæus*. TOOTH-LEAVED LAVENDER

(Bot. Mag., t. 400)

An evergreen well-branched shrub 1½ to 3 ft. high; young shoots four-angled, downy. Leaves dark green, opposite, 1 to 1½ ins. long, ⅛ to ¼ in. wide; linear in main outline, but regularly cut on each side into round-ended teeth halfway or more to the midrib; dull green and downy beneath. Main flower stem 3 to 12 ins. long, slender, square in cross section, downy, bearing at the top a spike, 1½ to 2½ ins. long, of densely packed flowers. A conspicuous and ornamental feature of the head of flowers is the lavender-blue bracts which are ovate or diamond-shaped, often three-lobed, pointed, strongly veined and downy. The base of the flowers themselves is hidden by these bracts, the exposed part of the corolla being about ¼ in. wide, five-lobed, pale lavender-blue; they are lavender scented but not very strongly so.

Native of Spain and the Mediterranean region, often in arid situations; it occurs on the Rock of Gibraltar. It was cultivated in Gerard's time (1597); he writes of it and L. Stoechas: "We have them in our gardens and keep them with great diligence from the injury of our cold climate, covered in winter or grown in pots and carried into houses." It prefers a climate like that of the Scilly Isles; in cooler parts elsewhere a sheltered sunny corner is needed for it, giving it protection in frosty weather. Even then it succumbs in hard winters. It is easily distinguished from other lavenders by its narrow much toothed leaves which give it a charming appearance. The foliage has a pleasant aromatic scent only faintly suggestive of lavender. Blooms from July onwards.

L. LANATA, *Boissier*

An evergreen shrub 1½ to 2 ft. high; young shoots and leaves covered with a close whitish wool. Leaves opposite, stalkless, linear or oblanceolate, tapered at the base, rounded or blunt at the end; 1 to 2 ins. long, ¼ in. or less wide. Flower-spikes 1 to 2 ft. high, four-angled, slender, not so woolly as the leaves, with the flowers crowded in a group (1½ to 3 ins. long) of whorls at the top. Flowers ⅓ in. long, bright violet and ⅛ in. wide at the mouth, downy outside. Calyx tubular, eight-ribbed, ¼ in. long; downy, toothed, with one tooth much enlarged.

Native of Spain, where it was discovered by Boissier in 1837, in calcareous mountainous regions, especially on the Sierra Nevada. It is very distinct from L. spica in the longer, much more thickly woolly leaves, but the habit is the same and the flowers are similarly arranged at the top of a long slender stalk. L. spica is distinct in the (up to) thirteen ribs of the calyx. Boissier observes that in Spain, where it flowers in July and August, it is "infinitely more fragrant, very much esteemed by the mountaineers for its medicinal virtues, and occupies a region more elevated than L. spica" (from 4000 to 6500 ft. altitude).

L. PEDUNCULATA, *Cavanilles*

An evergreen shrub 1½ to 2½ ft. high; the leaves, stems, and flower-stalks covered with a fine grey down. Leaves linear, ½ to 1½ ins. long, $\frac{1}{16}$ to ⅛ in. wide; margins recurved. Main flower-stalk 4 to 12 ins. long, four-angled, bearing the flowers at the top in a dense spike ½ to 1¼ ins. long and ½ to ⅝ in. wide. Bracts violet-purple, broadly wedge-shaped, ⅜ in. wide, downy, margined with hairs; they constitute the most attractive part of the inflorescence. Of the flower itself only the deep purple corolla shows and it is only ⅛ in. or a little more across. The spike is surmounted by a tuft of violet-purple, linear-oblong, leaf-like bracts which are up to 1½ ins. long and ¼ in. wide.

Native of Spain and Portugal, where it flowers from May and June onwards. It is closely related to L. Stoechas (with which it was associated as a variety by Linnæus and other botanists), but its spike of clustered flowers is shorter, comparatively broader, and borne on a much longer main-stalk; the terminal tuft of bracts also is longer. The ordinary bracts, too, are quite differently shaped. In general aspect the two plants are much the same. Occasional plants with white flowers and bracts are found in a wild state. On the whole this appears to be the handsomest of the lavenders, but unfortunately is not really hardy with us. It grows wild up to elevations of 4800 ft. in Spain, often in arid calcareous localities. Probably its tenderness with us is due as much to lack of summer sunshine as to winter cold. It should be grown at the foot of a sunny wall where it can conveniently be covered with a mat in times of severe frost.

L. SPICA, *Cavanilles*. COMMON LAVENDER

(L. officinalis, *Chaix*)

An evergreen, bushy shrub, 3 or 4 ft. high, with erect branches that are square when young, the whole plant covered with a close minute down which gives it a grey or, when the parts are quite young, a whitish, aspect; bark peeling. Leaves opposite, linear or slightly broadened towards the end, 1½ to 2 ins. long, ⅛ to ¼ in. wide, blunt, margins recurved. Flowers produced in July and August, at the top of slender, erect stalks up to 18 ins. long; they are arranged in whorls, crowded in dense spikes 1 to 2 ins. long. Corolla tubular at the base, ⅓ in. long, pale grey-blue, two-lipped at the mouth; calyx tubular, ribbed, ⅙ in. long, downy, of a deeper shade than the corolla.

Native of the Mediterranean region, known to have been cultivated in Britain since the middle of the sixteenth century, probably long before. This is the common lavender of gardens, a plant whose charm no other excels. Its flowers appear when few shrubs are in bloom, and their fragrance is, perhaps, more prized than that of any other except the rose. It is remarkably enduring; as I write, some dried flowering sprays gathered over thirty years ago fill the room with their fragrance. The leaves have a fragrance similar to that of the flowers, but not so strong and pure. The lavender likes a warm, sunny spot, and a soil rather light than heavy. A dense compact habit is induced by clipping the plants over every spring before growth commences. It is easily increased by cuttings made in August and placed under a bell-glass or in a cold frame.

L. STOECHAS, *Linnæus*. FRENCH LAVENDER

An evergreen shrub 2 to 3 ft. high, all of whose vegetative parts are covered with a fine grey down. Leaves stalkless, not toothed, linear, $\frac{1}{3}$ to $1\frac{1}{4}$ ins. long, $\frac{1}{16}$ to $\frac{1}{8}$ in. wide, the margins recurved. Main flower-stem from $\frac{1}{2}$ to $1\frac{1}{2}$ ins. long, carrying at the top a spike of closely set blossom 1 to 2 ins. long, $\frac{1}{2}$ in. wide. The variously-shaped bracts constitute the most conspicuous and beautiful part of the inflorescence, being purple, ovate or rhomboidal, $\frac{1}{4}$ to $\frac{3}{8}$ in. wide, downy, strongly veined. Flowers deep purple, the small exposed part of the corolla $\frac{1}{8}$ in. wide. The inflorescence has at the top a few enlarged leaf-like purple bracts of obovate outline and $\frac{1}{2}$ to 1 in. long.

Native of S.W. Europe, extending eastwards along the Mediterranean region to Greece; also of N. Africa. It flowers in its native haunts from April onwards, but commences later with us. It was in cultivation in the middle sixteenth century and is mentioned by Turner and Gerard in their Herbals as "French lavender." Its hardiness is about the same as that of L. dentata (*q.v.*). It is easily distinguished by its very short main flower-stalk and stout spike of flowers crowned with a tuft of large foliaceous bracts (but see also L. pedunculata). The shoots and leaves have a curious somewhat pine-like odour when crushed. It succeeds well on the chalk in Col. Stern's garden at Highdown, near Worthing.

Var. ALBIFLORA.—A white-flowered variety both as regards bracts and corolla. Messrs Ellman and Sandwith, in June 1925, found a plant growing near Villefranche, in the Eastern Pyrenees, bearing both white and typical purple bracts and flowers.

The name "Stoechas," once applied generically to this species and to L. pedunculata, is derived from the isles Stœchades of the ancients (now the îles d'Hyères). Plants growing there were most highly esteemed for their medicinal virtues.

L. VERA, *De Candolle*

In former times this lavender does not appear to have been recognised as distinct from L. spica. De Candolle, who first separated it and gave it the present name in 1815, points out its differences as follows: Leaves linear or narrowly oblong, never becoming wedge-shaped or spathulate, as is frequent in L. spica; usually $\frac{1}{12}$ to $\frac{1}{4}$ in. wide, greener. At the base of each whorl of flowers is a pair of bracts, oval with tapered points; in proportion to their length they are thrice as broad as those of L. spica. He observes, too, that the spike is simple (unbranched), but that is not the case in cultivation. L. vera is the superior plant for yielding lavender oil. At Mitcham, in Surrey, an ancient industry was that of growing it in fields, the spikes being hawked about London and bought by housewives for scenting bed-linen. They are also made into lavender water. L. spica yields the Oil of Spike, which is darker and less agreeable in odour than that obtained from L. vera. A white-flowered variety, ALBA, and a neat dwarf one, NANA, both appear to belong to L. vera.

LAVATERA ARBOREA, *Linnæus*. TREE MALLOW. MALVACEÆ

A shrub up to 6 or 8 ft. high, with stout, erect, woody, annual or biennial stems, 1 to 2 ins. thick, and resembling a small tree in form. Leaves long-stalked, very variable in size, from 3 to 9 ins. long, and as much broad; they are five- to seven-lobed, the lobes unequally round-toothed at the margins; the base heart-shaped; both surfaces are densely covered with soft hairs. Flowers borne very abundantly; covering as much as 1½ to 2 ft. of the terminal part of the branches, some on short leafy racemes, some clustered in leaf-axils. Each flower is 1½ ins. across, enclosed at first by a large, woolly, three-lobed involucre or epicalyx; calyx five-cleft; petals five, broadly wedge-shaped, pale purple-red, marked at the base with a patch of dark purple veins.

Native of S. Europe, this handsome plant is also found wild in Great Britain. It inhabits maritime situations on the south and west coasts from Hampshire to the Isle of Man, and occurs either naturalised or wild on Ailsa Craig, the Bass Rock, and other places on the coasts of Scotland. It is worth cultivating in the warmer parts of the kingdom, especially near the sea, its abundant seed making it easy of increase. It is chiefly known in inland gardens by var. VARIEGATA, whose leaves are handsomely marked with white. This form must be propagated by cuttings.

The genus commemorates two physicians and naturalists of Zurich, named Lavater.

L. BICOLOR, *Rouy*

(Bot. Mag., t. 8997)

An erect shrub 3 or 4 ft. high, shoots (like the leaves beneath) covered with minute, starry hairs, seen under the microscope to have six to ten rays. Leaves 1½ to 3 ins. long, 2 to 4 ins. wide, roundish ovate in main outline but with five triangular-toothed lobes; stalk as long or longer than the blade. Flowers 2¼ ins. across, single or in pairs from the leaf axils, each on a slender, scurfy stalk about 1 in. long, petals five, broadly obcordate, notched at the end, about 1 in. wide, tapering abruptly to a short stalk, white tinged with rose or mauve and with purple veins radiating from the base.

Native of S.E. Europe, it was for long cultivated at Kew and in the vicarage garden at Bitton. It is a handsome shrub, easily grown and with a flowering season from May to November. It is fairly hardy but also makes a useful flowering shrub for a cool greenhouse, grown in pots.

LEDUM. ERICACEÆ

A small genus of evergreen shrubs, with alternate, short-stalked leaves and white flowers, produced in terminal roundish clusters. Calyx teeth five; corolla of five distinct, spreading petals; stamens from five to ten, with the anthers opening by two apertures at the top. Seed-vessel a capsule, with five divisions which separate from the base upwards.

L. grœnlandicum and L. palustre inhabit moors and swampy districts in high northern latitudes, and like a peaty soil or sandy loam free from lime. They can be propagated by seeds, treated as recommended for heaths, also by layers and cuttings. No success has hitherto been achieved with L. glandulosum, and its reintroduction is desirable.

L. GLANDULOSUM, *Nuttall*

(Bot. Mag., t. 7610)

An evergreen bush, said to become as much as 6 ft. high in its native home. Leaves oval or ovate, ½ to 2 ins. long, ¼ to ¾ in. wide; dark green above, whitish and smooth beneath except for a covering of minute glistening scales; stalk ⅙ to ¼ in. long. Flowers white, ½ in. across, produced during May in a terminal cluster about 2 ins. across. Petals cupped, obovate, spreading; sepals minute, rounded, hairy on the margin; stalks ½ to 1 in. long, and, like the calyx and ovary, covered with tiny, scale-like glands.

Native of western N. America; originally discovered by Douglas in 1826. A batch of plants was raised at Kew in 1894 from native seed, which grew and flowered very well a few years later. For some indiscernible reason the plants died one by one until none was left. It would appear as if some peculiar condition were wanting necessary for its existence, and some knowledge of its native habitats is desirable. The species is possibly no longer in cultivation. It is easily distinguished from the two following species by its smooth stems and leaves.

L. GRŒNLANDICUM, *Oeder*. LABRADOR TEA

(L. latifolium, *Aiton*)

An evergreen shrub, 2 to 3 ft. high and as much in diameter; branches erect, clothed when young with more or less rust-coloured wool. Leaves

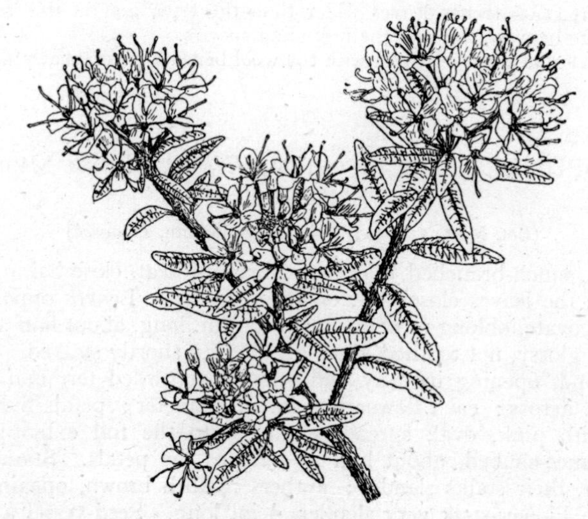

LEDUM GRŒNLANDICUM

aromatically fragrant when bruised, narrowly oblong or oval; ½ to 2 ins. long, ¼ to ½ in. wide; the margins much recurved, the base tapering or slightly heart-shaped; dark green with a few loose hairs above, covered beneath with a thick rust-coloured felt. Flowers in rounded terminal clusters 2 ins. across, consisting of one or more corymbs ; each flower ½ to ¾ in. across, white, borne on a slender, downy stalk ½ to 1 in. long. Calyx edged with very minute teeth ; petals oblong ; stamens five to eight ; seed-vessel somewhat cylindrical in shape.

Native of N. America, also of Greenland ; introduced in 1763. A very hardy and pretty shrub, the commonest of the ledums in gardens and the most useful. It flowers from the end of April to June. From L. palustre it is distinguished by its leaves being twice as wide, by having not more than seven or eight stamens to each flower, and by the seed-vessel being more tapered at the top. It extends over an enormous range of country, and varies to some extent in stature and shape of leaf.

Var. COMPACTUM.—Of dwarf habit, with short branches, very woolly stems, short broad leaves, and small flower clusters.

L. PALUSTRE, *Linnæus.* MARSH LEDUM

A dwarf evergreen shrub of thin habit, 1 to 4 ft. high ; young shoots clothed with rust-coloured wool. Leaves linear, ½ to 1¼ ins. long, $\frac{1}{12}$ to ¼ in. wide, the margins much recurved and thus reducing their width, dark dull green above, covered with rust-coloured wool beneath. Flowers white, ½ in. across, produced during April and May in terminal clusters ; calyx minutely toothed ; stamens more numerous than in L. grœnlandicum, usually seven to eleven ; seed-vessel egg-shaped.

Native of the northern and Arctic regions of Europe, Asia, and America, not of Britain ; introduced, according to Aiton, in 1762. As a garden shrub this ledum is inferior to L. grœnlandicum, and is much less common. The differences between them are pointed out under that species.

Var. DILATATUM has leaves wider than the type, and in this respect is intermediate between this and the preceding species.

Var. HYPOLEUCUM.—Leaves with the wool beneath permanently white.

LEIOPHYLLUM BUXIFOLIUM, *Elliott.* SAND MYRTLE. ERICACEÆ.

(Bot. Mag., t. 6752 ; Ledum thymifolium, *Lamarck*)

A low, much-branched, evergreen shrub of neat, close habit, 9 to 18 ins. high, the leaves closely set on the branches. Leaves opposite and alternate, ovate, oblong or obovate ; ¼ to ½ in. long, about half as wide ; glabrous, glossy, not toothed, dark green, very shortly stalked. Flowers rosy in bud, opening in May and June, in crowded terminal clusters ¾ to 1 in. across ; each flower is ¼ in. in diameter ; petals five, white, tipped with pink, oval, spreading almost to the full extent ; sepals narrow lance-shaped, about half as long as the petals. Stamens ten, spreading, their stalks slender ; anthers reddish brown, opening down the side. Flower-stalk very slender, ¼ in. long. Seed-vessel a two- to five-celled capsule, many-seeded.

Native of eastern N. America, from New Jersey southwards ; introduced in 1736 by Peter Collinson. From its near allies in the heath family it is distinguished by the quite free petals and small box-like leaves. Ledum is one of its nearest allies, but in that genus the pollen escapes from the anther by a hole at the top. It is a charming little shrub of neat aspect, and is at its prettiest just before the flowers expand, when the buds are very rosy. It blossoms very freely, the flowers almost hiding the foliage. The best method of propagating it is by cuttings made of shoots 1 to 1½ ins. long in July or August, dibbled in sandy

LEIOPHYLLUM BUXIFOLIUM

peat, and placed in gentle bottom heat; they should be covered with a bell-glass until rooted.

The species exhibits considerable variation in the size of the leaf, and in the comparative lengths of sepals and capsule, and of the petals and stamens. Some botanists make three species, but they appear to be no more than varieties. Ordinary L. buxifolium has the leaves mostly alternate; seed-vessels smooth, and thrice as long as the sepals; stamens twice as long as the petals.

Var. HUGERI.—Leaves mostly alternate, but longer than in the type; seed-vessels smooth, twice as long as the sepals; stamens about the same length as the petals. The commonest garden form as figured above.

Var. PROSTRATUM.—Leaves mostly opposite; seed-vessels toothed on the outside.

LEITNERIA FLORIDANA, *Chapman*. CORKWOOD.

LEITNERIACEÆ

A deciduous shrub or small tree, usually 5 to 10, sometimes 20 ft. high, with a stem 3 to 5 ins. in diameter; young shoots downy. Leaves alternate, entire, narrowly oval, tapered at both ends; 3 to 7 ins. long,

1½ to 3 ins. wide; covered with short hairs at first above, grey-felted beneath; stalk downy, 1 to 1½ ins. long. Flowers unisexual, the sexes on separate trees. Males in erect, axillary catkins, 1½ ins. long, each flower consisting of three to twelve stamens borne on a hairy bract, calyx and corolla absent. Female catkins smaller and more slender than the males; all of a greyish hue and of little beauty. Fruit an oval, flat, dry drupe, ¾ in. long, ¼ in. wide.

Native of Missouri, Florida, etc., inhabiting swamps; discovered about 1835; introduced to Kew in 1910. This remarkably interesting tree constitutes in itself the natural order Leitneriaceæ, and its position in the vegetable kingdom is variously estimated; most botanists, however, concur in placing it near the Myrica or gale family. I saw it in 1910 thriving quite well in the Arnold Arboretum, Mass., in Highlands Park, Rochester, N.Y., and in the New York Botanic Garden. It seemed to grow as well in ordinarily moist as in damp spots. All these places have considerably greater extremes than we have of heat and cold, and its capability of permanently supporting our duller climate has yet to be ascertained. Plants have so far succeeded fairly well. According to Prof. Trelease it often grows in rich soil, mostly covered with 6 ins. or more of water. But many American trees found in such places succeed better here under drier conditions. Still a site moderately moist should be given it. Its wood is probably the lightest known, and only weighs 12½ lb. per cubic foot.

LEPTODERMIS. RUBIACEÆ

A genus of about thirty species of deciduous shrubs native of the Himalaya, Japan, and China. They belong to the cinchona family, which is very meagrely represented in the open air with us. They have opposite, entire leaves and the often stalkless flowers are borne on the growing shoots. Corolla tubular, five-lobed; stamens five; style dividing into five at the top. The cultivated species are sun-lovers, being often found wild in dry stony places and in open situations.

L. OBLONGA, *Bunge*

(Hamiltonia oblonga, *Franchet*)

A deciduous twiggy shrub 3 or 4 ft. high; young shoots purplish, downy. Leaves opposite, ovate to oblong, entire, pointed, tapered at the base; ½ to 1 in. long, ⅛ to ⅓ in. wide; roughish above, slightly downy beneath; stalk $\frac{1}{10}$ in. or less long. Flowers produced from July to September in stalkless axillary clusters, a few together. Corolla violet-purple, ½ to ¾ in. long, tubular, with five oblong lobes, downy outside and in the throat.

Native of N. China, where it has been collected by Purdom and others. The plants in cultivation now in England were probably all raised from seed sent home by Farrer (No. 259). He calls it "a sturdy little bush with panicles of Persian lilac-like flowers in July." Evidently very hardy as it succeeds well in the Arnold Arboretum, Mass., where it is described as being attractive in late summer and autumn.

L. PILOSA, *Diels*

(Hamiltonia pilosa, *Franchet*)

A deciduous shrub 6 to 10 ft. high; young shoots downy. Leaves opposite, grey-green, ovate, pointed, wedge-shaped at the base, entire; $\frac{1}{2}$ to $1\frac{1}{4}$ ins. long, $\frac{1}{3}$ to $\frac{5}{8}$ in. wide; hairy on both sides; stalk $\frac{1}{4}$ in. or less long. Flowers fragrant, borne in axillary clusters towards the end of the current season's shoots and forming there a panicle several inches long. Corolla lavender-coloured, downy outside, $\frac{1}{2}$ in. long, slenderly funnel-shaped at the base, spreading at the mouth into five ovate lobes and measuring there $\frac{1}{4}$ in. wide.

Native of Yunnan, China; discovered by the Abbé Delavay in 1887; introduced by Forrest in 1904 from the Lichiang Valley. In the milder parts of the country it can be grown in the open, but in colder places like Edinburgh it needs the protection of a wall, one preferably with a southern exposure. It commences to flower in July and keeps on until the early frosts. The daphne-like fragrance of the pleasingly coloured blossom and the long period over which the flowering continues appear to make this shrub well worth its place in gardens. It is distinguished from the other two species here described by its larger hairy leaves.

L. PURDOMII, *Hutchinson*

A deciduous shrub up to 5 ft. high, with long very slender, wiry young shoots, covered with a close down at first. Leaves opposite, borne in clusters at the joints, linear; $\frac{1}{4}$ to $\frac{1}{2}$ in. long, $\frac{1}{10}$ to $\frac{1}{8}$ in. wide; glabrous, margins recurved. Flowers produced towards the end of the current season's growth in August and September in a slender panicle several inches long. Corolla slenderly tubular, $\frac{1}{2}$ in. long, five-lobed, pink.

Native of N. China; discovered by Purdom; introduced by Farrer in 1914 (No. 260). It was, I believe, first distributed as L. virgata, a Himalayan shrub of similar habit, but Dr Hutchinson made it a new species in 1916. Farrer describes it as a "shrub of inimitable grace with its delicate stems bowed down beneath long and lilac-like panicles that open in August." It flowered at Highdown, near Worthing, in 1921, and judging by Farrer's description of its habitat, the chalk cliffs of Col. Stern's sunny garden would seem to be as favourable a place as could be found for it in this country. The thin, wiry shoots and small, narrow, glabrous leaves amply distinguish it from the preceding species.

LEPTOSPERMUM. MYRTACCÆ

A genus of some thirty species of evergreen, small trees or shrubs, mostly natives of Australia but found also in New Zealand, New Caledonia, and the Malay Archipelago. The leaves are small, alternate, entire. Flowers solitary or in pairs or threes; petals five, spreading; stamens numerous; seed-vessel woody. Provided they are grown in a climate sufficiently mild, they are of easy cultivation, but none is genuinely hardy in the average climate of Britain. Leptospermum is from the Greek and refers to the small seeds.

L. FLAVESCENS, *Smith*

A tall evergreen shrub of which Bentham in his *Flora Australiensis* makes five varieties; of these the one I know as a shrub of the open air in this country is the var. OBOVATUM. There is a fine bush of this in the garden at Sheffield

Park, Sussex, which grows outside and was 10 ft. high when I saw it in 1928. The leaves are $\frac{1}{4}$ to $\frac{5}{8}$ in. long, $\frac{1}{8}$ to $\frac{1}{4}$ in. wide; almost uniformly obovate, except that some are rather wider in proportion to their length than others and they are very frequently notched at the apex, the base wedge-shaped. Flowers scarcely stalked, white, $\frac{5}{8}$ in. wide, opening in July, solitary on short twigs or in the leaf-axils; calyx glabrous. It was figured by Sweet in his *Flora Australasica*, t. 36, published in 1828, as "L. obovatum." He mentions that the plant figured was raised in the nursery of Messrs Whitley, Brames & Milne at Fulham, from seed sent by a Mr C. Frazer from New South Wales. Sweet observes that the plant will "without doubt stand our winters very well in the open air with a slight covering in severe frost." Its distinguishing characters are its five-celled ovary, its glabrous calyx-tube, and its notch-ended leaves. Besides New South Wales, this shrub is also wild in Victoria, Queensland, and Tasmania.

L. LIVERSIDGEI, *Baker and Smith*

An evergreen shrub 6 to 12 ft. high, of graceful habit and with drooping branches, devoid of down in all its parts; young twigs very slender with over twenty leaves to the inch. Leaves $\frac{1}{6}$ to $\frac{1}{4}$ in. long, linear-oblong to obovate, specked very freely with oil glands. Flowers solitary, very shortly stalked, coming from the leaf-axils, $\frac{1}{4}$ to $\frac{1}{3}$ in. in diameter, white. Petals orbicular, clawed. Seed-vessel circular, much flattened. Blossoms in June.

Native of New South Wales; first described in 1905. Port Macquarie appears to be one of its chief habitats. It is a very distinct species on account of the smallness of its leaves and flowers, also in the slender, virgate character of the branches. It is finely grown at Ludgvan Rectory, near Penzance, and lived and flowered on the west side of a sheltered wall at Kew for a good many years, but the latter plant was killed by the severe weather during the winter of 1946-47. In the winter of 1928-29 it was cut to the ground but sprang up again freely afterwards. The leaves when crushed have a lemon-like odour and from them can be obtained a fragrant oil. The species is known in Australia as the "lemon-scented tea-tree." In our cultivated plants the odour is rather faint, possibly owing to lack of sunshine.

L. NITIDUM, *Hooker fil.*

An evergreen shrub 3 to 12 ft. high, bark peeling; young shoots hairy, erect, densely leafy. Leaves oval-lanceolate to oblong, sharply pointed, tapered to the base, $\frac{1}{3}$ to $\frac{3}{4}$ in. long, $\frac{1}{8}$ to $\frac{1}{4}$ in. wide, shining green and glabrous above, more or less hairy beneath and on the margins; both surfaces are covered with minute oil glands; stalks very short. Flowers white, reddish inside, $\frac{1}{2}$ to $\frac{3}{4}$ in. wide, short-stalked and closely packed in the terminal leaf-axils of short shoots.

Native of Tasmania, where it was discovered in flower as far back as February 1845. Mr H. F. Comber collected it on his Tasmanian journey and describes it as a very "beautiful, dwarf, 1 to 2 ft. high." It was exhibited in flower from Nymans at Vincent Square, 16th June 1934. It appears to vary considerably in height in different districts.

L. PUBESCENS, *Lamarck*

(L. lanigerum, *Smith*; Gardeners' Chronicle, 4th Oct. 1879, fig. 65)

An evergreen shrub or small tree of erect habit, the slender twigs clothed with outstanding pale hairs. Leaves alternate, set about ten or twelve to the inch, obovate-oblong or oval, abruptly pointed, variable in size but usually $\frac{1}{3}$ to $\frac{1}{2}$ in. (occasionally $\frac{3}{4}$ in.) long, about $\frac{1}{8}$ in. wide, more or less silky, especially beneath, but sometimes glabrous and glossy green above. Flowers white, solitary at the end of short leafy twigs, about $\frac{1}{2}$ in. wide, the centre filled with a cluster of twenty to thirty stamens. Seed-vessel woody, nearly globose, $\frac{1}{4}$ to $\frac{1}{3}$ in. wide.

Native of Australia and Tasmania; introduced in 1774. This species seems to be hardier than the commoner L. scoparium. It was grown on a south wall at Kew and the winter of 1928-29, which very much injured L. scoparium, left it unaffected; it succumbed, however, during the hard winter of 1946-47. As long ago as 1879, a writer in the *Gardeners' Chronicle* remarked on its hardiness against a wall in Lancashire. It is quite an attractive, very leafy evergreen, flowering from June onwards. It is variable in the size and silkiness of its leaves, also in the size of its flowers, which in *Loddiges' Cabinet*, t. 1192, are depicted as 1 in. wide.

L. RODWAYANUM, *Summerhayes and Comber*

(Gardeners' Chronicle, 5th Sept. 1936, fig. 74)

An evergreen shrub 10 ft. high, of spreading habit, young shoots covered with fine grey down. Leaves grey-green, obovate to narrowly oval, $\frac{1}{3}$ to 1 in. long, $\frac{1}{8}$ to $\frac{3}{8}$ in. wide, tapered to a very short stalk, pointed or rounded at the apex, at first with minute white hairs beneath and pitted with tiny dark glands. Flowers solitary, terminal on short lateral twigs, pure white, scarcely stalked, $1\frac{1}{4}$ ins. wide, the mainly orbicular petals contracted to a short stalk. Fruit woody, persisting many years, broadly top-shaped, $\frac{3}{8}$ to $\frac{1}{2}$ in. wide, scaly on the flatly rounded summit.

Native of Tasmania; introduced by Comber in 1930. Plants were raised from his seeds at Nymans, Handcross, Sussex, and flowering shoots were shown by Colonel Messel at Vincent Square on 5th August 1936.

L. SCOPARIUM, *Forster*

A compact evergreen bush of rounded, very twiggy habit, attaining the dimensions of a small tree in a wild state; young wood sparsely hairy. Leaves alternate, linear-oblong, $\frac{1}{3}$ to $\frac{1}{2}$ in. long, $\frac{1}{12}$ to $\frac{1}{6}$ in. wide; sharply pointed, fragrant when bruised, dotted with transparent oil-glands. Flowers white, $\frac{1}{2}$ in. diameter, produced singly from the leaf-axils in spring; petals round, set well apart from each other, the triangular calyx-lobes showing between them. Fruit woody, globose, the size of a pea, many-seeded.

Native of Australia and New Zealand. It thrives outside in the south-western counties; and at Killerton, in Devon, as well as in other gardens there are bushes 15 to 20 ft. high. At Kew it has to be grown against a wall, and even there is apt to be killed in severe weather. Easily increased by cuttings. The var. NICHOLLSII, *Turrill* (Bot. Mag., t. 8419), is a remarkable and beautiful form with carmine-red petals. Introduced from New Zealand in 1908, by Captain Dorrien-Smith: said to have been first found on sandhills north of Christchurch.

Var. EXIMIUM, *Burtt.*—Probably the finest of the varieties in cultivation. Flowers about $\frac{3}{4}$ in. wide, pure white. Introduced from Tasmania by Comber. Given an Award of Merit at Vincent Square in May 1938. (Bot. Mag., t. 9582.)

Var. PROSTRATUM, *Hooker fil.*—Small frequently prostrate shrub, branchlets erect; leaves ovate to almost round. A mountain form, possibly the hardiest.

LESPEDEZA. Bush Clover. LEGUMINOSÆ

Of the fifty or more species belonging to this genus, not more than half a dozen are cultivated in gardens. Many are really semi-herbaceous, dying back to ground-level every winter, but sending up in spring from a woody root-stock a crowd of shoots which flower during late summer and autumn. Leaves trifoliolate; flowers pea-shaped; pods roundish, flat, one-seeded, and thus very distinct from the long, narrow, jointed, several-seeded pods of desmodiums with which some lespedezas have been confounded, and which they resemble in mode of growth. The species mentioned in the following notes succeed in ordinary loamy soil in an open position. Where seeds are not available, the most woody ones may be increased by cuttings; others by division. (See under L. Thunbergii.)

L. bicolor, *Turczaninow*

(Garden and Forest, 1892, fig. 18)

A deciduous shrub becoming in some climates a bush 8 or 10 ft. high, although at Kew its stems are only annual and grow from 3 to 7 ft. high during the season, dying down to ground-level every winter. Leaves trifoliolate, slender-stalked; leaflets varying in size from ¾ to 2 ins. in length by about two-thirds as much wide; broadly oval or obovate, the midrib enlongated into a small terminal bristle; the middle leaflet is larger and longer stalked than the others, all being dark green above, pale beneath, and clothed sparsely on both sides with appressed hairs or glabrous above. Racemes slender-stalked, 2 to 5 ins. long, produced in the leaf-axils from the uppermost 2 ft. of the stem. Flowers rosy purple, less than ½ in. long, confined to the terminal part of the raceme. Calyx ⅙ in. long, hairy, the teeth not so slender and sharp-pointed as in L. Thunbergii. Pod ovate, downy, ⅓ in. long, one-seeded.

Native of Manchuria, N. China, and Japan; introduced to Europe by Maximowicz, the Russian botanist, in 1856. It is not so handsome and desirable a plant as L. Thunbergii, with which it has been much confounded. In countries with a hotter summer than ours, the stems made each year do not die back more than half their length, and the plant thus increases gradually in height. In the Arnold Arboretum, Mass., it forms a bush comparable with a colutea. Flowers in August and September.

Var. alba.—Flowers white.

L. cyrtobotrya, *Miquel*

A small deciduous shrub, which in this country sends up from the base every summer a number of erect, woody stems 2 to 3 ft. high, that do not survive the winter, but die back to ground-level; bark downy. Leaves trifoliolate, 3 to 5 ins. long; leaflets 1 to 1¾ ins. long, ½ to ¾ in. wide; oval or obovate, covered beneath with a fine down especially early in the season; apex rounded or slightly notched, the midrib ending in a short bristle; base tapered. Flowers crowded at the end of umbel-like racemes 1½ ins. long, which spring from the axils of the upper leaves of the shoot; rosy purple, ½ to ⅝ in. long. Pod ovate, ¼ in. long, one-seeded.

Native of Japan and Korea; introduced to Kew in 1899. It is a pretty plant scarcely known in cultivation, and blossoms in August.

L. JUNCEA, *Persoon*

A semi-woody plant in this country, sending up annually from a woody root-stalk a crowd of slender, grooved stems 2 to 3 ft. high, covered with whitish hairs. Leaves trifoliolate, with a slender main-stalk $\frac{1}{4}$ to $\frac{1}{2}$ in. long; leaflets oblanceolate, $\frac{1}{3}$ to $\frac{3}{4}$ in. long, broadest near the apex, where they are $\frac{1}{12}$ to $\frac{1}{8}$ in. wide and short-pointed, tapering thence to a short stalk, covered beneath with fine grey hairs. Flowers in very short-stalked, two- to six-flowered umbels, produced from the leaf-axils; each flower $\frac{1}{4}$ to $\frac{1}{3}$ in. long, white or partly blue; the calyx half as long, hairy, with slender, linear lobes.

Native of the Himalaya, China, and Siberia; introduced to Kew in 1895. It is not a showy plant, but distinct and striking for its long slender stems of rather broom-like appearance, very densely clothed with the erect, rather appressed leaves. It flowers in September.

Var. CUNEATA (L. cuneata, *G. Don*).—Leaflets wedge-shaped, the end of each one being cut squarely off, except for the bristle-like prolongation of the midrib. Native of China. Other forms of L. juncea have much smaller leaves than those here described.

L. THUNBERGII, *Nakai*

(L. bicolor, *Hooker fil.*, Bot. Mag., t. 6602; L. Sieboldii, *Miquel*)

A semi-woody plant, producing stout, pithy, rather herbaceous, grooved stems, 4 to 8 ft. high, from a woody root-stock; they die back to ground-level during the winter, and are replaced by a fresh crop the following year. Leaves trifoliolate; leaflets $1\frac{1}{2}$ to 2 ins. long, one-third as much wide, becoming smaller towards the upper part of the stem, the centre one longer-stalked than the side ones; oval or oval-lanceolate; coated beneath, especially on the midrib, with appressed greyish hairs. Racemes numerous, up to 6 ins. long, produced from the leaf-axils of the upper part and at the end of the shoot, the whole constituting a loose panicle 2 to $2\frac{1}{2}$ ft. in length. Each flower is $\frac{1}{2}$ to $\frac{5}{8}$ in. long, pea-shaped, rosy purple; calyx $\frac{1}{4}$ in. long, covered with greyish hairs, and divided half-way down into five awl-shaped teeth. Pod ovate, flat, silky, $\frac{1}{3}$ in. long.

Native of N. China and Japan; introduced to Europe about 1837, by Siebold. Although strictly speaking it is scarcely a shrub, it is shrub-like. It is a plant with a luxuriant annual growth of great elegance and beauty, although, flowering late in the season, it does not always reach its best before the frosts come. This is more especially the case after dull wet summers. It commences to flower in September. A single fully grown plant will form a mass 10 ft. or more across, the outer stems arching outwards. It is not suitable for planting by itself in large groups in conspicuous places, as it starts into growth late in the season and is still bare of leafage when most other shrubs are in their full spring greenery. The old dead stems must be cut away in spring. Propagated by pulling or chopping the root-stock into smaller pieces about April. Pieces small enough, with root attached, may be potted and placed in a house where there is bottom heat.

LEUCOPOGON FRASERI, *A. Cunningham*. EPACRIDACEÆ

A dwarf evergreen shrub 3 to 6 ins. high, of close compact growth, forming a dense mat and spreading by underground stems. Branchlets more or less erect, very slender, minutely downy when young, almost entirely hidden by the foliage. Leaves stalkless, alternate, overlapping each other, obovate-oblong, abruptly tapered at the apex to a slender, bristle-like tip; $\frac{1}{8}$ to $\frac{3}{16}$ in. long, $\frac{1}{16}$ to $\frac{1}{12}$ in. wide; dull green, the longitudinal veins distinct beneath; margins fringed with tiny hairs. Flowers sweetly scented, solitary in the leaf-axils; corolla a slender tube $\frac{3}{8}$ in. long, pinkish white, divided at the mouth into five short triangular lobes which are downy on the under side; inside of tube hairy. The four brown anthers are fixed near the top of the corolla tube and have very short stalks. Style slender, downy. Fruit an oblong drupe, $\frac{1}{3}$ in. long, yellowish orange, sweet and edible.

Native of New Zealand up to 4500 ft. altitude, where it was found by C. Fraser in 1820; also of Tasmania and Australia. I do not know when this interesting little shrub was originally introduced, but I first saw it in Messrs Cunningham and Fraser's nursery at Comely Bank, Edinburgh, in 1911, and obtained it for Kew, where it has grown out-of-doors unprotected ever since, making a mat now 3 to 4 ft. wide. It does not flower freely enough to render it very noticeable, but it makes a neat tuft a few inches high very suitable for the rock garden, and its flowers have a hay-like fragrance. It is the only representative of its Natural Order hardy at Kew, although a few species of an allied genus, Epacris, are occasionally grown in our milder parts. It flowers in May and June. The family to which it belongs is closely allied to the heaths and is confined to Australasia.

LEUCOTHOË. ERICACEÆ

A genus of evergreen and deciduous shrubs, the hardy species found in N. America and Japan. The leaves are alternate; flowers in racemes, white, or slightly pink-tinted. Calyx of five free, or nearly free, sepals; corolla cylindrical or pitcher-shaped, five-toothed at the top. Stamens ten, enclosed within the corolla. Seed-vessel a round flattened capsule.

The chief cultural need of the leucothoës is a moist peaty soil, or a sandy lime-free loam with abundant leaf-soil added. L. Catesbæi thrives very well in semi-shade, and may be propagated by division.

EVERGREEN

1. *Grayana.* Racemes erect, terminal, usually solitary; leaves subsessile with bristly margins.
2. *Keiskei.* Racemes erect, terminal or axillary, solitary; leaves shortly petioled, margins glabrous.
3. *Davisiæ.* Racemes erect, terminal or subterminal, panicled; leaves shortly petioled, glabrous.
4. *Catesbæi.* Racemes axillary along the shoot, nodding; petioles up to $\frac{2}{3}$ in. long.
5. *Axillaris.* Racemes axillary along the shoot, nodding; petioles $\frac{1}{4}$ in. or less long

DECIDUOUS

6. *Racemosa.* Anthers with four awns; capsule not lobed.
7. *Recurva.* Anthers with two awns; capsule five-lobed.

L. AXILLARIS, *D. Don*

(Andromeda axillaris, *Lamarck*)

An evergreen shrub, 2 to 4 ft. high, with spreading branches zigzagged towards the end, clothed with very short down when young. Leaves leathery, ovate-lanceolate, 2 to 4½ ins. long, $\frac{3}{4}$ to 1½ ins. wide; usually abruptly pointed, spine-toothed, dark glossy green and glabrous above, pale and with scattered

airs beneath ; stalk $\frac{1}{4}$ in. or less long. Flowers produced during April and
May in axillary racemes 1 to $2\frac{1}{2}$ ins. long, crowded, and very shortly stalked.
Corolla white, cylindrical or pitcher-shaped, narrowing slightly towards the
nouth, where are five ovate teeth ; sepals ovate ; flower-stalks minutely downy.

Native of the south-eastern United States from Virginia southwards;
ntroduced in 1765. It is not so common in cultivation as L. Catesbæi, which
t much resembles, and with which it is much confused. Its leaves, however,
re comparatively shorter and broader, and abruptly pointed ; their stalks
re also shorter, and the sepals are broader. Coming from the lowlands of
'irginia, Florida, etc., it is much less hardy than L. Catesbæi, which inhabits
he mountains. Personally, I have only seen one or two plants, and they were
ot in good health. A dwarf form of L. Catesbæi is usually offered for it.

L. CATESBÆI, *A. Gray*

(Andromeda Catesbæi, *Walter* ; Bot. Mag., t. 1955)

An evergreen shrub, 2 to 6 ft. high, with slender, arching, zigzagged
ranches, which when young are reddish, and covered with a very short down.
eaves glabrous and leathery, narrowly lanceolate ; 3 to 5 ins. long, 1 to $1\frac{1}{2}$ ins.
vide ; with a long tapering point, rounded or shortly tapered at the base,
pine-toothed ; dark lustrous green above, paler and with scattered hairs
eneath ; stalks $\frac{1}{3}$ to $\frac{2}{3}$ in. long. Flowers produced during May, crowded on

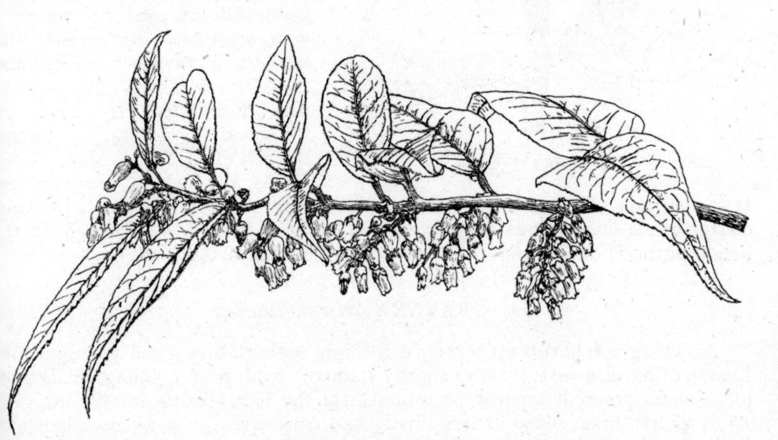

LEUCOTHOË CATESBÆI

xillary racemes 1 to 2 ins. long, occasionally in panicles 3 ins. long. Corolla
in. long, slenderly pitcher-shaped, white ; sepals narrowly ovate, pointed ;
ower-stalks very short.

Native of mountainous regions in the south-eastern United States ; intro-
uced in 1793. When fully in blossom, a well-grown plant with its long arching
ranches, laden for 12 to 18 ins. of their length with racemes, is decidedly
andsome. But owing to the flowers being all produced on the lower side,
ie branch often requires elevating for its full beauty to be seen. During the
owering season it is worth while to elevate a few of the branches by means
f forked sticks.

Var. ROLLISONI.—A variety with smaller, narrower leaves, 2 to 4 ins. long,
to $\frac{3}{4}$ in. wide.

L. DAVISIÆ, *Torrey*

(Bot. Mag., t. 6247; Andromeda Davisiæ, *C. K. Schneider*)

An evergreen shrub, 1 to 3 ft. high in cultivation, of neat, very sturd habit; branches erect, stiff, perfectly glabrous. Leaves ovate-oblong, rounde or slightly heart-shaped at the base, short-pointed or blunt at the apex lustrous dark green, of firı texture, $1\frac{1}{4}$ to $2\frac{1}{2}$ ins. long, $\frac{3}{4}$ t 1 in. wide; very slightly an evenly toothed; stalk $\frac{1}{8}$ to $\frac{1}{4}$ in long. Flowers produced in mi or late June in a cluster of ere racemes springing from the en of the shoot and its termin leaf-axils, each raceme 2 to 4 in long, and furnished with shor scattered bristles. Corolla nod ding, pitcher-shaped, white, $\frac{1}{4}$ in long, five-toothed. Sepals, shor ovate, edged with a few glandul teeth; flower-stalk $\frac{1}{8}$ in long.

LEUCOTHOË DAVISIÆ

Native of the Sierra Nevad California, at 5000 ft., where was originally discovered, an introduced in 1853 by Willia Lobb, for Messrs Veitch, and first distributed by them "Leucothoë Lobbii." Subs quently found by Miss N. Davis, after whom it was name It is, perhaps, the most beautiful in the genus, because its erect, termin cluster of racemes stands well above the foliage. It thrives very well in th neighbourhood of London. Propagated by cuttings in August.

L. GRAYANA *Maximowicz*

An evergreen shrub up to 3 or 4 ft. high, with glabrous, red young shoot Leaves of hardish texture, very shortly stalked; oval, ovate, oblong, or incline to obovate, pointed, tapered or roundish at the base, bristly on the margin $1\frac{1}{2}$ to $3\frac{1}{2}$ ins. long, more or less bristly and conspicuously net-veined beneatl Racemes terminal, up to 4 ins. long, erect, bearing the flowers at $\frac{1}{8}$ to $\frac{1}{2}$ in apart. Corolla bell-shaped, ivory-white to pinkish, $\frac{1}{4}$ in. long, hairy inside calyx-lobes ovate to ovate-lanceolate, membranous. Each flower springs fro the axil of a linear or awl-shaped bract. Fruit flattened-globose, $\frac{1}{5}$ in. wide.

Native of Japan; erroneously identified with L. chlorantha, *De Candoll* by Asa Gray in 1859; given its present name by Maximowicz in 1873 introduced in 1890, but not very common. It is a gaultheria-like shrub, b dry-fruited. Nakai, the Japanese botanist, includes under it five varietie viz., typica, glabra, glaucina, venosa, and intermedia, based mainly on le characters, but judging by a long series of specimens in the Kew Herbariur it will be difficult to differentiate them. It belongs to that section of the gen with evergreen leaves, a terminal inflorescence and anthers without awn L. Davisiæ differs in its glabrous, more distinctly stalked leaves. L. Grayar flowers in June and July and is quite hardy.

L. KEISKEI, *Miquel*

An evergreen shrub with slender, zig-zagged, glabrous young shoots. Leaves leathery, ovate-lanceolate, rounded at the base, drawn out into a long slender apex, inconspicuously toothed; 1½ to 3½ ins. long, ½ to 1½ ins. wide; glabrous except for a few appressed bristles beneath; stalk ⅙ to ¼ in. long. Flowers few, borne during July in short racemes at or near the end of the young shoots. Corolla nodding, pure white, cylindrical, ½ to ⅝ in. long, ¼ in. wide, with five small, erect, triangular teeth; calyx lobes broadly ovate, minutely ciliate; stamens hairy; fruit flattened-globose, ¼ in. wide.

Native of Japan; introduced in 1915 by Wilson. Charles Maries collected it wild in flower in August 1880, but I am not aware that he sent home seeds. It is hardy, and is rather distinct on account of the size of its flowers, which are the largest in the cultivated species. It is grown in Japanese gardens. It attains probably some 3 or 4 ft. in height. I have seen only young plants in cultivation, and these having shining red young shoots, and the leaves are red when young, deep red in autumn. Evidently an attractive shrub.

The late Mr Fred Stoker, who grew it well in Essex, considered it one of the best of the Ericaceæ. He held the opinion that partial shade and a lime-free soil were essential conditions. He considered that there are two forms in cultivation: one erect, the other semi-procumbent and not more than 8 ins. high.

L. RACEMOSA, *A. Gray*

(Andromeda racemosa, *Linnæus*; A. spicata, *Watson*)

A deciduous shrub of bushy, erect habit, generally 4 to 6 ft. high in cultivation, but occasionally twice as high; young shoots usually finely downy. Leaves narrowly oval or inclined to obovate; 1 to 2½ ins. long, ½ to 1¼ ins. wide; pointed at both ends, shallowly round-toothed, of firm texture, downy on the midrib beneath; stalk ⅛ in. or less long. Flowers produced during June in one-sided racemes 1 to 4 ins. long, sometimes branched, usually terminating short twigs of the previous year. Corolla white, cylindrical, ⅓ in. long; sepals triangular-ovate, finely hairy on the margin; flower-stalk very short, glabrous, with two bracts close beneath the calyx; each anther is terminated by four awns, two to each cell.

Native of the eastern United States from Massachusetts southwards; introduced in 1736. This is a perfectly hardy, free-growing shrub which flowers abundantly, and is one of the prettiest of June flowering shrubs. It requires an occasional thinning out of the older wood. Propagated by cuttings of nearly ripened young shoots. Allied to L. recurva (*q.v.*).

L. RECURVA, *A. Gray*

(Garden and Forest, 1896, fig. 33; Andromeda recurva, *Buckley*)

A deciduous shrub, usually 3 to 8 ft. high, the young shoots slightly downy or glabrous. Leaves narrowly oval or lanceolate, tapering at both ends, thin but firm, toothed, 1½ to 4 ins. long, ½ to 1¼ ins. wide; downy on the veins and midrib beneath; stalk very short. Flowers produced during May and June in decurved racemes, 2 to 3 ins. long, terminating short twigs of the previous year. Corolla white, cylindrical, ¼ in. long; sepals ovate, pointed; flower-stalk very short and stout; anthers terminated by two awns, one to each cell.

Native of the southern Allegheny Mountains from Virginia to Alabama; introduced to England by Prof. Sargent about 1890, but very rare. It is probably not so hardy, nor so good a garden plant as its near ally, L. racemosa, from which it differs chiefly in its more diffuse habit, the recurved racemes, and very distinctly grooved seed-vessel; each pollen bag, too, is surmounted by only one bristle instead of two.

LEUCOTHOË RACEMOSA (see p. 215)

LEYCESTERIA. CAPRIFOLIACEÆ

A genus of three deciduous shrubs natives of the Himalaya and China and named after Wm. Leycester, Chief Justice in Bengal in the early nineteenth century, who, "during a long series of years pursued every branch of horticulture with munificence, zeal and success."

L. CROCOTHYRSOS, *Airy-Shaw*

(Hooker's Icones Plantarum, t. 3165)

A shrub apparently 6 to 8 ft. high, producing long, slender, hollow young shoots thinly furnished with glandular hairs. Leaves 2 to 6 ins. long, 1 to $2\frac{3}{4}$ ins. wide, ovate, slenderly pointed, rounded at the base, sparsely toothed, rich dull green above, rather glaucous, minutely downy and conspicuously net-veined beneath, margins slightly hairy; stalk about ⅛ in. long. Each joint of the stem is furnished with a pair of conspicuously large, kidney-shaped stipules, ¼ to ¾ in. wide. Inflorescence an arching terminal raceme 5 to 7 ins. long on which the flowers are closely arranged in whorls of six, the whorls set about 1 in. apart. Corolla rich yellow, ¾ in. long and as much wide, five-lobed, the base tubular, hairy outside. Calyx green, five-lobed, ⅜ in. wide; ovary ovoid, ¼ in. long, covered with sticky glandular hairs. Fruit ⅝ in. long, globose-ovoid, very like a small gooseberry, with the calyx adhering at the top.

Native of the Delei Valley, Assam, at 6000 ft. altitude; discovered and introduced by Kingdon Ward in 1928. He describes it as a "small lax shrub growing on steep sheltered gneiss face, in dense thickets." Seeds were originally distributed under the name "Golden Abelia," No. 8180. In Col. Stern's chalk-pit garden at Highdown, near Worthing, a very sunny spot, I saw a large plant in perfect health flowering abundantly in early June, 1934. It promises to be quite hardy there. But at Exbury, near the Solent in Hants, it survives the winter in the open air unhappily, and is cultivated in a cool greenhouse where it flowers in April. At Kew it was promptly killed the first winter it was put in the open air. This species is very distinct from L. formosa.

L. FORMOSA, *Wallich*

(Bot. Mag., t. 3699)

A half-woody, deciduous plant, with erect, hollow stems, 4 or 5 ft. sometimes much more high, covered with glaucous bloom, glabrous, very leafy. Leaves opposite, ovate, heart-shaped at the base, with long tapered points; varying in size according to the vigour of the shoot from 2 to 7 ins. long, about half as wide; entire or with small teeth; deep green above, greyish and slightly downy when young beneath; stalk ¼ to 1 in. long. Flower-spikes produced from June to September, either at the end of the shoot or in the uppermost leaf-axils, 1 to 4 ins. long. Flowers stalkless, arranged in tiers, each tier supported by handsome claret-coloured bracts of the same shape as the leaves and from ½ to 1½ ins. long, which persist until the fruit is ripe. Corolla ¾ in. long and wide, funnel-shaped, five-lobed, purplish, slightly hairy; calyx one-third the length of the corolla, with five erect, awl-shaped, hairy lobes. Berry like a small gooseberry, reddish purple, glandular-downy, about ½ in. long, many-seeded, surmounted by the persistent sepals; ripe in October.

Native of the Himalaya in shady forests; introduced in 1824. This handsome shrub likes a rich soil, and, in spite of its natural habitats, a sunny spot. The bracts and fruits colour better under a full exposure. Birds, especially pheasants, are very fond of the berries, for which reason it is sometimes planted as covert. It should be propagated by seed, which ripens in such abundance and germinates so freely that an enormous stock can soon be raised.

A shrub sold in nurseries as "L. formosa variegata" is really a variegated form of BOSEA AMHERSTIANA, a Himalayan shrub belonging to the Amarantaceæ, with small greenish flowers, bright crimson berries, and alternate leaves. It is a rank-growing shrub not so hardy as Leycesteria, and needing wall protection but scarcely worth it. It has no relationship with Leycesteria, from which its alternate leaves at once distinguish it.

LIBOCEDRUS. CONIFERÆ

Eight species of this genus are known, which have a remarkably scattered distribution: two are found in Chile, two in New Zealand, and one each in western N. America, China, New Caledonia, and New

Guinea. They are evergreen trees, closely allied to Thuya, with male and female flowers borne on the same tree but on different catkins. Leaves tiny, scale-like, more or less flattened to the branchlet. Only three species, L. CHILENSIS, L. DECURRENS and L. BIDWILLII have any claim to be considered hardy, and one of these is doubtful. They should be grown from seed if possible, but failing seeds, cuttings may be employed.

Of the other two species described the handsome L. MACROLEPIS, *Bentham*, recently introduced from China, is unfortunately not hardy except in the milder counties, but is an admirable winter-garden tree; as is also L. DONIANA, *Endlicher*, from New Zealand. From Thuya, Libocedrus differs chiefly in the scales of the cone being always six or less, and in the seeds being unequally winged.

L. CHILENSIS, *Endlicher*

A tree 60 to 80 ft. high in nature, at present 20 to 50 ft. high in cultivation; bark peeling. Young trees have a pyramidal habit, the branches being much divided and leafy at the ends. Leaves in four ranks, arranged in two opposite, very unequal pairs; the top and bottom ones are very small, the lateral ones $\frac{1}{8}$ to $\frac{3}{16}$ in. long, bluntish, dark green on the upper side of the branchlet, with white stomatic bands underneath. Cones $\frac{1}{3}$ in. long.

Introduced from Chile by Mr T. Bridges, who sent it to Messrs Low, then of Clapton, in 1847. In gardens it is a very pretty small tree, with frondose, laterally spreading sprays, very distinct from the vertical sprays of L. decurrens, from which it differs also in the unequal size and length of the leaves and their whiteness underneath. It is a rather tender tree, best suited in such places as Cornwall and Devon; at Whiteway in the latter county there is a tree 48 ft. high. A couple of plants growing in a very sheltered spot at Kew are healthy, but slow-growing. Comber found a variegated form at St Martin de las Andes in the Argentine, in October 1926.

L. DECURRENS, *Torrey*. INCENSE CEDAR (Plate 18)

A tree 125 to 150 ft. high in a wild state, with a trunk occasionally 7 ft. in diameter. Numerous trees between 50 and 70 ft. high are to be found in this country, all marked by a stiff columnar or narrowly pyramidal habit. The branches are erect, and have their branchlets and leaves set vertically or edgewise instead of horizontally, so that they are equally exposed to the light on both sides, and are uniformly green on both surfaces. Leaves in four rows and in opposite pairs; about $\frac{1}{8}$ in. long, free only at the sharp points, the lower part appressed to and completely covering the branchlet, dark glossy green. Cones erect, $\frac{3}{4}$ in. long, $\frac{1}{4}$ to $\frac{1}{3}$ in. wide at the base, tapered. Seeds four, $\frac{1}{3}$ in. long, awl-shaped, with a large wing on one side and a small one on the other.

Native of Oregon and California; introduced by Jeffrey for the Oregon Association of Edinburgh in 1853; discovered seven years previously by Col. Fremont. It is frequently called Thuya gigantea (*Carrière*) in gardens, but is quite distinct from the tree to which that name properly belongs, whose horizontally spreading branchlets showing white stomata beneath are quite different (see *Thuya plicata*).

Libocedrus decurrens grows rather slowly, but should be represented in every garden large enough to accommodate it, because of its distinct and formal shape—admirable for a group planted as Lombardy poplars sometimes are. A very fine tree about 70 ft. high, and quite columnar, perhaps the best in the country, is in the Royal demesne of Frogmore. A hardy species, thriving best in moist, deep loam. In Italy the branches are more spreading and the tree more broadly pyramidal than is usual with us.

Vars. COMPACTA and NANA of gardens are compact and dwarf in growth.

Var. VARIEGATA.—Pieces of the shoots entirely yellow. These pieces vary in size from bits of branchlet ½ in. long to pieces 2 to 3 ins. across, giving the tree a curious spotted appearance.

L. DONIANA, *Endlicher*. KAWAKA

An evergreen tree 30 to 70 ft. high, with a trunk 6 to 13 ft. in girth, the bark falling away in long, thin ribbons. In the young state the ultimate branchlets are flat, arranged in two opposite rows, ½ to 1 in. long, and (with the leaves) about ⅙ in. wide. Leaves in four rows as in Thuya, the side ones ⅛ to ⅕ in. long, flattened to form a keel, pointed, overlapping the small upper and lower ones, of which only the quite small triangular tips are exposed. In the adult state (as with many New Zealand conifers), the branchlets and leaves are quite different; the distichous (two-rowed) arrangement of the branches is not so conspicuous and they are narrower, about $\frac{1}{12}$ in. wide, less flattened, with the leaves proportionately smaller, blunter, and more equal in size. Cones egg-shaped, ½ in. long, composed of four scales, each having a pointed curved spine nearly ¼ in. long at the back.

Native of New Zealand on both islands, but more frequent on the North, where it is said to be often rare and local; discovered in the Bay of Islands by Robert Cunningham in 1833. Kirk describes it as a noble tree. We know it only in a small state in cultivation, but it is a handsome conifer of the thuya type. At home it reaches altitudes of 2000 ft., but is only hardy in our milder counties.

L. BIDWILLII, *Hooker fil.*, is the only other species of Libocedrus in the Australasian region. It is often confused with L. Doniana, but differs in the juvenile state from that species in the branchlets being narrower, and still more in the adult state when they become distinctly four-sided and $\frac{1}{15}$ to $\frac{1}{12}$ in. wide, with the leaves almost uniform, triangular, pointed, cypress-like, and closely pressed to the stem. Cones as in L. Doniana, but only ¼ to ⅓ in. long. It is an evergreen tree, rarely more than 50 ft. high. As it reaches altitudes of 3000 to 4000 ft. in New Zealand it should be hardy with us. There is a healthy plant 10 ft. high at Nymans in Sussex.

L. MACROLEPIS, *Bentham and Hooker*

(Garden, 13th Sept. 1902, p. 183; Calocedrus macrolepis, *Kurz*)

An evergreen tree up to 100 ft. high, of graceful pyramidal shape; the bark of the trunk described by Henry as "remarkably white." Branchlets flat and frondose, the ultimate divisions on young trees ⅛ to ⅙ in. wide, bright green above, glaucous beneath. Leaves in four rows, very much compressed, the side ones folded lengthwise with their margins joined to the upper and lower ones so that only the short sharp points of all four are free; each set of four leaves is from ⅛ to ⅜ in. long, being considerably smaller in mature trees than in juvenile ones. Cones cylindrical, ⅝ in. long, composed of six scales.

Native of S. Yunnan, China; first described and named "Calocedrus macrolepis" in 1873 from a specimen collected in 1868 by D. J. Anderson; introduced by Wilson in 1899 from Szemao in Yunnan. It was given a First-Class Certificate by the Royal Horticultural Society in 1902, which was perhaps rather in excess of its merits, for although it is a quite handsome conifer of the thuya type, it is only hardy in our mildest counties. The free tips of the leaves are not so conspicuous in adult trees as in the young ones we cultivate.

LIGUSTRUM. PRIVET. OLEACEÆ

There are about sixteen hardy species of Ligustrum introduced to this country, all of which are natives of China or Japan, with the exception of the common privet, found in Europe and England. The genus is exclusively Old World, and reaches from China through the Himalaya, etc., to Java, the Philippines, and Australia. Leaves opposite, never toothed. Flowers of some shade of white, borne in terminal panicles. Calyx scarcely or only minutely toothed; corolla tubular, with four spreading lobes. Stamens two, attached to the tube of the corolla. Fruit a berry, usually black, or black with a purplish bloom.

Whilst the privets as a whole are not amongst the most attractive of hardy shrubs, a few of them are either striking or useful. One of the worst points about them is the penetrating odour of the flowers—heavy, and to most people objectionable. The privets are easily cultivated in any soil that is not very impoverished, and they can be rooted from cuttings about as easily as any shrubs, either with or without a little heat. A selection for the garden would be as follows:—

For flower—sinense and Quihoui; *for foliage*—lucidum, japonicum, ovalifolium aureum; *for planting in dark damp places*—vulgare, ovalifolium; *for hedges*—ovalifolium (tall), Delavayanum (dwarf).

L. CONFUSUM, *Decaisne*

A deciduous or, in warm localities, a more or less evergreen shrub or small tree, said to be sometimes 40 ft. high in Sikkim; young shoots clothed with down. Leaves 1½ to 3½ ins. long, ½ to 1 in. wide, lanceolate, pale glossy green, quite glabrous; stalk ⅛ to ⅜ in. long, grooved on the upper side. Panicles downy like the young shoots, produced in June and July at the end of leafy twigs that spring from the previous year's branches. Flowers white, ⅙ in. wide, scarcely stalked; calyx cup-shaped, glabrous, with shallow triangular lobes; stamens white with pink anthers. Fruit black, covered with a plum-like bloom, ½ in. long, ⅓ in. wide.

Native of Sikkim, Khasia, Bhotan, etc.; introduced to Kew in 1919 by means of seeds from Calcutta. It is not genuinely hardy in the open at Kew (although it survives) but grows luxuriantly on a south wall. There it flowers very freely, producing its panicles, each 3 or 4 ins. long and 2 or 3 ins. wide, numerously in a cluster at the end of the previous year's growth. It is one of the best of the privets in regard to blossom, the corolla being of a purer white than is usual, but it is even more striking when thickly hung with its panicles of black-purple berries. I believe it would make a handsome small tree in the southern and western maritime counties. The specific name refers to its having been confused with L. robustum, which has more cylindrical fruits and larger leaves.

L. CORIACEUM, *Carrière*

(Bot. Mag., t. 7519)

An exceedingly stiff-habited evergreen shrub, 4 to 6 ft. or perhaps more high; young shoots short, stunted, covered with very minute dark down the first season. Leaves crowded, 1 to 2½ ins. long, from two-thirds to fully as wide; broadly oval or round, very blunt or notched at the apex, dark glossy green, thick and leathery; stalk $\frac{1}{5}$ in. long. Flowers white, in erect pyramidal panicles 2 or 3 ins. high, and as much through at the base. Fruit black, globose, about $\frac{1}{5}$ in. diameter.

Native of Japan; found by Robt. Fortune in a garden there, and introduced in 1860. It is in all probability a stunted form of L. japonicum obtained under cultivation in Japan, and non-existent in a wild state. It has in fact been called L. japonicum coriaceum. It is now grown in many gardens in the south, but surely as a curiosity only, for its flowers have little beauty, and it has no elegance of habit or foliage. It is fairly hardy, but grows better in the south and west than elsewhere.

Var. INVOLUTUM.—A form of freer growth; leaves more incurved.

L. DELAVAYANUM, *Hariot*

(L. Prattii, *Koehne*)

An evergreen shrub, eventually 8 ft. or more high, with long graceful branches covered with a dense coat of short down which persists on the year-old branches. Leaves oval, $\frac{1}{2}$ to $1\frac{1}{4}$ ins. long, $\frac{1}{4}$ to $\frac{5}{8}$ in. wide; tapering towards both ends, quite glabrous except for some minute down on the midrib above; dark shining green; stalk $\frac{1}{12}$ in. long. Panicle very downy, flowers white; calyx glabrous; fruit egg-shaped.

Native of Yunnan, China; raised by Mr Maurice de Vilmorin from seed sent to him by the late Abbé Delavay in 1890. In its small state this is a pretty, small-leaved, flat-branching bush with the habit of a dwarf cotoneaster. As it gets older it makes a rounded elegant bush. Allied to L. strongylophyllum, it is apparently hardier. I have seen it 12 ft. high in Suffolk.

L. FORMOSANUM, *Rehder*. FORMOSAN PRIVET

An evergreen shrub up to 10 ft. high; young shoots purplish, minutely downy. Leaves leathery, broadly ovate or oval, or almost round, finely pointed, broadly wedge-shaped or almost rounded at the base; $\frac{1}{2}$ to $1\frac{1}{4}$ ins. long, $\frac{1}{2}$ to $\frac{3}{4}$ in. wide; dark green and quite glabrous; stalk $\frac{1}{12}$ in. long, purplish. Flowers small, produced in a terminal panicle 1 to 2 ins. long, lax and slightly downy.

Native of Formosa; discovered by Henry in 1894, but of much later introduction. I only know of it in cultivation at Werrington and Caerhays in Cornwall, where it has hitherto grown vigorously. I have not seen living flowers, but in the privets they do not vary much and they are no doubt of some shade of white. The leaves in texture resemble those of L. japonicum, but they are of course much smaller. Dr Rehder compares it also with the Chinese L. Henryi, which differs in its thinner leaves rounded at the base, its denser inflorescence, and its more conspicuously downy young twigs. L. formosanum is probably not very hardy, but in the west country it may make a useful evergreen hedge plant.

L. HENRYI, *Hemsley*. HENRY'S PRIVET

An evergreen bush, up to 12 ft. high, of neat habit especially when young; young shoots very downy. Leaves glabrous, variously shaped, from roundish ovate or almost round to ovate-lanceolate, $\frac{3}{4}$ to $1\frac{1}{2}$ ins. long, inconspicuously veined, of an almost black, shining green above. Flowers white, scented, in short-stalked terminal pyramidal panicles 2 to 6 ins. long. Corolla $\frac{1}{4}$ in. long; calyx and individual flower-stalk glabrous. Fruit oblong, black, $\frac{1}{3}$ in. long.

Native of Central China; discovered by Henry; introduced by Wilson in

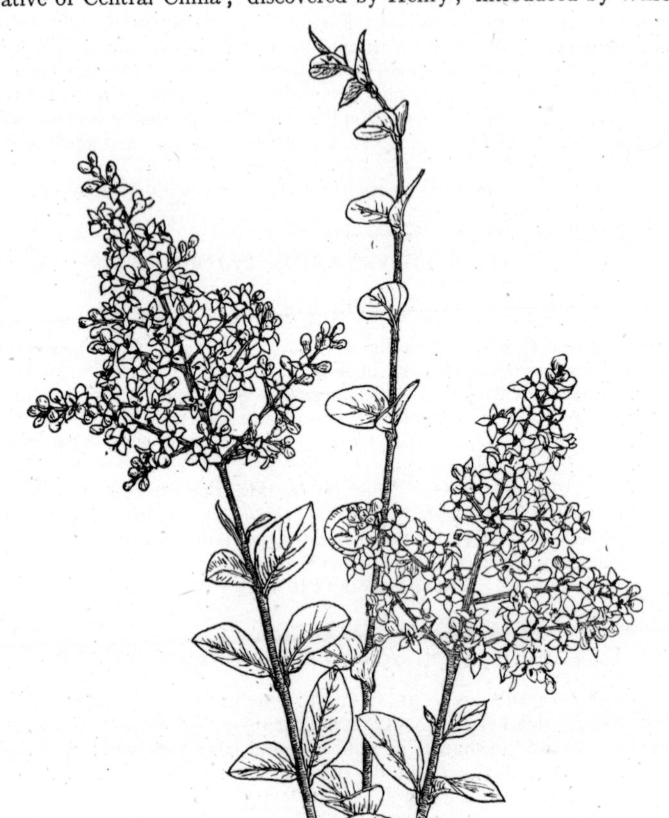

Ligustrum Henryi

1901 for Messrs Veitch. As a small shrub it makes a neat and pleasing evergreen, effective because of the black-green lustre of its leaves. Perhaps not absolutely hardy in severe winters.

L. IONANDRUM, *Diels*

(Journal, Royal Hort. Society, 1924, fig. 5)

An evergreen shrub up to 10 ft. high, of dense habit; young shoots thickly clothed with short fine down, becoming greyish. Leaves glabrous, of thin texture, ovate, oval or obovate, mucronate or bluntish at the apex, rounded or wedge-shaped at the base; $\frac{1}{2}$ to $1\frac{1}{4}$ ins. long, about $\frac{1}{2}$ in. wide; dark bright green above. Flowers white, scented like common privet, densely packed in terminal panicles which are $\frac{3}{4}$ to $1\frac{1}{2}$ ins. long, augmented sometimes by axillary racemes. Corolla $\frac{1}{6}$ in. long, anthers violet-coloured; flower-stalks downy. Fruit black, roundish ovoid, $\frac{1}{4}$ in. wide, produced in closely packed clusters.

Native of Yunnan, China; discovered in blossom in May 1906 by Forrest, on the eastern flank of the Lichiang Range at 9000 to 10,000 ft. altitude. Judging by the figure quoted above, which shows this privet in a wild state, it is of dense spreading habit and wider than it is high. I have heard Mr Forrest speak highly of its attractiveness in a wild state, but I fear it is not going to do itself justice in a climate like that of Kew where, although it has survived every winter since its introduction, its growth is stunted. Against a wall, however, it grows freely, making shoots 2 ft. or more long in a season and flowering in June. It succeeds very well in the southern and western maritime counties; at Exbury in Hampshire it makes a handsome, horizontally branching shrub and bears fruit freely. Mr Diels places it near L. Henryi, which has a more open growth and broader leaves. Its most distinctive character would appear to be the short panicles of densely packed flowers and fruit. It promises to make a good evergreen hedge. Dr Rehder now considers this privet identical with L. Delavayanum.

L. JAPONICUM, *Thunberg*. JAPANESE PRIVET

An evergreen shrub, rarely more than 6 to 12 ft. high in this country, of

LIGUSTRUM JAPONICUM

bushy habit; twigs covered when young with minute dark down, becoming quite glabrous. Leaves glabrous, almost black-green, very glossy, ovate,

1½ to 4 ins. long, ¾ to 2 ins. wide; usually rounded, sometimes tapering at the base, taper-pointed at the apex; stalk ¼ to ½ in. long. Flowers white, borne on terminal pyramidal panicles 4 to 8 ins. high and as much wide. Flower-stalks clothed with minute down. In bloom from July to September.

Native of N. China, Korea, Japan; introduced to Europe by Siebold in 1845. It is closely allied to L. lucidum, and much confused with it in gardens, but is a less vigorous shrub, its leaves are darker green, shorter, more rounded at the base, and the nerves beneath are raised, whereas in lucidum they are sunken; the inflorescence is looser, and the young shoots minutely downy. It is a useful and effective evergreen because of the intensely dark shining foliage, but needs a sheltered spot.

L. LUCIDUM, *Aiton*

(Bot. Mag., t. 2565)

An evergreen shrub of erect habit, 10 to 18 ft. high, or a small tree up to 30 ft.; devoid of down in all its parts. Leaves narrowly oval or ovate, from 3 to 6 ins. long, 1 to 2½ ins. wide; tapering at the base, long-pointed, glossy dark green above; stalk ⅓ to ½ in. long. Flowers white, produced during August and September in erect terminal panicles 6 to 8 ins. high and nearly as much wide. Fruit oblong, ⅓ to ½ in. long, blue-black; not frequently produced with us.

Native of China; introduced in 1794. Of the truly evergreen privets, this is the handsomest and best. A well-grown plant with the large lustrous leaves and a crowd of erect panicles is one of the most effective of autumn garden pictures. According to Henry, this privet is 20 to 30 ft. high, and the commonest evergreen tree in some parts of Hupeh, China. Wilson, in the Min River Valley, found one example 60 ft. high and 10 ft. in girth. I have seen it as a tree in the Dalmatian towns—there is one in the public park at Spalato 35 ft. high. In China it possesses some economic importance in being the tree on which the "white-wax" insect deposits its eggs. It is sometimes confused with L. japonicum (*q.v.*).

Var. ALIVONI.—Leaves longer, narrower, thinner, and less glossy, often variegated; they are 3 to 7 ins. long, and 1 to 2 ins. wide; young twigs minutely downy; fruit black, rounded at the top. It is not so handsome as L. lucidum, and is perhaps a distinct species.

Var. AUREO-VARIEGATUM.—Leaves variegated with dull yellow; ineffective.

Var. TRICOLOR.—A tender form which needs the protection of a wall. Leaves with a broad but irregular border of white, pinkish when young. Very striking when well grown.

L. OBTUSIFOLIUM, *Siebold and Zuccarini*

(L. Ibota, *Siebold*)

A deciduous shrub, dense with luxuriant leafage but of graceful habit, ultimately 8 to 10 ft. high; twigs downy. Leaves oval or slightly obovate, 1 to 2 ins. long, ⅓ to 1 in. wide, always tapered at the apex; glabrous except on the midrib beneath, and on the margins when young. Flowers white, produced in July in terminal, nodding clusters 1½ ins. long on short side twigs. Calyx bell-shaped, scarcely toothed, downy; corolla ⅓ in. long. Fruit globose, ultimately black, but at first covered with a purplish bloom.

Native of Japan; introduced in 1860. This privet is a strong and vigorous grower, and when well furnished with its short clusters is distinctly ornamental. But it does not make so good a display here as in countries with a hotter summer. I saw it in the Arnold Arboretum in July 1910, and was much struck with its beauty and grace. As a flowering or fruit-bearing shrub it is at Kew inferior to L. sinense. It is allied to L. ovalifolium, but is distinct in habit and in the downy midrib. Both species have a corolla tube two or three times as long as the lobes, but ovalifolium is nearly devoid of down.

Var. REGELIANUM, *Rehder* (L. Regelianum, *Koehne*).—A dwarfer shrub of dense habit, branches spreading horizontally. Leaves oblong or narrowly oval, downy beneath. Calyx hairy; corolla shorter; anthers broader and shorter; fruit smaller.

The true L. Ibota of Siebold and Zuccarini is an inferior shrub and has been grown as L. ciliatum.

L. OVALIFOLIUM, *Hasskarl*. OVAL-LEAVED PRIVET

A semi-evergreen or, in severe winters or in poor soil, a deciduous shrub 10 to 15 ft. high, of vigorous growth, forming a dense thicket of erect stems; young shoots usually quite glabrous. Leaves 1 to 2½ ins. long, ½ to 1¼ ins. wide; oval, wedge-shaped at the base, blunt or pointed at the apex, glossy green and glabrous on both surfaces; stalk ⅛ in. long. Flowers produced during July in a stiff, erect, terminal panicle, 2 to 4 ins. high and about the same wide; they are very crowded in the panicle, dull white, and have a heavy, unpleasant odour. Corolla ⅓ in. long. Fruit globose, shining, black. Calyx and individual flower-stalk smooth.

Native of Japan. The oval-leaved privet is a worthy associate of the common one for dark corners or places starved by roots of trees where scarcely anything else will grow. For hedges it is preferable to the common privet because of its more evergreen nature; it has, in fact, almost entirely displaced it for that purpose. It is not worthy of being put to better use, being of stiff, ungainly habit, its flowers dull, and to most people evil-smelling.

Var. ARGENTEUM.—Leaves bordered with creamy white. This pale variegation is not as rich and effective as that of the following.

Var. AUREUM. Golden Privet.—Leaves green only in the centre, with a border of varying width of rich golden yellow. This is the most popular of all variegated shrubs, and has been propagated by hundreds of thousands for town planting. Although it is the fashion to revile it, it certainly produces a very bright effect and brings colour into many a hemmed-in garden or dull city yard where little of any kind will grow. It is also useful in a small state for town window-boxes. In habit it is less rigid and more graceful than the type, and the young shoots, seen under the lens, are thickly but very minutely downy.

L. QUIHOUI, *Carrière*

(L. brachystachyum, *Decaisne*)

A rounded, deciduous bush of thin, diffuse, but elegant habit, 6 to 10 ft. high; branches thin, wiry, rather rigid, covered with a darkish minute down when young. Leaves 1 to 1½ ins. long, one-third to half as wide, oval or obovate, tapering to a short stalk at the base, often bluntish at the apex; glabrous on both surfaces, but minutely downy on the stalk. Flowers white, fragrant, produced in September and October in slender downy panicles, 4 to 8 ins. long, 1½ to 3 ins. in diameter. Fruit ovoid, shining, purplish.

Native of China; introduced to France about 1862. The habit of flowering so late in the season gives this species a special value in the garden, for it is one of the prettiest and most elegant of privets in bloom. Its flowers do not always open if September be dull and cold, but it deserves to be more extensively grown. The specific name was given in compliment to Mr Quihou, once superintendent of the Jardin d'Acclimatation at Paris.

L. SINENSE, *Loureiro*. CHINESE PRIVET (Plate 19)

A deciduous or, in mild winters, nearly evergreen shrub, 12 to 20 ft. high, occasionally taking the form of a small tree, of dense habit, rounded or flat-topped; twigs covered with a short, dense, brownish down. Leaves pale green, thin, oval; 1 to 3 ins. long, ½ to 1 in. broad; tapering at the base, bluntish or notched at the apex, downy on the midrib beneath; stalk ⅛ to ¼ in. long. Flowers white, produced in July in numerous downy panicles, 3 or 4 ins. long, 1½ to 2 ins. wide. Fruit globose, black-purple, about ⅙ in. diameter, remaining on the branches until after the New Year.

Native of China; introduced by Fortune about 1852. I consider this the best and most ornamental of deciduous privets. It bears immense feathery masses of blossom in July, and they are usually followed by a wealth of dark purple fruits about the size of large shot, which make the shrub interesting through the winter. It is never seriously injured by cold, although in hard winters the twigs are occasionally cut back. Still, a sheltered position for it is preferable to one bleak and exposed, as it grows and flowers better then.

Var. MULTIFLORUM, *Paul*.—Anthers reddish brown, not yellowish as in the type.

Var. NANUM.—A dwarfer, more spreading form, with smaller leaves (? L. Stauntoni, *De Candolle*). There is also a variegated form, the leaves irregularly bordered with yellow; of no value so far as I have seen.

L. STRONGYLOPHYLLUM, *Hemsley*

(Bot. Mag., t. 8069)

An evergreen shrub of elegant, loose habit, occasionally a small tree in a wild state, sending out long, slender branches each season which, whilst young, are covered with a dense, minute down. Leaves nearly round, broadly oval or ovate, ⅓ to ¾ in. long, often ending in a short abrupt tip; of firm texture, dark glossy green; margins slightly recurved; stalk $\frac{1}{20}$ in. long. Flowers white, ¼ in. diameter, produced during July in a terminal pyramidal panicle, 2 to 4 ins. high and as much wide at the base. Corolla tube ⅛ in. long; lobes pointed, ⅛ in. or less long.

Native of China; introduced by Maries for Messrs Veitch in 1879. Maries no doubt collected it in the Yangtze Kiang valley, about Ichang, where it was afterwards found by Henry. It is an elegant privet, and its numerous, small, almost round leaves give it a distinct appearance. But it is not very hardy, and at Kew has only flowered satisfactorily on a south wall.

L. VULGARE, *Linnæus*. COMMON PRIVET

A deciduous or more or less evergreen shrub, 6 to 10 ft. high, of rather lax habit; young shoots covered with minute down. Leaves narrowly oval or lance-shaped, 1 to 2½ ins. long, ¼ to ⅝ in. wide, glabrous. Flowers dull white, produced during June and July on erect compact panicles 1 to 2 ins. long, terminating the twigs; they have a heavy odour objectionable to most people. Fruit globose or egg-shaped, black.

Native of Europe, including Britain, where it is considered wild from

Yorkshire southwards. The common privet may nowadays be regarded almost as the Cinderella among shrubs. It is relegated to dark corners and other damp out-of-the-way places under the drip of trees, where scarcely anything else will grow. But one can scarcely wish it a better fate. With so many beautiful things available the privet is not needed; even in its own genus it is about the least attractive, and for hedges is now superseded by the oval-leaved species. Its flowers are under suspicion of producing a kind of hay-fever. The berries are eaten by birds.

Var. AUREUM.—A yellow-leaved form.

Var. BUXIFOLIUM.—Leaves oval, scarcely 1 in. long; habit dense.

Var. GLAUCUM.—Leaves of a grey-green tint, not sufficiently marked to give it any value.

Var. ITALICUM (sempervirens).—A more regularly evergreen shrub than the type.

Besides the ordinary form with black berries, three others, differing in their fruits, are, or have been, in cultivation: CHLOROCARPUM, green-berried; LEUCOCARPUM, white-berried; and XANTHOCARPUM, yellow-berried.

Akin to the common privet is L. INSULARE, *Decaisne*, a species of unknown origin with linear-oblong leaves 2 to 4½ ins. long, ½ to 1 in. wide, taper-pointed; young shoots velvety-downy. Flowers in a panicle 3 ins. long and broad; fruit roundish oblong, ⅓ in. long, black.

L. YUNNANENSE, *L. Henry*. YUNNAN PRIVET

(L. compactum, *Hooker fil. and Thomson*)

A deciduous, sometimes partially evergreen shrub, 10 to 15 ft. high, of open, vigorous habit; branches spreading or somewhat pendent, slightly warted, and at first clothed with a very minute down, which mostly falls away by the end of the year. Leaves oval lance-shaped, tapering at both ends; 3 to 6 ins. long, about one-third as wide; glabrous. Flowers creamy white with an odour like common privet, produced in July in numerous terminal panicles 6 or 7 ins. high, and the same or more wide at the base. Fruit ¼ in. long, rounded at the top, covered with purple bloom at first, then black.

Native of Yunnan, China; introduced to France by the Abbé Delavay, who sent seeds to the Jardin des Plantes at Paris in 1888. The plants raised from them flowered in 1902. In its general aspect it is very like L. lucidum Alivoni; but it flowers before that privet does, and regularly sets its fruit. It is also nearly deciduous.

LINDERA. LAURACEÆ

The linderas are spicily aromatic shrubs or small trees allied to the bay laurel. There is in cultivation one hardy American species, and several, scarcely so hardy, from Japan and China. None of them is showy in flower, and they do not bear fruit freely, if at all in this country. The genus is not represented in the European flora; but in Japan, Sargent remarks that the linderas make a notable feature in the shrubby growth of the hillsides and on the borders of streams and lakes. Leaves alternate, flowers unisexual, small, yellowish. Fruit a drupe. Besides the species mentioned below, another, L. SERICEA, *Blume*, is occasionally grown. Its leaves are covered with silky hairs when they unfold, which mostly fall away as the season advances. It used to flower freely at Coombe Wood in March and April, bearing its blossoms in small umbels; stalks short, very silky. I have not heard that it develops fruit. On the low levels of Kew it is so injured by spring frosts that it never lives long out-of-doors.

L. Benzoin, *Blume*. Spice Bush

(Laurus Benzoin, *Linnæus*; Benzoin æstivale, *Nees*)

A spicily aromatic, deciduous shrub, 6 to 12 ft. high, forming a rounded bush as much in diameter; young shoots glabrous or slightly downy. Leaves obovate, 2 to 5 ins. long, 1 to 2½ ins. wide; tapered towards both ends, but more gradually towards the stalk; not toothed, thin, glabrous above, glabrous or slightly downy and glaucous beneath, margins ciliate; stalk ¼ to ½ in. long. Flowers greenish yellow, small, and not showy; produced in tiny clusters during April from the joints of last year's naked shoots; the sexes are on separate plants; corolla none; calyx with six lobes. Fruit red, oval, ⅓ in. long, juicy.

Native of the eastern United States; introduced in 1683. When crushed the leaf emits a pungent spicy odour too strong to be quite pleasant. This species is perfectly hardy at Kew, where it makes a neat bush of no particular merit or distinction.

L. megaphylla, *Hemsley*

(Benzoin grandifolium, *Rehder*.)

An evergreen shrub or tree; young shoots darkish purple, marked with a few pale lenticels; terminal bud woolly. Leaves oblong to oblanceolate, entire, pointed, tapered to a wedge-shaped or rounded base; 4 to 9 ins. long, 1 to 2¼ ins. wide; brilliantly glossy and dark green above; dull, pale and glaucous beneath, perfectly glabrous; midrib yellow; stalk ½ to 1 in. long. Flowers produced numerously in short-stalked, axillary umbels about 1 in. wide. Fruit black, egg-shaped, about ¾ in. long.

Native of Central China; introduced by Wilson about 1900. The above description is based on the plants raised in the Coombe Wood nursery, where it formed a very handsome evergreen and proved quite hardy, remaining, however, a shrub. The leaves rather suggest, in their sheen and size, those of a cinnamon; they are aromatic when crushed.

L. obtusiloba, *Blume*

(Benzoin obtusilobum, *Kuntze*)

A deciduous shrub or small tree, 20 to 30 ft. high, the brown branchlets not downy, but marked with pale, narrow lenticels. Leaves variable in shape; mostly broadly ovate, sometimes entire, but usually more or less conspicuously three-lobed towards the apex, the lobes pointing forward; base heart-shaped, rounded or wedge-shaped; 2½ to 5 ins. long, 1½ to 4 ins. wide; dark shining green and glabrous above; pale and downy on the veins beneath; prominently triple-nerved; stalk ½ to 1 in. long, downy. Flowers yellowish, produced in March and April from the joints of the leafless wood in small dense clusters; each flower is about ⅙ in. across, borne on a stalk ⅙ in. long, clothed thickly with silky hairs. Fruits described by Sargent as shining black, globose, ¼ in. across, and as forming a very handsome contrast to the yellow autumn foliage.

Native of Japan and Korea; introduced by Maries in 1880, and grown and flowered in the Coombe Wood nursery. It is a very handsome-leaved shrub, but is hardier and succeeds better in France than with us. Mr de Vilmorin has it very vigorous at Les Barres.

L. PRAECOX, *Blume*

(Benzoin praecox, *Siebold and Zuccarini*)

A deciduous shrub or bushy tree, 15 to 25 ft. high, young shoots shining dark brown, not downy, but prominently warted. Leaves thin, ovate or oval, occasionally rotund; 1 to 3½ ins. long, ½ to 1½ ins. wide; taper-pointed or blunt at the apex, dark green above, pale and glaucous beneath, usually glabrous; stalk ¼ to ¾ in. long. Flowers small, greenish yellow, produced in March and April in small short-stalked umbels about ½ in. diameter. Fruit ¾ in. diameter, reddish brown, marked with numerous pale dots.

Native of Japan and Korea. This Lindera is fairly hardy at Kew, but only flowers well on a wall. It forms its umbels usually in pairs or threes during the summer; in the leaf-axils they remain through autumn and winter as little round knobs, bursting in the first warm days of spring. I have not seen it in fruit in this country. The leaves die off yellow.

LINNÆA BOREALIS, *Gronovius*. TWIN-FLOWER.
CAPRIFOLIACEÆ

A creeping evergreen plant, a few inches high, with a woody base; branches long, slender, wire-like, hairy when young. Leaves opposite, obovate, oval or ovate; ¼ to ¾ in. long, ⅛ to ½ in. wide; rounded or broadly tapered and coarsely toothed at the apex, wedge-shaped and entire at the base; with scattered hairs on the margin, upper surface, and on the midrib below; stalk $\frac{1}{12}$ to ⅙ in. long. Flowers produced in summer, in a pair at the top of an erect, thread-like stalk, 1½ to 3 ins. high, terminating short, erect, lateral twigs; each flower has its own secondary stalk ½ to ¾ in. long. Corolla pink or white, ½ in. long, nodding, funnel-shaped, with five rounded lobes, hairy inside; calyx with five linear lobes; stamens four; ovary hairy. Fruit dry, yellow, one-seeded, downy.

This little plant, named after the great Linnæus, is found in the high latitudes of the northern hemisphere, including a few places in the north-east of Britain. It is a dainty plant, with pretty, fragrant flowers, best adapted for some shady moist spot in the rock garden in rather sandy soil. Allied to Abelia and the honeysuckles.

LINUM ARBOREUM, *Linnæus*. TREE FLAX. LINACEÆ

(Bot. Mag., t. 234)

A low, compact, evergreen, glabrous shrub from 9 ins. to 2 ft. high, more in hotter countries. Leaves of a conspicuously blue-white colour, 1 to 2 ins. long, ⅛ to ½ in. wide; broadest near the apex, tapering thence to the base, with little or no stalk. Panicles erect, terminal, 3 to 6 ins.

long, continuing to produce flowers as they lengthen from May until July or August. Flowers bright, clear yellow, 1½ ins. across when fully expanded, but opening indifferently in dull weather and lasting in good condition but one day. Petals five, each 1 to 1¼ ins. long, of very fragile texture. Sepals five; green, narrow-lanceolate, fine-pointed, ⅓ in. long.

This gay little shrub is a native of the eastern Mediterranean region; introduced in the eighteenth century. It is not so much grown as it deserves, for when it is in flower few plants of its character are so bright. It makes a neat little tuft, and although the flowers are so fugitive, they are borne so freely on fine summer days that the plant is almost hidden by blossom. It is hardy at Kew in all but the severest winters, but is not a long-lived plant in our climate. It is very easily increased by means of cuttings taken whilst the wood is comparatively soft, and placed in brisk heat. Seeds are borne freely, but it helps to prolong the life of the plant if they are not allowed to develop. The soil need not be very rich, but as sunny a spot as possible is desirable. Even out of flower its vividly glaucous foliage is pleasing.

LIPPIA CITRIODORA, *Kunth*. LEMON-SCENTED VERBENA. VERBENACEÆ

(Aloysia citriodora, *Orteg*; Verbena triphylla, *L'Heritier*, Bot. Mag., t. 367)

A deciduous shrub (naturally a small tree), reaching in the southern parts of the British Isles 10 to 15 ft. or more in height; young shoots angular. Leaves mostly in threes, very fragrant, lance-shaped; usually 3 to 4 ins. long, ½ to ⅞ in. wide; wedge-shaped at the base, taper-pointed, not toothed; both surfaces glandular, especially the upper one, pale green; margins set with appressed bristles. The veins are parallel, springing at right angles from the midrib. Flowers numerous, small, pale purple, produced in August in slender, terminal, stalked, downy panicles, 3 to 5 ins. high; corolla tubular, ⅙ in. long, downy, as is also the cylindrical, toothed calyx.

Native of Chile; introduced in 1784. Near London this well-known shrub needs the protection of a wall, and is often grown in cold conservatories for the pleasant lemon-like scent of the leaves. In the Isle of Wight and the Channel Islands it becomes a large bush without any protection. Easily increased by summer cuttings.

LIQUIDAMBAR. HAMAMELIDACEÆ

A small genus of trees with a remarkably scattered distribution in nature; one species being found in Asia Minor, one in eastern N. America, and one or more in China. In general appearance they bear most resemblance to the maples (Acer), but are easily distinguished by their alternate, not opposite leaves. The flowers have no beauty, being greenish or yellowish, and borne in small globose heads. Male and female flowers are in separate heads, the male flower-heads in short racemes; the female heads solitary. The male flowers consist of stamens only; the females of calyx and carpel only.

The best known and most useful of liquidambars is L. styraciflua, which, like the rest, should, if possible, be raised from imported seeds. These frequently do not germinate until the second year. Failing them, layering must be resorted to. Young plants are apt to be injured by late spring frosts.

L. FORMOSANA, *Hance*

(L. acerifolia, *Maximowicz*)

A tree up to 80 ft. high in China; young shoots hairy. Leaves maple-like, 3 to 4½ ins. wide, with three or five oblong or triangular lobes; finely glandular-toothed, hairy on both sides, but especially beneath; stalks downy, 1½ to 2½ ins. long. It has never, or only lately, flowered in this country, but from specimens collected in China the seed-vessels are seen to be in a globular cluster 1½ ins. across and spiny.

Native of the central and southern provinces of China, where its timber is largely employed for making tea-chests. There is a plant growing on a wall at Kew which was raised from seed sent from Hankow in 1884. For long this was the only one in the country, but, in 1908, Wilson sent seeds from W. China; also of a glabrous variety—MONTICOLA, *Rehder and Wilson*, the latter is, no doubt, a hardier tree. The typical L. formosana is distinguished from the American and Asia Minor species by its hairy young shoots and leaves.

L. ORIENTALIS, *Miller*. ORIENTAL SWEET GUM

(L. imberbe, *Aiton*)

A deciduous tree up to 100 ft. high; but rarely one-fourth as high in this country, bushy-headed. It has a rugged trunk covered with small squarish plates of thick bark; young shoots glabrous. Leaves 2½ to 3½ ins. wide, scarcely as long; maple-like, five-lobed, the lobes oblong and reaching half or two-thirds of the depth of the blade, coarsely toothed or even lobed again, especially the three upper ones, the margins set with fine glandular teeth; quite glabrous on both surfaces; stalk 1 to 2 ins. long. Flowers (rarely or never seen in Britain) greenish, produced in globose heads from the terminal part of the shoot with the young leaves in spring. Seed-vessels woody, in a rounded cluster 1 in. across.

Native of Asia Minor; introduced about 1750. Fine specimens are to be found on the Continent, the best I have seen being in the Bologna Botanic Garden—90 to 100 ft. high, and 5 ft. in diameter of trunk. In Britain it is an interesting small tree, growing very slowly. It is quite hardy, but coming from one of the hottest parts of the Levant it lacks in this country the sunshine necessary for its complete development. From the inner bark of this tree the soft, viscid, balsamic resin known as "liquid storax" is obtained. This substance has certain medicinal properties of reputed value in bronchial affections, and is said to form part of the popular preparation known as "friar's balsam."

L. STYRACIFLUA, *Linnæus*. SWEET GUM

A deciduous tree up to 150 ft. high in a wild state, but not much more than half as high in England. It has a straight, erect trunk, with slender branches forming (as the tree is usually seen in this country) a narrow, pyramidal head. Branchlets glabrous and round at first, but during their second year they turn grey, and often begin to form corky wings after the fashion of the English elm. Leaves maple-like, usually five- sometimes seven-lobed, 5 to 7 ins. wide, scarcely as long, heart-shaped at the base; the lobes minutely toothed, ovate-lanceolate; upper surface glabrous and glossy, the lower one with tufts of hair in the axils of the veins; stalk slender, 2½ to 4 ins. long. Male flowers in small round heads arranged on a downy spike 2 or 3 ins. long; female inflorescence rather larger, ½ in. wide. Seed-vessels in a roundish cluster 1 to 1½ ins. across.

Native of the eastern United States, often in swampy ground. It was introduced in the seventeenth century, and has long been valued for its stately form and handsome foliage. It is often mistaken for a maple, but from all maples is, of course, distinguished by the alternate leaves. In autumn its foliage turns to brilliant shades of crimson and orange. The tree produces a fragrant resin, known as "sweet gum." The timber, although not of first quality, is largely imported under the name of "satin walnut," for furniture-making. Under cultivation it likes a good loamy soil, and a moderately moist but not a swampy position. Elwes mentions a tree at Godinton, near Ashford, as the tallest known to him in this country; in 1907 it was 82 ft. high. The species occasionally bears fruit at Kew.

Var. PENDULA, *Rehder*, has pendulous branches "forming altogether an almost columnar head." Var. ROTUNDIFOLIA, *Rehder*, has the leaves with three or five rounded lobes.

LIRIODENDRON. MAGNOLIACEÆ

A genus of two species, one North American, one Chinese. They are deciduous trees closely related to the magnolias, but differing from them in the truncate, never pointed leaves, the differently shaped, terminal winter bud, and closed seed-vessels. Leaves alternate; flowers solitary at the end of a short branch; sepals three; petals six; carpels densely packed on a spindle-shaped column.

The tulip trees are gross feeders, and will only attain their best in good deep soil. They are impatient of disturbance at the root, and should be given a permanent place early. Like magnolias, they are probably most successfully transplanted in May. Seeds are produced in immense quantities, but comparatively few are fertile. Even in America it is said of the native species that barely 10 per cent. can be expected to grow. Still seeds can now be cheaply obtained from American nurserymen, and they afford the best means of increase. The varieties may be grafted on seedlings of L. Tulipifera in March; given a little heat in a propagating case, they unite very readily.

L. CHINENSE, *Sargent*. CHINESE TULIP-TREE

(L. Tulipifera chinense, *Hemsley*)

Introduced to this country in 1901, this tree is perfectly hardy, and is growing admirably at Kew, where one of the original specimens is about 50 ft. high. It was first noticed in China in 1875, in the Lushan Mountains, and was subsequently found by Henry, in Hupeh, at 3000 to 6000 ft. altitude. Living plants were first introduced by Wilson for Messrs Veitch. It never appears to become so large as L. Tulipifera, and the greatest height recorded for it is

60 ft. The leaves are of very much the same shape as those of the American species, having the same truncate apex and two lateral lobes; they are, however, more glaucous beneath, and narrower waisted, the sinus between the lobes being deeper and the midrib more prolonged. The flowers are smaller, the petals narrower and expanding more widely, and the fruit is more elongated. The apices of the carpels are not so acute, and not recurved as in the American tree. The leaves beneath, seen with a strong lens, are found to be covered with tiny warts (papillæ). It flowered at Borde Hill, Sussex, in July 1927. It is easily grafted on seedlings of L. Tulipifera.

L. TULIPIFERA, *Linnæus*. TULIP-TREE

A tree of the largest size, reaching in its native haunts 150 to 190 ft. in height, with a magnificent columnar trunk 8 or 9 ft. in diameter. In the British Isles it has attained a stature of over 100 ft. The leaves vary in size,

LIRIODENDRON TULIPIFERA

but are usually 3 to 8 ins. long, and about one-third more in width, and by their form distinguish this from all other hardy trees except its Chinese ally; they are usually saddle-shaped, the apex being broad, and cut off almost square, or to a very shallow notch, the base truncate, or slightly hollowed, and extended at each side into an acute lobe with occasionally one or two more subsidiary ones. The leaf-stalk is slender, 2 to 4 ins. long; the midrib is slightly extended beyond the blade. Flowers produced in June and July, and except for the three deflexed sepals, resemble a tulip in form. Petals oblong, $1\frac{1}{2}$ ins. long, greenish white with an orange-coloured spot at the base, erect with their edges overlapping, thus giving the flower its cupped shape.

In the centre is the large, pointed pistil surrounded by numerous stamens. The foliage turns rich yellow in autumn.

In a wild state the tulip tree extends from Nova Scotia south to Florida, reaching its finest development in the south Allegheny region. It was one of the earliest introductions from N. America, and is known to have been cultivated by Bishop Compton at Fulham in 1688; but it was probably introduced some time before, because it is on record that a tree at Waltham Abbey, in 1745, was already 96 ft. high and 9 ft. in girth of trunk. When once it has attained the adult stage, the tree flowers very abundantly in this country, but the colouring of its blossoms is too dull to render them very noticeable. It is for its noble trunk and stately dimensions, its fine and unique foliage, that it is so much prized in gardens. The timber is extensively used in N. America under the name of "white wood," especially for indoor purposes. It is yellowish, smooth, and fine-grained, and although not strong, does not split easily. The bark of both root and branches has a pleasant, rather pungent scent.

Several forms are cultivated in gardens, of which the following are the most important:—

Var. AUREO-MACULATUM.—Leaves blotched in the centre with yellow.

Var. CONTORTUM.—Leaves with wavy margins.

Var. INTEGRIFOLIUM, *Kirchner*.—Leaves without the lateral lobes, and therefore of almost rectangular outline. This is the juvenile condition persisting; the first leaves of all tulip-trees are of this form.

Var. PYRAMIDALE, *Lavallée*.—A form with erect branches like a Lombardy poplar. The finest specimen I have seen was in the nursery of Messrs Simon-Louis, near Metz—a shapely spire 40 ft. high.

LITHOSPERMUM. BORAGINACEÆ

A genus of about fifty species of herbs and sub-shrubs, with a few shrubs. Leaves alternate, entire; calyx five-parted; corolla funnel-shaped or salver-shaped spreading at the mouth into five lobes. The generic name refers to the hard, stone-like seeds. The genus is found in the temperate parts of both hemispheres.

L. DIFFUSUM, *Lagasca*

(L. prostratum, *Loiseleur*)

A prostrate evergreen shrub, growing from 6 to 12 ins. only above the ground, but forming a wide-spreading mass. Shoots semi-herbaceous, slender trailing, thickly covered with pale, bristly hairs. Leaves alternate, linear-oblong; ½ to ¾ in. long, ⅙ in. wide; stalkless, blunt at the apex, dark dull green, clothed on both surfaces with pale hairs. Flowers stalkless, borne in the axils of leafy bracts on a terminal leafy elongated inflorescence; of a beautiful gentian blue, faintly striped with reddish violet. Corolla ½ in. long, tubular at the base, spreading into five rounded lobes at the mouth; calyx with erect hairy, awl-shaped lobes.

Native of S. Europe; introduced in 1825. A singularly beautiful sub-shrubby plant, very effective in the rock garden, or at the top of banks over which its trailing shoots may hang. It does not need a rich or wet soil, but one of a light nature, and well-drained. It should be planted in full sun. Increased by cuttings in summer, and kept in pots the first winter. Where the soil and exposure are suitable it makes delightful patches in front of a low shrubbery or border, flowering continuously during May and June, often again later.

L. OLEIFOLIUM, *Lapeyrouse*

(Bot. Mag., t. 8994 and t. 9559)

An evergreen prostrate shrub, 3 ft. or more wide, forming a dense mass of branches only 5 or 6 ins. high; young shoots clothed with silky hairs. Leaves obovate or oval, rounded or slightly pointed at the apex, tapering to a very short stalk; ½ to ¾ in. long, ¼ to ⅜ in. wide on flowering shoots, sometimes twice as long and wide on barren shoots; dull dark green with appressed silky hairs above, completely covered with whitish silky hairs beneath. Flowers blue, opening successively in May and June on flattish curving racemes 1 in. or more long, of the type common to the borage family, five to seven flowers on each raceme. Corolla ¾ in. long, ⅜ in. wide, hairy outside, glabrous inside, slenderly tubular at the base, more bell-shaped towards the top, with five rounded, slightly notched lobes there. Calyx five-lobed, the lobes narrowly linear, ¼ in. long; stamens five, hidden in the corolla; style shorter than the corolla.

Native of Spain; discovered on the eastern Pyrenees in 1814, growing in crevices of rocks. No one probably in this country succeeded so well in cultivating this rare and beautiful shrub as Miss Willmott, who grew it in her rock garden at Warley, in Essex, for over thirty years. She recommended for it a dry, well-drained position, with some old mortar rubble about the roots, and that it should be protected from excessive moisture. It can be propagated by cuttings and by division in the absence of seeds.

LOISELEURIA PROCUMBENS, *Desvaux*. ALPINE AZALEA.

ERICACEÆ

A procumbent evergreen shrub, much-branched, forming low tufts 3 to 6 ins. high; branches tortuous, very leafy, glabrous, rooting freely along the ground. Leaves opposite, oval or oblong, ⅛ to ⅓ in. long, scarcely half as wide, with the margins so much recurved as almost to hide the under-surface; glabrous and dark glossy green above, glabrous or sometimes with a whitish mealy down beneath; stalk one-fourth to half as long as the blade. Flowers rosy or nearly white, about ¼ in. diameter, produced in May in short terminal clusters, two to five together. Corolla erect, bell-shaped, with five lobes. Calyx with five deep lobes half as long as the corolla. Stamens five, shorter than the corolla. Seed-vessel a dry capsule, with two or three divisions, many-seeded.

Native of the Alpine summits and sub-Arctic regions of the three northern continents, and the only species known. Found on the Scottish highlands. It resembles Leiophyllum in its opposite leaves and small pink flowers, but is readily distinguished by its five (not ten) stamens included within the corolla. It needs a peaty soil. In the south of England it does not thrive well; the summer is usually too hot and dry for it. Some cool damp spot on the lower part of the rock garden should be selected for it.

LOMATIA. PROTEACEÆ

A genus of about a dozen species of evergreen small trees or shrubs with alternate or opposite leaves, the cultivated species of which come from South America and Australia. The generic name is from the Greek and refers to the winged seeds.

L. FERRUGINEA, *R. Brown*

(Bot. Mag., t. 8112; L. pinnatifolia, *Hort.*)

An evergreen shrub or a tree up to 30 ft. high, of erect growth when young; branchlets clothed with a rich brownish red, velvety down. Leaves mostly pinnate, with the pinnæ (*i.e.* primary divisions) deeply and pinnately lobed; but some of the smaller leaves have unlobed segments. They vary from 3 to 8 ins. in length and in main outline are oblong to ovate; the pinnæ are usually up to 2 or 3 ins. long, and vary from six to fifteen in number, decreasing in size towards each end; the ultimate segments being of oblong or obovate shape, pointed, about ½ in. long, dull dark green and at first downy above, covered beneath with down which is whitish, becoming tawny with age. The main and secondary leaf-stalks are covered with velvety down like that of the young shoots. Racemes axillary, 1½ to 2 ins. long, carrying a dozen or more flowers, each about ½ in. long, tawny yellow and red; there are four perianth segments, the style is curved and terminated by the large stigma characteristic of the genus; flower-stalks and petals downy. Flowers in July.

Native of Chile and Patagonia; introduced by Wm. Lobb between 1845 and 1848 for Messrs Veitch; it is frequent on the island of Chiloe. Its foliage is of a fern-like character and in this respect it is one of the handsomest trees that have come from S. America. The flowers, which are not particularly handsome, are of curious structure, the segments of the perianth bearing the stalkless anthers on their recurved tips. This tree is happiest in the Cornish gardens where, at Penjerrick, Lanarth, and other places, are examples 25 to 30 ft. high. It is incapable of withstanding the winters at Kew and the place nearest to London in which I have seen it successfully cultivated is the garden at South Lodge, Horsham, where a healthy plant was 7 ft. high in 1932. The description given above is based on the foliage, etc., as usually seen in this country, but there is a leaf collected on the island of Chiloe and preserved at Kew which is 20 ins. long and 10 ins. wide.

L. OBLIQUA, *R. Brown*

An evergreen shrub or small tree, 20 or more ft. high; young stems slightly downy. Leaves alternate, leathery, ovate, 1½ to 4 ins. long, ¾ to 2½ ins. wide; wedge-shaped or rounded at the base, blunt at the apex, coarsely round-toothed; as they unfold they are covered with tawny down, but afterwards become perfectly glabrous, and of a deep glossy green; stalk brownish, about one-fourth the length of the blade. Flowers borne in axillary racemes 2 to 3 ins. long, pale greenish-yellow, not showy.

Native of Chile, Peru, etc.; introduced by Mr Elwes in 1902. It proved hardy at Kew, planted on an outside border near one of the plant-houses where it was 9 ft. high until the winter of 1946-47 when it was killed by the severe weather. This species would no doubt be better suited growing under the same conditions as Embothrium in Cornwall.

LONICERA. HONEYSUCKLE, WOODBINE. CAPRIFOLIACEÆ

A genus of about 150 deciduous or sometimes evergreen species of bushy or climbing shrubs, with usually peeling bark, named by Linnæus after Adam Lonicer, a German naturalist who flourished in the middle part of the sixteenth century. The leading generic characters are: Leaves opposite, shortly stalked or stalkless; flowers five-parted, subtended by bracts and usually bractlets ; calyx five-toothed ; corolla tubular or bell-shaped and five-lobed, the lobes sometimes equal, but more frequently forming two "lips," the upper lip composed of four short lobes, the lower lip of a single strap-shaped lobe. Fruit a fleshy berry. The flowers often change from white to yellow with age.

In the British Isles the genus is represented by three species, two of which are typical examples of, and give the name to, two great sections into which it is divided, viz., L. Periclymenum and L. Xylosteum. The leading characteristics of these two sections (many authors have regarded them as distinct genera) are as follows :—

PERICLYMENUM. Woodbine, Honeysuckle.—Climbers or semi-climbers, with hollow branchlets, one or more of the uppermost pairs of leaves, usually (but not in L. Periclymenum itself) joined together by their bases ; flowers stalkless, usually in threes, forming whorls at the end of the branches, often crowded on somewhat elongated spikes. Fruits never united. (This group is also known as CAPRIFOLIUM.)

XYLOSTEUM. Bush Honeysuckle.—Shrubs of bushy habit ; leaves never united ; flowers always in pairs, produced in the leaf-axils, each pair on one stalk ; each pair of fruits often partially, sometimes wholly, cohering. (This group has also been given the generic name of CHAMÆCERASUS.)

There is a third group, distinguished as NINTOOA, which to some extent combines the characters of the other two. They are climbing or creeping shrubs with usually hollow stems ; leaves never joined at their bases ; flowers in axillary pairs ; fruits not cohering in any cultivated species. This group of honeysuckles is commonly represented in gardens by L. japonica and its varieties.

Although the value of the genus in gardens is not commensurate with its size, it does contain a number of extremely beautiful species, and of the Periclymenum or climbing group, every species that is hardy is worth growing. The free-growing woodbines are best accommodated on pergolas or similar supports, or planted to ramble over small trees or bushes ; but some of the less rambling ones may be at first trained up stout posts 4 or 6 ft. high, and then allowed to form loose, spreading shrubs, needing no further support. The Periclymenum group are very subject to attacks of aphides in summer, especially during hot dry spells ; if these are not repelled by applications of some insecticide (tobacco water and soft soap diluted is as good as anything), they sometimes destroy the crop of blossom. All the species like a good loamy soil, and especially cool moist conditions at the root—given these, the attacks of aphides are often naturally overcome.

The bush honeysuckles are in this country somewhat disappointing shrubs. Many of them, especially those of North Asiatic origin, are almost invariably cut by spring frosts and much of their blossom destroyed. Consequently we never see their full beauty of flower or of fruit—and many species are extremely handsome when bearing full crops of red, yellow, black, blue, or white, often translucent, berries. The propagation of those species that do bear fruit is easily effected by seed, but I do not know of any species that cannot be increased by cuttings of firm young shoots, placed in gentle bottom heat about July or August. If heat be not available, cuttings of somewhat harder wood may be dibbled in sandy soil under handlights out-of-doors.

L. ALBERTI, *Regel*

(Bot. Mag., t. 7394; L. spinosa Alberti, *Rehder*)

A deciduous shrub of low, spreading habit, unarmed, becoming about 4 ft. high and twice as much in diameter; young shoots glabrous or glandular, slender. Leaves linear-oblong, ⅝ to 1¼ ins. long, about ⅛ in. wide; bluntish at the apex, with often a few teeth near the base; blue-green, glabrous; stalks very short. Flowers rosy lilac, fragrant, produced in pairs from the leaf-axils, each pair on a stalk about ¼ in. long. Corolla-tube ⅓ to ½ in. long, slender, cylindrical, glabrous outside, downy inside; lobes spreading horizontally, oblong, giving the flower a diameter of about ¾ in. Stalk of the stamens twice as long as the anthers. Berries ⅓ in. in diameter, purplish red, not united.

Native of the mountains of Turkestan; introduced by Albert Regel to St Petersburg about 1880. It is sometimes regarded as a variety of L. spinosa, which inhabits the inner, arid ranges of the north-western Himalaya. This differs from L. Alberti in its sturdier, spiny, sometimes leafless, branches; in the ovate lobes of the corolla, and in the stalks of the stamens being only as long as the anther. L. Alberti is a pleasing shrub of graceful habit, very distinct from cultivated honeysuckles in its narrow bluish foliage.

L. ALPIGENA, *Linnæus*. CHERRY WOODBINE

A deciduous shrub, 4 to 8 ft. high, with erect branches; young shoots mostly glabrous. Leaves oval, oblong, or somewhat obovate; usually tapered, sometimes rounded at the base; slender-pointed; 2 to 4 ins. long, 1 to 2 ins. wide; sometimes glabrous, but usually with hairs on the midrib and veins both above and below when quite young; margins always hairy; stalk ½ in. or less long. Flowers yellow, deeply tinged with red, borne during May in pairs at the end of a stalk 1½ to 2 ins. long; corolla ½ in. long, with a very short tube protruded on one side near the base, distinctly two-lipped, very hairy inside, the lower part of the stamens hairy. Fruit red, up to ½ in. long, cherry-like.

Native of Central Europe; cultivated since the sixteenth century. The species is very distinct among cultivated bush honeysuckles in its long flower-stalks, large leaves, and large fruits, but has no particular garden value.

Var. NANA, *Dippel*.—A dwarf form whose leaves have scattered hairs all over the lower surface, more densely on the veins and midrib.

L. ALSEUOSMOIDES, *Graebner*

A climbing evergreen shrub, with slender, glabrous, young shoots. Leaves narrowly oblong, tapered at both ends, 1¼ to 2 ins. long, averaging about ¼ to ⅓ in. wide, the decurved margins furnished with appressed hairs; otherwise glabrous. Flowers produced from July to October at the apex of the shoot, and in the terminal leaf-axils, the whole forming a short broad panicle. Corolla purple within, yellow outside, funnel-shaped, ½ in. long, glabrous outside, downy within. Fruit globose, ⅙ to ¼ in. in diameter, black covered with purple bloom, borne in a close head.

Native of China; introduced by Wilson for Messrs Veitch about 1904. An interesting and pretty climber, which first flowered at Coombe Wood in 1909. Closely akin to L. Henryi, which has hairy young shoots and bigger leaves.

L. ALTMANNII, *Regel*

A deciduous shrub 6 to 8 ft. high; young shoots purplish, hairy. Leaves ovate or oval, ¾ to 2 ins. long, half to three-fourths as wide; rounded or tapered at the base, mostly pointed, ciliate, more or less hairy; stalk ⅙ in. or less long. Flowers in pairs, each pair subtended by two hairy bracts ¼ in. long; corolla white, ½ in. long, the slender tubular base rather longer than the lobes, and with a proturberance near the base; hairy outside; flower-stalk about ¼ in. long. Berries ⅓ in. wide, orange-red.

Native of Turkestan; introduced from St Petersburg in 1899, but very rare. It belongs to the same group as hispida, but has comparatively inconspicuous bracts, and the corolla-tube differs in being longer than the lobes. Flowers in April and May.

L. ANGUSTIFOLIA, *Wallich*

A deciduous shrub, 8 to 10 ft. high, of rounded elegant habit, the outer branches pendulous. Leaves ovate-lanceolate, rounded or tapering at the base, slender pointed, ¾ to 2 ins. long, ¼ to ½ in. wide, bright green and glabrous above except at first, paler and slightly downy beneath, especially on the midrib; stalk $\frac{1}{12}$ in. or less long, woolly. Flowers pinkish white, produced in May and June in pairs from the lower leaf-axils of the young branchlets, each pair on a slender drooping stalk ½ to ⅝ in. long. Corolla tubular, the tube ⅓ in. long, the lobes equal, about one-third as long as the tube. Style quite short and hidden. Berries red, edible; each pair united.

Native of the Himalaya; introduced by Sir Joseph Hooker about 1849. If it flowered more freely it would be an attractive shrub, as it is perfectly hardy and of elegant growth; its flowers are fragrant.

L. CŒRULEA, *Linnæus*

(Bot. Mag., t. 1965)

A deciduous sturdy bush of rounded habit, 2 to 4 ft. high; branchlets stiff, glabrous, or hairy only when young. Leaves oval, obovate or oblong, rounded at the apex, ½ to 1½ ins. long, ¼ to 1 in. wide; more or less (sometimes very) hairy beneath, especially on the midrib and veins; stalk hairy, ⅛ in. or less long. Flowers twin, produced from the leaf-axils, yellowish white. Corolla ½ to ¾ in. long, funnel-shaped, hairy outside, with a sac at the base of the tube; bracts awl-shaped, ciliate. Fruit blue.

A widespread species inhabiting, in one or other of its numerous forms, the higher altitudes and latitudes of the three northern continents. It has little or no merit for gardens, but has some botanical interest. The single oval berry which constitutes the fruit is not, as was long supposed, the wholly united ovaries of each pair of flowers, but really a pair of free ovaries enclosed by the cupula—an upgrowth of the bractlets.

A variable shrub, the leaves and branches in some forms much more hairy or downy than in others, and the fruit sometimes roundish. They are all distinguished by the curious character mentioned, where two flowers appear to rise from one ovary.

L. CAPRIFOLIUM, *Linnæus*. PERFOLIATE WOODBINE

A deciduous climber, up to 20 ft. high, not downy on any part except sometimes the outside of the corolla. Leaves obovate or oval, usually tapered at the base, rounded at the apex; 2 to 4 ins. long, about half as wide; glaucous, especially beneath. The lower leaves of the shoot are stalked, the higher pairs are sessile; finally, the uppermost one to three pairs are united round the stem, each pair forming a cup, and in their axils the flowers are borne. Flowers in whorls, fragrant, produced from June onwards. Corolla yellowish white, tinged with pink, 1½ to 2 ins. long, two-lipped, the tube slender. Fruit orange-coloured.

Native of Europe, naturalised in Britain, possibly wild in the south-east of England; also naturalised in the eastern United States. This beautiful fragrant honeysuckle differs from L. Periclymenum in the uppermost pairs of leaves (in whose axils the flowers are borne) being united. It is often confused with L. italica (*q.v.*), a hybrid between itself and L. etrusca, and a still more ornamental climber.

LONICERA CHÆTOCARPA

L. CHÆTOCARPA, *Rehder*

(L. hispida chætocarpa, *Batalin*)

An upright deciduous shrub, 5 to 7 ft. high; shoots bristly and glandular. Leaves ovate to oblong, sometimes oval, 1½ to 3 ins. long, blunt to pointed at the apex, bristly, especially beneath. Flowers in pairs or solitary, borne on hairy stalks up to ¾ in. long; corolla tubular, 1¼ ins. long, dividing at the mouth to five roundish spreading lobes, primrose yellow, hairy and glandular outside; ovary densely glandular and bristly. Berry bright red.

Native of W. China; introduced for Messrs Veitch by Wilson in 1904. It is an attractive shrub of comely habit, closely akin to L. hispida, which differs in its more slender corolla-tube and its glabrous or glandular ovary. It is quite hardy and flowers in June.

L. CHRYSANTHA, *Turczaninow*

A deciduous shrub up to 12 ft. high; young shoots usually rather shaggy at first, but variable in this respect and sometimes nearly glabrous. Leaves oval to ovate-lanceolate, pointed, broadly tapering or rounded at the base; 2 to 4½ ins. long, about half as wide; downy on the midrib above, also beneath especially on the veins; stalk ⅛ to ¼ in. long. Flowers twin, each pair borne on a slender hairy stalk ½ to ¾ in. long, springing from the leaf-axils; they are pale yellow becoming deeper in shade with age, $\frac{3}{4}$ in. long, slightly downy outside; stamens downy at the lower part; ovaries glandular. Fruit coral-red.

Native of Siberia, N. China, and Japan. It has long been in cultivation and was in the Kew collection in 1880. As a flowering bushy honeysuckle it is one of the most ornamental and very hardy.

Var. REGELIANA, *Zabel* (L. Regeliana, *Kirchner*), has smaller but deeper yellow flowers. Var. TURKESTANICA, *Rehder*, has broader, stouter leaves, less downy beneath. It resembles L. Ruprechtiana in many respects, but that species has a glabrous ovary.

L. chrysantha belongs to the group of bush honeysuckles with hollow branchlets and distinct ovaries. It blooms in May and June.

L. CILIOSA, *Poiret*. WESTERN TRUMPET HONEYSUCKLE

A twining honeysuckle of the same group as L. sempervirens, but differing in having leaves hairy on the margins, but otherwise glabrous; the style also is hairy. Leaves ovate or oval, 2 to 3 ins. long, glaucous beneath, the upper pairs united by their bases round the stem. Flowers $1\frac{1}{4}$ to $1\frac{1}{2}$ ins. long, yellow or orange scarlet, sometimes purplish, downy outside; they are produced in a terminal stalked spike of several whorls. Corolla slightly two-lipped, more so than in L. sempervirens.

Native of western N. America from British Columbia southwards; introduced in 1824, but now very rare in gardens.

L. DEFLEXICALYX, *Batalin*

(Bot. Mag., t. 8536)

A deciduous shrub of elegant spreading habit; branches often horizontal or drooping, the branchlets in opposite rows; young shoots purple, downy. Leaves $1\frac{1}{2}$ to 3 ins. long, scarcely half as wide, rounded at the base, narrowly ovate, pointed, dull green and downy above, greyish and hairy beneath, especially when young; stalk $\frac{1}{8}$ in. long. Flowers in pairs from each axil along the branchlets, all expanding upwards; corolla yellow, $\frac{5}{8}$ in. long, downy outside, the lower lip much deflexed, tube shorter than the lobes; stamens hairy at the base; style wholly hairy; stalk $\frac{1}{4}$ in. long; fruit orange-red.

Native of China and Tibet; introduced in 1904. A notably elegant, free-growing shrub, very hardy and floriferous, showing its flowers to good advantage by producing them on the upper side of the long feathered branches. It flowers in May and June, and grows probably 8 ft. or so high.

L. DELAVAYI, *Franchet*

(Bot. Mag., t. 8800; L. similis Delavayi, *Rehder*)

This species was sent to Kew in 1907 from France by Mr Maurice de Vilmorin, who had received it from W. China in 1901, and with whom it first flowered three years later. It is an evergreen climber of the L. japonica group. Its leaves are ovate-lanceolate, rounded or slightly heart-shaped at the base, taper-pointed; 2 to 5 ins. long, $\frac{3}{4}$ to 2 ins. wide; glabrous above, grey-felted beneath; stalk $\frac{1}{6}$ to $\frac{1}{4}$ in. long. Flowers sweet-scented, in axillary pairs, and at the end of the shoot forming a kind of panicle. The corolla is pale yellow, and has a very slender cylindrical tube 2 ins. long, and a two-lipped apex; the larger lip $\frac{3}{4}$ in. long, with four short lobes, the smaller one linear; calyx-lobes awl-shaped, edged with hairs. The species was originally discovered in Yunnan by the Abbé Delavay, in 1888. It flowers in August.

L. DIOECA, *Linnæus*

(Bot. Reg., t. 138; L. glauca, *Hill*)

A spreading or twining deciduous shrub; young stems and leaves quite glabrous. Leaves oval or oblong, tapered at both ends, 1½ to 4 ins. long, 1 to 2 ins. wide; green above, vividly glaucous beneath. Flowers yellow, tinged with purple, produced during June and July in terminal clusters, two or more

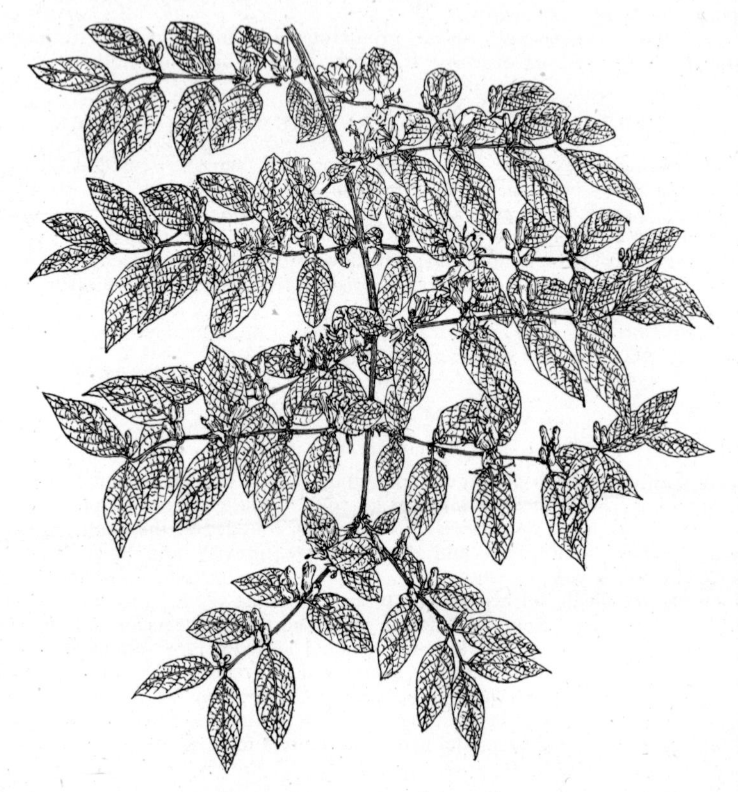

LONICERA DEFLEXICALYX (see p. 241)

pairs of leaves beneath being united. Corolla ¾ in. long, the tube about equal to the lips in length, swollen at the base, glabrous outside. Berries red.

Native of eastern N. America; introduced in 1776. This honeysuckle succeeds very well under cultivation in good loam; if given the support of a stout central stake, it will form a low, spreading, rather elegant bush, and although without any great beauty of flower is striking for the very glaucous under-surface of the leaf.

Nearly allied to the above, and sometimes confused with it, is L. GLAUCESCENS, *Rydberg*. This differs chiefly in having the leaves downy beneath and the corolla downy outside; as a rule only the uppermost pair of leaves is united. The style and the base of the stamens are downy; the corolla-tube rather longer than the lips.

L. ETRUSCA, *Santi*

A very vigorous half evergreen or deciduous climber, young shoots (in the cultivated form) reddish purple. Leaves oval or obovate, rounded at both ends or broadly tapered at the base; 1½ to 3½ ins. long, 1 to 2 ins. wide; glaucous and usually somewhat downy beneath. The lower ones are shortly stalked; approaching the top they become stalkless; whilst the uppermost pairs are united at the base (connate). Flowers fragrant, at first yellowish, suffused with red, becoming deeper yellow with age; borne from July onwards in terminal and axillary groups of three long-stalked heads. Corolla 1¾ ins. long, the tube slender, sometimes glabrous, sometimes glandular; conspicuously two-lipped.

Native of the Mediterranean region; introduced probably two hundred years ago, but not often seen. At its best, perhaps it is the most gorgeous of all honeysuckles, but I have not seen it at its best out-of-doors, although no doubt it may reach perfection in the south-western counties. Farther north it is hardy, but not wholly satisfactory out-of-doors; in an unheated greenhouse it is wonderfully beautiful in late summer, the long shoots branching and forming immense bouquets. The species varies very much in the amount of down on the leaves, but the form now cultivated is downy on both sides of the leaf. It is

Var. PUBESCENS, *Dippel* (also known in gardens as gigantea, gigantea superba, etc.).

Var. SUPERBA.—Very vigorous; panicles larger. Bot. Mag., t. 7977.

Var. VISCIDULA, *Boissier*.—Leaves very glandular above, less so beneath; young shoots also glandular. Native of Asia Minor; rather tender.

L. FERDINANDI, *Franchet*

A very robust, deciduous shrub, of spreading, open habit, becoming in a few years 8 or 9 ft. high and more in diameter; buds awl-shaped, at first hairy; young shoots glandular when quite young. Leaves ovate, rounded or heart-shaped at the base, slender-pointed, 1½ to 4 ins. long, ¾ to 1¾ ins. wide; dull green, hairy on both sides and on the margins. On the vigorous barren shoots the leaf-stalks (each about ¼ in. long) are attached to a pair of stipules, which are united and form a shield-like disk surrounding the stem at each joint. These are not present on the flowering branches. Flowers yellow, produced in pairs during early June from the apex of the shoot, and in the upper leaf-axils. Corolla two-lipped, ¾ in. across, with a bellied tube ⅓ in. long, downy outside. Each pair of flowers is subtended by two leaflike bracts. Fruit bright red.

Native of Mongolia and China; introduced in 1900. It is a remarkably distinct species, and flowers freely. The shield-like stipules mentioned above persist through the winter and become brown, stiff, and brittle the second year.

L. FLAVA, *Sims*

(Bot. Mag., t.1318)

The real L. flava is perhaps not now in cultivation, or, if it be, it is extremely rare. It appears to be very local in its distribution, and was originally discovered on the summit of Paris Mountain, in S. Carolina, by John Fraser; introduced early in the nineteenth century. The plants that go in cultivation under the name are either L. prolifera or L. glaucescens, both of which are inferior to it. It is about the most beautiful of American honeysuckles. The bright orange-yellow flowers are about 1¼ ins. long, the corolla-tube glabrous outside, slenderly tapered downwards, not bellied. The flowers are produced in two or more whorls on a stalked, terminal inflorescence; style glabrous. Leaves rather glaucous beneath, glabrous, the uppermost one to three pairs united into disks, not glaucous above as they are in L. prolifera.

L. FRAGRANTISSIMA, *Lindley and Paxton*

(Bot. Mag., t. 8585)

An evergreen, partially evergreen, or deciduous bush, 6 to 8 ft. high, glabrous except for the bristly margins of the young leaves and sometimes the midrib. Leaves oval, rather stiff and leathery, 1 to 2 ins. long, two-thirds as wide; broadly wedge-shaped at both ends, but terminated by a short bristle-like tip, and bristly on the margins when young; dark dull green above, rather glaucous beneath; stalk ⅛ in. or less long. Flowers produced from December to March in several pairs at the joints, creamy white, very fragrant, ⅝ in. long; stalk glabrous, ¼ in. long.

Native of China; introduced by Fortune in 1845. This is not a showy plant, but is valued in gardens for its early, charmingly fragrant blossoms. It varies from deciduous to evergreen according to the severity of the winter, but is rarely devoid of foliage. Often confused with L. Standishii, it is, nevertheless, very distinct in the absence of bristles on the young shoots, flower-stalks, and corolla; the leaf, too, is shorter, and the apex is not drawn out as in L. Standishii. L. fragrantissima, which is the superior shrub, commences to grow very early in the year. Both are distinct in their early flowering from all the rest of the honeysuckles.

L. GIRALDII, *Rehder*

(Bot. Mag., t. 8236)

An evergreen climber forming a dense tangle of twining branches, thickly clothed with yellowish erect hairs when young. Leaves narrowly oblong, with a lance-shaped apex and a heart-shaped base; 1½ to 3½ ins. long, ½ to 1 in. wide; densely hairy on both sides; stalk ⅓ in. or less long, hairy. Flowers purplish red, borne in a short terminal panicle 1½ ins. across; corolla two-lipped, ¾ in. wide, yellowish hairy outside; the tube slender, ½ in. long; the entire flower 1 in. long; bracts inconspicuous. Fruit purplish black.

Native of Szechuen, China, whence it was introduced to France in 1899, and first grown by Mr Maurice de Vilmorin. I first saw it growing against a wall in the garden of Mr Phillipe de Vilmorin at Verrières-le-Buisson, near Paris, in June 1908, then in flower. Plants were obtained for Kew the following autumn, and these, so far as I am aware, represent its first introduction to Britain. As I saw it, it was a striking honeysuckle forming a dense thicket, the whole plant having a yellowish tinge, very downy, the rather small flower clusters striking in the contrast of lurid red corolla and yellow stamens. It is hardy in the south and west of England.

L. GRIFFITHII, *Hooker fil. and Thomson.*
GRIFFITH'S HONEYSUCKLE

(Bot. Mag., t. 8956; Gardeners' Chronicle, 22nd July 1916, fig. 16)

A deciduous twining shrub up to 20 ft. high, the older bark peeling off in flakes; young shoots glabrous. Leaves broadly ovate, oblong or roundish in main outline; the terminal pair close to the inflorescence are always roundish and in cultivated plants the lower pairs are often very deeply lobed; 1 to 2 ins. long, half to nearly as much wide; glaucous green, quite glabrous; stalk 1/8 to 1/2 in. long. Inflorescence a terminal, stalked head of flowers closely arranged in two or three tiers opening in May. Corolla rosy white, of the two-lipped, common honeysuckle shape, 1 in. long, 3/4 in. wide, the tube downy and glandular outside, glabrous within; stamens glabrous; style hairy. The main-stalk of the inflorescence is downy and the bracts beneath each tier of flowers are hairy.

Native of Afghanistan; discovered in 1840 by Griffith (Superintendent of the Botanic Garden, Calcutta, in the early nineteenth century). The plants at present in cultivation were obtained by Lt.-Col. Mainwaring of Upwey in Dorset, who had seeds sent to him in 1910. Dr Aitchison collected it in 1879 during his notable travels in Afghanistan, and records that he found it in association with Quercus Ilex, Rosa Ecæ, and Populus alba, all very hardy. It does not appear, nevertheless, to have taken kindly to our climate, although it succeeds at Abbotsbury, not far from Upwey. None of the wild specimens in the Kew Herbarium have the deeply lobed leaves shown in the illustrations quoted above, but the plants cultivated at Upwey and Abbotsbury have them. Botanically, the species is closely related to our native L. Periclymenum. Both Dr Aitchison and Col. Mainwaring found it festooning Quercus Ilex, and all who have seen it in a wild state have been impressed by its beauty.

L. GYNOCHLAMYDEA, *Hemsley*

A deciduous shrub of erect habit, with glabrous, purplish young shoots. Leaves lanceolate, rounded or broadly tapered at the base, drawn out at the apex to a long slender point; 2 to 4½ ins. long, 3/4 to 1½ ins. wide; downy along the midrib above, with usually a conspicuous strip of down towards the base of the midrib beneath; stalk about 1/8 in. long. Flowers twin, produced in May from the leaf-axils on stalks 1/8 to 1/4 in. long, white tinged with pink; corolla 1/3 to 1/2 in. long, the tube stout, much bellied at the base, downy outside; stamens and style more or less downy. Fruit white or purplish, rather translucent.

Native of Hupeh and Yunnan, China; discovered by Henry, introduced by Wilson in 1901. Henry states that he found it 10 ft. high. Although very different in mode of growth, it is botanically akin to L. pileata, both having a "remarkable downward cap-like production of the calyx covering the united bracteoles" (Hemsley).

L. HECKROTTII, *Rehder*

A deciduous shrub, of loose, spreading, scarcely climbing habit, thought by Dr Rehder to be a hybrid between L. sempervirens and L. italica. It is a strikingly handsome honeysuckle, its leaves being oblong or oval, glabrous, scarcely stalked, 1½ to 2½ ins. long, glaucous beneath. The uppermost pairs are united by their bases (connate). Flowers 1½ ins. long, rich pink outside, yellow within; produced in whorls on a rather long-stalked, terminal spike. Corolla-tube not downy outside, slender, slightly hairy inside. Blossoms from June onwards. This hybrid originated or was first noticed in the United States, but its history is unrecorded. It is quite hardy, and one of the best of its type of honeysuckle.

L. HENRYI, *Hemsley*

(Bot. Mag., t. 8375)

An evergreen climber, with slender, very downy young shoots. Leaves oblong, with a lance-shaped apex and a rounded or heart-shaped base; 1½ to 4 ins. long, 3/4 to 1½ ins. wide; dark green above, paler and rather glossy beneath; downy only on the midrib and margins; stalk $\frac{1}{8}$ to $\frac{1}{2}$ in. long. Flowers purplish red, produced during June at the end of the shoot in a cluster 2 or 3 ins. across; each stalk is twin-flowered. Corolla two-lipped, $\frac{3}{4}$ in. across, the lips much reflexed, the tube about $\frac{1}{2}$ in. long, hairy within, glabrous outside; stamens slightly downy; style hairy, protruded $\frac{1}{2}$ in. beyond the corolla; bracts awl-shaped, about $\frac{1}{4}$ in. long. Fruit blackish purple.

Native of China and Tibet; introduced by Wilson in 1908, and first flowered at Nuneham in 1910. It is a free-growing climber of the same character as L. japonica, which is, however, very distinct in the big leaf-like bracts. Botanically, it is more closely allied to alseuosmoides and Giraldii.

L. Hildebrandiana, *Collet and Hemsley*. Giant Honeysuckle

(Bot. Mag., t. 7677)

A vigorous evergreen climber (or nearly deciduous in cool places) growing 60 to 80 ft. high, without down in all its parts. Leaves broadly ovate, oval or roundish oval, abruptly contracted at the apex to a short point, broadly tapered at the base; 3 to 6 ins. long, half to two-thirds as wide; dark green above, paler and with scattered glands beneath; stalk $\frac{1}{3}$ to $\frac{3}{4}$ in. long. Flowers fragrant, produced from the leaf-axils and in a terminal raceme, always in pairs, each pair joined to a short stalk $\frac{1}{4}$ to $\frac{3}{4}$ in. long. Corolla $3\frac{1}{2}$ to 6 ins. long, creamy white changing to rich orange, the long slender tube dividing at the mouth into two lips, one of which consists of four short lobes, the other of a single narrow lobe much recurved; they give the flower a diameter of 2 to 3 ins. Fruit ovoid, 1 to $1\frac{1}{4}$ ins. long.

Native of Burma, Siam, and China; discovered by Sir Henry Collet in 1888 on the Shan Hills. Henry found it also in Yunnan, China. The species is of great interest as the largest in size, leaf, flower, and fruit of all the honeysuckles. It is not hardy at Kew, but is grown in the Temperate House, where it climbs to the roof. Shy-flowering in its early years, it commences to flower when of full size if exposed to full sunshine. It is grown out-of-doors in several mild localities. The late Rev. H. Ewbank flowered it at Ryde, Isle of Wight, in 1910, grown on a west wall. It is also grown by Lord St Leven on St Michael's Mount and at Trewidden near Penzance. It first blossomed in the British Isles at Glasnevin in August 1898, and it flowered at Kew the following June.

L. hirsuta, *Eaton*

(Bot. Mag., t. 3103; L. pubescens, *Sweet*)

A deciduous twiner, with glandular-downy, slender young shoots. Leaves oval, 2 to $3\frac{1}{2}$ ins. long, $1\frac{1}{4}$ to 2 ins. wide; dark dull green above, grey beneath, downy on both sides especially beneath, ciliate; uppermost one or two pairs connate, pointed; lower ones stalked. Flowers orange-yellow, about 1 in. long, produced in several whorls on short-stalked spikes at the end of the shoot, and sometimes from the axils of the connate leaves beneath. Corolla two-lipped, the tube slender but slightly swollen towards the base; covered outside with sticky glandular down; hairy within.

Native of N.E. America; introduced in 1822. It is now uncommon, and L. glaucescens is often made to do duty for it in nurseries and gardens, but that species is not glandular on the branchlets or corolla, and its leaves are not downy above.

L. HISPIDA, *Pallas*

A deciduous shrub, 3 to 5 ft. high, with bristly young shoots. Leaves ovate-oblong, rounded or broadly tapered at the base, short-pointed or often blunt at the apex; 1½ to 2½ ins. long, about half as wide; hairy on the margins, and more or less so on both surfaces; dark green above, greyish beneath; stalk ⅛ in. long. Flowers produced at the base of the young shoots at the end of May; corolla funnel-shaped, about 1 in. long, ⅝ in. wide at the mouth, yellow or yellowish white, the tube longer than the lobes. Each pair of flowers is subtended by two roundish ovate membranous bracts up to 1 in. long, edged with bristles; stalk ⅓ to ½ in. long, bristly.

Native of Turkestan; introduced early last century. Interesting on account of the large bracts.

Var. BRACTEATA, *Airy-Shaw*.—Leaves oblong-lanceolate to oblong, apex drawn out, softly downy. Bot. Mag., t. 9360.

L. IBERICA, *Bieberstein*

A deciduous shrub, of dense, bushy, rounded habit, up to 10 ft. high and 12 ft. through; young shoots hairy. Leaves mostly heart-shaped, sometimes

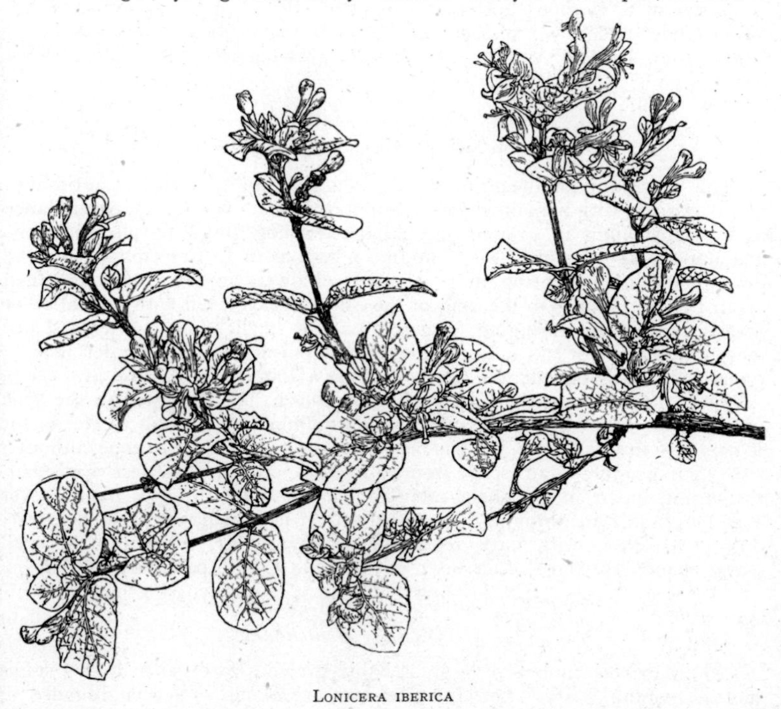

LONICERA IBERICA

roundish, the apex scarcely pointed; dark dull green above, grey beneath, both surfaces downy. On the vigorous barren shoots some of the leaves are 2 ins. long and nearly as much wide; on the flowering branchlets they are mostly ½ to 1 in. long; stalk ⅛ to ⅓ in. long. Flowers produced in pairs from the end and upper leaf-axils of short shoots; corolla two-lipped, ¾ in. long and the same wide, pale yellow, not fragrant, downy outside, the tube curved and about as long as the slightly lobed limb. Bracts like the leaves but ovate, and ¼ to ½ in. long; flower-stalk very short.

Native of the Caucasus, Persia, etc.; introduced in 1824. A very robust shrub of neat habit, free-flowering without being showy. Botanically, it is distinguished by the bractlets coalescing into a cup-shaped organ enveloping the two ovaries, which, however, grow out of the cup and develop into bright red berries which are very attractive.

L. IMPLEXA, *Solander*. MINORCA HONEYSUCKLE

(Bot. Mag., t. 640)

An evergreen climber, 8 ft. or more high, with slender, purplish, usually glabrous young shoots. Leaves oval, ovate or oblong, stalkless, blunt or pointed, ¾ to 2 ins. long, ⅓ to 1 in. wide; very glaucous beneath, glabrous. The upper pairs of leaves are united at the base so as to form a kind of cup-shaped bract, in the axils of which the stalkless flowers are produced in a whorl. Corolla 1½ to 2 ins. long, yellow suffused with pink outside, white within, changing to yellow.

Native of S. Europe; introduced in 1772. It is a pretty honeysuckle, but rather tender and slow-growing, and best with the shelter of a west wall. It flowers from June to August. It probably grows much higher in its native haunts.

L. ITALICA, *Tausch*

(L. americana, *K. Koch*; L. grata, *Aiton*)

This interesting and beautiful woodbine is a hybrid between L. Caprifolium and L. etrusca, with both of which it is often confused. It has most resemblance to L. Caprifolium in growth and foliage; young stems purple, glabrous. The uppermost pairs of leaves unite into a cup, as in L. Caprifolium, but the lower ones differ in being more pointed. Flowers in whorls not confined (as in L. Caprifolium) to the axils of the connate leaves, but with several other whorls above them springing from the axils of small bracts. Corolla 2 ins. long, yellow more or less suffused with reddish purple, the tube slender, usually glandular, downy outside, the two lips giving a diameter of 1 to 1½ ins.

The origin of this lovely hybrid is not known, but it existed in the time of Linnæus, who confused it with L. Caprifolium. According to Rehder, it is very rare in a wild state, but has been found in S. and S.E. Europe, although even there possibly as an escape from cultivation. It is a very effective climber, the terminal part of the shoot often branching and forming a panicle over 1 ft. long and 8 in. through. Several forms of it are cultivated, such as var. ATROSANGUINEA, with dark red-purple flowers; var. QUERCIFOLIA, with leaves shaped like those of an oak; var. RUBELLA, with pale purplish flowers.

L. JAPONICA, *Thunberg*

An evergreen climber of vigorous habit, growing 20 to 30 ft. high; stems hollow, twining, hairy. Leaves ovate, oval or oblong, somewhat rounded or broadly wedge-shaped at the base, pointed, 1½ to 3½ ins. long, half as wide; occasionally wavy or lobed at the margin, more or less downy sometimes on both sides. Flowers fragrant, produced from June onwards in pairs from the leaf-axils of the young shoots, towards the end of which they are often much crowded; flower-stalk ½ to ¾ in. long, carrying two ovate bracts similar to the leaves, but only ½ to ¾ in. long. Corolla 1¼ to 1½ ins. long, two-lipped;

the tube slender, hairy, white changing to yellow with age, and sometimes tinged with red. Fruit black.

At least four forms of this honeysuckle are in cultivation, but which of them is the type as seen by Thunberg it is now difficult to say. Dr Rehder, the greatest authority on honeysuckles, is of opinion that var. Halliana comes nearest to it.

Var. AUREO-RETICULATA, *Nicholson* (L. brachypoda reticulata).—Leaves mostly less than 2 ins. long, sometimes pinnately lobed, the veins and midrib picked out in bright yellow. A very effective variegated plant in summer, but usually killed back a good deal in winter. Shy-flowering.

Var. FLEXUOSA, *Nicholson* (L. flexuosa, *Thunberg*, Bot. Reg., t. 712).—Stems reddish purple, leaves nearly smooth, except for the ciliated margins and a few hairs on the veins, which are also purple; flowers pale red outside, white within; young shoots very hairy.

Var. HALLIANA, *Nicholson* (L. flexuosa Halliana, *Dippel*).—Leaves downy on both sides when young, more especially beneath; flowers white, changing to yellow with age.

The species is native of Japan, whence it was introduced in 1806, also of Korea and China. During the winter of 1908-9 it was, in open spots, very much injured at Kew—the var. flexuosa was killed to the ground, but in ordinary seasons and always, I think, in sheltered spots, it is quite hardy. The species, however, is not represented at Kew at the present time, having been killed during the winter of 1946-47. It lasts in flower a couple of months, and its blossoms have a charming fragrance. In good soil it grows vigorously, and if given the chance will soon cover (and smother) a small tree. It has become naturalised in parts of the United States (Long Island, etc.). The name "confusa" is sometimes given to it, but the true L. CONFUSA, *De Candolle*, is quite distinct in its awl-shaped bracts. Probably more tender. China and E. Indies.

L. KOROLKOWI, *Stapf*

(Garden and Forest, 1894, fig. 4)

A deciduous shrub of loose, spreading, graceful habit, 6 to 10 ft. high; young shoots very downy. Leaves ovate to oval, usually tapered at the base, pointed, $\frac{3}{4}$ to $1\frac{1}{4}$ ins. long, $\frac{1}{2}$ to $\frac{7}{8}$ in. wide; pale glaucous green, downy on both surfaces, especially beneath; stalk up to $\frac{1}{4}$ in. long. Flowers produced in pairs from the leaf-axils of short lateral branchlets in June, pale rose-coloured; corolla $\frac{2}{3}$ in. long, two-lipped, the tube slender and about as long as the lobes, downy inside; flower-stalk $\frac{1}{3}$ in. long, downy. Berries red.

Native of Turkestan; first cultivated apparently by the late Mr A. Lavallée, of Segrez, in France, but first distinguished as a species in 1893 from a plant growing in the Arnold Arboretum. Its most striking character when in leaf is the pale grey hue of the whole plant. I saw it in flower in Mr Späth's nursery near Berlin, many years ago, and was much struck with its grace and beauty, but it has not flowered so freely in this country.

L. LEDEBOURII, *Eschscholtz*

(Bot. Mag., t. 8555)

A deciduous shrub, of sturdy, erect habit up to 8 or 9 ft. high, and as much through; young shoots stout, four-angled, soon glabrous. Leaves ovate-oblong, rounded or narrowed at the base, pointed; 2 to 4 ins. long, 1 to $1\frac{3}{4}$ ins. wide; dull dark green above, bright green and downy beneath; margins downy; stalk $\frac{1}{4}$ in. long. Flowers deep orange-yellow tinged with red, produced in pairs from the leaf-axils in June, each pair on a downy stalk 1 to 1¾ ins. long, and subtended by two large, reddish, heart-shaped, bracts ⅝ in. wide, and two smaller ones; all glandular. These bracts grow after the flower is fertilised. Corolla downy outside, tubular, ⅜ to ¾ in. long, $\frac{3}{16}$ in. wide, with a curious sac at the base; the lobes rounded, erect; stamens not longer than the tube, glabrous or nearly so; style longer, also glabrous. Berries black.

Native of California; introduced in 1838. A robust species very distinct from all others except involucrata (see below). In habit, foliage, and the long flower-stalk it has some resemblance to L. alpigena, but the short-tubed, two-lipped corolla with spreading lobes, and the tiny, linear bracts of that species are very different. L. Ledebourii grows well close to the sea.

L. INVOLUCRATA, *Banks*.—Closely allied to L. Ledebourii, but has longer stamens; flowers yellow; the leaves are thinner, not so downy (sometimes glabrous), and more tapered at the base; var. HUMILIS is a dwarf form 2 ft. high; var. SEROTINA, *Koehne*, flowers later, in July and August. Native of western N. America.

L. MAACKII, *Maximowicz*

A deciduous shrub 10 to 15 ft. high, with wide-spreading branches, often arranged in a flat, distichous manner; young shoots downy. Leaves oval-lanceolate, with long, slender points, and tapered at the base; 1½ to 3 ins. long, ½ to 1½ ins. wide; dark green, downy on both surfaces; stalk ⅓ in. or less long. Flowers fragrant, pure white at first, turning yellowish with age, all produced in pairs on the upper side of the branchlets, where they form a dense row. Corolla two-lipped, the tube ¼ in. long, the narrowly oblong, round-ended lobes ½ in. long, the two outer ones of the upper lip deeper than the middle ones; stamens about twice as long as the corolla tube, downy at the base; style hairy. Flower-stalk about ⅛ in. long. Fruit dark red.

Introduced to St Petersburg, about 1880, from Manchuria; and from China by Wilson in 1900. It is one of the most beautiful of bush honeysuckles, especially the Chinese form, which is distinguished as var. PODOCARPA, *Franchet*, " having the ovaries, together with the bractlets, on a short, stalk-like elongation above the bracts " (Rehder). This seems also to be of freer growth than the Manchurian form, and is remarkable for the abundance and purity of its blossom. L. Maackii belongs to the same section of the genus as L. Xylosteum and L. Morrowi, from both of which it is distinguished by the very short flower-stalks and pure white corolla. It varies in the amount of down on the leaves, and is sometimes almost glabrous.

Of very much the same character as L. Maackii is L. KOEHNEANA, *Rehder*; introduced from China by Wilson in 1908. It is a vigorous grower, with softly downy, often rather diamond-shaped leaves up to 3 or 4 ins. long, and yellow flowers. From L. Maackii it is at once distinguishable by the slender, much longer flower-stalks (up to 1 in. long).

L. MAXIMOWICZII, *Regel*

A deciduous shrub of erect habit, up to 10 ft. high; young shoots glabrous or slightly bristly. Leaves oval, tapered or rounded at the base, pointed, 1½ to 3 ins. long on flowering shoots (up to 4½ ins. long on vigorous barren shoots) about half as wide; glabrous, dark green above, furnished more or less with pale down beneath. Flowers deep purplish rose, produced in pairs, each pair on a slender stalk up to 1 in. long. Corolla scarcely ½ in. long, two-lipped, short-tubed, glabrous outside, hairy within; stamens hairy at the base, style hairy the whole length. Fruit ovoid, red.

Native of Amurland; cultivated in this country since about 1878. The flowers are rather brightly coloured, but the species has no outstanding merit with us, although favourably mentioned in more sunny climates.

L. MICROPHYLLA, *Willdenow*

A deciduous shrub, of stiff, sturdy habit, up to 3 ft. high; branchlets short, glabrous. Leaves oval or obovate, ½ to 1 in. long, ¼ to ½ in. wide; dull grey green above; glaucous, finely downy, and with well-defined nerves beneath; stalk $\frac{1}{16}$ in. long. Flowers pale yellow, produced in pairs from the leaf-axils, on stalks ¼ in. long. Corolla two-lipped, scarcely ½ in. long, the tube about as long as the lips. Berries bright red, united.

Native of the arid parts of the north-west Himalaya, Tibet, Siberia, etc.; introduced in 1818. It is a suitable plant for the rock garden, where, however, its chief attraction would be its low, neat habit and grey aspect, for it bears flowers and fruits very sparingly in our climate.

L. MORROWI, *A. Gray*

A vigorous, deciduous shrub, 8 ft. or more high, of loose, spreading habit; young shoots grey with down. Leaves oval or ovate, 1 to 2½ ins. long, half as wide; rounded or tapering at the base, rounded or with a short slender point at the apex; downy and dull green above, greyish and woolly beneath; stalk ⅙ in. long. Flowers creamy white changing to yellow with age, produced in pairs from the middle or upper leaf-axils of short branchlets, in May and June. Corolla downy, two-lipped, with a slender tube ¼ in. long, the deep spoon-shaped lobes ½ in. long, spreading; style hairy; flower-stalk up to ⅗ in. long. Bracts hairy on the margins; fruit dark red, rarely yellow.

Native of Japan; allied to L. Xylosteum, from which it differs in having a glabrous, not glandular, ovary. It is useful for furnishing semi-wild parts of the grounds.

L. BELLA, *Zabel*, is a hybrid between this species and L. tatarica. Its leaves are frequently rounded or slightly heart-shaped as in tatarica.

L. MYRTILLUS, *Hooker fil. and Thomson*

A deciduous shrub, of dense, compact, rounded habit, 3 or 4 ft. high; shoots downy when quite young. Leaves oval or ovate, ⅓ to 1 in. long, about ¼ in. wide; dark green above, rather glaucous beneath, glabrous on both surfaces, margins decurved. Flowers pinkish white, fragrant, borne in very shortly stalked pairs; corolla between tubular and bell-shaped, ¼ in. long, glabrous outside, hairy at the mouth inside; lobes equal, spreading; style much shorter than the tube, glabrous; bracts linear, ⅙ to ¼ in. long. Fruit orange-red, ¼ in. wide.

Native of the Himalaya and Afghanistan. It forms a neat, pleasing bush, but our climate is too dull for it to flower sufficiently freely to produce any effect. It is one of the bush honeysuckles which are distinguished by a very short style and a tubular, regularly lobed corolla, hairy at the mouth inside. From the others of this group here mentioned it is distinguished by its stiff branches and small leaves, and from all except angustifolia by the two-celled ovary. Blossoms in May.

Var. DEPRESSA, *Rehder* (L. depressa, *Royle*).—Differs only from the above by the flower-stalks being twice as long, and the broader, oval bracts.

L. NERVOSA, *Maximowicz*

A deciduous shrub up to 8 ft. high, with glabrous young shoots and leaves. Leaves oval or inclined to oblong, abruptly pointed, tapered to rounded at the base; $\frac{3}{4}$ to 2 ins. long, $\frac{1}{2}$ to 1 in. wide; reddish at first, turning bright green above, the midrib and veins remaining reddish; stalk $\frac{1}{8}$ to $\frac{1}{6}$ in. long. Flowers pale pink, $\frac{2}{5}$ in. long, produced in pairs on a slender stalk of the same length; the pairs are borne in the leaf-axils of very slender leafy shoots in May and June. Fruit black.

Native of China; discovered in Kansu by Przewalski in 1872; introduced from St Petersburg to Kew in 1892. It succeeds well in the Arnold Arboretum, Mass., where it is valued as a graceful bush honeysuckle with handsomely veined leaves and plentiful crops of black berries. The specific name refers to the reddish-veined leaves.

L. NIGRA, *Linnæus*

A deciduous shrub, of stiff, rounded habit, 3 to 5 ft. high, with mostly oval leaves, 1 to 2 ins. long, downy along the midrib beneath, sometimes over the entire surface when quite young. Flowers produced in axillary pairs, each pair on a glabrous or slightly downy, slender stalk $\frac{3}{4}$ to over 1 in. long; pink, about $\frac{1}{3}$ in. long and broad; corolla two-lipped, the tube short and broad. Berries bluish black, united only at the base.

Native of the Alpine regions of Middle and S. Europe; introduced in the sixteenth century, but of little value in gardens. Several forms, varying chiefly in the degree of pubescence on the leaves, flower-stalks, etc., have been distinguished, but are not of sufficient importance to be noticed here. It is best marked by its slender flower-stalks and black fruit.

L. NITIDA, *Wilson*

(Bot. Mag., t. 9352)

An evergreen shrub, 5 to 12 ft. high, of densely leafy habit; young shoots slender, erect, purplish, downy, and sparsely bristly. Leaves of stout texture, closely set on the shoot, ovate to roundish, heart-shaped at the base, blunt at the apex; $\frac{1}{4}$ to $\frac{5}{8}$ in. long, dark and glossy above, pale beneath, glabrous except for a few minute bristles which ultimately fall away; stalk $\frac{1}{20}$ in. long, minutely bristly. Flowers produced in axillary, short-stalked pairs, creamy white, fragrant; corolla $\frac{1}{4}$ in. long. Fruit globular, blue-purple, about $\frac{1}{4}$ in. across, transparent. A good sea-side shrub.

Native of W. Szechuen and Yunnan, China, at altitudes of 4500 to 7000 ft. introduced by Wilson in 1908. Botanically allied to L. pileata, this is very distinct in its dense habit and smaller leaves. Young plants in cultivation have the aspect of an exceedingly dainty, very leafy, evergreen privet. It is hardy and is now being used very extensively for making low hedges, but is best in mild districts.

L. ORIENTALIS, *Lamarck*

A deciduous shrub of bushy habit, up to 8 or 9 ft. high, rather more in diameter; shoots quite glabrous. Leaves oval or ovate, broadly wedge-shaped or rounded at the base, pointed; $1\frac{1}{2}$ to 4 ins. long, $\frac{1}{4}$ to $1\frac{1}{2}$ ins. wide; dull green above, greyish beneath; glabrous, or with a few scattered hairs beneath stalk $\frac{1}{4}$ in. or less long. Flowers borne during May and June in pairs from the leaf-axils of the current year's shoots, pink, slightly fragrant, $\frac{1}{2}$ in. long corolla two-lipped; tube very short, much swollen on one side, downy within; stamens and style exposed, both downy; flower-stalk ½ to ¾ in. long, glabrous. Fruits black, each pair wholly united by the inner edges.

Native of Asia Minor; introduced in 1825. Apparently variable. The above description applies to the form in cultivation, which is a shrub of no particular merit. Known as var. CAUCASICA.

L. KESSELRINGII, *Regel* (L. savranica, *Späth*), is by some considered a variety of orientalis and called var. LONGIFOLIA, *Dippel*. It has oblong or oval-lanceolate leaves 1½ to 2½ ins. long, rarely more than ¾ in. wide. Flowers pink, smaller than in orientalis, he corolla tube only slightly swollen; stalk ⅓ in. long. Introduced from Kamtschatka n 1888.

L. PERICLYMENUM, *Linnæus*. WOODBINE, HONEYSUCKLE

A twining shrub scrambling in a wild state over bushes and hedgerows; stems often over 20 ft. long, hollow when young, downy or glabrous. Leaves ovate, oval, or obovate, more or less tapered at the base, mostly pointed,

LONICERA PERICLYMENUM BELGICA

sometimes blunt, 1½ to 2½ ins. long, 1 to 1½ ins. wide; green above, rather glaucous beneath, slightly downy or glabrous; lower pairs of leaves stalked, uppermost ones almost or quite stalkless, but never united as in L. Caprifolium. Flowers yellowish white and red in varying proportions, produced in a series of close whorls at the end of the shoot, forming a terminal stalked inflorescence. Corolla 1½ to 2 ins. long, two-lipped, the tube slender, tapering, glandular-downy outside. Berries red.

The common woodbine, best known of British species, reaches eastward to Asia Minor, the Caucasus, and W. Asia. No wild plant adds more to the charm of our hedgerows and thickets in July and August than this, especially in the cool dewy morning or evening when the fragrance of its blossoms is richest. Of several varieties, the following are the most noteworthy:—

Var. BELGICA, *Aiton*. Dutch Honeysuckle.—Of more bushy habit; stems

purplish and, like the leaves, glabrous. Flowers purplish red outside, fadin
to yellowish ; yellow within.

Var. QUERCINA, *Weston* (var. quercifolia, *Aiton*). Oak-leaved Woodbine.-
Leaves lobed after the fashion of those of the common oak.

Var. SEROTINA, *Aiton*. Late-flowering Honeysuckle.—Flowers da
purple outside, becoming paler with age ; inside of lips creamy white, changin
to yellow. A late-flowering form and one of the best. Also known as " sempe
florens," under which name it was figured in *The Garden*, 14th April 189
pl. 957.

L. PILEATA, *Oliver*

(Bot. Mag., t. 8060 ; Gard. Chron., 9th April 1910, fig. 102)

An evergreen or partially deciduous shrub of low, spreading, neat habi
branches often horizontal ; young shoots purple, very downy. Leaves bo
like, ovate-oblong or somewhat lozenge-shaped, tapered at the base, blunt
rounded at the apex ; $\frac{1}{2}$ to $1\frac{1}{4}$ ins. long, $\frac{1}{6}$ to $\frac{1}{2}$ in. wide ; dark lustrous gree
nearly glabrous on both surfaces, scarcely stalked. Flowers yellowish whi
produced in May in very short-stalked pairs ; corolla-tube downy outside, $\frac{1}{4}$ i
long ; stamens hairy, one and a half times the length of the corolla. The fru
is a translucent amethyst colour, $\frac{1}{5}$ in. wide, and is invested at the top by
curious outgrowth from the calyx. This shrub does well close to the sea.

Native of China ; discovered by Henry, and introduced for Messrs Veit
by Wilson in 1900. Although it has but little flower beauty, and is (as yet
least) very shy in bearing fruit, its neat habit and dark shining foliage a
pleasing. The pairs of leaves are often only from $\frac{1}{4}$ to $\frac{1}{2}$ in. apart on the sho
Young plants are more inclined to be evergreen than older ones.

L. PLANTIERENSIS, *André*

A twining honeysuckle with a considerable affinity to L. sempervirens, b
much hardier. It has lived without protection at Kew (where sempervirens
tender) for upwards of twenty-five years. It is derived from that species a
probably L. hirsuta. Leaves downy and glaucous beneath, upper pair unite
Flowers 1 to $1\frac{1}{2}$ ins. long, of a glowing red outside, the mouth and lobes ri
orange ; corolla-tube glandular, downy outside, hairy within ; lobes ve
short, rounded, and almost regular. Style slightly downy. It flowers fro
June onwards, bearing the blossom in a terminal stalked spike composed
several whorls. The honeysuckles grown in nurseries as L. Brownii,
fuchsioides, and L. punicea have an origin similar to that of plantierens
and vary only in slight details. All are beautiful plants, bringing into the ou
door garden much of the beauty of L. sempervirens without having
tenderness.

L. PROLIFERA, *Rehder*

(L. Sullivantii, *A. Gray* ; Garden and Forest, 1890, fig. 34)

A deciduous spreading shrub, with stems up to 6 ft. long, lax, but scarce
climbing. Leaves oval, obovate or oblong, 2 to 4 ins. long, $1\frac{1}{4}$ to $2\frac{1}{2}$ ins. wid
glaucous and slightly downy beneath, more glaucous on the upper sid
one or more of the upper pairs are united at the base, and form a roundi
disk clasping the stem ; of thickish substance. Flowers yellow, not fragra
produced in June at the end of the current season's growth in a termin
stalked spike, composed of two or more whorls, sometimes branched at t

ase. Corolla two-lipped, about 1 in. long, the tube longer than the lips, ender, slightly swollen on one side; glabrous outside, style slightly hairy. erries reddish yellow, $\frac{1}{4}$ to $\frac{1}{2}$ in. diameter.

Native of central N. America; long grown in gardens—in early times as . flava, which is a rarer and more beautiful shrub than L. prolifera. The .tter is closer to L. dioica, a species distinguished by its shorter corolla, the ıbe of which is about as long as the lips, the leaves and style quite glabrous. . prolifera does not need a support except when quite young and may be rown in the open as an elegant, loose bush.

L. PROSTRATA, *Rehder*

A deciduous bush, of low, rounded habit, forming a hemispherical mass of ender hollow branches; young shoots slightly hairy and purplish. Leaves val or ovate, tapered at both ends, but more abruptly at the base; $\frac{3}{4}$ to $1\frac{1}{8}$ ins. ng, $\frac{1}{4}$ to $\frac{1}{2}$ in. wide; ciliate, upper surface downy at first, becoming glabrous; idrib and chief veins sparsely downy beneath; leaf-stalk hairy, $\frac{1}{10}$ in. long. lowers pale yellow, not fragrant, borne in pairs from the leaf-axils on slightly owny stalks, $\frac{1}{4}$ in. long; corolla $\frac{5}{8}$ in. long, two-lipped, the tube not so long as e lips, hairy within and without; stamens and style hairy at the base: racts linear, hairy, $\frac{1}{6}$ in. long; bractlets rounded, ciliate. Berries distinct, g-shaped, reddish, $\frac{1}{4}$ to $\frac{1}{3}$ in. long.

Native of W. China; discovered and introduced by Wilson about 1904. does not promise to be of any special beauty in flower, but its prostrate abit is distinct, and will make it useful for ground covering. It used to thrive the Coombe Wood nursery, where it flowered about the beginning of June. kin to L. trichosantha.

L. PURPUSII, *Rehder*

A deciduous shrub of dense, rounded habit, up to 10 ft. high, more in ameter. Leaves ovate to oval, 2 to $3\frac{1}{2}$ ins. long, 1 to $1\frac{3}{4}$ ins. wide, pointed, oadly tapered to rounded at the base, glabrous above, hairy on the midrib d veins beneath. Flowers white, fragrant, in axillary clusters of two to four; rolla $\frac{5}{8}$ in. long, $\frac{1}{2}$ in. wide, the short rounded lobes reflexed; stamens glisten- g white, anthers bright yellow, conspicuously exposed.

A hybrid between L. fragrantissima and L. Standishii. Flowering like em early in February, it makes an attractive addition to early flowering shrubs.

L. PURPURASCENS, *Walpers*

A sturdy bush, 5 to 8 ft. high; young shoots stiff, purplish, covered with a ft, fine down. Leaves oblong or somewhat obovate, tapered or bluntish at e apex, rounded or tapered at the base; 1 to 2 ins. long, $\frac{1}{2}$ to 1 in. wide; ll green above, grey beneath, downy on both surfaces but especially beneath; lk $\frac{1}{6}$ to $\frac{1}{4}$ in. long, downy, purplish. Flowers in pairs from the leaf-axils a slender downy stalk, $\frac{1}{3}$ in. or more long. Corolla $\frac{3}{5}$ in. long, with five ort nearly equal lobes, which are purple; the tube paler, hairy, funnel- aped, and protruded at the base; bracts awl-shaped. Berries more or less ited, blue-black.

Native of the Himalaya up to altitudes of 13,000 ft., and very hardy; roduced to Kew in 1884. A neat bush with a purplish cast, but of little erit.

L. PYRENAICA, *Linnæus*

(Bot. Mag., t. 7774)

A deciduous shrub, 2 to 3 ft. high, branches erect; free from down in all its parts. Leaves obovate to oblanceolate, tapered to a stalkless base, abruptly pointed, $\frac{3}{4}$ to $1\frac{1}{4}$ ins. long, $\frac{1}{4}$ to $\frac{3}{8}$ in. wide; glaucous, especially beneath. Flowers produced during May and June in pairs from the terminal leaf-axils of short branchlets or the lower leaf-axils of stronger ones, each pair subtended

LONICERA PYRENAICA

by two rather sickle-shaped bracts $\frac{1}{4}$ in. long, and borne on a stalk $\frac{1}{4}$ to $\frac{1}{2}$ in long. Corolla rosy-tinted white, $\frac{5}{8}$ in. diameter; the tube scarcely as muc long, swollen on one side at the base; the lobes roundish ovate, spreading Berries red, globose, $\frac{1}{4}$ in. diameter; each pair united only at the base.

Native of the eastern Pyrenees and the Balearic Isles; introduced, accordin to Aiton, in 1739. A very pretty shrub, perhaps the most pleasing in flower o all the dwarf bush honeysuckles. This plant is no longer represented in th Rock Garden at Kew, but another young plant there is growing in the surround ing border of the North Gallery.

L. QUINQUELOCULARIS, *Hardwick*

(Bot. Reg. xxx., t. 33; L. diversifolia, *Wallich*)

A large deciduous shrub, 12 to 15 ft. high in cultivation, said to be som times a small tree where wild; young shoots purplish, very downy. Leave oval, sometimes inclined to obovate and orbicular, rounded or tapered at th base, mostly short-pointed, but sometimes rounded at the apex; 1 to $2\frac{1}{2}$ in long, $\frac{5}{8}$ to $1\frac{1}{2}$ ins. wide; dull green and at first downy above, greyish an more downy beneath. Flowers creamy white changing to yellow; arrange in pairs, produced on a stalk $\frac{1}{12}$ in. long from the leaf-axils in June. Coroll two-lipped, $\frac{3}{4}$ in. across; the upper lip round-toothed; tube $\frac{1}{4}$ in. long, bellied stamens about as long as the upper lip, downy at the base. Berries transluce white, round to oval.

Native of the Himalaya and China; long cultivated at Kew. It is robust, and, when in flower, rather handsome shrub, flowering more free than the majority of bush honeysuckles do with us. It is very distinct on account of its white transparent fruits, which distinguish it from deflexicalyx, Maackii, Xylosteum, and other of its immediate allies.

Var. TRANSLUCENS, *Zabel* (*Gardeners' Chronicle*, vol. lxiv., p. 194).—Leaves longer pointed, more markedly ciliate, and the upper surface rougher than in quinquelocularis; the corolla tube also is shorter and more protuberant on one side. A sturdy bush, 10 ft. high, that flowers freely.

L. RUPICOLA, *Hooker fil. and Thomson*

A very dense bush, forming a rounded mass of interlacing branches 6 to 8 ft. high; branchlets slightly downy or glabrous when young; bark peeling off in thin strips the second year. Leaves often in threes, oblong or ovate, rounded or slightly heart-shaped at the base, blunt at the apex; ½ to 1 in. long, about half as wide; dull green and glabrous above, paler and downy beneath, often becoming glabrous; stalk ⅛ in. or less long. Flowers produced in May and June in pairs from the shoots of the current year, often six at one joint, fragrant; corolla pale pink, ½ in. across, the tube ¼ in. long, downy on both sides; lobes rounded-ovate, equal. Calyx-lobes narrow-oblong, downy; style and flower-stalk very short.

Native of the Himalaya; long cultivated at Kew. It is closely allied to L. thibetica, but is distinguished by the dull green, blunt-ended leaves not being white-felted beneath. These two species differ from all other cultivated honeysuckles in their globose shape and impenetrable mass of branches. It is striking, but does not blossom freely.

L. RUPRECHTIANA, *Regel*

A deciduous shrub forming a shapely bush 8 to 10 ft. high; young shoots downy. Leaves ovate to oblong, pointed (often slenderly so), tapered at the base; 1½ to 4 ins. long, ⅝ to 1½ ins. wide; dark green and downy only on the sunken midrib above, paler and downy beneath; stalk ¼ in. or less long. Flowers not fragrant, produced during May and June in pairs, each pair on a slender downy stalk ½ to ¾ in. long, borne in the leaf-axils; corolla white at first, changing to yellow, ¾ in. long. Stamens and style hairy. Fruit bright red, ⅓ in. wide, rather transparent.

Var. CALVESCENS, *Rehder*.—Leaves shorter and comparatively broader, slightly downy only on the veins beneath; fruit dull red.

Var. XANTHOCARPA, *Zabel*.—Fruit yellow; flowers smaller.

Native of N.E. Asia; introduced to Kew from St Petersburg in 1880. According to Maximowicz, who discovered it, it is sometimes 20 ft. high. As a flowering shrub it is pretty, although in no way outstanding amongst the bush honeysuckles. But as I saw it in the Arnold Arboretum in June 1910, laden with its scarlet fruit, it struck me as one of the best in the fine collection then in full fruit-bearing there. It is very hardy, but is subject to injury with us by late spring frosts.

L. NOTHA, *Zabel*, is a hybrid between Ruprechtiana and tatarica which originated in the St Petersburg Botanic Garden in 1878. Flowers ⅝ in. long, in pairs from the leaf-axils. Several forms of this hybrid are in cultivation with blossom of different shades of pink on opening, turning yellow later. The most attractive of these are *grandiflora* with large rose-tinted flowers and *carnea* with the deepest rose-coloured ones. These are amongst the best of the numerous hybrid bush honeysuckles.

L. SEMPERVIRENS, *Linnæus*. TRUMPET HONEYSUCKLE

(Bot. Mag., t. 781)

A vigorous, climbing shrub, evergreen in mild localities; young shoots glabrous, glaucous. Leaves oval or somewhat obovate, 1½ to 2¾ ins. long, ¾ to 2 ins. wide; rich green and glabrous above, bluish and slightly downy beneath; stalk ¼ in. or less long; one or two of the uppermost pairs of leaves are united and form a circular or oblong disk. Flowers unscented, rich orange scarlet outside, yellower within, 1½ to 2 ins. long, produced in three or four whorls (each whorl of usually six flowers), forming a terminal stalked spike. Corolla-tube slender, slightly swollen near the base; the four upper lobes are smaller than the lower one, but the corolla is not markedly two-lipped; style glabrous.

Var. MINOR.—Leaves narrower. Flowers rather longer and more slender.

Native of the south-eastern United States, but reaching as far north as Connecticut; introduced in 1656. Unfortunately this beautiful honeysuckle succeeds only really well in the south and west. Farther north it needs winter shelter. It has, however, given much of its beauty to hybrid progeny, two at least of which are hardy (see *Heckrottii* and *plantierensis*).

L. SPLENDIDA, *Boissier*

(Bot. Mag., t. 9517)

This beautiful woodbine is very rare in cultivation; but I had specimens a few years ago from Messrs W. Smith & Sons of Aberdeen, who informed me that it was a vigorous grower in their nursery, throwing shoots 6 or 8 ft. long in one season, perfectly hardy, and free flowering. It is evergreen and belongs to the same group as Etrusca and Periclymenum, but differs from the latter in having the upper pairs of leaves united round the stem (connate); and from etrusca it differs in having the flowers in a terminal stalkless spike, springing directly from the uppermost pair of leaves. The corolla is 1½ to 2 ins. long, reddish purple outside, yellowish within. Perhaps the most distinctive feature of the plant is the very glandular inflorescence. Leaves oval or oblong, stalkless, 1 to 2 ins. long, very glaucous; young sterile shoots hairy.

Native of Spain; distinguished by Boissier as long ago as 1838. In spite of Messrs Smith's experience, I suspect that this honeysuckle may be in some way delicate or tender, otherwise it is difficult to understand why so beautiful and distinct a plant, which fully deserves its specific name, should be so scarce in gardens. It ought in any case to thrive in the south-west counties.

L. STANDISHII, *Carrière*. STANDISH'S HONEYSUCKLE

(Bot. Mag., t. 5709)

A deciduous or partially evergreen bush, 6 or 8 ft. high in the open, 12 ft or more against a wall; the bark of the stem and older branches peeling; young shoots warted and bristly. Leaves oblong-lanceolate, 2 to 4½ ins. long ¾ to 2 ins. wide; rounded or broadly wedge-shaped at the base, slenderly pointed, prominently veined beneath; bristly on the margins and on both sides of the midrib, also more or less over the lower surface; stalk bristly ⅛ in. long. Flowers produced from November to March (according to the mildness of the season), often in two pairs at each joint; flower-stalk has downward pointing bristles. The flowers are creamy white, very fragrant, about ½ in. wide, the tube of the corolla bristly outside. Fruit ripe in early June, red, the two ovaries united nearly to the top and forming an inversely heart-shaped berry; stalk ½ in. long, bristly.

Native of China; introduced by Fortune in 1845. It is in no way showy, but has always been a favourite because of the early date at which it flowers and for its charming fragrance. Although the first flowers come as early as November, it is usually at its best in February. It is perfectly hardy, and is only grown on walls for the sake of protection for its early flowers.

Var. LANCIFOLIA, *Rehder*.—Leaves narrowly lanceolate, usually under 1 in. in width. Introduced by Wilson in 1908, from W. China.

L. SYRINGANTHA, *Maximowicz*

(Bot. Mag., t. 7989)

A deciduous shrub of graceful, spreading habit, up to 6 ft. high; young shoots slender, quite glabrous. Leaves in pairs or threes; oblong or inclined to ovate, the base rounded or slightly heart-shaped, the apex bluntish or broad-pointed; ½ to 1 in. long, 3/16 to ⅜ in. wide; dull rather glaucous green, quite glabrous; stalk 1/12 in. long. Flowers in axillary pairs, produced on a slender stalk ¼ in. long during May and June from the middle joints of the young shoots; soft lilac in colour, lilac-scented. Corolla-tube ½ in. long, slender, cylindrical, glabrous outside, hairy within; the flower is ½ in. across the rounded-ovate lobes. Calyx-lobes lance-shaped, glabrous. Style quite short. Fruit red.

Native of China and Tibet; introduced about 1890. A very elegant and pleasing shrub, with delicately coloured and charmingly fragrant flowers, which are not always abundantly borne. It is allied to thibetica and tomentella, differing in the quite glabrous leaves.

L. TANGUTICA, *Maximowicz*

A deciduous spreading bush 4 to 6 ft. high, with slender, usually glabrous twigs. Leaves obovate, more gradually tapered towards the base than towards the bluntish apex; ½ to 1½ ins. long, ¼ to ¾ in. wide; sprinkled with appressed hairs on both surfaces and on the margins; stalk 1/12 to ⅛ in. long. Flowers twin, yellowish white tinged with pink, about ½ in. long, each pair pendulous from the leaf-axils on a very slender stalk ½ to 1½ ins. long; corolla tubular, bellied at the base, glabrous, opening in May and June. Fruit scarlet.

Var. GLABRA, *Batalin*.—Leaves quite glabrous.

Native of Kansu, where it was discovered by Przewalski in 1872; of Hupeh and Szechuen, where it was found by Henry and Wilson; and of S.E. Tibet (Forrest). It has been in cultivation since 1890 and has lately become more common through seed sent home by Farrer from Kansu. It is distinct on account of its small obovate leaves and the long stalk on which each pair of flowers is borne. It is also one of the most beautiful in its pendulous scarlet fruits. Wilson's Hupeh and Szechuen plants have generally leaves that are larger (up to 2½ ins. long) and proportionately narrower than those from Kansu. Forrest's specimen has downy shoots and is probably a distinct form.

L. TATARICA, *Linnæus*

(Bot. Mag., t. 8677)

A deciduous shrub of vigorous growth and bushy habit, 8 to 10 ft. high; young shoots glabrous. Leaves oblong-ovate, slightly heart-shaped or rounded at the base, pointed; on vigorous growths they are 1½ to 2½ ins. long, 1 to 1½ ins. wide; on the flowering branches less than half the size; green above, rather glaucous beneath, glabrous; stalk ⅛ in. long. Flowers white or pinkish, borne in pairs on a slender stalk, ½ to 1 in. long; corolla two-lipped, glabrous outside, hairy within, ¾ to 1 in. long; tube much shorter than the reflexed oblong lobes. Berries globose, red.

In a wild state this species reaches from Central Asia to Russia. It was introduced in 1752, and is so perfectly adapted to our conditions that it is now the commonest of bush honeysuckles, running semi-wild in some gardens. It is a variable plant so far as the colour of the flowers is concerned, and the best red forms should only be selected. They are often very showy at flowering time, which is May and early June.

Var. LATIFOLIA, *Loudon* (also known as speciosa and splendens), is perhaps the best, having rich, rosy red flowers.

Var. NANA, *Alphand.*—A shrub of low, compact habit; leaves tapered at the base.

Var. SIBIRICA, *Persoon* (also known as var. rubra), is a handsome rich pink-flowered sort; the leaves are larger than in the type, and as much as 3½ ins. long. The "L. punicea," *Sims*, of the Bot. Mag., t. 2469, appears to be this plant.

L. TATSIENENSIS, *Franchet*

A deciduous shrub up to 8 ft. high; young shoots glabrous. Leaves oval, slightly obovate, or oblong-lanceolate, pointed, wedge-shaped to rounded at the base, entire or wavy margined on flowering shoots, often (by no means always) deeply lobed on virgin shoots; 1 to 2½ ins. long, ⅝ to 1 in. wide; sometimes with scattered hairs on both surfaces, sometimes glabrous; stalk ⅛ to ⅓ in. long. Flowers ½ in. long, borne in a pair at the end of slender stalks 1 to 1½ ins. long; corolla dark purple, short-tubed; stamens downy at the base; fruits red, each pair ¾ in. wide. Flowers in May.

Native of Szechuen, China; originally discovered by Père Faurie in the environs of Ta-tsien-lu; introduced by Wilson in 1910. Like some forms of L. japonica and L. Griffithii (both climbers and very different in other respects) this species is well marked by its frequently deeply lobed leaves. Combined with its large red fruits and purple flowers, this character makes it distinct.

L. TELLMANNIANA, *Hort.* (Plate 20)

(Gardeners' Chronicle, 5th Dec. 1931—Supplement plate)

This is a hybrid between L. tragophylla and L. sempervirens superba raised in the Royal Hungarian Horticultural School, Budapest, from which institution it was acquired and, in 1927, put into commerce by Messrs Späth of Berlin. It was first seen in flower in London on 16th June 1931, when Sir Wm. Lawrence showed it at Westminster from his garden at Burford, near Dorking. It was then given an Award of Merit. It is one of the most successful results in the hybridisation of honeysuckles that has been achieved, uniting in itself as it does perhaps the showiest of Chinese species and not far from the most beautiful of American ones. It is a deciduous climber with elliptical-ovate leaves 2 to 3½ ins. long, the upper pair united by their bases and forming a collar round the stem. The slender-tubed flowers are borne in terminal heads of six to twelve, each bloom about 2 ins. long and measuring about 1 in. across the two lips of the corolla, which is of a beautiful yellow, flushed in the bud state and at the tips with bronzy red. In habit it is luxuriant and is said to be hardy, a quality it would inherit from tragophylla. Like all this class of honeysuckle, it likes a good loamy soil and will prefer to have its roots and lower branches in the shade.

L. THIBETICA, *Bureau and Franchet*

A deciduous shrub of low, spreading habit when young, forming in the dult state a dense rounded mass of intertwined branches 6 ft. high and 10 ft. r more through; young shoots purplish, downy, the bark peeling in thin trips the second year. Leaves often in threes, narrowly oblong, rounded at he base, pointed, $\frac{1}{3}$ to 1 in. long, $\frac{1}{8}$ to $\frac{1}{3}$ in. wide; dark glossy green and glabrous

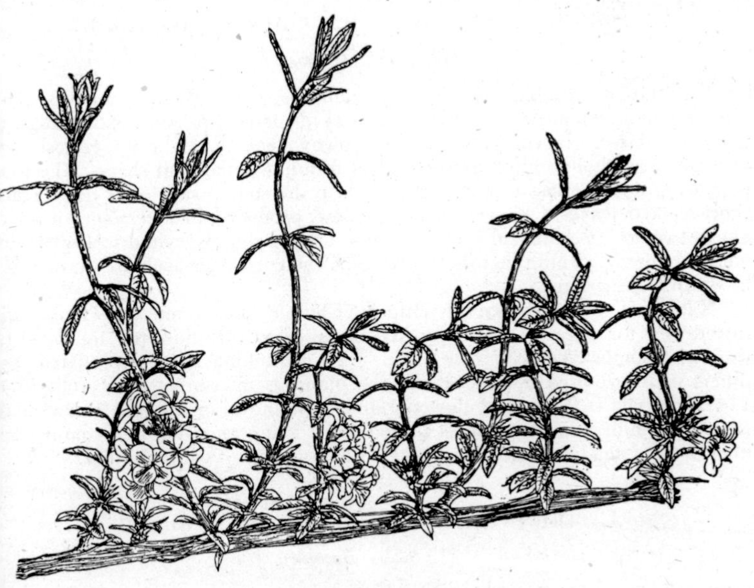

LONICERA THIBETICA

bove, covered with a dense white felt beneath; stalk $\frac{1}{12}$ in. or less in length. 'lowers produced in pairs during May and June from the leaf-axils of the oung shoots, often six flowers at each joint, fragrant, $\frac{1}{3}$ in. across, lilac-coloured. Corolla-tube $\frac{1}{2}$ in. long, downy within and without; lobes equal, roundish vate. Calyx-lobes awl-shaped, downy, as long as the style. Berry red, blong, $\frac{1}{4}$ in. long, three-celled.

Native of Tibet; introduced in 1897. A very pretty and distinct honeyuckle, allied to L. rupicola, but easily distinguished by the white-felted underurface of the leaves, and deeper coloured smaller flowers. The flowers are erfumed like lilac.

L. TOMENTELLA, *Hooker fil. and Thomson*

(Bot. Mag., t. 6486)

A deciduous shrub of erect habit, 6 to 10 ft. high; branchlets woolly, uter bark splitting and becoming detached the second season. Leaves in airs, ovate, sometimes inclined to oblong; $\frac{3}{4}$ to $1\frac{1}{2}$ ins. long, $\frac{1}{4}$ to $\frac{2}{5}$ in. wide; ounded or slightly heart-shaped at the base, bluntish or broad-pointed at the pex; dull green and sparsely downy above, grey-woolly beneath; stalk $\frac{1}{6}$ in. long. Flowers produced towards the end of June, pendulous, in pairs from the leaf-axils of the young shoots, white with a pinkish tinge. Coroll about ½ in. long, downy; calyx-lobes ovate, very short, pink-tipped; style a long as the corolla-tube. Berries blue-black.

Native of Sikkim; introduced by Sir Joseph Hooker in 1849. This specie has some affinity with and resemblance to L. rupicola, but is more erect; th leaves are in pairs, the style is longer, and the calyx-lobes shorter.

L. TRAGOPHYLLA, *Hemsley*. CHINESE WOODBINE

(Bot. Mag., t. 8064)

A deciduous climbing shrub, with glabrous young shoots. Leaves ova tapering about equally to both ends; 2 to 4½ ins. long, ¾ to 2 ins. wide; slightl glaucous above, glaucous and slightly downy beneath. The uppermost pa of leaves are wholly united by their bases forming a diamond shape; the nex pair lower down is less united, but still clasp the stem; still lower down com short-stalked leaves. Flowers bright yellow, produced in a terminal head ten to twenty. Corolla-tube 2½ to 3½ ins. long, slenderly cylindrical, glabrou outside, downy within; across the two lips the corolla measures 1 in. or mor in width. Berries red.

Native of the province of Hupeh, China; discovered by Henry an introduced for Messrs Veitch by Wilson in 1900. It flowered for the fir time at Coombe Wood in July 1904. L. Caprifolium is closely related, bu differs in its whorled flowers and in the glabrous interior of the corolla-tub L. tragophylla is the largest flowered and most showy of the true honeysuckl (Periclymenum) group. It likes a deep moist loam, and Wilson recommende for it a semi-shaded position. Flowers not fragrant. A tall climber.

L. TRICHOSANTHA, *Bureau and Franchet*

(L. ovalis, *Batalin*)

A deciduous bush, of vigorous growth and rounded, dense, leafy habi probably 8 ft. or more high, the whole plant with a pale greyish aspect young shoots at first downy, becoming glabrous later in the season. Leave oval, often inclined to obovate, rounded or broadly wedge-shaped at the bas and short pointed or rounded at the apex, 1 to 2 ins. long, ½ to 1¼ ins. wide dull grey-green above, paler beneath, both sides at first downy becomin almost glabrous, especially above; stalk ⅛ to ¼ in. long. Flowers pale yellow fading to a deeper shade; corolla ½ to ¾ in. long, hairy outside. Calyx bel shaped, but split into two parts. Berries dark red.

Native of Szechuen, China; discovered by the Russian traveller Potanin Introduced in quantity by Wilson about 1908. A robust species of the sam class as deflexicalyx and quinquelocularis.

L. XYLOSTEUM, *Linnæus*. FLY HONEYSUCKLE

A deciduous shrub up to 10 ft. high, more in diameter, very bushy; youn shoots downy. Leaves oval or obovate, rounded or broadly tapered at th base; mostly with a short abrupt apex, 1¼ to 2½ ins. long, half or more tha half as wide; downy on both surfaces; stalk ¼ in. long, downy. Flowe not scented, yellowish white, tinged sometimes with red, produced in pairs o downy stalks up to ⅝ in. long. Corolla very downy, conspicuously two-lippe ⅝ in. across, the tube short and bellied. Fruits red, often showy in August.

Native of Europe and W. Siberia, found wild in parts of S.E. England, here it may be a true native.

Var. LUTEA.—Fruits yellow. There are numerous other varieties varying ı the degree of pubescence on the plant, etc., which need not be adverted) further.

L. YUNNANENSIS, *Franchet*

A low creeper, with slender, glabrous stems. Leaves oblong or narrowly bovate, 1½ to 3 ins. long, about one-third as wide; glabrous above, glaucous nd glabrous or slightly downy beneath, very shortly stalked. The upper air or pairs of leaves are united into a round or oblong disk, in the axils of hich the stalkless flowers are borne. Corolla yellow, ¾ to 1 in. long, glabrous utside, hairy within.

Native of Yunnan; discovered by Delavay. It is allied to the American . dioeca.

Var. TENUIS, *Rehder*.—A smaller-leaved form found by Henry at Mengtze ı Yunnan, inhabiting rocky mountains up to 6000 to 7000 ft. Corolla ¾ in. ›ng, white changing to yellow. It was introduced in 1901 by Wilson to the oombe Wood nursery.

LOROPETALUM CHINENSE, *Oliver*. HAMAMELIDACEÆ

(Bot. Mag., t. 7979)

An evergreen shrub of bushy, very twiggy habit, 5 or 6 ft. high; ranchlets crooked, wiry, covered thickly with brownish stellate down. ,eaves ovate or oval, 1 to 2½ ins. long, ¾ to 1¼ ins. wide; markedly nequal at the base, pointed at the apex; rough and with scattered hairs bove, paler beneath; margin finely toothed; stalk about ⅛ in. long, airy. Flowers very like those of witch-hazel in appearance, but white; ıey are produced in February and March, three to six crowded in a ead; petals four to each flower, strap-shaped, ¾ in. long, 1/16 in. wide; ower-stalk and outside of calyx clothed with white stellate down. eed-vessel a woody, ovoid, nut-like capsule.

Native of China; introduced by Maries for Messrs Veitch in 1880. 'his singular and pretty shrub is too tender to thrive near London without rotection, and can only be recommended for trial in the mildest parts f these islands. In its narrow, strap-shaped petals and four-parted owers it resembles Hamamelis, but its white flowers and evergreen ature amply distinguish it. Grown out-of-doors in summer, and 'intered in the coolest conservatory, it makes a very pretty shrub in 'ebruary when covered with blossom. It likes a proportion of peat in ıe soil, and is easily increased by cuttings.

LUPINUS. LEGUMINOSÆ. LUPIN

A genus of some 300 species, mostly herbs but containing a few shrubs, ıost abundant in western N. America, but represented also in eastern '. America, South America, and the Mediterranean region.

L. ARBOREUS, *Sims*. TREE LUPIN

(Bot. Mag., t. 682)

An evergreen shrub of remarkably quick and luxuriant growth, becomin
6 to 9 ft. high, and nearly as much through, in three or four years when plant
in rich soil. Branchlets round, semi-woody, covered with silky hairs. Leav
alternate, digitate, with seven to eleven (usually nine) grey-green leaflets
each $\frac{3}{4}$ to 2 ins. long, varying in size according to the vigour of the plant
they are oblanceolate, pointed, downy beneath, the common leaf-stalk rath
longer than the leaflets. Flowers in erect, terminal racemes 6 to 10 ins. lon
fragrant, sulphur-yellow in the type, but in the varieties blue, purplish, or whit
Seed-pods $1\frac{1}{2}$ to 3 ins. long, $\frac{1}{2}$ in. wide; covered with a sort of felt, and contai
ing five to twelve blackish seeds.

Native of California in the coast region; of unrecorded introductio
This beautiful, half-woody shrub is apparently quite hardy near Londo
but is sometimes short-lived, especially if grown in rich soil. Young plant
it has been noticed, will pass through a winter quite unharmed which, a fe
years later, will succumb during another winter not any more severe. Th
is not an unusual characteristic of plants which grow so rapidly and produ
seed in such abundance as this does. It points to the advisability of removin
all seed-pods that are not required as soon as they are formed, also to th
necessity of renewing the stock from seed (or, in the case of special varietie
from cuttings) every few years. For so beautiful a shrub this is trouble we
repaid. Cuttings should be made in July and August of short side-shoots wit
a heel attached, and placed in gentle heat. This lupin likes a good but n
close or heavy soil, and it should have a sunny position. It succeeds well o
dryish banks, but does not grow so large there. The typical yellow form
very beautiful, as is also a comparatively new white variety, "Snow Queen.
Varieties are also obtainable with flowers pale blue, blue and white, variou
shades of purple, lavender, etc. The flowers continue to appear from May
August, but are at their best in June and July.

L. CHAMISSONIS, *Eschscholtz*

(Bot. Mag., t. 8657)

A sub-shrubby plant from $1\frac{1}{2}$ to 3 ft. high, woody at the base; youn
shoots silky-hairy. Leaves digitate, made up of five to seven leaflets, whic
are lanceolate, abruptly pointed, tapered at the base; $\frac{1}{2}$ to $1\frac{1}{4}$ ins. long, $\frac{1}{8}$
$\frac{1}{4}$ in. wide; silvery with appressed hairs on both surfaces; main-stalk $\frac{1}{2}$
1 in. long. Raceme 3 to 6 ins. long, erect, slender, the flowers more or le
whorled, each on a silky stalk which is $\frac{1}{4}$ in. long and bears a silky linear bra
at the base of the flower. Corolla $\frac{5}{8}$ in. long, the standard petal blue or lila
with a large yellow blotch at the base; wing petals and keel of the same blu
or lilac shade, both paling towards the base. Calyx $\frac{1}{4}$ in. long, two-lippe
Pod 1 to $1\frac{1}{4}$ ins. long, $\frac{3}{16}$ to $\frac{1}{4}$ in. wide, silky.

Native of California, often on sandy hill-slopes near the shore betwee
San Francisco and San Diego. Although originally described in 1826, abo
which period it was collected by David Douglas, it never appears to have bee
common in cultivation. Its combination of silvery leaves and blue or lavende
coloured flowers is very charming. As is the case with so many California
shrubs cultivated in this country, its tenure no doubt is shortened by lack
sunshine. But I do not think the shrubby lupins are ever particularly long-live
in our gardens. L. Chamissonis should be planted in well-drained soil at th
foot of a sunny south wall. It has been confused in gardens with L. argenteu

ıother silver-leaved but more herbaceous species, a native of Colorado. . Chamissonis is distinguished amongst the silvery lupins by the large yellow lotch on the standard petal. It flowers at Kew from June onwards till autumn ıd ripens seed there.

LUZURIAGA RADICANS, *Ruiz and Pavon*. LILIACEÆ

(Bot. Mag., t. 6465)

A creeping evergreen shrub from a few inches to over 1 ft. in height, ften found in a wild state growing on the trunks of trees in shady forests, ttached by roots springing from the joints of the stem. Its young shoots re thin, ribbed, wiry, and like the rest of the plant quite devoid of down. eaves stalkless, set in two opposite rows, ovate-oblong, or oval to arrowly linear, tapered at both ends; ½ to 2 ins. long, ⅛ to ⅝ in. wide; right green above, rather glaucous beneath, with six to twelve distinct ibs running lengthwise. Flowers produced singly or two or three ɔgether from the leaf-axils, each drooping on a slender stalk up to 1 in. ɔng; they are white, 1 to 1½ ins. across; the six "petals" ⅛ to ¼ in. ide, pointed; anthers yellow, stalkless, forming a slender cone in the entre of the flower. Berry the size of a pea, brilliant orange.

Native of Chile; introduced by the middle of the nineteenth century, ince when it has been cultivated at Kew. It is not hardy there, but can e grown out-of-doors in the milder south and south-western districts. t is interesting as one of the shrubby members of the lily family, like apageria and Ruscus. It flowers in June in the Temperate House at Kew. Whether grown under glass or out-of-doors it should have a haded position. It loves a peaty soil and abundant moisture. Mr I. F. Comber, who collected it on his Chilean journey (1925-7), says bears its flowers and fruits most freely when growing on tree trunks. With us it will probably succeed best out-of-doors treated as a rock arden plant; in a greenhouse grown against stones or on tree-fern stems.

LYCIUM. BOX THORN. SOLANACEÆ

A genus of about one hundred species of loose-habited shrubs allied to he deadly nightshade (Atropa Belladonna), with usually spiny branches. eaves alternate, often in clusters. Flowers from one to four in the eaf-axils, their parts usually in fives; corolla funnel-shaped or tubular. ruit a berry, very ornamental.

The lyciums or box thorns are easily cultivated; they do not need rich soil, flowering and fruiting better in a well-drained one of moderate uality. L. afrum needs a wall, but the others here described are erfectly hardy. They are best propagated by seeds when these are btainable, but cuttings and layers may also be used. The nomenclature f the few hardy species is rather involved, owing to the many names nder which the common L. chinense is grown. The two commonest ames met with in gardens—"L. europæum" and "L. barbarum"— oth rightly belong to plants that are not in cultivation.

L. AFRUM, *Linnæus*. AFRICAN BOX THORN

A deciduous shrub, much branched, spiny, growing 8 to 10 ft. high again a wall; young shoots pale, slightly angled, glabrous. Leaves clustered, $\frac{1}{2}$ 1 in. long, $\frac{1}{12}$ to $\frac{1}{8}$ in. wide; linear, tapered at the base, grey-green, glabrou Flowers on stalks $\frac{1}{3}$ in. long, produced in May and June. Corolla tubula $\frac{1}{4}$ in. wide, $\frac{3}{4}$ to 1 in. long, with five shallow, erect lobes; very dark purpl Calyx bell-shaped, $\frac{1}{4}$ in. long, with five triangular teeth; stamens enclose within the corolla, each with a tuft of hairs half-way down. Berry red, final purple-black, egg-shaped, $\frac{1}{3}$ in. long, with the calyx persisting at the base.

Native of the Cape of Good Hope; introduced in 1712. This speci requires a sunny wall for it to be seen at its best. It was highly spoken of b early writers growing in such a position, and it has flowered with great freedo in the garden at Bitton. It is cultivated in N. Africa, about Algiers, etc., b does not appear to be a genuine native of that region.

L. CHINENSE, *Miller*. CHINESE BOX THORN

A rambling or scandent shrub, of very vigorous, quick growth, especial when young; branches long, arching or pendulous, angled, small on occasionally spine-tipped. Leaves variable in size and shape; on vigorou shoots 2 to 4 ins. long, $\frac{1}{2}$ to over 1 in. wide; ovate-lanceolate, but on othe obovate to linear, and down to $\frac{1}{2}$ to $\frac{3}{4}$ in. long. Flowers usually in pairs c threes at each joint, each on a slender stalk $\frac{1}{2}$ to $\frac{3}{4}$ in. long. Corolla purpl $\frac{1}{2}$ in. long, short-tubed, the five spreading, ovate lobes being rather longer tha the tube. Calyx lobed to various depths, persistent. Stamens bearded at th base. Berry scarlet or orange, oblong or egg-shaped, $\frac{3}{4}$ to 1 in. long, half a wide. Blossoms May to July.

Native of China; long known in gardens, and now naturalised in man parts of Britain and Europe. This is the shrub very common on the clif of south coast towns like Eastbourne and Bournemouth. It is very ofte grown as L. europæum and L. barbarum, neither of which is in cultivation c probably hardy. Few plants are better for seaside planting than L. chinens and when laden with its abundant, pendent, highly coloured fruits it i extremely ornamental. Birds appear to eat the fruits, as plants may frequent be seen growing on the tops of old walls, and suchlike places. In village between London and the south coast, plants may often be seen beautifully i fruit on cottage walls in August and September.

Var. MEGISTOCARPUM.—A name sometimes given to a form with large fruits, but probably not really distinguishable.

Var. OVATUM (L. rhombifolium, *Dippel*).—Leaves broader and mor lozenge-shaped than in the type. Fruits blunter at the end.

L. GREVILLEANUM, *Gillies*

A deciduous shrub, 4 to 6 ft. high, forming a dense mass of overlayin branches; young shoots pale, more or less downy or scurfy. Leaves obovat or oblanceolate, $\frac{1}{2}$ to 2 ins. long, $\frac{1}{8}$ to $\frac{1}{2}$ in. wide; tapered to the base, mor abruptly towards the apex, densely arranged, ciliate, rather fleshy. Th larger-sized leaves are only on young vigorous sucker-growths; most of th leaves are less than 1 in. long. Flowers solitary or in pairs in the leaf-axils $\frac{1}{2}$ in. diameter; corolla funnel-shaped, deeply five-lobed (the lobes longer tha the tube), purple and yellowish white; calyx bell-shaped, the triangular-pointe lobes ciliate; stamens hairy at the base. Fruit orange-red, globular, $\frac{1}{3}$ in diameter.

Native of the Argentine, but hardy. It flowers freely, but does not develop fruit well; distinct from all the other hardy species in the downy stems, leaves and calyx, although this character is much more evident in wild than in cultivated examples.

L. HALIMIFOLIUM *Miller*

(L. vulgare, *Dunal*)

A deciduous shrub, with slender, glabrous branches, and sometimes 8 or 9 ft. high; twigs glabrous, spiny. Leaves variable, narrowly oval or lance-shaped, 1 to 2½ ins. long, blunt or pointed at the apex, wedge-shaped at the base, grey-green. Flowers axillary, produced each on a slender stalk singly, in pairs, or threes; corolla dull lilac-purple, ½ in. across, the tube longer than the lobes; stamens bearded at the base. Berry scarlet, oval, ⅜ in. long.

Native of S.E. Europe and W. Asia. It is very closely allied to L. chinense, and scarcely specifically distinct. It is considered to be of less vigorous growth and of more bushy, less rambling habit. The lobes of the corolla as compared with the tube are distinctly shorter in halimifolium than in chinense, neither is the fruit so long.

This species, like L. chinense, is often grown as L. EUROPÆUM, a species that differs from both in having quite glabrous stamens (not bearded at the base), in the longer-tubed corolla, and smaller narrow leaves.

L. PALLIDUM, *Miers*. FREMONT'S BOX THORN

(Bot. Mag., t. 8440)

A deciduous shrub of rather thin, lax, sprawling habit, at present 5 or 6 ft, high in cultivation; branches long, tortuous, or semi-pendulous, quite glabrous, but armed with spines which are really arrested branches, often bearing leaves. sometimes flowers. Leaves oval lance-shaped, up to 2 ins. long by ⅜ in. wide on the young, non-flowering shoots; but narrowly obovate, 1 in. or less long, and produced in rosettes on the year-old, flowering shoots; quite glabrous, entire, of a glaucous green; tapering at the base to a short stalk. Flowers nodding on stalks ¼ in. long, often solitary or in pairs at each joint. Corolla funnel-shaped, ¾ in. long, ½ in. wide at the mouth, where are five shallow, rounded lobes; pale green veined with darker lines, and tinged with purple. Calyx bell-shaped, about ⅛ in. long, with five pointed lobes. Style much protruded; stamens rather shorter. Fruit scarlet, globose, ⅜ in. long; ripe in August.

Native of the south-eastern United States; discovered by Fremont on one of the tributaries of the Colorado River in 1844; introduced to Kew in 1886. It is a distinct and quite hardy shrub, whose prettily coloured flowers hang in profusion from the under-side of the branches, and make it the best of the lyciums in flower. It is also ornamental in fruit, but with us the crop is uncertain. It is best propagated by layering, in the absence of seed. The foliage varies in the intensity of its glaucous hue.

LYONIA. ERICACEÆ

A genus of evergreen or deciduous shrub found in E. Asia and the Himalaya, also in N. America and the West Indies. About thirty species are known. They are peat-loving plants closely related to Oxydendrum. The genus commemorates John Lyon, a famous collector of North

American plants, who died about 1818 during one of his expeditions to the mountains of the south-eastern United States—the "savage and romantic mountains which had so often been the theatre of his labours."

LYCIUM PALLIDUM (see p. 267)

L. LIGUSTRINA, *De Candolle*

A deciduous shrub, 3 to 8 ft. high; young shoots either covered with a close soft down or nearly glabrous, and of a rather zigzag growth. Leaves alternate, oval or obovate, 2 to 3 ins. long, $\frac{1}{2}$ to $1\frac{1}{4}$ ins. wide; entire or nearly so, pointed, covered with short down and dark green above, more downy beneath and paler, the nerves very prominent; stalk $\frac{1}{8}$ in. long. Flowers produced in July and August on the leafless terminal portion of the preceding year's growth, in downy racemes or small panicles 1 to $1\frac{1}{2}$ ins. long, the whole forming a compound panicle from 3 to 6 ins. long. Corolla downy, dull white, $\frac{1}{8}$ to $\frac{3}{16}$ in. wide, globose or orange-shaped, with five small, reflexed teeth at the nearly closed mouth. Calyx pale green or white, downy, appressed to the corolla. Seed-vessel a dry, five-celled capsule, with the calyx persisting at the base.

Native of eastern N. America; introduced in 1748. This is not one of the most attractive of the heath family, but is desirable through flowering so late in the season. It grows naturally in moist situations, but in cultivation thrives in ordinary peat or light sandy loam. Propagated by seed or by cuttings taken with a slight heel from the shoots that spring freely from beneath the flower panicle.

Var. PUBESCENS, *Gray*.—The most pubescent form of this species (which varies considerably in this respect), and entirely of a greyish aspect.

L. MACROCALYX, *Airy-Shaw*

(Bot. Mag., t. 9490)

A shrub 3 to 6 ft. high; shoots glabrous, greyish brown. Leaves oblong-ovate, varying to lanceolate and ovate, 2 to 4 ins. long, about half as wide, rounded at the base or occasionally slightly cordate there, slenderly pointed, entire, glabrous and bright green above, very glaucous and with minute, appressed, reddish down beneath. Flowers fragrant, pendulous in axillary racemes 3 or 4 ins. long; corolla white, globose-ovoid, $\frac{2}{5}$ in. long, $\frac{3}{8}$ in. wide, with five minute, triangular lobes at the mouth, slightly red-downy outside, glabrous within; sepals $\frac{1}{4}$ in. long, erect. Blossoms in July.

Native of Yunnan, China, and found in 1924 by Forrest and Kingdon Ward, both of whom sent home seeds. From these, flowering plants were raised by Mr G. H. Johnstone of Trewithen, Cornwall, and by the late Lord Headfort at Kells, Co. Meath.

LYONOTHAMNUS FLORIBUNDUS, *Gray*, var. ASPLENIFOLIUS, *Brandegee*. ROSACEÆ

(L. asplenifolius, *Greene*)

An evergreen tree 30 to 50 ft. high, of slender form, with a red-brown peeling bark; young shoots glabrous. Leaves opposite, pinnate, 4 to 8 ins. long, made up of three to nine leaflets. Leaflets stalkless, 2 to $4\frac{1}{2}$ ins. long, $\frac{1}{2}$ to $\frac{5}{8}$ in. wide; cut up into hatchet-shaped segments $\frac{1}{4}$ to $\frac{1}{2}$ in. long by incisions reaching to the midrib; veins set at right angles to the midrib; dark green and glabrous above, paler and downy beneath. Flowers white, $\frac{1}{4}$ in. across, produced numerously on terminal paniculate corymbs 3 to 6 ins. broad; petals five; stamens fifteen. "Fruit of two woody, glandular, four-seeded parts, splitting on both sides" (Eastwood).

Native of the islands of Santa Catalina, Santa Cruz, etc., off the coast of California; not yet found on the mainland. Although the typical L. floribundus differs from this variety only in foliage (its leaves being simple, oblong, lanceolate, and either toothed minutely or not at all) it is far from being so ornamental a tree. But between it and var. asplenifolius there is every intermediate state. So far as I know, the fern-leaved variety is the only one introduced to this country. A tree raised from seed sent to Kew in 1900 grew to be 20 ft. high in a corner facing east outside the wall of the Temperate House, where it attracted much admiration for the beauty of its fern-like leaves, its luxuriance and graceful habit. It was so much injured by the cold winter of 1928-9 that it did not recover its health again. The arrangement of the leaves opposite each other on the twig and their distinctive shape make this tree easily recognisable in the rose family. It would appear to be an admirable tree for the milder counties. The generic name commemorates W. S. Lyon, who discovered the tree in 1884 on Santa Catalina.

"On Santa Cruz Island, perhaps the most satisfying of all sights are large stands of Lyonothamnus. It grows high up the canyons and in these protected places is able to attain its full beauty. The foliage is fern-like and very lovely, and the small white flowers, borne in broad terminal panicles, overspread the top branches, so that when a colony of the tree, cupped in the hollow of a hill, is seen from a vantage point above, the aspect is of a sea of creamy white upon green" (L. Rowntree).

MAACKIA. Leguminosæ

A genus of six deciduous trees natives of E. Asia and named after Richard Maack, a Russian naturalist who died in 1886. They are nearly akin to Cladrastis and have by some authorities been put in that genus. But they are really very distinct in that the wood is not brittle as in Cladrastis; the leaf-buds are solitary and not hidden by the base of the leafstalk; the leaflets are opposite and the flowers are densely packed in more or less erect racemes. They are very hardy and grow well in good open loam in full sunshine, but they have no very outstanding merits. They flower in July and August and occasionally bear seed.

M. amurensis, *Ruprecht*

(Cladrastis amurensis, *Bentham*, Bot. Mag., t. 6551)

A small deciduous tree, said to be 40 ft. or more high in a wild state, with

Maackia amurensis

peeling bark, but usually shrubby in cultivation in this country; young shoots minutely downy. Leaves 8 to 12 ins. long, pinnate, with seven to eleven leaflets;

the main-stalk rather swollen at the base, but leaving the bud quite exposed; leaflets opposite, ovate, blunt at the top, 1½ to 3 ins. long, dark green above, paler and glabrous beneath. Flowers pea-shaped, dull white, closely set on stiff, erect racemes, 4 to 6 ins. long, sometimes branched at the base. Each flower is ½ in. long on a short stalk about half its length; calyx bell-shaped, ⅙ in. long. Pod 2 to 3 ins. long, ⅓ in. wide, flat, with the seam slightly winged.

Native of Manchuria; introduced in 1864.

Var. BUERGERI, *C. K. Schneider*, is a native of Japan and differs chiefly in the leaflets beneath being furnished with appressed hairs, also the calyx.

M. CHINENSIS, *Takeda*

(M. hupehensis, *Takeda*)

A deciduous flat-headed tree 16 to 50 ft. (rarely more) high, the largest trees with a trunk 7 ft. in girth; young shoots glabrous by summer. Leaves pinnate, 5 to 8 ins. long, composed usually of nine to thirteen leaflets, the lower ones of which are ovate and about 1 in. long, the others becoming larger and more oblong or oval in outline towards the end of the leaf and 1¾ to 2½ ins. long by ¾ in. wide; they are bluntish at the apex, tapered to rounded at the base, silvery grey with down when young, remaining densely covered beneath with velvety appressed down; stalk ⅛ in. long, downy. Flowers opening in July and August on a terminal panicle 6 to 8 ins. long and 4 to 5 ins. wide, consisting of several cylindrical downy racemes densely crowded with flowers. These are a dull white, ⅖ in. long; calyx bell-shaped, toothed, ⅛ in. long and, like the short flower-stalk, downy.

Native of Hupeh and Szechuen, China; discovered by Wilson and introduced by him in 1908. He observes that it is common in W. Hupeh in moist open country, but that large specimens are rare. It flowered in the Arnold Arboretum, Mass., in 1920, and at Kew four years later. Its chief beauty is in the silvery sheen of the young unfolding leaves; the flowers are of little account. It appears to be closely related to M. amurensis, differing in the smaller shorter leaves and in the narrower more downy leaflets.

M. FAURIEI, *Takeda*

(Cladrastis Fauriei, *Léveillé*)

A deciduous tree up to 25 ft. high, with a trunk 2 ft. in girth, but often a bush 6 ft. or more high; young shoots glabrous. Leaves pinnate, about 8 ins. long; leaflets nine to seventeen, oval or ovate, rounded or broadly wedge-shaped at the base; 1½ to 2 ins. long, ⅝ to ⅞ in. wide, rather downy when young, becoming glabrous; stalk of leaflet ⅛ to $\frac{3}{16}$ in. long. Flowers white, ⅖ in. long, produced on a panicle made up of slender racemes 2 to 3 ins. long, on which they are closely packed; calyx bell-shaped, scarcely toothed, finely downy. Pod 1½ to 1¾ ins. long.

Native of Quelpaert Island, Korea; discovered by the Abbé Faurie in 1907 at an altitude of 3700 ft. E. H. Wilson collected seeds on the island in 1917, which represent its first introduction to cultivation. It flowers there in August at the end of leafy shoots. Introduced to Kew in 1922.

M. TASHIROI (Cladrastis Tashiroi, *Yatabe*), from the Loochoo Islands, appears to be a small form of M. amurensis, always shrubby. Probably not in cultivation in this country.

MACLURA POMIFERA, *C. K. Schneider*. OSAGE ORANGE. MORACEÆ

(M. aurantiaca, *Nuttall*)

A deciduous tree, occasionally 40 ft. or more high; branches armed with spines up to 1¼ ins. long; young shoots downy, soon becoming glabrous. Leaves alternate, ovate or oval to oblong-lanceolate; 1½ to 4 ins. long, about half as wide; pointed, mostly rounded at the base; dark green and glabrous above, paler and downy beneath, especially on the veins and midrib; stalk ½ to 1½ ins. long. Male flowers green, produced in June along with one or two leaves from the joints of the previous year's wood, numerous in a short-stalked roundish cluster; they are quite inconspicuous, as are also the female ones, borne on separate trees. Fruit like an orange in shape, 2 to 4 ins. across, yellowish green.

Native of the South and Central United States; introduced in 1818. This tree is remarkable for its large, ornamental, but quite inedible fruits, rarely seen in this country, perhaps because the two sexes are not often associated. They are full of a milky juice. In the United States this tree is largely used as a hedge plant, and I have also seen it used for the same purpose in Central Europe. It is an ally of the mulberry, and the only species known. Named in honour of William Maclure, an American geologist. Propagated by layers or root-cuttings, in the absence of seeds. Where only one tree is grown, an endeavour should be made to graft the other sex upon it.

Var. INERMIS, *André*, is without spines, and worth noting as being female.

Var. PULVERULENTA.—Leaves spotted with white; I only know it as a small plant, but it appears to be of little value.

MAGNOLIA. MAGNOLIACEÆ

A genus of deciduous or evergreen trees and shrubs named by Linnæus in honour of Pierre Magnol, a professor of botany and medicine at Montpelier, who died in 1715. The species in cultivation come from two widely separated areas, one group being native of the eastern United States, the other and larger one native of India, China, and Japan. Outlying members of each group occur in Mexico and Malaya. In one respect magnolias are the most splendid of all hardy trees, for in the size of their individual flowers they are easily first; the evergreen species, too, have some of the largest leaves of all evergreen trees hardy with us. The flowers are produced singly at the end of a shoot, the calyx consisting of three sepals, the corolla of usually six or nine, sometimes fifteen or eighteen, petals. The fruit is more or less cone-shaped, and, like the seeds, often richly coloured. The young branches are very pithy; the leaves alternate and always entire. In most of the species, the bark when crushed emits a pleasant aromatic odour, and some of the American species, as well as the Chinese M. officinalis, have medicinal properties.

Perhaps no group of exotic trees gives more distinction to a garden than a comprehensive collection of magnolias. There is not one that is not worthy of cultivation, the early-flowering or Yulan section being especially noteworthy for the brilliant effect they produce in spring.

The only difficulty experienced in cultivating these trees is in establishing some of them after transplanting. The roots are thick and fleshy, and apt to decay if disturbed and lacerated when the trees themselves are at rest. Any planting, therefore, which involves root injury should be done when active growth has commenced, so that the wounds may heal and new roots be formed immediately. May is a suitable month. The more delicate-rooted species like parviflora and stellata like a proportion of peat in the soil, more especially when they are young. But for the strong-growing sorts like Soulangiana, tripetala, acuminata, etc., a good loam is very suitable. All of them like abundant moisture, and where the soil is shallow and poor, holes 18 ins. deep and 2 to 4 yards in diameter should be prepared by mixing good loam, and if possible one-fourth peat and decayed leaves with the ordinary soil. The dimensions of the prepared ground should, of course, be proportionate to the vigour of the species. In most gardens the ordinary soil, well trenched and improved by adding decayed leaves, will be found suitable, but for such delightful plants as these a little extra labour and expense at the outset will be repaid.

Magnolias are propagated by seed, layering, and grafting. For the pure species, seeds no doubt are preferable, but their production in this country is uncertain, and it has to be remembered that being of an oily nature they retain their vitality but a short time if kept dry. It is advisable to sow them singly in small pots of light soil under glass. Layering is a very useful means of increase; it is now much practised in the great Dutch nurseries, whence magnolias are sent to England every year in large quantities for forcing. Where layering is inconvenient or impossible, grafting will have to be employed. One of the best stocks is the American M. acuminata. For M. stellata the Japanese gardeners use M. Kobus as a stock, and for M. Watsoni they use stocks of M. obovata. But grafting should be the last resource.

With regard to the matter of the attitude of magnolias towards chalk in the soil, Col. F. Stern tells me that, according to his experience at Highdown, near Worthing, Wilsonii, parviflora and Dawsoniana dislike it, but that Delavayi, Kobus, stellata, Veitchii, sinensis, and Lennei succeed well there.

It may be worth mentioning that seeds of magnolias are sometimes very long in germinating. A batch of about two hundred seeds of M. Wilsonii, ripened at Kew a few years ago, remained dormant after sowing for over two years, then germinated simultaneously with scarcely a failure.

M. ACUMINATA, *Linnæus*. CUCUMBER TREE

(Bot. Mag., t. 2427)

A large deciduous tree, 60 to 90 ft. high, forming a trunk 6 to 12 ft. in girth. Branches at first erect, ultimately arching. Leaves oval to oblong, 5 to 10 ins. long, about half as wide; green on both sides, downy beneath;

they narrow to a point at the end, the base is rounded. Flowers comparatively inconspicuous, dull greenish yellow; sepals 1 to 1½ ins. long; petals erect, 2 to 3 ins. long, in two sets of three each. Fruit dark red, columnar, 3 ins. long.

Native of eastern N. America, from New York State southwards, reaching its finest development in the S. Allegheny region. This tree, the noblest of American magnolias in growth and the least effective in blossom, was discovered by John Bartram, and introduced by him to England in 1736. It was raised from seed by Peter Collinson, and flowered with him for the first time 20th May 1762. The flowers have a slight fragrance. The popular name of "cucumber tree" refers to the shape and colour of the fruits when quite young. It ripens seed freely, and young plants make perhaps the best stocks for grafting other magnolias upon. A fine tree at Kew is 5 ft. 3 ins. in girth of trunk.

Var. MAXIMA.—Trees under this name are grown at Kew, but except for a possibly more vigorous growth and larger foliage there is nothing to distinguish them. Sent out by the firm of Loddiges about 1830.

Var. VARIEGATA.—Leaves handsomely blotched with golden yellow.

M. CAMPBELLII, *Hooker fil.*

(Bot. Mag., t. 6793; Garden, 24th Aug. 1895 (plate).)

A deciduous tree, occasionally 150 ft. high, with oval leaves tapering towards both ends, from 6 to 10 ins. long, glabrous above, covered with appressed hairs beneath. Flowers produced in spring before the leaves; very fragrant, cup-shaped at first, the petals very thick, 4 to 5 ins. long and about 2 ins. wide, varying in colour from deep rose to crimson.

Native of the Sikkim Himalaya at 8000 to 10,000 ft. altitude. It is only in the milder parts of the kingdom, like the south and west, that this fine tree—perhaps the most magnificent of magnolias—can be expected really to thrive. It flowers from February to early April, and its flower-buds are susceptible to injury by storm and frost. It flowered with Sir E. Loder at Leonardslee, Horsham; and a tree outside at Kew, 35 ft. high, has been raised from seed that may have been gathered at the highest part of its altitudinal range, which is considerable. Hooker described it, wild near Darjeeling, as an immense, black-barked, sparingly branched tree.

M. CORDATA, *Michaux*

(Bot. Mag., t. 325; M. acuminata cordata, *Sargent*)

Although this magnolia is said to have been found by the elder Michaux growing near rivers in Georgia, its exact counterpart, according to Sargent, is not now known in a wild state. Sargent regards it as a variety of M. acuminata, from the typical form of which it is very distinct. The leaves are 3 to 5 ins. long, comparatively broader and less pointed than those of M. acuminata, but rarely cordate as the name implies. The flowers are faintly and not agreeably scented, canary yellow; petals 1½ to 2 ins long. Compared with the free-growing M. acuminata, of which it may be a high mountain form, it is a low, stunted tree. At Kew, where M. acuminata succeeds exceptionally well, a tree of M. cordata fifty years old is only 15 ft. high, and others only 3 or 4 ft. high flower abundantly. In beauty of blossom it is superior to its ally. Introduced in 1801.

M. Dawsoniana, *Rehder and Wilson*

A deciduous tree 25 to 40 ft. high, with a trunk up to 6 ft. in girth; young shoots glabrous. Leaves obovate to oval, shortly pointed or blunt at the apex, usually tapered to the base; 3½ to 6 ins. long, about half as much wide, of firm leathery texture, lustrous green above, paler and rather glaucous beneath; glabrous except for down each side the midrib; stalk ½ to 1¼ ins. long. Fruit shortly stalked, cylindrical, 4 ins. long, 1½ ins. wide; seeds ⅖ in. long, orange scarlet.

Native of W. Szechuen, China; discovered and introduced to the Arnold Arboretum in 1908 by Wilson. Introduced to England from Messrs Chenault's nursery at Orleans in 1919. Wilson never saw the tree in flower in China, but it flowered at Lanarth in Cornwall in March 1937. The petals were 3 to 4 ins. long, 1 to 2 ins. wide, white faintly streaked and tinged with rosy purple. It grows wild at elevations of 7000 to 8000 ft. and is quite hardy; it has not at any rate shown any sign of tenderness at Kew. Wilson notes that it is rare and known only from one, rather remote, locality. The name commemorates Mr Jackson Dawson, first Superintendent of the Arnold Arboretum, Mass., and Professor Sargent's chief assistant in its foundation.

M. Delavayi, *Franchet*

(Bot. Mag., t. 8282)

A spreading, flat-topped, evergreen tree, up to 30 ft. high. Leaves 8 to 14 ins. long, 5 to 8 ins. wide; greyish dull green above, glaucous and with fine down beneath; the stalk one-fourth the length of the blade, stout; the midrib prolonged beyond the blade into a short tip. The flowers are 7 to 8 ins. across, cup-shaped and fragrant; the petals about 4 ins. long, half as wide, dull, creamy white. The cone-like fruit is 6 ins. long.

Native of Yunnan, China; introduced by Wilson in 1899. It grows on mountain-sides at from 4500 to 7500 ft. elevation, but in spite of these considerable altitudes it has not proved hardy at Kew in the open ground. Against a wall, both there and at the Coombe Wood nursery, it has succeeded admirably. It flowered first in 1908. From the other (and hardier) evergreen cultivated magnolia—M. grandiflora—this is very distinct in the larger leaves, dull green above, glaucous beneath. It ought to be a valuable tree in the south-western counties.

M. denudata, *Desrousseaux*. Yulan

(M. conspicua, *Salisbury*; M. Yulan, *Desfontaines*)

A rather low, rounded, deciduous tree, much branched, rarely more than 30, but sometimes 45 ft. high. Leaves 3 to 6 ins. long, 2 to 3½ ins. wide; oval to obovate, the apex contracting abruptly to a point; downy beneath. Flower-buds conspicuous all the winter by reason of their large scales being covered with grey, shaggy hairs. Flowers pure white, opening from March to May according to the season; petals 3 ins. long, at first erect, afterwards spreading, thick, about nine in number. Fruit spindle-shaped, 5 ins. long.

Native of China; introduced in 1789. One of the most beautiful and distinctive of all flowering trees, this magnolia is, unfortunately, an occasional victim to the inclemency of an English spring. Its flowers respond quickly to premature warmth in late February or March, only too often to be trapped by succeeding frost. A cold February and March suits it best. It never fails to set an abundance of blossom, and the white flowers gleaming in the sunshine of an early spring day render it the most conspicuous of all trees at that season. It was for long an uncommon tree, the most famous specimens being at Kew, Syon, and Gunnersbury House. It is now propagated in the Dutch nurseries by grafting on M. Soulangiana, and sold cheaply for forcing early into flower. By the Chinese the yulan has been cultivated for at least thirteen hundred years, especially near temples and in the Imperial gardens.

M. FRASERI, *Walter*. FRASER'S MAGNOLIA

(M. auriculata, *Lamarck*, Bot. Mag., t. 1206)

A deciduous tree, 30 to 40 ft. high, of open, spreading habit. Leaves produced in a cluster at the ends of the branches, pale green, of thin texture, glabrous on both sides, obovate, pointed and with two distinct auricles (or lobes) at the base, extending below the point where the stalk joins the blade; the

MAGNOLIA DENUDATA (see p. 275)

entire blade is from 8 to 15 ins. long about half as wide; the stalk 2 to 4 ins. long. Flowers 8 ins. or more across, strongly and not very agreeably scented—at any rate close at hand; produced on the leafy shoots in May and June. Sepals three, oblong-obovate, greenish, larger than the petals, deflexed. Petals six, at first pale yellow, afterwards milky white; narrowly obovate, 3 to 4 ins. long; at first erect, afterwards spreading. Seeds red, produced on a rose-coloured cone 4 or 5 ins. long.

Native of the south-eastern United States; first discovered in S. Carolina, in 1776, by William Bartram, and introduced to England ten years later. This handsome and distinct tree is distinguished from all other magnolias, except the rare M. pyramidata and the much larger-leaved M. macrophylla, by the auricles at the base of the leaves. It is well worth growing as a lawn tree. The specific name commemorates John Fraser, who sent to England many North American plants between 1780 and 1810—including this magnolia.

M. GLOBOSA, *Hooker and Thomson*

(Bot. Mag., t. 9467; M. tsarongensis, *W. W. Smith*)

A deciduous shrub or small tree 10 to 20 ft. high; young shoots at first densely clothed with tawny velvety down. Leaves oval, rounded or slightly heart-shaped at the base, shortly pointed at the apex; 4 to 10 ins. long, nearly half as wide; dark glossy green above with a little rusty down on the midrib and veins, permanently downy beneath; veins in about twelve to fifteen pairs; stalk 1½ to 3 ins. long. Flowers fragrant, slightly creamy white, rather globose, about 3 ins. across, produced in June at the end of a leafy shoot, each on a stout stalk 2 ins. or more long, which is covered thickly with a tawny felt. Sepals and petals numbering together nine to twelve; stamens numerous, very short, bearing richly tinted anthers ½ in. long. Fruit cylindrical, 2 to 2½ ins. long, 1 in. wide, pendulous, crimson.

The type, named by Hooker and Thomson, is a native of the Sikkim Himalaya, but the same plant or one nearly the same, was found by Forrest in July 1919 in W. China and was introduced by him. This was named M. tsarongensis by Wright Smith and was for some time cultivated as such. The Himalayan M. globosa is rarer and I have only seen it at Caerhays. I saw a healthy Chinese plant about 4 ft. high showing flower-buds at Loch Inch, Wigtownshire, as long ago as May 1931. The flowers developed handsomely and were exhibited the following month by the Earl of Stair at Westminster, when the species was given an Award of Merit. It flowered with Major G. H. Johnstone of Trewithen, Cornwall, during June 1932. Nearly akin to M. globosa is M. sinensis.

M. GRANDIFLORA, *Linnæus*. LAUREL MAGNOLIA

(M. fœtida, *Sargent*)

An evergreen tree, 60 to 80 ft. high, of dense pyramidal form, but as usually seen with us less than half as high and more rounded. Leaves oval to oblong and obovate, from 6 to 10 ins. long, less than half as wide; tapered to both ends; leathery in texture, glossy dark green above, covered beneath, especially when young, with a thick red-brown felt; stalk 1 to 2 ins. long. Flowers among the finest in the genus, globular, 8 to 10 ins. across, very fragrant with a spicy or fruity odour, produced continuously during the late summer and autumn. Petals thick and concave, creamy white, broadly obovate, and 4 or 5 ins. long. Seeds ripen at Goodwood.

Introduced from the southern United States to England early in the eighteenth century, this still remains the finest flowered of evergreen trees; and until the advent of the Chinese M. Delavayi it was the only really evergreen hardy magnolia. It never suffers from cold at Kew, but grows slowly, especially in height, and is very different from the magnificent pyramids one sees along the Riviera and in Italy. It is apt to have its branches broken during heavy falls of snow, for which reason it is sometimes wise to brace the main branches together by stout wires. In cold localities it makes an admirable wall tree. Many varieties, mostly of S. European origin, have been, and continue to be, put on the market.

Var. ANGUSTIFOLIA (syn. M. Hartwegii).—Leaves narrow, 6 to 8 ins. long, 1½ to 2 ins. wide, with little or no brown-red felt beneath.

Var. FERRUGINEA, *Hort.*—A form with the red felt beneath the leaf more developed than usual.

Var. GLORIOSA.—A broad-leaved form which bears flowers of great size and substance—one of the finest.

Var. LANCEOLATA, *Aiton* (var. exoniensis, *Loddiges*).—Exmouth Magnolia. Leaves rather narrower than in the type, lanceolate or oval, rusty coloured beneath; of a rather erect or fastigiate habit. Said to have originated in the garden of Sir John Colliton at Exmouth in the eighteenth century; hardier, and flowering younger. Bot. Mag., t. 1952.

Var. UNDULATA.—Broad-leaved, with conspicuously wavy margins.

It is neither necessary nor possible to distinguish the various other forms that have been named. The tree ripens seeds freely in the south of Europe, and it is among the plants raised from them that these forms appear.

M. KOBUS, *De Candolle*

(Bot. Mag., t. 8428; M. Thurberi, *Parsons*)

A deciduous tree, ultimately 30 or 40 ft. high, with a trunk 3 ft. in girth, of quick growth and pyramidal form when young, but eventually round-headed. Young branches aromatically fragrant when crushed; winter leaf-buds downy. Leaves obovate, 3 to 6 ins. long, often contracted at the apex to a short point, tapering at the base to a short stalk. Flowers amongst the smallest in the genus, often under 4 ins. in diameter when fully expanded; petals six, pure white, obovate; sepals small, soon falling; flower-stalk downy. Fruit pinkish, seeds bright red. Flowers in April.

Native of Japan. Although one of the less attractive of magnolias when young, when it does not flower freely, this species is an interesting addition to cultivated Japanese trees on account of its vigorous constitution. It is much used by Japanese gardeners as a stock on which they graft M. stellata, and it blooms profusely when older. There are two forms of it, one more robust and with larger leaves than the other and attaining 70 to 80 ft.—var. BOREALIS, *Sargent*. The tree referred to by Loudon in vol. i. of the *Arboretum and Fruticetum*, p. 283, as M. Kobus cannot, from the description, be this species. It was probably first introduced to England by Maries; there was a fine tree in the Coombe Wood nursery sent home by him in 1879.

M. LENNEI, *Van Houtte*

(Flore des Serres, t. 1693)

One of the most beautiful of all hybrid magnolias, this tree is said to have had the same origin as M. Soulangiana, viz. denudata × liliflora, or probably its var. purpurea. It is, at anyrate, very different from the average forms of that hybrid, the leaves being larger and broader (as much as 8 ins. by 5 ins.), and more strongly ribbed; the flowers, too, are finer and more richly coloured. Petals very fleshy, broadly obovate, often 4 ins. deep and 4 ins. wide; concave like a broad spoon, and of a beautiful shade of rose-purple outside, white inside. The main crop of flowers commences to open in late April, and lasts through May, so that they are not often injured by frost. It occasionally flowers a second time in autumn.

This remarkable magnolia is said to have originated accidentally in Lombardy, where it was noticed by an Erfurt nurseryman named Topf in 1850, and by him introduced to Germany. It was figured by Van Houtte in the place quoted above, and named in honour of Mr Lenné, a royal gardener in Berlin. There is a fine tree at Enys, in Cornwall.

M. RUSTICA RUBRA is of a similar type to M. Lennei, and was raised in a nursery at Boskoop, near Gouda, in Holland, in a batch of seedlings from M. Lennei. In this variety the petals are more rose-coloured than in M. Lennei, and proportionately shorter and broader. It is much grown in the Boskoop nurseries from layers which are used as a stock for grafting M. denudata, etc., on.

M. LILIFLORA, *Desrouseaux*

(M. obovata, *Willdenow*; M. purpurea, *Curtis*, Bot. Mag., t. 390)

A deciduous bush of rather straggling growth, rarely more than 12 ft. high in the open (although twice as high on walls); young wood aromatic. Leaves ovate, oblong, or obovate, 3 to 8 ins. long, 2 to 5 ins. wide; tapering rather abruptly to a point, dark green above, downy beneath. Flowers opening from April to June; petals 3 ins. long, 1¾ ins. wide, erect, obovate, vinous purple and white outside, white within.

Introduced from Japan in 1790, this handsome shrub is now considered to be a native of China, and as existing in Japan as a cultivated plant only. It varies to a considerable extent in the colour of the flowers when raised from seed, but is always purple or a combination of purple and white outside, and white within.

Var. NIGRA, *Nicholson*, has larger flowers with petals 4 or 5 ins. long, very dark purple outside.

Var. PURPUREA has larger flowers than the type, wholly purple outside, very deep towards the base of the petals (see *Bot. Mag.*, figure quoted above); but there appears to be no well-marked distinction between them.

Quite hardy near London, it usually requires wall protection in the north. The later flowers are accompanied by full-sized leaves.

M. MACROPHYLLA, *Michaux*

(Bot. Mag., t. 2189)

A deciduous tree, 20 to 50 ft. high, with an open, spreading head of branches, and a trunk 1 to 1½ ft. in diameter. Leaves the largest of all magnolias, measuring 15 to 25 ins., sometimes 3 ft. in length, and from 7 to 12 ins. wide; oblong-obovate, widest above the middle, bluntish at the apex, broadly heart-shaped or auriculate at the base; bright green and glabrous above, silvery grey and downy beneath. Flowers on leafy shoots 8 to 10, sometimes 14 ins. across, fragrant; petals six, dull creamy white, fleshy, 5 to 7 ins. long, half as wide. Fruit roundish, egg-shaped, rose-coloured, 3 ins. long.

Native of the south-eastern United States, where it is rare, and only occurs in small isolated stations. It was discovered by the elder Michaux in 1759 in the mountains of S. Carolina; introduced to Europe in 1800. In foliage this is the most remarkable of magnolias; and is indeed one of the most interesting of the world's trees; but it is, unfortunately, spring tender in a young state. That it will withstand severer frosts than any we experience is shown by two healthy trees growing in front of the museum of the Arnold Arboretum, Boston, U.S.A. The most famous specimen in England was at Claremont, near Esher, a healthy tree which, when I saw it in 1912, was 40 ft. high, its trunk 3 ft. in girth.

M. MOLLICOMATA, *W. W. Smith*

A deciduous tree 50 to 80 ft. high in a wild state; young shoots downy at first, becoming glabrous. Leaves broadly oval to obovate, rounded or somewhat heart-shaped at the base, shortly pointed or rounded at the apex; 6 to 10 ins. long; 4 to 5 ins. wide; glabrous and dull green above, downy beneath, especially on the midrib; lateral veins in ten to fourteen pairs; leaf-stalk 1 to 2 ins. long, downy like the midrib. Flowers appearing before the leaves in spring, cup-shaped, 6 or 7 ins. wide, rose-coloured. Fruit cylindrical, 5 or 6 ins. long, 1 to 1¾ ins. wide.

Native of S.E. Tibet and Yunnan; discovered by Forrest. This magnolia is closely related to the Indian M. Campbellii. Judging by dried specimens it appears to be a Chinese and Tibetan ally of that species, distinguished as a rule by a more copious down beneath the leaves when young, but evidently no hard and fast line can be drawn between them even in this respect.

M. NITIDA, *W. W. Smith*

A widely branched evergreen tree or shrub 20 to 30 (occasionally over 40) ft. high; young shoots glabrous. Leaves of leathery texture, oval, oblong or inclined to ovate, shortly pointed, broadly wedge-shaped or sometimes rounded at the base; 2¼ to 4½ ins. long, 1 to 2 ins. wide; dark shining green above, paler beneath, perfectly glabrous; stalk ½ to 1 in. long. Flowers fragrant, creamy white, 2 to 3 ins. wide; petals nine, oblanceolate to narrowly obovate, 2 ins. long, ½ to ⅝ in. wide; sepals three, narrower. Fruit 2 to 3 ins. long, 1¼ ins. wide, composed of fifteen to twenty carpels, each containing one or two bright orange-red seeds.

Native of Yunnan, China, and S.E. Tibet, at altitudes of 9000 to 12,000 ft.; discovered by G. Forrest in 1917; plants raised from seed he collected later are in cultivation at Kew and elsewhere. The leaves are very much smaller than, but have some resemblance to, those of M. grandiflora; they do not at all resemble those of Delavayi, the third and only other evergreen species in cultivation. Forrest found it flowering in June and he remarks that it is strongly aromatic when in fruit. It is found in the same region and at the same elevations as M. rostrata, which is evidently going to be fairly hardy, but that species is deciduous and as a rule evergreens are more tender in cultivation. Writing after a severe frost at Caerhays in Cornwall, in March 1931, Mr J. C. Williams described its foliage as by far the most brilliant to be seen there and absolutely without a trace of injury. It is not hardy at Kew.

M. OBOVATA, *Thunberg*

(M. hypoleuca, *Siebold and Zuccarini*; Bot. Mag., t. 8077)

A deciduous, erect-growing tree, 50 to 80, sometimes 100 ft. high, with a trunk 6 to 9 ft. in girth; young bark dark brown-purple. Leaves in a cluster at the end of the shoot, leathery, obovate, 8 to 18 ins. long, half as much wide; tapering at the base to a stalk 1 to 2½ ins. long; glaucous green above, blue-white and slightly downy beneath. Flowers produced in June, 8 ins. across, strongly scented, sepals and petals creamy white; stamens bright purplish red, forming, with the yellow anthers, a conspicuous circular mass 3 ins. across in the centre of the flower. The fruit is brilliant red until mature, cone-shaped, rather pointed, 5 to 8 ins. high, 2½ ins. wide.

Native of Japan; introduced in 1884. It attains apparently its largest size in the forests of Yezo, where it is highly valued for its light, soft, easily worked timber. One of the most beautiful of all northern trees both in leaf and flower, this magnolia is also quite hardy. When young its habit is open and sometimes rather gaunt. It must not be confounded with the obovata of Willdenow (see M. liliflora).

M. OFFICINALIS, *Rehder and Wilson*

A deciduous tree 20 to 50 ft. high, its young shoots at first silky downy, yellowish grey. Leaves obovate, rounded at the apex, tapered at the base; 14 to 21 ins. long, 5 to 10 ins. wide; glabrous and rather pale green above, glaucous and clothed with pale fine down beneath; lateral veins twenty to thirty, prominent beneath; stalk 1 to 1½ ins. long. Flower white, fragrant, cupped, 6 to 8 ins. across, produced in early summer at the end of the leafy young growth; flower-stalk thick and downy. Sepals and petals nine to twelve, fleshy, up to 4 ins. long and 1½ ins. wide; stamens numerous, red. Fruit oblong to egg-shaped, flat at the top, 4 to 5 ins. high, 2½ ins. wide.

Native of W. Hupeh, China; discovered by Henry about 1885, introduced by Wilson in 1900. At first it was confused with the beautiful M. obovata, with which it is identical in foliage. It differs in the yellowish grey young shoots (purplish in obovata) and flat-topped fruit. It is not so large a tree although equally beautiful in flower and noble in leaf. It is cultivated in W. China for its bark and flower-buds, which yield a drug valued by the Chinese for the medicinal properties. It is quite hardy. As it was sent out from Coombe Wood Nursery as the "Chinese hypoleuca," it no doubt exists unrecognised in some gardens under that name.

Var. BILOBA, *Rehder and Wilson.*—Leaves deeply and conspicuously notched at the apex, otherwise similar to the type. I do not think this remarkable variety has been introduced. Cultivated in W. China.

M. PARVIFLORA, *Siebold and Zuccarini*

(Bot. Mag., t. 7411; M. Sieboldii, *K. Koch*)

A small deciduous tree or large shrub, with slender branches. Leaves oblong or obovate-oblong, 4 to 6 ins. long, the apex contracting rather abruptly to a point, rounded at the base, dark green and glabrous above, glaucous and downy beneath, usually with seven to nine pairs of veins; leaf-stalk $\frac{3}{4}$ to $\frac{1}{2}$ in. long, pubescent when young. Flowers fragrant, at first cup-shaped, borne on a stalk 1 to $2\frac{1}{2}$ ins. long; petals pure white, about 2 ins. long, obovate, very concave. Stamens numerous, forming a rosy crimson disk 1 in. across. Fruit 2 ins. long, carmine; seeds scarlet.

Native of Japan and Korea. The most distinctive character of the species is the comparatively long flower-stalk. The flowers are not always borne in one large crop, but appear often a few at a time from May until August on the leafy shoots. The crimson stamens show in attractive contrast with the white sepals. It is not so robust a grower as most magnolias are, and likes a proportion of leaf-soil or peat in the soil. It has ripened seeds at Kew from which plants have been raised. Introduced to Kew in 1893.

M. PYRAMIDATA, *Pursh*

(Bot. Reg., t. 407)

Originally discovered by William Bartram in Georgia, on the banks of the Altamaha River, and recognised by him as a species, this magnolia was by later botanists confused with M. Fraseri. Although closely allied, the two are now considered quite distinct. The leaves of the present species are much smaller (usually less than 8 ins. long), of thinner texture, narrowing to a waist near the base, the basal lobes spreading. The flowers, too, are smaller, 3 to 5 ins. across, and the tree more erect and pyramidal, as is implied by the name. Whilst M. Fraseri is an inland mountain plant, this species affects low-lying regions of Georgia and the Carolinas. Whether it is at present in cultivation I am not aware. It was introduced early in the nineteenth century, and grew in Messrs Loddiges' nursery at Hackney about 1837. The late Mr G. Nicholson saw it in the Trianon Gardens in 1887, and quite possibly it survives in some of the old gardens in the warmer parts of the country under the name of Fraseri. It is, no doubt, more tender than M. Fraseri.

M. ROSTRATA, *W. W. Smith*

A deciduous tree 40 to 80 ft. high, with silvery grey bark and glabrous purplish young shoots. Leaves obovate, rounded at the end, usually tapered to a narrow or slightly heart-shaped base, the largest over 20 ins. long by 12 ins.

wide; purplish red and clothed with tawny down when quite young, becoming glabrous above, glaucous and thinly furnished with down beneath; the midrib and chief veins (of the latter there are frequently over thirty pairs) often clothed with reddish brown hairs; stalk 1 to 3 ins. long. Flowers creamy white or pink, large, terminal, and solitary on leafy shoots of the current season, opening in June; petals tapered to a point, at first erect enough to give the flower a cupped shape. Fruit cylindric, bright red, 5 or 6 ins. long, 1½ ins. wide.

Native of Yunnan, S.E. Tibet, and Upper Burma; discovered in Yunnan by Forrest in 1917. There appears to have been much confusion between this species and M. mollicomata (or Campbellii) which bears its rosy pink flowers in spring on the leafless shoots of the preceding year. The original description of the flowers by Sir W. W. Smith in *Notes, Royal Botanic Garden, Edinburgh*, vol. xii., p. 213, really refers to those of M. mollicomata. Farrer, who found it in Upper Burma in 1919, also confused the two. Kingdon Ward describes the flowers as white, small, borne immediately above the huge leaves and practically invisible from below, and the tree itself as certainly not the magnificent sight in flower Forrest and Farrer originally believed it to be. It seems, nevertheless, to be undoubtedly the finest of all Asiatic magnolias in foliage. It is too early yet to write decisively as to its hardiness, but young plants at Kew withstood the hard winter of 1928-9 with slight protection and during the wet summer of 1931 made growths 2 to 3 ft. long. At Exbury and Caerhays it is quite hardy and flowered at both places in 1935. Kingdon Ward's opinion that the tree will never be any good in this country, not even moderately hardy, and be blown down in the first gale that catches it in full foliage, seems unduly pessimistic. At Kew the terminal bud is very liable to be destroyed in winter.

M. SALICIFOLIA, *Maximowicz*

(Bot. Mag., t. 8483)

A slender deciduous tree, 20 to 40 ft. high, with a trunk 1 ft. in diameter; young shoots very slender, smooth the first year, slightly warted the second; leaf-buds quite smooth. Leaves narrowly oval to lanceolate, tapered at both ends, blunt or pointed at the apex; 1½ to 4 ins. long, ⅝ to 1½ ins. wide; dull green and glabrous above, slightly glaucous and covered with minute down beneath; stalk slender, ¼ to ⅝ in. long. Flowers 3 to 4 ins. across; petals six, pure white; the three outer ones 2 ins. long, ½ in. wide, oblong, pointed; the three inner ones rather shorter and wider, slightly obovate; sepals short, lanceolate, very soon falling; flower-stalks quite glabrous; flower-buds hairy. Fruit rosy pink, 2 to 3 ins. long; seeds scarlet.

Native of Japan, chiefly of Mount Hakkoda, at 2000 to 3000 ft.; introduced in 1906. A very distinct species which makes an elegant tree, perfectly hardy. It blossoms in April on the naked shoots. The flower is similar to that of M. Kobus, but otherwise the species is very distinct in its narrow leaves, smooth leaf-buds and flower-stalks. It first flowered at Kew in 1911. The bark when bruised emits a pleasant odour, like that of Lippia citriodora (lemon-scented verbena).

Var. CONCOLOR, *Miquel*.—There is another magnolia in gardens, also called M. salicifolia, which is not quite the same. Dr Sprague of Kew, who kindly looked into the matter, recognises it as the var. concolor of Miquel. This variety differs from the typical form in its more spreading habit, its stouter branchlets, larger flowers, broader petals (1⅛ ins.), broader leaves (up to 3 ins. wide), differently scented bark, and in flowering a fortnight or so later. It used to be grown in the Veitchian nursery at Coombe Wood, and was probably introduced from Japan by J. H. Veitch about 1892.

Millais in his book *Magnolias*, p. 213, described the willow-leaved form as var. "fasciata." There is, of course, nothing fasciated about this tree in its normal state and "fasciata" is, no doubt, a misprint for "fastigiata." But as it is the typical tree which Maximowicz called salicifolia, Millais' name, in any case, has no standing. We are expecting a monograph on the Magnoliaceæ from Mr J. E. Dandy, but I do not know what conclusion he has arrived at on

MAGNOLIA SALICIFOLIA

this matter. Some years ago he held to the view that the two forms will be found to be joined by intermediates and that in any case they were not worth distinguishing by the botanist pure and simple. From a garden point of view they are quite distinct.

M. SARGENTIANA, *Rehder and Wilson*

A deciduous tree often 50 to 80 ft. high in nature; young shoots glabrous yellowish, afterwards becoming grey, dotted with small warts. Leaves obovate, rounded at the apex or with a short pointed tip, tapered towards the base; 4 to 8 ins. long, 2½ to 4½ ins. wide; firm in texture, glabrous and dull green above, paler and clothed with a dense grey down beneath (glabrous in young plants); leaf-stalk 1 to 2 ins. long, glabrous. Flowers opening in April or early May on the naked shoots, consisting of twelve sepals and petals, the former oblong-oval, 3 ins. long by 2 ins. wide, the latter up to 5 ins. long and 2½ ins. wide, rounded at the apex; they are rosy pink outside, deepest in shade towards the base, much paler inside. Flower-stalk thick, yellow, downy, ⅝ in. long. The column of stamens is ovoid, 1 in. long, rosy carmine. Floral bracts dark brown, hairy, heart-shaped, 2¾ ins. long by 2 ins. wide, dropping soon after the flowers open. Fruits cylindrical, 4 to 5½ ins. long; seeds scarlet.

Native of Szechuen, China; discovered by David in 1869 and again by Wilson in 1903. Introduced to the Arnold Arboretum, Mass., by Wilson in 1908, and to Kew three years later. It first flowered in this country with Mr J. C. Williams at Caerhays, Cornwall, in April 1931. It is evidently one of the largest magnolias, for Wilson found a tree over 80 ft. high and 10 ft. in girth of trunk. It is quite hardy at Kew, but will always no doubt show to better advantage in the south-west. It is at least as beautiful as Campbellii, besides being hardier and flowering later. To Lt.-Col. Messel of Nymans, Sussex, belongs the credit of being the second to flower this magnolia in April 1932.

M. SINENSIS, *Stapf* (Plate 21)

(M. globosa sinensis, *Rehder*; M. Nicholsoniana, *Hort.*, not *Rehder and Wilson*)

A deciduous tree or shrub up to 20 ft. high; young shoots clothed at first with pale brown silky hairs; becoming glabrous and greyish the second year. Leaves oval, oval-oblong and obovate to roundish; rounded or abruptly pointed at the apex, wedge-shaped or rounded at the base; 3 to 7 ins. long, 2 to 5½ ins. wide; glabrous and bright green above, slightly glaucous and at first very velvety beneath; stalk ¾ to 2½ ins. long and, like the midrib, densely silky hairy. Flowers saucer-shaped, white, fragrant, 4 to 5 ins. wide, produced at the end of young leafy shoots on a stalk 1 to 2 ins. long in June; sepals and petals usually nine, oblong-obovate, 1 to 2 ins. wide. Stamens numerous, ⅖ in. long, rosy crimson. Fruit pendulous, cylindrical, 3 ins. long, 1½ ins. wide, pink; seeds at first pink, ultimately scarlet.

Native of W. Szechuen, China; discovered and introduced to the Arnold Arboretum in 1908 by Wilson. It was found by him at altitudes of 7500 to 9000 ft. and is perfectly hardy. Introduced to England through Messrs Chenault's nursery at Orleans in 1920 and distributed under the name "M. Nicholsoniana." The magnolia to which that name was originally given is now regarded as the same as M. Wilsonii (*q.v.*). M. sinensis is a pleasant addition to hardy shrubs; a tree over 15 ft. high bore its handsome fruits in abundance with Mr P. D. Williams at Lanarth, Cornwall, in 1930. Col. Stern informs me that it grows very happily in his chalky garden at Highdown, near Worthing.

M. SOULANGEANA, *Soulange-Bodin* (Plate 22)

(M. Yulan Soulangeana, *Lindley*, Bot. Reg., t. 1164)

A hybrid raised in the garden of Mr. Soulange-Bodin at Fromont, near Paris, from seed borne by M. denudata fertilised by pollen of M. liliflora. The plant first flowered in 1826, and has since become the most popular of all magnolias in European gardens. In habit it is similar to denudata, forming a low, spreading, but more shapely tree. It flowers in April, rather later than the yulan, and is usually at its best when the flowers of that species are fading. Leaves 3 to 6 ins. long, mostly narrower than those of the yulan, and especially more tapering towards the apex; they are downy beneath. The flowers appear first and make their great display on the naked shoots, but continue to develop until early June, when the tree is full of foliage. Numerous forms of this magnolia have appeared since 1826, raised mostly from its seeds. They are all alike in having the petals white inside and stained more or less with purple on the outside; but they vary in depth and shade of colour, and in the width and shape of the petals. The following names have been given; Alexandrina, cyathiformis, Hammondii (with very narrow petals), Norberti, speciosa, superba, spectabilis (nearly pure white, very large), triumphans, etc. Many are so similar that it is not possible to distinguish them from each other in words, but all are attractive.

M. Sprengeri, *Pampanini*

(Bot. Mag., t. 9116 (forma diva); M. denudata purpurascens, *Rehder and Wilson*; M. conspicua purpurascens, *Bean*; M. diva, *Stapf*)

This tree appears first to have been found by Henry about 1885 in Hupeh and a year or two later in Szechuen. It was found again by Wilson in 1900 and introduced the following year by him to the Coombe Wood nursery. He and Rehder subsequently named it "denudata var. purpurascens" in *Plantæ Wilsonianæ*, vol. i., p. 401. The name "Sprengeri" was given to specimens collected by the Italian missionary, Silvestri, in N. Hupeh, about 1912, and as the tree is not now considered to belong to M. denudata (syn. conspicua) that is the first valid name.

Two forms are in cultivation: one with large rosy carmine flowers ("diva"); the other with smaller pure white ones and smaller leaves, which has been distinguished as "elongata." The continued existence of the former in gardens is due to the late Mr J. C. Williams, who obtained apparently what was the only plant from Coombe Wood. It has since grown very successfully at Caerhays, where it is now over 30 ft. high. I first saw it in flower there in April 1919, and was much impressed with the beauty of its blossoms which, in colour and in their erect pose at the end of leafless shoots, resembled M. Campbellii. That species is distinct in its much larger oval or oblong leaves without the wedge-shaped base. The Caerhays tree ripens good seed from which young trees have been raised. One of them is growing well at Kew and is to all appearance perfectly hardy.

It is a deciduous tree up to 65 ft. high, the bark on the old branches and trunk light grey and peeling off in small flakes; young shoots glabrous, yellowish. Leaves obovate, tapering to a wedge-shaped base, contracted near the apex to a short point; dark dullish green above and downy on the midrib; paler and more downy on the midrib and veins beneath; 4 to 7 ins. long, 2 to 5 ins. wide; stalk up to 1¼ ins. long. Flowers opening in April, 6 to 8 ins. wide, erect, very shortly stalked, terminating last year's shoots; made up of twelve sepals and petals which are rosy pink outside, paler and streaked with dark lines within. Stamens scarcely ½ in. long, rosy red. Of the

Var. ELONGATA, *Stapf*, there are three examples at Kew, the largest 20 ft. high and 20 ft. across, very bushy. They were obtained from Coombe Wood, where they had been raised from seed sent home by Wilson in 1901. Leaves obovate, 3 to 4½ ins. long, 2 to 3 ins. wide; glabrous by late summer. Flowers pure white with the twelve sepals and petals 2 to 3 ins. long. It will develop probably about the same garden value as M. Kobus. I should be inclined to regard it as specifically distinct from the Caerhays tree.

M. stellata, *Maximowicz* (Plate 23)

(Bot. Mag., t. 6370; M. Halleana, *Hort.*)

A much-branched deciduous shrub of rounded, compact habit, 10 to 15 ft. high, usually half as much more in diameter; young bark very aromatic, at first silky hairy; winter buds shaggy. Leaves 2½ to 4 ins. long, narrow oblong or obovate, tapering at the base to a short stalk. Flowers fragrant, pure white at first changing to pink; produced on the naked shoots in March and April. Petals twelve to eighteen, more numerous than in any other magnolia; 1½ to 2 ins. long, narrowly oblong or strap-shaped, at first spreading, then reflexed. In var. ROSEA, *Veitch*, the flowers are rosy especially on first opening.

Native of Japan in the woods of Fujiyama; introduced to England about

1877. For small gardens this is the most desirable of all magnolias. Its only defect is that its delicate petals are very susceptible to injury by frost, or even excessive wind and rain. But it flowers most profusely, and the first crop of blossoms if destroyed is succeeded by others. It sets its flowers unfailingly, and flowers even when less than 1 foot high. An attractive picture is made by planting this shrub in a group and growing beneath it, thickly, the blue grape hyacinth (*Muscari comosum*). The two flower together. This magnolia is much benefited by an admixture of peat in the soil, even to the extent of one-third.

M. THOMPSONIANA, *Sargent*.

(M. glauca major, *Sims*; Bot. Mag., t. 2164)

About the year 1808 a Mr Thompson, then a nurseryman at Mile End, noticed a distinct plant amongst some of his seedlings of Magnolia virginiana. He propagated it and ultimately distributed it under the above name. It is now usually regarded as a hybrid between virginiana and tripetala, although there is much less evidence of tripetala than of virginiana. It is a shrub of loose, ungainly habit, producing very vigorous unbranched growths of great length in one season. The leaves are 4 to 10 ins. long, very glaucous beneath, and otherwise similar to those of M. virginiana. The flowers are creamy white, much larger and less globular than those of M. virginiana, the petals being from 2 to 3½ ins. long. I have not seen or heard of its producing seeds, but if it did and these were sown, the question of its hybrid or other origin would probably be settled.

M. TRIPETALA, *Linnæus*. UMBRELLA TREE

(M. umbrella, *Lamarck*)

A deciduous tree, 30 to 40 ft. high, with a wide-spreading, open head of branches. Leaves among the largest in the genus, usually 12 to 20 ins. long, and 6 to 10 ins. wide (sometimes still larger); broadly oblanceolate, acute, tapered at both ends, pubescent beneath when young, strongly ribbed; stalk 1 to 2 ins. long. Flowers produced in May and June, heavily and not agreeably scented. Petals six to nine, creamy white, 4 to 5 ins. long, 2 ins. wide (inner ones smaller). Fruit 4 ins. long, cone-shaped, of a fine rosy red; produced freely in this country, and very handsome; seeds scarlet.

Native of eastern N. America in the Allegheny region, from Pennsylvania southwards; introduced in 1752, and first flowered with Peter Collinson, 24th May 1760. Once the commonest and best known of American magnolias. It is called the "umbrella tree" from the pose of its radiating cluster of large decurved leaves produced at the apex of the shoots. From the other big-leaved American species it is distinguished by the tapering base of its leaves. As a fruit-bearing tree it is the handsomest of all the magnolias in this country. The finest specimen I know of is in the gardens at Sandon Hall, Weston, Stafford, which has a main trunk 9 ft. 9 ins. in girth near the ground, and is about 25 ft. high and through. There is another at Hartlebury Rectory, Kidderminster, whose trunk is 6 ft. in girth at 1 ft. from the ground.

M. VEITCHII, *Bean*

A deciduous tree probably 30 to 40 ft. high eventually; young wood purplish, clothed at first with appressed hairs, becoming brown the second year. Leaves obovate or oblong, mostly rounded at the base, shortly and abruptly pointed; 6 to 12 ins. long, 3 to 7 ins. wide; dark green when mature but purplish (especially beneath) when young; midrib and chief veins clothed with grey down; stalk ¾ to 1 in. long, downy. Flowers 6 ins. long, blush pink, opening in April on the naked twigs, each borne on a short thick stalk; sepals and petals nine, 1½ to 2 ins. wide, rounded and broadest towards the apex, tapered at the base; stamens ½ in. long. Fruit not seen.

A hybrid between M. Campbellii and M. denudata, raised by the late Mr Peter C. M. Veitch of the Royal Nurseries, Exeter, who made the cross in 1907, the seed-bearer being M. denudata. It first flowered in 1917. The hybrid is very vigorous in growth and has noble foliage; moreover it is quite hardy. I first saw the blooms in April 1919, and was much impressed by their beauty. A tree at Bodnant, N. Wales, is over 20 ft. high.

Five plants were raised from the original crossing in 1907, four of which bore creamy white flowers. It is the fifth, with pink blossom showing the influence of the pollen parent, M. Campbellii, to which the name Veitchii was given. It was a creditable achievement to have hybridised two such fine magnolias.

M. VIRGINIANA, *Linnæus*. SWEET BAY

(M. glauca, *Linnæus*)

A shrub or small tree in Great Britain, but said to be occasionally 50 ft. high in its native localities. Leaves oval or oblong, sometimes obovate, 2½ to 5 ins. long, scarcely half as wide; often blunt at the apex; lustrous green and glabrous above, blue white and downy beneath, especially when young. Flowers globular, 2 to 3 ins. wide, delightfully scented; produced in no great numbers, but continuously, on leafy shoots, from June to September. Petals oblong or slightly obovate, 1½ to 2 ins. long, at first creamy white, becoming deeper with age. The fruit develops indifferently in this country, but in the eastern United States the fine red cones produce a bright effect. This magnolia varies in the persistence of its leaves; and of two trees at Kew, growing within a few yards of each other, one retains some of its foliage all the winter, the other, var. DECIDUA, is quite deciduous.

Native of the eastern United States from Massachusetts to Florida, often in swampy places. It was one of the early introductions from America, and is known to have been cultivated by Bishop Compton at Fulham Palace Gardens before the end of the seventeenth century. It is a most charming plant, readily distinguished by its comparatively small leaves, vividly glaucous beneath (but see also M. Thompsoniana). It is, or has been, valued in medicine for its tonic and diaphoretic properties.

M. WATSONII, *Hooker fil.*

A deciduous shrub or small tree of stiff habit. Leaves obovate, 4 to 8 ins. long, tapering at the base to a stalk ¼ to 1 in. long, apex blunt, dark green above, rather glaucous and finely downy beneath. Flower 5 to 6 ins. across, with a strong aromatic odour. Petals obovate, the inner ones ivory-white, outer ones tinged with rose; stamens crimson, forming a conspicuous mass of rich colour across the centre of the flower. Flower-stalks stout, about 1 in. long.

This magnolia is probably a hybrid and M. obovata and M. parviflora have been suggested as its parents. It first appeared in Europe at the Paris Exposition of 1889, when it was exhibited in the Japanese Court. Like many imported Japanese plants, those originally introduced were badly grafted, and many of them died; the shrub thereby got the reputation of being difficult to manage. It thrives admirably when once established, and flowers freely in June and July on leafy shoots. It is quite hardy at Kew, and in Devonshire is already 20 ft. high. Often confused with M. parviflora, this species is readily distinguished by its shorter-stalked, larger flowers, and by the larger, more leathery leaves, with ten to fifteen pairs of nerves.

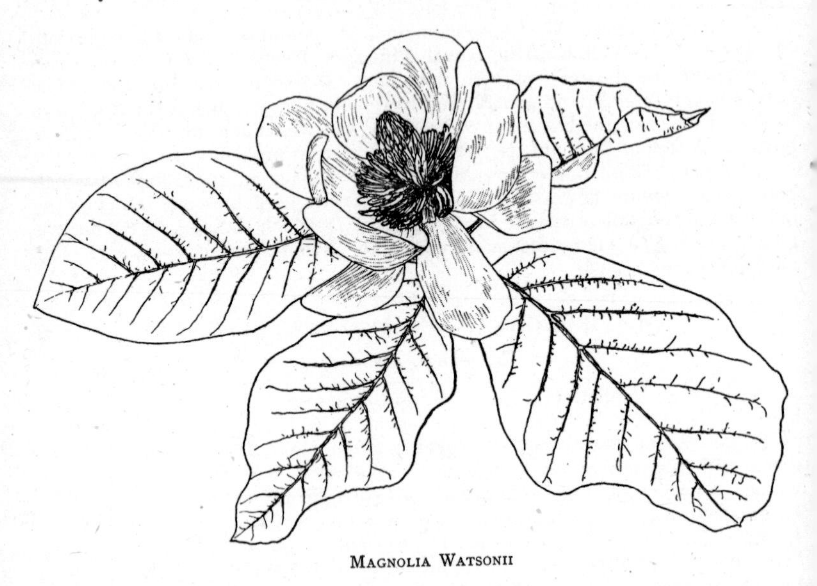

MAGNOLIA WATSONII

M. WILSONII, *Rehder*

(Bot. Mag., t. 9004; M. Nicholsoniana, *Rehder*; M. taliensis, *W. W. Smith*)

A deciduous shrub or small tree up to 25 ft. high, the slender young shoots clothed at first thickly with pale brown felt; glabrous and purplish brown the second year. Leaves ovate-lanceolate to narrowly oval; pointed at the apex; rounded, tapered, or slightly cordate at the base; 3 to 6 ins. long, nearly half as much wide; dull green and soon glabrous above, velvety beneath with a dense coating of pale-brown wool; leaf-stalk ½ to 1½ ins. long, woolly, marked midway by a scar. Flowers white, 3 to 4 ins. wide, cup-shaped, pendulous, fragrant, developing in May and June with the young foliage, each on a woolly stalk 1 to 1½ ins. long. Sepals and petals usually nine, incurved, the largest obovate, rounded at the top, 2½ ins. long, 1¾ ins. wide. Stamens numerous, ½ in. long, rich red. Fruit cylindric-ovoid, 2 to 3 ins. long, 1 in. wide, purplish pink; seeds scarlet-coated.

Native of W. Szechuen, China, at 7000 to 8500 ft. altitude; discovered by Wilson in 1904, introduced in 1908. This magnolia is one of the most beautiful of Wilson's introductions. The finest example in cultivation is at Caerhays in Cornwall, where I have seen it in flower several times in May. It is there a small tree of open habit over 20 ft. high and bears scores of its pure white blossoms, each with its conspicuous ring of crimson stamens. The height of this tree enables one to appreciate the beauty of the pendulous flowers to the full extent from the ground, and it is difficult to imagine one more lovely. It is related to M. parviflora and M. sinensis, both of which have more abruptly pointed leaves. At Kew it is hardy, but never seems likely to get beyond the shrubby state, and it is frequently injured there by late spring frosts. It prefers a semi-shaded spot. There appear to be two forms in cultivation, one with larger, broader leaves and larger flowers than the other, and they vary also in the amount of pubescence beneath the leaf.

MAHOBERBERIS NEUBERTI. *C. K. Schneider*

(Berberis ilicifolia—of gardens, not of *Forster*)

An evergreen, or partially evergreen shrub, of loose, open habit, 4 to 6 ft. high. Leaves very variable; sometimes simple, obovate, 1½ to 3 ins. long, with fine marginal teeth like those of Berberis vulgaris; others stiff, hard, and holly-like, with a few large spiny teeth resembling the leaflets of Mahonia; others trifoliolate or pinnate. Flowers and fruits not seen.

A hybrid between Mahonia Aquifolium (the seed-bearer) and Berberis vulgaris, which appeared in Baumann's once famous nursery at Bolwiller, in Alsace, about 1850. It has but little to recommend it as a garden plant, being in my experience a sterile, flowerless mule. As a scientific curiosity it is interesting, for it unites the two sections of the genus, although remarkably distinct from either of its parents. The form with spiny-toothed leaves like holly is usually and erroneously called "ilicifolia" in nurseries.

MAHONIA. BERBERIDACEÆ

A genus of evergreen shrubs very closely related to Berberis and often united with it. They are very distinct in their invariably evergreen character, in their simply pinnate foliage and in the absence of spines from their branches. The genus contains some very handsome species, the usually prickly-margined leaves being dark and shining. They are not generally so hardy as the true barberries, but those that are hardy are amongst the handsomest of evergreens. All thrive in a good loamy soil. The generic name commemorates Bernard M'Mahon, an American horticulturist who died in 1816. Some fifty species are known.

M. AQUIFOLIUM, *Nuttall*. OREGON GRAPE

(Bot. Reg., t. 1425; Berberis Aquifolium, *Pursh*)

An evergreen shrub reaching a height of 6 ft., but as commonly seen usually 2 to 3 ft. high. Stems spineless, but little branched, spreading by underground suckers; bark grey-brown, glabrous. Leaves 6 to 12 ins. long, pinnate, consisting of five to nine leaflets, which are stalkless, or nearly so, of variable shape, but usually broadly and (except the terminal one) obliquely ovate; 1½ to 3½ ins. long, glossy dark green, turning purplish in winter; the apex and margin set with slender, spiny teeth. Racemes erect, produced in a crowded group from just beneath the terminal bud, each 2 to 3 ins. long, thickly set with golden yellow, slender-stalked flowers. The first flowers begin to open in February, or in mild seasons even earlier, but the great flowering time is April and May. Berries very abundant and ornamental, black, but covered with a fine violet-coloured bloom.

Native of western N. America from Vancouver Island southwards;

introduced in 1823. For some time after that date it remained very expensive, costing as much as ten pounds per plant, but in 1837 the price had been reduced to five shillings. Prior to 1914 small plants could be obtained for thirty shillings per thousand. Few evergreen shrubs introduced from abroad have proved so valuable in British gardens as this. It is very hardy; I have seen it thriving on the bleak elevations of the Yorkshire wolds. For forming a low evergreen covering for the ground in moderately shaded positions, such as beneath deciduous trees, there is no evergreen so beautiful and so thriving as this. It is also admirable for planting as a groundwork for flowering shrubs that are leafless when in blossom, like the forsythias and Jasminum nudiflorum. It is not particular as to soil. Easily increased by seed, but an abundance of plants can be obtained by dividing the old plants in spring and planting the pieces on a gentle hot-bed.

Raised from seed it varies to a considerable extent, and names have been given to several varieties. It appears also to have hybridised with other W. American species like M. pinnata (Berberis fascicularis) and M. repens, as is shown by the dull glaucous-leaved forms seen in gardens, very different from the polished dark green of the type.

Var. LATIFOLIA and MACROPHYLLA have much larger, broader leaves than ordinary.

Var. MURRAYANA.—Leaflets dull green, shorter, broader and more wavy than those of the type; perhaps a hybrid with M. repens.

Var. ROTUNDIFOLIA HERVEYI.—Leaflets often in threes, large and broad, the plant forming a low tuft. Probably a hybrid with M. repens.

M. FORTUNEI, *Fedde*. FORTUNE'S BARBERRY

(Berberis Fortunei, *Lindley*)

An evergreen shrub, 5 to 6 ft. high, with erect, unbranching stems. Leaves 6 to 8 ins. long, pinnate, consisting usually of seven leaflets, which are linear-lanceolate, taper gradually to both ends, and are 3 to 4 ins. long, and about ½ in. wide; margins except towards the base set with forward-pointing teeth; under-surface marked with prominent, netted veins. Flowers yellow, densely crowded on narrow, cylindrical racemes 2 to 3 ins. long, erect. Blossoming in late autumn (October and November), the species rarely develops fruit in this country.

Robert Fortune found this shrub cultivated in a nursery at Shanghai, and introduced it in 1846. It has since been found wild in several parts of China. It is rather tender, and will not thrive in the open ground at Kew. In milder districts it grows quite well, as in Canon Ellacombe's garden at Bitton, near Bath, where it used to flower annually in October. It is distinct from all the other pinnate-leaved barberries in the narrow, dull green leaflets, and in the slender racemes, less than ½ in. in diameter; but is one of the least effective.

M. FREMONTII, *Fedde*. FREMONT'S BARBERRY

(Berberis Fremontii, *Torrey*)

An evergreen shrub, 3 to 12 ft. high, with pinnate leaves composed of five or seven leaflets of a vividly glaucous colour. Leaflets ¾ to 1¼ ins. long, spine-tipped, and with one or more spiny teeth at each side; the terminal leaflet is stalked and ovate to lanceolate, the others sessile and shorter. Flowers yellow, and produced four to eight together towards the end of a raceme 2 to 3 ins. in length; each flower on a slender stalk ½ to ¾ in. long. Fruit blue, becoming dry and inflated at maturity, enclosing six to eight seeds.

Native of the hot, dry, south-western United States (Texas, Arizona, etc.). A striking and handsome species, but too tender for the open ground except n the milder counties. It may be grown on a south wall, and, wherever ultivated, should be given the sunniest position available. The only species in ultivation likely to be confused with this is M. trifoliolata, which has leaflets of the same form and very glaucous hue, but only three of them to each leaf.

M. HÆMATOCARPA, *Fedde*

(B. hæmatocarpa, *Wooton*)

An evergreen shrub from 6 to 12 ft. high in a wild state; young shoots glabrous, eventually grey. Leaves pinnate, $1\frac{1}{2}$ to 4 ins. long, made up of three o nine leaflets. Leaflets oval, ovate, or lanceolate, with three to five spine-tipped teeth at each side and a slender spine-tipped apex; $\frac{1}{2}$ to $1\frac{3}{4}$ ins. ong, $\frac{1}{4}$ to $\frac{5}{8}$ in. wide; of a conspicuous glaucous hue and quite glabrous; all except the terminal leaflet stalkless. Flowers pale yellow, $\frac{1}{4}$ in. wide, produced n slender-stalked racemes 1 to $1\frac{1}{2}$ ins. long, carrying about six flowers. Fruit blood-red, globose, $\frac{1}{4}$ to $\frac{1}{3}$ in. wide.

Native of western N. America in the States of New Mexico, Colorado, and California; introduced to Kew in 1916. In general appearance this species bears a strong resemblance to M. Fremontii. It is, nevertheless, very distinct from that species in its rich red fruits. It has not been affected by cold up to the present. As sunny a position as possible should be allotted to it. It seems disinclined to branch and makes slender erect shoots densely furnished with eaves. The fruits are used for making jam in its native country, but our climate is doubtless too dull for it to bear them freely enough to be of any value in that respect here.

Mahonia Swaseyi, *Fedde*, is a species from Texas also with red fruits and closely related to the foregoing. It is distinguished by having broadly ovate bracts up to $\frac{1}{3}$ in. long on the flower-stalk (see also M. Nevinii).

M. JAPONICA, *De Candolle*. JAPANESE MAHONIA

(Berberis japonica, *R. Brown*)

An evergreen shrub of very stiff, sturdy, erect habit; its thick, unbranched stems, 10 ft. or perhaps more high, bearing a few leaves at the top. Leaves 1 to $1\frac{1}{2}$ ft. long, composed of seven, nine, eleven, or thirteen leaflets, which are 2 to 5 ins. long, $1\frac{1}{2}$ to $3\frac{1}{2}$ ins. wide, obliquely ovate, very hard and stiff; dark dull green, armed on each margin with four to six large spiny teeth; the lowest and smallest pair situated at, or very close to, the base of the leaf-stalk (a good distinction from M. nepaulensis). Flowers lemon-yellow, delightfully fragrant, borne in a cluster of numerous slender, erect racemes 6 to 9 ins. long, terminating the stem; the fragrance resembles that of the lily of the valley. Berries oblong, as much as $\frac{1}{2}$ in. long, purple.

Var. BEALEI.—A distinct variety of great vigour, the leaflets larger, broader, more rounded, and with fewer spines; the bases of each pair often overlap. The racemes also are finer, the flower-stalks shorter. It is the most striking of all the mahonias, the leaflets being sometimes 8 ins. long and 6 ins. wide. Introduced from China in 1845, by Fortune, who regarded it as a distinct species; it was figured as Berberis Bealei in the *Botanical Magazine*, t. 4852.

These two mahonias, with others of an intermediate character, are the most striking of all the group to which they belong. Their flower-clusters commence to open in February, and continue in beauty for several weeks. Allied to M. nepaulensis, M. japonica is readily distinguished in its typical form by its duller leaves, having the lowest pair of leaflets close to the base of th leaf-stalk. The variety Bealei is much hardier, and will thrive (as at Kew where M. nepaulensis fails. It should, all the same, be given a sheltered spot and settled in its permanent position as early as possible, for few shrubs suffe more from transplanting. This operation may be successfully done during showery time in May.

Var. GRACILLIMA is described as having smaller leaflets than the type—about 2 ins. long and ¾ in. wide—but I do not know that it is in cultivation in Britain.

M. LOMARIIFOLIA, *Takeda*

(Bot. Mag., t. 9634)

An evergreen shrub 8 to 12 ft. high; stems erect. Leaves pinnate, 10 to 24 ins. long, carrying 9½ to 18½ pairs of leaflets, each leaflet 1½ to 4 ins. long usually ½ to 1 in. wide, stalkless, linear-lanceolate, oblique at the base, more or less incurved towards the apex, the margins and apex spiny-toothed, stiff leathery, glabrous. Flowers fragrant, bright yellow, densely crowded on erect cylindrical spikes 4 to 8 ins. long by 1 in. wide, which are clustered as many as eighteen or twenty together at the apex of the shoots; petals oblong, about ¼ in. long, the apex rounded and notched. Fruit oval, ⅖ in. long, blue-black.

Native of Burma, W. China, and possibly also of Formosa, where several mahonias grow which may be forms of M. lomarifolia but have not yet been thoroughly studied. Major Johnston of Hidcote Manor, Gloucestershire originally introduced the species to cultivation by means of seeds he collected near Tengueh, Yunnan, in 1931. He raised plants and distributed them from his garden at Menton. This is probably the handsomest of the mahonias, but is not perfectly hardy except in the maritime counties to the south and west

Sometimes, as seen wild, it is 30 to 40 ft. high, its erect trunk and stems each carrying a tuft of foliage at the summit. Its time of flowering seems to be variable. A plant in bloom was given an Award of Merit at Vincent Square on 24th May 1938, and a First Class Certificate on 24th October 1939.

M. NEPAULENSIS, *De Candolle*

(Berberis nepalensis, *Sprengel*)

An evergreen shrub, sometimes 20 ft. high in the Himalaya, but rarely more than one-third as high in Britain. Leaves with as many as twenty-five leaflets, usually about fifteen. Leaflets dark glossy green, obliquely ovate, lanceolate, 1½ to 4½ ins. long, the lowest pair broader and shorter than the others, spine-toothed, of firm, leathery texture. Flowers yellow, borne in slender racemes 6 to 12 ins. long. Berries oval or nearly globose, about ¼ in. diameter, covered with blue-white bloom.

Native of the Himalaya, this barberry is too tender to thrive well except in the milder parts of Britain, or in exceptionally sheltered spots. At Kew it lives but a short time out-of-doors, although it succeeded well in a sheltered spot in the gardens of Belvoir Castle for a good many years. It has by some authorities been united with M. japonica, but is sufficiently distinguished by its more numerous, smaller, even-sized and more tapering leaflets, and the brilliantly polished upper surface. For the milder counties it is a most desirable shrub, commencing to flower as early as October, but at its best in March and April. Several forms of it exist, some of which approach M. japonica.

M. NERVOSA, *Nuttall*

(Berberis nervosa, *Pursh*; Bot. Mag., t. 3949. B. glumacea, *Sprengel*)

A low, suckering evergreen shrub, with stems rarely more than 12 or 15 ins. high, and handsome pinnate leaves up to 18 ins. long, composed of usually eleven to fifteen leaflets. Leaflets stalkless, 1½ to 3 ins. long, obliquely ovate, very firm and leathery in texture, prominently three-veined beneath, the margins armed with large, spiny teeth. Racemes erect, 8 ins. or even more in length, with short-stalked, yellow flowers. Fruit roundish oblong, ¼ in. diameter, purplish blue.

Native of western N. America, especially of the State of Washington; introduced in 1822. It is a handsome and striking barberry, but does not appear to thrive very well in this country generally; it always has been and still remains rare. It can be propagated by suckers. The foliage most nearly resembles that of M. nepaulensis, but M. nervosa is readily distinguished by its dwarf habit, and the greater distance of the lowest pair of leaflets from the base of the common leaf-stalk.

M. NEVINII, *Fedde*

(Berberis Nevinii, *Gray*)

An evergreen shrub up to 7 or 8 ft. high; young shoots slender, purplish. Leaves pinnate, 2 to 2½ ins. long; leaflets usually five, sometimes three or seven, the lowest pair very close to the stem; they are of hard texture, glaucous, glabrous; ¾ to 1½ ins. long, ¼ to ⅜ in. wide; oblong-lanceolate, rounded at the base, tapered to a slender spine-tipped apex; margins set with needle-like spines. Flowers bright yellow, ¼ in. wide, produced about seven together in racemes ¾ to 1½ ins. long; stalks slender, glabrous. Fruit egg-shaped, juicy, black, covered with abundant white bloom.

This mahonia was discovered by a Mr Nevin on a sandy plain near Los Angeles, California, and originally named after him in 1895. It is figured in *Garden and Forest*, vol. ix., p. 415, and is there described as "exceedingly rare . . . handsome and distinct." Introduced to this country in 1928, it was first flowered by Mr T. Hay in Hyde Park in March 1931. It is closely related to M. hæmatocarpa, but the red fruits of that species well distinguish it. To the black-fruited M. Fremontii it is also allied, but that species has leaflets broader in proportion to their length, with marginal teeth larger and fewer, and venation more distinctly marked. M. Nevinii has survived several winters in the open air at Kew, but would evidently prefer a sunny spot on the south coast.

M. PINNATA, *Fedde*

(Berberis pinnata, *Lagasca*; B. fascicularis, *Sims*, Bot. Mag., t. 2396).

This very distinct mahonia has been regarded by some authorities as a variety of M. Aquifolium, but there is little doubt that it deserves to rank as a species. In stature alone it is very different, for in favourable situations it is 12 to 16 ft. high. A beautiful specimen stands near the entrance door to the vicarage at Bitton, 12 ft. high, and a still taller one in Phœnix Park, Dublin, is 16 ft. In foliage it differs in being of a dull greyish green, and in the narrower leaflets numbering sometimes thirteen to each leaf. There are also two tiny bracts on the pedicels, absent in M. Aquifolium. Flowers yellow, produced in erect racemes about 3 ins. long, not confined to the top, but developed also down the stem.

Native of western N. America (California, New Mexico, etc.), and thus having a more southern distribution than M. Aquifolium; introduced in 1819. It is not so hardy as M. Aquifolium, but thrives well at Kew, being one of the most desirable of the mahonia group. Very fragrant in blossom.

M. REPENS, *G. Don*. CREEPING BARBERRY

(Berberis repens, *Lindley*, Bot. Reg., t. 1776)

An evergreen shrub of dwarf, stiff habit, usually less than 1 ft. high, spreading by underground stems. Leaves pinnate, consisting of three, five, or seven leaflets, which are ovate, pointed, 1 to 2½ ins. long, spine-toothed, of a dull bluish green. Racemes 1½ to 3 ins. long, produced in a cluster at the end of the branch. Flowers deep yellow, open in April and May. Fruit black, ¼ in. wide, covered with a blue bloom.

Native of western N. America; originally discovered during the famous expedition under Lewis and Clarke, who crossed the North American continent for the first time, 1804-1806. It ought to be useful in positions where a close evergreen covering is desired, but it has never been extensively grown. It can be propagated by removing the creeping shoots, but has never adapted itself to our conditions as M. Aquifolium has, for instance. From that species it differs markedly in its dull bluish foliage, which also shows itself in some hybrids between the two species. It is quite distinct from M. nervosa which has glossy foliage, and twice as many leaflets.

M. TOLUACENSIS, *Hort*.

(Berberis toluacensis, *Hort.*, Mahonia heterophylla, *C. K. Schneider*)

In the *Gardeners' Chronicle* for 1868, p. 435, there is a note, headed by the name given above, in which the writer asks if anything is known of the shrub so-called, beyond that it was said to come from Mexico. The editors were unable to give any information. The shrub is still in cultivation and is offered by a few nurserymen. It is an evergreen shrub, 3 to 6 ft. high, glabrous in all its parts; young shoots purplish. Leaves pinnate, 6 to 12 ins. long, composed usually of five or seven leaflets. Leaflets lanceolate or narrowly oblong, often unequal-sided; 1 to 3½ ins. long, ¼ to ¾ in. wide; each margin set with one to ten slender teeth or sometimes entire; shining green on both sides; stalk of leaflets slender, up to 1 in. long or almost stalkless.

Judging from the name, it is possible this mahonia was found near, or was sent to England from, Toluca in Mexico, where mahonias are known to have been collected. I have not seen the plant in flower. The leaflets are usually curiously twisted or even curled and their stalks vary much in length. It is perhaps most nearly related to Mahonia arguta, *Hutchinson*. There is or used to be a plant 6 ft. high growing against a wall at Glasnevin.

M. TRIFOLIOLATA, *Fedde*. MEXICAN BARBERRY

(Berberis trifoliolata, *Moricand*, Bot. Reg., Vol. 31, t. 10)

An erect, rigid shrub, 6 or 8 ft. high, with only three leaflets to each leaf. Leaflets glaucous or almost white, shaped like a spear-head; 1 to 2 ins. long, ¼ to ⅗ in. wide; tapering to a long, spine-tipped point, and bulging at each side into one or two spine-tipped lobes. Flowers yellow, borne in short corymbs. Fruit oval or roundish, black with a blue bloom.

This rare shrub comes from rocky hills in New Mexico, and is only hardy against a sunny wall, or in exceptionally mild districts. Some years ago I aw an old bush, 8 ft. high, growing against the house wall at Bayfordbury. The species differs from all other mahonias in cultivation in the vividly glaucous-white leaves with only three leaflets.

MALLOTUS JAPONICUS, *Mueller*. EUPHORBIACEÆ

(Rottlera japonica, *Sprengel*)

A deciduous shrub, 10 or 12 ft. high, with very pithy young wood, covered at first with minute specks of white starry down. Leaves like hose of a catalpa, ovate, rounded or broadly tapered at the base, gradually tapered at the apex to a long slender point; they vary much n size, the largest being 9 or 10 ins. long by 6 ins. wide; the smallest less han one-third those dimensions; at first they are clothed with down like hat on the shoots, but this soon falls away, leaving them nearly or quite glabrous; the lower surface is specked with minute, transparent glands. Flowers small, crowded on erect, terminal, pyramidal panicles, 3 to 6 ins. high; they have little beauty, being small and covered with white down. Males and females occur on separate plants.

Native of Japan and Central China. The best plant I have seen was n Mrs Chambers' garden at Haslemere, where it flowered in autumn. It s only worth growing for its handsome foliage.

MALUS. CRAB. ROSACEÆ

A genus of some twenty-five to thirty deciduous trees, including a few shrubs, spread thinly over the north temperate parts of Europe, N. America, and Asia. They differ from true Pyrus, with which they were long generically united, by their styles being united at the base—free in Pyrus proper. The fruits also vary in shape from rounded to ovoid, but not pear-shaped. Flowers usually in umbel-like clusters, white to various shades of pink or purplish; stamens fifteen to fifty, anthers usually yellow.

As ornamental trees, and especially in regard to flower, the crabs rank first among all the groups of the old genus Pyrus. In all the range of flowering trees and shrubs there is nothing more beautiful and effective than the best of this group, such as M. floribunda, Scheideckeri, spectabilis, etc. In regard to fruit also it includes some particularly valuable species, such as M. baccata, M. prunifolia, M. Sargentii, etc. The Malus group is peculiarly liable to attacks of the white woolly aphis, known as "American blight," and scale insects. A winter dressing of the caustic soda wash should be applied, and in summer a spraying with an emulsion of paraffin and soap. So far as I am aware, there s no hybrid between this group and any other of the sections of the old genus Pyrus, and the fact that it will not intergraft with them seems to show that a greater gap separates it from them than the older botanists imagined, and that there are good grounds for treating it as a distinct genus. The various members have hybridised with each other very freely, so that with many one cannot rely on seeds reproducing the parent exactly. The following species, for instance, are all linked together by a series of hybrids: baccata, prunifolia, pumila, and Sieboldii. Some, probably most of them, can be rooted from cuttings made of leafless shoots in early winter, and put in a cold frame, but most of them are increased by grafting on the various crab and apple stocks used in nurseries for garden apples.

M. ANGUSTIFOLIA, *Michaux*

(Pyrus angustifolia, *Aiton*)

A small tree, semi-evergreen in mild winters, 20 ft. or more high; shoots glabrous except when quite young. Leaves oval or oblong, sometimes lanceolate; 1 to 3 ins. long, ½ to 1¾ ins. wide; dark shining green above, paler beneath, and nearly or quite glabrous when fully grown; base usually tapering, margins coarsely toothed, especially towards the apex. On the flowering twigs the leaves are small, 1 to 1½ ins. long, oblong, and entire, or with a few teeth only towards the apex. Flowers fragrant like violets, rosy or almost white, 1 to 1¼ ins. across, produced usually in clusters of four; each flower on a slender stalk, 1 to 1½ ins. long; calyx teeth white, woolly inside. Fruit ¾ in. across, yellowish green, fragrant, harsh, acid.

Native of eastern N. America; introduced, according to Aiton, in 1750. The true plant was evidently known to Loudon, but it had disappeared from cultivation until a few years ago, when it was reintroduced from the United States. It is closely allied to M. coronaria, and has been regarded as a variety of it. It has, however, a more southern distribution in a wild state, and is quite distinct in the shape of its leaves, which are only about half as wide in proportion to their length, and have wedge-shaped bases. The tree known in cultivation as "M. angustifolia plena" is a double-flowered variety of another closely allied species—M. ioensis—distinguished from this and M. coronaria by the persistently woolly leaves.

M. ARNOLDIANA, *Sargent*

(M. floribunda × baccata)

This beautiful crab originated in the Arnold Arboretum, Mass., where it appeared amongst some seedlings of M. floribunda and was first distinguished about 1905. Sargent suggests that it is probably a hybrid between floribunda and one of the garden forms of M. baccata. A plant obtained for Kew in 1912 has proved to be a very charming addition to its group. In habit it is extremely graceful, producing as it does long arching or semi-pendulous shoots which, when young, are redder than those of M. floribunda. The foliage is similar but of larger average size. The flowers are more than half as large again and are about 1¼ ins. wide. In the bud state the petals are a rich ruby red, paling with age to deep rose outside and pale rose inside. As with M. floribunda the beauty of the tree is greatest when half the flowers are still in the bud state. Flower-stalk 1½ to 2 ins. long, reddish; lobes of the calyx awl-shaped, ¼ in. long; both are nearly glabrous (downy in floribunda). Fruits egg-shaped, ¾ in. long, tapering to the flat apex which is marked with the scars of the fallen calyx, pale yellow, changing finally to dull red. Blooms in April.

M. BACCATA, *Borkhausen*. SIBERIAN CRAB (Plate 24)

(Pyrus baccata, *Linnæus*; Bot. Mag., t. 6112)

A tree 20 to 40 ft. high, forming a rounded, wide-spreading head of branches, the lower ones arching or pendulous at the extremities; trunk 1 to 2 ft. in diameter. Leaves $1\frac{1}{2}$ to $3\frac{1}{2}$ ins. long, about half as much wide; oval or ovate, rounded or tapering at the base, shallowly and bluntly toothed; glabrous above, and either glabrous or downy beneath; stalks slender, 1 to 2 ins. long. Flowers white, produced during April in umbels; each flower $1\frac{1}{2}$ ins. across, and borne on a slender stalk 1 to $1\frac{1}{2}$ ins. long. Fruit $\frac{3}{4}$ to $\frac{7}{8}$ in. thick, globular, bright red, hollowed at the insertion of the stalk, and with a round scar, but no calyx teeth at the top.

Widely spread in nature, this species reaches from Lake Baikal in Siberia, eastwards to Manchuria and N. China, and the same or a similar tree is found in the Himalaya. Introduced to Kew in 1784. It varies considerably in the downiness of the various parts. Some of the trees in the Kew collection have glabrous young shoots, leaves, calyx-tube, and flower-stalks; others have all these parts downy. The lobes of the calyx appear to be invariably silky-hairy inside. As a tree for gardens the Siberian crab stands in the first rank. It is pretty in April when laden with its abundant white flowers, but its great value and charm are most apparent in autumn, when its plentiful crop of cherry-like crabs turns a brilliant red. They remain long on the leafless branches, and I have seen them lighting up the garden on fine days as late as February. This tree is closely allied to M. prunifolia, but the fruit of the latter is more elongated, not indented at the base, and nearly always crowned with the calyx teeth. The late Dr Regel, about thirty years ago, sent seeds to Kew of about a dozen varieties with names, but when the trees flowered and bore fruit they proved indistinguishable. The fruit of M. baccata, although harsh when eaten raw, makes a very excellent jelly.

Var. MICROCARPA, *Regel*.—Fruit about half the size of those described above. Some regard this as the typical wild plant.

M. CORONARIA, *Miller*

(Pyrus coronaria, *Linnæus*; Bot. Mag., t. 2009)

A tree 20 to 30 ft. high, with a short trunk and a wide-spreading, open head of branches; young shoots downy the first summer. Leaves ovate to three-lobed, 2 to $4\frac{1}{2}$ ins. long, sometimes nearly as much wide, but usually 1 to $2\frac{1}{2}$ ins. wide, pointed, the base rounded or slightly heart-shaped, sometimes tapering; very soon quite glabrous on both surfaces; margins sharply, deeply, and irregularly toothed; stalk downy, 1 to $1\frac{1}{2}$ ins. long. Flowers white, tinged with rose, fragrant like violets, $1\frac{1}{2}$ to 2 ins. across, produced in clusters of four to six, each flower on a slender stalk, 1 to 2 ins. long. Fruit 1 to $1\frac{1}{2}$ ins. across, orange-shaped, yellowish green, very harsh and acid.

Native of eastern N. America; introduced in 1724, but not so common as one might expect from the beauty and fragrance of its flowers, which come in May and June—later than any other of the Malus group, except its two immediate allies. There are two American crabs closely allied to this species: they are M. angustifolia, with narrower leaves tapering at the base, and M. ioensis, in which the foliage is much more downy (and persistently so) beneath. The larger, broader leaves of M. coronaria frequently suggests those of our native Sorbus latifolia in shape. "M. coronaria plena" is a wrong name for M. ioensis plena, a very beautiful crab (*q.v.*).

M. Eleyi, *C. K. Schneider*. Eley Crab (Plate 25)

(Pyrus Eleyi, *Bean*; Gardeners' Chronicle, Vol. LXXII, fig. 37)

A hybrid crab raised by Mr Charles Eley of East Bergholt, Suffolk, from M. Niedzwetzkyana crossed with pollen of M. spectabilis. It is a deciduous tree, eventually no doubt 30 ft. high, its young shoots downy, both they and the leaves being reddish purple like those of the mother tree, but of a brighter and not so dark a hue. Leaves ovate, with a short, sharply pointed apex, rounded or wedge-shaped at the base, finely toothed; 2 to 4 ins. long, 1 to 2½ ins. wide; downy beneath especially on the dark purple midrib and veins; stalk dark purple, ½ to 1 in. long; stipules linear to awl-shaped, toothed, ¼ in. long. Flowers in apple-like clusters and of apple-blossom shape, each 1¼ ins. wide, of a rich vinous red. Fruit rich purplish red, conical, 1 in. long, ⅝ in. wide at the base, each on a slender stalk 1½ ins. long, the apex hollow when the calyx falls away.

M. aldenhamensis, raised by the late Hon. Vicary Gibbs at Aldenham, Herts, very much resembles M. Eleyi. Its fruits differ in being flattened globose, or orange-shaped, instead of conical; they are 1 in. wide, the calyx persists at the top and the stalks are thicker. The leaves are often slightly lobed, and their toothing is coarser and more uneven.

From the time the flowers open in April until the fall of the leaf in autumn these crabs are beautiful. Their charm is greatest when the thickly clustered, pendulous fruits have acquired their rich colour. They are also very attractive when in bloom in April and May.

M. Lemoinei, another hybrid from M. Niedzwetzkyana raised at Nancy, has bronzy purple foliage and dark crimson flowers. It was given an Award of Merit by the Royal Horticultural Society on 8th May 1928. It is perhaps the best of these Niedzwetzkyana hybrids.

M. florentina, *C. K. Schneider*

(Pyrus cratægifolia, *Savi*; Bot. Mag., t. 7423)

A bush or small tree of rounded habit, with slender, dark brown branches; branchlets woolly when young. Leaves rather hawthorn-like, 1½ to 2½ ins. long, ¾ to 1¾ ins. wide; broadly ovate in the main, but with the margins always cut up into several lobes which are themselves toothed; base rounded or heart-shaped; dark green above, with scattered hairs when young, paler and downy beneath; stalk downy, reddish, up to 1 in. long. Flowers pure white, about ¾ in. diameter, produced in June five to seven together on lax open corymbs 2 or 3 ins. across, each flower on a slender, downy, pinkish stalk 1 to 1¼ ins. long; calyx very woolly, the lobes narrow, pointed. Fruit roundish oval, ½ in. long, yellowish changing to red, the calyx fallen away.

Native of N. Italy, and very rare both in a wild state and in cultivation. There are few more charming small trees than this in June, the long, slender shoots of the previous summer being then clothed with abundant short twigs, each with its cluster of white flowers. The leaves are very similar in form to those of the wild service (Sorbus Torminalis) only much smaller. Its fruit is not particularly bright, but the foliage often turns a brilliant orange-scarlet before falling. It is very suitably placed as an isolated specimen on a lawn. Plants at Kew now 20 ft. high were introduced by the late Mr H. Groves from near Florence in 1886.

M. FLORIBUNDA, *Siebold* (Plate 26)

(Pyrus floribunda, *Kirchner*)

A tree ultimately 20 to 30 ft. high, with a spreading tangle of branches forming a rounded head wider than the tree is high; often shrubby; young shoots downy at first, becoming glabrous later. Leaves on the flowering and weaker shoots usually narrowly or broadly ovate, and from 1½ to 3 ins. long; rounded or tapering at the base, rather coarsely toothed; on strong shoots they are occasionally three- or five-lobed, 3 to 4½ ins. long, and half as wide; upper surface dark dullish green, glabrous; lower one paler and downy; stalk ½ to 1 in. long, downy. Flowers 1 to 1¼ ins. across, rosy red in bud, pale pink when open, produced in clusters of four to seven, each on a stalk 1 to 1½ ins. long. Fruit round, ¾ in. diameter, yellow, with the calyx fallen away.

Introduced from Japan about 1862, and perhaps the most beautiful of all crabs in flower. It blossoms towards the end of April, producing then an amazing profusion of flowers, each branch a garland. Perhaps its beauty is greatest when half the flowers are expanded, the pale pink contrasting with the rich rose of the other half still in bud. This crab is not considered to be a true wild species, but a hybrid from M. Sieboldii and perhaps M. baccata. The deeply three- or even five-lobed leaves occasionally seen on strong branches certainly indicate affinity with M. Sieboldii (*q.v.*). The largest tree I have seen is in the botanic garden at Herrenhausen, Hanover. In the summer of 1908 it was 35 ft. high, 42 ft. in diameter, its trunk girthing 4 ft. 3 ins.

Var. ATROSANGUINEA.—Flowers of a richer rose than the type, especially when fully open, otherwise similar. Foliage shining green.

M. HALLIANA, *Koehne*

(Pyrus Halliana, *Voss*; P. Parkmanni, *Hort.*)

A small tree, 12 to 18 ft. high; young branches purple, soon quite glabrous. Leaves ovate or oval, 1½ to 3 ins. long, half as wide, rounded or tapering at the base, rather long-pointed, slightly toothed; the midrib glandular and slightly hairy above, otherwise the leaf is quite glabrous on both surfaces and of a dark polished green above, often purple-tinted, especially on the midrib; stalk ½ in. or less long. Flowers deep rose, 1 to 1½ ins. across, from four to seven in a cluster, each flower on a glabrous, reddish purple stalk 1 to 1½ ins. long; petals five to eight; calyx reddish purple and glabrous outside, white-woolly within. Fruit round, purple, the size of a small pea, marked at the top with the scar of the fallen calyx.

Native of western Szechuen, China. It was first introduced to America from Japan about 1863 by Dr G. R. Hall, after whom it is named, but it does not appear ever to have been found wild there. It has some affinity with M. floribunda and has been known in gardens as "M.f. plena," the flowers being often semi-double. M. Halliana is abundantly distinct in habit, in the nearly glabrous character of its parts, and it never appears to have the deeply lobed leaves occasionally seen in floribunda. In my experience, M. Halliana is by no means so beautiful a flowering tree as M. floribunda.

M. IOENSIS, *Britton*. IOWA CRAB

(Pyrus ioensis, *Bailey*, Bot. Mag., t. 8488)

A tree of the same character as M. angustifolia and M. coronaria (*q.v.*), but differing in the much more downy branches, the down on which persists until the summer of the following year; side branchlets often spine-tipped.

Leaves ovate or oval, 3 to 4 ins. long, half or a little more than half as wide; persistently woolly beneath, coarsely toothed towards the apex. Flowers 1½ to 2 ins. across, white or rosy, four to six in a corymb; stalks 1 to 1½ ins. long, covered with white wool; calyx very woolly. Fruit 1¼ to 1½ ins. diameter, dull yellowish green.

As has already been stated under M. coronaria, this tree is one of a closely allied group of N. American crabs, but it has a more western habitat than the other two, being found in the Central United States. It differs from both its allies in the much more downy branchlets, leaves, and other young parts of the tree (a frequent characteristic in the most western forms of American trees).

Var. PLENA. The Bechtel Crab.—In the year 1891, Messrs Bechtel, of Stanton, Illinois, U.S.A., sent out this beautiful double-flowered crab under the name of "M. angustifolia plena." In the prevailing confusion as to the identity of these three species, it has also been called "M. coronaria plena." The individual flower, which on young healthy plants measures 2 to 2½ ins. across, is the finest of all the Malus group, the numerous petals being of a lovely delicate pink. With a delightful odour suggestive of violets, and coming into bloom in early June, this crab has a claim to recognition in every garden.

M. KANSUENSIS, *C. K. Schneider*

(Pyrus kansuensis, *Batalin*; Eriolobus kansuensis)

A deciduous shrub or small tree of bushy habit 10 to 25 ft. high; young shoots downy. Leaves ovate in main outline, but usually deeply three-lobed at the terminal part, sometimes five-lobed, the smaller leaves scarcely lobed; lobes slenderly pointed, toothed, often curved outwards, the base rounded or slightly heart-shaped; 1 to 3½ ins. long, ¾ to 2½ ins. wide; slightly downy at first on both surfaces, becoming nearly or quite glabrous; stalk ½ to 1½ ins. long. Flowers white, ½ to ¾ in. wide, produced four to ten in May in a terminal corymb 2 to 3 ins. wide; main and secondary flower-stalks downy; calyx-lobes awl-shaped, they and the tubular part clothed with pale hairs; stamens about twenty; styles three, united, glabrous or downy at the base only. Fruit scarlet, dotted, egg-shaped, ⅓ to ½ in. long, its stalk 1 to 2 ins. long, the calyx fallen away from the summit.

Native of Kansu, Hupeh, and Szechuen, China; introduced by Wilson in 1910 for the Arnold Arboretum, possibly before for Messrs Veitch. A tree raised from Wilson's number 4115 flowered at St Clere, Kemsing, Sevenoaks, in May 1919, and from a specimen received from there the above description was made—apart from the fruit. It is a handsome species with brightly coloured fruits, very distinct in the three-lobed leaves with three main veins at the base. It is allied to M. toringoides, which differs in the more pinnate lobing of the leaf and in having one or two more styles to each flower.

Var. CALVA, *Rehder*, differs from the type in having the flower-stalk and calyx devoid of down. Except for some down on the veins beneath, the leaves are also glabrous. A plant at Kew with creamy-yellow petals, received from Messrs Veitch in 1909 under Wilson's seed number 1097, appears to be this variety.

M. LANCIFOLIA, *Rehder*

(Pyrus lancifolia, *Bailey*)

A deciduous tree up to 25 ft. high with frequently spiny branches; young shoots at first woolly, soon glabrous. Leaves ovate or ovate-lanceolate, pointed, usually rounded at the base, those on the barren shoots larger, broader, more strongly toothed than on the flowering shoots; 1½ to 3½ ins. long, 1¼ to 3 ins. wide; woolly beneath when young, soon becoming almost glabrous; stalk to 1 in. long. Flowers 1¼ to 1½ ins. wide, produced in May in clusters of ree to six each on a glabrous, slender stalk 1 to 1¼ ins. long. Fruit roundish, in. wide, green.

Native of the United States (Missouri, Illinois, etc.); introduced to ltivation in 1912. It belongs to the same group of crabs as M. coronaria, I. angustifolia, and M. ioensis; ioensis is easily recognised by the often bed, very downy leaves. From the other two Prof. Bailey notes that lancifolia distinguished by its acuminate, less leathery leaves, by the longer calyx-lobes nd by the styles being woolly below the middle. Like its allies it is an ornaental flowering tree with larger flowers than is usual amongst crabs in general. he specific name is more applicable to the leaves of the flowering shoots than those of the barren ones.

M. MAGDEBURGENSIS, *Schoch*

A very handsome hybrid crab raised in Germany about the end of last entury from M. spectabilis crossed with some form of M. pumila and therefore robably of the same origin as M. micromalus or M. Kaido, but even finer. he Magdeburg crab has a rather erect habit and bears in May dense clusters f "double" flowers, each about 1 in. wide, the numerous petals of a lovely eep rose outside, paler towards the base and inside. Fruit sub-globose, ellowish, about 1 in. wide.

M. NIEDZWETZKANA, *Dieck*

(M. pumila Niedzwetzkyana; Pyrus Niedz., *Hemsley*; Bot. Mag., t. 7975)

A small tree of about the size and character of the ordinary apple; young ark reddish purple. Leaves 3 to 5 ins. long, 2 to 2½ ins. wide; ovate or oval, ound-toothed, downy all over the lower surface when young, afterwards on ie midrib only; stalk downy, ¾ to 1½ ins. long. The stalk and midrib are right red, the blade also is of a decided red tinge when young, becoming urplish later in the season. Flowers in apple-like clusters, deep red-purple, ½ ins. across; flower-stalks ½ to ¾ in. long and, like the calyx, covered with hitish wool. Fruit conical, with a few broad grooves running lengthwise; ins. long, of a deep vinous red.

I do not think this tree can be considered anything more than a variety of I. pumila. Some years ago five seedlings from it were raised at Kew, and f these, three came as green in branch and leaf as the ordinary apple, and ie flowers were merely pink—not the beautiful red which makes this one of ie most striking of its group. This would seem to show that it is only a olour sport from M. pumila. It was introduced to cultivation by Dr Dieck, f Zoeschen, in Germany, who states that it is abundant in S.W. Siberia and the aucasus. The fruit is not of high quality as we know apples, being of rather urnip-like consistency. So completely is the tree permeated with red colouring natter that the young wood, when cut, shows red right through, as does also ie fruit. Introduced to England in 1894.

M. PRATTII, *C. K. Schneider*

(Pyrus Prattii, *Hemsley*)

A deciduous tree up to 30 ft. high; young shoots furnished with whitish airs when quite young, soon glabrous. Leaves ovate, ovate-lanceolate or oval; he apex slenderly pointed, the base rounded; sharply and doubly toothed; ½ to 5½ ins. long, 1 to 2¾ ins. wide; soon glabrous except for occasional down eneath on the midrib and chief veins; stalk 1 to 1½ ins. long. Flowers white,

$\frac{3}{4}$ to 1 in. wide, borne during May in clusters ten or twelve together; style five, glabrous. Fruit roundish egg-shaped, $\frac{1}{2}$ in. wide, red, specked with tin white dots, the woolly calyx persisting at the top; flesh gritty; fruit-stal 1 in. long.

Native of Szechuen, China; discovered by A. E. Pratt, introduced b Wilson for Messrs Veitch in 1904. It bears fruit regularly at Kew and is distinc on account of the largish leaves and handsome, dotted fruits. The foliag often colours well in autumn. Akin to M. yunnanensis (*q.v.*).

M. PUMILA, *Miller*. WILD APPLE

(Pyrus Malus, *Linnæus* (partly); M. communis, *De Candolle*)

The wild crab of W. Europe and N.W. Asia is of interest as being th parent of the cultivated garden apples, and the type of one of the chief section of the genus. But for itself it need not be given a place in the garden, as i is not so beautiful as the bulk of its numerous progeny. It is a tree 20 to 30 ft high, with a usually crooked trunk and a rounded head of ultimately more o less pendulous branches, the young shoots, leaves, and flower-stalks clothe more or less with greyish down. Leaves roundish oval or ovate, $1\frac{1}{2}$ to $2\frac{1}{2}$ ins long, round toothed, stalk about half as long. Flowers white or rosy, i corymbs. Fruit red or yellow, round, crowned with persistent calyx-lobes and indented at the base where it joins the stalk. Botanists find two distinc forms among the wild crabs, viz., var. SYLVESTRIS or acerba and var. MITIS Var. sylvestris is not so downy as the other, the leaves and young shoots becom ing glabrous during the season. The fruit is sourer. Var. mitis is considere to be the parent of the sweeter apples, and all the younger parts of the plan are more woolly; fruit-stalk shorter.

Var. ASTRACANICA, *Dumont*. Red Astrachan Apple.—Fruit bright red covered with plum-like bloom, long-stalked.

Var. PARADISIACA.—A dwarf variety of the mitis type and the famou stock for grafting apples known as "Paradise stock" or "Adam's apple."

Var. PENDULA (Elise Rathke).—A delightful tree with weeping branche and abundant beautiful blossom followed by fine crops of handsome yellov fruits of good flavour.

CRABS.—Among the ornamental trees of autumn a high place must b given to several crabs, mostly of unrecorded but undoubtedly hybrid origin Such of them as are not certainly known to belong to the species of Malu described on other pages (like baccata and prunifolia) may be mentioned here

Dartmouth or Hyslop is of American origin. It has plum-like fruits covere with a red-purple bloom, and may be partially derived from Red Astrachan.

Fairy.—Deep yellow, flushed with crimson.

John Downie.—Perhaps the finest of all crabs as regards the fruits; it wa raised by Mr E. Holmes in his nursery at Whittington, near Lichfield. It fruits are conical, $1\frac{1}{4}$ ins. long by 1 in. wide, tapering to the apex, bright orang and scarlet, and produced in wonderfully profuse clusters.

Orange.—Fruits of a pretty pale yellow, 1 in. or so across.

Transcendent.—Fruit deep yellow, carmine on the sunny side.

Transparent.—Fruits translucent yellow with a red tinge on one side Long known in gardens. See also M. Niedzwetzkiana.

M. PRUNIFOLIA, *Borkhausen*

(Pyrus prunifolia, *Willdenow*; Bot. Mag., t. 6158)

A small tree with downy young shoots and ovate or broadly oval leaves 2 to 4 ins. long, half or more than half as wide, unequally toothed, downy beneath. Flowers white, $1\frac{1}{2}$ ins. across, produced in April in umbels of six to ten blossoms ; calyx with long, narrow, woolly lobes. Fruit round or slightly ovoid and elongated, 1 in. in diameter, yellowish or red, crowned with the persistent calyx.

There is some doubt as to the origin of this crab. Aiton gives the date of its introduction to England as 1758, and its native country as Siberia, to which other authors have added N. China. But there appears to be no genuine

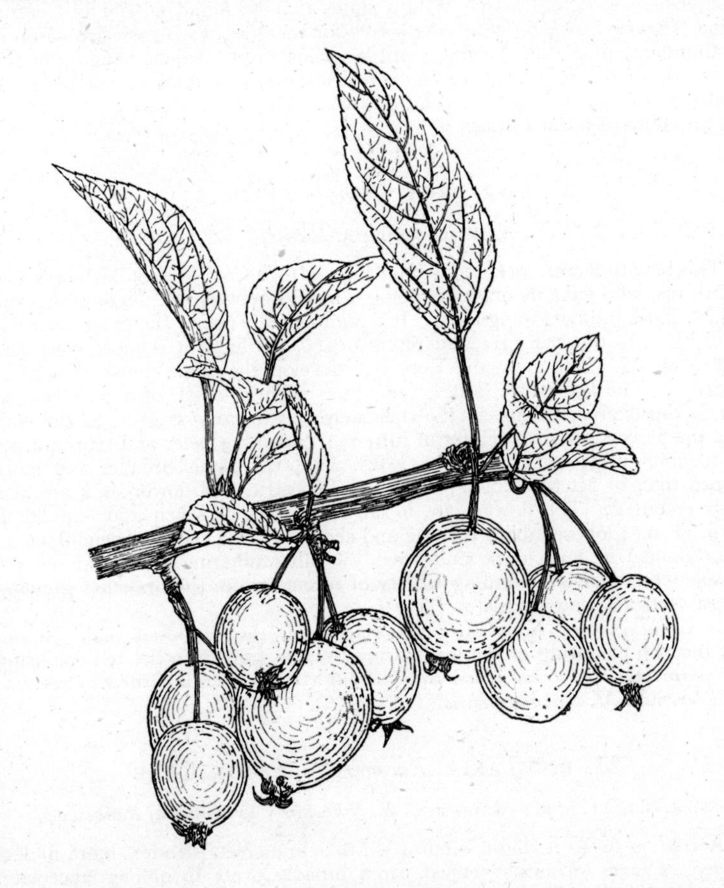

Malus prunifolia Rinki

proof of its existence in either country. It has been suggested that it is a hybrid between M. baccata and M. pumila. It is distinguishable from M. baccata in fruit by having the calyx-lobes nearly always adhering at the top, although not invariably. Although longer cultivated in Britain than M. baccata, it does not appear to have reached so large a size.

Vars. dulcis and edulis have sweet, greenish yellow fruits.

Var. lutea.—Fruit golden yellow, with a pleasantly acid juicy flesh (syn. xanthocarpa).

Var. pendula.—Branches weeping.

Malus cerasifera, *Spach*, is a cross between M. prunifolia and M. baccata, and is a very beautiful crab. Flowers white, fruit about the size of a cherry, coloured purplish red. The calyx teeth sometimes remain on the fruit, as in M. prunifolia—sometimes fall away.

Var. RINKI (Pyrus Ringo, *Wenzig*; Bot. Mag., t. 8265); Malus Ringo, *Carrière*).—This tree appears to have been originally introduced to Europe by Siebold from Japan about the middle of last century, but it is not known to be anywhere wild in Japan. Wilson states that he found it wild in Central China (*Plantæ Wils.*, ii., 280). As a tree for the garden its great attraction is its abundant, gracefully pendent, bright yellow fruits, which hang from the lower side of the branches in long crowded rows, and make it probably the handsomest of our yellow-fruited hardy trees. They have an apple-like flavour and are quite pleasant eating.

M. PURPUREA, *Rehder* (Plate 27)

(Pyrus purpurea, *Hillier*)

This beautiful crab was obtained for Kew in 1912 from Messrs Barbier & Co. of Orleans, who gave its origin as being a hybrid between M. Niedzwetzkyana and M. floribunda atrosanguinea. It is undoubtedly one of the most beautiful acquisitions to flowering trees of recent years. In habit it is more erect and open than M. floribunda and does not develop the same dense thicket of branches. The leaves are larger, sometimes slightly lobed, of a purplish red that is especially pleasing in the delicately tinted early stage. In the bud state the flowers are of a delightful ruby red, becoming paler and more purple on opening fully; they are 1 to 1¼ ins. wide, the petals broader and more cupped than in M. floribunda; the stamens, calyx, and flower-stalk are also richly coloured. The flowers are in clusters of six or seven and expand in April. Fruit globose, about the size and shape of large cherries, pendulous on stalks about 1 in. long, dark vinous red, the calyx adhering at the end.

Var. PENDULA is a weeping variety of recent origin, the branches growing almost vertically downwards.

It is, of course, from M. Niedzwetzkyana, the supposed male parent, that the rich colouring of the leaves, flowers, and fruit (also the red colouring that permeates the young wood right through) have been inherited. (See also *M. Eleyi* and *M. aldenhamensis*.)

M. RIVULARIS, *Roemer*. OREGON CRAB

(Bot. Mag., t. 8798; M. fusca, *C. K. Schneider*; Pyrus fusca, *Rafinesque*)

A tree 20 to 40 ft. high, often a shrub; branchlets slender, more or less downy. Leaves variously shaped, from broadly ovate to oblong-lanceolate, often three-lobed; the largest 4 ins. long, and 2½ ins. wide, more often 1 to 3 ins. long, and half as wide; the base tapering, rounded or slightly heart-shaped, pointed at the apex, sharply toothed; downy on both sides; stalk downy, 1 to 1½ ins. long. Flowers white or rose-tinted, ¾ in. across, produced in clusters of six to twelve. Fruit egg-shaped, ½ to ¾ in. long, red, yellow, or greenish yellow, the calyx teeth fallen away; stalks 1 to 1½ ins. long, slender.

Native of western N. America; introduced in 1836, according to Loudon, but little known in cultivation now, although it is offered sometimes in tree catalogues of continental firms. It belongs to the Sieboldii group of crabs, but appears to have no special value for the garden. The fruit has an agreeable sub-acid taste, and the wood, being close and hard, is valued in the western States for uses similar to those of apple- and pear-wood in this country.

M. SARGENTII, *Rehder*

(Pyrus Sargentii, *Bean*; Bot. Mag., t. 8757)

A shrub of bushy habit 5 to 8 ft. high; young shoots downy. Leaves ovate or oval, 2 to 3 ins. long, 1 to 2 ins. wide; pointed at the apex, rounded or slightly heart-shaped at the base, often three-lobed, sharply toothed; woolly when quite young, becoming nearly glabrous before falling; stalks downy, $\frac{1}{3}$ to 1 in. long. Flowers pure white, 1 in. across, produced in clusters of five or six, each on a stalk 1 to $1\frac{1}{4}$ ins. long; calyx glabrous outside, woolly within. Fruit orange-shaped, $\frac{1}{3}$ in. wide, bright red, the apex marked by the scar of the fallen calyx.

This very attractive species was sent to Kew by Prof. Sargent in 1908. It is distinct among crabs by its purely bushy habit. It was originally discovered by Sargent in 1892 near a brackish marsh, Mororan, Japan, and was named in his honour by Dr Rehder in 1903. The author observes that it is most nearly related to M. Sieboldii, but differs in its larger, pure white flowers with broad overlapping petals and in its larger fruits. From another ally, M. zumi, it is distinguished by "its broader, often lobed leaves, the shape of the [broader based] petals, the glabrous calyx-tube and the habit."

M. SCHEIDECKERI, *Zabel*

(Pyrus Scheideckeri, *Späth*)

A tree eventually 20 to 30 ft. high, branches somewhat erect on young trees; shoots grey-downy early in the season, becoming glabrous later. Leaves ovate, rounded or tapering at the base, pointed, coarsely and sharply toothed; glabrous and dark shining green above, paler and at first downy beneath, becoming glabrous in autumn except on the midrib; on the flowering twigs the leaves are 2 to 3 ins. long and about half as wide, but on vigorous maiden shoots as much as $4\frac{1}{2}$ ins. long by 3 ins., and sometimes lobed. Flowers often semi-double, $1\frac{1}{2}$ ins. across, pale rose, produced in May in umbels of six to ten flowers each on a downy stalk 1 to $1\frac{1}{2}$ ins. long; calyx woolly, especially inside. Fruits globose, yellow, $\frac{5}{8}$ in. thick, calyx-teeth usually persisting at the top.

A hybrid between floribunda and perhaps spectabilis put into cultivation by Späth of Berlin in 1888. Through floribunda it inherits the "blood" of M. Sieboldii, as is occasionally evidenced by the lobing of leaves on vigorous branches. It is a tree wonderfully profuse in blossom, and of vigorous growth. On young trees clean shoots 3 or 4 ft. long are made in one season, at every bud of which there appears the following May a cluster of six to ten large blossoms. It is thus possible to cut branches a yard or more long, wreathed from end to end with flowers. This and M. floribunda are the two finest of flowering (as distinct from fruiting) crabs, and as M. Scheideckeri is two or three weeks the later, both should be grown.

M. SIEBOLDII, *Rehder*. TORINGO CRAB

(Pyrus Toringo, *Siebold*; P. Sieboldii, *Regel*)

A small tree, rarely seen more than 10 to 15 ft. high, sometimes a low shrub, but said by Sargent to become 30 ft. high in a wild state; branches arching or pendulous; young shoots downy the first year. Leaves dull green, very variable in shape, and either narrowly oval, ovate, deeply three-lobed, or of some intermediate shape; they are 1 to 2½ ins. long, sharply, irregularly, and often coarsely toothed; downy on both sides, but especially beneath; tapering at the base to a downy stalk ¼ to ¾ in. long. Flowers pale pink to deep rose, ⅜ in. in diameter, produced during April in clusters of three to six, each flower on a downy, slender, almost thread-like stalk ¾ to 1 in. long. Fruit globose, the size of a small pea, red or brownish yellow, with no calyx-lobes at the top.

Native of Japan; introduced by Siebold about the middle of last century, and a small tree of very graceful habit, distinct among crabs for its variable, often deeply cut leaves, and its tiny fruits (see also M. Sargentii and M. zumi). It is allied to M. floribunda, but is not so valuable a garden tree, its blossoms being shorter-lived.

M. SIKKIMENSIS, *Koehne*. SIKKIM CRAB

(Pyrus sikkimensis, *Hooker fil.*; Bot. Mag., t. 7430)

A small tree branching low and of bushy habit, distinct among all other crabs in cultivation through the excessive development of stout, rigid branching spurs on the trunk; young shoots downy. Leaves 2 to 4½ ins.

MALUS SIKKIMENSIS

long, 1 to 2 ins. wide; narrowly oval, tapering or rounded at the base, slender-pointed; very woolly beneath, and more or less so above; stalks downy, ½ to 1½ ins. long. Flowers 1 in. across, white (rosy in bud), produced during May in corymbs of four to nine blossoms; calyx downy, with slender-pointed lobes; flower-stalks 1¼ to 1½ ins. long, slender. Fruit somewhat pear-shaped, ⅝ in. wide and long, dark red with paler dots, the apex marked with the scar left by the fallen calyx.

Native of Himalaya; introduced to Kew a century ago by Sir Joseph Hooker, who found it in the interior of Sikkim up to elevations of 10,000 ft. It is strange that so distinct and striking a tree has not spread more in cultivation. The original tree, is still at Kew and, although not in such vigorous health as formerly, is now 27 ft. high and rather quaint in form.

It flowers freely, and annually produces enormous crops of fruits, which are in colour by September. Brandis observes that this crab is scarcely specifically distinct from M. baccata, but, as represented at Kew, it is easily distinguished by the low-spreading habit, the excessive development of spurs on the stems, the more woolly leaves and the smaller pear-shaped fruit. A pleasing lawn tree.

M. SPECTABILIS, *Borkhausen*

(Pyrus spectabilis, *Aiton* ; Bot. Mag., t. 267)

A tree rarely more than 30 ft. high, forming a rounded head of branches often as wide as high ; young twigs downy. Leaves oval or obovate to almost round, 2 to 3½ ins. long, up to 2 ins. in width ; toothed, shortly and abruptly pointed, tapering or rounded at the base ; glossy green and glabrous above, downy when young beneath, becoming almost or quite glabrous by autumn ; stalk ¼ to 1 in. long. Flowers deep rosy red in the bud state, paling to a blush tint when fully open, and then nearly 2 ins. across ; they are borne each on a downy stalk ¾ to 1¼ ins. long, in umbels six or eight together ; petals normally five, but in var. PLENA up to ten ; calyx and flower-stalk downy. Fruit globose, yellow, ¾ to 1 in. wide, bitter and harsh ; calyx persisting at the top.

Native of N. China. The date of its introduction is not known, but it was cultivated by Dr Fothergill in 1780. One of the most beautiful of all the Malus group in its flowers, this has no beauty in its fruit. It flowers almost invariably in great profusion from the middle of April to the second week of May. From M. baccata and M. prunifolia its fruits and larger flowers amply distinguish it.

Malus Kaido, *Wenzig*.—Perhaps a hybrid between spectabilis and pumila. It has larger, more deeply coloured flowers than the former.

M. THEIFERA, *Rehder*

(M. hupehensis, *Rehder* ; Pyrus theifera, *Bailey*)

A deciduous tree up to 25 ft. high of stiffish habit ; young shoots at first covered with whitish down. Leaves ovate or oval, shortly and slenderly pointed, rounded at the base on virgin shoots but wedge-shaped on flowering ones ; finely toothed ; 2 to 4 ins. long, 1 to 2½ ins. wide ; dark bright green and glabrous at maturity above, purplish when young, pale beneath and downy on the midrib and chief veins ; stalk up to 1⅛ ins. long. Flowers white tinged with rose on first opening, fragrant, 1 to 1½ ins. wide, produced in April in clusters of three to seven, each on a slender downy stalk 1 in. long ; calyx lobes downy inside, glabrous and purplish outside ; styles usually three. Fruit globose, ⅓ in. wide, greenish yellow tinged on the exposed side with red, with the calyx fallen away from the summit.

Native of Central and Western China, where it is widely distributed, and of Assam ; introduced by Wilson for Messrs Veitch in 1900, but not named until 1915. It is a beautiful tree when in full bloom with its very profuse white or pink-tinted flowers. It is perfectly hardy and a valuable addition to the flowering crabs. The late Mr Vicary Gibbs showed it several times at Westminster in great beauty. The name refers to the use of the leaves by the peasants of Central China, who prepare a beverage from them which they call " red tea."

Var. ROSEA, *Rehder*.—Flowers of a pretty, rosy pink. Found by Wilson in W. Hupeh and raised from his seed at Coombe Wood in 1900.

Nearly related to M. baccata and M. Halliana, the flowers of both of which have usually five styles.

M. TORINGOIDES, *Hughes*

(Bot. Mag., t. 8948; Pyrus toringoides, *Osborn*)

A deciduous tree up to 25 ft. high, of loose, graceful habit; young shoots long, slender, at first closely covered with grey down, becoming glabrous later. Leaves ovate to lanceolate in main outline, but usually deeply lobed, the pointed or bluntish lobes numbering three to seven, basal leaves of shoot often entire; the apex of the leaf is pointed, sometimes slenderly so, and the base varies from narrowly wedge-shaped to truncate; 1¼ to 3½ ins. long, ¾ to 2 ins. wide; both surfaces are slightly downy at first, but the upper one becomes quite glabrous, the lower one remaining more or less downy on the midrib and veins; margins slightly toothed; leaf-stalks slender, downy, ¾ to 1½ ins. long. Flowers six to eight together in corymbs terminating short leafy spurs, opening in May; each flower is ¾ to 1 in. wide, borne on a slender downy stalk ¾ to 1 in. long; petals creamy white; calyx-tube bell-shaped, the lobes awl-shaped, the whole clothed with grey down. Fruit pear-shaped to globose, ⅓ to ½ in. wide, pendulous, yellow, flushed deeply with scarlet on the sunny side, the calyx fallen away from the top.

Native of W. Szechuen, China; introduced by Wilson for Messrs Veitch in 1904. This is a very beautiful addition to cultivated crabs, uniting a graceful habit with exquisite colouring of fruit. It is in its highest beauty in September and October. The late Miss Willmott showed it at Westminster in October 1919, when it was given an Award of Merit.

M. TRANSITORIA, *C. K. Schneider*, which Rehder originally placed under M. toringoides as a variety, is in cultivation. It has more downy leaves with narrower deeper lobes, the calyx-lobes are shorter and more triangular and the flowers and fruits are smaller. Native of N.W. China.

M. TRILOBATA, *C. K. Schneider*

(Eriolobus trilobata, *Roemer*; Bot. Mag., t. 9305; Pyrus trilobata, *De Candolle*)

A small tree, perhaps up to 20 ft. high, or a shrub, with very downy young twigs. Leaves with three deep main lobes, the terminal one usually three-parted, the side ones two-parted. The leaf thus often becomes seven-parted, but the shape is not uniform, and although the three main lobes are always there, the subsidiary divisions vary in number. Some of the leaves have a maple-like appearance, the blade being 2 to 4 ins. wide, scarcely as long, heart-shaped at the base; the stalk ¾ to 2 ins. long. The upper surface is glabrous and bright, the lower one downy, more especially on the veins and midrib; margins finely toothed. Flowers white, 1½ ins. across, in small terminal corymbs, calyx-lobes long, triangular, with a dense white wool on both sides. Fruit usually reduced to from one to three in a corymb, ⅝ to ¾ in. across, globular or pear-shaped, crowned with the calyx-lobes, red or yellow.

Native of Mount Lebanon and other parts of Syria, but rare both in a wild state and in gardens. Two small trees in the Kew collection are quite hardy. Some of the leaves resemble those of Sorbus Torminalis. An interesting small tree.

M. Tschonoskii, *C. K. Schneider*

(Pyrus Tschonoskii, *Maximowicz*; Bot. Mag., t. 8179)
Eriolobus Tschonoskii, *Rehder*

A tree 30 to 40 ft. high, of erect, open, rather pyramidal habit; young ranches covered with a greyish down. Leaves broadly ovate, or rounded; to 5 ins. long, $1\frac{1}{2}$ to 3 ins. wide; pointed, unevenly toothed, the base rounded; overed with loose down above when young, afterwards becoming glabrous; ermanently grey-felted beneath; veins in six to ten pairs, parallel; stalk owny, $\frac{1}{2}$ to 1 in. long. Flowers 1 to $1\frac{1}{4}$ ins. across, white, suffused at first ith rose, produced four to six together in umbels, each flower on a woolly alk $\frac{1}{2}$ to $\frac{5}{8}$ in. long; calyx covered with white wool. Fruit globose, 1 in. ide, brownish yellow flushed with purple, erect on a stalk 1 to $1\frac{1}{2}$ ins. long, owned with the persistent calyx teeth.

Native of Japan, and first discovered at the foot of Fujiyama. It does not ppear to be anywhere common, and was first introduced to cultivation by rof. Sargent, who, in 1897, sent plants to Kew, raised from seed he had llected five years previously. It is a tree of more interest than beauty, so r as one has yet been able to judge, for it does not flower very copiously, d its fruits have no attraction in colour. In North America its leaves are scribed as changing in autumn into beautiful shades of orange and yellow.

M. yunnanensis, *C. K. Schneider*

(Pyrus yunnanensis, *Franchet*, Bot. Mag., t. 8629)

A deciduous tree 20 to 40 ft. high; young shoots at first felted, afterwards abrous and reddish brown. Leaves ovate, finely and irregularly toothed, metimes slightly lobed, pointed, rounded or slightly heart-shaped at the ise; 2 to $4\frac{1}{2}$ ins. long, $1\frac{1}{2}$ to 3 ins. wide; chief veins in six to nine pairs, dull een and ultimately glabrous above, clothed beneath with a pale brown felt; alk $\frac{3}{4}$ to $1\frac{1}{2}$ ins. long. Flowers white or with a faint pink tinge, $\frac{5}{8}$ in. wide, oduced during May in flattish clusters 2 to $2\frac{1}{2}$ ins. wide at the end of short afy side twigs. Calyx clothed with white wool at first, its lobes triangular; tals round; stamens twenty with yellow anthers; styles five. Fruit globose, in. wide, deep red sprinkled with whitish dots, the reflexed calyx-lobes rsisting at the top; flesh gritty, harsh, acid.

Native of Hupeh, Szechuen, and Yunnan, China; discovered by Delavay in unnan, introduced by Wilson in 1900. It is more commonly represented in rdens by var. Veitchii, *Rehder*, a form with more distinctly lobed leaves t united with the type by intermediates. It was first exhibited and put on e market as "P. Veitchiana" and under that name was given an Award of erit at Westminster on 8th October 1912. The fruit-bearing branches en shown by Messrs Veitch bore a wonderful crop of red crabs and were ceedingly ornamental. I consider this one of the best of Wilson's introctions amongst crabs, for in addition to the beauty of its fruits its leaves rn to scarlet and orange in autumn. M. Prattii, a near ally having also itty, white-dotted, red fruits with a persisting calyx, differs in the leaves on becoming smooth beneath and in never being lobed. M. Tschonoskii s somewhat similar but never so distinctly lobed leaves, and larger brownish llow and purple fruits.

M. Zumi, *Rehder*

(Pyrus Zumi, *Matsumura*)

A small tree of pyramidal habit; young wood slightly downy. Leaves ate or oblong; $1\frac{1}{2}$ to $3\frac{1}{2}$ ins. long, $\frac{3}{4}$ to $1\frac{1}{2}$ ins. wide; tapering or rounded at e base, glabrous except when quite young; stalks about 1 in. long. Flowers pink in bud, becoming white after opening, 1 to 1¼ ins. diameter, produce in clusters of four to seven; calyx-lobes woolly, especially inside; flowe stalks 1 to 1½ ins. long. Fruit ½ in. diameter, globose, red.

Native of Japan; introduced to N. America in 1892 by Sargent, an thence to Kew in 1905. It is one of the group of Japanese crabs to whic M. Sieboldii and M. Sargentii belong, distinguished by small fruits marked a the apex by the scar of the fallen calyx. It is said to be superior to M. Siebold as a garden tree in the Arnold Arborteum, being covered there in May b a mass of flowers, and in autumn by "attractive bright red fruits." It diffe from both its allies in its oblong leaves being only slightly or not at all lobec and from M. Sargentii in its wider flowers and less crowded petals. The frui are larger than the pea-like ones of M. Sieboldii.

MANDEVILLA SUAVEOLENS, *Lindley*. APOCYNACEÆ

(Bot. Mag., t. 3797)

A deciduous climbing shrub growing 12 ft. or more high; youn shoots very slender, glabrous, hollow, exuding a milky juice when cu Leaves opposite, heart-shaped, tapering at the apex to a long fine poin toothless; 2 to 3½ ins. long, 1¼ to 2 ins. wide; dark dull green an glabrous above, paler beneath, with tufts of white down in the axils of th veins; stalk ½ to 2 ins. long. Flowers sweetly scented, produced six eight together in corymbs from the leaf-axils, from June to Septembe Corolla white or creamy white, funnel-shaped, 2 ins. long, 1½ ins. wid five-lobed, the lobes roundish ovate, spreading, overlapping; glabro outside, hairy inside the tube. Anthers five, yellow, scarcely stalke ⅜ in. long, crowded together in a column towards the base of the tu and concealing the stigma. Calyx green, with five awl-shaped lob ⅜ in. long. Seed-pods usually in pairs, each from 12 to 16 ins. lon slenderly cylindrical, ¼ in. wide. Seeds bearded.

Native of the Argentine; introduced in 1837 by Mr H. J. Mandevill at that time British Minister at Buenos Ayres, and in compliment to who the genus was named. Usually grown in greenhouses, where it is valu for the abundant, sweetly scented blossoms, it can, in the milder parts the country, be grown on a sunny wall, planted in well-drained, ligh loamy or peaty soil. It has succeeded well and borne its remarkab seed-pods in the Vicarage Garden at Bitton in Gloucestershire, and Leonardslee in Sussex. In Cornwall it is even more luxuriant. It botanically allied to Vinca and Trachelospermum, and is sometim known as "Chilean jasmine."

MANGLIETIA. MAGNOLIACEÆ

This genus is very nearly related to Magnolia, and has the sar solitary, terminal blossoms, but is distinguished by having often s ovules to each carpel, whereas the magnolias have only two. "Ma glietia" appears to have been adapted by Blume from the native nar in Malaya of the first species of the genus he described.

M. HOOKERI, *Cubitt and W. W. Smith*

A medium-sized or tall evergreen tree with a conical head of branches; young shoots covered with a close, greyish down. Leaves leathery, oblanceolate to oblong, narrowed at the apex to a short point, tapered at the base; 6 ins. to 1 ft. long, 1½ to 3½ ins. wide; dark glossy green above, paler but also glossy beneath, quite glabrous but finely and distinctly net-veined; stalk ½ to 1⅛ ins. long. Flowers solitary, terminal, 4 ins. wide; sepals three, oblong, blunt, cream-coloured; petals nine, white. Fruit ovoid or almost globose, 2½ ins. long.

Native of Upper Burma at 5000 to 6000 ft., and of Yunnan at 9000 ft. altitude. It was originally discovered in 1909 by Mr Cubitt in the former country and later by Forrest in Yunnan. The tree is said to yield a timber highly valued by the Burmese. Most or all of the plants in cultivation have been raised from Forrests' seeds, and they are growing vigorously in Cornish gardens, being already handsome and striking evergreens.

M. INSIGNIS, *Blume*

(Plant Introductions of Reginald Farrer, t. 4, p. 32)

An evergreen tree 40 ft. or more high, the young shoots, leaf-stalks and leaf-buds more or less downy at first, becoming nearly or quite glabrous later; branchlets ringed at the joints. Leaves rather leathery, oblanceolate to narrowly oval, finely pointed, gradually tapered from the middle to the base; 4 to 8 ins. long, 2 to 3 ins. wide; dark glossy green above, pale and slightly glaucous beneath; stalk ½ to 1 in. long. Flowers magnolia-like, odorous, solitary, terminal, erect, 3 ins. wide, opening after the young leaves. The flowers are variously described as "white or yellowish tinged with pink," "splendid rose pink," "richest creamy carmine"; sepals three; petals nine; flower-stalk stout, ¾ to 1 in. long. Fruit ovoid-cylindric, 2 to 4 ins. long, 1 to 1½ ins. wide, purple. Seeds three or four to each carpel, suspended on a slender filament on becoming free.

Native of the Himalaya, where it has long been known; found by Forrest in Yunnan in 1912 and several times since; also by Farrer in Upper Burma; both introduced seeds from which plants have been raised that are now growing in Cornwall and elsewhere. In the garden at Exbury it was 10 ft. high in 1931, but had been somewhat injured during the winter of 1928-9. At Kew in a sheltered shrubbery well protected from the north and east, it was 8 ft. high in 1932 and perfectly healthy, but unfortunately this tree is no longer at Kew.

MARGYRICARPUS SETOSUS, *Ruiz and Pavon*. PEARL FRUIT.

ROSACEÆ

A low, prostrate shrub, with glabrous, pale, straw-coloured branches, nearly covered by large, similarly coloured, clasping stipules. Leaves pinnate, about ¾ in. long; leaflets green, finely linear, ⅛ to ⅓ in. long; stipules membranous, furnished at the edges with white, silky hairs. Flowers solitary, stalkless, very inconspicuous, without a corolla; produced singly in the leaf-axils. Fruit a small white berry, about the size of a peppercorn, with a pleasant acid flavour. Evergreen.

Native of the mountains of Chile, on dry mountain-sides. This curious little shrub may be grown by those interested in out-of-the-way plants; but beyond its finely cut leaves it has little to recommend it, although when its pearl-like fruits are borne freely it is distinctive. It appears to be hardy except during the hardest winters. It should have a sunny position on the rock garden, and not a rich soil. I have seen it bearing fruit freely in Mr Notcutt's nursery at Woodbridge, where probably the dry, sunny East Anglian climate suits it. It blooms in July and August but is of no great merit.

MARSDENIA ERECTA, *R. Brown*. ASCLEPIADACEÆ

(Cynanchum erectum, *Linnæus*)

A deciduous climber, with slender, twining stems, 20 ft. or more high, furnished with a little loose down when young. Leaves opposite, heart-shaped, 1½ to 2½ ins. long, from two-thirds to as much wide; with short, abrupt points; pale rather glaucous green, with a little loose down on the midrib and veins beneath; stalk ½ to 1¼ ins. long. Corymbs terminal and axillary, the latter often in pairs, but only borne in the axil of one of each pair of leaves, 2 to 4 ins. long, erect. Flowers white, ⅓ in. across, sweetly scented, the five segments of the corolla narrow oblong, ¼ in. long, rounded at the end. Calyx-lobes ovate, transparent at the margins. Fruit narrowly cone-shaped or spindle-shaped, 3 ins. long, ½ in. wide at the base, tapering to a point; each seed has a brush-like attachment of silky white hairs 1 in. long. Blooms in June and July.

Native of S.E. Europe and Asia Minor; cultivated in England in the sixteenth century, but long regarded as a greenhouse plant. It is the hardiest member of a large genus, and succeeds very well against a sunny wall, but is liable to be killed in the open. It is not quite so hardy as its ally, Periploca græca. When cut, the stems exude a milky juice, which has a blistering effect on the skin, and is very poisonous taken internally.

MEDICAGO ARBOREA, *Linnæus*. MOON TREFOIL. LEGUMINOSÆ

This shrub is chiefly interesting as a woody member of a genus represented in the British flora by about half a dozen herbaceous plants known as "medicks," and including the "lucerne." It is not hardy at Kew in the open, but will live against a wall; it is said to have been 11 ft. high at one time in the Chelsea Botanic Garden. It is best adapted for the south and south-western counties. A shrub, evergreen where it thrives, usually 6 or 8 ft. high; its stems very leafy but little branched, covered with grey down. Leaves trifoliolate, 1 to 1½ ins. long; leaflets ¼ to ¾ in. long, wedge-shaped, sometimes toothed, sometimes notched at the apex, silky beneath, glabrous above. Flowers yellow, ½ in. long, crowded at the end of short axillary racemes which continue to appear as the shoot extends, from April well into autumn, but never making a great display at one time. Easily increased by soft cuttings in bottom heat. The leaves are produced in clusters at each joint, and as the joints are usually about ½ in. apart, the stem has a very leafy aspect. The pod is flat, but curled round like a ram's horn. In the south of Europe it makes a pleasing undergrowth in thinnish woodland and at the outskirts of plantations, especially in maritime districts. Abundant near Antibes.

MELIA AZEDARACH, *Linnæus*. MELIACEÆ. BEAD-TREE

(Bot. Mag., t. 1066 ; M. japonica, *G. Don*)

A deciduous tree up to 30 or 40 ft. high in warm countries ; variable in habit. Leaves alternate, doubly pinnate, 12 to 24 ins. long, half as much wide ; leaflets ovate to oval, slender-pointed, unequally tapered at the base, toothed or lobed ; 1½ to 2 ins. long, ⅓ to ¾ in. wide ; quite glabrous, or sometimes slightly downy on the midrib and main-stalks when young. Flowers fragrant, ¾ in. wide, numerous in clusters of loose axillary panicles 4 to 8 ins. long on the young leafy shoots. Calyx five-lobed, the lobes oblong, pointed, downy, ⅛ in. long. Petals five, lilac-coloured, narrow-oblong, ⅛ in. wide, spreading or slightly reflexed. Stamens, ten or twelve, their stalks united into a slender, erect, violet-coloured tube about ¼ in. long, the anthers only free. Fruit yellow, roundish egg-shaped, ½ in. long, containing a hard, bony seed.

Native of N. India and of Central and W. China ; now cultivated or naturalised in almost every warm temperate or sub-tropical country, often as a street tree. According to Gerard, it was cultivated by John Parkinson in England at the end of the sixteenth century. Miller says he flowered it at Chelsea three or four years successively, and that he found it resisted cold extremely well in the open ground. I have never heard of its being grown near London in recent years except under glass. So far as I know, Mr Hiatt C. Baker of Oaklands, near Bristol, succeeded as well as any one with it. He grew it out-of-doors against a wall, where it stood uninjured for over twenty years. He showed a spray gathered from this plant at Westminster in June 1930. I have seen it in flower in S. Italy, in Dalmatia, and on the Riviera, and have always been charmed by the grace and beauty of its foliage and blossom. It is easily raised from imported seed, is of easy cultivation, and flowers at an early age. The name of "bead-tree" originated through the seeds being strung by monks and others to form rosaries.

Var. UMBRACULIFORMIS, *Berckmans*, is much grown in the S.W. United States, as the "Texan Umbrella Tree." It forms a dense, flattened, spreading head of branches, and has narrower leaflets. Said to have appeared originally on the battlefield of San Jacinto, Texas.

MELICYTUS RAMIFLORUS, *Forster*. VIOLACEÆ

(Bot. Mag., t. 8763)

A deciduous shrub or small tree up to 30 ft. high, with glabrous young shoots and leaves. Leaves alternate, oblong-lanceolate, tapered towards both ends, coarsely toothed ; 2 to 6 ins. long, ¾ to 2 ins. wide ; bright dark green above; stalk $\frac{1}{3}$ to $\frac{3}{4}$ in. long. Flowers small, produced in June in clusters of three to nine from the joints of the previous season's growth; each flower about $\frac{1}{5}$ in. wide, yellowish green, on a stalk $\frac{1}{5}$ to $\frac{2}{5}$ in. long. Petals five, triangular. Fruit a globose berry, $\frac{1}{5}$ in. wide, violet-blue, very abundant.

Native of New Zealand; long cultivated in the Temperate House at Kew, where a plant flowers but does not bear fruits. As, however, the species is usually, if not always, unisexual, both male and female plants will be necessary to obtain them. The greatest success with it in this country probably has been achieved by the late Canon Boscawen at Ludgvan Rectory, near Penzance, in whose garden it stood ten degrees of frost without injury, and in May 1930 was 20 ft. high and wide. He sent to Kew some beautiful sprays covered with fruit in November 1917, which had been gathered from his plants raised ten years before from New Zealand seed. The species is one of those curious shrubs belonging to the violet family, of which Hymenanthera crassifolia is the best known representative in gardens.

MELIOSMA. SABIACEÆ

A genus of trees and shrubs, with alternate, simple or pinnate leaves, natives of Eastern Asia and America—the hardy ones all from China and Japan, and deciduous. They produce their flowers, which are small and white, in large terminal panicles. Petals five, the three outer ones concave, orbicular, and larger than the two inner ones. Fruit a drupe containing one seed, which is remarkable for its twisted radicle. The name refers to the honey-like fragrance of the flowers of some of the species. M. Veitchiorum, the most imposing in leaf of all the meliosmas, flowered for the first time in this country at Caerhays, Cornwall, in June 1930, and one flowered and bore fruit at Nymans in Sussex in 1931; the fruit is globose, violet coloured, $\frac{3}{8}$ in. wide. Unfortunately this tree is still very rare. There are two distinct sections of this genus, one with pinnate, the other with simple leaves.

M. Beaniana, *Rehder and Wilson*

A deciduous tree ranging from 40 to 80 ft. high in a wild state, the trunks of the largest 6 ft. in girth; young shoots slightly rusty-downy at first. Leaves pinnate, 6 to 12 ins. long, composed of five to thirteen (usually nine) leaflets, which are oval to ovate, pointed, tapered at the base, the margins remotely and finely toothed or entire; the lower pairs are the smallest and 1 to 2 ins. long, the remainder increasing in size towards the end, where they are 2 to 5 ins. long and 1 to $2\frac{1}{2}$ ins. wide; upper surface rather rough, dullish green; lower one with tufts of down in the vein-axils; stalks $\frac{1}{12}$ in. long. Flowers creamy white, borne in axillary, spreading or pendulous panicles up to 8 ins. long and 4 ins. wide, with rusty downy stalks. Individually the flower (as in all meliosmas) is small and about $\frac{1}{4}$ in. wide. Fruit globose, black, $\frac{1}{4}$ in. wide.

Native of Hupeh and Szechuen, China; discovered by Wilson and introduced in 1907. He praises it highly and describes it as one of the most striking and handsome of Chinese trees. It flowers in May, when the bloom is so abundant as to cover the tree. It is often planted near temples and wayside shrines. It differs from all other pinnate-leaved meliosmas (which have terminal panicles) in the inflorescence being axillary. It grows healthily at Kew and is very hardy. A tree, newly transplanted from Aldenham, bloomed at Borde Hill, Sussex, May 1933.

M. CUNEIFOLIA, *Franchet*

(Bot. Mag., t. 8357)

A deciduous shrub, described as up to 20 ft. high in nature; branches erect, glabrous or nearly so. Leaves simple, 3 to 7 ins. long, 1½ to 3 ins. wide; obovate or wedge-shaped, broadest near the apex, where they narrow abruptly to a point; upper surface rough to the touch, lower one clothed at first with a brownish down, especially on the midrib and axils of the veins. The veins of

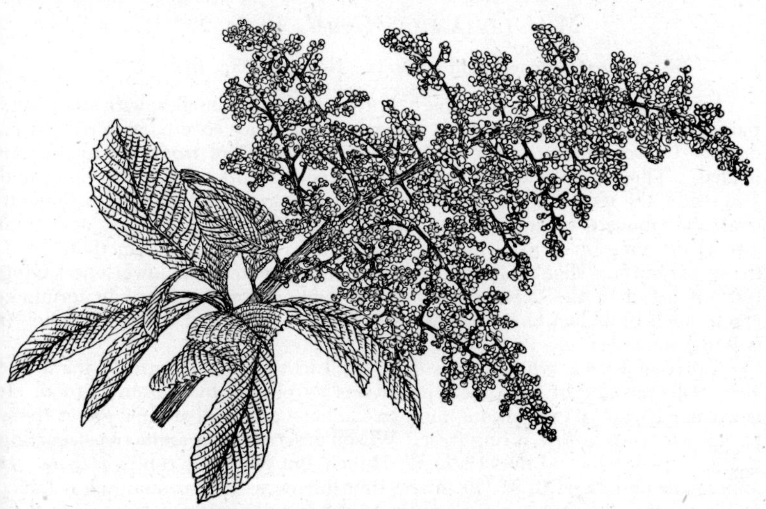

MELIOSMA CUNEIFOLIA

he leaf are in fifteen to over twenty pairs, parallel, and about $\frac{3}{16}$ in. apart; nargins set with bristle-like teeth. Flowers yellowish white at first, then almost pure white, deliciously scented, $\frac{1}{6}$ in. across; produced in downy pyramidal panicles terminating the branches, 5 to 9 ins. high, and as much hrough. Fruit globose, about the size of peppercorns, black.

Native of W. China; introduced by Wilson in 1901 for Messrs Veitch, and first flowered in their nursery at Coombe Wood in July 1909, when I saw t, and was much attracted by its fine panicles, and especially by the hawthorn-ike fragrance. It is, no doubt, allied to the older M. myriantha, but is a hardier plant, easily distinguished by the shape of the leaves, the lower two-hirds of which is uniformly and distinctly wedge-shaped.

M. MYRIANTHA, *Siebold and Zuccarini*

A deciduous shrub or small tree of spreading habit, 20 ft. high. Leaves imple, oval-lanceolate, 3 to 8 ins. long, 1½ to 3 ins. wide; shortly pointed, harply and regularly toothed, the stalk (½ to 1 in. long) and midrib covered with eddish brown hairs; veins parallel, as in a sweet chestnut. Panicles terminal, ins. or more long, and about the same wide, much branched; the main-stalk and all its ramifications covered with brown hairs. Flowers minute, about $\frac{1}{8}$ in. diameter, very numerous, yellowish white, very fragrant. Fruit crowded in a broad panicle, each one about the size of a peppercorn, dark red.

Native of Japan and the Korean Archipelago; introduced from the former to the Coombe Wood nursery in 1879 by Maries. The original plant, now unfortunately no longer at Kew was a fine spreading bush about 8 ft. high and 12 ft. through, and flowered with freedom every year in late June and July. It is, nevertheless, a rather tender subject when young; plants unprotected in the open at Kew have often perished. When once a strong woody base has been formed it will probably survive, but until then some winter protection is necessary. It will certainly thrive in the warmer counties.

M. Oldhamii, *Miquel* (Plate 28)

(Gardeners' Chronicle, 2nd Nov. 1929, fig. 160)

A deciduous tree up to 60 ft. high, but usually much smaller, with stout, very pale grey, glabrous young shoots; terminal winter buds covered with red-brown down. Leaves pinnate, 7 to 15 ins. long, composed of from five to thirteen leaflets. The lowest ones are usually rounded to ovate, about 1 in. long and $\frac{3}{4}$ in. wide, the remainder gradually increasing in size and changing in shape to oval and obovate towards the terminal one, which is the largest and from 3 to $5\frac{1}{2}$ ins. long by $1\frac{1}{4}$ to $2\frac{1}{2}$ ins. wide; they are pointed and distinctly toothed, the upper surface slightly downy when the leaf is young, the lower one having tufts of down in the vein-axils. Flowers pure white, produced in terminal, erect, much branched, downy panicles 6 to 12 ins. high and wide; each flower is $\frac{1}{6}$ to $\frac{1}{4}$ in. wide.

Native of Korea, where it was discovered in 1863 by Richard Oldham, the Kew collector, and of China, whence it was introduced by Wilson in 1900. It is extremely rare in cultivation, but a tree about 15 ft. high at Kew grows freely except when cut by late spring frost. Wilson describes it as a fine tree occurring in the moist woods and thickets of W. Hupeh, but not really common there. It appears to be related to M. Beaniana, but differs in the terminal inflorescence and in flowering later when the leaves are nearly fully grown. The tree at Kew flowered in July 1942.

M. pendens, *Rehder and Wilson*

A deciduous shrub up to 16 ft. high, with graceful branching; young shoots purplish, hairy. Leaves simple, mostly obovate, approaching oval, with usually slender points, but tapering more gradually towards the base, the margin set with distant, bristle-like teeth; 2 to 6 ins. long, 1 to $2\frac{1}{2}$ ins. wide; dull green above, with short scattered hairs and a bristly midrib, paler beneath and more conspicuously hairy, especially on the midrib and on the twelve to twenty pairs of veins; stalk $\frac{1}{4}$ to $\frac{1}{2}$ in. long. Panicles terminal, pendulous, many flowered, 4 to 8 ins. long, scarcely as wide. Flowers white, $\frac{1}{6}$ in. wide, fragrant; main and secondary flower-stalks downy.

Native of W. Hupeh, China; introduced by Wilson in 1907. A plant obtained from the Coombe Wood Nursery flowered at Kew in July 1920. It is evidently near to M. cuneifolia, but that species is distinguished by the broader, more erect panicles, also, when out of flower, by the conspciuous tufts of down in the vein-axils beneath the leaves which are absent in M. pendens. It is quite hardy but does not grow so freely as M. cuneifolia.

M. TENUIS, *Maximowicz*

A deciduous shrub, perhaps a small tree in a wild state; young shoots purplish, downy when quite young; winter-buds elongated, covered with tawny down. Leaves simple, oval to obovate, abruptly slender-pointed, tapered to the base, toothed; 2 to 5 ins. long, half as wide; dark green above and with scattered hairs there, pale beneath with axil-tufts of pale down and hairs on the midrib; veins in ten to fifteen pairs; leaf-stalk 1/4 to 3/8 in. long, downy. Flowers produced in loose, slender panicles about 6 ins. long, very small, yellowish white. Fruit 3/16 in. wide, globose, black, covered at first with a purplish bloom.

Native of Japan; introduced in 1915. This shrub flowered at Wakehurst, Sussex, in August 1930, but it does not promise to be as ornamental as M. cuneifolia. It has the same type of small flower as that species but the panicles are not so large nor nearly so thickly packed with blossom. It suffered badly at Kew in the winter of 1928-9 and is apparently best fitted for the milder counties.

M. VEITCHIORUM, *Hemsley* (Plate 29)

A deciduous tree, 30 to 40 ft. high, with very stout, rigid, erect branches. Leaves pinnate, 1½ to 2½ ft. long, with about nine or eleven leaflets, which are each 3½ to 7 ins. long, about half as much wide; of ovate or oblong outline, occasionally rather heart-shaped at the base, glabrous except on the midrib beneath; margins entire or sparsely toothed. Panicles as much as 18 ins. long, and 12 ins. wide at the base, more open and less densely furnished with flowers than either of the simple-leaved species before mentioned; flowers creamy white, 1/4 in. across. Fruit rich violet, globose, 5/8 in. wide.

Native of W. China at elevations of 5000 to 7500 ft., whence it was introduced by Wilson in 1901. It is in cultivation in several places including Kew, and is noteworthy for its fine pinnate foliage, and curiously stout, rigid branchlets. It is evidently a perfectly hardy tree and has flowered in several places and borne fruit in recent years. It is at present extremely rare.

MENISPERMUM. MOONSEED. MENISPERMACEÆ

Climbing, woody or semi-woody plants, with alternate, long-stalked, peltate leaves, and separate male and female flowers. Sepals six; petals six or nine; stamens nine to twenty-four. The black or purple-black fruit encloses one half-moon or crescent-shaped seed—giving the popular name. The plants spread rapidly by means of underground stems, and are easily increased by division. Cocculus is nearly allied, but has the leaf-stalk attached at the margin of the leaf, and only six stamens.

M. CANADENSE, *Linnæus*. CANADIAN MOONSEED

(Bot. Mag., t. 1910)

A deciduous climber, producing a dense tangle of slightly downy, slender, twining shoots 12 or 15 ft. high. Leaves 4 to 7 ins. wide, ovate to heart-shaped and roundish, with usually three, five, or seven angular lobes; strongly veined and pale beneath, dark green above. Leaf-stalk slender, 3 to 4 ins. long, attached to the blade near, but not at the base (peltate). Flowers numerous, inconspicuous, greenish yellow, borne on a slender, long-stalked raceme, one of which is produced a little above each leaf-axil. Fruit in long loose racemes, nearly black when mature, about the size of a black currant. Each fruit contains one crescent-shaped seed.

Native of eastern N. America, where it is widely spread; cultivated in England since the end of the seventeenth century. Its stems although truly woody have a herbaceous appearance, and do not live long. The exceptional vigour of the plant and its habit of spreading rapidly by means of underground suckers render it unsuitable for planting near delicate or slow-growing shrubs, which it is apt to smother. But it makes a good summer covering for a wall or summer-house, and is distinctly ornamental when in fruit. It can be pruned back to the ground every winter.

M. DAURICUM, *De Candolle*. DAVURIAN MOONSEED

Scarcely different from the American species in stem, leaf, and general aspect, this can be recognised when in bloom by the flowers being more closely packed together in a shorter raceme, and by the racemes being produced in pairs a little above each leaf-axil. In both the leaves have the same three or five lobes, but the apex is usually more drawn out, the spaces between the lobes are more deeply hollowed, and the stalk is attached to the blade farther away from its margin.

Native of N.E. Asia from Siberia to China, requiring the same conditions and treatment as the American species.

MENZIESIA. ERICACEÆ

A genus of deciduous shrubs containing about ten species, three of which are native of N. America, the rest of N.E. Asia. They have alternate leaves without teeth and are often clustered at the end of the twig. Flowers in terminal clusters, the parts in fours or fives; corolla bell-shaped, urn-shaped, or cylindrical with the stamens enclosed; calyx and flower-stalks usually bristly. They succeed under the same treatment as rhododendrons but enjoy more sunshine; a moist, well-drained, lime-free, loamy or peaty soil suits them. The Japanese species grow slowly and are quite suitable for the rock garden.

The name commemorates Archibald Menzies, who served as surgeon-botanist on Vancouver's great expedition of survey, 1790-5, during which he discovered and introduced many plants—a western North American species of Menziesia among them.

M. CILIICALYX, *Maximowicz*

A deciduous shrub 2 to 3 ft. high, with glabrous, slender young shoots, ofte produced in tiers. Leaves mostly clustered at the end of the twigs; obovat to oval, tapered towards both ends, usually more abruptly towards the apex edged with bristle-like hairs and having a few larger bristles on the midrib otherwise glabrous; $\frac{3}{4}$ to 3 ins. long, $\frac{1}{2}$ to $1\frac{1}{4}$ ins. wide; stalk $\frac{1}{8}$ in. or less long Flowers nodding, produced in May in umbel-like clusters at the end of th shoots of the previous year. Corolla bell-shaped, $\frac{5}{8}$ in. long, $\frac{1}{4}$ in. wide, wit four or five small lobes, yellowish green at the base, purplish at and near th lobes; glabrous outside, downy within. Stamens eight or ten, shorter than th corolla, very downy at the lower part. Calyx slightly lobed, fringed with glandular bristles. Flower-stalk $\frac{1}{2}$ to $1\frac{1}{8}$ ins. long, glandular-bristly.

Native of Japan, named by Maximowicz in 1870; introduced about 1914. It is nearly related to M. multiflora (*q.v.*) and is quite a pretty shrub when flowering as freely as one sees it in the garden at Exbury, Hants.

M. FERRUGINEA, *Smith*

A deciduous shrub usually 2 to 6 ft. high; young shoots glandular-ciliate and finely downy; afterwards with peeling bark. Leaves narrowly oval or obovate, pointed, tapered at the base; $\frac{3}{4}$ to 2 ins. long, $\frac{1}{2}$ to $\frac{3}{4}$ in. wide; bristly hairy above and on the margins, less so beneath. Flowers nodding, in clusters of two to five, each on a glandular stalk $\frac{1}{2}$ to 1 in. long. Corolla cylindrical, $\frac{3}{8}$ in. long, four-lobed, dullish white tinged with pink. Stamens eight, with downy stalks.

Native of western N. America from Alaska to Oregon; in the Cascade Mountains of the latter State it has been found up to 12 ft. high. It is very closely related to M. pilosa, which differs in its more rounded, bell-shaped corolla and glabrous stamens. This was the species discovered on the N.W. Coast of America by Archibald Menzies during his voyage with Vancouver, 1790-5, and the one on which Sir James Smith founded the genus. Flowers in May but of no great worth in gardens.

M. MULTIFLORA, *Maximowicz*

(M. ciliicalyx multiflora, *Makino*)

This species is evidently nearly related to M. ciliicalyx described above, and is connected with it by intermediate forms. It was originally described and named by Maximowicz in 1870, and he distinguished it from ciliicalyx by its shortly racemose instead of umbellate inflorescences, and its obovate rather than oval leaves. His own specimens, however, show little or no difference in shape of leaf. In these specimens the most obvious distinction of multiflora is in the linear lobes of the calyx being as much as $\frac{3}{8}$ in. long and $\frac{1}{6}$ in. wide. Some authors have relied on the glabrous flower-stalks of multiflora as distinct from the glandular-bristly ones of ciliicalyx, but in specimens of the former collected by Wilson in Japan in 1914, whose flowers have very distinctly linear-lobed calyces, the flower-stalks are as glandular-bristly as in ciliicalyx. The corolla of M. multiflora is somewhat shorter and more urn-shaped than that of ciliicalyx; its colour varies from pale purple to nearly white with deeper coloured lobes.

Native of Japan. It was collected in flower in that country by Veitch's collector, Charles Maries, during August 1880, on Mt. Fuji-yama, but if he sent home seeds at that time the plant never became established in gardens. It has occasionally been cultivated since the war of 1914-1918.

M. PENTANDRA, *Maximowicz*

A deciduous shrub up to 4 ft. high, with an often bi- or tri-furcate mode of branching; young shoots slender, bristly. Leaves narrowly oval, tapered at both ends, margined with hairs, bristly above, less so beneath; 1 to 2 ins. long, $\frac{1}{2}$ to 1 in. wide; stalk about $\frac{1}{8}$ in. long, bristly. Flowers nodding, a few in an umbel, each on a slender, sparsely glandular stalk $\frac{1}{2}$ to 1 in. long. Corolla roundish urn-shaped, $\frac{1}{4}$ in. long, dull greenish white, five-lobed. Stamens five, glabrous. Calyx five-lobed, ciliate.

Native of Japan and Saghalien; introduced about 1905, originally named in 1867. It is one of the least attractive of the menziesias, abundantly distinct from the other Asiatic species in having only five stamens, which are glabrous.

M. PILOSA, *Jussieu*

(M. globularis, *Salisbury*; M. ferruginea var. globularis, *Sims*, Bot. Mag., t. 1571)

A deciduous shrub, 3 to 6 ft. high, rigid and erect in habit, the bark on the older branches hanging in loose shreds; young shoots downy and hairy. Leaves alternate, obovate or narrowly oval; $\frac{3}{4}$ to 2 ins. long, $\frac{3}{8}$ to 1 in. wide; tapered at both ends, more or less glandular-hairy on the upper surface and on the margins, with a few bristles on the midrib beneath. Flowers yellowish

MENZIESIA PILOSA

white, nodding, produced along with the young shoots in May in few-flowere clusters terminating the previous year's branches. Corolla bell-shaped, $\frac{1}{4}$ in long, mostly four-lobed; sepals with small, slender teeth; flower-stal decurved, glandular-downy, $\frac{1}{4}$ to $\frac{3}{4}$ in. long. Seed-vessel dry, egg-shaped, $\frac{1}{4}$ in long, covered with gland-tipped hairs; stamens 8.

Native of eastern N. America from Pennsylvania southwards, mostly i mountain woods; introduced in 1806. This is not one of the most attractiv of the American Ericaceæ, but was commonly grown in the older collection and is still obtainable in nurseries. It likes a peaty soil, and should be increase by seeds.

Nearly allied to it, and often associated with it as a variety, is M. GLABELL *A. Gray*. This differs in having downy stamens (those of pilosa being glabrous) the leaves are almost glabrous, as is also the seed-vessel. It is a native of th North Central and North-West United States.

M. PURPUREA, *Maximowicz*

A deciduous shrub said to be up to 8 ft. high, with glabrous, slender shoo often produced in tiers of three or four. Leaves oval to obovate, tapered at tl base, the apex rounded except for a minute tip (mucro); 1 to $1\frac{1}{2}$ ins. lon $\frac{1}{2}$ to $\frac{7}{8}$ in. wide; with scattered bristles above and some on the midrib beneatl stalk $\frac{3}{16}$ in. or less long. Flowers nodding, produced in May and June at the er of the previous year's twigs in umbel-like clusters of four to eight. Corolla red, bell-shaped, ½ in. long, ¼ in. wide, with four or five shallow, minutely ciliate lobes. Stamens very hairy, in number twice as many as the corolla lobes. Calyx four- or five-lobed; lobes ovate-oblong, ⅙ in. long, glandular-ciliate. Flower-stalk ½ to ¾ in. long, very slender, glandular-bristly.

Native of Japan, named in 1867 by Maximowicz; introduced about 1914. It is the prettiest and brightest coloured of the menziesias, distinguished from all the preceding species by its bell-shaped, bright red corolla, whose lobes are edged with minute hairs, and its round-ended mucronate leaves. Occasionally exhibited at the Royal Horticultural Society's Shows, but still rare.

MESPILUS GERMANICA, *Linnæus*. MEDLAR. ROSACEÆ

A low deciduous tree of crooked, picturesque habit, usually under 20 ft. high; young branchlets very hairy, older ones often armed with stiff, straight spines ½ to 1 in. long. Leaves almost without stalks, lanceolate or oval, 2 to 5 ins. long, minutely toothed; downy on both surfaces, but more so beneath. Flowers solitary at the end of short leafy branches; 1 to 1½ ins. across, white or slightly pink, produced on a very short woolly stalk, in May or early June. Petals five, roundish; sepals covered with grey wool, triangular at the base, drawn out into a long, narrow point standing out beyond the petals. Fruit 1 in. wide, five-celled, apple-shaped, brown, with a broad open eye, surrounded by the persistent calyx, and showing the ends of the bony seed-vessels.

The wild medlar is a native of Europe and Asia Minor, and is found wild in the woods of several counties in the south of England, notably Sussex and Kent, but it is not believed to be truly indigenous. It has long been cultivated for its fruit in English orchards, and several named varieties exist. The cultivated forms are distinguished by thornless or nearly thornless branches, by larger, broader leaves, and by larger fruits up to 1½ or 2 ins. across. Although much esteemed by those who have acquired the taste for them, medlars are not a popular fruit. They should be left on the tree until the end of October or later, then stored in a fruit-room until they are "bletted"—a term given to indicate a state of incipient decay. A jelly made from the fruits meets a more general taste. The medlar is most closely allied to Cratægus, differing in the solitary flower, etc. It is very hardy, and not particular as to soil.

METAPLEXIS STAUNTONI, *Roemer*. ASCLEPIADACEÆ

(M. japonica, *Makino*)

A deciduous climber, with twining stems covered at first with more or less loose down. Leaves opposite, heart-shaped, tapered to a point at the apex, 2 to 4½ ins. long, half to two-thirds as wide near the base, which is deeply notched; somewhat downy on the midrib beneath, dull green; stalk 1 to 3 ins. long. Flowers produced from July to September in racemes 3 to 5 ins. long, in but one of the axils of each pair of leaves; flower-stalk downy. The flowers are frequently crowded at the end of the inflorescence as in an umbel. Corolla dull rosy white, about ½ in. diameter, with five reflexed lobes united into a bell-shaped base; the lobes are narrow, curled back at the points, and covered with pale hairs on the upper side. Seed-vessel 4 ins. long, spindle-shaped, the seeds furnished at one end with a tuft of beautiful silky hairs $1\frac{1}{4}$ ins. long.

Native of China and Japan; introduced in 1862. It is not often seen in gardens, but it flowers and has borne seed in the vicarage garden at Bitton, near Bristol. It usually dies back to the ground in winter in the open. It is interesting, but not particularly attractive, being allied to Marsdenia erecta, which has smaller leaves, sturdier stems, and more rounded petals.

METASEQUOIA GLYPTOSTROBOIDES, *Hu and Cheng*. METASEQUOIACEAE. See p. 635

MICHELIA COMPRESSA, *Sargent*. MAGNOLIACEÆ

This is the only really hardy species of a genus of trees closely allied to Magnolia, but distinguished by the flowers being axillary, and the ovules more numerous in each carpel. M. compressa is an evergreen tree, at least 40 ft. high, with a trunk 1 ft. or more in diameter, and a compact, rounded head of branches. Leaves 3 ins. in average length, oblong or obovate, tapering at the base to a slender stalk $\frac{1}{2}$ to 1 in. long; glabrous, leathery, and glossy green. Flowers (rarely seen in this country) $1\frac{1}{2}$ to 2 ins. across when fully expanded, magnolia-like, fragrant; sepals and petals pale yellow. Fruits on a cone 2 ins. long, each containing usually three seeds.

Native of Japan and, according to Hayata, of Formosa, it was introduced to England in 1894. It has proved hardy at Kew, although slow-growing, increasing in height about 3 or 4 ins. annually. Still rare.

M. DOLTSOPA, *Buchanan-Hamilton*

(Bot. Mag., t. 9645)

A shrub or tree 20 to 40 ft. high, or sometimes 50 to 80 ft. in the Himalaya; young stems slightly warted, soon glabrous. Leaves of firm texture, oval-oblong, 3 to 7 ins. long, $1\frac{1}{4}$ to 3 ins. wide, tapering to an often bluntish apex, rounded to tapered at the base, dark glossy green above, pale beneath; stalk $\frac{1}{2}$ to 1 in. long. Flowers very fragrant, soft pale yellow to white, solitary in the leaf-axils, very shortly stalked, 3 to 4 ins. across; petals twelve to sixteen, obovate to oblanceolate, rounded at the apex, $\frac{1}{2}$ to 1 in. wide. The flowers reach the bud state in autumn but do not open until the following spring.

Native of W. China, Tibet and E. Himalaya. Introduced from W. China by Forrest about 1918, first flowered in this country at Caerhays Castle in Cornwall in April 1933. Judging by Kingdon Ward's pictures in the *Gardeners' Chronicle*, vol. xcii (1932) it flowers very freely and must give a fine effect. The blossom has much the appearance of a large-sized Magnolia stellata. The tree is only likely to be a permanent success in the south-west. A specimen at Nymans got to be a big bush and flowered profusely in 1938 but died the following winter.

M. FUSCATA, *Blume*

(Magnolia fuscata, *Andrews*, Bot. Mag., t. 1008; Liriopsis fuscata, *Spach*)

An evergreen shrub ultimately 10 to 20 ft. high, of bushy habit; young shoots densely clothed with short brown hairs. Leaves narrowly oval or slightly obovate, tapering towards both ends, the apex blunt; 1½ to 4 ins. long, ⅝ to 2 ins. wide, furnished with brown down at first, finally nearly glabrous, dark glossy green; stalk ⅛ in. long, hairy like the shoots. Flowers very fragrant, produced in the leaf-axils, each on a brown, downy stalk ½ in. long; sepals and petals yellowish green stained with dull purple, ¾ to 1 in. long; flower-buds at first enclosed by brown downy bracts.

Native of China; introduced according to Aiton in 1789. At Kew this shrub has to be given the protection of a cool greenhouse, but in the mildest parts of our islands it is hardy. It is a cheerful evergreen, not conspicuous for beauty of flower but one of the most fragrant of all shrubs. Two or three blossoms will fill a small greenhouse with their fruity perfume, which strongly recalls that of an old-fashioned sweet known as "pear-drops." A succession of flowers is produced from April to summer. A plant at Cann House, near Plymouth, is 16 ft. high and 10 ft. in diameter. Closely allied to the magnolias, the michelias are readily distinguished by their axillary flowers.

MICROGLOSSA ALBESCENS, *C. B. Clarke*. COMPOSITÆ

(Bot. Mag., t. 6672; Aster cabulicus, *Lindley*; Amphiraphis albescens, *De Candolle*)

A plant with semi-woody, erect stems, growing in tufts about 3 ft. high, very pithy, and clothed with a grey down. Leaves alternate, lance-shaped, 2 to 5 ins. long, ½ to 1 in. wide; tapered to both ends, the margins entire or with minute teeth; grey and downy beneath. Flower-heads ⅓ in. diameter, produced during July, in compound corymbs 3 to 6 ins. across, terminating the current season's growth. Ray florets about fourteen, narrow; pale lilac-blue or bluish white; disk flowers yellow.

Native of the Himalaya, up to 12,000 ft.; introduced to the Chiswick gardens of the Royal Horticultural Society about 1840. It is nearly allied to Aster. The shoots made during the summer die back considerably during the winter, almost to the ground in severe seasons. The flowers are of a rather indeterminate blue, and the plant has no particular merit except in flowering in late summer. Propagated by cuttings of the young growths in heat, or by dividing old plants.

MITCHELLA. PARTRIDGE BERRY. RUBIACEÆ

A genus of two species named after John Mitchell, a botanist in Virginia and a correspondent of Linnæus in the eighteenth century. They are attractive little plants for the rock garden given a moist, lime-free, well-drained soil and some shade.

M. REPENS, *Linnæus*

(Loddiges' Botanical Cabinet, t. 979)

An evergreen, creeping, half-woody plant scarcely reaching above the ground; young shoots wiry, squarish, with traces of down when quite young. Leaves opposite, glabrous, dark glossy green, ovate to roundish, rounded at the apex, truncate or slightly heart-shaped at the base; ¼ to ⅝ (sometimes ⅞) in.

long and wide; stalk scarcely so long as the blade, downy on the upper side when quite young; stipules minute. Flowers fragrant, opening during June and July at the end of the shoot in scarcely stalked, erect pairs. Corolla up to ½ in. long, tubular at the base, dividing at the top into four spreading ovate lobes which are hairy inside and give the flower a diameter of about ⅜ in., white, often tinged with purple; calyx small, four-toothed; stamens four. Fruit globose, about ¼ in. wide, scarlet, formed by the union of the two ovaries, the two calyces persisting at the top, carrying normally eight seeds.

Var. LEUCOCARPA has white fruits.

Native of eastern and central N. America from Nova Scotia to Florida and westwards to Texas; introduced by John Bartram about 1761. It is very hardy, loves some shade, and is suitable for a moist spot in the rock garden. As its prostrate branches root freely as they lie, it is easily increased by division, also by cuttings. A pleasing little plant, perhaps scarcely woody enough to justify inclusion here, very much resembling Linnæa borealis in its creeping habit, small leaves, and twin flowers, but the latter belongs to the honeysuckle family, has the parts of its flower in fives, and the blossoms are borne at the top of a thread-like stalk as much as 3 ins. long.

M. UNDULATA, *Siebold and Zuccarini*

An evergreen, subshrubby plant with very slender, glabrous stems, self rooting. Leaves opposite, ¼ to 1 in. long, heart-shaped to truncate at the base, pointed at the apex, glabrous, margin undulated; stalk about ⅛ in. long. Flowers terminal, mostly in pairs, very shortly stalked; corolla slenderly cylindrical, ½ in. long, four-lobed and ¼ in. wide at the end, pink, becoming darker towards the tips, downy inside; calyx cup-shaped, ⅛ in. long, four-lobed.

Native of Japan, collected by the late H. J. Elwes in an Arbor-vitæ forest near Asmoni in the north, where it was growing in dense shade and flowering in July. Apparently not introduced until 1933, when it reached the late Mr Fred Stoker, who retrieved two plants from some packing material that had come from Japan. It is very hardy and flowers a month later than its American ally, which is distinct also in its more rounded leaves. In M. undulata they often approach triangular in shape.

MITRARIA COCCINEA, *Cavanilles*. GESNERACEÆ

(Bot. Mag., t. 4462)

A slender-stemmed prostrate or climbing evergreen shrub; young shoots densely clothed with short down. Leaves opposite, rather leathery, ovate or oval, pointed, rounded or tapered at the base, toothed; ½ to ⅞ in. long, ¼ to ⅜ in. wide; dark glossy green and with short hairs above when young; pale, rather glaucous, more or less downy on the midrib beneath; stalk $\frac{1}{16}$ in. long, downy. Flowers solitary on a slender downy stalk 1 to 1½ ins. long, produced from the axils of the leaves. Corolla rich scarlet, tubular, 1 to 1¼ ins. long, ⅙ to ¼ in. wide and rather bellied, downy. Sepals five, of unequal size, lanceolate, clasped on one side by downy bracts. Stamens four, the yellow anthers protruding beyond the corolla. Fruit an ovoid berry ⅜ in. wide, surmounted at first by the persistent style which is 1½ ins. long.

Native of the island of Chiloe and other parts of Chile; introduced by Wm. Lobb for Messrs Veitch of Exeter about 1846. The brilliant red flowers of this creeper, with its neat glossy foliage, are very attractive. Unfortunately it requires greenhouse treatment at Kew, but it can be grown out-of-doors in the south-west in shady moist positions. Mr Armytage Moore has it in his rock garden at Rowallane, Co. Down, a luxuriant mass 10 ft. across. At Leonardslea, Horsham, with the late Sir Edmund Loder, it flowered and developed fruit in a carefully selected spot. There is also a broad patch of it at Wakehurst, near Hayward's Heath, which suffers only in very hard winters. It comes into blossom during May and June and continues more or less until autumn. It dislikes drought and hot sunshine. On wild specimens the leaves are often much larger than we are accustomed to see them on cultivated plants, sometimes $1\frac{1}{2}$ ins. long and half as much wide.

MOLTKIA. BORAGINACEÆ

A genus of some half a dozen species of herbs or subshrubs. Leaves alternate, entire; corolla tubular to funnel-shaped, purple blue or yellow. The genus was named after Count J. G. Moltke, a Danish naturalist who died in 1818.

M. PETRÆA, *Grisebach*

(Lithospermum petræum, *De Candolle*, Bot. Mag., t. 5942)

A small semi-evergreen, bushy shrub, 1 to 2 ft. high; stems erect, and covered with grey hairs pointing upwards. Leaves alternate, narrow-linear, $\frac{1}{2}$ to $1\frac{1}{2}$ ins. long, about $\frac{1}{8}$ in. wide; covered like the stems with appressed, forward-pointing hairs on both surfaces. Flowers produced during June, in small crowded clusters terminating the young shoots, the whole inflorescence 1 to $1\frac{1}{2}$ ins. across. Corolla pinkish purple in bud, becoming violet-blue on opening, tubular, $\frac{1}{3}$ in. long, with five short, erect, rounded lobes. Stamens longer than the corolla lobes.

Native of Dalmatia, Albania, etc.; first introduced about 1840, and treated as a cool greenhouse plant. It was afterwards lost to cultivation, but was reintroduced by Messrs Backhouse of York thirty years later. It is not a robust plant and is certainly not adapted for shrubberies, but on a well-drained ledge in the rock garden at Kew it has lived for thirty years. Probably damp is more detrimental to its welfare than cold. Certainly no little shrub of its type deserves better care; it lasts in flower a good while, and no prettier or more dainty plant exists when every twig is crowned by the brilliantly coloured blossoms. The flowers have much the same arrangement as in the common borage; they are closely set, and open successively on the upper side of a stalk which becomes decurved. Summer cuttings take root readily. It needs a light, well-drained soil and a sunny position. Out of flower it has much the appearance of lavender.

M. SUFFRUTICOSA, *Brand*

(M. graminifolium, *Nyman*; Lithospermum graminifolium, *Viviani*)

A low, semi-evergreen shrub of tufted habit 6 to 18 ins. high when in flower; young shoots, leaves, flower-stalks and calyx all covered with appressed silky grey hairs. Leaves linear, pointed, the basal ones up to $4\frac{1}{2}$ ins. long,

⅛ in. or less wide; those of the flowering stems 1 to 2 ins. long, silvery beneath. Flowers borne at the top of a leafy stalk 4 to 8 ins. high in a branched pendulous cluster 1 to 2½ ins. wide; they are blue with a tinge of purple (pink in the bud state), about ½ in. long; calyx-lobes linear, stamens about as long as the corolla or rather shorter. The branches of the inflorescence often curve outwards and have the flowers set on the top, as is common in the borage family.

Native of Italy; put into commerce by Messrs Backhouse of York in 1888. Mr H. Correvon in *The Gardeners' Chronicle*, 2nd April 1910, p. 212, writes:

"I was once ascending Monte Summano, near Vicenza, when my eyes were suddenly arrested by a slope covered with a glorious azure of blue flowers. Judge my surprise when I recognised an old friend in Lithospermum graminifolium. It seemed as if the whole mountain were covered with it."

The plant is essentially one for a sunny place in the rock garden. I have never seen it better than in Major R. Emmet's garden at Moreton Paddox in Warwickshire, and it succeeds exceptionally well in the chalk in Col. Stern's garden at Highdown, near Worthing. M. petræa is easily distinguished from it by its shorter, comparatively broader leaves and well exposed stamens. There is a hybrid between the two grown in gardens as M. (or, more often, Lithospermum) intermedia, a taller, more shrubby plant with broader leaves.

MORUS. MULBERRY. URTICACEÆ

Of the dozen or so species of mulberry known, four or five can be grown without protection in the south of Britain. These are (with us) small, bushy-headed trees with alternate, deciduous, toothed, and often variously lobed leaves. The flowers are unisexual, the sexes borne on separate spikes, which are small, more or less cylindrical, axillary, and of no beauty. The "fruit" of the mulberry is really a fruit cluster, composed of closely packed drupes, each enclosed by the persistent, enlarged, succulent sepals.

Mulberry trees like a warm, well-drained, loamy soil, and M. nigra especially is worth growing for its luxuriant leafage and picturesque form. It is not much planted now, but nothing gives to a garden fortunate enough to possess it a greater sense of old-world charm and dignity than a rugged old mulberry standing on a lawn. It can be increased by summer cuttings with the greatest ease—the old writers say pieces 8 ft or more long will grow. Branches broken down but not detached will usually take root if they touch the ground. M. alba will also root from autumn or winter cuttings.

M. ACIDOSA, *Griffith*

(M. indica, *Roxburgh*, not *Linnæus*; M. australis, *Poiret*; M. japonica, *Bailey*)

A deciduous bushy tree up to 25 ft. high or, more usually, a shrub up to 10 or 15 ft. high; young shoots glabrous. Leaves very variable in size and shape, ordinarily ovate with a truncate or heart-shaped base and toothed, but often very deeply three- or five-lobed, the lobes themselves deeply scalloped; 2 to 6 ins. long and from two-thirds to quite as much in width; upper surface dull dark green and covered with minute warts which make it slightly rough to the touch; sparsely downy beneath, soon becoming nearly or quite glabrous stalk ¾ to 1½ ins. long. Male catkins up to 1¼ ins. long; female ones one-third as much long, silky-hairy. Fruits dark red, juicy, sweet, ½ in. or rather more long.

Native of China, Japan, and Korea; introduced by Wilson in 1907, but cultivated a good many years previously as "M. alba stylosa." Griffith (whose name for this mulberry is adopted by Schneider in *Plantæ Wilsonianæ*, vol. iii., p. 297) found it common in woods near Cheikwar (now spelt "Saikhoa"), a small town in Upper Assam on the Brahmaputra river. It is quite hardy and grows freely in this country although it is not so large a tree as the white or the common mulberry. It has been confused with M. alba, from which it differs in the stigma being borne on a distinct style; in M. alba the style is nearly or quite absent. The fruit of M. acidosa has, in consequence, a much more bristly appearance. When not in fruit a good distinction is the absence of tufts of down in the vein-axils of the leaf (present in M. alba). The leaves are not used to feed silkworms.

M. ALBA, *Linnæus*. WHITE MULBERRY

A deciduous tree, 30 to 45 ft. high, with a rounded head of branches and a trunk 6 ft. in girth; young shoots downy at first, becoming more or less glabrous by autumn. Leaves broadly ovate with a heart-shaped base, usually pointed, sometimes rounded at the apex, frequently three-lobed; varying much in size, from 3 to 8 ins. long and up to 6 ins. wide; coarsely toothed, lightish green and only slightly roughened above, downy near the veins and midrib beneath; stalk ½ to 1 in. long. Flowers produced during May in the leaf-axils and at the base of the new shoots; females on stalked cylindrical spikes ⅓ to ½ in. long; male spikes longer. Fruit-clusters ½ to 1 in. long, white or pinkish, sweet, insipid.

Native of China, and possibly of other parts of temperate Asia; cultivated from time immemorial in many South European and Eastern countries. In the old Dalmatian towns, like Ragusa and Spalato, old trees with rugged trunks give great charm to the streets; they are pruned back every winter. The white mulberry is the tree on which the silkworm is fed. It succeeds quite well in the south of England, but no success has ever been achieved in establishing the silkworm industry there in spite of several attempts, the first of which was made under the auspices of James I. The climate is considered to be too dull and damp. Nevertheless the tree is quite hardy at Kew, and over 30 ft. high, with a trunk 12 to 18 ins. in diameter; succulent, over-vigorous shoots are injured by frost. The tree, however, lacks the quaint charm of the common mulberry.

Many varieties of white mulberry are in cultivation, but those that differ chiefly in their influence on the silk produced by worms that feed on them have little interest to British arboriculturists. The following deserve mention:—

Var. FEGYVERNEKIANA.—A pigmy, usually under 3 ft. high.

Var. HETEROPHYLLA.—Leaves variously and unequally lobed.

Var. LACINIATA.—Leaves raggedly and deeply toothed.

Var. MACROPHYLLA, *Loddiges*.—One of the largest-leaved forms; leaves 7 to 9 ins. long.

Var. PENDULA.—A tree of very weeping habit forming an umbrella-like head. It is of so pendulous a nature that it is necessary to tie up a leading shoot every year to enable a trunk to be formed of the desired height. It should be trained up 20 ft., and will then make one of the most notable of weeping trees.

Var. VENOSA.—Leaves tapered at both ends, the veins very prominent, yellowish.

M. CATHAYANA, *Hemsley*

A tree 10 to 25 ft. high, young shoots downy at first, becoming smoother and greyish. Leaves heart-shaped, 3 to 6 ins. long on adult plants, three-fourths as wide (considerably larger on young vigorous plants), terminated at the apex by an abrupt slender point, margins roundish-toothed (often three-lobed in young trees); rough with short hairs above, softly downy beneath; primary veins in five or six pairs; stalk about 1 in. long, hairy. Male spikes ¾ in. long, borne on a slender stalk about the same length; female spikes of similar size, but with the flowers more closely packed. Fruit about 1 in. long, white, black, or red.

Native of Central China; first discovered about 1888, by Henry, in Hupeh; introduced twenty years later by Wilson. Young trees have hitherto grown freely, and promise to be quite hardy.

M. MONGOLICA, *C. K. Schneider*

(M. alba mongolica, *Bureau*)

A deciduous tree up to 25 ft. high, or a shrub; young shoots glabrous or soon becoming so. Leaves ovate, with a long, slender, often tail-like apex, heart-shaped at the base, coarsely triangular-toothed, each tooth terminated by a bristle; 3 to 6 ins. long, 2 to 3¼ ins. wide; nearly glabrous except for axil-tufts beneath when young; stalk 1 to 1⅝ ins. long. Male catkins 1 to 1½ ins. long, with a bare stalk one-third as long; female ones much shorter. Fruit described by Wilson as "pale red, sweet, palatable," also as "black."

Native of China and Korea; discovered by the Abbé David in 1864; introduced by Wilson in 1907. Originally regarded as a variety of M. alba, it was made a species by Schneider in *Plantæ Wilsonianæ*, vol. iii., p. 296. It is very distinct by reason of the coarse, bristly toothed margins of the leaves. Henry describes it as common on the mountains around Pekin and the fruit as "insipid." The style is longer than in M. alba and in this character the species approaches M. acidosa.

Var. DIABOLICA, *Koidzumi*, has leaves scabrid above, downy beneath and frequently deeply lobed. Var. VESTITA, *Rehder*, is distinguished by its leaves being densely downy on both surfaces.

M. NIGRA, *Linnæus*. COMMON MULBERRY (Plate 30)

A deciduous tree, 20 to 30 ft. high, of rugged, picturesque aspect, forming a dense spreading head of branches usually wider than the tree is high, and a short rough trunk; young shoots downy, exuding a milky juice when cut. Leaves broadly ovate or two- to five-lobed, always heart-shaped at the base, and with a short, tapered point; coarsely toothed; upper surface rough with short flattened hairs, deep glossy green; lower surface paler and downy. On vigorous barren growths the leaves will be 6 to 9 ins. long, and both lobed and unlobed; on fruiting shoots they are 2½ to 5 ins. long; stalk 1 in. or less long. Flower-spikes cylindrical, those carrying male flowers about 1 in. long, the females half as long; both on very downy stalks. Fruit clusters oval, ¾ to 1 in. long, dark red, with an agreeable sub-acid flavour.

The black mulberry is, no doubt, a native of one or more Oriental countries but having been cultivated for thousands of years and naturalised, its original limits have long been obliterated. It is known to have been cultivated in England since the early part of the sixteenth century, quite possibly long before. Trees at Syon, in Middlesex, are believed to have been planted there in 1548. It is better adapted for the southern part of Britain than the northern, but is always of slow growth. The famous "Shakespeare mulberry" (of which descendants are at Kew) was planted in the poet's garden at Stratford-on-Avon in 1609. Although not so good for the purpose as M. alba, the leaves

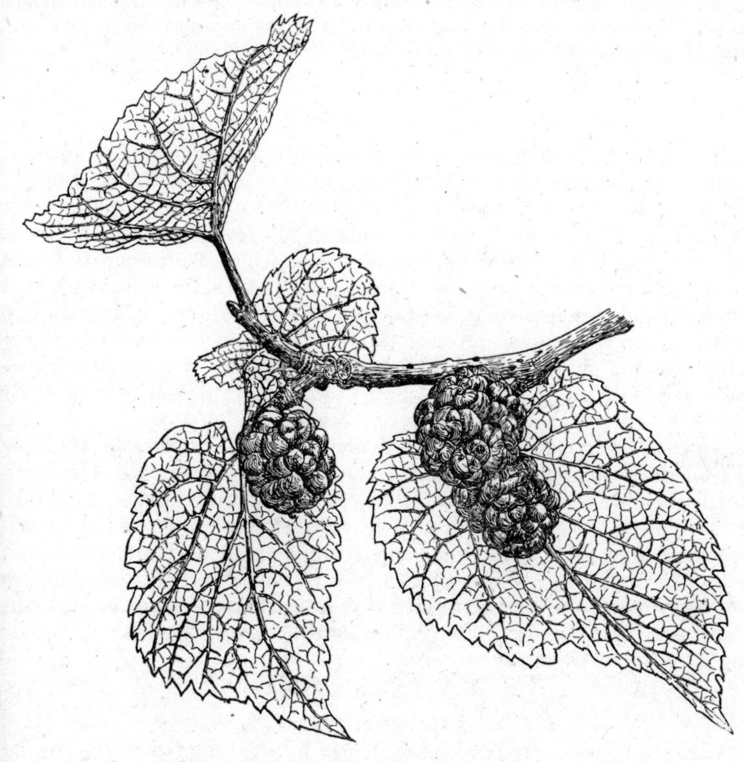

Morus nigra

of common mulberry have been much used to feed silkworms upon. The fruits are sometimes eaten at dessert, and they are also made into various conserves and drinks. So far as I am aware, the mulberry has never produced any variation from the type—a very unusual circumstance in a tree so long cultivated.

M. rubra, *Linnæus*. Red Mulberry

A deciduous tree, 40 to over 60 ft. high in a wild state, with a trunk 3 or 4 ft. in diameter. Leaves broadly ovate to roundish, heart-shaped at the base, slender-pointed, occasionally two- or three-lobed, toothed, 3 to 5 (occasionally 7 or 8) ins. long, three-fourths to about as much wide; somewhat rough above with scattered stiff hairs, or the remains of them, very downy beneath; stalks ½ to 1 in. long. Male spikes 1 to 2 ins. in length, slender and catkin-like; females 1 in. long; both downy. Fruit cluster 1 to 1¼ ins. long, cylindrical; at first red, then dark purple; sweet.

Native of the eastern and central United States; introduced in 1629. In my experience this mulberry thrives the worst of those here mentioned. At Kew it always has an unhappy appearance, and I do not know of good trees elsewhere. Probably our climate is as unsuited for it as for several other trees from the same region. In the United States it produces a light, tough, durable timber, and, according to Sargent, is planted in the southern States for the value of its fruit as food for poultry and hogs. Several named varieties are also cultivated there for human use. It is distinguished from alba and nigra by the leaves being much more downy beneath.

MUEHLENBECKIA. POLYGONACEÆ

A genus of about fifteen species of shrubs or semi-woody climbers, chiefly Australasian, some South American. Leaves alternate, stalked; flowers small, greenish or whitish, of little or no ornament, the sexes sometimes on separate plants. Perianth deeply five-lobed, stamens eight; fruit a nutlet, three-angled, and enclosed in the perianth, which persists and sometimes becomes fleshy. The species are so variable that it is difficult to define their limits, but I believe there to be only two species commonly grown out-of-doors in this country, viz., M. axillaris, a tiny creeping shrub, and M. complexa, a climber. The latter is sometimes met with as "australis" and "adpressa," names which really belong to species with much larger leaves up to 3 ins. long. M. AUSTRALIS, *Meissner*, is from New Zealand, and M. ADPRESSA, *Meissner* (nearly allied to it), is Australian; both have panicled inflorescences, and neither is likely to be hardy, except in our very mildest localities. Of the real M. VARIANS I am able to ascertain little. It was described by Meissner in 1852 as having panicled inflorescences 3 to 4 ins. long; its country unknown. Cheeseman in his recent *Monograph of the New Zealand Flora* does not mention it. It is, perhaps, a form of australis or adpressa, with smaller, often fiddle-shaped leaves, usually 1 to 1½ ins. long.

M. AXILLARIS, *Walpers*

(M. nana, *Hort.*)

A tiny, deciduous, creeping shrub, 1 or 2 ins. high, forming a dense mat upon the ground of thin wiry branches, and spreading indefinitely by underground stems. Ultimately it may make a tangled mass of stems 1 foot high. Young shoots minutely downy. Leaves ovate to round, ⅛ to ⅓ in long, glabrous, not toothed; the stalk scarcely so long. Flowers pale green, very tiny, produced singly or in pairs in the axils of the terminal leaves during July.

Native of the mountainous districts of New Zealand, Tasmania, and Australia. This little shrub, which is one of the very dwarfest in cultivation, may be recommended to lovers of curiosities. Its flowers are scarcely perceptible, but its thread-like stems, tiny round leaves, and matted growth, make it interesting. It may be grown on some rock garden ledge. Easily increased by division or cuttings.

M. COMPLEXA, *Meissner*

(Bot. Mag., t. 8449)

A climbing deciduous shrub, forming dense masses of slender, wiry, much interlaced stems; minutely warted when young. Leaves very variable in shape and size, being roundish, heart-shaped, oblong and fiddle-shaped, sometimes on the same plant; they are thin, dull green, quite glabrous, $\frac{1}{8}$ to $\frac{3}{4}$ in. long; stalk rough with minute warts, $\frac{1}{8}$ to $\frac{1}{4}$ in. long. Flowers greenish white, $\frac{1}{6}$ in. long, produced in autumn in small terminal and axillary spikes about $\frac{2}{3}$ in. long; the perianth with its five erect, oblong, blunt-ended lobes persists to the fruiting stage, becoming enlarged and glistening waxy white and enclosing the black shining nutlet.

Native of New Zealand, often found at considerable altitudes. It differs from australis in its usually smaller leaves and in having its flowers nearly always in short spikes. It makes a dense and interesting cover for old tree-stumps and rubble-heaps; and it is even worth while allowing it to ramble over a common or unimportant shrub 6 to 10 ft. high, which it will in time smother by an amazingly thick tangle of dark wiry stems. Hardy in the south and west; killed to ground-level by severe frost at Kew.

M. EPHEDROIDES, *Hooker fil.*

A deciduous shrub of prostrate sprawling habit, forming a thicket of slender stems which are rush-like the first year, deeply grooved and without down. Leaves linear to halberd-shaped, $\frac{1}{3}$ to 1 in. long, $\frac{1}{16}$ to $\frac{1}{6}$ in. wide, glabrous, usually inconspicuous or even absent. Flowers small, mostly unisexual, produced from the leaf-axils in short spikes or few-flowered clusters; on the spikes the flowers are predominantly of one sex but often have a few flowers of the other sex mixed with them; they have no beauty. The fruit is black, triangular in cross section, about $\frac{1}{8}$ in. long, subtended by the persisting, more or less succulent perianth.

Var. MURICATULA, *Cheeseman*, is a distinct variety grown by Mr E. A. Bowles at Myddleton House, Waltham Cross, Herts. It differs from the type in its very slender, almost thread-like young shoots, in the smaller leaves ($\frac{1}{6}$ to $\frac{1}{2}$ in. long) and in the segments of the perianth becoming membranous in fruit. I saw it in July 1932, bearing a large crop of its three-angled seeds rather like miniature beechnuts, but black. (M. muricatula, *Colenso.*)

Native of the North and South Islands of New Zealand. Of interest chiefly to botanists and lovers of curiosities.

MUSA BASJOO, *Siebold.* JAPANESE BANANA. MUSACEÆ

(Bot. Mag., t. 7182; M. japonica, *Hort.*)

Stems cylindrical, slightly tapering upwards, 6 to 9 ft. high, as many or more inches wide at the base, crowned by four to six leaves. Leaves oblong, bright green, the largest 8 or 9 ft. long, and 2 ft. wide; the smallest one-third those dimensions; all have the close parallel veins springing at nearly right angles from the midrib that are characteristic of all the musas; stalk 6 to 12 ins. long, winged. Flowers borne on a stout arching inflorescence proceeding from the apex of the stem, the main-stalk of which is 1 to $1\frac{1}{2}$ ft. long and 2 ins. or more in diameter. The flowers (yellowish, cylindrical, of no beauty) open successively over a long season in clusters, each cluster consisting of two rows enclosed in the early stages by a large, concave, leathery bract. Fruit banana-like, 3 or 4 ins. long, about 1 in. thick, three-angled, attaining full-size at the base whilst the terminal flower-clusters are still expanding.

It is doubtful if this plant has a claim to notice in these pages, for there is nothing woody about it, even at the root. Yet it is tree-like, has a clean stem and persistent evergreen foliage. It was introduced from Japan by Charles Maries about 1881 when collecting for Messrs Veitch, and was first grown out-of-doors in this country at the Coombe Wood Nursery in Surrey. It will live in the open air at Kew for a few years but becomes more enfeebled each successive season and finally succumbs. Dr Wilfrid Fox grows it successfully a few miles south of Godalming, but it is only really at its best in the south-west. There is a large mass of it at Caerhays Castle in Cornwall which bears fruit regularly. In general appearance it is a smaller replica of the common banana tree (M. Sapientum) and quite unlike anything else in the open air in this country. It has therefore considerable interest, but otherwise I do not consider it worth its place in the garden except in some out-of-the-way spot. It must be given a well-sheltered place or the wind will tear the leaves to ribbons. Although with wind protection it may be a handsome and really striking object for a few late summer months, it usually wears a dismal aspect in our climate for the rest of the year with its dead or tattered foliage. The species is grown in Japan for the fibre obtained from the leaves. I do not know that the fruit is edible. Given shelter from wind and a sufficiently mild climate, its only other requirement is a rich loam to grow in. It can be increased by its sucker growths.

MUTISIA. Compositæ

A genus of evergreen composites notable on account of their mostly climbing habit and showy flower-heads, inhabiting various tropical and temperate parts of S. America, especially Chile, where according to Reiche, the author of a flora of that country, thirty-four species are to be found; altogether about sixty species are known. The leaves are alternate and in one cultivated species, M. Clematis, they are pinnate; in all the others we grow the leaves are simple, varying from broadly elliptical to linear and from deeply toothed to entire. The midrib is very frequently prolonged into a tendril, sometimes branched. The flowers are crowded in "heads," as is the case with all composites, and they are terminal, their beauty depending mainly on the ray-florets, which are often beautifully and brilliantly coloured.

Most of the species are only suited for the milder parts of the country and even there are not easily kept in health for a long term of years, although in certain places they go on indefinitely (see note on M. decurrens at Killerton). Some are apt to die off suddenly without any apparent cause. M. Clematis is an exception and quite amenable to cultivation. Often they grow wild pretty much as the honeysuckle does in our English copses, scrambling over other shrubs. They probably prefer to have their roots and main-stems in the shade, but the younger parts in full sunshine. A perfectly drained light sandy loam, with which stones are freely mixed, is recommended by those who have succeeded best with them.

The genus was named after J. C. Mutis, who was born at Cadiz in 1732, afterwards teacher of anatomy at Madrid, and a student of S. American plants; died about 1808.

M. CLEMATIS, *Linnæus fil.*

(Bot. Mag., t. 8391; Gardeners' Chronicle, 29th Nov. 1913, supplement)

A vigorous evergreen climber 30 ft. or more high; young stems slender, ribbed, and clothed like the undersurface of the leaves, the flower-stalks, and the outer bracts of the flower-head with a thick, soft, whitish wool. Leaves alternate, pinnate, composed of six, eight, or ten leaflets, the woolly main-stalk lengthening out at the end into a slender, forked tendril several inches long, by which the plant supports itself in climbing. Leaflets oblong-ovate, pointed, rounded or widely tapered at the base, entire; $\frac{2}{3}$ to $1\frac{1}{2}$ ins. long, $\frac{1}{3}$ to $\frac{1}{2}$ in. wide; woolly on both surfaces at first, the upper one wearing clean; very shortly stalked. Flower-heads solitary, terminal, pendulous, the lower part cylindrical, 2 to $2\frac{1}{2}$ ins. long, enclosed in an involucre of four or five series of erect, oblong-lanceolate bracts. Ray-florets nine or ten, brilliant orange-scarlet, spreading horizontally or slightly recurved, giving the flower-head a diameter of 2 to $2\frac{1}{2}$ ins.

Native of the Andes of Colombia and Ecuador, one of its natural sites being on the high slopes of Mt. Pichincha, almost on the equator; introduced in 1859. Near London it has to be given cool greenhouse treatment, but it is hardy in the milder counties. A large plant climbs up the Rectory at Ludgvan, near Penzance. A plant formerly grown in the Temperate House at Kew commenced to flower in May and continued until October; the plant there was pruned back and its weak shoots thinned out before growth commenced in spring. Unlike some of the mutisias this species is very amenable to cultivation and is really so rampant a grower that this annual pruning soon becomes necessary under glass, and desirable out-of-doors. Propagated by cuttings of half-ripened shoots quite easily.

M. DECURRENS, *Cavanilles*

(Bot. Mag., t. 5273)

A climbing evergreen shrub, growing 8 to 10 ft. high; stems slender, glabrous, but little branched. Leaves narrow-oblong, stalkless; the blade 3 to 5 ins. long, $\frac{1}{2}$ to 1 in. wide; the base being extended down each side of the stem as a pair of narrow wings, the apex terminating in a forked tendril which curls round any available support, and thus holds up the stem. Flower-heads 4 to 5 ins. across, solitary at the end of the shoot, and borne on a glabrous stalk 3 to 5 ins. long. Ray florets about fifteen, each $\frac{1}{2}$ in. wide, and of a brilliant orange or vermilion colour; disk florets yellow. The flower-head is supported at the base by a columnar mass of overlapping thin scales tipped with greyish hairs, and has much the aspect of a Gazania or single dahlia.

Native of Chile; introduced for Messrs Veitch in 1859 by Richard Pearce. Except in comparatively few places it has not proved a success in this country, and is now uncommon. One of the greatest successes with it has been obtained in Sir Thomas Acland's garden at Killerton, near Exeter. A plant there is grown against a wall facing south-west, and Mr J. Coutts, who planted it and cultivated it for several years, tells me that it has borne over three hundred flower-heads during one summer. He ascribes his success with it, first, to the position and climate; second, to the soil, which is not the ordinary red soil of Devon, but volcanic trap; and lastly, to the practice of placing stones on the ground about the roots. The Killerton plant produces suckers freely, and by them can be propagated; it also ripens seed from which many plants have been raised. This mutisia is capable of withstanding severe cold; soon after it was introduced it experienced 26° of frost at Exeter without injury.

M. ILICIFOLIA, *Cavanilles*

(Bot. Mag., t. 6009; Gardeners' Chronicle, 29th Nov. 1913, fig. 135)

A slender-stemmed evergreen climbing plant whose young shoots, as seen on cultivated plants, are furnished with toothed ridges (wings); they are clothed with a whitish or pale brown wool, as are also the leaves beneath and the flower-stalks. Many wild specimens in the Kew Herbarium show that those parts of the plant are often glabrous and the stems merely ribbed. Leaves holly-like, leathery, simple, stalkless, ovate-oblong, deeply heart-shaped at the base, 1 to 2¼ ins. long, the margins strongly spiny-toothed, the midrib prolonged 1 to 4 ins. so as to form a slender curling tendril; upper surface dark bright green. Flower-heads solitary, terminal, borne on a stalk usually less than ½ in. long. Ray-florets eight to twelve, of various shades of pink or pale mauve, oblong-lanceolate, pointed, giving the flower-head a diameter of 2 to 3 ins. Disk-florets yellow, numerous, forming a circular mass in the centre 1 in. wide. Bracts of the involucre erect, roundish ovate to lanceolate, often constricted at the apex to a short point, but variously shaped. It flowers at almost all seasons.

Native of Chile; introduced in 1832. Generally it is regarded as a cool greenhouse plant, but it is grown as a wall plant in Cornwall and even in the rock garden at Edinburgh Botanic Garden has survived twenty winters. Mr Clarence Elliott collected it in Chile at 5000 to 6000 ft. altitude, flowering in November 1927. He notes that it was climbing over and smothering bushes up to 10 and 15 ft. high. Easily recognised by its sessile, simple, holly-like leaves and shortly stalked flower-heads, but sometimes found to be difficult to keep in good health. There is a healthy plant on a wall at Trewithen, Cornwall, which I saw flowering freely in July 1932.

M. OLIGODON, *Poeppig and Endlicher*

(Bot. Mag. t. 9499; Gardeners' Chronicle, 13th Oct. 1928, fig. 136;
M. Gayana, *Remy*)

An evergreen semi-climbing, semi-prostrate shrub with ribbed young shoots covered at first with a loose, pale wool. Leaves 1 to 1½ ins. long, ¼ to ⅞ in. wide, oblong, stalkless, the base mostly bi-lobed, the lobes clasping the stem, the midrib prolonged into a slender, curling tendril ½ to 3 ins. long; margins coarsely triangularly toothed; dark bright green above, covered with pale wool beneath. Flower-heads solitary, terminal, borne on a slender stalk 1 to 3 ins. long; ray-florets six to twelve, elliptical to oblanceolate, roundish or blunt at the end, 1¼ ins. long, ⅜ in. wide, of a beautiful silky pink. Bracts of the involucre closely overlapping, roundish-ovate, with down at the margin and a short mucro at the apex.

Native of Chile at 3000 to 4000 ft. altitude. Originally described in 1835, and afterwards found by Veitch's collector, Richard Pearce (1859-66), it seems first to have been introduced to cultivation by H. F. Comber during his Andean Expedition, 1925-7. He describes it as covering large areas, spreading by means of underground stems, a single plant often filling a space of 8 to 10 sq. yds. He found it common in rocky places and on hot, dry pastures. It appears usually to be dwarf, often only 6 to 12 ins. high, but in one of his field notes he gives it as 2 to 4 ft. high and in another as a "climber 4 to 8 ft." It is growing well with Mr Musgrave at Hascombe in Surrey and at Nymans, near Crawley, in a loose mixture of loam, leaf-mould, stones, and sand. Mr Comber, the gardener at Nymans, considers it a beautiful plant although its persisting dead leaves tend to make it look untidy—a characteristic, Mr Clarence Elliott tells me, of several species in a wild state. At Logan in Wigtownshire I saw it in May 1931, just coming very freely into blossom, the flower-heads salmon pink. The plants were prostrate and growing over stones.

M. RETUSA, *Remy*

An evergreen climber whose height is given by recent collectors as 10 to 20 ft. Leaves 1 to 2¼ ins. long, half as much wide, stalkless, elliptical or oblong, lobed at the base, notched at the apex; the margins varying from entire to coarsely and triangularly toothed down the whole length; but often with the dentation confined to one or two teeth near the apex; dark green and glabrous above, varying from glabrous to loosely woolly beneath; the midrib extended into a tendril up to 3 ins. long. Flower-heads borne on stalks up to 3 ins. long; ray-florets about eight, pink, oblanceolate, 1¼ ins. long, ¼ to ½ in. wide.

Native of Chile; originally named by Remy in Gay's *Flora of Chile* in 1847. It was collected by Richard Pearce for Veitch's in 1868 and flowered at Kew in 1894. The plants at present in cultivation were introduced by H. F. Comber during his Andean expedition, 1925-7. It is succeeding very well at Nymans, in Sussex, scrambling over a large hawthorn where it flowers freely and where self-sown seeds germinate in the borders. This species, as Mr C. Elliott has observed, is not very distinct from ilicifolia from a gardener's point of view, but the flower-head in ilicifolia is very shortly stalked as a rule, sometimes almost sessile, and the leaves are harder, more uniformly coarsely toothed and more distinctly net-veined. Mr Elliott considered, from what he saw of the two species in Chile, that ilicifolia had superior flowers, but retusa may be more amenable to cultivation.

Var. ALBA has white ray-florets. Var. GLABERRIMA, *Philippi*, has more uniformly glabrous leaves than the type, but they are not always glabrous, and the species is so variable in this respect that it may be difficult to draw a line between them. The Nymans plant is of this variety.

M. SUBULATA, *Ruiz and Pavon*

(Bot. Mag., t. 9461; Gardeners' Chronicle, 13th Sept. 1930, fig. 75)

An evergreen, slender-stemmed climber reported by collectors as growing 6 to 10 ft. high; young shoots grey, ribbed, much zigzagged. Leaves glabrous, linear, 1 to 3 ins. long, $\frac{1}{16}$ in. or so wide, grey green, grooved above, the midrib prominent beneath and often prolonged at the apex into a curling tendril. Flower-heads with some eight or ten ray-florets of an orange-scarlet colour, each floret of lanceolate shape, 1½ ins. long by ¼ in. wide. Involucre cylindrical, 1½ ins. long by ½ in. wide; scales overlapping, ¼ to ⅜ in. wide, broadly ovate, tipped with down.

Native of Chile; originally named in 1798 and collected in a wild state many times since, but not introduced apparently until 1928, when seeds reached Britain through the agency of Messrs C. Elliott and G. W. Robinson; a living plant brought home by the latter flowered in 1930. It is very distinct from the species previously mentioned in its stems which are scarcely thicker than an ordinary strand of worsted. Like other species, it should be planted to grow over a bush or small tree, on which it should eventually form a mass of interlaced branches and flower about midsummer. It is of doubtful hardiness, but would, no doubt, find the south-western counties warm enough. Related to this species is

M. LINEARIFOLIA, *Cavanilles*, but it has its dark shining leaves much more crowded on the stem, sometimes, judging by wild specimens, a dozen or more to the inch; they are also shorter, mostly only 1 to 1½ ins. long and up to ⅛ in. wide, linear-subulate and pointed. Flower-heads "rich and brilliant crimson-scarlet"; involucre bottle-shaped, 1¼ ins. long. Mr C. Elliott introduced it from Chile in 1928. He writes that at 6000 ft. altitude (below which he did not find it) it was a wiry climber trailing over shrubs up to 8 or 10 ft. At 9000 ft. it grew flat upon desolate screes, forming clumps 3 or 4 ft. wide, with thick woody root-stocks not rising more than 3 ins. above ground level and suggesting when in flower colonies of scarlet gerberas. Considering the altitudes which it reaches, it should be hardy in many parts of Britain. Personally I have only seen it in a living state in Mr Musgrave's garden at Hascombe, Surrey. Judging by wild specimens, the midribs of the leaves do not lengthen out into tendrils, at least on the flowering parts of the plant.

MYRICA. GALE, BAYBERRY. MYRICACEÆ

Deciduous and evergreen shrubs or small trees, with scented alternate leaves and unisexual flowers, the sexes sometimes on the same plant, sometimes separated. Flowers in catkins, and produced in the axils of bracts. There are neither sepals nor petals, the male flower consisting of a varying number of stamens, the female of a one-celled ovary with two stalkless stigmas.

The myricas are not much grown in gardens, but are worth a place for their sweetly scented leaves, and, in the American kinds, their white, wax-coated fruits. They thrive in any ordinary soil. Increased by seed or layering.

M. CALIFORNICA, *Chamisso*. CALIFORNIAN BAYBERRY

An evergreen shrub, usually 10 to 14 ft. high, with vigorous shoots, hairy when young. Leaves oblanceolate or somewhat oval, tapered at both ends, regularly and angularly toothed, sometimes almost to the base; 2 to 4 ins. long, ½ to ¾ in. wide; dark glossy green, glandular on both surfaces, especially beneath, downy only on the midrib above, slightly fragrant when crushed; stalk ¼ in. or less long. Male catkins borne in the axils of the year-old leaves, about 1 in. long; female catkins usually on the same plant. Fruit globular, ⅙ in. across, purple, but covered with white wax.

Native of California, where it is sometimes a tree 40 ft. high. In very hard winters this shrub is cut back to ground-level at Kew, but in ordinary winters survives without injury except to the tips of the young shoots. It is a cheerful, vigorous evergreen, but its leaves are not so strongly scented as those of the other species here mentioned. Very well adapted for the milder parts of the country. It is 30 ft. high at Tregrehan in Cornwall.

M. CERIFERA, *Linnæus*. WAX MYRTLE

A deciduous, or more or less evergreen shrub in this country, but said to be at times a small evergreen tree, 20 to 40 ft. high in a wild state; young shoots reddish, downy. Leaves narrowly obovate or oblanceolate, very variable in size in different forms, the largest 4½ ins. long and 2 ins. wide, but normally

$1\frac{1}{2}$ to 3 ins. long, $\frac{1}{3}$ to $\frac{3}{4}$ in. wide; usually toothed towards the apex, glossy green and glabrous above, dotted with yellowish resin-glands beneath, and downy on the midrib; stalk $\frac{1}{8}$ to $\frac{1}{4}$ in. long. Male catkins $\frac{1}{4}$ to $\frac{1}{2}$ in. long. Fruits globular, $\frac{1}{8}$ in. wide, coated with white glistening wax, stalkless, densely crowded in clusters of two to six on the growths of the previous year.

Native of the south-eastern United States; introduced in 1699. In the early part of the occupation by Europeans of its native region, this shrub was valued by the settlers for the wax yielded by the fruits. This white, waxy coating, which gives so distinctive a character to the plant in autumn, was removed by boiling, and then made into candles. According to Kalm, the Swedish traveller, these candles burnt better and more slowly than ordinary tallow ones, and gave an agreeable smell when extinguished. The species is very variable in leaf, especially in size and toothing.

Var. LATIFOLIA, *Aiton*.—A form grown for many years at Kew. It has obovate leaves 2 to $4\frac{1}{2}$ ins. long, 1 to 2 ins. wide; dark glossy green and glabrous above, hairy over the whole surface beneath, especially on the midrib; young shoots hairy. It is a shrub up to 9 ft. high and 12 ft. through.

Closely allied to M. cerifera, and perhaps a more northerly form of it, is the "Bayberry"—M. CAROLINENSIS, *Miller*. This reaches into Canada, and extends in a wild state from Nova Scotia, New Brunswick, and Prince Edward Island south to Florida, etc. If differs in its leaves being more often oblong and oval than obovate, more abruptly tapered at the base, and blunter at the apex than in M. cerifera; downy above. Young wood downy. The fruit is coated with white wax, as in the other, but is somewhat larger ($\frac{1}{6}$ in. wide). This species is always shrubby and up to 8 or 9 ft. high. It is, no doubt, hardier than the true cerifera and probably is grown under that name in many gardens.

M. GALE, *Linnæus*. SWEET GALE

(Gale palustris, *Chevalier*)

A deciduous shrub, 2 to 4 ft. high, bushy; wood and leaves fragrant when crushed. Leaves oblanceolate, tapering and entire at the base, toothed and broadest near the apex; 1 to $2\frac{1}{2}$ ins. long, $\frac{1}{3}$ to $\frac{3}{4}$ in. wide; glossy and dark green above; paler, more or less downy, and with scattered shining glands beneath; stalk $\frac{1}{8}$ in. long. Flowers of the male plant produced during May and June in crowded, stalkless catkins, each catkin $\frac{1}{3}$ to $\frac{5}{8}$ in. long, set with close, overlapping, shining, concave scales. Fruit catkins about as long, but stouter; composed of closely set, resinous nutlets $\frac{1}{12}$ in. wide. The flowers are borne on the naked wood of the previous year; the sexes usually on separate plants.

Native of the higher latitudes of all the northern hemisphere; common in Great Britain, especially in the north, usually in moist peaty places, and on moors. In gardens the sweet gale is sometimes grown for the sake of its pleasant fragrance when handled. On the Yorkshire moors branches were, and perhaps still are, used to flavour a kind of home-made beer known as "gale beer," considered to be very efficacious for slaking thirst.

VAR. TOMENTOSA.—Young wood, both surfaces of the leaf (but especially the lower one), very downy. Siberia, Japan.

MYRICARIA GERMANICA, *Desvaux*. TAMARICACEÆ

A deciduous shrub, 6 to 8 ft. high, glaucous grey, and of rather gaunt habit. Branches erect, plume-like, clothed with flat round-pointed, linear leaves, from $\frac{1}{16}$ to $\frac{3}{16}$ in. long, glabrous and dotted with glands.

Flowers densely set in slender racemes 3 to 8 ins. long, which terminate the branchlets all over the top of the shrub; each flower is about ¼ in. long, produced in the axil of a bract longer than itself; petals narrow, pink or pinkish white. Stamens ten; seeds feathery.

Native of Europe, Himalaya, Afghanistan, etc.; cultivated in England since 1582. It inhabits river banks, mountain streams, and other sandy, occasionally inundated places, where it often fills the ground over long distances. Closely allied to Tamarix (from which it differs chiefly in the more numerous and united stamens), it is not so ornamental as various members of that genus. It is easily propagated by cuttings made of stout wood of the current year placed in sandy soil in the open ground in October. It flowers from May to August.

MYRSINE. MYRSINACEÆ

This genus consists of some 150 species of trees and shrubs. The flowers are usually small, or even minute and inconspicuous, often unisexual. Fruit a pea-like drupe, one-seeded and either dry or rather fleshy. The parts of the flower are mostly in fours or fives. The New Zealand species, including two of the following, are sometimes put in a separate genus—SUTTONIA.

M. AFRICANA, *Linnæus*

(Bot. Mag., t. 8712)

An evergreen shrub, usually from 2 to 4 ft. high, bushy, and very leafy; young shoots angled, covered with short down. Leaves alternate, about ⅛ in. apart on the twigs, oval to narrowly obovate, rounded or tapering at the apex, always tapered at the base; ¼ to ¾ in. long, $\frac{3}{16}$ to ½ in. wide; toothed at the terminal half only, glabrous on both surfaces, lustrous dark green above; stalk downy, $\frac{1}{16}$ in. long. Flowers of one sex only on a plant, very tiny, pale brown, produced in stalkless clusters of three to six at the leaf-axils. Berries on the female plant pale blue, orange-shaped, ¼ in. or less across, with the persistent calyx at the base, containing a single seed.

Native of the Himalaya, China, Azores, and the mountains of E. and S. Africa. This curious little shrub, which is of neat habit and has a general resemblance to Ilex crenata, is spread widely over the Old World. It has no flower-beauty. The plants in cultivation are mostly, if not entirely, of Himalayan or Chinese origin. It appears to be very hardy; a plant raised from seed in 1895 at Kew grew for many years in the rock garden unprotected. This plant, which was only 1 ft. high was killed during the hard winter of 1946-47. There is a female plant which bears fruit in Lord Ilchester's garden at Abbotsbury, near Weymouth; and there used to be one in Mr A. Waterer's nursery at Knap Hill. I have had it also in fruit from Devonshire, Ireland, etc.

M. CHATHAMICA, *F. Mueller*

(Suttonia chathamica, *Mez*)

A small evergreen tree up to 20 ft. high; young shoots furnished with short, stiff hairs. Leaves alternate, leathery, obovate, notched at the rounded apex, tapered at the base, not toothed; 1 to 2½ ins. long, ¾ to 1½ ins. wide; glabrous except for down along the midrib beneath, pale green on both surfaces, dotted with glands beneath; stalk 1/6 in. or so long. Flowers 1/10 in. wide, unisexual, produced in dense clusters in the leaf-axils and on the lower naked part of the shoot; petals four, ciliate, thickly dotted with reddish glands. Fruit globose, purplish, 1/4 to 1/3 in. wide, containing one seed.

Native of Chatham Islands (New Zealand); introduced by Major A. A. Dorrien-Smith, who visited the islands in December 1909 and found it common there in certain woods. One of its companion trees, then in full bloom, was Veronica gigantea, 20 ft. high. The myrsine—inconspicuous in its flowers—should succeed where Olearia semidentata, perhaps the most beautiful of Chatham Island shrubs, succeeds.

M. NUMMULARIA, *Hooker fil.*

(Suttonia nummularia, *Hooker fil.*, Flora of New Zealand, vol. i., t. 45)

A prostrate evergreen shrub only an inch or two high, with very slender, wiry, reddish brown, slightly downy shoots. Leaves alternate, set on the twigs eight to twelve to the inch, rather leathery, broadly obovate to orbicular, toothless, often slightly indented at the apex; 1/6 to 1/3 in. long and wide; dark green, glabrous, rather wrinkled, dotted beneath with numerous translucent glands; stalk 1/16 in. long, grooved and downy on the upper side. Flowers unisexual, very small and inconspicuous, produced during May and June singly, in pairs, or in threes in the leaf-axils; they are very shortly stalked, only 1/6 in. wide, yellowish white; petals four, edged with tiny hairs, concave; anthers almost as large as the petals. Fruit berry-like, globose, blue-purple, 1/5 to 1/4 in. wide, containing one seed.

Native of the North and South Islands of New Zealand, at altitudes of 2000 to 5000 ft.; also of Stewart Island, where it occurs at sea-level. It is fairly hardy at Kew, also at Edinburgh, where I saw it in flower in June 1931. It is really of more interest than beauty unless the fruits, which I have not seen, are abundant enough to be attractive. In general appearance it suggests one of the dwarf, small-leaved vacciniums or a small Cotoneaster microphylla, and is best adapted for the rock garden.

MYRTUS. MYRTACEÆ. MYRTLE

A genus of evergreen shrubs, mostly from S. America and Australia. Leaves opposite, covered with translucent dots. Calyx and corolla of four or five parts. They are tender in our average climate.

M. BULLATA, *Solander*

(Bot. Mag., t. 4809)

An evergreen shrub 10 to 15 ft. high, or a small tree; young shoots downy. Leaves opposite, orbicular or ovate, entire, most usually 3/4 to 1 1/4 ins. long, scarcely as wide (sometimes over 2 ins. long), of rather leathery texture, purple and downy when young on both surfaces, changing to reddish brown, the blade conspicuously puckered and blistered between the veins; stalk 1/8 to 1/4 in. long, very downy. Flowers 3/4 in. wide, white, solitary in the leaf-axils, each on a downy stalk 1/2 to 5/8 in. long; calyx purple; petals round; stamens numerous, with white stalks and yellow anthers. Fruit a black-red, egg-shaped berry 1/3 in. long.

Native of New Zealand; introduced originally to Kew, where it flowered as long ago as June 1854. It is scarcely hardy there, but succeeds well in the south-west, where it has reached nearly or quite 20 ft. in height. Its chief feature is the curiously bullate or blistered appearance of the leaves, which makes it quite distinct from any other shrub that, so far as I know, can be grown in the open air in this country. So far as I have seen, it is shy-flowering.

M. COMMUNIS, *Linnæus*. COMMON MYRTLE

An evergreen, very leafy shrub, up to 10 or 12 ft. high, sometimes a small tree; young wood downy. Leaves opposite, ovate or lanceolate, pointed, 1 to 2 ins. long, ⅓ to ¾ in. wide; dark glossy green above, paler beneath, glabrous on both sides, fragrant when crushed, and covered with transparent dots; margins entire, decurved; stalk very short or none. Flowers white, ¾ in. across, fragrant, nearly always solitary on a slender stalk ¾ to 1 in. long arising from the leaf-axils, the most conspicuous features being the crowded stamens ⅓ in. long, produced in a brush-like cluster, and the five rounded petals; calyx green, with five erect, short, broadly ovate lobes. Fruit a purplish black berry, roundish oblong, ½ in. in length (white in variety LEUCOCARPA, *De Candolle*).

The common myrtle is now very abundant in S. and E. Europe and the Mediterranean region generally, but is believed to have been introduced there from W. Asia, probably Persia or Afghanistan. It was probably one of the first shrubs introduced to our islands from the Levant, and was well known in the sixteenth century. One of the favourite plants of the ancients, and held sacred by them to the goddess of Love, a sprig of myrtle still carries its ancient significance in being indispensable in the composition of wedding bouquets. It is not hardy except in the mildest parts of the country, but thrives well upon a south wall. It blossoms usually in July and August.

Of the several varieties of myrtle, which vary in the colour of the fruit (sometimes yellowish white) and in the form of the leaves, the following only need be mentioned here. Most of them pertain rather to the cold greenhouse than the open air.

Var. TARENTINA, *Linnæus*. Tarentum Myrtle.—Leaves small, narrowly oval, ½ to ¾ in. long, ⅛ to ¼ in. wide, often alternate; young shoots, leaf-stalks, and base of midrib very downy. This, like the bigger-leaved type, needs wall protection. It bore its whitish fruits at Kew in 1911. Recognisable twigs have lately been found in Roman tombs of 2000 years ago. An open well-drained loam suits the myrtles, and cuttings readily take root in gentle heat.

M. LUMA, *Molina*

(Eugenia apiculata *De Candolle*; E. Luma, *Bergius*; Bot. Mag., t. 5040)

In Ireland this handsome evergreen succeeds remarkably well. At Kilmacurragh, Co. Wicklow, I have seen a bush 20 ft. high and 25 ft. in diameter, but it can only be grown against a wall in the average climate of this country. At Kew, it has more than once been killed, even with that protection. Branchlets clothed with a fine reddish down. Leaves ½ to 1 in. long, rather more than half as wide, oval, usually tapered at the base, and terminated by a short, abrupt point; dark dullish green, paler beneath, with a well-defined marginal vein. Flowers white, about ⅝ in. diameter. Fruit black, sweet, insipid. Introduced by W. Lobb from Chile. It differs from M. Ugni in having four petals; roundish, not reflexed sepals; and more conspicuous stamens. Old trees have beautiful cinnamon-coloured trunks.

M. NUMMULARIA, *Poiret*

An evergreen shrub, usually prostrate and growing into a thick mat only a few inches above the ground ; young shoots wiry, glabrous, reddish. Leaves opposite, oval, rounded at both ends, shortly stalked ; usually $\frac{1}{6}$ to $\frac{1}{4}$ in. long, half to two-thirds as wide ; bright dark green, glabrous on both sides, margins decurved. Flowers white, $\frac{1}{4}$ to $\frac{1}{3}$ in. wide, produced singly from the terminal leaf-axils, each on a very short stout stalk. Calyx four-lobed ; corolla of four rounded petals ; stamens numerous ; fruit an oblong pink berry $\frac{1}{4}$ in. long, crowned with the persisting calyx lobes.

Native of the southern parts of S. America, especially in the Straits of Magellan and the Falkland Islands. It has long been known, having been described and named in 1796 ; it was collected originally by Commerson. Charles Darwin gathered it on Tierra del Fuego in 1833 during the voyage of the *Beagle*, and many others have found it since then, but it seems to have been comparatively recently introduced. It is well suited for carpeting moist shelves and stones in the rock garden. It is quite hardy at South Lodge, Horsham, and in other places towards the south coast ; elsewhere it should be as hardy at least as Oxalis enneaphylla. It flowers during November and December in S. America, equivalent to our May and June. The whole plant is rather suggestive of Gaultheria trichophylla.

M. OBCORDATA, *Hooker fil.*

(Bot. Mag., t. 9417 ; Eugenia obcordata, *Raoul*)

An evergreen shrub 10 to 15 ft. high, of dense, very twiggy habit ; young shoots downy. Leaves opposite, obcordate (*i.e.*, inversely heart-shaped), conspicuously notched at the apex, tapered to the short downy stalk ; otherwise glabrous ; usually $\frac{1}{5}$ to $\frac{1}{2}$ in. long, $\frac{1}{4}$ to $\frac{3}{8}$ in. wide ; dark green above, pale and dotted with oil-glands beneath. Flowers $\frac{1}{4}$ in. wide, dull white, solitary, produced from the axils of the leaves on a slender downy stalk $\frac{1}{3}$ to $\frac{1}{2}$ in. long. Calyx four-lobed, the lobes ovate, the tube downy ; petals four, round, ciliate ; stamens very numerous and the chief attraction of the flower. Fruit a dark red or violet subglobose berry, $\frac{1}{4}$ in. wide.

Native of New Zealand ; introduced long ago. This pleasing shrub just misses being hardy at Kew, but survives the winters safely thirty or forty miles south of London. In the gardens of the south-west it is quite at home. It rarely blossoms with freedom, and if it did the flowers would not add much to the attractiveness of the plant. This is mainly to be found in its neat habit, slender branching, and in the plenitude of its small, unusually shaped leaves.

M. UGNI, *Molina*. MYRTILLA

(Eugenia Ugni, *Hooker*, Bot. Mag., t. 4626)

A Chilean evergreen, with leathery ovate leaves very like those of the myrtle, but with smaller flowers, shorter inclosed stamens, and reflexed, awl-shaped sepals. Petals five. It is sometimes grown on walls, and is only about as hardy as the myrtle itself. It bears a blue-black, juicy, and very palatable fruit.

NANDINA DOMESTICA, *Thunberg*. BERBERIDACEÆ

(Bot. Mag., t. 1109)

nA evergreen shrub, with erect, unarmed, and unbranched stems, 6 to 8 ft. high in this country, even taller in warmer ones, the lower part covered with the bases of fallen leaves. Leaves 1 to $1\frac{1}{2}$ ft. long, much divided (doubly or trebly pinnate), composed of numerous, linear-lanceolate leaflets, which are 1½ to 4 ins. long, long-pointed, quite glabrous, tinged with red when young, becoming purplish in autumn. Flowers in an erect panicle, 8 to 15 ins. long, borne at the top of the stem, each flower ¼ to ½ in. across, white, with large yellow anthers. Berries two-seeded, globular, ⅓ in. in diameter, bright red normally, but in some forms more purplish red; the stigma persisting, as in barberry fruits.

Introduced in 1804 from Japan, where it is much cultivated, but really a native of China. Its chief merit in this country is its elegant bamboo-like form, for its flowers are not very showy, nor are its fruits freely produced. It has lived outside at Kew for many years in a sheltered spot, but has never really succeeded well. It requires the greater warmth of the south-western counties, where, given a good moist soil and shelter from wind, it thrives admirably. It is best propagated from seeds, which, however, do not, as introduced, germinate freely. Cuttings put in a mild heat will root in time, but they too are slow. The young plants should be grown under glass for a year or two. Most of the plants in cultivation have been introduced direct from the nurseries of Japan.

NEILLIA. ROSACEÆ

A genus represented on both sides of N. America, in the Himalaya, Burma, Manchuria, and China. It is allied to Spiræa (under which generic name some of the following species were at one time known), but differs in the shining, very albuminous seeds. It is itself now frequently divided into two genera, viz., Neillia proper and PHYSOCARPUS. The former—represented in gardens by N. sinensis and N. thyrsiflora, and confined in a wild state to Asia—are distinguished by a racemose inflorescence and a solitary, podlike, many-seeded fruit. The Physocarpus section, represented in most gardens by N. opulifolia and its golden-leaved variety, has a corymbose inflorescence, and the fruit is composed of two to five pods. Leaves alternate, lobed, and toothed. Flowers white or pale rose. Sepals and petals five.

In gardens this genus (named in honour of Dr Patrick Neill, a prominent member of the botanical circle in Edinburgh at the beginning of the nineteenth century), is chiefly known by N. opulifolia. All the species are of easy culture, loving a moist loamy soil; they are propagated by cuttings of half-ripened wood.

N. AMURENSIS, *Bentham and Hooker fil.* MANCHURIAN NINE BARK

(Physocarpus amurensis, *Maximowicz*)

A deciduous shrub, 6 to 8 ft. high, the larger branches covered with a loose peeling bark. Leaves three- or five-lobed, up to 4 ins. long by 3 ins. wide; more or less downy beneath, the lobes pointed, margins double-toothed. Flowers white, ⅓ in. across, produced each on a slender downy stalk in corymbs 1½ to 2 ins. across, terminating short twigs. Calyx with five thickly downy, triangular lobes. Stamens about forty, purple; petals downy on the outside. Fruit downy.

Native of Manchuria; much resembling N. opulifolia. The leaves appear generally to be larger, more downy beneath and more distinctly five-lobed; the downy pods too are distinctive, and much shorter in proportion to the calyx.

N. BRACTEATA (Plate 31)

(Physocarpus bracteatus, *Rehder*; Opulaster Ramaleyi, *A. Nelson*)

This is a shapely deciduous shrub up to 6 ft. or more high and more in width, of free and elegant growth, with grey, flaky bark; young shoots glabrous, yellowish. Leaves 1½ to 3½ ins. long, nearly or quite as wide, roundish ovate in main outline, often heart-shaped at the base, usually three- sometimes five-lobed, the lobes doubly toothed; both surfaces are free from down, the lower one pale; stalk about one-third as long as the blade. Flowers white, ⅓ in. wide, opening in June, closely packed in rounded clusters 1½ to 2 ins. wide which come on short leafy twigs from the previous season's growths, thus forming handsome sprays. Calyx with five-pointed ovate lobes; flower-stalks slender, ½ to 1 in. long; both densely covered with starry down.

Native of the mountains of Colorado, at altitudes of 5000 to 6000 ft. The illustration (Plate 31) for which I am indebted to the Arnold Arboretum, shows it to be an admirable shrub for Massachusetts. It was introduced in 1904 under the specific name of "Ramaleyi," but subsequently seems to have disappeared. It was reintroduced in 1930. It is most nearly akin to N. malvacea and N. Torreyi, having, like them, only two carpels to each fruit which are united half their length, whereas in the common N. opulifolia there are three to five carpels united only at the base. It differs from them in the obovate or spatulate floral bracts being more persistent. The neillias like a good, moist, loamy soil, also to be grown in full sunshine.

N. CAPITATA, *Greene*. WESTERN NINE BARK

(Spiræa opulifolia mollis, *Torrey*; S. capitata, *Pursh*)

A deciduous shrub, 6 to 10 ft. high (in a wild state over 20 ft.). Leaves three-lobed, broadly ovate, 2 to 4 ins. long, doubly toothed, downy beneath. Flowers white, produced in a corymb, each flower on a downy stalk about ½ in. long; calyx very downy. Fruit glabrous or nearly so, composed of three to five inflated pods ⅓ in. long, containing usually two obliquely pear-shaped seeds.

Native of western N. America from British Columbia to California, where it is said to have stems often more than 20 ft. long interlaced with willow branches, and forming impenetrable thickets on the banks of streams (Greene). It is really a western form of N. opulifolia, from which it differs chiefly in the more downy leaves and in the pear-shaped seeds. Introduced in 1827.

N. LONGIRACEMOSA, *Hemsley*

A deciduous shrub 3 to 6 ft. high; young shoots angular, downy. Leaves ovate, sometimes indistinctly three-lobed, irregularly toothed, slender-pointed, rounded to heart-shaped at the base; 1½ to 4 ins. long, 1 to 2½ ins. wide; more or less downy on both surfaces, especially beneath and on the midrib; stalk ⅙ to ½ in. long; stipules lanceolate (not toothed). Racemes terminal, 2 to 6 ins. long, slender. Flowers opening in May and June, rosy-pink, ⅓ in. long. Calyx tubular with five erect lanceolate lobes very downy like the main and secondary flower-stalks, ultimately glandular-bristly; petals rounded, only showing between the calyx lobes; ovary hairy only at the top.

Native of W. China; discovered by A. E. Pratt in 1890; introduced by Wilson in 1904. It is a true neillia (as distinguished from the sub-genus Physocarpus, which has an umbel-like inflorescence). Of the species mentioned in previous editions it is most closely related to N. sinensis which is well distinguished from it by its glabrous shoots and calyx and much shorter raceme. N. longiracemosa is a pretty, elegant shrub and is frequently given a place in the exhibits at the Royal Horticultural Society's Shows. Akin to this species is

N. THIBETICA, *Franchet.*—According to Rehder its chief distinctions from the above are in the ovate, toothed stipules, the more downy leaves, and in the ovary being silky all over. In both species the calyx-tube becomes glandular-bristly at the fruiting stage. Wilson introduced seeds of N. thibetica in 1910 under the number 4220, but some at any rate of the plants raised from these seeds are N. longiracemosa.

N. MALVACEA, *Greene*

(Physocarpus malvaceus, *Kuntze*, 7; Bot. Mag., t. 7758 (as N. Torreyi))

A deciduous shrub, 3 to 5 ft. high, with erect stellately downy stems. Leaves three-lobed, sometimes obscurely five-lobed on the non-flowering shoots; from 1½ to 3 ins. wide, scarcely so long; usually roundish or broadly oval in general outline; variable in the amount of down on the lower surface. Flowers ⅓ in. wide, white, produced in corymbs 1½ ins. wide; calyx downy. Fruit composed of two or three pods, each one- or two-seeded.

Native of western N. America, reaching from Oregon and Idaho through Utah and Nevada to W. Texas. It is allied to N. Torreyi, which has a more eastern distribution, differing chiefly in the more robust habit, larger leaves, and sometimes more numerous carpels. Introduced to Kew in 1897. The pods are described as indehiscent, until after falling.

N. OPULIFOLIA, *Bentham and Hooker fil.* NINE BARK

(Physocarpus opulifolius, *Maximowicz*; Spiræa opulifolia, *Linnæus*)

A deciduous shrub, 6 to 10 ft. high, occasionally much more in diameter; bark glabrous, peeling. Leaves usually broadly ovate and three-lobed, sometimes only very slightly lobed or not at all; doubly toothed, 1½ to 3 ins. long and from half to fully as wide, glabrous; stalk ¼ to ¾ in. long. Flowers numerous, in hemispherical corymbose clusters 2 ins. wide, produced in June at the end of leafy twigs from the previous year's branches. Each flower is white tinged with rose, ¼ to ⅓ in. across, and borne on a slender downy or glabrous stalk. Stamens about thirty, purplish. Fruit consisting of three to five pods ¼ in. long, which are inflated, glabrous or nearly so, and usually carry two egg-shaped seeds.

Native of eastern N. America; introduced, according to Aiton, in 1687, and a common shrub in gardens. The largest I have seen was in Sir A. Smeaton-Hepburn's garden at Smeaton, N.B., which was 30 ft. across and 10 ft. high when I measured it some years ago. The shrub is a handsome one in blossom, and useful for rough shrubberies where plants are left largely to take care of themselves.

Var. LUTEA.—Leaves of a beautiful golden yellow when young, but soon becoming green and almost of the same shade as the type. Once popular, this, like others of its class of golden-leaved shrubs, is being superseded by varieties which retain their colour until autumn.

N. SINENSIS, *Oliver*

(Hooker's Icones Plantarum, t. 1540)

A deciduous shrub, 5 or 6 ft. high, with glabrous, brown, peeling bark. Leaves ovate, 2 to 4 ins. long, $1\frac{1}{4}$ to $2\frac{1}{2}$ ins. wide; the apex long drawn out, the margins set with coarse teeth or small lobes which are again sharply toothed;

NEILLIA SINENSIS

there is down on the main veins and in their axils at first, but both surfaces become almost or quite glabrous. Flowers nodding, produced in a slender, terminal raceme 1 to $2\frac{1}{2}$ ins. long, carrying twelve to twenty flowers. The remarkable feature of the flower is the smooth cylindrical white calyx, $\frac{1}{2}$ in. long and $\frac{1}{8}$ in. wide, dividing at the end into five narrow triangular lobes. Petals small, broadly ovate, about as long as the calyx-lobes. Fruit many-seeded.

Native of Central China; discovered by Henry, and introduced to cultivation by Wilson in 1901. It is a shrub of elegant habit and very distinct in its racemose inflorescence from all cultivated neillias, except the Himalayan N. thyrsiflora, and it is hardier and altogether better than that species, which has a shorter, bell-shaped hairy calyx.

N. THYRSIFLORA, *D. Don*

A low deciduous bush, of neat, rounded habit, about 3 ft. high; young shoots angular, glabrous, sometimes reddish. Leaves $1\frac{1}{2}$ to 3 ins. long, two-thirds as wide; three-lobed (most markedly so on the barren shoots), ovate with a long, narrow point; sharply, often doubly toothed; the base mostly heart-shaped; dark green and glabrous above, the bright green under-surface downy on the chief veins; stalk $\frac{1}{4}$ to $\frac{1}{2}$ in. long. Flowers in a downy raceme, terminating the shoot, or springing from the axils of the uppermost leaves. Each flower is about $\frac{1}{3}$ in. long; the calyx bell-shaped, five-lobed, silky hairy, the lobes lance-shaped and pointed; petals roundish ovate, white. Fruit consisting of one pod enclosed by the persistent calyx, and containing four to eight seeds.

Native of Sikkim and the Khasia Hills, where it is common. It suffers during hard winters, and is said to prefer a semi-shaded as well as a sheltered position. Allied to N. sinensis (*q.v.*).

N. TORREYI, *S. Watson*

(Garden and Forest, 1889, fig. 84; Physocarpus Torreyi, *Maximowicz*)

A dwarf deciduous bush, about 2 ft. high in a wild state, with erect, much-branched stems. Leaves ¾ to 1½ ins. long, roundish ovate, three-lobed; the lobes irregularly and doubly toothed, sometimes very downy beneath, sometimes only slightly so. Flowers ¼ in. diameter, of a clear or slightly rose-tinted white, produced in early June in few-flowered corymbs ¾ to 1¼ ins. across. Fruit downy, usually composed of two pods cohering for more than half their length, but sometimes only one; each contains one obovoid seed.

Native of the Rocky Mountains of Colorado up to elevations of 9000 ft. It is a pretty little shrub with small leaves often lobed and toothed, like a ribes. Its dwarf habit, small leaves, and few downy seed-vessels well distinguish it in the Physocarpus group.

NEMOPANTHUS MUCRONATUS, *Trelease*. MOUNTAIN HOLLY. AQUIFOLIACEÆ

(N. canadensis, *De Candolle*)

A deciduous shrub, 3 to 10 ft. high, with glabrous young wood. Leaves alternate, oval, oblong or ovate, thin, not (or very slightly) toothed, tapered more abruptly towards the base than the apex, quite glabrous; 1 to 2½ ins. long, ½ to 1⅛ ins. wide; stalk ¼ to ½ in. long. Flowers often unisexual, small, of no beauty; produced from the leaf-axils usually singly, occasionally a few together on a thread-like stalk ½ to 1 in. long. Fruit a globose berry, ¼ to ⅓ in. wide, pale crimson, containing four or five hard bony seeds (nutlets).

Native of eastern N. America; introduced in 1802. It is similar in aspect and nearly related to the deciduous (or *Prinos*) group of hollies, from which it differs botanically in having strap-shaped petals free from the stamens (they are attached together in the hollies). Whilst some plants have flowers of both sexes as well as perfect flowers, others have those of one sex only. Although introduced so long ago, this shrub never appears to have obtained much recognition in this country. Unless it bears its fruits freely it is of no garden value, and our summer sun is probably not hot enough to develop its best qualities in that respect. I have never seen it bearing fruit anything like so freely in Britain as it does in N. America.

NESÆA SALICIFOLIA, *Kunth*. LYTHRACEÆ

(Heimia salicifolia, *Link*)

A deciduous shrub, said to grow to a height of 5 or 6 ft., but usually shorter than that in this country, where, in the open ground, its stems are frequently cut back to the ground in winter, springing up 2 to 4 ft. high the following summer. Stems erect, leafy, much-branched, quite glabrous. Leaves linear and willow-like, opposite on the lower portion of the stem, alternate towards the top; 1 to 2 ins. long, $\frac{1}{8}$ to $\frac{1}{4}$ in. wide; quite glabrous. Flowers yellow, $\frac{1}{3}$ to $\frac{1}{2}$ in. across, very shortly stalked, produced singly in the leaf-axils of the current year's growth from July to September; petals five to seven; stamens ten to eighteen.

Native of N. and S. America, reaching from Mexico to Buenos Aires, in many places a weed; introduced in 1821. It will live in the open ground at Kew, and flowers there, but its stems do not become more than half woody, and do not survive the winter.

VAR. GRANDIFLORA, *Lindley* (Bot. Reg., vol. 27, t. 60), is the Buenos Aires variety. The flowers are 1 to $1\frac{1}{2}$ ins. across, and the leaves often $\frac{1}{2}$ in. wide. It is a much finer plant than the type and decidedly prettier in flower, but is not so hardy. It is said to be common on the pasture-lands about Buenos Aires. Introduced in 1839. Both can be propagated by cuttings in late summer.

NEVIUSIA ALABAMENSIS, *A. Gray*. ROSACEÆ

(Bot. Mag., t. 6806)

A deciduous shrub, 4 to 6 ft. high, with erect stems and spreading branches, making a rounded bush, wider than it is high; branchlets at first covered with fine down. Leaves alternate, ovate-oblong, 1 to $3\frac{1}{2}$ ins. long, those of the barren shoots shallowly lobed, finely double-toothed; downy on the veins beneath; stalk up to $\frac{1}{3}$ in. long, downy. Flowers produced in a cluster at the end of short leafy side-shoots in April and May. Each flower is borne on a slender, downy stalk $\frac{3}{4}$ to 1 in. long; it has no petals, but a conspicuous bunch of white stamens $\frac{1}{4}$ to $\frac{1}{3}$ in. long, and a calyx about $\frac{3}{4}$ in. across, with leaflike, toothed lobes.

Native of Alabama, where, apparently, it is only known in one or two spots. It was found on the cliffs of Black Warrior River, at Tuscaloosa, in 1858, by the Rev. R. D. Nevius, after whom the genus was named by Asa Gray. It is quite hardy in England, and is easily increased by fairly soft cuttings placed in heat. Its beauty in some parts of N. America is so great that it has been called the "Alabama Snow-wreath," owing to the snowy whiteness and profusion of its feathery blossom. But out-of-doors in England it is never really pure white, but of a dull greenish white. Forced early into blossom under glass, its colour is much purer, and it is then very elegant and beautiful. In March 1907, about fifty years after its discovery, a letter was received at Kew from Mr Nevius, then at Tacoma, Washington, from which it appears that this shrub is not always a success in its native land. He says: "I have had it growing in many places in the open, but it does not do well. Even at Tuscaloosa, where I discovered it, a hedge I planted of it in the churchyard flowered but sparingly." Neviusia is related to Spiræa, Kerria, etc., from which, and other allied genera, its apetalous flowers distinguish it.

NICOTIANA GLAUCA, *R. Graham*. SOLANACEÆ

(Bot. Mag., t. 2837)

A semi-evergreen or deciduous shrub of erect, thin habit, 10 ft. and upwards high in this country; branches slender, at first only semi-woody; perfectly glabrous. Leaves alternate, variable in shape, usually ovate and tapered towards both ends, sometimes heart-shaped at the base, pointed, quite entire; 1½ to 4 ins. long, 1 to 3 ins. wide, sometimes much larger; glaucous and perfectly glabrous on both surfaces; stalk slender and about as long as the blade. Inflorescence a lax terminal panicle bearing numerous flowers. Corolla bright yellow, tubular, 1½ ins. long, ⅙ in. wide, five-lobed at the mouth where it is ⅜ in. wide, downy outside, glabrous within; calyx green, tubular, ½ in. long, with five pointed triangular teeth, glabrous; stamens five, 1 in. long.

Native of the Argentine, Brazil, and other parts of S. America; introduced in 1827. Although an ally of the common tobacco plant this is very different in general appearance, being an almost tree-like shrub of lax growth. It flowers from June onwards and is quite ornamental, the yellow flowers contrasting well with the vividly glaucous foliage. It was cultivated for several years in a sheltered sunny nook at Kew, but was not genuinely hardy there, being killed in hard winters. Even so, it is well worth cultivating, especially in the warmer counties.

NOTHOFAGUS. SOUTHERN BEECHES. FAGACEÆ

The northern beeches, of which Fagus sylvatica is the type, form a very homogeneous group of invariably deciduous trees with broad leaves; they are confined to the temperate latitudes of the northern hemisphere. The beeches found in S. America and Australasia are evergreen as well as deciduous, and have usually much smaller leaves. At first classed under Fagus, they are now commonly regarded as generically distinct, and are distinguished as NOTHOFAGUS. They have the characteristic three-cornered nuts of the beeches, but the male flowers, instead of being borne numerously in globose heads as in Fagus proper, are usually solitary, never in more than threes; the nuts too are frequently three in each husk (invariably two in Fagus). The differences in general aspect are, however, much more strikingly apparent than mere botanical details.

None of the Australasian species has proved to be hardy at Kew. The S. American ones, however, are considerably hardier and N. obliqua and N. antartica have lived in the open uninjured for thirty to forty years. Unlike the Northern beeches they are not suitable for a calcareous soil. They love best a deep open loam. Increase can be effected by layering.

A. EVERGREEN

1. *betuloides*. Leaves round-toothed, dotted beneath.
2. *Cunninghami*. Leaves round-toothed, not dotted beneath.
3. *Menziesii*. Leaves doubly round-toothed, with one or two downy pits beneath.
4. *fusca*. Leaves coarsely toothed; up to 1½ ins. long.
5. *Moorei*. Leaves sharply toothed; up to 3 ins. long.
6. *cliffortioides*. Leaves not toothed.
7. *Blairii*. Leaves not toothed, rounded or almost truncate at base; up to ¾ in. long.

8. *Dombeyi*. Leaves finely and unevenly toothed; up to $1\frac{1}{2}$ ins. long.
9. *Solandri*. Leaves not toothed, broadly wedge-shaped; up to $\frac{5}{8}$ in. long.

B. DECIDUOUS; LEAVES TOOTHED

10. *antartica*. Leaves usually less than $1\frac{1}{4}$ ins. long; shoots very downy.
11. *obliqua*. Leaves 2 to 3 ins. long; shoots smooth or slightly downy.
12. *procera*. Leaves up to 4 ins. long; shoots with brownish hairs.

N. ANTARCTICA, *Oerstedt*. ANTARCTIC BEECH

(Bot. Mag., t. 8314; Fagus antarctica, *Forster*)

A deciduous tree of large size; young shoots very downy. Leaves $\frac{1}{2}$ to $\frac{1}{4}$ ins. long, often nearly as much wide; broadly ovate, or somewhat triangular,

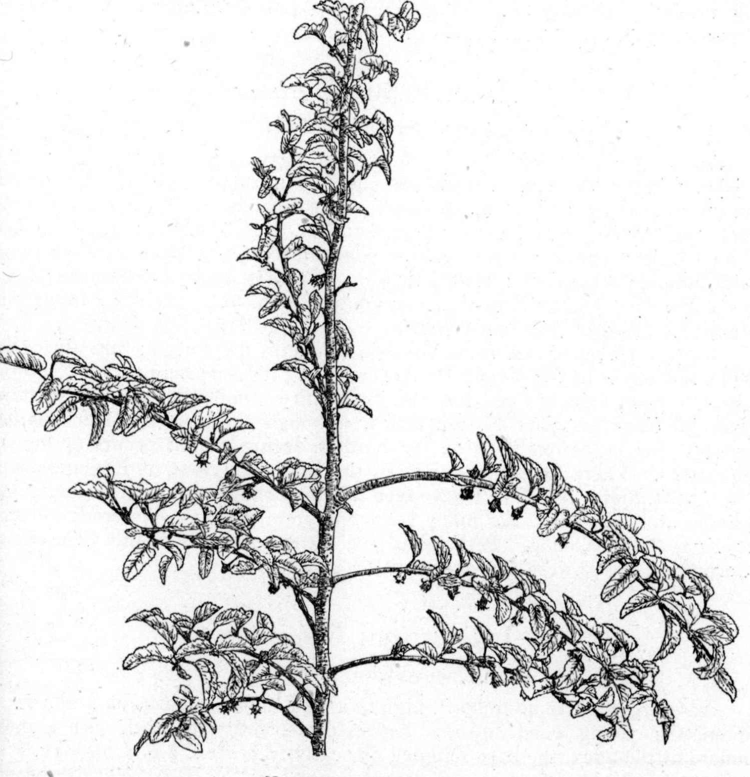

NOTHOFAGUS ANTARCTICA

eart-shaped or truncate at the base, rounded at the apex, sometimes slightly bed, always irregularly and minutely toothed, the teeth often rounded; labrous on both sides except for a minute down on the midrib beneath; stalk owny, $\frac{1}{12}$ to $\frac{1}{6}$ in. long. Flowers produced during May, the males singly, in airs, or in threes in the basal leaf-axils of small twigs, pendulous, each about in. across; calyx broadly funnel-shaped, five-lobed. Husk of fruit four-bed, enclosing three nuts.

Native of S. America from Tierra del Fuego northwards to Chillan; first introduced, according to Loudon, in 1830. Seeds were again sent home by Sir Joseph Hooker to Kew about 1843, and it has, no doubt, been introduced several times subsequently. All the trees at present in cultivation, with the exception of one at Hafodunos in Denbighshire, were introduced by means of seeds collected by Mr H. J. Elwes, in 1902. These plants have hitherto succeeded very well at Kew and other places, but seeing that almost all those introduced during the previous seventy years have disappeared, it would be rash to conclude that the species is going to survive permanently. In the south-western counties and similarly situated places it will almost certainly be hardy, but elsewhere I am afraid there are potentialities in the English climate that may be fatal to it.

Few trees have greater elegance and distinction than this when it is young. It makes unbranched shoots as much as 3 ft. long in a season, furnished over the whole length with small crumpled leaves $\frac{1}{4}$ to $\frac{3}{4}$ in. apart. The habit is thin and open. Increased by layers.

N. BETULOIDES, *Blume*

(Fagus betuloides, *Mirbel*)

An evergreen tree of large size, and dense, very leafy habit; young shoots sticky, minutely downy. Leaves set about $\frac{1}{4}$ in. apart on the twigs, ovate, wedge-shaped, or rounded at the base, pointed or blunt at the apex, minutely and regularly toothed; $\frac{1}{2}$ to 1 in. long, $\frac{1}{4}$ to $\frac{3}{4}$ in. wide, glabrous; upper surface dark varnished green; lower surface paler, finely net-veined, often sprinkled with minute dark glands; stalk $\frac{1}{8}$ in. long. Flowers (male) produced in May, the calyx funnel-shaped, downy, many-lobed, $\frac{1}{4}$ in. long, enclosing numerous stamens. Husk of fruit four-lobed.

Native of S. America from Valdivia to Tierra del Fuego; introduced in 1830, and again by Sir Joseph Hooker in 1843. It has since, no doubt, several times been introduced, and has obtained a firmer foothold in Great Britain than its close associate N. antarctica, although, judging by their relative habitats the latter ought to be the hardier, seeing that it occurs at higher elevations. There are several trees in the south and west of England from 30 to 50 ft. high. The best I have seen near to London was in Mrs Chambers' garden at Haslemere. For many years one grew in Mr A. Waterer's nursery at Knap Hill, Woking. Perhaps as fine a tree as any is one at Pencarrow, Cornwall; this flowers, but does not give good seed.

N. BLAIRII, *Krasser*

(Fagus Blairii, *T. Kirk*)

An evergreen tree 40 to 60 ft. high in a wild state, with a trunk 2 to 3 ft. in diameter; young wood downy. Leaves ovate, entire, pointed, with a short mucro at the apex, the base rounded or nearly truncate; $\frac{2}{3}$ to $\frac{3}{4}$ in. long, $\frac{3}{8}$ to $\frac{1}{2}$ in. wide; bright green above, clothed beneath with a close, yellowish-brown felt; veins four to six each side the midrib; stalk $\frac{1}{16}$ in. long. Male flowers produced in the leaf-axils, usually solitary. Husk of fruit, four-lobed, $\frac{1}{4}$ to $\frac{1}{3}$ in. long.

Native of New Zealand on the North and South Islands up to 2500 ft. altitude. Other species, amongst them N. cliffortioides, have been grown under this name, and I am not sure that the true plant is yet in cultivation. It belongs to the same group as cliffortioides and Solandri, having evergreen toothless leaves, but they are larger than in either of those species, always vate and much broader towards the base. Cockayne, the New Zealand otanist, regarded it as "certainly a polymorphic hybrid," its parents being olandri, cliffortioides and fusca. As in those species, the leaves may be labrous on young trees.

N. CLIFFORTIOIDES, *Oerstedt*. MOUNTAIN BEECH

(Fagus cliffortioides, *Hooker fil.*)

An evergreen tree, becoming 50 ft. high in New Zealand; young shoots rownish, thin and wiry, covered with down. Leaves oval, oblong or ovate; to ½ in. long, $\frac{3}{16}$ to ¼ in. wide; set alternately and very regularly along the ranches, ⅛ to ¼ in. apart, in two rows; they are usually more or less pointed, bliquely rounded or broadly wedge-shaped at the base; not toothed, glabrous n both surfaces, net-veined, with four or five pairs of distinct veins; stalk ery downy, short. On adult trees the leaves are said to be downy beneath.

Native of New Zealand. The largest trees in the country are at Enys in ornwall. A smaller one for long stood in Messrs Veitch's nursery at Coombe Vood. The tree is essentially one for the milder parts of the kingdom. From ll the cultivated southern beeches, this is distinguished by its evergreen leaves eing entire. It is sometimes offered as N. Solandri, a different but nearly llied species with blunt leaves, also from New Zealand.

N. CUNNINGHAMI, *Oerstedt*. CUNNINGHAM'S BEECH

(Fagus Cunninghami, *Hooker fil.*)

An evergreen tree of large size, young shoots wiry, covered with short ark down. Leaves ovate, approaching diamond-shape or often almost quilaterally triangular; ¼ to ⅝ in. long, from half to quite as much wide; ne base broadly wedge-shaped or truncate, and entire; the upper part more apering, pointed and blunt toothed; both surfaces glabrous; stalk downy, ery short.

Native of Tasmania, where, according to the elevation at which it grows, it aries from a shrub to an enormous timber tree. There is a good specimen n the Royal Gardens at Osborne, Isle of Wight, which I saw abundantly in ower in September 1907. The husk, which encloses three nuts, is very urious; it is divided into four narrow lobes scarcely ¼ in. long, each bristled ver with short decurved scales terminated by a globular gland—very much esembling the stigma of many flowers. Two of the nuts are three-sided, the hird is two-sided. The tree is rare in cultivation, and is only suited for the nilder counties. The best specimen is at Fota, near Cork (50 ft. high).

Bearing a close resemblance in general habit to N. Cunninghami is a New Zealand species—N. MENZIESII, *Oerstedt* (Fagus Menziesii, *Hooker fil.*). ts foliage and twigs are very much like those of Cunningham's beech, but he leaves are readily distinguished by having the margin doubly instead of ingly round-toothed, and still more by one or two curious little pits situated eneath the leaf. These pits are placed in the axils of the second pair of veins rom the base, and are lined with brownish down. The trunk of this tree is aid to be silvery, like a birch.

N. DOMBEYI, *Blume*. COIGUE

(Fagus Dombeyi, *Mirbel*)

An evergreen or semi-evergreen tree of very large size; young shoots lothed with very minute down. Leaves of firm texture, ovate or ovate-anceolate, rounded or broadly wedge-shaped, pointed, finely and unevenly toothed; $\frac{3}{4}$ to $1\frac{1}{2}$ ins. long, $\frac{3}{8}$ to $\frac{5}{8}$ in. wide; dark glossy green above, paler bright green beneath, sometimes specked when older with minute blackish glands on both surfaces, but more thickly beneath; chief veins inconspicuous; stalk $\frac{1}{12}$ in. long. Stamens bright red. Seeds $\frac{3}{16}$ in. long.

Native of Chile, including the island of Chiloe, and of the Argentine. According to Elwes, it is a common tree in Chile, and is usually associated there with N. obliqua. Introduced to England by Mr F. R. S. Balfour, who presented a large quantity of seeds to Kew in 1916. Of these only four germinated, but as subsequent importations of seed have been made, and as plants can be raised from cuttings, it has become quite established in cultivation. It is remarkable that so fine and common a tree should not have been introduced before. As a young tree it grows quickly and is very elegant, making slender shoots 1 to 2 ft. long annually. Up to the present it has proved hardy at Kew, although occasionally during bitter winds in February and March it has lost most of its foliage. Near the Baths of Chillan Mr Elwes found trees whose trunks at five feet from the ground measured 22 to 27 ft. in circumference. Along with N. obliqua it provides the chief timber supplies of Chile.

N. FUSCA, *Oerstedt*

(Fagus fusca, *Hooker fil.*)

An evergreen tree of the largest size, described as 100 ft. high in nature; young shoots minutely downy, and in cultivated specimens very zigzagged Leaves broadly ovate to roundish, $\frac{3}{4}$ to $1\frac{1}{2}$ ins. long, glabrous except on the coarsely toothed margins, which are ciliate, especially on the notches, wedge-shaped to truncate at the base; leaf-stalk downy, about $\frac{1}{8}$ in. long; veins ir usually three or four pairs. Husk of fruit nearly $\frac{1}{2}$ in. long, four-lobed, con taining three nuts.

Native of New Zealand, where it yields a useful timber. The largest I have noted in the British Isles is at Castlewellan, Co. Down, which, when I saw i in February 1913, was from 20 to 25 ft. high. There used to be a health young tree in the Coombe Wood nursery, of bushy habit and about 12 ft. high which seems to show that it is hardier than is generally supposed. The ol leaves turn red before they fall.

N. MENZIESII, *Oerstedt*

(Fagus Menziesii, *Hooker fil.*)

An evergreen tree 60 to 80 ft. (occasionally 100 ft.) high in a wild stat with a trunk 6 to 16 ft. in girth and silvery white when young; young shoo clothed with yellowish brown down. Leaves roundish ovate to diamond-shape broadly wedge-shaped at the base, rounded or pointed at the apex, doub round-toothed; $\frac{1}{3}$ to $\frac{5}{8}$ in. long, $\frac{1}{4}$ to $\frac{1}{2}$ in. wide; glabrous on both surfac except for one or two pits in the blade near the base beneath, which are line with brown hairs; stalk $\frac{1}{16}$ in. long, downy. Male flowers solitary. Nu three in each husk, two of them with three wings, the other with two; hus $\frac{1}{4}$ to $\frac{1}{3}$ in. long.

Native of New Zealand on both North and South Islands, up to 3500 above sea level. It is allied to N. Cunninghami, but that species has sing (not doubly) toothed leaves, and the curious hairy pits beneath seen in Menziesii are absent. It was cultivated for many years in the Temperate Hou at Kew but was taken out in 1931 and planted near the Pagoda. To the sou and west it succeeds well; in April 1931 I measured a tree at Wakehurst Sussex 25 ft. high, and a rather larger one is in the garden at Lanarth Cornwall.

N. Moorei, *Maiden*. Australian Beech

(Fagus Moorei, *Mueller*)

Of the Nothofagus group of beeches, this has the largest leaves of any ultivated out-of-doors in this country. They are glossy dark green, ovate-anceolate or ovate; $1\frac{1}{2}$ to 3 ins. long, $\frac{3}{4}$ to $1\frac{1}{2}$ ins. wide; the base wedge-haped, the apex taper-pointed; sharply toothed; stalk $\frac{1}{12}$ in. long. The whole leaf is glabrous except the stalk and the upper surface of the midrib; he lateral veins are prominent, and in nine to fifteen pairs. Young twigs overed with brownish down; stipules very narrow, $\frac{1}{3}$ to $\frac{1}{2}$ in. long.

This is an evergreen tree described as becoming 150 ft. high, and was liscovered in New South Wales by the late Charles Moore of Sydney. There ised to be a tree over 20 ft. high growing in the grounds of Kilmacurragh, Co. Wicklow, but this beech is only likely to be hardy in the very mildest parts of the British Isles. Introduced to Kew in 1892.

N. obliqua, *Blume*. Roble Beech (Plate 32)

(Fagus obliqua, *Mirbel*)

A large deciduous tree, up to 100 ft. high in a wild state; young shoots glabrous. Leaves arranged alternately in two opposite rows, ovate to oblong, nostly blunt at the apex, rounded or broadly wedge-shaped at the base, inequal sided; $1\frac{1}{2}$ to 3 ins. long, $\frac{3}{4}$ to $1\frac{1}{2}$ ins. wide; irregularly set with small, riangular teeth, and with shallow round lobes also near the base; dark green above, pale and rather glaucous beneath, glabrous; stalk $\frac{1}{8}$ in. long. Male flowers produced singly in the leaf-axils, consisting of a calyx and thirty o forty stamens. Husk of fruit four-lobed, containing a pair of three-sided iuts and one flattened one.

Native of Chile, and according to Elwes the most northerly of the South American beeches. It was first introduced by Wm. Lobb for Messrs Veitch n 1849, but like N. antarctica seems to have died out. The largest trees at present in cultivation were introduced by Mr Elwes in 1902. At Kew and elsewhere they have grown with remarkable rapidity and have withstood he frosts of forty years uninjured. As a young tree it is of elegant habit, naking long, slender shoots annually. In Chile it is a valuable timber tree, known as " Roblé." It flowers at Kew in spring.

A note may be made of the excellent progress of the trees of this species aised from seed sent from Chile by the late Mr H. J. Elwes in 1902. The argest of these was, in 1931, over 70 ft. high, its trunk 4 ft. 2 ins. in girth. This represents a growth in height of some $2\frac{1}{2}$ ft. per annum, which is a rather emarkable rate for a deciduous tree coming from south of the equator.

N. procera, *Oerstedt*. Rauli

(Fagus procera, *Poeppig*)

A large deciduous tree 80 ft. and upwards high; young shoots clothed with mall brownish hairs; winter buds $\frac{1}{4}$ in. long, slender, pointed. Leaves oblong r narrowly oval, blunt or rounded at the apex, rounded or broadly wedge-haped at the base, very finely toothed; $1\frac{1}{2}$ to 4 ins. long, $\frac{3}{4}$ to $1\frac{1}{2}$ ins. wide; ellowish green above and downy, especially on the midrib and on the raised art of the blade between the sunken veins; paler green beneath and downy n the midrib and veins; stalk $\frac{1}{12}$ to $\frac{3}{16}$ in. long, hairy. Veins fourteen to eighteen each side the midrib, parallel, sunken above, prominent beneath. Fruit shortly stalked, $\frac{1}{3}$ in. long, ovoid, the husk covered with narrow, gland-tipped scales.

Native of Chile; introduced to Kew in 1913 through the Dendrological Society of France. This species is distinct from all the other Chilean nothofaguses in its large conspicuously ribbed leaves, which resemble those of a hornbeam or Alnus firma. It has proved hardy at Kew so far and grows well in cultivated ground, making a welcome addition to a very interesting group of trees. It can be increased by means of cuttings put in gentle heat in July or August. Elwes describes it as a stately tree in Valdivia, and Comber as producing the best of Chilean timbers. The largest cultivated tree I have seen is one at East Bergholt in Suffolk, which in July 1933 was 40 to 45 ft. high and 2 ft. 9 ins. in girth of trunk. The leaves often turn to good yellow before falling, occasionally rich red.

N. SOLANDRI, *Oerstedt*

(Fagus Solandri, *Hooker fil.*)

An evergreen tree said to be 40 to 80 ft. high in a wild state, with a trunk 2 to 5 ft. in diameter; young shoots clothed with a dense fine down. Leaves oval, sometimes rather ovate, not toothed, broadly wedge-shaped at the base, blunt at the apex; $\frac{1}{4}$ to $\frac{5}{8}$ in. long, $\frac{1}{4}$ to $\frac{3}{8}$ in. wide; glabrous and glossy above, covered with a close down beneath; stalk $\frac{1}{16}$ in. long; veins usually four or five each side the midrib. Male flowers produced one to three together in the leaf-axils. Husk of fruit usually three-lobed, $\frac{1}{4}$ in. long; nuts two- or three-winged.

Native of New Zealand on both North and South Islands, mostly in hilly districts up to 2500 ft. altitude. This tree appears to be most closely related to N. cliffortioides, but that species has smaller leaves on the whole, more rounded or even somewhat heart-shaped at the base. I believe N. Solandri was introduced to cultivation after the publication of the first edition of this work in 1914 and it is as yet quite uncommon. It is only likely to be hardy in the south and west. Cheeseman says the leaves of young trees are often nearly or quite devoid of down beneath.

NOTHOPANAX. ARALIACEÆ

This is one of the genera of araliads into which the old genus Panax has been divided. They are evergreen trees or shrubs, with simple or digitate leaves; the ovary usually two-celled and the styles separate. Easily grown in loamy soil, they are also easily propagated by cuttings. (See also Pseudopanax.)

N. ARBOREUM, *Seemann*

(Bot. Mag., t. 9280; Panax arboreum, *Linnæus fil.*)

A small, unisexual, evergreen tree of rounded shape, freely branched and 12 to 25 ft. high, all its parts free from down; young shoots stout. Leaves digitate; the three, five, or seven leaflets arranged at the end of a main-stalk as in the horse chestnut. Leaflets elliptic-oblong to narrowly obovate, coarsely and bluntly toothed, tapered to both ends, often more abruptly at the apex; 3 to 8 ins. long, 1 to 3 ins. wide; dark glossy green above, paler beneath.

stalks of leaflets ½ to 1 in. long; main-stalk up to 8 ins. long, the base dilated and clasping the stem. Flowers in compound umbels terminating the shoot, their main-stalks short and thick or almost non-existent; from the end of each radiate eight to twelve primary divisions each on a stalk 2 to 4 ins. long, and from the end of each of these radiate divisions of a third dimension to the number of ten or twenty, each ½ to 1½ ins. long and bearing at the end a rounded umbel of some ten or fifteen flowers. These flowers are ¼ in. wide, greenish brown and of no beauty; petals five, obovate; stamens five, spreading. Fruit purplish black, rather compressed-globose, ¼ in. wide, crowned by the recurved styles.

Native of New Zealand, mostly of the lowlands, but ascending to 2500 ft.; long introduced. It is not hardy at Kew, but there used to be a good tree in the Temperate House, where it grew for many years and became eventually as large apparently as it is found at home. There is a good tree, 20 ft. high, in the open air in the garden at Lanarth, and another in the Rectory garden at Ludgvan. These, of course, are in the mildest part of England, but it is also very healthy at Exbury, Hants, and at Wakehurst, Sussex. In New Zealand the tree often begins life as an epiphyte on the stems of tree-ferns, down which it extends its roots until they reach the ground. It is a handsome foliage tree of a type unusual in the open air, but common enough in glass houses.

N. Davidii, *Harms*

(Panax Davidii, *Franchet*; Acanthopanax diversifolium, *Hemsley*)

A small evergreen tree 10 to 20 ft. high; young shoots and leaves quite glabrous. Leaves leathery, very variable in shape, and either simple, bifoliolate (rarely), or trifoliolate; the simple leaf and the individual leaflets of the compound leaves are similar in size and shape, being narrowly lanceolate, tapered towards both ends, especially towards the apex which is very long and slender-pointed; margins remotely toothed; 3 to 6 ins. long, ¾ to 1½ ins. wide; dark glossy green; leaf-stalk 2 to 8 ins. long, grooved on the upper side. The simple leaves have normally three longitudinal veins starting from the base; where the leaf consists of two leaflets one has a single vein, the other (usually larger) one has two; where there are three leaflets each has a single vein. Thus every leaf, whatever its shape, has three veins. Flowers small, greenish yellow, opening in July and August, and produced in pyramidal or rounded panicles 3 to 6 ins. long composed of small umbels. Fruit black, roundish, compressed, ⅙ in. wide.

Native of Hupeh and Szechuen, China; introduced by Wilson to the Arnold Arboretum in 1907, and three years later to Kew. It has survived all the winters since 1910 without injury, but grows slowly. It finds the south-western counties more to its liking, and in the garden at Duffryn, near Cardiff, succeeds admirably. It makes a neat evergreen, quite distinct from any other hardy one in the diversity of its leaves. Originally found in 1869 by the French missionary, David, and later by Henry. Easily increased by late summer cuttings.

NOTOSPARTIUM Carmichaeliæ, *Hooker fil.* LEGUMINOSÆ

(Bot. Mag., t. 6741)

An almost leafless shrub, 4 to 10 ft. high in its native state, with slender, rush-like, mostly arching or pendulous branches, which are slightly flattened and grooved. Leaves (only seen on young plants) simple, roundish or orbicular, often notched at the apex, ¼ in. long. Racemes downy, 1 to 2 ins. long, axillary, carrying from twelve to twenty flowers. Each flower is ⅓ in. long, pea-shaped, purplish pink; calyx densely covered with silky down, five-toothed; teeth triangular; flower-stalk hairy, ⅛ in. long. Pod ¾ to 1 in. in length, slender, three- to eight-jointed, with one seed to each joint. It blooms in July.

Native of New Zealand, in the South Island, where it is said to be rare and local. It is not absolutely hardy at Kew, a fine plant about 4 ft. high being killed by the trying winter of 1908-9. It had flowered beautifully for ten or twelve years previously, and ripened seed freely. Young plants are better with some protection during winter for the first few years of their existence, and may be grown in pots, for although not killed entirely the branches are so badly cut back that the progress of the plant is very slow. When once a firm woody base has been formed, they weather ordinary winters quite well. Seeds afford the best means of increase. The best soil is a light loam, and the position should be well drained and sunny. So lovely a plant deserves special care. A plant at East Bergholt was 8 ft. high when I saw it in 1939.

N. GLABRESCENS, *Petrie*. LEGUMINOSÆ

(Bot. Mag., t. 9530)

A round-headed tree, 15 to 30 ft. high; young shoots flattened, slightly grooved, not much spreading, glabrous, finally terete. Leaves reduced to triangular scales, scarcely visible. Flowers in a crowd of axillary racemes 1½ to 2 ins. long towards the end of the shoot, each raceme carrying fifteen to twenty-five blossoms. Standard petal nearly ½ in. across, erect, oval, notched at the tip, white with a conspicuous purple blotch at the base and with similarly coloured nerves radiating upwards from it; wing-petals and keel much smaller, oblong; calyx bell-shaped with ciliate, triangular lobes. Pod ¾ to 1 in. long, carrying about six seeds.

Native of the South Island of New Zealand, in the valley of the Clarence River, first flowered in this country in 1933. A very attractive tree described as resembling in habit a weeping willow, its lower branches being more or less pendulous. It blossoms quite freely, however, as a shrub and is evidently as hardy as N. Carmichæliæ, to which it is closely related. But its flowers are somewhat larger and more purplish, the pods are larger and the axis of the racemes is glabrous.

NUTTALLIA CERASIFORMIS, *Torrey*. OSO BERRY. ROSACEÆ

(Osmaronia cerasiformis, *Greene*)

A deciduous shrub, usually 6 to 8 ft. (occasionally more) high, with the habit of a black currant, the stems springing erect from the ground in great numbers, and forming ultimately a dense thicket several feet through; branchlets glabrous, bright green. Leaves alternate, narrow oblong or lance-shaped; 2 to 3½ ins. long, ¾ to 1¼ ins. wide; of thin texture, green and quite glabrous above, greyish beneath; margin entire, narrowed at the base to a stalk ¼ in. or less long. Male and female flowers usually on different plants; both borne on stiff, pendent, copiously bracted racemes 1½ to 2 ins. long. Each flower is about ¼ in. across, the five petals white ; the calyx green, bell-shaped, five-lobed. Male flowers have fifteen stamens ; females five carpels. Fruit plum-like, oval, ¾ in. long, purple when ripe, usually not more than two of the carpels of each flower developing.

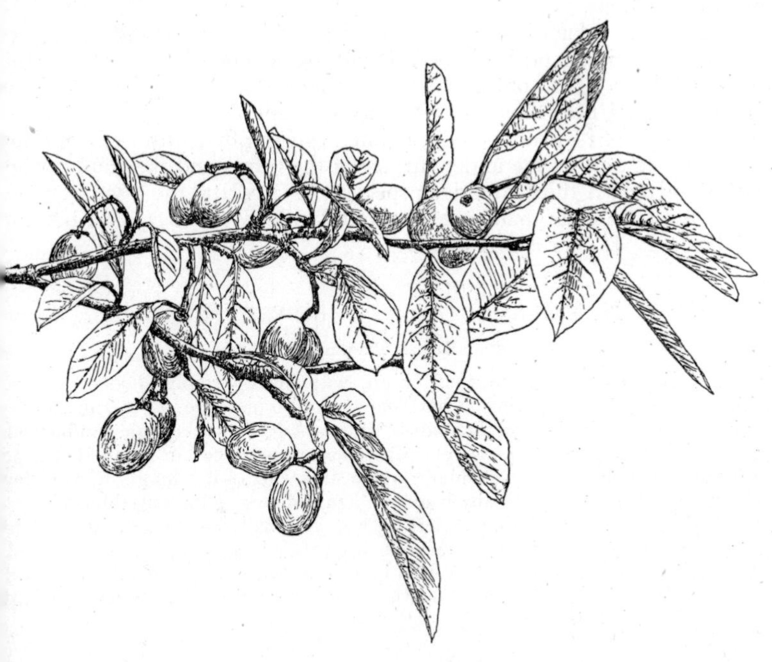

NUTTALLIA CERASIFORMIS (in fruit)

Native of California ; introduced in 1848, and a close ally of Prunus, rom which it differs in the five-carpelled female flower. In gardens the)so berry is useful for its early, almond-scented blossoms, which are ısually fully open by the third week in March, being produced from the eafless shoots of the previous year. The female plant is of coarser habit han the male and not so pretty nor so free in blossom, but it is worth ssociating with the male for the sake of its abundant fruits. The pecies is very hardy and thrives in a well-drained, loamy soil. It is asily propagated by taking off small pieces from old plants, also by eeds. The fruits are very bitter and strongly almond-scented. A form vith hermaphrodite or self-fertilising flowers has recently been introduced. The genus is named after Thomas Nuttall, an American botanist, 786-1859.

NYSSA. NYSSACEÆ

Of the half-dozen or so species of Nyssa known, which are natives f N. America, Himalaya, and China, only one (N. sylvatica) has hitherto ucceeded in the British Isles. A new species from China is promising, but is long likely to be too scarce to count. They used to be placed in the Cornel family, but except in the fruit, have little obvious relationship to the other hardy members of that order. They transplant badly and should be given a permanent place as early as possible, preferably in good moist loam.

Besides N. sinensis and N. sylvatica, which are described below, another American species is occasionally seen, viz., N. AQUATICA, the "Tupelo gum." According to Henry there is a fair specimen of it at White Knights, near Reading. It is easily distinguished from N. sylvatica by the shape of its ovate-oblong, pointed leaves, often with a few distant coarse teeth, and by the under-surface of the leaves and the young twigs being downy. A third American species, N. OGECHE, the "sour Tupelo tree," has been more than once introduced to Kew, but has never become established. It is probably tender.

N. SINENSIS, *Oliver*. CHINESE TUPELO

(Hooker's Icones Plantarum, t. 1964)

A deciduous tree, 20 to 50 ft. high, with downy young shoots. Leaves thin, narrowly oval, tapering at both ends; 4 to 6 ins. long, 1½ to 2 ins. wide hairy at the margins and on the midrib, dull dark green above, pale and lustrous beneath; stalk ¼ in. long, hairy. Male flowers produced in a rounded head ½ in. across at the end of a slender, downy stalk 1 to 1½ ins. long; females few on longer stalks, neither of any beauty. Fruit oblong, ½ in. long, bluish.

Native of Central China, where it was originally discovered in 1888 by Henry, who describes it as a rare tree occurring in mountain woods. Seeds were sent to Messrs Veitch by Wilson in 1901-2, but only one plant was raised This tree grew in the Coombe Wood nursery, where it was in the best of health and apparently quite hardy.

N. SYLVATICA, *Marshall*. TUPELO, PEPPERIDGE

(N. multiflora, *Wangenheim*)

A deciduous tree, occasionally 100 ft. high in a wild state, with a trunk 5 ft. in thickness. Leaves of variable shape, but oftenest obovate or oval with a tapering base; 3 to 6 ins. long, 1½ to 3 ins. wide; entire, usually perfectly glabrous in this country except on the young stalks and midrib which are slightly hairy; stalk ½ to 1 in. long, frequently reddish. Flowers appearing in June, males and females on separate heads, ½ in. or less across greenish, produced on a slender downy stalk about 1 in. long in the axil of the scales or lowermost leaves of the young shoots; male flowers numerous females ones usually two to four in a head; they have no beauty. Fruit usually in pairs, each one ⅓ to ⅔ in. long, egg-shaped, bluish black.

Native of Eastern N. America, chiefly found in swamps and ill-drained land; introduced sometime in the first half of the eighteenth century. It was, until lately, quite scarce in cultivation, and few trees of any size exist in Britain. But the late Mr Soames of Sheffield Park raised some four hundred plants from seed, many of which are now scattered about the grounds, vigorous and healthy. Of older trees Mr Elwes gives the palm to one at Strathfieldsaye which is probably about 80 ft. high and 6 ft. in girth. There is a curious diversity in the leaves, not only in shape, but in lustre. Of two healthy trees at Kew growing within a few yards of each other, one has dull-surfaced leaves the other has larger shining ones. The chief value of the tupelo in gardens, over and above its great interest, is the brilliant red and yellow of its autumnal foliage. Like many other American trees growing in wet situations at home, it thrives best in ordinary good loam when transplanted to our gloomier climate.

OLEA EUROPÆA, *Linnæus*. OLIVE. OLEACEÆ

An evergreen tree of rugged, much-branched habit and slow growth, generally 20 to 40 ft. high, with grey-green foliage. Leaves opposite, narrowly obovate or oval; 1½ to 3 ins. long, ⅓ to ¾ in. wide; glaucous or silvery beneath, leathery. Flowers white, ⅕ in. diameter, in axillary racemes 1 to 2 ins. long, the corolla with four ovate lobes; stamens two. Fruit an oval, oily drupe, ¾ in. long, containing a bony seed.

Native of Asia Minor and Syria, now largely cultivated all over the Mediterranean region. In many parts of Italy, as in the environs of Florence, its grey tints give the prevailing tone to the landscape. In Britain it can only be cultivated out-of-doors in the mildest parts. It has borne fruit in Lord Mount Edgcumbe's garden, near Plymouth, and in several other places in the south-west. At Kew it has lived for a good many years on a south wall, but in such a place is only worth growing for its interest and associations.

OLEARIA. DAISY BUSHES. COMPOSITÆ

Of this large group of evergreen shrubs and small trees, numbering over one hundred species, all of which belong in nature to the Australasian region, only one has yet been proved generally hardy. This is O. Haastii. O. myrsinoides is promising, and in the southern and western counties, in various parts of Ireland and the west of Scotland, some thirty species are grown. They are probably the most ornamental shrubs of the Composite order that are as hardy in the British Isles. They like a light loamy or peaty soil free from lime, and most of them can be increased by cuttings made of moderately ripened wood and placed in gentle heat.

Olearias are nearly allied to asters and have much the same type of flowers. The leaves are opposite or alternate, and more or less felted beneath.

There is occasionally also some confusion in gardens between the genera Senecio and Olearia, the former being also represented in Australasia by many shrubby species. They can be distinguished in flower by the bracts (scales) of the involucre being confined to a single row, or sometimes two rows, in Senecio, but produced in several rows in Olearia.

O. ALBIDA, *Hooker fil.*

(Eurybia albida, *Hooker fil.*)

An evergreen shrub or small tree 10 to 20 ft. high in a wild state; young shoots grooved and, like the leaf-stalks and flower-stalks, clothed with pale brown, closely appressed down. Leaves alternate, entire, narrowly ovate or narrowly oval, rounded or abruptly tapered at the base, blunt or rounded at the apex; 1 to 4 ins. long, ½ to 1½ ins. wide; dark dull green and without down above when mature, clothed beneath with very close, white, soft felt; stalk ¼ to ⅓ in. long. Corymbs about 2 ins. wide, terminal and from the uppermost leaf-axils on slender pale brown stalks 2 to 3 ins. long. Flower-heads white, cylindrical, ¼ in. long, the outer bracts erect, more or less downy and ciliate, each head carrying three to six florets, of which one to three are ray-florets.

Native of New Zealand in the North Island; said by Cheeseman to be uncommon and usually found near the sea. From this one would expect it to be more tender than its ally, O. avicenniæfolia, but it has lived and grown well at Kew for several years not only on a wall but in the open ground. These two species are closely akin and have been confused with each other in gardens, but avicenniæfolia can be distinguished by its leaves being more tapered at the base and longer stalked, by its fewer florets in one head, and by the glabrous or nearly glabrous bracts of the flower-head. O. albida is a pleasant evergreen where it succeeds. It flowers in July and August.

O. ANGUSTIFOLIA, *Hooker fil.*

(Kirk's Forest Flora of New Zealand, t. 138)

An evergreen shrub or small tree 6 to 20 ft. high, occasionally as much as 30 ft. in diameter; young shoots, lower surface of leaves and flower-stalks all clothed with a soft, white felt. Leaves linear-lanceolate, pointed, tapered to a broad stalkless base, the margins finely and regularly set with small blunt teeth; 2 to 5 ins. long, ⅓ to ¾ in. wide; glabrous and glossy green above, more or less distinctly three-veined beneath. Flower-heads two to ten at the top of the branches, each head on its own stalk and 1½ to 2 ins. wide; ray-florets pure white; disk-florets rich deep purple. Main flower-stalk 2 to 4 ins. long, stiffly erect, ⅛ in. thick, furnished with narrow, leaf-like bracts 1 to 2 ins. long.

Native of the South Island of New Zealand and of Stewart Island; discovered in 1848 by Dr Lyall; described and named by the younger Hooker in 1853. This beautiful species seems always to have been either very rare or absent from cultivation in this country, yet Kirk described it long ago as "standing unrivalled in a genus which contains many species of great beauty." It is closely related to, and comparable in beauty with, the now well-known O. semidentata, but should be hardier. Seeds collected on the southernmost point of Stewart Island were distributed in this country in 1932 by Mr Stead, who told me that it grows there close to the shore, bears the brunt of the fierce Antarctic gales, and is frequently drenched with sea spray. In the same group, which includes also O. operina and O. chathamica, comes

O. TRAILLII, *Kirk*, seed of which, collected on Stewart Island, was also distributed by Mr Stead in 1932 in English gardens. It is a shrub or small tree and grows 10 to 20 ft. high; young shoots, undersurface of leaves and flower-stalks all clothed with white wool. Leaves oblanceolate, 3 to 6 ins. long, ¾ to 1½ ins. wide, finely and irregularly toothed. Flower-heads borne three to eight together in racemes 3 to 8 ins. long, near the end of the branches. Each head is 1 in. wide, ray-florets white, disk-florets violet-purple. It was discovered by T. Kirk in 1883, and is a native of Puysegue Point on the South Island, as well as of Stewart Island; rare in both localities. Its racemose (instead of solitary) flower-heads well distinguish it in its group. O. Colensoi, also closely akin and having a racemose inflorescence, differs very much in having no ray-florets and much broader leaves.

O. ARGOPHYLLA, *Mueller*. MUSKWOOD

(Aster argophyllus, *Labillardière*; Bot. Mag., t. 1563)

An evergreen shrub or small tree up to 30 ft. high; young shoots slightly ribbed and clothed with a closely appressed silvery down. Leaves alternate, leathery, oblanceolate or oval, tapered about equally towards both ends, ɔinted, toothed unevenly; 2 to 6 ins. long, 1 to 2½ ins. wide; grey green ıd slightly downy above when young, especially on the midrib; clothed ɛrmanently beneath with a close, fine, silvery, glistening felt; stalk grooved, to 1 in. long. Flower-heads produced very numerously in corymbs 3 or 4 ins. ide at the end of the shoots of the previous year's growth the whole forming hanging cluster 8 ins. or more wide. Ray-florets three to five, narrow, :arcely ¼ in. long, creamy white; disk-florets six to eight, yellow.

Native of New South Wales, Victoria, and Tasmania; introduced in 1804. lthough not particularly attractive in its flowers, this is a handsome foliage lant on account of its silvery appearance. It has also a very pleasant musky :ent which may be detected by rubbing the leaves, and which is also erceptible in the atmosphere near a bush after a shower. It has been grown gainst a wall at Kew, but that amount of protection is insufficient to keep it ive permanently. In Cornwall and the Isle of Wight it is 20 to 30 ft. high. : flowers in June.

O. AVICENNIÆFOLIA, *Hooker fil.*

(Eurybia avicenniæfolia, *Hooker fil.*)

An evergreen shrub or small tree varying from 8 to 20 ft. in height in a ild state; young shoots ribbed and clothed with a close, white, scurf-like ɔwn. Leaves alternate, oval-lanceolate, tapered towards both ends, pointed : bluntish at the apex, entire; 2 to 4 ins. long, ⅞ to 1¾ ins. wide; greyish een and glabrous above, the undersurface furnished with a close, thin, white : yellowish white felt; stalk ¼ to ¾ in. long, grooved and downy like the ɔung shoots. Flower-heads produced in erect, rounded corymbs from the rminal leaf-axils in August and September, each corymb 2 to 3 ins. wide ıd borne on a slender stalk 2 to 3 ins. long, grooved and downy. Each ower-head is ¼ in. long, cylindrical, white, the outer bracts erect; there are sually two or three florets in each head, one or two (or sometimes none) of hich are ray-florets.

Native of New Zealand in the South Island up to 3000 ft. altitude. This hardy in the milder parts of the British Isles, and was grown outside by Ir Robinson at Gravetye in Sussex for some years. Mr Beamish succeeds ell with it at Ashbourne in Co. Cork, where, exposed to full sunshine, it owers very freely; it is 9 ft. high and in admirable vigour at Exbury in Hamp-ire. At Kew it is grown in the outside recesses of the wall of the Temperate Iouse. Considering the elevation at which it grows wild it ought, indeed, to e one of the hardier olearias. It has been confused with O. albida (*q.v.*).

O. CHATHAMICA, *Kirk*

(Bot. Mag., t. 8420)

An evergreen shrub 3 to 7 ft. high; young shoots stout, furrowed, and like e undersurface of the leaves and flower-stalks, clothed with a soft white felt. eaves alternate, 1½ to 5 ins. long, ½ to 1½ ins. wide, thick, leathery; ɔlanceolate or oblong-lanceolate, pointed, the margins set with rather :gular blunt teeth, tapering at the base to a short broad stalk; green and abrous above; the midrib is raised beneath and at each side of it are one or vo similarly prominent veins running lengthwise. Flower-heads aster-like, ¾ to 2¼ ins. wide, solitary on stalks 4 to 6 ins. long. Ray-florets numerous, sually pale mauve, occasionally white, ⅝ in. long, linear, pointed. Disk-orets dark violet-purple, forming a conspicuous centre to the flower-head ¾ in. ide. Outer bracts linear, pointed, ⅓ in. long, woolly towards the top.

Native of the Chatham Islands ; introduced by Major A. A. Dorrien-Smit in 1910. It has been very successfully grown in the Rectory garden at Ludgva near Penzance, planted in peat, leaf-soil and grit. It flowers in May and Jun According to Cheeseman its nearest ally is O. operina, *Hooker fil.*, a Ne Zealand species I have not seen in gardens. Among cultivated olearia O. chathamica most resembles O. semidentata and is equally beautiful. differs from that species in its larger, broader, more conspicuously toothe leaves with prominent veins beneath.

O. COLENSOI, *Hooker fil.*

An evergreen shrub 10 to 16 ft. high, sometimes a small tree twice as hig with a trunk 1 to 2 ft. in diameter. Leaves of very leathery texture, usual obovate to obovate-lanceolate, pointed or occasionally bluntish at the ape tapering at the base to a stout stalk ½ to ¾ in. long, toothed (often doubl so) at the margin ; 3 to 6 ins. long, half or more than half as much wide dark shining green above except when young, clothed permanently beneat with a thick white wool ; veins netted, prominent beneath. Racemes clustere at ends of the branches, each 4 to 6 ins. long and bearing five to eight or mo flower-heads which are up to 1 in. wide and dark brownish purple. The are no ray-florets.

Native of the North and South Islands of New Zealand, where it regarded as one of the most handsome of the daisy-bushes. It was discovere on Mt. Hikurangi by Colenso at altitudes up to 5000 ft. I do not think it very common in cultivation, and by far the finest example I know of in Englan was a bush in the Ludgvan Rectory garden, near Penzance, which was abo 14 ft. high, rather more in diameter, and flowered in July. At Kew it nee the shelter of a cool greenhouse. It constitutes an important part of th vegetation of Stewart Island near the sea, but with O. angustifolia usual in front of it.

O. ERUBESCENS, *Dippel*

(Eurybia erubescens, *De Candolle* ; E. myrsinoides erubescens, *Mueller*)

An evergreen shrub, 3 to 5 ft. high ; young shoots often long and slende covered like the undersurface of the leaves with a pale, brownish, shinin down. Leaves alternate, scarcely stalked, stiff and leathery ; narrowly ov or oblong, pointed, tapered or rounded at the base, conspicuously toothed ½ to 1½ ins. long, ¼ to ¾ in. wide ; dark glossy green and glabrous abov Inflorescence branched, up to 3 ins. long and carrying several flower-heads, o often unbranched and only one. Flower-heads 1 in. wide, with three to fiv pure white ray-florets and six to eight yellow disk-florets in the centre. The open in May and June. The inflorescences come from the leaf-axils of th previous year and form altogether an elegant, densely flowered, cylindric panicle 1 to 1½ ft. long.

Native of Tasmania, Victoria, and New South Wales ; cultivated at Kew i the 'forties of last century. It needs wall protection there although, in a wel sheltered spot like the foot of a house wall facing south, it may pass throug several winters without serious injury. When seen at its best it is a charmin shrub and is admirable for the south and west. It has been much confuse in gardens with O. myrsinoides (*q.v.*), but is more ornamental and is quit distinct in its much larger, pointed, more conspicuously toothed leaves and it larger flower-heads with as many as five spreading pure white florets, plus si to ten yellow disk-florets.

Var. ILICIFOLIUS, *De Candolle*.—I do not think a strict line can be drawn between this variety and typical erubescens, but the name may well be used to distinguish the largest and longest-leaved forms whose leaves are occasionally as much as 3 ins. long and 1 in. wide. The inflorescences are larger and bear more numerous flowers and the whole plant is more vigorous. It is cultivated in Messrs Stewart's nursery at Ferndown in Dorset, at Trebagh in Cornwall, and in various places in Ireland.

O. FORSTERI, *Hooker fil.*

(O. paniculata, *Cheeseman*; Shawia paniculata, *Forster*)

An evergreen shrub or a small tree up to 20 ft. high in its native country; young shoots ribbed and furnished with a dark brown scurf, as are also the leaf-stalks and flower-stalks. Leaves alternate, leathery, ovate or oval, rounded or slightly heart-shaped at the base, mostly blunt at the apex, the margins entire but conspicuously wavy; 1½ to 3½ ins. long, 1 to 1¾ ins. wide; shining green and without down above, clothed beneath with a grey-white, closely appressed felt; stalk ⅓ to ¾ in. long, grooved. Flower-heads dull white, produced in small, pyramidal, axillary panicles in October and usually about 2 ins. long; each flower-head is cylindrical, ¼ in. long, composed of a solitary tubular floret enclosed by erect, slightly downy, dull white scales.

Native of both Islands of New Zealand, up to 1500 ft. It is not hardy near London except against a wall, but is grown outside in several parts of the British Isles, especially in the west and near the sea. It is 12 ft. high at Castlewellan in Co. Down, and I have had specimens in flower from a garden near Bristol. It has no beauty of flower, but the blossoms are fragrant and continue to open during November and December. It is very distinct among cultivated olearias by reason of the very undulated margins of the leaves.

O. FURFURACEA, *Hooker fil.*

(Aster furfuraceus, *A. Richard*; Eurybia furfuracea, *De Candolle*)

An evergreen shrub of bushy habit, sometimes a small tree up to 20 ft. high; young shoots covered with a whitish soft down, which persists to the second year and becomes brown. Leaves alternate, very leathery, mostly ovate or inclined to oblong, abruptly pointed or blunt at the apex, rounded or broadly tapered and often unequal at the base; margins entire or remotely and shallowly toothed; 2 to 4 ins. long, 1½ to 2½ ins. wide; glabrous and dark glossy green above, silvery beneath with a closely appressed down; leaf-stalk ½ to 1 in. long. Flower-heads numerously produced in axillary, much branched corymbs 3 to 5 ins. wide, the main-stalk up to 6 or 8 ins. long. Each head is ⅓ to ½ in. wide, carrying two to five ray-florets and three to seven disk-florets, the former white, oblong, ⅛ to ¼ in. long; the latter yellow. March and April.

Native of the North Island, New Zealand. In its shining green foliage—in size and colouring rather like that of a Portugal laurel, only stiffer and shining grey-white beneath—this olearia is quite handsome, and its flowers are abundant enough to give a pleasing effect. It survives mild winters in a sheltered spot at Kew, but is, of course, happier farther south and west. Among cultivated olearias it comes nearest to O. nitida, but that species has thinner, less leathery leaves, whose margins are usually more conspicuously wavy and toothed and whose flowers each carry fifteen to twenty florets.

O. Gunniana, *Hooker fil.*

(Bot. Mag., t. 4638; O. stellulata, *Bentham* (in part))

An evergreen shrub, 5 to 10 ft. high, naturally much branched; young shoots covered with a close white felt. Leaves alternate, oblong or narrowly obovate, ½ to 1½ ins. long, about one-fourth as wide, roundish at the apex, tapering towards the base, the margins sinuously or very shallowly toothed,

Olearia Gunniana

dark dull green above, white, and closely felted beneath; very shortly stalked. Flower-heads pure white with a yellow disk, 1 to 1¼ ins. across, produced during summer in erect, loose, slender-stalked corymbs. Ray-florets ten to sixteen.

Native of Tasmania; introduced to Kew about 1848. It is the least hardy of the olearias here described, and can only be grown out-of-doors permanently in the mildest districts. It is a handsome plant when grown outside in pots during the summer, and housed through the winter. Grown in this way it comes into flower in March and April. This species was by Bentham united with O. STELLULATA, *De Candolle*. The true plant of that name is very distinct and has leaves up to 4 ins. long. Probably not in cultivation.

Mr H. F. Comber, during his expedition to Tasmania (1929-30), found some forms of O. Gunniana with coloured flowers. The form hitherto cultivated has white flowers, but he describes these new ones as ranging from white to pale pink, deep pink, mauve, purple and blue. The seed he sent home germinated freely, and some attractive new olearias have been established in cultivation, especially those with blue flowers.

O. HAASTII, *Hooker fil.*

(Bot. Mag., t. 6592)

An evergreen shrub of bushy, rounded habit, 4 to 9 ft. high; young branches covered with a close, greyish white down. Leaves crowded on the branches, alternate, oval or ovate, ½ to 1 in. long, about half as wide; not toothed, rounded or blunt at the apex, thick and leathery, dark shining green and glabrous above, white-felted beneath; stalk about ⅛ in. long. Flower-heads produced during July and August in a series of axillary corymbose clusters standing out beyond the leaves, the whole forming a flattish cluster 2 to 3 ins. across at the end of each twig. Ray-florets white, disk-florets yellow; each flower-head is ⅓ in. across.

Native of New Zealand, in the province of Canterbury, at 4000 ft. to 5000 ft. elevation; introduced in 1858 by Veitch of Exeter. This is the only olearia at Kew of proved hardiness. I have never seen it killed outright by cold, although in February 1895 it was cut to the ground, but sprang up again freely a few months later. It flowers when there are few shrubs in blossom, and its abundant white flowers show up well against the dark green leaves; they have besides the charm of a sweet hawthorn-like fragrance. The flower-heads in the seeding state are covered with brown-grey down, which some people object to and cut off, as it persists through the winter. This shrub is admirable for maritime districts. In the late Sir Herbert Maxwell's garden at Monreith some years ago I saw a specimen 9 ft. high and 15 ft. in diameter. I believe it thrives extremely well in the Orkneys. Pruning, which it bears well, should be done in early spring. It should consist merely of a shortening back of plants that have become lanky or too large for their place.

O. OLEIFOLIA, *Kirk*, sometimes offered in catalogues, is a species very nearly related to O. Haastii; in fact Cheeseman, the New Zealand botanist, says it "only differs in its more erect habit and longer narrower leaves." The latter are 1½ to 3 ins. long by ¼ to ½ in. wide, and of oblong-lanceolate to lanceolate shape. Intermediate forms have been found in New Zealand.

O. ILICIFOLIA, *Hooker fil.*

(O. multibracteolata, *Colenso*; Eurybia dentata linearifolia, *Hooker fil.*)

An evergreen bush of spreading habit up to 10 ft. or more high; young shoots rather downy. Leaves alternate, hard and leathery, linear-oblong to lanceolate, pointed, rounded or truncate at the base; margins conspicuously wavy and sharply and coarsely toothed; glabrous and green at maturity above, clothed beneath with a close whitish felt; 2 to 4 ins. long, ½ to 1 in. wide; stalk ½ to ¾ in. long. Flower-heads fragrant, produced during June in branched, rounded corymbs 2 to 4 ins. wide from the end of the previous year's growths on a main-stalk 3 to 6 ins. long. Each flower-head is daisy-like, about ½ in. wide, with ten or more white ray-florets.

Native of New Zealand on both North and South Islands extending to 4000 ft. altitude. It is closely related to O. macrodonta and is somewhat similar in general appearance. Both have the same musk-like odour. The leaves of ilicifolia are more oblong in shape, usually narrower, more wavy at the margin, and the veins stand out from the midrib at right angles (pointing forward in macrodonta). The whole plant in this country is smaller and less vigorous. It is about as hardy as O. macrodonta and therefore of uncertain tenure in a climate like that of Kew, even against a wall. It does not promise to become so beautiful a shrub.

O. INSIGNIS, *Hooker fil.*

(Bot. Mag., t. 7034; Pachystegia insignis, *Cheeseman*)

A low, spreading, evergreen shrub, described as growing 6 ft. high in a wild state; young shoots thick and, like the undersurface of the leaves, leaf-stalks and flower-stalks, clothed with a white or pale brown woolly felt. Leaves crowded at the ends of the shoots, very stout and leathery, entire, oval or obovate; tapered, rounded, or slightly heart-shaped at the base, blunt at the apex; 3 to 7 ins. long, about half as wide; upper surface at first woolly, ultimately dark glossy green and glabrous except on the midrib and margins; stalk stout, ½ to 2 ins. long. Flower-heads produced from the end of the shoot or in the terminal leaf-axils; each solitary on a slender stalk 4 to 8 ins. long. Each flower-head is 1½ to 2½ ins. wide; the ray-florets very numerous in two or more rows, white, linear, toothed at the end, ½ in. long. Disk-florets very crowded, forming a yellow centre to the flower-head 1¼ ins. wide. Outer scales small, overlapping, woolly, arranged in many rows.

Native of New Zealand on the South Island up to 4000 ft. altitude; discovered by Capt. Rough about 1850. A very handsome species and very distinct among olearias by reason of its large leaves; its large, white and yellow, long-stalked flower-heads; and large egg-shaped involucre of very numerous scales beneath the flower-head. As many as five heads may be borne on one shoot and they open in summer. It is not really happy out-of-doors at Kew although it survives at the foot of a warm wall. At Wakehurst in Sussex is a plant near the house 4 ft. across and 2 ft. high. It is well worth cultivation wherever it can be grown. Blooms about August.

O. LACUNOSA, *Hooker fil.*

(O. alpina, *Buchanan*)

An evergreen shrub 5 ft. or more high (in a wild state sometimes a small tree 15 ft. high); young shoots, undersurface of leaves, leaf-stalks and flower-stalks all densely clothed with a pale greyish or rust-coloured down. Leaves of leathery texture, linear to linear-oblong, obscurely or not at all toothed, pointed, very shortly stalked; 3 to 7 ins. long, ⅓ to 1 in. wide; margins recurved; upper surface glabrous, the veins conspicuously sunken above, very prominent beneath, proceeding from the midrib to the leaf margins at almost right angles; midrib yellow on the upper surface. Panicles terminal and several together, forming a group of flower-heads 4 ins. or more wide. Flower-heads ⅕ in. wide, each carrying from eight to twelve florets, four or five of which have rays about ⅛ in. long.

Native of North and South Islands, New Zealand, up to 5000 ft. altitude; discovered by W. T. L. Travers in 1864 on the mountains near Rotoroa. It was grown at Kew, but although it survived mild winters out-of-doors in sheltered spots, it was not genuinely hardy there. Like most of the olearias it will only be seen at its best in the mildest counties. The leaves make it one of the most distinct in the genus; the midrib is very prominent beneath and the veins, leaving it at right angles, divide the lower surface into a long series of roughly rectangular hollows. It grows well in the Rectory garden at Ludgvan, near Penzance.

O. MACRODONTA, *Baker*

(Bot. Mag., t. 7065)

An evergreen shrub up to 20 ft. high, or even a small tree in a wild state, with bark peeling in long strips; young shoots angled, downy. Leaves alternate, firm and leathery, ovate to narrowly oval, rounded or tapering at the base, pointed at the apex; 2 to 5 ins. long, 1 to 2 ins. wide; the margins wavy and furnished with coarse sharp teeth, the hollows between them rounded; upper surface dark glossy green, downy only when quite young, lower surface covered with a close, silvery white felt; leaf-stalk ½ to ¾ in. long. Flower-heads produced in one or more branched clusters 3 to 6 ins. across, at the termination of the previous season's growth, each cluster on a silvery white, downy stalk 3 to 6 ins. long. The flower-head is ½ in. across, with ten or more white ray-florets and a few reddish disk-florets.

Native of New Zealand up to elevations of 4000 ft., and only hardy in the mild parts of the kingdom. It succeeds in Ireland, Cornwall, on the west coast of Scotland, and even in Sussex, where in July I have seen bushes 15 ft. through, almost hidden by their own white blossom. At Kew it has to be grown on a wall, where it flowers in June. The plant has a musky odour when crushed. This species is often grown as O. tomentosa, but the true shrub of that name has its leaves clothed with a thick red-brown felt beneath, and is very uncommon.

Var. MINOR (syn. nana).—A very dwarf, compact form with much smaller leaves.

O. MOSCHATA, *Hooker fil.*

An evergreen shrub of dense, bushy, much branched habit, 3 to 6 ft. high, with a distinct musk-like scent and slightly viscid; young shoots, flower-stalks, involucres and undersurface of leaves covered with a close white felt. Leaves of leathery texture, alternate, closely set on the branches, oval inclined to obovate, rounded at the apex, tapered at the base to a very short stalk, quite without teeth; ⅓ to ¾ in. long, ⅛ to ⅜ in. wide; greenish grey and scurfy above. Corymbs axillary, made up of three to five flower-heads produced on a slender main-stalk up to 2 ins. long, the stalks of the individual flower-head much shorter. There are twelve to twenty florets in a head; ray-florets white, usually seven to nine, linear, giving each flower-head a diameter of ⅓ to ½ in.; disk-florets yellow.

Native of the South Island, New Zealand; discovered by Sir Julius von Haast in 1862. This daisy bush is very distinct on account of its silvery-grey colour, its musky scent, small leaves, and close compact habit. When in bloom the leaves are almost hidden by the wealth of blossom. It needs winter shelter at Kew, but farther south succeeds well in the open air. In July 1930 it was flowering well at Wakehurst in Sussex, and in Col. Stern's garden at Highdown, near Worthing, there is a healthy rounded bush about 4 ft. high, whose silvery grey hue makes it very conspicuous and handsome.

O. MYRSINOIDES, *Mueller*

An evergreen shrub said to be usually low and straggling or densely bushy in a state of nature; young shoots angled, silvery, with a scale-like covering like the undersurface of the leaves. Leaves alternate, mostly obovate, sometimes narrowly oval, tapered at the base, rounded at the apex, toothed; $\frac{1}{4}$ to $\frac{1}{2}$ in. long, $\frac{1}{8}$ to $\frac{1}{4}$ in. wide; shining green and glabrous above. Flower-heads three to five together in axillary clusters, borne on stalks up to 1 in. long; ray-florets white, two or three to each head; disk-florets two to five, yellow.

Native of Tasmania and Victoria. In shape and size the leaves often resemble those of Myrsine africana. I do not know that the true plant is in cultivation. What has been grown under the name is O. erubescens, a very distinct thing.

O. NITIDA, *Hooker fil.*

(O. arborescens, *Cockayne*; Eurybia alpina, *Lindley and Paxton*, Flower Garden, ii., p. 84)

An evergreen shrub up to 12 ft. high; young shoots grooved, clothed with fine, close, pale brown down. Leaves alternate, slightly leathery, ovate to roundish-ovate, pointed, usually rounded (sometimes broadly tapered) at the base, wavy or indistinctly toothed at the margins; $1\frac{1}{2}$ to $3\frac{1}{2}$ ins. long, $\frac{3}{4}$ to 2 ins. wide; dark shining green above and either glabrous or with appressed whitish hairs when young; clothed beneath with a silvery, satiny, closely appressed down; stalks about $\frac{1}{2}$ in. long. Flower-heads in corymbs opening in May and June, from the end of the shoots and the terminal leaf-axils, the whole forming a cluster 4 to 6 ins. wide; the main-stalks 2 to 3 ins. long, grooved and downy like the young shoots, secondary stalks more downy. Each flower-head is $\frac{1}{2}$ to $\frac{5}{8}$ in. wide, aster-like, the fifteen to twenty ray-florets being white, the disk-florets yellowish. Outer scales linear-oblong, clothed with short brown hairs.

Native of New Zealand from sea-level to 4000 ft. altitude. It was cultivated at Kew for at least seventy years, but was killed during the severe winter of 1946-47. The late Mr Chambers used to grow it well at Grayshill, Haslemere, where it flowered excellently. The garden there is some hundred feet above sea-level; on the low flat area of Kew it will not live for long out-of-doors, It is really at its best in the southern and western maritime counties. Mr Armytage Moore of Rowallane, Co. Down, for instance, has a bush 22 ft. across; and there is a similar one at Loch Inch in Wigtownshire. I am told the noted example at Castlewellan, Co. Down, is now 30 ft. across. It is well distinguished by the satiny sheen of the undersurface of the leaves, and is quite pretty in bloom. It grows well in chalky soil.

O. NUMMULARIFOLIA, *Hooker fil.*

(Eurybia nummularifolia, *Hooker fil.*)

An evergreen bush of dense growth up to 10 ft. high; young shoots thinly downy or almost glabrous. Leaves alternate, thick and leathery, closely set on the branchlets (twelve or more to the inch), oval or obovate to almost round, tapering at the base to a very short stalk, rounded at the apex, toothless, the margins recurved; $\frac{1}{4}$ to $\frac{1}{2}$ in. long, from half to nearly as much wide; glossy green above, clothed beneath with a very close, yellowish-white felt. Flower-heads solitary, produced from the axils of the terminal leaves, beyond which they stand out slightly. Each flower-head is $\frac{1}{3}$ to $\frac{1}{2}$ in. long and each has three to five creamy white or yellowish ray-florets. The scales of the involucre are erect, in several rows, often nearly glabrous except at the points and margins.

Native of New Zealand on the North and South Islands, ascending to altitudes of 4500 ft. It is one of the hardier olearias and survives ordinary winters at Kew, but still cannot be relied on there like O. Haastii. It is usually seen as a rather low bush in this country, distinct in its crowded, small, thick leaves and is well worth growing in the milder counties. It flowers in July. I have not seen a better example than one in the late Sir Herbert Maxwell's garden at Monreith, Wigtownshire, which in May 1931 was 6 ft. high and 5 ft. across.

O. ODORATA, *Petrie*

A shrub up to 10 ft. high of thin, sparse habit, with slender, wiry, terete, little-branched stems; leaves opposite, linear or spathulate, $\frac{3}{4}$ to $1\frac{1}{2}$ ins. long, $\frac{1}{8}$ to $\frac{1}{4}$ in. wide near the rounded apex; bright green and glabrous above, silvery beneath with appressed, glistening, white hairs; tapering at the base to a short stalk. Flower-heads $\frac{1}{4}$ in. across, borne on short, arrested, bud-like branches, which usually also carry a pair of leaves; they are scented and dull greyish brown; the bracts of the involucre brown, and viscous-glandular.

Native of New Zealand, where it is very common in the lake district of Otago. It is a curious, not particularly ornamental, shrub introduced a few years ago, and put in commerce as "O. virgata." The true virgata has four-angled instead of cylindrical stems.

O. RAMULOSA, *Bentham*. TWIGGY DAISY BUSH

(Aster ramulosus, *Labillardière*; Eurybia ramulosa, *De Candolle*)

A much-branched evergreen shrub 3 to 5 ft. high, with graceful arching shoots clothed with pale hairs or scurf when young and very slender. Leaves alternate, linear, linear-obovate or almost round; $\frac{1}{12}$ to $\frac{1}{3}$ in. long, $\frac{1}{12}$ in. wide; margins recurved; dark green and at first slightly woolly or minutely warted above, permanently woolly beneath; stalk $\frac{1}{8}$ in. or less long. Flower-heads $\frac{5}{8}$ in. wide, solitary on very short, leafy twigs; ray-florets pure white, six to ten in number, linear; disk-florets also white, with yellow anthers.

Native of Tasmania and Australia. It has long been cultivated, having flowered in a garden near Paris as long ago as 1822. It was treated as a cool greenhouse plant at Kew where it flowered from February onwards. It is grown out-of-doors in specially favoured places in the south-west, but must be regarded sa one of the tenderest of the olearias. The flowers stand erect on the arching shoots and make very elegant sprays. H. F. Comber found it in dry, open pastures in Tasmania, fully exposed to the sun. In flower, he observes, the plant became simply a white mass. The plant figured in the *Botanical Magazine*, t. 8205, as var. COMMUNIS is the form grown in this country. Comber's form is of closer growth and may be hardier.

O. SEMIDENTATA, *Decaisne*

(Bot. Mag., t. 8550; Eurybia semidentata, *Mueller*)

An evergreen bush of rounded habit 6 to 12 ft. high and as much or more in diameter; young shoots slender, clothed with a white, woolly felt. Leaves alternate, linear to lanceolate, pointed, tapered slightly to a stalkless base with a few shallow teeth at the upper half; $1\frac{1}{2}$ to 3 ins. long, $\frac{1}{6}$ to $\frac{5}{8}$ in. wide; upper surface dark green, wrinkled; lower one clothed with soft, silvery white wool.

Flower-heads solitary at the end of the twigs, each one about 2 ins. wide, aster-like in form, the numerous spreading or slightly decurved ray-florets pale purple and about ¾ in. long by ⅙ in. wide; disk-florets of a darker, more violet-purple, forming a conspicuous circular centre to the flower-head ½ to ¾ in. wide. The outer scales of the involucre are linear, pointed, closely set in about three rows, and almost hidden by a white cottony down.

Native of the Chatham Islands; introduced to England in 1910 by Major A. A. Dorrien-Smith, who gives a very interesting account of a visit made to the native habitat of this beautiful shrub in the *Kew Bulletin*, 1910, p. 120. On this occasion he found a white form, ALBIFLORA. Since its introduction, O. semidentata has spread in cultivation and become, in the milder parts of the British Isles, one of the most popular of the genus, which it well deserves to be. It first flowered at Tresco Abbey in Scilly in July 1913. In the garden at Ludgvan Rectory, near Penzance, there is a plant 12 ft. high, taller than it is usually found in a wild state. I saw two fine bushes in Lord Stair's garden at Loch Inch, Wigtownshire, in June 1931, which were then 8 ft. by 10 ft. and 6 ft. by 8 ft. respectively. In colour beauty of blossom this surpasses all other olearias I have seen in cultivation. It is not adapted for the open air in places with a climate similar to that of Kew, only surviving there the mildest winters and even then not unscathed. It likes a light, well-drained or even stony soil. Closely related to O. chathamica (*q.v.*).

O. SOLANDRI, *Hooker fil.*

(O. fasciculifolia, *Colenso*; Eurybia Solandri, *Hooker fil.*)

An evergreen shrub up to 15 ft. high in a wild state, of erect habit, branches broom-like; young shoots angled, clothed with yellowish down. Leaves opposite or in opposite clusters, about ¼ in. long, $\frac{1}{20}$ in. wide (twice as long on quite young plants); linear inclined to obovate, rounded or bluntish at the end, tapered at the base to a very short stalk; dark green and glabrous above, the midrib deeply sunken; clothed beneath with a yellowish white felt; margins recurved. Flower-heads solitary from the centre of the leaf-clusters, stalkless, yellowish, ¼ to ⅓ in. long, each containing eight to twenty florets. Outer scales of involucre in four rows, bright tawny yellow, rather downy.

Native of New Zealand on both the North and South Islands up to 1500 ft. altitude. It is distinct amongst cultivated olearias in its rather heath-like foliage and habit and its clusters (fascicles) of leaves. In general aspect it resembles Cassinia fulvida. It can be grown in a sheltered spot near a wall at Kew and has made healthy bushes there 6 ft. high, apt nevertheless to be severely injured in hard winters. The whole plant has a yellowish tone due to the colour of the down on the shoots, underneath the leaves, and on the involucral scales. It blooms from August to October, but on the whole is a dull shrub.

O. SPECIOSA, *Hutchinson*

(Bot. Mag., t. 8118)

An evergreen shrub described as of straggling habit and 3 to 4 ft. high; young shoots densely clothed with pale brown wool. Leaves alternate, stout and leathery, narrowly oblong or oval, the margins recurved and toothed—sometimes coarsely and iregularly; 1½ to 4½ ins. long, ⅝ to 1½ ins. wide; dark glossy green and finely wrinkled above, clothed beneath with a thick, soft, pale brown felt; stalk ¼ to ½ in. long. The flower-heads are produced about midsummer in rather lax corymbs 4 to 8 ins. wide, the main and secondary stalks woolly like the young shoots. Each head is borne on a slender stalk

$\frac{1}{2}$ to 2 ins. long and measures about 1 in. wide. Ray-florets five or six, white, $\frac{1}{6}$ in. wide, tapering towards both ends. Disk-florets about twice as many, yellow. Outer bracts woolly, forming a funnel-shaped involucre $\frac{1}{3}$ in. wide.

Native of Australia. The plant figured in the *Botanical Magazine* was raised at Kew from seed obtained in 1888 from Melbourne. The species had, however, been introduced previously to Kew and had flowered in 1883, but was confused with O. tomentosa. To this species (*q.v.*) it is related, but differs in its thicker, short-stalked leaves and fewer ray-florets, which in tomentosa are rose-tinted. It thrives well at Tresco Abbey in the Isles of Scilly but needs winter protection at Kew.

O. SUBREPANDA, *Hutchinson*

(Eurybia subrepanda, *De Candolle*)

In the first edition of this work, published in 1914, I accepted the then prevailing conception of the name "Olearia stellulata" which, following Bentham, the author of *Flora Australiensis*, was made to include O. Gunniana. Bentham was a confirmed "lumper," and not only did he sink O. Gunniana under stellulata but also two other species, viz., O. lyrata and O. subrepanda. In the second and subsequent editions I adopted the name O. Gunniana for the plant described as "O. stellulata."

O. subrepanda is an evergreen shrub closely akin to O. Gunniana, but is well distinguished by its more compact habit and its smaller leaves, which are from $\frac{1}{4}$ to $\frac{5}{8}$ in. long, $\frac{1}{8}$ to $\frac{3}{16}$ in. wide, oblong-obovate, rounded at the end, tapered at the base, rather coarsely and bluntly toothed, wrinkled above, stellately downy beneath like the young shoots. Flowers white with a yellow disk, $\frac{5}{8}$ to $\frac{3}{4}$ in. wide, ray-florets linear; flower-stalks stouter and much shorter than in O. Gunniana. Native of Tasmania on mountain sides at 3000 ft. elevation, where it makes a rounded bush 4 or 5 ft. high. In the confusion with O. Gunniana and O. stellulata it would be difficult to ascertain when it was first introduced, but it was cultivated by Messrs Veitch in the Coombe Wood Nursery, in 1881, as "Eurybia Gunniana." It is still grown in gardens as a small-leaved, dwarfer form of O. Gunniana and is a charming spring-flowering shrub.

O. LYRATA, *Hutchinson* (Aster liratus, *Sims*, Bot. Mag., t. 1509), is very distinct, especially in foliage, from O. Gunniana and O. subrepanda. It is evergreen, grows 9 to 10 ft. high; young shoots grey-downy, very pithy. Leaves lanceolate, long-pointed, 3 to 6 ins. long, $\frac{1}{2}$ to $1\frac{1}{4}$ ins. wide; the margins toothless, wavy, or toothed; glabrous and wrinkled above, covered with a close grey felt beneath. Flower-heads white with a yellow disk, $\frac{3}{4}$ in. wide, borne in rounded terminal clusters 2 or 3 ins. across. Native of Australia (Victoria and New South Wales), also of Tasmania. It was cultivated by Loddiges of Hackney as a greenhouse plant in 1813, by the late Mr W. E. Gumbleton, near Queenstown, Co. Cork, in 1890, and at Bowood in 1910, but is now very uncommon. It is only hardy in our mildest counties, and is not so well worth cultivation as its close allies. All of them have star-shaped down. It is probable that the true O. stellulata is not in cultivation.

O. TOMENTOSA, *De Candolle*

(O. dentata, *Moench*, Bot. Mag., t. 5973; Aster tomentosus, *Schrad*)

A stout, much branched, evergreen shrub; young shoots clothed with a felt of rusty brown, forked hairs. Leaves alternate, oval, ovate, pointed or blunt, mostly tapered at the base but sometimes rounded or slightly heart-shaped, with four to six shallow teeth on each margin or almost entire; 1 to $2\frac{1}{2}$ ins.

long, about half as wide; dark green and rough to the touch above, clothed beneath with a felt of forked hairs similar to that which covers the branchlets; stalk $\frac{1}{4}$ to $\frac{5}{8}$ in. long. Flower-heads in a terminal panicle of sometimes nine to a dozen, each head 1 to $1\frac{1}{2}$ ins. wide. Ray-florets numerous, linear, often notched at the end, pale rose-coloured. Disk-florets forming a compact yellow centre $\frac{1}{3}$ in. wide. Outer scales of flower-head linear, pointed, clothed with a red-brown felt like that of the other parts, very numerous in several rows and forming an ovoid involucre nearly $\frac{1}{2}$ in. wide.

Native of E. Australia, and suitable only for the milder parts of our islands. It has long been cultivated and was raised in Lee and Kennedy's nursery at Hammersmith in 1793 and flowered there a few years later. It has been grown at Tresco Abbey in Scilly since the middle of last century and Sir Joseph Hooker records the existence of a fine bush there in 1872. I believe the true plant is now very rare. For some time the very different O. macrodonta went under the name of "dentata," one of the synonyms of this species. It is certainly one of the most beautiful of the olearias, for few of them have flower-heads combining size, pretty colouring and number to such an extent. The flowering season is apparently an extended one and I have seen specimens collected in March and July. Andrews, who figured the plant in his *Botanist's Repository*, t. 61, gives the flowering season as extending from December to August.

O. TRAVERSII, *Hooker fil.*

(Eurybia Traversii, *Mueller*)

An evergreen shrub or small tree from 15 to 35 ft. high in a wild state; young shoots four-angled, clothed with a silvery white, closely appressed felt as are also the leaves beneath, the leaf-stalks and the flower-stalks. Leaves opposite, obovate or oval, tapered at both ends, but usually more abruptly towards the mucronate apex, quite untoothed, leathery; $1\frac{1}{2}$ to $2\frac{1}{2}$ ins. long, $\frac{3}{4}$ to $1\frac{1}{2}$ ins. wide; at first furnished with appressed silky hairs above, but ultimately quite glabrous and bright dark green; stalk $\frac{1}{8}$ to $\frac{1}{4}$ in. long. Panicles 1 to 2 ins. long, produced during June in the leaf-axils and carrying usually five to twelve flower-heads, each $\frac{1}{4}$ in. long. From five to fifteen florets occur in each head, the outer ones of which are female. There are no ray-florets and the dull greyish flowers have little beauty.

Native of the Chatham Islands, where it was discovered in 1840. Although this olearia has so little flower beauty to recommend it, the fine silvery sheen beneath the leaves is quite attractive. It is a free grower where the conditions suit it, and it has proved hardy at Kew but not on other inland sites. It thrives in the milder counties and is especially adapted for the seaside. Even on the east coast as far north as Scarborough, it succeeds in exposed situations if planted close to the sea. It is well distinguished by its short-stalked, opposite leaves, numerous short axillary panicles, and squarish twigs.

O. VIRGATA, *Hooker fil.*

(O. quinquefida, *Colenso*; O. parvifolia, *Colenso*; Eurybia virgata, *Hooker fil.*)

An evergreen shrub up to 10 or 15 ft. high and as much wide, often forming dense tangled bushes; young shoots very slender, wiry, usually four-angled and glabrous. Leaves opposite or in opposite clusters; linear-obovate, $\frac{1}{4}$ to $\frac{3}{4}$ in. long, $\frac{1}{16}$ to $\frac{3}{16}$ in. wide, rounded or abruptly narrowed to a point at the apex, tapered at the base; upper surface usually glabrous and dark green; lower surface clothed with white felt; stalk very short or absent. Flower-heads in opposite clusters, each about $\frac{1}{6}$ in. long and wide and borne on very short downy stalks. Florets in each head five to twelve; ray-florets three to six, yellowish white. Outer scales of the involucre in about three rows, linear-oblong, usually silky-downy.

Native of New Zealand in the North and South Islands, from sea level up to 3000 ft. altitude. This curious shrub has no great beauty and is chiefly interesting for its long, slender, wire-like branches furnished with small leaves and clusters of short flower-heads which open during May and June in this country. It is not very hardy and needs wall protection in most places. Still I saw it in bloom in Mr Berkeley's garden at Spetchley, near Worcester, some years ago. The finest specimen I know of is in Mr M'Douall's garden at Logan in the Rhinns of Galloway; this, in June 1931, was 15 ft. high and as much wide. O. virgata and O. odorata are closely related, but the latter has terete branchlets, broader leaves, many more (20 to 25) florets in each head, and the outer scales of the involucre are viscid and glandular. Still more nearly akin is

O. LINEATA, *Cockayne* (O. virgata lineata, *Kirk*), but it differs in the more slender and pendulous branchlets which are often downy when young. Still more does it differ in the opposite leaf-clusters being set farther apart, and in the narrowness of the leaves themselves, which are only $\frac{1}{16}$ in. wide, but from $\frac{1}{2}$ to $1\frac{1}{2}$ ins. long. The ray-florets are about twice as many to each head as in virgata, and number from eight to fourteen. Native of the South Island, New Zealand; also of Stewart Island. There is a good example in Messrs Hillier's nursery at Winchester 15 ft. high, and others in Messrs Wallace's nursery at Tunbridge Wells, where it is evidently hardy.

ONONIS. LEGUMINOSÆ

Of this genus—to which belongs the common "rest-harrow" (O. arvensis) of our waysides and fields—only two or three species can be included amongst hardy shrubs, the majority being herbaceous or only slightly woody. They are natives of S. Europe. The leading characteristics of the genus are the alternate, trifoliolate, toothed leaves, the five long, narrow divisions of the calyx, the pea-shaped flowers, the stamens united in one bundle, and the slightly swollen seed-pods. The under-mentioned are useful in flowering later in the season than the bulk of hardy shrubs, and are easily cultivated in moderately good soil in a sunny spot. Propagated by seeds, or, failing them, cuttings. Besides the three here described, O. NATRIX, *Linnæus* (Bot. Mag., t. 329), is sometimes included in lists of shrubs. It is a rather showy plant with yellow flowers, the standard petal 1 in. across, but it is only partially woody and not long-lived. A native of S. Europe and popularly called "Goat-root."

O. ARAGONENSIS, *Asso*

A deciduous bushy shrub, $1\frac{1}{2}$ to 2 ft. high, of sturdy habit, with crooked branches and pale greyish young shoots. Leaves from $\frac{1}{2}$ in. long on the flowering twigs, to $1\frac{1}{2}$ ins. long on the stronger flowerless shoots of the year; leaflets three, glossy green, roundish, irregularly toothed, glabrous, from $\frac{1}{8}$ to $\frac{3}{8}$ in. wide, the middle one stalked and larger, the side ones stalkless, or nearly so. Flowers yellow, $\frac{1}{2}$ in. long, produced often in pairs along a crooked, hairy, terminal raceme, 3 to 6 ins. high. The standard petal is $\frac{1}{3}$ in. across, and the calyx consists of five-pointed, awl-shaped lobes covered with glandular hairs. Pod glandular-hairy, with the calyx persisting at the base.

ONONIS ARAGONENSIS

Native of the Pyrenees southward into Spain; introduced in 1816. This is a pretty dwarf shrub, flowering from mid-May onwards. It bears its erect racemes very freely, the larger ones carrying ten or twelve pairs of blossoms. It does not ripen seed freely here, but can be increased by cuttings of half-ripened wood. It must have a sunny position, and the soil should be light loam. Suitable for the rock garden. It is perfectly hardy.

O. fruticosa, *Linnæus*

(Bot. Mag., t. 317)

A deciduous shrub of spreading habit, 2 or 3 ft. high, with pale, crooked branchlets. Leaves trifoliolate, short-stalked, clasping the stem by the stipule at the base; the stipule is terminated by four slender teeth—two long and two short; leaflets narrowly obovate, ½ to 1 in. long, ⅛ to ¼ in. wide; not downy, but wrinkled, unevenly toothed, all stalkless. Flowers ¾ in. long, pale pinkish purple, borne (usually three on a stalk) on a short terminal panicle 2 to 3 ins. long. Pod ¾ to 1 in. long, stout, covered with bristly hairs, and containing two to five seeds.

Native of S. Europe, especially in the Dauphiné Alps; known in our gardens since 1680. It flowers from June to August, and should only be propagated by seeds, which it ripens in plenty. Well distinguished from the other two by the shape of the leaflets, and by all three of them being stalkless.

O. rotundifolia, *Linnæus*

(Bot. Mag., t. 335)

A deciduous, half-shrubby species, 1½ to 2 ft. high, with very glandular-hairy, zigzag stems; the leaf-stalk, flower-stalk, and calyx are also glandular-hairy. Leaves trifoliolate, 1 to 3 ins. long; leaflets roundish, sometimes obovate, the terminal one the largest, stalked, and ¼ to 1¼ ins. long; side ones half to two-thirds as large, stalkless; all are toothed and hairy, especially below and on the margins. Flowers ¾ in. long, pink, produced from the axils of the leaves, three together towards the end of a stalk ½ to 2½ ins. long. Pod very hairy, 1 to 1¼ ins. long.

Native of S. and Central Europe; cultivated for more than three hundred years in England. Increased by seeds.

OPUNTIA. Prickly Pear. Cactaceæ

The only members of the cactus family that can be grown continuously in the open air in our average climate belong to this genus. It is purely American, and species are found as far north as Massachusetts in the United States, and as far south as the Straits of Magellan. The greatest aggregations of species occur in the S.W. United States, Mexico, and Chile. Several species have become naturalised in the Old World, notably in the Mediterranean region, and in N. and S. Africa. In Australia there is a fear that they may become as great a pest in the plant world as the rabbit has proved to be in the animal world. E. H. Wilson, in a wild mountainous spot in Western China, at elevations of 4000 to 5000 ft., found a large colony of opuntia covering miles of barren rocky slopes. Here the plants, which he identified as O. Dillenii, grow 6 to 10 ft. high and flower profusely. He offers no explanation as to how an American plant such as this became established (it must have been many years ago) in the Chinese-Tibetan borderland—a really remarkable occurrence.

In the common type of prickly pear, the younger parts of the plant consist of stems in the shape of thick fleshy plates or "slabs" of obovate or oval outline, varying from 2 or 3 ins. to over 1 ft. in length. These are jointed together at the ends, and each face is covered with a green bark more or less thickly sprinkled with clusters of slender needle-like spines up to 1½ ins. long (in some species over 3 ins.), which spring from tufts of tiny, often barbed bristles. But not all the opuntias have these flat slab-like stems; many have them more or less terete, but jointed and armed in the same way as the others.

They vary much in stature; those that can be grown in the open air in this country are at most a few feet high, and consist entirely of jointed sections. But in warmer regions some species attain the dimensions of small trees with a distinct trunk. The flowers are usually borne on the margins of the stems, and have usually a saucer- or cup-shaped arrangement of sepals and petals and measure 2 to 4 ins. across, the colour being oftenest of some shade of yellow or orange, sometimes red, rarely white. What leaves they produce are small and soon fall. The fruits of some species are edible, notably O. tuna, which produces the "tuna fruit," and O. Ficus-indica, the "Indian fig."

In most places in this country the opuntias can only be regarded as curiosities and not beautiful ones at that, but on sunny dry spots on the south coast the hardy species should flower and give some interest. They should be grown on perfectly drained raised mounds or slopes of light sandy soil mixed with an equal amount of stones or rubble and in full sunshine. Several species are perfectly hardy as regards mere frost. Some years ago I saw a group made up of various kinds, very healthy and flowering freely in the New York Botanic Garden, where the winters are much more severe than ours, but the summers much hotter and more sunny. Damp is a greater drawback than cold, nor do they like shade. The best collection of prickly pears grown in the open air in Britain is in the Cambridge Botanic Garden, one of our driest and sunniest localities, but very far from being the warmest. It is the practice there to cover them with glass lights in winter to shield them from excessive wet.

In a small collection grown for a good many years on the south side of the Palm House at Kew the following species are included: O. ARENARIA, *Engelmann*, S.W. United States; O. BICOLOR, *Philippi*, Andes of Chile; O. CANTABRIGIENSIS, *Lynch*, Mexico; O. ELATA, *Link*, Brazil; O. ENGELMANNII, *Salm-Dyck*, Mexico; O. FRAGILIS, *Haworth*, W. N. America; O. MEGACANTHA, *Salm-Dyck*, Mexico; O. MESACANTHA, *Rafinesque*, E. United States (syn. O. Rafinesquei, *Engelmann*, *Bot. Mag.*, t. 7041); O. POLYACANTHA, *Haworth*, W. United States.

Of these the best in health is O. elata, but mesacantha (in several varieties), megacantha, cantabrigiensis, Engelmannii, and bicolor are good. Very distinct and growing well is O. fragilis with its dark green sections of stem almost circular in cross section (not flat and slab-like as is more usual). It is found wild as far north as British Columbia, and takes its name from the easy way its joints break apart. This makes it a great nuisance to grazing animals in its native region.

In addition to the above, the following species are grown in the open air in the Cambridge Botanic Garden: O. FRAGILIS BRACHYARTHRA,

Coulter, N. America ; O. IMBRICATA, *De Candolle*, S. United States ; O. monacantha, *Haworth* (now regarded as a synonym of O. VULGARIS, *Miller*), S. America ; O. ROBUSTA, *Wendland*, Mexico, which Mr Preston, the Curator, informs me is by far the most handsome of the hardy species at Cambridge, putting on, as it does, a fine glaucous hue, and growing over 4 ft. high, being affected only by severe winters ; O. RHODANTHA, *Schumann*, S.W. United States.

ORIXA JAPONICA, *Thunberg*. RUTACEÆ

(Evodia ramiflora, *A. Gray* ; Celastrus japonica, *Koch*)

A deciduous shrub of graceful, spreading habit, with long slender branches, and 6 to 8 ft. high. Leaves aromatically scented, obovate or oblanceolate ; 2 to 5 ins. long, 1 to 2 ins. wide ; dark green, quite entire, and glabrous except on the nerves of the young leaves. Flowers unisexual ; the parts in fours ; males in short racemes produced from the joints of the previous year's wood, green, scarcely ¼ in. across, with downy stalks. Female flowers on separate plants, solitary. Fruits about ¾ in. across, brown, and composed usually of four compressed, one-seeded carpels.

Native of China and Japan. As this pleasing and elegant shrub bears its male and female flowers on different plants, its fruits are only obtainable when both sexes are grown. Mr Wilson, who saw them in China, once told me they have the curious and interesting faculty when ripe of shooting out the seed a distance of several feet in the same way as Impatiens does. I have not seen this shrub anywhere except at Kew, and as only the male plant exists there the fruit is unknown to me on the living plant. The leaves have a pleasant, spicy odour when crushed. This shrub is said to be largely used by the Japanese as a hedge plant. In the *Genera Plantarum* of Bentham and Hooker it was erroneously put under Celastrus.

OSMANTHUS. OLEACEÆ

A small group of evergreen shrubs and small or medium-sized trees, two of which inhabit the southern United States, the rest being Asiatic. The species cultivated out-of-doors in Britain are all from China and Japan. They are closely akin to the olive (Olea), and have opposite leaves ; flowers white or yellowish, in small axillary or terminal clusters. Calyx and corolla four-lobed ; stamens two. Fruit an oval drupe, usually dark blue or violet.

These shrubs are handsome evergreens with a holly-like appearance. They are sometimes propagated by grafting on privet—an undesirable method—for they are healthier and better on their own roots. Cuttings taken about the end of July strike readily if given a little bottom heat. They like a good loamy soil.

O. FRAGRANS, *Loureiro* (Olea fragrans, *Thunberg*), is too tender for general cultivation. It has large, broad leaves shining green beneath, and white flowers so strongly fragrant that one or two of them, tiny though they are, will fill a fair-sized conservatory with sweet perfume. The Chinese use them for perfuming tea. It may be grown out-of-doors fully in the open in Cornwall, but I do not remember to have seen it there. Mr Thurston mentions a plant growing against a wall at Boslowick. In the Bot. Mag., t. 9211 is figured var. AURANTIACUS, *Makino*, which has pale to deep orange-coloured flowers.

O. AQUIFOLIUM, *Siebold and Zuccarini*

(O. ilicifolius, *Mouillefert*)

An evergreen shrub of rounded, dense, bushy habit, 10 ft. or more high near London, twice as high in milder localities; young shoots minutely downy. Leaves oval, 1½ to 2½ ins. long, 1 to 1½ ins. wide, with two to four large spine-tipped teeth down each side; the largest teeth ½ in. long, triangular. In the adult stage the leaves on the top of the plant become oval or ovate, and quite entire at the margins, like a myrtle. The upper surface is of a dark, very glossy green, the lower one paler, both quite glabrous; stalk ¼ to ½ in. long. Flowers white, fragrant, ⅛ to 3/16 in. across, borne during September and October, four or five together, in short-stalked, axillary clusters. Fruit oblong, ⅝ in. long, ⅜ in. wide, blue; not often seen in this country.

Native of Japan, where it is described by Sargent as attaining the dimensions of a tree sometimes 30 ft. high, with a trunk 1 ft. or more in diameter. Introduced by Thomas Lobb in 1856. As far as its foliage is concerned, it is one of the handsomest of evergreens. Its leaves are very like those of the holly, and the shrub is often mistaken for one, but it can, of course, even without flower or fruit, be at once distinguished by its opposite leaves. It has been used with success as a hedge plant. It has a number of varieties, of which the following are the most important :—

Var. MYRTIFOLIUS.—As stated above, when O. Aquifolium gets to the adult stage the upper part of the shrub bears quite entire leaves, 1 to 2 ins. long, narrow oval, and unarmed except for the sometimes spine-tipped apex. A similar transformation in the shape of the uppermost leaves is seen in the holly, the assumption being that having grown out of reach of browsing animals, the armature of spines on the leaves is no longer needed. Cuttings of these uppermost branches take root easily, and as they do not revert to the spiny-leaved type, they are known as the "myrtle-leaved osmanthus." On its own roots this state of O. Aquifolium is dwarfer and more spreading than the type with toothed leaves.

Var. PURPUREUS.—In this variety, which was raised at Kew in 1880, the young leaves are of a black-purple shade; they and the very young shoots, in their black glossiness, have much the aspect of having been dipped in tar. It is the hardiest of all the forms of this osmanthus. The frosts of February 1895 left it quite unaffected, whilst all the others here mentioned were more or less seriously injured at Kew.

Var. ROTUNDIFOLIUS.—A dwarf, very slow-growing shrub, with rigid, leathery leaves, 1 to 1½ ins. long, half to two-thirds as wide, more or less obovate, with a marginal vein, wavy at the margins. It is usually regarded as a variety of O. Aquifolium, but I think it may, when it flowers, prove to be a distinct species.

There are several variegated forms of O. Aquifolium whose leaves are bordered with creamy white or yellow, and one of var. myrtifolius bordered with yellow. They are less hardy than the type.

O. ARMATUS, *Diels*

(Bot. Mag., t. 9232)

An evergreen shrub or small tree, 8 to 15 ft. high; young shoots stiff, at first clothed with minute down, turning greyish white by autumn; slightly warted. Leaves very leathery, oblong-lanceolate, 3 to 6 ins. or even more long on young specimens, ¾ to 1½ ins. wide, abruptly narrowed to the rounded or slightly heart-shaped base, taper-pointed; coarsely toothed, the teeth triangular and with slender spiny points, dark dull green, prominently net-veined and quite glabrous, minutely dotted beneath; stalk ⅛ to ¼ in. long, reddish. Flowers produced during autumn in clusters in the leaf-axils, creamy white, ¼ in. diameter, fragrant; each on a slender glabrous stalk ¼ in. long. Fruit dark violet, egg-shaped, ¾ in. long.

Native of W. China; introduced for Messrs Veitch by Wilson in 1902, and strikingly distinct in the length of the leaf from the other hardy species. Although the spine-tipped teeth are a prominent feature of the leaves of young plants, they are often quite absent in adult specimens. According to Wilson, it grows on humus-clad cliffs and boulders, either in dense shade or fully exposed to sunshine.

O. DELAVAYI, *Franchet*

(Bot. Mag., t. 8459; Siphonosmanthus Delavayi, *Stapf*)

An evergreen shrub, described as reaching 6 to 10 ft. in height; branches spreading, stiff, downy when young. They are densely clothed with stiff leathery leaves that are dark glossy green above, dotted with tiny dark spots beneath, ovate or oval, tapered about equally at both ends, toothed; ½ to 1 in. long, half as wide; shortly stalked. Flowers fragrant, pure white, in terminal and axillary clusters of four to eight; corolla with a cylindrical tube ½ in. long, spreading at the mouth into four reflexed oblong lobes, and about ½ in. across. Fruit roundish egg-shaped, blue-black.

Native of Yunnan, China; raised from seeds sent to M. Maurice de Vilmorin in 1890 by the Abbé Delavay, of which only one germinated. This charming shrub is very distinct from the well-known Aquifolium group in having terminal as well as axillary flower clusters that open in April; in the long-tubed corolla; and in the small leaves. It has proved itself to be one of the most beautiful of white-flowered evergreens. In Sussex and Hampshire, and thence westwards especially, one sees it every April almost hidden by its own wealth of scented blossoms.

O. FORRESTII, *Rehder*

An evergreen shrub 10 to 25 ft. high, with glabrous, yellowish grey young shoots. Leaves of firm hardish texture, dull green, ovate-lanceolate to oblong, wedge-shaped to rounded or heart-shaped at the base, mostly slender-pointed, sometimes quite entire, sometimes conspicuously spiny-toothed; 3 to 8 ins. long, 1 to 2¼ ins. wide; not downy but prominently net-veined and sprinkled thickly with minute black dots on both surfaces; stalk ⅛ to ⅓ in. long. Flowers creamy white to pale yellow, sweetly fragrant, produced numerously in clusters from the leaf-axils, each flower on a slender stalk ⅜ in. long; corolla ⅜ in. wide, deeply four-lobed; lobes oblong; anthers yellow, attached near the base. Fruit egg-shaped, ½ to ⅝ in. long, "deep blue-purple with a heavy waxy bloom much resembling the ripe fruits of Prinsepia utilis" (Forrest).

Native of N.W. Yunnan, China; introduced by Forrest in 1923. Dr Rehder considered it to be most closely related to O. armatus, which is easily distinguished by its downy young shoots and leaf-stalks. Judging by dried specimens it appears often to produce spine-toothed leaves at the base of the shoot and entire ones towards the end. It occurs at altitudes of 6000 to 11,000 ft. and has proved hardy in a sheltered corner at Kew, but it will probably need the conditions of the southern and south-western counties to develop

Osmanthus Delavayi

its best qualities. In respect of its foliage it should be one of the finest in this genus, but it can scarcely be regarded as promising, at present, to be a first-rate evergreen for our average climate.

O. Fortunei, *Carrière*

(O. ilicifolius, *Hort.*; Gard. Chron., 1877, vii., fig. 37 (as O. Aquifolium))

An evergreen shrub of rounded, bushy habit, rarely more than 6 ft. high in inland counties, but 15 to 20 ft. high in Cornwall, the whole plant devoid of down. Leaves leathery, 2½ to 4 ins. long, 1½ to 3 ins. wide; oval or slightly ovate, broadly wedge-shaped at the base, taper-pointed and spine-tipped, the margins armed like one of the large broad-leaved forms of common holly with large, triangular, spine-tipped teeth; stalk ⅓ in. long. Some of the leaves, however, especially those at the base of the twig, are not toothed at all. Flower about $\frac{1}{3}$ in. across, white and delightfully fragrant, produced in clusters in the leaf-axils during autumn.

A hybrid of Japanese origin between O. Aquifolium and O. fragrans; introduced by T. Lobb in 1856 and by Fortune in 1862. It is usually cultivated in gardens either as O. ilicifolius or O. Aquifolium, and in this country appears to be known only in the male state. It is quite hardy at Kew, and has only once been seriously injured in my recollection, which was in the great frosts of February 1895, when the temperature fell to nearly zero on three successive nights. It does not flower profusely except in such places as Cornwall. It is easily distinguished from O. Aquifolium by its larger, broader leaves, less glossy on the upper surface, and with more numerous (eight to ten) teeth on either margin. For the history of this shrub and the elucidation of its confused naming, see *Kew Bulletin*, 1911, p. 177.

O. SERRULATUS, *Rehder*

An evergreen shrub 6 to 12 ft. high; young shoots minutely downy. Leaves oval-lanceolate to oblong or narrowly obovate, slender-pointed, wedge-shaped at the base, sharply toothed to entire; $2\frac{1}{2}$ to $4\frac{1}{2}$ ins. long, $\frac{5}{8}$ to $1\frac{1}{2}$ ins. wide; of leathery texture, dark shining green above, paler and dotted beneath; stalk about $\frac{1}{4}$ in. long. Flowers fragrant, produced in spring from four to nine in a cluster from the leaf-axils; corolla white, deeply four-lobed, $\frac{1}{2}$ in. wide; flower-stalk $\frac{1}{3}$ to $\frac{1}{2}$ in. long, slender. Fruit $\frac{3}{8}$ in. long, oblong, blue-black.

Native of W. China; discovered by Wilson in 1904, introduced to the Arnold Arboretum in 1910 and to Kew in 1912. It is hardy at Kew and has grown into a stiff bush 4 ft. high, but gives the impression that it would prefer a warmer locality. It resembles O. suavis in leaf, but belongs to the same section of the genus as O. fragrans and O. Forrestii, having the stamens inserted near the base of the corolla.

O. SUAVIS, *King*

(Siphonosmanthus suavis, *Stapf*, Bot. Mag., t. 9176)

An evergreen shrub up to 12 ft. high, sometimes a small tree; young shoots greyish, minutely downy. Leaves lance-shaped inclined to oblong, wedge-shaped at the base, more or less slender-pointed, sharply toothed to almost entire; $1\frac{1}{2}$ to $3\frac{1}{2}$ ins. long, $\frac{1}{2}$ to $1\frac{1}{4}$ ins. wide; dark glossy green above, paler and minutely dotted beneath; stalk $\frac{1}{8}$ to $\frac{1}{4}$ in. long. Flowers white, fragrant, produced in axillary clusters of as many as eight; corolla $\frac{1}{4}$ to $\frac{3}{8}$ in. wide, with four roundish-ovate, spreading lobes and a tube $\frac{1}{4}$ in. long; calyx bell-shaped, four-lobed, the lobes edged with minute hairs; flower-stalk $\frac{1}{8}$ to $\frac{1}{4}$ in. long, minutely downy. Fruit roundish egg-shaped, $\frac{2}{5}$ in. long, bluish black.

Native of N. India (Sikkim, Bhotan, Manipur), where it reaches altitudes of 10,000 ft.; discovered by Griffith in 1838. It is hardy but grows slowly at Kew. Along with O. Delavayi, Dr Strapf removed it from Osmanthus and constituted of the pair a new genus, SIPHONOSMANTHUS, on account of the almost stalkless stamens attached close to the mouth of the corolla and the cylindrical tube of the corolla. It bears both unisexual and bisexual flowers, and is an attractive evergreen at Headfort in Co. Meath, where it opens its fragrant blossom in mid-winter. In still milder parts of our islands it should be even more effective.

OSMAREA BURKWOODII. OLEACEÆ

This is a bigeneric hybrid between Osmanthus Delavayi and Phillyrea decora, raised by Messrs Burkwood and Skipwith of Kingston-on-Thames. It is an evergreen with downy young shoots and shortly stalked, oval to ovate leaves 1 to 2 ins. long, slightly toothed, glabrous, leathery and dark, rather glossy, green. Flowers white, fragrant, borne in terminal and axillary clusters of six or seven, opening in April. Corolla $\frac{1}{5}$ in. long, with lobes nearly as long. Very hardy, rather slow in growth and bushy.

OSTEOMELES. ROSACEÆ

A genus of trees and shrubs found in the Andes of S. America, and in various parts of Asia from the west of China to New Zealand. Two Asiatic species are in cultivation, both rather tender evergreen shrubs of very distinct appearance, with unequally pinnate leaves, white flowers, and haw-like fruits containing five seeds. From other genera of the pomaceous group of Rosaceæ with pinnate leaves, they are distinguished by the entire-margined, bristle-tipped leaflets of small size. They need wall treatment, and grow well in loam.

Wilson, in 1908, introduced an Osteomeles from W. China which has been called O. Schwerinæ microphylla, *Rehder and Wilson.* It is distinguished from the type by its dainty, less downy foliage, glabrous calyx and dwarf habit, and appears to be hardier. (No. 1016, Wilson.)

OSTEOMELES SCHWERINÆ

O. SCHWERINÆ, *C. K. Schneider*

(Bot. Mag., t. 7354 (as O. anthyllidifolia))

An evergreen shrub, growing probably 6 to 8 ft. high in the open, considerably more against a wall; the long, slender, flexible branchlets covered with short grey hairs. Leaves pinnate, 2 to 4 ins. long, composed of eight and a half to fifteen and a half pairs of leaflets, covered, more especially beneath, with grey down; main-stalk hairy, channelled above. Leaflets oblong-oval or obovate, with a short abrupt point, stalkless; ¼ to ⅝ in. long, about one-third as wide. Flowers white, ½ to ⅔ in. diameter, produced in June in branching corymbs 1½ to 3 ins. across, terminating lateral twigs; calyx-lobes ovate-lanceolate, hairy outside, glabrous within. Fruit egg-shaped, ¼ to ⅜ in. long, at first dark red, blue-black when ripe, glabrous, crowned by the persistent calyx; five-seeded.

Native of Yunnan and other parts of W. China, originally raised in the Jardin des Plantes at Paris from seed which had been sent from Yunnan by the Abbé Delavay in 1888; introduced to Kew in 1892. Forms nearly allied to this Chinese plant occur through the south-east Pacific region as far as the Sandwich Islands and New Zealand. The whole were at first included under O. ANTHYLLIDIFOLIA, *Lindley*, but the west Chinese plant has been separated on the strength of its glabrous fruit, less hairy calyx-lobes, and usually but not always narrower leaves, thus leaving Lindley's name for the tropical and subtropical woolly-fruited plants. They are extremely closely allied, but perhaps the latter could not be grown out-of-doors with us.

O. Schwerinæ is a shrub of distinct appearance, its foliage very suggestive of some of the Leguminosæ; it is also very elegant in habit and attractive in blossom. But we do not find it hardy in the open, although it survives mild winters. It makes a very delightful wall plant. It can be increased by cuttings made of moderately ripened wood placed in gentle heat. Seed only ripens in favourable years.

O. SUBROTUNDA, *C. Koch*

A dwarf, slow-growing, evergreen shrub, the tortuous branches covered with silky down when young. Leaves pinnate, ¾ to 1½ ins. long, composed of four and a half to eight and a half pairs of leaflets, the main-stalk hairy and grooved above. Leaflets obovate or oblong, ⅛ to ¼ in. long, stalkless, the apex broad and rounded; lower surface silky-hairy, the upper one less hairy and shining. Flowers white, ½ in. across, borne in axillary leafy corymbs.

Native of China; first introduced to the Jardin des Plantes at Paris from Japan (of which country it may also be a native), thence to Kew in 1894. Botanically, this species is, no doubt, closely allied to the two species discussed in the preceding note, but its stunted branches, slow growth, and obovate smaller leaflets amply distinguish it. Increased by cuttings. Not very hardy in the open.

OSTRYA. HOP HORNBEAM. BETULACEÆ

Four species of Ostrya are usually recognised, all of which are in cultivation. They are curiously isolated in nature, one species occurring in Europe and Asia Minor, one in Eastern Asia, one in Western and one in Eastern N. America. They are medium-sized trees, with deciduous, alternate, parallel-nerved leaves, quite closely related to the hornbeams (Carpinus), and in the foliage especially similar. The chief botanical differences are in the female flowers and fruits. In both genera the female flowers are borne on slender catkins, and in pairs at the base of deciduous scales. In Ostrya, however, each flower is set in a bag-like husk (involucre), which at first is open at the top, but closes up after fertilisation takes place. The husk afterwards grows very considerably, and is the pale, membranous, ovate, flattish, bladder-like organ which, congregated and overlapping in hop-like clusters, and completely enclosing the nutlet, gives the trees of this genus their popular name. In Carpinus this involucre remains open and does not enclose the nutlet.

These three ostryas should be raised from seed; they thrive in any soil of good or moderate quality, all being perfectly hardy.

O. CARPINIFOLIA, *Scopoli*. HOP HORNBEAM

(O. vulgaris, *Willdenow*)

A tree 50 to 60 ft. high, with a short, stout trunk covered with greyish, ultimately rough, bark, and a rounded head of branches; young shoots covered with short hairs (not gland-tipped). Leaves ovate, sometimes inclining to oval, rounded at the base, pointed and tapered at the apex; 2½ to 4 ins. long, half as wide; prettily double-toothed, dark green above, with appressed hairs mostly between the ribs; paler beneath and sparsely hairy, chiefly on the midrib and veins, and in the axils of the latter; veins in twelve to fifteen pairs; stalk about ¼ in. long, hairy. Male catkins nodding; 1½ to 3 ins. long, ¼ in. wide; scales finely and abruptly pointed. Fruit clusters 1½ to 2 ins. long; the nutlets (commonly called "seeds") ⅙ in. long, stalkless, enclosed at the base of an ovate, hairy, flat, bladder-like husk, ½ in. long.

Native of S. Europe and Asia Minor; introduced early in the eighteenth century. This tree has very much the aspect of the American species (*q.v.*), but is distinguished by never having any glands on the hairs of the twigs. It is pretty and rather striking when furnished with the pendent hop-like fruit clusters in autumn. The timber has the same bony texture and hardness as hornbeam.

O. JAPONICA, *Sargent*. JAPANESE HOP HORNBEAM

A tree occasionally 80 ft. high in nature, trunk 18 ins. in diameter; winter buds ovoid, shining; young shoots clothed with soft pale hairs, which persist through the winter. Leaves ovate or ovate-oblong; 3 to 5 ins. in length, 1½ to 2¼ ins. in width, on young trees; rounded or slightly heart-shaped at the base, tapered at the apex to a long slender point, coarsely, sharply, and irregularly toothed; dark green and hairy above, paler, more downy and velvety to the touch beneath. Fruit clusters 1½ to 1¾ ins. long, ¾ in. wide.

Native of Japan, where it is said to be somewhat uncommon; introduced to Kew by Prof. Sargent in 1897. It succeeds well, and is now 35 ft. high, being easily distinguished from the European and American species by the veins each side the midrib (nine to twelve) being fewer and farther apart, and by the more uniformly downy, softer, more velvety surfaces of the leaves. According to Henry, the same tree is sometimes, though very rarely, found in Central China.

O. KNOWLTONII, *Coville*

(Garden and Forest, 1894, fig. 23)

A small deciduous tree, 12 to 30 ft. high; young shoots downy, greenish brown, becoming grey at two years old; buds cylindrical, very downy. Leaves ovate to oval, toothed, tapered, rounded or slightly heart-shaped at the base; pointed or bluntish at the apex; 1 to 2½ ins. long, ¾ to 1¼ ins. wide; downy on both surfaces; veins in five to eight pairs; stalk ⅛ to ¼ in. long. Male catkins 1 to 1¼ ins. long, with downy stalks and scales. Fruit clusters 1 to 1¼ ins. long, $\frac{3}{4}$ in. wide; the membranous husks or involucres that enclose the nutlets $\frac{1}{2}$ to $\frac{3}{4}$ in. long, oval. Nutlets $\frac{1}{4}$ in. long, hairy towards the apex.

Native of Arizona and Utah; discovered by Mr F. H. Knowlton in 1889 on the southern slope of the Grand Cañon of the Colorado river; introduced to cultivation in N. America in 1914 and to Kew in 1916. It differs from the hop-hornbeam of the E. United States (O. virginica) by its much smaller size, its more abruptly pointed or round-ended leaves with about half as many pairs of veins. It is hardy in the Arnold Arboretum, Mass.

O. VIRGINICA, *Willdenow*. IRONWOOD

A round-headed tree, 30 to 50 ft. high, similar in habit to O. carpinifolia; young shoots furnished with gland-tipped hairs. Leaves 2 to $4\frac{1}{2}$ ins. long, 1 to 2 ins. wide; oval-lanceolate, rounded or sometimes slightly heart-shaped at the base, taper-pointed, sharply toothed (not so markedly double-toothed as in O. carpinifolia); dark green and hairy on the midrib and between the veins above, paler and more downy beneath; stalk $\frac{1}{4}$ in. long, glandular downy. Male catkins 2 ins. long. Fruit clusters $1\frac{1}{2}$ to $2\frac{1}{2}$ ins. long, $\frac{2}{3}$ to $1\frac{1}{2}$ ins. wide. Nutlet $\frac{1}{3}$ in. long, the pale bladder-like membranous bag enclosing it being ovate, $\frac{3}{4}$ to 1 in. long, hairy at the base.

Native of eastern N. America; introduced by Compton, Bishop of London, in 1692. Cultivated specimens differ from the closely allied O. carpinifolia in the glandular hairs on the twigs and leaf-stalks, in the usually fewer ribs of the leaf, and in the larger nut. The timber, as the common name denotes, is very hard and durable, and is used for mallets, handles of tools, etc. Although not very common in English gardens, this interesting tree thrives well. At Kew there are several specimens 25 to 30 ft. high, of handsome pyramidal form and very healthy.

OSTRYOPSIS DAVIDIANA, *Decaisne*. BETULACEÆ

A deciduous shrub of bushy, rounded habit, 5 to 10 ft. high, suckering from the base like a hazel; young shoots downy. Leaves alternate, broadly ovate, heart-shaped at the base, short-pointed, 1 to 3 ins. long, $\frac{3}{4}$ to 2 ins. wide; sharply, irregularly and often doubly toothed; upper surface dull green with scattered hairs, lower surface much more downy; stalk $\frac{1}{4}$ in. or less long. Flowers unisexual, both sexes on the same bush. Male catkins $\frac{1}{2}$ to $\frac{3}{4}$ in. long, slender, nodding, produced from the joints of the old wood. Female inflorescence terminal on the new shoot of the year, erect, very short. Fruit a conical nut enclosed in an outer covering or husk (involucre), which is also narrowly conical, $\frac{1}{2}$ to $\frac{3}{4}$ in. long, downy, terminating in three slender points. At first this husk completely encloses the nut, but finally liberates it by splitting down one side. The fruits are crowded eight to twelve together in a cluster at the end of the twig.

Native of N. China and Mongolia; discovered by the Abbé David, after whom it is named. It was introduced from the mountains near Pekin to Kew, in 1883, by the late Dr Bretschneider. It is an interesting little shrub, with the habit and foliage of a hazel, to which it is closely akin, but differs much in the shape of the nut. It has no particularly ornamental qualities to recommend it, but is interesting and quite hardy.

OVIDIA ANDINA, *Meissner*. THYMELÆACEÆ

(Daphne andina, *Poeppig*)

A deciduous shrub, often of spare habit, up to 7 ft. high; shoots downy when quite young. Leaves oblanceolate to narrowly elliptical or oval, bluntish or rounded at the apex, tapered to a stalkless base; 1 to 5 ins. long, ½ to 1 in. wide, dull grey green and glabrous above, glaucous and furnished with appressed hairs beneath. Flowers produced in July along with and terminating the young shoots, crowded thirty or more together on a solitary umbel which is 1 to 1½ ins. wide, and has a stout, downy main-stalk ¾ to 1 in. long. Each flower is about ¼ in. wide, white to creamy white with red anthers, the calyx (perianth) funnel-shaped, downy, dividing at the mouth into four oval or obovate lobes. Fruits pure white, egg-shaped, ¼ in. long, with the stigma persisting at the end. Individual flower-stalks very slender, ¼ to ½ in. long.

Native of Chile up to 5000 ft. altitude; introduced by H. F. Comber during his Andean expedition, 1925-7; it has also been collected by Mr Clarence Elliott, who found it in flower in January 1928. It is a diœcious shrub, *i.e.*, the male and female flowers are borne on separate plants. The female flowers are smaller than the males and shorter-stalked. Comber observes that he found it in semi-shady situations where the soil was moist and varying from peaty to loamy in character. Coming from such an altitude it should be hardy. In Major Pam's garden at Wormley Bury, Herts, I have seen some very sturdy plants.

O. PILLOPILLO, *Meissner* (syn. Daphne p. *Gay*) was also introduced by Comber from Chile in 1927. It is closely related to O. andina, but is described as 10 to 30 ft. high. It can be distinguished from that species by the glabrousness of its leaves, which are stalkless, oblanceolate, 1 to 3 ins. long, ¼ to ½ in. wide; dull, pale, rather glaucous green. Judging by wild specimens the young shoots are mostly very downy. Flowers white, very downy outside, ½ in. wide; fruit reddish and purple when ripe. "Pillo-pillo" is the Indian name for this shrub.

Ovidia is a genus of some four species closely akin to Daphne, both having four-parted flowers with eight stamens and very supple young shoots. Daphne differs from Ovidia in its cylindrical perianth and in its style being very short or even absent. At present, neither of the above species promises to be a first-rate garden plant.

OXYCOCCUS. CRANBERRIES. VACCINIACEÆ

Only two species of Oxycoccus are known, which, although closely allied to Vaccinium, are very distinct in their long, slender, wiry, creeping stems, clothed with alternate leaves, and still more in the corolla, the four parts of which are so deeply divided that they become practically separate petals.

The cranberries like a moist or semi-boggy, peaty soil, and can be increased by seed or by layers. They have little garden value, although a broad patch of either kind forming a dense mass of interlacing stem is interesting and unusual. The berries are used for making tarts and in confections of various kinds.

O. MACROCARPUS, *Persoon*. AMERICAN CRANBERRY

(Vaccinium macrocarpum, *Aiton*; Bot. Mag., t. 2586)

A creeping evergreen shrub of prostrate habit, with long, thin, wiry stems. Leaves oval or oblong, $\frac{1}{3}$ to $\frac{2}{3}$ in. long, $\frac{1}{8}$ to $\frac{1}{3}$ in. wide; rounded at both ends, entire, very short stalked, pale or bluish white beneath, usually recurved at the margins. Flowers produced during the summer in a raceme about 1 in. long, beyond which the leaf-bearing shoot continues to grow; each flower is borne on a curving, slightly downy stalk, but is itself drooping. Petals pink, $\frac{1}{3}$ in. long, rolled back so as fully to reveal the eight stamens, which stand up in a close cluster. Calyx with shallow, triangular lobes. Berry red, acid, $\frac{1}{2}$ to $\frac{3}{4}$ in. diameter, globose.

Native of eastern N. America from Newfoundland to N. Carolina, generally inhabiting boggy ground. It has much the same general appearance as our native cranberry, but differs in its larger, rounder-tipped leaves and larger berries, in having a leafy shoot above the raceme, and in the stalk of the stamens being shorter in comparison with the anthers. This shrub is now being largely cultivated in the United States for its fruit. Hundreds of acres have been specially adapted for it by means of a water-supply which admits of the land being flooded at will. On well-prepared ground a crop of 500 bushels per acre has been gathered in a single season.

O. PALUSTRIS, *Persoon*. SMALL CRANBERRY

(Vaccinium Oxycoccus, *Linnæus*)

A prostrate, evergreen shrub with long, thin, wiry stems. Leaves ovate, $\frac{1}{4}$ to $\frac{3}{8}$ in. long, pointed, dark green above, very glaucous beneath. Flowers nodding, produced during summer in a terminal cluster of up to four, each flower on a slender downy stalk, $\frac{3}{4}$ to 1 in. long. Petals rosy pink, bent backwards, $\frac{1}{4}$ in. long. Berry red, globose, $\frac{1}{3}$ in. across.

Native of N. Europe, N. Asia, and N. America; widely spread in the British Isles, but most abundant in the north of England and the south of Scotland. At one time the gathering of cranberries was a considerable industry for women and children of that part of Great Britain, and in some of the markets of the northern towns (at Longtown in Cumberland, near the Solway Firth, for instance), £30 worth of cranberries would be sold in a day. But the draining and enclosing of boggy land induced by the high prices for corn during and after the Napoleonic wars destroyed many extensive and favourite haunts of the cranberry, and the plant is much less abundant than in former times. The berries are perhaps the most pleasantly flavoured of wild fruits.

OXYDENDRUM ARBOREUM, *De Candolle*. SORREL TREE

(Andromeda arborea, *Linnæus*, Bot. Mag., t. 905)

A deciduous tree, occasionally 50 to 70 ft. high in a wild state, the slender trunk 1 to $1\frac{1}{2}$ ft. in diameter. In this country it is occasionally 25 to 30 ft. high, but is more often a tree-like shrub under 20 ft. high; young shoots quite glabrous. Leaves alternate, oblong-lanceolate, with a long, tapering point; 4 to 8 ins. long, 1½ to 3½ ins. wide; almost or quite glabrous; midrib sometimes bristly beneath; entire or minutely toothed, thin in texture, dark green, turning red in autumn; leaf-stalk ½ to 1 in. long. Flowers white, ¼ in. long, cylindrical, but narrowing towards the mouth, produced during July and August in a lax panicle 6 to 10 ins. long, composed of several slender racemes from the end of the shoot or the terminal leaf-axils; flower-stalks, calyx, and corolla downy, the two latter five-lobed; stamens ten, enclosed within the corolla. Fruit a dry, woody, five-celled capsule, many-seeded.

Native of eastern N. America; introduced in 1752. It is the only species of its genus. Belonging to the heath family, this tree thrives under the same conditions as azaleas and rhododendrons. The finest specimens I have seen were in the Knap Hill nursery, near Woking, where they were about 30 ft. high, with well-formed trunks and a slender head of branches. It is usually propagated by seed obtained from the United States. The leaves have a pleasant acid taste, to which its popular and scientific names refer. A beautiful late-blooming tree, the foliage turning scarlet in autumn.

OZOTHAMNUS ANTENNARIA, *Hooker fil.* COMPOSITÆ

(Bot. Mag., t. 9152; Helichrysum Antennarium, *Mueller*; Swammerdamia Antennaria, *De Candolle*)

An evergreen shrub of dense leafy habit up to 10 ft. high; young shoots glutinous, angled, they and the undersurface of the leaves not downy but covered with a close grey or tawny scurf. Leaves oblanceolate or obovate, tapered to the base, broad and rounded at the apex, set from ⅛ to ¼ in. apart on the twigs; ½ to 1¼ ins. long, ⅛ to ⅝ in. wide; glabrous and dark green above; leaf-stalk very short. Flowers produced in June and July in dense clusters terminating short axillary shoots; each flower-head consists of twenty or more florets and is ¼ in. wide, dullish white, the most conspicuous feature being the pappus, which is really the calyx converted into a ring of silk-like hairs surmounting the ovary. Scales of the involucre and main flower-stalk downy.

Native of Tasmania, especially on Mt. Wellington and the Western Mountains. This shrub has proved hardier than it was first thought to be. For nearly twenty years a plant grew outside at Kew and remained in perfect health without any shelter other than that given by the wall of the Temperate House, which protected it from north and east winds. It was killed, however, during the severe winter of 1946-47. One collector records that he found it in May on Mt. Wellington where the ground was covered with three feet of snow. The foliage when crushed has a slightly acrid although not unpleasant odour. Recently introduced to cultivation is

O. LEDIFOLIUS, *Hooker fil.* (syns. Helichrysum led., *Bentham*; Cassinia led., *De Candolle*).—An evergreen shrub of stiff, erect habit, 3 to 5 ft. high, with a distinct odour; young shoots downy, conspicuously yellow, rather viscid. Leaves ⅙ to ½ in. long, $\frac{1}{20}$ to $\frac{1}{16}$ in. wide, closely arranged on the twigs, stalkless, linear, entire, the margins much rolled back; dark green above, of the same yellow beneath as the young shoots. Flower-heads white, densely packed in terminal clusters ½ to 1 in. wide; each head is about ⅙ in. long and as much wide; ray-florets about six; involucral bracts oblong, downy; flower-stalks very downy.

Native of the mountains of Tasmania up to altitudes of 3000 to 4000 ft., whence it was introduced in 1929-30 by Comber, who suggested it should be quite hardy. It is growing quite healthily at Exbury, near the Solent. Wild specimens show it to be remarkably free-flowering, the whole bush being completely hidden by the densely clustered flower-heads. The yellow colouring of the young shoots and the undersurface of the leaves is suggestive of Cassinia fulvida, but the ozothamnus is a much sturdier shrub and more ornamental in blossom.

PACHYSANDRA. BUXACEÆ

A group of four or five species of curious semi-woody plants of tufted habit, allied to Buxus, but very distinct in general appearance, being in habit low and more or less prostrate. Leaves dullish green, alternate, mostly aggregated near the apex of the season's growth. Flowers unisexual on erect spikes, the males numerous, the females solitary or few; both sexes on the same spike, the females at the base. Petals none; sepals and stamens four in the male; sepals four to six, and ovary three-celled in the female. Fruit a two- or three-celled capsule, with the styles persisting at the top like three curved horns. The generic name is in allusion to the thick stamens.

The pachysandras thrive in any moist soil, and do not mind shade; they make neat tufts, but are of only moderate decorative value. Easily increased by summer cuttings. The three following species are easily differentiated by their inflorescence as follows:—

1. *Axillaris.* Inflorescences in the leaf-axils.
2. *Procumbens.* Inflorescences clustered at the naked base of the stem.
3. *Terminalis.* Inflorescences solitary at the end of the stem.

P. AXILLARIS, *Franchet*

An evergreen, semi-woody plant with prostrate root-stocks, from which rise the young stems 4 to 10 ins. high, at first minutely downy. Leaves three to six near the summit of each stem; ovate, broadly wedge-shaped or rounded and entire at the base, coarsely toothed at the upper part, 2 to 4 ins. long, 1¼ to 2¼ ins. wide. Flowers white, produced in April in erect spikes ¾ to 1 in. long, from the axils of the leaves. Fruit about the size of a pea, with two or three long, curly-ended styles persisting at the top.

Native of China; discovered in Yunnan by the Abbé Delavay; introduced by Wilson in 1901. Of little beauty, it may by lovers of curiosities be given a place in some shady corner of the rock garden.

P. PROCUMBENS, *Michaux*. ALLEGHENY SPURGE

(Bot. Mag., t. 1964)

A semi-herbaceous plant forming low masses, with stems 6 to 12 ins. high, springing unbranched from a root-stock; downy, bearing the leaves in a cluster at the top. Leaves broadly ovate, obovate, or somewhat rhomboidal; 2 to 3½ ins. long, often almost as wide; the upper part usually very coarsely toothed, the lower part entire and tapering to a stalk ½ to 1½ ins. long. The lower leaves are the largest and longest stalked; all are furnished with minute, scattered hairs. The unisexual flowers are borne at the base of the stem (between the flowers and the leaves the stem is bare), crowded on several erect, cylindrical spikes 2 to 4 ins. high; female flowers few, and confined to the base. The most conspicuous part of the spike is the stamens, with their pale, flattened stalk ⅓ in. long; the sepals are greenish or purplish.

Native of the south-eastern United States from Virginia and Kentucky southwards; introduced in 1800. It grows vigorously in sheltered shady places. The inflorescence is formed in autumn, and expands in spring. Flowers unpleasantly scented.

P. TERMINALIS, *Siebold and Zuccarini*

An evergreen, semi-woody plant, 6 to 10 ins. high; stems glabrous, the lower portion procumbent and matted. Leaves diamond-shaped, 1 to 2¼ ins. long, ½ to 1¼ ins. wide; coarsely and bluntly toothed on the upper half, entire and tapering below, glabrous, prominently three-veined at the base; stalk ¼ to ¾ in. long. The leaves persist two or three years, and each year's crop is produced in a whorl-like cluster at the end of its growth, being separated from the previous one by several inches of naked stem. Flowers green tinged with purple, produced in spring at the end of the previous year's shoot in a spike about 1 in. long.

Native of Japan. Not so striking a plant as the American P. procumbens, from which it is readily distinguished by its terminal spikes and smaller leaves, but hardier. It ultimately forms a dense low mass several feet across.

Var. VARIEGATA.—Leaves bordered and striped with white.

PACHYSTIMA. CELASTRACEÆ

Two North American, low, glabrous shrubs, with small evergreen opposite, leathery leaves and tiny inconspicuous flowers. They have four petals, four stamens, and a two-celled ovary; the fruit is small, oblong, white. These two shrubs thrive best in a soil that is partly peat, partly sandy loam, and are, perhaps, best adapted for a nook in the rock garden, where, however, their interest will be chiefly botanical. They need only be recommended to people who love rare, out-of-the-way plants, irrespective of their beauty. At the same time the pachystimas make neat, rather dainty tufts. Both are easily increased by cuttings The name implies "thick stigma."

P. CANBYI, *A. Gray*

A low evergreen shrub up to 1 ft. in height, with linear or narrow-oblong leaves, ½ to 1 in. long, $\frac{3}{16}$ in. or less wide, shallowly toothed towards the apex the margins decurved; quite glabrous. Flowers very small, greenish, borne on very slender-stalked cymes ½ in. long in the leaf-axils. Fruit $\frac{3}{16}$ in. long, white

Native of steep rocky slopes on the mountains of Virginia and N. Carolina introduced to Kew in 1893, where it has proved hardy. It has no beauty o flower, and its only merit as a garden shrub is its neat low habit, for it does not bear fruit freely with us. It is also of scientific interest in being confined to comparatively small areas in a wild state. It blossoms from May to August

P. Myrsinites, *Rafinesque*

An evergreen shrub, 6 to 18 ins. high, ultimately spreading in habit. Leaves oblanceolate to narrow-oblong or ovate, from $\frac{1}{3}$ to $1\frac{1}{4}$ ins. long, from $\frac{1}{16}$ to $\frac{1}{4}$ in. wide, toothed towards the tip. Flowers $\frac{1}{8}$ in. across, reddish, produced singly, or two or three together in the leaf-axils. Fruit white, $\frac{1}{6}$ in. long.

This is the Western representative of the genus, being found in woods on the north-western coast of N. America, and in the valleys of the Rocky Mountains. It is much more widely spread and abundant than its Eastern ally, but has no more value in the garden. If differs from P. Canbyi in its freer more robust growth, its wider, larger leaves not so much decurved at the margins, and in its shorter flower-stalks. It blossoms in April and during the two or three succeeding months.

PÆONIA. Pæony. RANUNCULACEÆ

A genus composed mainly of herbaceous plants, but including the three following shrubs. Leaves alternate, deeply divided; flowers solitary, produced at the end of the shoot. Fruit consisting of five carpels.

P. Delavayi, *Franchet*. Delavay's Pæony

(Gardeners' Chronicle, 21st Aug. 1920, fig. 43)

A deciduous shrub 3 to 6 ft. high, increasing by sucker growths from the base, devoid of down in all its parts. Leaves doubly pinnatifid, the ultimate divisions lanceolate, slender-pointed, 2 to 4 ins. long, dark green above, glaucous beneath. The entire leaf with its stalk is from 6 to 18 ins. long and it persists in its dead condition through the winter. Flowers one to three on a stalk, each $2\frac{1}{2}$ to 4 ins. wide, cup-shaped, rather drooping, opening in June. Petals five to ten, rounded, incurved, overlapping, of a rich, almost blood red. their beauty heightened by the clustered golden anthers in the centre. Seed-vessels $\frac{3}{4}$ to $1\frac{1}{4}$ ins. long, glabrous.

Native of China; originally discovered by the Abbé Delavay in 1884; introduced about 1908. It is related to P. lutea, differing mainly in the colour of the flowers. Still, Forrest records that he found numerous plants in W. China with flowers of an indeterminate colour between red and yellow, sometimes orange-brown, which gave him the impression that they might be hybrids between the two species. Some of this mongrel type reached cultivation, but they are very inferior to the type described above. P. Delavayi is a handsome shrub seen at its best, although it has the defect when small of hiding the face of its flowers. It likes a rich soil with occasional dressings of manure and succeeds well in chalky districts. Unlike P. suffruticosa, it does not appear to suffer from late spring frosts.

Var. alba.—Flowers creamy white; not very common but succeeding well at Highdown, near Worthing, in very chalky soil. Var. angustiloba, *Rehder*, differs from the type in the narrow final divisions of its leaves, which are only $\frac{1}{8}$ to $\frac{1}{2}$ in. wide, also in its lower stature. Introduced by Wilson in 1908 and flowered in the Coombe Wood Nursery in June 1911. A handsome shrub in regard to its foliage, but inferior to the type in blossom.

P. lutea, *Franchet*. Yellow Pæony

(Bot. Mag., t. 7788)

A dwarf, sub-shrubby, deciduous plant, with a short, woody stem; entirely glabrous. Leaves leathery, 12 to 15 ins. long, strongly nerved, deep green above, glaucous beneath; ternate, with the three divisions pinnatifid and deeply cut at the margin. Outer sepals narrow-lanceolate, acuminate; inner ones roundish concave, yellowish green. Petals six to ten, golden yellow, roundish concave, with usually crenate margins and a carmine stain at the base. The flower is 2½ ins. across, and is sometimes slightly "double," both in a wild state and cultivated. Seed-vessels glabrous.

Native of the mountains of Yunnan, where it was originally discovered by the French missionary, Delavay, in 1882. This beautiful pæony is not so decidedly a shrub as P. suffruticosa, but it forms a short, woody stem. Its large, rich yellow blossoms make it a splendid acquisition to gardens, although, in some forms at least, the flowers are apt to be hidden by the foliage. Messrs Lemoine of Nancy have sent out a fine variety called SUPERBA, with larger flowers and a stronger and more robust habit.

P. SUFFRUTICOSA, *Andrews*. MOUTAN PÆONY

(P. Moutan, *Sims*, Bot. Mag., t. 2175)

A stiff-branched, deciduous shrub, of rather gaunt habit when in the leafless state, but of luxuriant aspect when in full leaf; rarely more than 5 ft. high in this country, but said to be twice that height in China. Branchlets thick, rugged, soft with abundant pith, dying back more than half their length after flowering. Leaves doubly pinnate or doubly ternate; 9 to 18 ins. long. In the typical state, now rarely seen, the flowers have from five to ten petals and numerous stamens; but in the popular double varieties petals have taken the place of stamens, and, being very numerous, form a full, exceedingly "double" flower from 6 to 12 ins. across. The original type has rosy purple flowers, but in the varieties the colours range from white to pink, deep rose, vermilion, and crimson, sometimes striped, the petals having a crinkled, satiny appearance. Such odour as the flowers possess is not pleasant. They expand in May and June.

This shrub, one of the most gorgeous of all exotics hardy in England, has been cultivated for centuries by the Chinese and Japanese. The name "Moutan" is derived from "Meu-tang," the king of flowers in Chinese myth. It is said to grow wild in the province of Kansu, China, north of the river Hoang-ho. It was introduced in 1789 from China to Kew, where the original plant remained until 1842, when, owing to building operations, it had to be removed. In many parts of the country the tree pæony is very unsatisfactory. At Kew it grows too early in spring, and the young growths and flowers are almost invariably destroyed by late frosts. It is these, not genuine winter cold, that have to be feared. In the north-eastern counties, where it is not excited into growth so easily, one may see fine robust bushes 4 or 5 ft. high and more in diameter, such as it is hopeless to obtain in low-lying districts near London. But no doubt the fine highly bred varieties now in favour are more delicate than the old sorts first imported from China. The unnatural practice, too, of grafting the plant on the herbaceous pæony is probably also responsible for many failures. Propagation is best effected by layering, first slitting the stem and, when pegged down, covering it with 2 or 3 ins. of soil. This should be done before the growing season commences. The layers when rooted should be established in pots.

The tree pæony is seen to best advantage as an isolated shrub on a sheltered lawn where the early morning sun does not strike the plants, and thus induce rapid thawing after frosty nights. It is a gross feeder, and may be grown in good loamy soil. An occasional dressing of manure is advisable.

PALIURUS SPINA-CHRISTI, *Miller*. CHRIST'S THORN. RHAMNACEÆ

(P. aculeatus, *Lamarck*. P. australis, *Gaertner*)

A deciduous shrub or small tree, up to 20 ft. high in this country, with shoots downy when young, and armed at each joint with a pair of spines, one straight and pointing more or less upwards, the other shorter, curved, and pointing downwards. Leaves alternate, 1 to 1½ ins. long, broadly ovate, three-nerved, and entire or slightly toothed; stalk ½ in. or less long. Flowers very numerous, and produced in a short branching umbel from each leaf-axil of the current year's shoots; the individual flowers small, greenish yellow, but rather striking, wreathed as the shoot is with them, the parts in fives. Fruit ¾ to 1 in. wide, consisting of a three-celled, roundish body, developing at the top a curious flat wing which runs all round, giving the whole fruit the aspect of a low-crowned, wide-brimmed hat.

Native of S. Europe eastwards to W. Asia; cultivated in this country for over three hundred years. In some of its native places it is used as a hedge plant. I remember seeing it put to this use on the road between Spalato and Salona, in Dalmatia. It is perfectly hardy at Kew, and I have never seen it even touched by frost there. It grows very well in ordinary loam, and although the flowers have no great beauty they are pretty, and abundantly produced in rows of umbels on the upper side of the shoot. The flat, disk-like, greenish yellow fruits, too, have an interesting appearance, quite distinct from that of any other hardy shrub. The branches are pliable and excessively spiny, and the tree has a legendary interest as the one of whose branches the Crown of Thorns was believed to have been made. It flowers in July and August. Well worth cultivation.

PANAX SAMBUCIFOLIUM, *Sieber*. ARALIACEÆ

(Bot. Mag., t. 6093)

A shrub or small tree free from down in all its parts. Leaves pinnate, 3 to 10 ins. long, usually made up of nine to eleven leaflets. Leaflets stalkless; lance-shaped or narrowly oval, finely pointed, tapered at the base, quite toothless; 1 to 3 ins. long, ¼ to ¾ in. wide; dark green above, glaucous beneath, the midrib raised to a knife-like edge above. Flowers greenish, borne in panicles made up of spherical umbels ½ in. wide, of no beauty. Fruits produced in a group of globose clusters 1 in. or so wide, each fruit globose, ⅓ in. wide, of a watery, translucent, faint blue colour, very handsome and persisting a long time. Except in colour they resemble white currants.

Native of New South Wales, Victoria, and Tasmania; introduced to Kew, where it first flowered in 1873. I have only seen this distinct and beautiful araliad growing out-of-doors at Nymans, Sussex. Miss Messel in *A Garden Flora* recorded that, in 1916, three trees, then 8 ft. high, had been planted in 1913. The description given above is made, except as regards the fruits, from specimens kindly furnished from these trees, which unhappily succumbed during the trying winter of 1928-9. The species would appear, nevertheless, to be a promising tree for southern and western maritime counties, for it has handsome foliage quite unlike that of any other araliad, and beautiful fruits. The trees at Nymans agreed with the figure in the *Botanical Magazine* in having simply pinnate leaves and entire leaflets. But there are specimens in the Kew Herbarium with doubly pinnate leaves and toothed leaflets. It flowered at Nymans in August.

PARASYRINGA SEMPERVIRENS, *W. W. Smith*. OLEACEÆ

(Gardeners' Chronicle, 29th Sept. 1928, fig. 116; Bot. Mag., t. 9295; Ligustrum sempervirens, *Lingelsheim*; Syringa sempvirens, *Franchet*)

An evergreen shrub 6 to 10 ft. high, of bushy shape; young shoots minutely downy. Leaves oval, suborbicular, broadly ovate, or obovate, not toothed, widely tapered at both ends, pointed or bluntish; $\frac{1}{2}$ to $2\frac{1}{2}$ ins. long, $\frac{3}{8}$ to $1\frac{3}{4}$ ins. wide, dark glossy green above; dull, paler and with numerous black dots beneath; of thick leathery texture; stalk $\frac{1}{12}$ to $\frac{1}{4}$ in. long. Flowers creamy white, fragrant, produced in August and September in mostly terminal, pyramidal or cylindrical panicles 2 to 4 ins. long. Corolla tube about $\frac{1}{4}$ in. long, the oblong rounded lobes half as long; calyx cup-shaped, indistinctly toothed. Fruit oval, $\frac{1}{4}$ in. long, black, at first juicy, ultimately splitting downwards into two halves, unless, as frequently happens in cultivation, they are abortive.

Native of Yunnan, China, where it was discovered by the French missionary, Delavay; also of Szechuen; introduced by Forrest in 1913. We apparently owe its existence in British gardens to Mr J. C. Williams, who raised it at Caerhays Castle from Forrest's seeds. It was originally called Syringa in 1886 by Franchet from Delavay's specimen, on account of its splitting fruit, but it has a much greater resemblance to the privets, especially in flower and mode of growth. It is very healthy, grows freely, and appears to be perfectly hardy at Kew in a sheltered position but without artificial protection. In the warmer counties it is a really good evergreen of shapely form and the leaves become larger and more leathery than in colder places, resembling those of Ligustrum coriaceum. It can also be regarded as one of the best flowering shrubs of the privet tribe and may prove to be a useful evergreen hedge plant. It was given an Award of Merit at Westminster in September 1928, when exhibited in flower by Mr Armytage-Moore from North Ireland. Easily grown in ordinary soil and easily propagated by cuttings. I have not seen the fruits split on cultivated plants, and judging by them one would never regard this shrub as anything but a ligustrum.

PARROTIA. HAMAMELIDACEÆ

Two deciduous, small trees, with alternate leaves and small flowers crowded in terminal globose heads, subtended by several bracts. The flowers have no petals, but numerous stamens, which furnish their chief attraction; although in P. Jacquemontiana this is supplemented by the large white bracts. Both species are quite hardy, and thrive in good loamy soil. Seeds afford the best means of increase, but failing these, both may be propagated from layers. P. Jacquemontiana can be raised from cuttings—possibly the other also. Their nearest allied genera are Sycopsis, which is evergreen, and Fothergilla, which has no bracts beneath the head of flowers. The genus is named after the German, Mr F. W. Parrot, who made the first ascent of Mt. Ararat in 1829. The two species are very distinct, and P. Jacquemontiana has been made into a separate genus.

P. Jacquemontiana, *Decaisne*

(Bot. Mag., t. 7501; Parrotiopsis involucrata, *C. K. Schneider*)

A deciduous tree, ultimately 15 to 20 ft. high, with a smooth grey trunk and a much-branched bushy head; sometimes a shrub; young twigs covered with clustered (stellate) hairs. Leaves roundish or very broadly ovate, 2 to 3½

Parrotia Jacquemontiana

ins. long and nearly as wide; margins set with broad open teeth; both surfaces furnished with stellate hairs, the upper one thinly so and finally almost glabrous, the lower one densely on the nerves; stalk ¼ to ½ in. long. Flowers stalkless, produced from April to July, about twenty together in a shortly stalked globose head about ⅝ in. across, the chief feature of which are the numerous yellow stamens. Beneath the head of flowers are four to six conspicuous petal-like bracts of the same shape as the leaves, but only ½ to 1 in. long, and white; they constitute the chief feature of the inflorescence. Seeds shining, oblong, ⅙ in. long.

Native of the western Himalaya, especially in Cashmere; where it was discovered by Dr Falconer in 1836. It does not appear to have reached cultivation until 1879, when seeds were sent to Kew. The largest specimen is now about 12 ft. high, quite hardy and vigorous in an exposed position, and flowers annually. It has no claim to a place among showy plants, but belongs to a family of exceptional interest, and when well furnished with its flower-heads it is at least pretty. The leaves remain long on the tree after those of P. persica have fallen. The largest inflorescences, with the surrounding bracts, are sometimes 2 ins. across, especially those that open late. The main crop is borne in April and May, but flowers continue to open intermittently through the summer. The twigs are very rough and are largely used for making rope bridges in the western Himalayas. The wood, too, is useful in being hard and close-grained.

P. PERSICA, *C. A. Meyer*

(Bot. Mag., t. 5744)

A deciduous tree, 30 to 40 ft. high, with a stout trunk from which the smooth, grey bark comes away in flakes, as in the plane, and horizontal wide-spreading branches; young twigs at first furnished with stellate hairs. Leaves ovate, oblong or obovate; 2½ to 5 ins. long, 1 to 2½ ins. wide; rounded or tapering at the base, coarsely, shallowly and unevenly toothed, or merely wavy towards the apex; almost glabrous above, sparsely furnished beneath with stellate hairs; stalk ¼ in. long, downy. Flowers produced during March in short clusters ½ in. across, often terminal on short leafy twigs, and only conspicuous for their numerous red stamens. Bracts brown and hairy outside, green within, ¼ to ⅓ in. long, ovate. Seed-vessels nutlike, opening at the top; seeds ⅜ in. long, bright brown, pointed at one end.

Native of N. Persia to the Caucasus; introduced to Kew about 1841. The great charm of this tree is in the beautiful tints of gold and crimson its foliage assumes in autumn. Few trees are more effective then. In the early spring, too, when in flower, the numerous red-anthered stamens and rich brown bracts give to the still leafless branches a hazy effect of red which is very pleasing in sunshine The species is very hardy, but unless trained up in its early stages and its lower branches pruned away, it is apt to remain stunted and shrubby. There is a fine tree at Vicar's Hill, Lymington, which frequently bears fruit, as does another across the Solent in Osborne gardens. Doubtless there are others, and the numbers will increase as the years go by; but Parrotia persica is not so plentiful as its charm and interest entitle it to be.

PASSIFLORA CŒRULEA, *Linnæus*. PASSION-FLOWER.

PASSIFLORACEÆ

(Bot. Mag., t. 28)

A climbing plant of great vigour and more or less evergreen, attaching itself to its supports by tendrils; devoid of down in all its parts. Leaves palmate, five- or seven-lobed, 4 to 7 ins. across; lobes oblong with rounded ends; green above, somewhat glaucous beneath. Flowers borne on long, slender stalks from the leaf-axils of the young growing shoots; flat and open, fragrant, 3 to 4 ins. across, the five sepals and five petals whitish. Between the petals and the stamens is a conspicuous ring of thread-like, purplish growths 2 ins. across, known as the "corona." Fruit of the shape and size of a bantam's egg, with a tough, orange-coloured rind and numerous seeds inside, embedded in pulp.

Native of S. Brazil; introduced, according to Aiton, in 1699. It is not genuinely hardy near London, but will often survive several winters on a sheltered wall. As it grows very rapidly and is easily propagated from seeds or cuttings, it is worth growing for its beautiful and remarkably constructed flowers, which commence to appear in June, and continue until the end of September. There is a luxuriant plant on a house in Pirbright, Sussex.

Var. "CONSTANCE ELLIOTT," first shown by Messrs Lucombe, Pince, & Co., of Exeter, in 1884, has ivory-white flowers (see *Gard. Chron.*, 1884, i., p. 701).

The name of "passion-flower" by which this and all the passifloras are known, was given originally by the Spanish priests in S. America, because of the resemblance their piety led them to detect between the various parts of the flower and the instruments of Christ's Passion. The late Dr Masters, the historian of the family, has pointed these out to be as follows: The three stigmas represent the three nails, two for the hands and one for the feet; the five anthers represent the five wounds; the corona represents the crown of thorns or the halo of glory; the five sepals and five petals stand for ten apostles—Peter and Judas being absent; the hand-like leaves and whip-like tendrils represent the hands and scourges of His persecutors.

PAULOWNIA. SCROPHULARIACEÆ

A genus of about ten species of deciduous trees, all natives of China. Leaves opposite, varying from entire to slightly lobed; flowers in terminal panicles. Named after Anna Paulowna, princess of the Netherlands, 1795-1865.

P. LILACINA, *Sprague*

(Bot. Mag., t. 8927)

A deciduous, sparsely branched tree up to 60 or 70 ft. high; young shoots pale green, clothed with viscid gland-tipped hairs; brown and warted the second year. Leaves opposite, broadly ovate with a heart-shaped base, slender-pointed; 6 to 12 ins. long, 4 to 7 ins. wide; dull green, nearly glabrous above, downy beneath, especially on the veins and midrib when young; stalk thick, 2 to 4 ins. long, covered with sticky hairs similar to those of the young shoots. Panicles terminating the growths of the previous year, erect, pyramidal, 12 to 18 ins. high, two-thirds as much wide. Corolla 3 ins. long, tubular, divided at the mouth (where it is 2½ ins. wide) into five large rounded spreading lobes; downy outside; pale lilac with a large yellowish stain in the throat. Calyx bell-shaped, ½ in. long, with five deep recurved lobes covered with felt that is fawn-coloured inside, dark brown outside. Ovary and style glutinous; flower-stalk ¼ to ½ in. long, felted like the outside of the calyx. Fruit ovoid, 1½ to 1¾ ins. long, ¾ to 1 in. wide, tapering at the top to a short slender point, brown.

Native of China (probably Western). It was sent to Kew in 1908 by the late Maurice de Vilmorin and flowered there in June 1928. Judging by the behaviour of this tree it would seem better fitted for our average climate than P. tomentosa. It was sent to Kew as P. Fargesii and seeds of it were distributed under that name. When it flowered and was figured for the *Bot. Mag.* Dr Sprague found it to be quite distinct from that species and gave it the above name.

P. TOMENTOSA, *Steudel*

(P. imperialis, *Siebold*; Bot. Mag., t. 4666)

A round-topped, deciduous tree 30 to 50 ft. high, with thick, stiff branches and rather open habit; all the parts more or less downy. Leaves opposite, the small ones ovate, the larger ones three- to five-lobed, the lobes pointed but shallow, the base deeply notched; the dimensions are very variable; in adult trees they are 5 to 10 ins. long and wide, dark green, and with scattered hairs above, covered beneath with a soft, greyish wool; stalk nearly as long as the blade. Panicle terminal, up to 1 ft. long, the flowers forming in autumn but not opening until the following May. Corolla blue-purple, 1½ to 2 ins. long, shaped like a huge foxglove; calyx woolly, ½ in. long, bell-shaped, with five ovate teeth. Seed-vessel an ovoid, pointed capsule, 1½ to 2 ins. long, containing numerous winged seeds.

Native of China, but introduced from Japan to France in 1834. Few more beautiful flowering trees than this exist, but although the tree is fairly hardy and sets its flowers, they often do not develop in this country, owing to its curious habit of exposing them in bud through the winter. Perhaps they do not derive sufficient stamina from our dull summers, but more likely the unrest of our winters, with their alternate frosts and mild spells, prevents their proper development. In the milder counties, as at Abbotsbury, near Weymouth, in S. Wales, and even at Leonardslee in Sussex, the tree flowers and ripens seeds. In the Jardin des Plantes at Paris there are trees 40 or 50 ft. high, with trunks about 8 ft. in girth, which make a splendid picture when in bloom.

But whilst many gardens in Great Britain are denied the blossoms of this tree, it may, by another mode of cultivation, be made to provide a fine feature anywhere but in the coldest parts. This is to treat it simply as a fine-foliaged plant. To get the best effect the plants should be set out 3 or 4 ft. apart in a group of at least twenty, and be kept to a single stem, the object being to obtain leaves as large as possible. In spring the stem is cut back to within 2 ins. of the older wood. From the crowd of young growths that then push out the two strongest are selected, the rest rubbed off. Two are left for fear of accident only, and after they are fairly established the weaker one is removed. It then only remains to water when necessary and to feed the plants with manure. Well-grown plants will have huge pentagonal leaves 2 to 3 ft. across, and the sturdy erect stems will grow over 12 ft. high in the season. Paulownias need a rich soil and are best propagated from seed, which is produced in plenty on the Continent. Root-cuttings may also be used.

PENSTEMON. SCROPHULARIACEÆ

This genus is almost purely N. American and consists of some 150 species, most of which are perennial herbaceous plants. The shrubby species are mostly native of California. The leaves are opposite; the corolla tubular, two-lipped; stamens five, as the generic name indicates, but one of them is always sterile. The shrubby species are easily increased by cuttings of moderately ripened wood; they like a sunny position and a lightish well-drained soil. A very beautiful genus.

P. CORDIFOLIUS, *Bentham*

(Bot. Mag., t. 4497)

An evergreen shrub of straggling loose habit; young shoots opposite, very downy. Leaves heart-shaped, pointed, coarsely toothed; $\frac{1}{2}$ to 2 ins. long and about two-thirds as wide; glossy dark green, minutely downy on both sides; stalk $\frac{1}{8}$ in. or less long. Flowers produced in a large terminal pyramidal panicle as much as 12 ins. long and 9 ins. wide. Corolla $1\frac{1}{2}$ ins. long, scarlet, glandular-downy, with a cylindrical tube, two-lipped; upper lip hooded, the lower one decurved and divided into three linear lobes. Calyx very glandular, downy, $\frac{1}{3}$ in. long, cut deeply into five lanceolate lobes; flower-stalk glandular; anthers yellow, finally whitish.

Native of California; discovered by David Douglas in 1831; introduced by Hartweg in 1848 through the Horticultural Society. The sterile stamen is conspicuously bearded on one side with pale hairs. Like most of the shrubby penstemons this is not very hardy, but when grown at Kew on a south wall, it makes a fine display from late June until August or even later. In the winter of 1928-9 it was severely cut back by frost but sprang up freely again during the summer. It is undoubtedly one of the finest of the shrubby species.

P. ISOPHYLLUS, *B. L. Robinson*

(Bot. Mag., t. 9482)

A semi-shrubby plant of bushy habit, 2 to 3 or more ft. high; young shoots densely leafy and very minutely downy. Leaves opposite, elliptic-ovate, 1 to $2\frac{1}{2}$ ins. long, $\frac{1}{3}$ to 1 in. wide, pointed or blunt, rather fleshy, dark green, minutely warted and glaucous beneath, sessile or scarcely stalked. Flowers scarlet-crimson with pale lines in the throat, borne on loose, erect racemes 8 to 15 ins. long; corolla tubular, $1\frac{1}{2}$ to $1\frac{3}{4}$ ins. long, $\frac{2}{3}$ to 1 in. across, two-lipped, the upper lip two-lobed, the lower one three-lobed, the lobes rounded; fertile stamens four, white, two attached to the bottom of the corolla-tube, the other pair amalgamated with the corolla for the lower half inch. The flowering season is late summer and autumn.

Native of Mexico, introduced in 1908. It is a plant of great beauty but not quite hardy, although it may survive several mild winters in a sheltered position. If merely cut back to the base it will spring up again. It is an admirable plant for the milder parts. Colonel F. C. Stern records that it has withstood 20° of frost in his chalk garden at Highdown near Goring-on-Sea.

P. MENZIESII, *Hooker*

An evergreen shrub which varies from a bushy plant 8 to 12 ins. high to a prostrate creeper 2 ins. or so high. Hooker's type specimen at Kew has slender stems covered with minute down, and obovate leaves, glabrous, and shortly stalked, $\frac{1}{4}$ to $\frac{3}{4}$ in long, $\frac{3}{16}$ to $\frac{3}{8}$ in. wide, the base tapered, the apex rounded and more or less shallowly toothed. Flower stems erect, terminal, carrying two to six flowers. Corolla 1 to $1\frac{1}{4}$ ins. long, between tubular and funnel-shaped, two-lipped, the upper lip two-lobed, the lower one three-lobed, $\frac{1}{2}$ in. wide, hairy within, purple. Sepals five, ovate, pointed, $\frac{1}{4}$ to $\frac{1}{2}$ in. long, more or less downy.

Native of N.W. America. The mountain form of this gay little evergreen is a prostrate creeper with leaves $\frac{3}{8}$ in. or less long with scarcely noticeable toothing and dark bright green. It grows only an inch or two high and is admirable for a shelf in a rock garden, the flowers being of rather astonishing size for a shrub of this character of growth. Mr Musgrave grows it well in his garden at Hascombe, near Godalming. The flowering season is May and June.

P. SCOULERI, *Douglas*

(Bot. Mag., t. 6834—as P. Menziesii Scouleri)

A semi-shrubby plant woody only at the base, 1 to 1½ ft. high; young shoots minutely downy. Leaves opposite, narrowly lanceolate, 1 to 2 ins. long, ⅛ to ¼ in. wide; pointed, tapered to both ends, toothed, the smaller basal leaves of the shoot entire; scarcely stalked. Flowers blue-purple, arranged oppositely on erect terminal racemes opening in June; the funnel-shaped, two-lipped corolla is 1½ ins. long, expanded at the mouth into three lower lobes and two upper ones, and there 1 in. or more across. Stamens five, two-thirds as long as the corolla, one of them sterile; anthers very hairy; calyx-lobes awl-shaped.

Native of western N. America; introduced in 1828 by Douglas. It is, perhaps, no more than one of the more shrubby forms of a very variable species to which P. MENZIESII belongs.

Another fairly hardy penstemon is P. HETEROPHYLLUS, *Lindley*. It is of a shrubby nature, growing 1½ to 4 ft. high, and has slender stems furnished with glabrous, opposite, stalkless, linear leaves, 1 to 4 ins. long, ⅛ to ¼ in. wide. Flowers soft blue, 1 to 1¼ ins. long, anthers hairy at the margins. Introduced in 1828 for the Horticultural Society by David Douglas (*Bot. Mag.*, t. 3853).

P. CORYMBOSUS, *Bentham*, is sometimes grown against a wall, where it is 4 ft. high, its oval or ovate leaves ½ to 1¼ ins. long; flowers bright red, the tube about 1 in. long; anthers not hairy. Both these species are Californian.

PENTACTINA RUPICOLA, *Nakai*. ROSACEÆ

A deciduous shrub 2 to 2½ ft. high; young shoots angled, glabrous, reddish; winter-buds silky. Leaves without stipules, alternate, very shortly stalked, mostly oblanceolate to obovate, wedge-shaped at the base, with usually three or five lobes or large teeth towards the apex, the lobes fine-pointed, often toothed; ¾ to 1½ ins. long, ⅓ to ¾ in. wide; glabrous above, more or less furnished with silky hairs beneath. Flowers small, white, produced in June and July on slender terminal pendulous panicles 1½ to 3 ins. long. Petals five, linear, ⅕ in. long; sepals five, triangular, persisting to the fruiting stage when they become much reflexed; stamens twenty, white, exposed. Each flower has five dry seed-vessels about $\frac{1}{16}$ in. long.

Native of the Diamond Mountains of Korea and the only species known; introduced to the Arnold Arboretum in 1918 by Wilson, who found it common on cliffs. It is closely related to the spiræas but can be distinguished from all the species of that genus by its linear petals. The inflorescence resembles that of another near ally—Stephanandra—which genus differs in having stipules. It is a graceful dwarf shrub with clustered stems, usually found wild growing in the crevices of rocks, but with more beauty in leaf and habit than in flower. It is quite hardy, and judging from its native habitats should prefer a moderately shady position.

PERAPHYLLUM RAMOSISSIMUM, *Nuttall.* ROSACEÆ

(Bot. Mag., t. 7420)

A deciduous shrub, 6 to 10 ft. high in some of its native haunts, of spreading habit; branchlets at first downy, ultimately glabrous and bluish grey. Leaves 1 to 2 ins. long, about $\frac{1}{4}$ in. wide; narrowly oblanceolate, entire, tapering to a short stalk at the base, rather more abruptly to the point; downy beneath when young, becoming glabrous. On the young shoots the leaves are alternate; on one-year-old shoots

PERAPHYLLUM RAMOSISSIMUM.

they are in tufts. Flowers in short-stalked corymbs, produced in April and May with the leaves from the joints of the previous summer's wood; there are from one to three flowers in the cluster, each $\frac{5}{8}$ in. diameter; calyx and flower-stalk silky; petals white, orbicular. Fruit a berry, $\frac{1}{3}$ to $\frac{1}{2}$ in. diameter, globose, yellow with a reddish cheek, edible.

Native of western N. America on dry hillsides; introduced to Kew in 1870. It is closely allied to the amelanchiers, but differs in the narrow entire leaves, longer calyx-tube, and rounded petals. In English gardens it must be regarded more as a curiosity (being the only species of its genus) than as an ornamental shrub, for it flowers indifferently and rarely bears fruit. It comes from regions (Colorado, Utah, California, etc.) where the summers are infinitely hotter and brighter than ours, and this summer heat, no doubt, is what it misses here. It is, however, quite hardy, and can be increased by layers.

PERIPLOCA GRÆCA, *Linnæus.* SILK VINE. ASCLEPIADACEÆ

(Bot. Mag., t. 2289)

A deciduous climber of vigorous, twining habit, reaching 20 to 30 ft. in height; stems brown, quite glabrous, exuding a milky juice when cut. Leaves opposite, mostly oval or ovate; 2 to 4 ins. long, about half as wide; not toothed, pointed at the apex, rounded or wedge-shaped at the base, with prominent parallel veins merging into a marginal one; stalk ¼ to ½ in. long. Cymes 2 or 3 ins. across, terminating short lateral shoots, produced in July and August, and consisting of eight to twelve flowers. Flowers 1 in. across, the corolla composed of five narrow, oblong segments, 3/16 in. wide, rounded at the end and downy, especially at the edges, brownish purple inside, greenish yellow outside; calyx ¼ in. across, with five ovate lobes. Seed-pods in pairs; cylindrical, 5 ins. long, ¼ in. wide, tapering to a point where they are usually united; full of seeds, each with a remarkable tuft of silky hairs at the end 1¼ ins. long.

Native of S.E. Europe (Greece, etc.); cultivated since the sixteenth century. It thrives in any soil of moderate quality, and requires a sunny position. Best propagated by division of the root in spring. It is a free-growing, hardy climber, interesting in its curious flowers, and may be used for pergolas, etc. The milk that exudes from the broken stems is poisonous, and in the south of Europe it is believed to be injurious to health to inhale the heavy odour of the flowers.

P. SEPIUM, *Bunge*. CHINESE SILK VINE

A deciduous climbing shrub 6 to 10 ft. (perhaps more) high; young shoots glabrous. Leaves opposite, lanceolate to narrowly oval, not toothed, mostly slenderly pointed, tapered at the base; 1¾ to 4 ins. long, ½ to 1¼ ins. wide; shining green, glabrous on both surfaces; stalk ⅛ to ½ in. long. Flowers fragrant, about ¾ in. wide, produced two to nine together in axillary and terminal cymes during June and July; main flower-stalk 1 to 2 ins. long. Corolla greenish outside, dark purple inside, five-lobed, the lobes revolute and woolly towards the margin. Seed-pods in pairs, slenderly cylindrical, tapering at the end where they are connected, 4 to 6 ins. long, 3/16 in. wide; seeds furnished with a tuft of silky white hairs.

Native of N. China; introduced to America in 1905. It differs from P. græca in its narrower, often lanceolate leaves, more slender stems and somewhat hardier constitution. Chiefly interesting for the long, slender, cylindrical twin pods.

PERNETTYA. ERICACEÆ

This genus commemorates Antoine Joseph Pernetty, the historian of Bougainville's voyage to the Falkland Isles, the Straits of Magellan, and other parts of South America (1763-4). He was born in 1716 and died at Avignon in 1801. The genus, represented in Tasmania and New Zealand as well as America, is closely allied to Gaultheria, but its calyx never becomes so fleshy and enlarged as to enclose the real fruit in the way it does in that genus. Usually it remains small, dry and membranous, but an intermediate condition has appeared in P. Pentlandii described below.

P. FURENS, *Klotzsch*

(Bot. Mag., t. 4920; Arbutus furiens, *Hooker*)

An evergreen shrub 2 to 4 ft. high; young shoots hairy at first, becoming brown and glabrous. Leaves ovate to ovate-lanceolate, up to 1½ ins. long by ½ to ¾ in. wide, pointed, tapering to a very short red stalk sparsely toothed, ciliate when young, dark green. Flowers crowded in axillary racemes 1¼ ins. long, nodding; corolla waxy white, ovoid-globose, ¼ in. long, spreading at the apex into five quite short, broad, reflexed lobes, opening from April to June; calyx fleshy, with five short, spreading lobes; stamens ten, downy at the base.

Native of Chile; introduced by Standish and Noble about the middle of last century, but always rare. It is a rather anomalous shrub and has a distinct affinity with Gaultheria, especially in the fleshy, accrescent calyx. The elder Hooker placed it at first in Arbutus.

P. LEUCOCARPA, *De Candolle*

A low, creeping, evergreen shrub 6 to 12 ins. high, spreading much wider by underground stems and of dense habit. Leaves of much the same character as those of P. mucronata but smaller, up to ½ in. long, oblong-lanceolate, concave above, very slightly toothed, dark shining green, ciliate at first. Flowers white, more or less tinged with pink, solitary in the leaf-axils, opening in spring. Fruits very freely borne, so freely sometimes as almost to hide the leaves, each ⅓ to ½ in. wide, globose, white or tinged with pink, sweet and pleasantly flavoured.

Native of the Chilean Andes up to 6000 ft.; introduced by H. F. Comber in 1926. I have seen it in the late Mr Fred Stoker's garden in Essex and it has been very finely grown in Colonel Messel's garden at Nymans in Sussex. It varies in the colour-shades of both flower and fruit from white to pink. Comber collected one with "deep rose-coloured" berries. In all its forms it is very charming.

Var. LINEARIS.—Mr Marchant of Keepers' Hill Nursery lists this in his catalogue, describing it as "6 to 9 ins. high, with a mass of interlacing twigs crowded with linear leaves ½ to ¾ in. long, $\frac{1}{10}$ in. wide."

P. MUCRONATA, *Gaudichaud* (Plate 33)

(Bot. Mag., t. 8023)

An evergreen shrub, 2 to 5 ft. high, spreading freely by suckers and forming ultimately a dense, low thicket; young branches thin and wiry, sometimes furnished with a few appressed, forward-pointing bristles or short down, but usually becoming glabrous in a short time. Leaves alternate, dense upon the branches, ovate to oblong, very shortly stalked; ⅓ to ¾ in. long, ⅛ to ¼ in. wide; toothed and spiny-pointed, hard in texture. Flowers produced singly in the leaf-axils near the end of the shoot, in May. Corolla white, nodding, cylindrical, about ¼ in. long, five-toothed. Calyx five-lobed, green; stamens ten; flower-stalk ¼ in. long. Fruit a globose berry ⅓ to ½ in. diameter, containing many very small seeds; it varies in colour from pure white to pink, lilac, crimson and purple, or almost black.

Native of the region about the Straits of Magellan; introduced in 1828. This is one of the hardiest of South American shrubs, and is rarely severely injured by frost in the neighbourhood of London. Certainly it is one of the finest ornamental berry-bearing shrubs we have. Its berries attain their colour by early autumn, and remain on the branches through the winter and following spring. The pernettya was long strangely neglected, but a great fillip to its cultivation was given by an exhibit in London made about 1882 by an Irish nurseryman, Mr T. Davis, who showed a number of remarkably beautiful varieties he had raised during the previous twenty or more years in his own nursery. The pernettya is about the only shrub that has been cultivated and selected with a view to the beauty and variety of its fruit, apart from edible qualities. In Kew, the fruits are never touched by birds, although in some gardens they are said to be stripped in winter—possibly by pheasants.

The chief cultural requirements of pernettya are a cool, moist bottom, and a peat soil, or a loam with which either peat or decayed leaves or both should be freely mixed. It likes full sunshine, and can be propagated by seeds, division, or cuttings. The last two are best for selected varieties. I have been told that it grows well on mountain limestone.

Besides the various forms differing in colour of fruit, there is some variation also in the size and shape of leaf. The plant known in gardens as P. angustifolia is a narrower leaved form, but it is not the true P. ANGUSTIFOLIA, *Lindley*, a distinct and perhaps not hardy species.

It may be mentioned here that many if not all the plants of the well-known P. mucronata have been found to be functionally, if not structurally, unisexual, and that to get the best results they should be planted in groups, when a few certified male plants should be mixed with the bulk of equally undoubted female ones. I know of more than one group of perfectly healthy pernettyas where scarcely a fruit is ever seen. Once the sex is ascertained, the respective plants can easily be propagated by cuttings.

The pernettya in cultivation under the name of P. RUPICOLA, *Philippi*, seems to be very near P. mucronata, and Reiche, the Chilean botanist, has made it a variety of that species. The young shoots are very finely downy but they appear never to have the bristles in addition that occur in mucronata. The leaves are narrowly ovate-lanceolate and have the same spiny tip, but besides their being narrower the two to five teeth they have on each margin are less prominent than in mucronata. The red fruits are similar in size and shape.

P. PENTLANDII, *De Candolle*

(Bot. Mag., t. 6204; P. prostrata Pentlandii)

A dwarf evergreen shrub, sometimes prostrate; young shoots downy and sparsely bristly. Leaves shortly stalked, oblong-ovate, pointed, rounded or tapered at the base, bristly toothed, $\frac{1}{2}$ to $\frac{3}{4}$ in. long, $\frac{1}{8}$ to $\frac{1}{4}$ in. wide; dark glossy green and glabrous above, pale green and either glabrous or with a few dark bristles on the midrib beneath; there may be ten or more leaves to the inch. Flowers solitary in the leaf-axils, nodding, opening in June. Corolla ovoid-globose, white, $\frac{1}{3}$ in. long, contracted towards the mouth and there dividing into five pointed, recurved lobes. Stamens ten, with downy stalks swollen at the base; anthers with four short bristles. Calyx-lobes ovate, pointed, becoming, at any rate sometimes, swollen at the fruiting state and turning blue-purple. This is the colour also of the globose berry, which is $\frac{1}{4}$ to $\frac{3}{8}$ in. wide, nodding, with the remains of the stigma at the top and the fleshy lobes of the calyx at the base.

Native of S. America, from Venezuela to Chile, always on high mountains. In the Andes of Ecuador it grows on the higher slopes of Pichincha and Cotopaxi. It is a variable plant especially in the size and shape of the leaf. The description given above is made from a form which is grown at Kew and Wakehurst, but the var. PARVIFOLIA has leaves only half or less than half the size. Another form has leaves $\frac{5}{8}$ in. long but only $\frac{1}{12}$ in. wide. There is also a variety known as HUMILIS that may represent the cultivated plant, which is prostrate. The leaves turn purple in the winter. Plants from seed collected on the Andes of Quito were raised by Mr Anderson Henry in Edinburgh and flowered and bore fruit with him in 1874. He found it hardy there. The enlargement and fleshiness that is characteristic of the calyx in the fruiting stage is suggestive of the nearly allied gaultherias, but Sir Joseph Hooker suggests that it may not be constant, nor is there any indication of it in the dried specimens of wild plants I have examined in Kew Herbarium. The leaves are not spine-tipped as in mucronata.

P. PUMILA, *De Candolle*

(Bot. Mag., t. 6204)

A low, often prostrate evergreen shrub frequently only a few inches high, easily distinguished from P. mucronata by the smaller ovate or ovate-lanceolate leaves having no mucro at the apex; often they are blunt or even rounded there; they are $\frac{1}{8}$ to $\frac{1}{4}$ in. long and have cartilaginous, very minutely toothed margins. Flowers white, nodding, bell-shaped, $\frac{3}{16}$ in. wide, with five shallow reflexed lobes. Fruit globose, $\frac{3}{16}$ in. wide, white or pink.

Native of the Magellan Straits region and of the Falkland Isles. It has long been known, having been collected by Darwin and Joseph Hooker over 100 years ago. It makes an interesting plant for the rock garden, and should be quite hardy. In a wild state it bears fruit very abundantly; one collector states that they could be gathered by the bushel and cooked like huckleberries.

P. TASMANICA, *Hooker fil.*

(Flora of Tasmania, t. 73)

A dwarf, prostrate, evergreen shrub, forming large, dark green mats or carpets only a few inches high; branches much forked, slender and slightly downy when young. Leaves alternate, leathery, shortly stalked, oval-lanceolate, pointed, margins often wavy; $\frac{1}{4}$ to $\frac{1}{3}$ in. long, half as much wide, shining. Flowers $\frac{1}{8}$ in. wide, solitary on a short stalk in the upper leaf-axils; corolla white, bell-shaped, five-lobed; stamens ten. Fruit a globose red berry $\frac{3}{8}$ in. wide, the persistent calyx in which it is seated often becoming fleshy and coloured also.

Native of Tasmania, where, according to Hooker, it occurs on all the mountains, especially on a granite soil, forming large green cushions there. He records that the fruits, normally red, are sometimes yellow or cream-coloured. H. F. Comber found it only 2 ins. high in 1930 on an exposed moor at 4000 ft. altitude. It is a pleasing little evergreen for the rock garden where it can have a moist, preferably peaty soil.

Pernettya is predominantly a South and Central American genus. This Tasmanian species differs from all the American ones in not having awns at the back of the anthers as they have. P. NANA, *Colenso*, however, a mountain species of the South Island of New Zealand, resembles the American ones in this respect, but in all others is so nearly alike to P. tasmanica that Hooker made them one species.

PEROVSKIA ATRIPLICIFOLIA, *Bentham*. LABIATÆ

(Bot. Mag., t. 8441)

A deciduous, semi-woody plant, 3 to 5 ft. high, with a sage-like odour; branches long, stiffly erect, covered with a white, close down. Leaves opposite, 1 to 2 ins. long, $\frac{1}{3}$ to 1 in. wide; rhomboidal or slightly obovate, tapered at both ends, coarsely toothed, grey-green, and slightly downy; stalk $\frac{1}{12}$ to $\frac{1}{3}$ in. long. Panicles terminal, 9 to 12 ins. long, produced in August and September, and composed of numerous slender, opposite, leafless spikes, 2 to 5 ins. long. Flowers beautiful violet-blue, 1/3 in. long, produced in whorls; corolla two-lipped, tubular at the base with a five-lobed spreading limb 1/3 in. across; calyx shaggy, with white hairs. The whole inflorescence is covered like the stem with a white, powder-like down, which brings the colour of the blossoms into greater prominence.

Native of the Himalaya and Afghanistan. It covers large areas in the Chitral Valley, to the exclusion of other vegetation. Although woody at the base, the stems made during the summer die back considerably during winter. It should be planted in good loam, in a group of at least half a dozen plants, and then makes a pretty effect in late summer. A heat-lover, it should have the sunniest position available. The plants should be pruned over in spring, cutting off the dead portion and perhaps a little more. It rarely produces seed with us, but can easily be increased by July cuttings.

PERTYA SINENSIS, *Oliver*. COMPOSITÆ

A deciduous bush, 4 to 6 ft. high, with glabrous, slender, ribbed branches. Leaves alternate on the shoots of the year, ovate-lanceolate, long and taper-pointed; 2 to 3 ins. long, 3/4 to 1 in. wide; deep green, usually with one to three sharp teeth on each margin, but sometimes not toothed. On the year-old branches they are produced four to six together in rosette-like clusters from each joint, and are only half or less than half the size of the others, and without teeth. The leaves are either glabrous or have some small bristles on the midrib; stalks 1/8 in. or less long. Flower-heads pinkish purple, 1/2 in. across, surrounded by a series of oval, membranous, overlapping bracts; about a dozen are produced from the centre of each leaf cluster on the year-old shoots, each on a slender, slightly bristly stalk about 1/4 in. or more long. It flowers in June and July.

Native of Hupeh, China; discovered by Henry in 1889, and introduced by Wilson in 1901 for Messrs Veitch. It is a neat shrub, but perhaps of more botanical than garden interest. The leaves have an intense, Quassia-like bitterness. The chief interest of this shrub is in its being an addition to the few shrubby composites that are hardy in cultivation. The genus is named after J. A. Maximilian Perty, Swiss naturalist, 1804-1884.

PETTERIA RAMENTACEA, *Presl*. DALMATIAN LABURNUM. LEGUMINOSÆ

(Cytisus Weldenii, *Visiani*; Bot. Reg., 29, t. 40)

A deciduous, tree-like shrub of sturdy habit, 6 or 8 ft. high, closely allied to Laburnum and Cytisus. Leaves trifoliolate, with a slender stalk 1 to 1½ ins. long; leaflets oval or obovate, very shortly stalked, 1 to 2 ins. long, half as much wide, rounded at the apex, glabrous, entire. Racemes terminating short twigs of the year, erect, 1½ to 3 ins. long; flower-stalks short, hairy. Flowers fragrant, densely arranged, yellow, $\frac{3}{4}$ in. long, resembling those of a broom ; calyx tubular, downy ; standard petal

PETTERIA RAMENTACEA

erect. Seed-pod $1\frac{1}{2}$ to 2 ins. long, pointed at the end, dark brown when ripe, containing five or seven seeds.

Native of Dalmatia and Montenegro ; one may see it growing on the sides of the beautiful road that joins those two countries, between

Cattaro and Cettinje. It was introduced in 1837, but is not common. It is perfectly hardy, and flowers regularly in May and June, and ripens seeds which (like those of Laburnum) are poisonous. It differs from Laburnum in the longer tubular calyx and shortly stalked pods. The genus commemorates Franz Petter, Dalmatian botanist; died 1853.

PHELLODENDRON. RUTACEÆ

A small genus of deciduous trees found in N.E. Asia, with opposite, pinnate leaves which give off a rather aromatic odour when crushed, and whose leaf-stalks, swollen at the base, completely hide the bud. The inner bark is yellow. Male and female flowers appear on different trees, but both are inconspicuous; the fruits are roundish, about the size of large peas, juicy and aromatic, with a black, tough skin. The chief attraction of the phellodendrons is in their foliage and often picturesque habit. P. japonicum has fruited in this country, and the seed germinates freely. When seeds are not available, cuttings taken from the tree in July may be rooted in gentle heat; they should be made of short twigs with a "heel" of older wood. These trees are gross feeders, and like a deep rich loam.

The name is derived from the Greek *phellos* (cork) and *dendron* (tree) given in reference to the corky bark of P. amurense, the species first described by Ruprecht in 1853. The species have but little beauty of blossom.

P. AMURENSE, *Ruprecht*

A deciduous tree, 20 to 40 ft. high, of stiff habit, with a trunk 1 ft. or more in diameter, corky-barked; young shoots glabrous. Leaves pinnate, 10 to 15 ins. long, with five to eleven leaflets which are 2½ to 4½ ins. long, ovate or ovate-lanceolate, long-pointed, hairy only on the margin and at the base of the midrib, glossy green above. Panicles erect, 3 ins. high, 1½ to 3 ins. wide; few-branched. Flowers small, yellow green, ¼ in. long. Fruit about ½ in. in diameter, black.

Native of Amurland, Manchuria, etc. Although in a wild state this tree is perhaps handsomer than P. japonicum, it is not so in cultivation here. Like many other trees from the same habitat, it is very liable to have its young shoots injured by late frosts. This induces excessive branching and an unnaturally dwarfed, bushy habit. It has been in cultivation at Kew for over fifty years. There is, or was, a fine tree 40 ft. high in Späth's nursery near Berlin; and it thrives well in the Arnold Arboretum, Mass., but both these places have a more decided winter and a later spring than ours. It is distinguished from the following species by its bright green leaves and the silvery down on the winter buds.

P. CHINENSE, *C. K. Schneider*

A deciduous tree 20 to 35 ft. high, with young shoots at first thinly downy, brown and glabrous the second year. Leaves pinnate, up to 15 ins. long, with seven to thirteen leaflets, main-stalk downy. Leaflets 3 to 5 ins. long, 1 to 1¾ ins. wide; oblong-lanceolate, furnished with pale hairs beneath, especially on the midrib. Flowers small, yellowish green, crowded on a short, very downy panicle; ovary downy. Fruit black, globose, 2/5 in. wide, aromatic, closely packed in a panicle 2 to 3½ ins. long and half as much wide.

Native of W. Hupeh, China; introduced by Wilson in 1907, perhaps earlier, for Messrs Veitch. It is most closely akin to P. japonicum and has similar although less downy leaves, but the fruits are larger and their close, compact arrangement distinguishes the species well. It first bore fruit at Kew in 1920.

Var. GLABRIUSCULUM, *C. K. Schneider*, differs from the type in having the down on the leaves confined almost to the midrib and chief veins. Wilson found it in Hupeh and Szechuen up to 30 ft. high during the same year as the type. This and the following species flower in June.

P. JAPONICUM, *Maximowicz*

A deciduous, bushy-headed tree, of stiff habit, 20 to 35 ft. high, its trunk 8 to 12 ins. in thickness. Leaves 10 to 15 ins. long, pinnate, with seven to fifteen leaflets, which are very downy beneath, dull green, and soon nearly or quite glabrous above, broadly ovate, pointed, oblique at the base, 2 to 3 ins. long, with a short stalk. Panicle of male flowers about 4 ins. long, and 2 ins. wide, erect; the female one more slender. Flower ¼ in. across, yellowish green. Fruits orange-shaped, black, each nearly ½ in. across, borne on an erect downy panicle.

Native of China and Japan; introduced about 1870. It is distinguished from the other species by the thick, greyish down beneath the leaflets, and by their broader proportions. A well-grown tree is handsome when in full leaf and fruit. It flowers in July.

P. LAVALLEI, *Dode*

(Bot. Mag., t. 8945; P. amurense Lavallei, *Sprague*)

A deciduous tree with corky bark, 30 ft. high in cultivation and probably capable of attaining twice that stature; young shoots at first downy, soon nearly or quite glabrous, ultimately purplish brown. Leaves pinnate, 9 to 15 ins. long, composed of seven to eleven leaflets; main-stalk downy. Leaflets oval-lanceolate, with long, slender points, broadly tapered at the base; 1½ to 4½ ins. long, ⅝ to 1¾ ins. wide; dullish green and slightly downy on the veins above; midrib and chief veins furnished with white hairs beneath; margins hairy; stalk 1/12 to ⅙ in. long. Panicles about 3 ins. wide, many-flowered, lax; main-stalks downy. Flowers greenish yellow, small, each on a downy stalk about ⅛ in. long. Fruit ⅓ to ½ in. wide, globose, containing a juicy aromatic flesh.

Native of Japan and cultivated in England for fifty years either as P. japonicum or P. amurense. The former differs by the soft down which covers the whole of its much more rounded leaflets beneath; P. amurense has only a little down near the base of the midrib and the upper surface is glossy, dark green. Prof. Sargent once told me that, from what he saw in Japan, he should judge P. Lavallei to be the largest of the phellodendrons. It succeeds very well under cultivation and grows vigorously at Kew, bearing large crops of its black fruits. The leaves turn golden yellow before they fall.

P. SACHALINENSE, *Sargent*

A deciduous tree 30 to 40 ft. high, with a tall, straight trunk. Leaves 9 to 12 ins. long, with seven to fifteen leaflets, which are 2½ to 4½ ins. long, taper-pointed, ovate, downy beneath on the midribs, especially towards the base, dull green. Panicles glabrous, 2 to 4 ins. long. Flowers greenish yellow; females ⅜ in. long; males longer, with protruding stamens. Fruit ⅓ in. diameter, black.

Native of Japan, Korea, Saghalien; introduced to the Arnold Arboretum, Mass., in 1877; thence to Kew in 1904. By its quick growth and erect habit it promises to outstrip most of the other species and it is very hardy. From japonicum it can be distinguished by its nearly glabrous, longer, narrower leaflets and glabrous inflorescence; and from amurense, which it more closely resembles in foliage, by its dull green leaves and the brown-red down on the winter buds. Sargent also observes that the bark is thinner and not corky.

PHILADELPHUS. Mock Orange, Syringa.
SAXIFRAGACEÆ

A genus of deciduous shrubs most nearly related to Deutzia, from which they chiefly differ in having four petals and four calyx-lobes, and twenty to forty stamens, whilst in Deutzia the petals and the calyx-lobes are in fives and the stamens ten; the hairs in Deutzia, too, are stellate, in Philadelphus they are simple. Leaves opposite, stalked, often three- or five-nerved. Flowers often strongly scented, mostly pure white, occasionally yellowish or blotched with purple at the base of the petals. The inflorescence is always terminal, but varies from a solitary flower to a raceme or panicle. Fruit usually four-valved, dry, and woody, splitting lengthwise to liberate the numerous seeds. Flowers are not infrequently seen with the flower-parts in fives. In the majority of species the leaf-buds on the young shoots are completely hidden by the base of the leaf-stalk.

Perhaps no genus of shrubs presents so many difficulties in the differentiation of its species as this. A few of them are well marked, like microphyllus, with small entire leaves; hirsutus, with exposed leaf-buds and united stigmas; and mexicanus, with similar leaf-buds but divided stigmas; but the majority offer no really distinctive characters. The difficulty is further increased by free hybridisation under cultivation, so that now a large proportion of cultivated plants are not species at all, but garden hybrids.

These beautiful shrubs, commonly known as "Syringa"—a name which properly belongs to the lilacs—need no recommendation. They contribute to our gardens their most attractive pictures during June and July, when the great flowering time of shrubs is rapidly waning. They are useful in shrubberies where the vigorous ones can take care of themselves in competition with most things, and they also make very charming objects isolated on lawns. They grow best in a loamy soil, in a position at least moderately sunny, and are easily increased by cuttings made of softish young wood placed in bottom heat. They flower on short lateral twigs which spring from the shoots made the previous year, so that whatever pruning has to be done should consist of taking out old branches that have flowered and leaving the long, vigorous shoots of the current year to provide the succeeding crop of blossom. No mere shortening back should be done unless from considerations of space. The following selection may be recommended: microphyllus, Lemoinei, pubescens, insignis, Lewisii, "Virginal," and grandiflorus. Virginal, a variety of P. Lemoinei, with double white flowers, is considered by many to be the finest of all philadelphuses.

P. ARGYROCALYX, *Wooton*

(P. ellipticus, *Rydberg*)

A deciduous shrub of graceful spreading habit 6 to 8 ft. high; young shoots slender, downy, becoming black-brown the second year. Leaves ovate, up to 2 ins. long by 1 in. wide on the virgin shoots, smaller and narrower on the flowering ones; not toothed, pointed, tapered at the base; glabrous above, hairy on the midrib and veins and paler beneath; three-veined; stalk ⅛ in. or less long, downy. Flowers solitary or in threes, terminating leafy twigs 1 to 2 ins. long; white, 1¼ ins. wide. Calyx-tube hemispherical, the four lobes ovate, about ¼ in. long, covered with silvery grey down; petals obovate; anthers greenish; styles united; stigmas free; ovary quite glabrous.

Native of New Mexico; discovered in 1892, introduced in 1922. This charming philadelphus is the most distinct of the new species introduced since the first publication of this work. It is related to P. microphyllus and the flowers have a similar fruity fragrance, but that species has a nearly glabrous calyx whilst in this it is silvery-grey with down; P. argyrocalyx has also larger flowers and a more vigorous growth. It is very pretty in bloom, the flowers showing in two rows on the upper side of the previous year's (usually arching or drooping) shoots. Flowering in late June and July, being perfectly hardy and of a convenient size, it deserves to become popular in gardens.

P. CALIFORNICUS, *Bentham*

An elegant, pendulous-branched shrub up to 10 ft. high, the young shoots glabrous, the year-old bark peeling. Leaves three-nerved, ovate, 1½ to 3 ins. long, ¾ to 2 ins. wide; shortly and broadly toothed, or nearly entire (especially on the flowering twigs), either glabrous or slightly downy beneath. Flowers 1 in. or less wide, pure white, scentless, produced numerously in panicles at the end of the shoot, often over twenty flowers in each. Petals oblong-obovate; calyx glabrous outside the lobes, downy on the margins, and near the apex inside; styles united, stigmas separated.

Native of California. Although much confused with P. Lewisii, and sometimes regarded as a variety of it, this is really one of the most distinct of American species. On weak shoots its inflorescence may be only a simple raceme, but normally it is composed of several racemes, thus forming a true panicle. Flowers small and crowded. The base of the leaf-stalk does not hide the axillary bud, as it does in P. Lewisii.

P. CORONARIUS, *Linnæus*. MOCK ORANGE. SYRINGA (Plate 34)

(Bot. Mag., t. 391)

A shrub up to 12 ft. high, with erect stems, the year-old bark brown and peeling; young shoots ribbed. Leaves ovate to oval-lanceolate, broadly wedge-shaped or nearly rounded at the base, distantly toothed; 1½ to 4 ins. long, ⅝ to 2 ins. wide; glabrous except for a few hairs on one or both surfaces and on the leaf-stalk, which is ⅙ to ⅓ in. long. Flowers yellowish white, heavily scented, about 1 in. across, produced in terminal racemes of five to nine blossoms. Petals oval, ⅜ in. wide; calyx-lobes downy at the margins, the tube and flower-stalk either glabrous or slightly downy; styles separated at the upper third.

Native of S.E. Europe and Asia Minor; cultivated in Britain since the sixteenth century, probably before. It flowers in early June. This is the best-known species of mock orange in gardens, but is not in the first rank. The fragrance of its flowers is pleasing out-of-doors, but may become too insistent if the plants are numerous or near sitting-room windows. The odour is too strong for the flowers to be enjoyed in a cut state indoors. Over three hundred years ago Gerard, the herbalist, wrote :—

"They have a pleasant sweete smell, but in my judgment troubling and molesting the head in very strange manner. I once gathered the flowers and laid them in my chamber window, which smelled more strongly after they had lain together a few howers, but with such a pontick and unacquainted savor that they awaked me from sleepe, so that I could not take rest till I had cast them out of my chamber."

Var. DIANTHIFLORUS and var. PLENUS. Both double flowered; the former dwarf.

Var. FOLIIS AUREIS.—Leaves bright yellow, and very effective in spring, becoming duller after midsummer.

Var. NANUS.—Dwarf, and only 2 to 3 ft. high; rarely seen in flower.

Var. SALICIFOLIUS.—Remarkably distinct; leaves 2 to 4 ins. long, ½ to ¾ in. wide, sparsely toothed; shy-flowering.

Var. VARIEGATUS.—Leaves with a broad irregular border of creamy white.

P. DELAVAYI, *L. Henry*

(Bot. Mag., t. 9022)

A shrub up to 10 or 15 ft. high; shoots glabrous. Leaves ovate, rounded at the base, slender-pointed, toothed, dark green and hairy above, felted with whitish hairs beneath, 1 to 3 ins. long, ⅓ to 1½ ins. wide. Flowers fragrant, 1 to 1½ ins. across, produced in clusters of seven to eleven. Petals pure white, roundish oval, with tapered ends, often deeply toothed or undulated at the margins, spotted or margined with purple at the back; calyx glabrous outside, the lobes triangular-obovate, violet purple; style as long as the stamens, glabrous; stigmas separate. Fruit ¼ in. long.

Native of W. China; discovered and introduced by the Abbé Delavay in 1887. It flowered first at the Jardin des Plantes in 1890. In many of its characters it resembles P. tomentosus, *Wallich*, but the fruits are smaller. A pretty, fragrant species, producing its flowers in neat, dense clusters in June.

Var. MELANO CALYX has its calyx very dark purple.

P. FALCONERI, *Sargent*

(Garden and Forest, 1895, fig. 68)

A shrub up to 10 or 12 ft. high, forming a dense mass of slender, arching branches, which become a dark purplish brown the second year; young shoots nearly free from down, slightly ribbed. Leaves ovate to ovate-lanceolate, broadly wedge-shaped at the base, slender-pointed, distantly and minutely toothed; 1¼ to 3½ ins. long, ⅓ to 1⅝ ins. wide; glabrous except for a few hairs on the margins and ribs beneath when young. Flowers delicately scented, pure white, 1½ to 2 ins. across, produced at the end of twigs 2 to 4 ins. long in racemes of three to seven flowers. Petals oblong-lanceolate, ¼ in. wide, slender-pointed; calyx glabrous, except for minute down at the margins of the lance-shaped lobes; styles separated half-way down.

The origin of this mock orange is not known; it was first distinguished in Parson's nursery at Flushing, Long Island, U.S.A., and is probably a hybrid. It is not one of the best of the genus, and although elegant in habit is shy-flowering, at least in this country. Its long, narrow petals make it one of the best distinguished of the genus.

P. Gordonianus, *Lindley*

(Bot. Reg., vol. xxv., t. 32)

A shrub up to 12 ft., with slightly downy shoots. Leaves ovate to oval and oblong, 2 to 3½ ins. long, coarsely toothed, tapered to both ends more especially to the apex, usually strongly five-ribbed. Flowers in usually dense racemes of seven to nine, white, not very fragrant, each 1½ to nearly 2 ins. across; calyx of four ovate to ovate-lanceolate sepals; styles united from half to two-thirds their length.

Native of western N. America, from British Columbia to California, originally discovered over one hundred years ago by David Douglas. It is a handsome species and very hardy, flowering in July. According to Jepson the shoots were used by the native tribes of Indians as arrow-shafts.

P. grandiflorus, *Willdenow*

A shrub up to 12 ft. high, with the year-old bark peeling, young bark glabrous, becoming chestnut brown. Leaves ovate to ovate-lanceolate, rounded or tapered at the base; slender-pointed, sharply toothed, prominently three- or five-nerved; 1½ to 5 ins. long, ¾ to 2½ ins. wide; glabrous except for tufts of down in the vein-axils, and bristles along the chief veins. Flowers scentless, 2 ins. wide, pure white, produced at the end of leafy twigs, singly or in threes, and sometimes (in cultivated plants) in cymes of five flowers. Petals orbicular; calyx glabrous outside, the lobes slenderly pointed, downy at the margins and near the points outside. Fruit top-shaped, ½ in. long, gradually tapered to the stalk.

Native of the south-eastern United States; introduced in 1811. It is a vigorous and beautiful mock orange, useful in flowering later than most species, usually into July. It is allied to P. inodorus (*q.v.*). P. laxus, *Schrader*, is now usually regarded as a variety of P. grandiflorus, differing in its narrower leaves, more densely covered beneath with appressed down. Flowers small, 1 to 1½ ins. across, often solitary, not scented. (P. grandiflorus laxus, *Torrey*.)

P. hirsutus, *Nuttall*

(Bot. Mag., t. 5334)

A shrub up to 6 or 10 ft. high, of thin habit; young shoots covered with pale bristles; axillary buds not hidden by base of leaf-stalk. Leaves three-nerved, ovate (broadly so on the barren shoots), rounded or tapered at the base, taper-pointed; margins set with irregular, coarse, outstanding teeth; ¾ to 3 ins. long, ½ to 1¾ ins. wide; downy and dull green above, shaggy beneath; stalk ⅓ in. or less in length. Flowers 1 to 1¼ ins. across, sometimes solitary, often in threes on lateral twigs 1 in. or less long, bearing as a rule one pair of leaves. Petals creamy white; calyx shaggy, with triangular lobes; stigmas united.

Native of the south-eastern United States; introduced in 1820. Although one of the most easily recognised of a confusing genus, this species is one of the least attractive. Its flowers are scentless, and comparatively few. Its distinguishing marks are its exposed axillary buds, its short one- or three-flowered twigs, its dull shaggy leaves, etc., and united stigmas.

P. INCANUS, *Koehne*

A shrub up to 8 ft. or more high; young shoots more or less hairy. Leaves ovate or oval, broadly wedge-shaped or almost rounded at the base, slender-pointed, finely toothed; $2\frac{1}{2}$ to 4 ins. long, $1\frac{1}{4}$ to $2\frac{1}{4}$ ins. wide on the barren shoots; those of the flowering twigs mostly 1 to 2 ins. long; upper surface set with sparse minute hairs, the lower one thickly covered with appressed pale, stiff hairs giving it a dull grey hue; stalk $\frac{1}{12}$ to $\frac{1}{2}$ in. long, bristly. Flowers white, fragrant, about 1 in. across, produced five to nine (usually seven)

PHILADELPHUS INCANUS

together on downy racemes about 2 ins. long, at the end of leafy shoots of about the same length. Petals roundish; style about the average length of the stamens, glabrous, divided quite half-way down. Calyx and flower-stalk shaggy, like the under-surface of the leaves. Fruit top-shaped, $\frac{3}{8}$ in. long.

Native of Hupeh and Szechuen, China; discovered by Henry about 1887; introduced by Wilson in 1904. The plants at Coombe Wood used to flower late—from middle to late July—and the species is desirable on that account. It is also charmingly fragrant with an odour like that of hawthorn. It differs from P. Magdalenæ in its glabrous style.

P. INODORUS, *Linnæus*

(Bot. Mag., t. 1478)

A shrub of compact habit, 4 to 6 ft. high, usually more in diameter; bark glabrous, peeling the second year, of a chestnut-brown colour. Leaves ovate, with a rounded base and a fine point; $1\frac{1}{2}$ to 4 ins. long, $\frac{3}{4}$ to 2 ins. wide; sparsely and inconspicuously toothed; dark glossy green, with pale, appressed hairs above; paler, also glossy beneath, with only a few hairs on the veins. Flowers solitary, not scented, produced at the end of short twigs, pure white, 2 to $2\frac{1}{4}$ ins. across, petals overlapping, making the flower square in outline, with rounded corners.

Native of the south-eastern United States; introduced in 1738. For long this shrub was lost to cultivation, although many spurious plants were sold under the name. Through the Arnold Arborteum the true thing is again in gardens—one of the finest and most striking of the genus. It is distinguished by its glossy dark green leaves, and solitary, large, squarish flowers. Allied to P. grandiflorus, it differs in its less dentate, shorter pointed leaves and more abruptly pointed calyx.

P. INSIGNIS, *Carrière*

(P. " Souvenir de Billiard " ; P. Billiardi, *Koehne*)

The origin of this handsome mock orange is not known, but it is probably a hybrid in whose origin P. grandiflorus has shared. It is a vigorous bush up to 10 or 12 ft. high ; young shoots glabrous or nearly so ; bark of year-old ones not peeling. Leaves ovate or sometimes heart-shaped ; 1½ to 3½ ins. long, 1¼ to 2½ ins. wide ; minutely and sparsely toothed, glabrous and glossy green above, shaggy with pale hairs beneath. Flowers faintly perfumed, pure white, cupped, a little over 1 in. across, produced during late June in leafy terminal panicles of fifteen to over twenty blossoms. Petals roundish, ¾ in. long, overlapping ; calyx and flower-stalk hairy outside ; style shorter than the stamens, united just below the stigmas.

Although cultivated for over seventy years, this is not much grown in gardens yet, although certainly one of the most attractive of mock oranges. It is distinct in its many-flowered inflorescences, combined with its glossy green leaves, its cupped flowers, and overlapping petals. It is useful in flowering well into July.

P. LEMOINEI, *Hort*

A deciduous bush of graceful habit, round-topped, and 6 ft. or more high ; young stems covered with pale hairs. The leaves of the strong barren shoots of the year are ovate, with a rounded base, slender-pointed, with usually three to six coarse teeth on either margin about the middle ; 1 to 2½ ins. long, about half as wide ; dull green and with scattered hairs above, glossy and more hairy beneath. The leaves of the flowering shoots are about 1 in. long, narrowly ovate, and with few or no teeth. Flowers pure white, very fragrant, 1 in. across, produced during June in the leaf-axils, and at the end of short lateral branchlets, three to seven on each.

A hybrid between microphyllus and coronarius raised by Mr Lemoine of Nancy, about 1883. It represents one of the greatest successes ever achieved by the hybridiser's art, being the forerunner in gardens of a new and distinct type of philadelphus, and the first of a most beautiful race of summer-flowering shrubs. By a system of annual pruning, P. Lemoinei may be kept comparatively dwarf. The flowers are produced along slender wands (the barren shoots of the previous year), giving wreaths of blossom often 1½ to 2 ft. long. To keep the plants dwarf, these should be cut clean out to the base as soon as the flowers are past, leaving only the crowd of young barren shoots springing from the base, and already, at the time of pruning, 6 to 12 ins. long. These will provide the following year's crop of blossom, and if too numerous to develop properly should be thinned. This system of culture gives enormous quantities of flower, and keeps the plants about 3 ft. high, thus rendering them suitable for positions where, left to grow naturally, they might be too big.

There are numerous varieties now in cultivation of the Lemoinei race : they have not, however, all the same origin :—

Single.—Avalanche, Gerbe de Neige, Fantaisie, Pavillon blanc.

Double.—Boule d'argent, Manteau d'hermine, Virginal. The last has flowers 1½ to 2 ins. across, pure white, in dense clusters. Given a first-class certificate by the Horticultural Society, 20th June 1911, and perhaps the finest in the genus.

P. Lemoinei, as well as all these varieties, is very quickly and easily increased by cuttings of soft wood in June, placed in brisk bottom heat.

P. LEWISII, *Pursh.* See p. 635

P. MAGDALENÆ, *Koehne*

A shrub of bushy habit, up to 12 ft. high; young shoots downy; year-old bark peeling, glabrous. Leaves ovate-lanceolate or narrowly oval, tapered at both ends, finely toothed except towards the base; 1 to 2½ ins. long, ½ to ⅞ in. wide; furnished both above and below with pale, bristle-like, minute, appressed hairs, but especially dense and grey with them beneath. Flowers white, ¾ to 1 in. diameter, borne during early June in racemes of three to eleven; flower-stalk and calyx hairy, purplish; style downy towards the base, shorter than the stamens; stigmas separate; fruit top-shaped.

Native of Szechuen, China; introduced to France by Mr Maurice de Vilmorin in 1895, and sent by him to Kew in 1897. It belongs to the same Asiatic group as Satsumi, sericanthus, and incanus. Neither of the two former has the close leaf-covering of bristle-like down of Magdalenæ; in addition, sericanthus differs in its glabrous style, as does incanus also.

P. MEXICANUS, *Schlechtendahl*

(Bot. Mag., t. 7600)

A shrub up to 6 ft. high, with hairy young shoots; axillary buds not hidden by base of leaf-stalk. Leaves ovate-lanceolate, rounded at the base, slenderly pointed, sparsely toothed, three-nerved; 1 to 2½ ins. long, ½ to 1 in. wide, with appressed pale hairs on both surfaces, but more abundant beneath. Flowers cupped, solitary (rarely in threes) at the end of short, leafy shoots; 1½ to 2 ins. across, strongly fragrant, yellowish white; petals roundish, overlapping; calyx hairy, the lobes sometimes toothed; flower-stalk very short hairy; style about as long as the stamens; stigmas separate.

Native of Mexico; and not hardy except against a warm wall. It is a handsome and distinct species, most nearly allied to P. hirsutus, and, like it, distinguished by the buds being exposed at the base of the leaf-stalk. P. hirsutus, however, has smaller white flowers and the stigmas are united. (See also *californicus*, with exposed buds.)

Var. COULTERI, "Rose Syringa."—Petals with a blotch of rich reddish purple at the base. Neither species nor variety is very free-flowering in cultivation. (P. Coulteri, *S. Watson.*)

P. MICROPHYLLUS, *A. Gray*

A deciduous shrub of densely bushy, rounded habit, ultimately about 4 ft. high; branchlets slender but rigid, downy; bark shining brown the first year, peeling and almost black the second. Leaves ovate, pointed, not toothed; ½ to ¾ in. long, ¼ to ⅓ in. wide; bright green and almost glabrous above, grey and covered with pale, appressed hairs beneath; stalk $\frac{1}{16}$ in. long. Flowers very fragrant, pure white, about 1 in. across; produced in June, usually singly, at the end of lateral branches 1 to 2 ins. long, which spring from the joints of the previous year's shoots.

Native of Colorado, Arizona, etc.; introduced by Prof. Sargent to Britain about 1883. It is quite distinct from all other cultivated species of philadelphus in its small entire leaves and low, compact habit. The leaves in a state of nature are much more hairy than with us. The flowers have a strong pineapple-like odour, very pleasant in the open air. Although coming from such a hot and sunny climate, it succeeds remarkably well in Britain, and flowers profusely.

PHILADELPHUS MICROPHYLLUS

For small gardens and limited spaces it and its progeny are the most charming representatives of their kind. Hybridised with P. coronarius it has given birth to the beautiful race of philadelphuses of which P. Lemoinei was the first to appear.

P. PEKINENSIS, *Ruprecht*

A shrub up to 8 ft. high; young shoots glabrous, the bark peeling off the year-old branchlets. Leaves ovate to ovate-lanceolate, slender-pointed, toothed; 1½ to 3½ ins. long, ¾ to 2 ins. wide; three-nerved, glabrous or nearly so; stalk and veins beneath purplish. Flowers yellowish, about 1 in. across, slightly fragrant, produced in racemes of five to nine (sometimes eleven). Petals oval, rounded at the top; calyx glabrous outside, downy towards the points of the lobes inside; styles separated at the top only; flower-stalk glabrous.

Native of N. China, Mongolia, Korea. It flowers in late May and June and is distinct in its yellowish flowers, glabrous leaves with purplish stalks, and glabrous flower-stalks; but it is not one of the best, although free-flowering. Near it, and sometimes made a variety of it, is P. BRACHYBOTRYS, *Koehne*, introduced by Mr Maurice de Vilmorin from China in 1892. This also has yellowish flowers but smaller, and the young shoots are furnished with a few stiff hairs; the leaves entire or indistinctly toothed. It forms a rounded, dense-habited bush.

P. PUBESCENS, *Loiseleur*

(P. grandiflorus floribundus, *Gray*; P. latifolius, *Schrader*)

A robust shrub, 10 to 20 ft. high, as much or more in diameter; young shoots glabrous, green; the year-old shoots grey, not peeling. Leaves of the barren shoots oval or ovate, broadly tapered or rounded at the base, pointed, sparsely and irregularly toothed; 2 to 5 ins. long, about half as wide; dull and almost glabrous above, downy beneath; with three or five prominent veins. Leaves of the flowering twigs smaller. Flowers pure white, $1\frac{3}{4}$ ins. wide, not much scented; produced in June at the end, and in the uppermost leaf-axils of lateral twigs, usually seven or nine each. Calyx-lobes $\frac{2}{5}$ in. long, lanceolate, and, like the individual flower-stalks, downy.

Native of the S.E. United States; introduced early last century. It is a fine free-flowering shrub, not uncommon in gardens, distinguished chiefly by the year-old bark not peeling, the numerous flowers in each raceme, and the downy calyx. One of the finest and noblest of mock oranges.

P. PURPURASCENS, *Rehder*

(P. brachybotrys purpurascens, *Koehne*; Bot. Mag., t. 8324—as P. Delavayi)

A deciduous shrub up to 12 ft. high, with peeling bark; young virgin shoots slightly hairy, flowering twigs glabrous. Leaves ovate to ovate-lanceolate, slender-pointed, tapered or rounded at the base, distantly toothed sometimes almost or quite entire on the flowering twigs; $1\frac{1}{2}$ to 3 ins. long $\frac{1}{2}$ to $1\frac{1}{4}$ ins. wide; more or less hairy on both surfaces on the virgin shoots nearly or quite glabrous on the flowering ones. Flowers white, fragrant 1 to $1\frac{1}{4}$ ins. wide, produced during June mostly in five- (but also seven- and nine-) flowered racemes; petals roundish oval; calyx more or less purple, the lobes narrowly triangular, ciliate; styles united at the top.

Native of W. China; introduced for Messrs Veitch by Wilson in 1904 Its most distinctive character is the purple calyx, but this colouring is somewhat variable in amount. On a plant at Westonbirt which the late Sir George Holford showed me, the entire calyx was dark violet purple and it made a most effective contrast with the pure white petals. But in other plants the lobes only are coloured or merely their tips.

P. PURPUREO-MACULATUS, *Lemoine*

(Bot. Mag., t. 8193)

A hybrid of the Lemoinei type, but more bushy in habit; young wood reddish brown, hairy. Leaves of the barren shoots broadly ovate or roundish the base slightly heart-shaped; the largest $1\frac{3}{4}$ ins. long, $1\frac{1}{2}$ ins. wide; one to three teeth on either side, dull dark green, slightly hairy; stalk $\frac{1}{6}$ in. long The leaves of the flowering twigs are 1 in. or so long, with usually one tooth or entire. Flowers fragrant, $1\frac{1}{2}$ ins. across, solitary at the end of a short lateral branchlet, petals white, with a blotch of purplish rose at the base, opening in mid-June.

This beautiful philadelphus was raised by Mr Lemoine of Nancy, and is apparently derived from P. mexicanus Coulteri (*q.v.*), crossed with one of the microphyllus hybrids. It is the patch of colour in the centre of the flower, inherited from the former parent, that gives this philadelphus its value and distinctness in gardens. Although hardy in ordinary seasons, it is not quite so hardy as P. Lemoinei.

P. SATSUMANUS, *Miquel*

(P. acuminatus, *Lange*)

An erect shrub, 6 to 8 ft. high ; young shoots glabrous ; bark of the previous year's shoots dark greyish brown, more or less split lengthwise, but not peeling off. Leaves ovate or oval, with long drawn-out points ; those of the barren shoots 2 to 6 ins. long, half as wide, toothed, usually five-nerved, glabrous above, downy in the vein-axils beneath ; the leaves of the flowering shoots are smaller and proportionately narrower, and often quite or nearly entire. Flowers slightly scented, white, about $1\frac{1}{4}$ ins. across, produced in erect racemes of five to eleven flowers ; petals oval, rounded ; style rather shorter than the stamens, the stigmas separate ; calyx-lobes ovate, glabrous outside or nearly so.

Native of Japan ; introduced in 1851.

P. SCHRENKII, *Ruprecht*

(P. mandschuricus, *Nakai*)

A vigorous deciduous shrub up to 12 ft. high ; young shoots brown, slightly hairy ; bark peeling the second year. Leaves ovate, sparsely toothed, slender-pointed ; $1\frac{1}{2}$ to $4\frac{1}{2}$ ins. long and about half as much wide on the virgin shoots, smaller on the flowering ones ; slightly downy beneath, less so above. Flowers about $1\frac{1}{2}$ ins. wide, in five- or seven-flowered racemes ; style usually hairy at the base ; calyx-tube and flower-stalks hairy.

Native of Manchuria, Korea, and N. China ; introduced in 1874. This vigorous shrub is one of the earlier flowering species of philadelphus. A fine bush 12 ft. high in Col. Stern's garden, near Worthing, flowers in late May and early June. In the summer of 1930 I noticed the ground beneath it was freely sprinkled with seedlings that had sprouted from the seeds of 1929. It is quite an ordinary philadelphus, with no strongly marked qualities or characteristics ; but the racemose inflorescence, the peeling bark of the year-old shoots, and the style being hairy at the base are the more distinctive ones.

P. SERICANTHUS, *Koehne*

(Bot. Mag., t. 8941)

A shrub 6 to 12 ft. high, shoots glabrous, becoming reddish brown the first year, ultimately peeling. Leaves ovate to oval-lanceolate, tapered to both ends, especially to the slender acuminate apex, coarsely toothed with up to eleven pairs, $1\frac{1}{2}$ to 4 ins. long by 1 to $2\frac{1}{2}$ ins. wide, sometimes entire, sparsely hairy or glabrous above with a few hairs at the back and tufts in the vein-axils. Flowers about 1 in. wide in racemes of up to eleven, not scented ; petals pure white, rounded-oval to nearly orbicular ; calyx and stalks densely covered with appressed, stiff, white hairs ; style glabrous.

Native of Hupeh and Szechuen, China, discovered by Henry, 1888-9, introduced to England by E. H. Wilson in 1900. It is quite hardy, very free flowering and blossoms in June.

P. TOMENTOSUS, *Wallich*

A shrub 6 or 8 ft. high; young shoots glabrous, or slightly hairy when quite young only. Leaves 1½ to 4 ins. long, ¾ to 2 ins. wide; oval or ovate, with long slender points and a rounded or tapered base, unevenly toothed; dark green and hairy above, especially when young, grey and felted beneath; stalk ⅕ to ⅖ in. long. Petals oval, rounded at the end; calyx glabrous outside, downy inside; style about as long as the stamens; stigmas separate at the top.

Native of the Himalaya; introduced, according to Loudon, in 1822. It is often regarded as a variety of P. coronarius, but is amply distinguished from it by the grey-felted under-surface of the leaves. It is more nearly related to P. Delavayi (*q.v.*).

P. ZEYHERI, *Schrader*

A deciduous shrub of very vigorous spreading habit, up to 8 ft. high, considerably more in width; bark deep brown, slightly peeling; young shoots glabrous. Leaves broadly ovate to lanceolate, tapered at the base, slender-pointed, varying from coarsely toothed to nearly entire; 2½ to 4 ins. long, ¾ to 2 ins. wide; glabrous above, downy beneath along each side of the midrib and chief veins, with occasional hairs between. Flowers pure white, 1½ to 1¾ ins. across, produced during June in a terminal corymb of three to seven blossoms (sometimes solitary). Petals oval; style distinctly longer than the stamens; calyx glabrous, with slender lobes ½ in. long.

A hybrid of unrecorded origin, but with grandiflorus probably as one parent. The flowers have little or no fragrance, and the sepals are acuminate, as in that species. The young shoots are apt to be killed back in winter, which may be due to their sappy vigour. The plant is very distinct in its comparatively low, spreading habit, but it blossoms poorly, and is of inferior quality.

PHILAGERIA VEITCHII, *Masters*. LILIACEÆ

A hybrid between Lapageria rosea and Philesia buxifolia which was raised by Messrs Veitch at Chelsea, and flowered in their nursery there in 1872. It was named, described, and figured that year in the *Gardeners' Chronicle*, p. 358, fig. 119. The lapageria was the seed-bearer. It is a scrambling shrub with leathery, dark green, shining leaves about 1½ ins. long and ½ in. wide, with three prominent veins running lengthwise and converging at the apex. Flower pendulous, about 2 ins. long, ½ to ¾ in. wide, with a rosy purple calyx of three oblong, pointed fleshy sepals about 1 in. long; and a corolla of three bright rose-coloured overlapping petals twice as long; anthers ½ in. long, yellow; flower-stalk ¼ in. long.

This interesting hybrid bears more resemblance to the lapageria in habit, in the stamens and in the colour of the flower, than it does to the philesia. It is hardy in Cornwall and similar places but is now very rare.

PHILESIA BUXIFOLIA, *Lamarck*. LILIACEÆ

(Bot. Mag., t. 4738; P. magellanica, *Gmelin*)

A dwarf evergreen shrub, said to be 3 ft. high in its native country, but usually 6 to 12 ins. high in this; stems erect, bearing alternate, angled, glabrous branchlets. Leaves alternate, stiff and hard, dark green above, glaucous white beneath; about 1½ ins. long, ¼ to ⅜ in. wide, but made narrower by the reflexed margins, quite glabrous; midrib prominent beneath; stalk $\frac{1}{8}$ in. long. Flowers solitary, nodding, terminal; 2 to $2\frac{1}{2}$ ins. long, rich rosy crimson; petals three, oblanceolate, pointed, not expanding, and thus giving a tubular form to the flower. Calyx of three oblong sepals about $\frac{1}{4}$ to $\frac{3}{4}$ in. long, appressed to the petals. Fruit a roundish red berry.

Native of S. Chile; introduced by W. Lobb in 1847. It is one of the remarkable group of shrubs allied botanically to the lilies, to which Ruscus, Smilax, Lapageria, etc., belong. It is strikingly handsome, and quite distinct in its long red flowers from any other cultivated plant except Lapageria, and that is a climber. Philesia is grown out-of-doors in several parts of the country, and should be planted in peaty soil. In October 1911 I saw it flowering on the rockery in Messrs Cunningham & Fraser's nursery at Edinburgh. It succeeds very well in Cornwall; there is a plant 12 ft. wide in the Rectory garden at Ludgvan, and another at Caerhays 2 to 3 ft. high. Col. Stephenson Clarke has a fine patch in his garden at Binstead, Isle of Wight, which I have seen in full bloom in July.

PHILLYREA. OLEACEÆ

A group of evergreen shrubs or small trees, the hardy ones of which are natives of the Mediterranean region and of the country south-east of the Black Sea. They are nearly related to Osmanthus, and have opposite leaves, toothed or entire, and small white or greenish flowers borne in clusters in the leaf-axils of the previous year's growths. Calyx and corolla four-lobed; stamens two. Fruit a roundish oval, mostly one-seeded drupe.

They are all easily cultivated, and thrive in any soil that is of average quality. Cuttings made of the current season's wood in July take root readily. Except P. decora, they bear clipping well.

P. ANGUSTIFOLIA, *Linnæus*

A shrub of dense habit, up to 10 ft. high, and occasionally more in diameter; branches minutely downy and slightly warted. Leaves linear, 1 to $2\frac{1}{2}$ ins. long, $\frac{3}{16}$ to $\frac{3}{8}$ in. wide; tapering towards both ends, rarely toothed, dark dull green; glabrous on both surfaces. Flowers fragrant, dull white, produced during May and June in short axillary clusters $\frac{1}{2}$ in. or less long; flower-stalks minutely downy. Fruit blue-black, roundish-oval, $\frac{1}{4}$ in. long.

Native of N. Africa and S. Europe; cultivated in England before 1597. It is a neat, quite hardy evergreen, without any striking features, but easily distinguished from all the rest by its entire, long, narrow leaves.

Var. ROSMARINIFOLIA, *Aiton* (P. rosmarinifolia, *Miller*).—Leaves narrower and smaller than those of the type, $\frac{1}{8}$ to $\frac{3}{16}$ in. wide, and of a greyer, rather glaucous shade.

P. DECORA, *Boissier*

(P. Vilmoriniana, *Boissier*, Bot. Mag., t. 6800; P. laurifolia, *Hort.*)

A rigidly branched shrub, 5 to 10 ft. high, more in diameter; young shoots slightly warted, but not downy. Leaves pointed, narrowly oval or oblong, 2 to 5 ins. long, $\frac{1}{2}$ to $1\frac{3}{4}$ ins. wide, tapering at the base; of firm, almost hard texture; very dark, glossy green above, paler below. They are either quite entire, or there are a few scattered teeth on the margins; stalk $\frac{1}{2}$ in. or less long. Flowers about $\frac{1}{4}$ in. across, pure white, crowded in dense, axillary clusters, produced during April. Fruit oval, $\frac{1}{2}$ in. long, borne on slender stalks $\frac{1}{2}$ in. long, ripe in September, first reddish, then blackish purple.

Native of Lazistan, near the south-eastern coast of the Black Sea; discovered in 1866 by Balansa, and introduced to France by seeds the same year. The

PHILLYREA DECORA

first record I have of its flowering in this country is in the nursery at Knap Hill, in April, 1883. It is the most striking of the phillyreas, and very distinct from the others in size and shape of leaf; its flowers, too, are of a purer white. Owing to its being grafted on privet (an evil practice) in the early days of its cultivation, many of the plants were short-lived, and the reputation of the plant suffered. Raised from seeds or cuttings, it is quite satisfactory. It is very hardy. There is some variation in the foliage, one form being much narrower in leaf.

P. LATIFOLIA, *Linnæus*

Of the three commonly grown phillyreas from S. Europe, viz., this, P. media, and P. angustifolia, the name latifolia is given to the one with largest and broadest leaves. P. angustifolia is distinct enough, but I cannot see that any definite distinction between P. latifolia and P. media can be made; there appears to be no gap between the largest leaves of P. media and the smallest ones of P. latifolia; nor is there any other character discernible, as they grow in this country, sufficient to separate them. The largest leaves of what I regard as P. latifolia are ovate or roundish ovate; 2 to 2½ ins. long, 1 to 1½ ins. wide; pointed, sharply toothed, rounded or even slightly heart-shaped at the base; the smaller ones are often oval, indistinctly toothed, broadly tapered at the base. Young wood and flower-stalks minutely downy. Flowers dull white, in short axillary clusters. Fruit blue-black, roundish or orange-shaped, scarcely ¼ in. long. It is sometimes a small tree 15 ft. to 30 ft. high.

Var. ILICIFOLIA (P. spinosa, *Miller*).—A form with strongly toothed leaves, 1 to 1½ ins. long; ovate and rounded at the base.

Native of S. Europe and N. Africa; cultivated in England in the sixteenth century.

Of P. MEDIA, *Linnæus*, there is little to be added to what is said above. It is scarcely specifically distinct from latifolia, but the plant to which the name is attached has smaller leaves, ovate or oval, ½ to 1½ ins. long, slightly and bluntly toothed (not sharply as in latifolia), or quite entire and the fruit more ovoid or pointed. The form known as BUXIFOLIA has small, almost wholly entire leaves. There used to be a good bush 6 or 8 ft. high in Messrs Paul & Son's nursery, Cheshunt.

PHLOMIS FRUTICOSA, *Linnæus*. JERUSALEM SAGE. LABIATÆ

(Bot. Mag., t. 1843)

A vigorous evergreen shrub; branchlets soft, herbaceous, stout, square, thickly covered with grey, branched hairs. Leaves opposite, dull green, wrinkled, and with prominent veining like common sage; 2 to 5 ins. long, 1½ to 1¾ ins. wide, ovate-lanceolate; covered with branched hairs, sparsely above, thickly beneath; stalks ¼ to 1 in. long. Flowers stalkless, bright yellow, crowded at the leaf-bases in two dense clusters which together form a circular tier 2 ins. across. Corolla 1¼ ins. long, two-lipped, the upper lip hood-shaped; calyx green, funnel-shaped, hairy, with five projecting narrow teeth at the top.

Native of S. Europe; cultivated in England since the sixteenth century. It is only half hardy near London, and succumbs in severe winters. The flowers develop in late summer and autumn, and are very bright and interesting, forming curious, short, crowded clusters. The foliage is like that of a giant sage, but is weakly scented. The plant is seen at its best in the south-western counties and Ireland. Easily propagated by cuttings. The Jerusalem sage should have some sunny sheltered spot, such as a house corner facing south, or a dryish, sunny bank.

PHORMIUM. LILIACEÆ

Strictly speaking the phormiums are, I suppose, "herbs," but they are genuinely evergreen, their root-stocks are at any rate semi-woody, and they are so frequently included in nurserymen's lists of trees and shrubs that their perhaps anomalous inclusion here may be excused. They belong to the lily family but resemble closely in their mode of growth the common type of iris, having the same fleshy root-stock and the same flattened, two-edged, fan-like arrangement of the leaves.

Neither of thc phormiums here described has ever withstood the winters for long out-of-doors at Kew, but twenty or thirty miles south of London it begins to be possible to cultivate them. Dr Wilfrid Fox has healthy plants in a low, damp place in his garden at Winkworth Farm, near Godalming. They thrive in good loamy soil and plenty of moisture, but are really not very particular in their requirements and have been found to succeed well in peaty soil and even in boggy moorland. There is an interesting account in the *Kew Bulletin*, 1919, p. 174, by Lord Ventry of his experiments in growing P. tenax on a commercial scale in the south-west of Ireland. Some large plantations also have been made in Devonshire which it is hoped will in a few years show that the New Zealand flax may be a remunerative crop in the British Isles.

P. COLENSOI, *Hooker fil.* MOUNTAIN FLAX

(P. Cookianum, *Le Jolis*; P. Hookeri, *Gunn*, Bot. Mag., t. 6973)

This is, in general aspect, similar to the better known P. tenax described below, but its leaves are only 2 to 5 ft. high and 1 to 2½ ins. wide, pale green, rarely glaucous, and without the orange-coloured or red line on the leaf margins and midrib that characterises that species. The flowers, too, are yellow or yellowish red on the three outer segments, greenish yellow on the inner three; and the seed-vessel is twisted (not so in P. tenax). Like the larger species, it varies considerably, but is always characterised by the laxer foliage and pale yellow or yellowish flowers.

Native of both islands of New Zealand from sea-level up to 4500 ft. altitude. First seen by Captain Cook in 1770. There is a variegated form in cultivation.

P. TENAX, *Forster*. NEW ZEALAND FLAX

(Bot. Mag., t. 3199)

Leaves erect, of hard tough texture, rigid except at the points, up to 6 or 9 ft. long and 4 or 5 ins. wide, tapering near the top to a fine point, green inside, glaucous outside, with a red or orange-coloured line on the margins and midrib; they are stalkless, sheathing at the base, keeled, and V-shaped farther up, flattening out more towards the apex which is slit on old leaves. Flowers produced in summer on a panicle 5 to 15 ft. high, each flower 1 to 2 ins. long, with the six dull red segments separate but assuming a tube-like arrangement.

Native of New Zealand on both islands and from sea-level up to 4500 ft. altitude. With such a range both in latitude and altitude, it naturally varies a good deal in stature. The dwarfer mountain form is known as ALPINUM and one with bronzy purple leaves is called PURPUREUM. There are various garden forms such as VEITCHII with a broad yellow stripe up the centre of the leaf, and VARIEGATUM with stripes of sulphur yellow. The leaves yield one of the finest fibres known, which makes it the most important economic plant native of New Zealand; numerous forms, differing in value and character from this standpoint are cultivated there. It was seen by Sir Joseph Banks during Cook's first voyage (1769-70), but the seeds he then collected and brought home failed to germinate. Seeds were successfully introduced to Kew in 1789.

PHOTINIA. ROSACEÆ

A genus of North Asiatic shrubs and small trees allied to Sorbus and Cratægus. The leaves are simple and often somewhat leathery in texture. Flowers in corymbose clusters, white; petals and calyx-lobes five; stamens twenty. Fruit red, haw-shaped. They all like a warm, loamy soil, not too heavy and close. Propagation is best effected by seeds, but failing them cuttings of half to nearly ripened young wood should be tried in gentle heat. The practice of grafting them on hawthorn can only be condemned. P. serrulata has its foliage most richly coloured in spring, P. villosa in autumn.

P. BEAUVERDIANA, *C. K. Schneider*

A deciduous tree up to 20 ft. high, devoid of down in all its parts; young wood purplish brown, marked with very pale lenticels. Leaves lance-shaped to narrowly obovate, long and slenderly pointed, narrowly wedge-shaped at the base, finely and sharply toothed, the teeth frequently tipped with a small dark gland; 1½ to 5 ins. long, ½ to 1¾ ins. wide; of thin firm texture with some ten or twelve pairs of veins conspicuously raised beneath. Flowers in corymbs 1½ to 2 ins. wide, terminating short leafy twigs which spring from the previous season's growth. Each flower is scarcely ½ in. wide, white; petals roundish, tapering to a claw; sepals triangular. Fruit deep red, rather egg-shaped, nearly ¼ in. wide.

Native of W. China; discovered by Henry, introduced to the Coombe Wood Nursery in 1900 by Wilson, who describes it as a small, slender tree common in woods and copses. It has been cultivated at Kew since its introduction, is quite hardy and bears fruit regularly and usually freely enough to make it quite ornamental. A distinguishing character is the conspicuous veining, almost ribbing, of the leaves beneath. It flowers in May.

Var. NOTABILIS, *Rehder and Wilson* (P. notabilis, *C. K. Schneider*).—Easily distinguished from the type by the larger and especially broader leaves which are up to 5 ins. long, and the larger looser inflorescences which are 3 to 4 ins. wide. Superior to the type. Introduced by Wilson in 1908 from W. Hupeh, where he found it over 30 ft. high.

P. DAVIDSONIÆ, *Rehder and Wilson*

An evergreen tree, 20 to 45 ft. high, the young shoots reddish, appressed-downy. Leaves leathery, oblanceolate to narrowly oval, tapered towards both ends, usually more gradually towards the base; 2 to 6 ins. long, ¾ to 1¾ ins. wide, finely toothed; dark glossy green above, pale beneath, soon quite glabrous; stalk ¼ to ½ in. long. Flowers numerous, in terminal corymbs 3 or 4 ins. across; each flower scarcely ½ in. wide, white. Petals roundish, spreading; calyx funnel-shaped, with broadly triangular lobes, downy like the flower-stalks. Fruit roundish, orange-red, glabrous, about ⅓ in. long, the calyx-lobes persisting and incurved.

Native of W. Hupeh, China; discovered in 1900 by Wilson, who describes this as one of the handsomest evergreen trees in Central China, where it is frequently planted round shrines and tombs. It is most closely allied to P. serrulata, but is well distinguished by its shorter-stalked leaves and downy inflorescence; the fruit and flowers are also smaller in P. serrulata. It appears to be hardy.

P. GLABRA, *Maximowicz*

A glabrous evergreen shrub up to 8 ft. high, also said to be sometimes a small tree 15 to 20 ft. high. Leaves glossy dark green, narrowly oval, sometimes slightly obovate, 1½ to 3½ ins. long, one-third to half as wide, pointed, tapered at the base to a stalk $\frac{1}{4}$ to $\frac{1}{2}$ in. long, regularly and shallowly serrate. Flowers in loose, terminal, much-branched panicles 3 to 5 ins. across, scented like hawthorn, each blossom $\frac{1}{3}$ in. wide with five narrowly oval petals, white tinged with pink, opening in June. Fruit globose, $\frac{1}{8}$ to $\frac{1}{4}$ in. wide, red, ultimately black.

Native of Japan whence Wilson introduced it in 1914, but it may have appeared previously. It was originally placed in Cratægus by Thunberg, and another author has put it in Sorbus. It is a pleasant evergreen without any very outstanding merits. A very similar if not identical shrub is found in China.

P. PRIONOPHYLLA, *C. K. Schneider*

(Bot. Mag., t. 9134; Eriobotrya prionophylla, *Franchet*)

An evergreen shrub of stiff habit; young shoots covered with greyish down. Leaves of leathery texture, obovate or inclined to oval, wedge-shaped at the base, rounded or with a short point at the apex, sharply, almost spinily toothed; $1\frac{1}{2}$ to 3 ins. long, 1 to 2 ins. wide; finely downy above when quite young, becoming glabrous and dark green later, persistently downy and strongly veined beneath; stalk up to $\frac{1}{2}$ in. long. Flowers white, $\frac{1}{3}$ in. wide, produced in summer in flattish corymbs 2 to 3 ins. across. Petals obovate, incurved; stamens about twenty with yellow anthers. Calyx-tube woolly, the short triangular teeth downy or glabrous towards their tips where there is a small gland. Fruit globose, $\frac{1}{4}$ in. wide, crimson, woolly at the apex where the calyx remains.

Native of Yunnan, China, where it was discovered on limestone hills by the Abbé Delavay in 1888, and since collected by C. K. Schneider and Forrest, to the latter of whom we owe its introduction to cultivation. It was originally placed in the genus Eriobotrya by Franchet. It is distinguished amongst the cultivated photinias by the sharp, often coarse toothing of the hard-textured obovate leaves. The species appears first to have flowered with Mr E. J. P. Magor at St Tudy, Cornwall, in July 1922. It will probably need the protection of a wall away from the south and south-west.

P. SERRULATA, *Lindley*

(Bot. Mag., t. 2105)

An evergreen shrub, or a tree ultimately 30 to 40 ft. high in favoured situations; branchlets stout, glabrous. Leaves oblong, very firm and leathery, reddish when young, 4 to 8 ins. long and from $1\frac{1}{2}$ to $3\frac{1}{2}$ ins. wide, rounded or tapering at the base, shallowly toothed, perfectly glabrous on both surfaces; the stalk, however, which is from 1 to $1\frac{1}{2}$ ins. long, is clothed with whitish hairs which also extend up the midrib when young. Flowers white, $\frac{3}{8}$ in. in diameter, produced in April and May in large, terminal corymbose panicles 4 to 6 ins. through. Fruit about the size of common haws, red.

Native of China; first introduced by Captain Kirkpatrick of the East India Co., in 1804. Where it thrives, this is undoubtedly one of the finest evergreens ever introduced, but is only seen at its best in the south-western counties of England, etc. At Kew it is hardy in all but exceptional winters, but every plant was cut to ground-level by the frosts of February 1895, springing up again a few months later. It thrives remarkably well in Cornwall, where at Enys and at Pengreep there are trees 35 ft. high. It is also very fine at various places in Co. Cork, Ireland. It is most beautiful in spring, when the white flowers are associated with the rich brownish red, shining young leaves, but near London the latter are apt to be spoilt by late spring frosts.

Var. ROTUNDIFOLIA has shorter, proportionately broader leaves.

P. SUBUMBELLATA, *Rehder and Wilson*

(P. parvifolia, *C. K. Schneider*)

A deciduous shrub 6 to 9 ft. high, with dark red, glabrous young shoots. Leaves oval, ovate, or somewhat obovate, slenderly pointed, broadly wedge-shaped or almost rounded at the base, finely toothed; 1¼ to 2½ ins. long, ½ to 1⅓ ins. wide; dark bright green and soon quite glabrous; stalk ⅛ in. or less long. Corymbs 1 to 1½ ins. wide, terminating short leafy twigs and carrying few (rarely more than eight or nine) flowers; flower-stalks ½ to 1 in. long, slender, glabrous. Flowers about ½ in. wide, white; petals roundish with a few hairs inside the claw; calyx with a top-shaped tube and small, ovate, pointed lobes. Fruit oval, ⅓ in. long, not so much wide, dullish red or orange-red, crowned with the persistent sepals.

Native of Hupeh, China; introduced by Wilson to the Arnold Arboretum, Mass., in 1908. It is perfectly hardy at Kew, but neither in flower nor in fruit has it proved very ornamental up to the present. It blossoms in May.

P. VILLOSA, *De Candolle*

(P. variabilis, *Hemsley*)

A deciduous shrub or a small tree. Leaves obovate, or ovate-lanceolate, 1½ to 3½ ins. long, ¾ to 1½ ins. wide; the apex drawn out into a long fine point, tapered at the base, finely and regularly toothed, each tooth gland-tipped. Flowers white, in corymbs 1 in. long and 1½ ins. wide, produced in May; stalks conspicuously warted; each flower about ½ in. in diameter. Fruit the size and shape of common haws, red. The foliage, too, is often a beautiful red in autumn.

Native of Japan, China, and Korea. It is a variable plant especially in the amount of down on the leaves, young shoots, and flower-stalk. In the typical villosa the leaves are, as a rule, more obovate, and all the younger parts of the plant hairy; the flower-stalk is felted with grey down, and the fruit is about ⅓ in. long. In

Var. LÆVIS, *Dippel* (P. lævis, *De Candolle*), the leaves are usually longer pointed, and like the branchlets and flowers, glabrous or only slightly downy; the brilliant red fruits are ½ in. long. These two forms, whilst distinct enough in themselves, are united by various intermediate forms.

This photinia is sometimes met with as "Pourthiæa arguta," but the true plant of that name is not, so far as I know, in cultivation, and is possibly not hardy. It is from the Khasia Hills, India. (Bot. Mag., t. 9275.)

Var. SINICA, *Rehder and Wilson.*—This variety, which represents the species in Central and Western China, was discovered by Henry and introduced by Wilson about 1901. It is a slender deciduous tree 18 to 25 ft. high, with downy young shoots. Leaves oval to oblong, sometimes rather obovate, pointed, usually tapered but sometimes rounded at the base, finely and sharply toothed; 1½ to 3½ ins. long, ½ to 1½ ins. wide; bright green and soon glabrous above, paler beneath and downy especially on the midrib and veins, becoming glabrous by late summer; stalk $\frac{1}{12}$ to ⅕ in. long, downy. Flowers produced in May on racemose corymbs 1 to 2 ins. wide with downy stalks. Each flower is about ⅓ in. wide, with white rounded petals, a woolly bell-shaped calyx with triangular teeth and twenty stamens. Fruit egg-shaped, ½ in. long, orange-scarlet; the fruit stalks conspicuously warted.

The typical P. villosa, which does not occur in W. China, differs from this variety in its most frequently obovate leaves, thicker in texture. Both are notable for their fine red autumnal colouring of leaves and fruit.

PHYGELIUS CAPENSIS, *E. Meyer*. SCROPHULARIACEÆ

(Bot. Mag., t. 4881)

An evergreen shrub a few feet high; shoots erect, four-angled, very pithy, glabrous. Leaves opposite, glabrous, ovate, 1¼ to 5 ins. long, about half as wide, shallowly toothed, rounded or shallowly heart-shaped at the base, tapered to the bluntish apex; stalk ¾ to 2 ins. long, deeply channelled. Flowers nodding, borne on terminal erect panicles 6 ins. to 1½ ft. tall, loosely pyramidal, up to 6 ins. wide at the base. Corolla tubular, 1 to 1¼ ins. long, ½ in. wide at the five-lobed mouth, scarlet, yellowish in the throat. Stamens four, attached beneath the mouth of the corolla.

Native of S. Africa, introduced about 1850. The finest specimen I have seen was in the late Mr Osgood Mackensie's garden at Inverewe, Rosshire, which in 1906 was a bush about 7 ft. high. This region has, of course, a very mild climate. At Kew it has lived on a south wall for several years, but is not luxuriant, and is not worth struggling with in the open ground. For the milder parts like Hampshire and Sussex it is admirable. The shade of red in the flowers varies considerably in depth. Easily increased by cuttings.

P. ÆQUALIS, *Harvey*, is the only other species known and is not often seen in cultivation. Lady Byng of Vimy obtained an Award of Merit for it at Vincent Square, 15th September, 1936. It is a sub-shrub, woody below, more or less herbaceous above, 2 to 3 ft. high, shoots quadrangular. Leaves opposite, stiff in texture, 1 to 4 ins. long, about one-third as wide, ovate to lanceolate, bluntly toothed. Flowers quite pendulous on terminal panicles 6 to 9 ins. high; corolla slender, tubular, 1 to 1½ ins. long, scarlet to salmon-coloured. Native of S. Africa; flowers from August to October. The blossoms are shorter stalked and much more closely set on the panicles than in P. capensis. At Kew it was cut back to ground level in most winters. (*Gardeners' Chronicle*, 27th February 1843, fig. 43.)

PHYLLOCLADUS. TAXACEÆ

This curious genus of trees and shrubs is related to the yews, although they are very different in outward aspect. Of the species that are, or have been in cultivation, one is native of Tasmania and three of New Zealand. Two tropical species grow in Borneo and the Philippine Islands. They are evergreen and are chiefly remarkable because the branchlets are flattened out to resemble leaves and perform the functions of leaves, after the fashion of several acacias and the butcher's broom. They are known as "cladodes" (see *Ruscus*). The true leaves are small and linear or scale-like—scarcely noticeable except on young seedling plants. Flowers unisexual; both sexes occurring on one tree in some species, on separate trees in others.

The four species here described succeed in open loamy soil but need a copious rainfall and warmer conditions than our average climate affords. Propagation can be done by cuttings put in gentle heat in summer, but plants raised from imported seeds are preferable.

P. ALPINUS, *Hooker fil.* CELERY PINE

An evergreen shrub or small tree from 8 to 25 ft. high, but in exposed Alpine localities, according to Cheeseman, often reduced to a bush 3 to 6 ft. high. The "leaves" (cladodes) are usually very crowded and vary much in shape and size. On scrubby bushes growing on the mountains at 5000 ft. elevation the "leaves" are small and narrow, ½ to ¾ in. long and ⅛ to ¼ in. wide. But at lower elevations and growing under more favourable circumstances they are as much as 1½ ins. long and ¾ in. wide, ovate to rhomboid in shape, sometimes pinnately lobed, often merely irregularly toothed. Nuts produced a few together, each nut about the size of a radish seed, the apex exposed.

Native of the North and South Islands of New Zealand, most abundant at elevations of 1500 to over 5000 ft. It differs from the other two New Zealand species (glaucus and trichomanoides) in the irregularly disposed branchlets and "leaves," those two species having them pinnately arranged. It is more closely related to the Tasmanian P. rhomboidalis. Although the hardiest of all this genus and no doubt hardy in many parts, I do not remember to have seen it anywhere but in the Rectory garden at Ludgvan, near Penzance. Its rather congested growth and crowded cladodes make it the least elegant and effective of its genus.

P. GLAUCUS, *Carrière.* TOATOA

An evergreen tree 20 to 30 ft., sometimes more, high, of slender tapering habit, even somewhat fastigiate; branchlets stout, whorled. "Leaves" (cladodes) arranged on branchlets 4 to 10 ins. long in two opposite rows, very leathery, diamond-shaped to roundish ovate, the lower part entire and tapered to a short stalk, the upper part with often three to five shallow lobes on each side; 1 to 2¼ ins. long, ⅝ to 1¼ ins. wide; glaucous when young, becoming dark dull green. Male flowers in cylindrical spikes ¾ to 1 in. long, produced at the tips of the branchlets. Nuts about the size of radish seeds, ten to twenty of them stuck on one egg-shaped receptacle about ½ in. long, the nuts half exposed; these take the place of cladodes towards the base of a branchlet.

Native of New Zealand on the North Island up to 3000 ft. above sea level. Although most closely akin to P. trichomanoides, especially in the thick whorled branches and frond-like arrangement of the "leaves," this is very distinct. It has the largest "leaves" of any of these cultivated phyllocladuses and they are glaucous when young. As this tree is confined to the North Island, it is likely to be more tender than the other New Zealand species; still it should be hardy in the south-west. It has long been cultivated in the Temperate House at Kew and as far back as 1881 bore fruit there. It is described as a very elegant tree in its wild state, but is only one-third the height of its relative, P. trichomanoides.

P. RHOMBOIDALIS, *L. C. Richard.* ADVENTURE BAY PINE

(P. asplenifolius, *Hooker fil.*)

An evergreen tree up to 60 ft. high at low elevations but dwarfed and bushy at high altitudes; trunk usually slender; all the parts glabrous. "Leaves" (cladodes) irregularly arranged on the branchlets and resembling in this respect those of P. alpinus, but differing from the pinnately arranged ones of P. trichomanoides and P. glaucus; nor are the branchlets strictly whorled as in these two species although often clustered. The "leaves" have the usual rhomboid or diamond shape seen in this genus, being wedge-shaped and entire at the base, the upper part also tapering to the apex but always toothed and often lobed as well—sometimes deeply so; they vary from $\frac{3}{4}$ to $2\frac{3}{4}$ ins. in length and from $\frac{1}{3}$ to 1 in. in width, dark dull green.

Native of Tasmania where it is described as being a "beautiful tree, growing to a great height but not attaining any great size of trunk; found in rich, humid situations, and abundant on the Hampshire and Surrey hills." It has long been cultivated in England. The finest tree I have seen was in the pinetum at Bicton in S. Devon, a shapely, slender pyramid 32 ft. high. It was probably the most admirable example of phyllocladus ever seen in the British Isles, but during a recent visit to Bicton I learnt with great regret that it had suddenly died. This species is most nearly allied to the New Zealand P. alpinus, especially in the irregularly arranged, not pinnate, branchlets, but is a finer, free-growing tree with larger foliage.

P. TRICHOMANOIDES, *D. Don*

An evergreen tree of graceful habit from 50 to 70 ft. high in a wild state, with a trunk 3 to 9 ft. in girth; devoid of down; branchlets in whorls. "Leaves" (cladodes) arranged in opposite rows on short branchlets only 2 to 4 ins. long so as to resemble a pinnate leaf or certain fern fronds. Each "leaf" is $\frac{1}{4}$ to 1 in. long, not so much wide, obovate to diamond-shaped, the lower half entire, the upper half cut into several shallow lobes, dark dull green. Flowers of both sexes on the same plant, the males in cylindrical clusters $\frac{1}{3}$ to $\frac{1}{2}$ in. long at the tips of the branchlets, the females at the margins of small modified cladodes and usually solitary. Nut (seed) solitary and seated in a cup-shaped receptacle.

Native of New Zealand on the North and South Islands ascending from sea level to 2500 ft. The wood is white, close-grained, and is much valued in New Zealand for building purposes. The Maoris obtain a red dye from the bark. It is hardy in Cornwall, the south of Ireland, and in similar places. It is easily recognised from the other species except P. glaucus by the whorled arrangement of the branches combined with a pinnate arrangement of the cladodes; from P. glaucus it is well distinguished by the much smaller average size of the cladodes which have a reddish-brown tinge when quite young.

PHYLLODOCE. ERICACEÆ

A small group of some six or seven species of dwarf evergreen shrubs, similar in habit to the heaths, but with stouter stems and larger leaves. Leaves alternate, linear. Flowers bell-shaped or pitcher-shaped, slender-stalked, produced in terminal racemes, umbel-like clusters, or even solitary. Corolla and calyx five-parted; stamens usually ten; seed-vessel a dry, subglobose, five-celled capsule, carrying numerous small seeds.

The genus has by some botanists been united with BRYANTHUS, but the general practice now is to keep them apart and to confine Bryanthus to one species, B. GMELINI, *Don*, on which the genus was originally founded. It has four-parted flowers, and a deeply divided corolla, and is a dwarf, moss-like shrub from Kamtschatka, etc.; not, so far as I am aware, in cultivation at present.

With the exception of P. empetriformis, these little shrubs require rather special care in the south of England. They inhabit cool, moist altitudes and latitudes, and dislike dryness in the air or at the root. A cool, moist nook on the lower levels of the rock garden, where the soil is peaty, is as good a place as any. Propagation is effected in the same way as recommended for Erica.

P. ALEUTICA, *A. A. Heller*

(Menziesia aleutica, *Sprengel*; Bryanthus aleuticus, *Gray*; Phyllodoce Pallasiana, *D. Don*)

A dwarf evergreen shrub 5 to 9 ins. high, the young shoots entirely hidden by the leaves. Leaves linear, tapered at the base, bluntish at the apex, finely toothed; $\frac{3}{8}$ in. long, $\frac{1}{16}$ in. wide; bright green above, yellowish-green beneath with a white line down the centre; very shortly stalked. Flowers nodding, each on a downy glandular stalk $\frac{1}{2}$ to $1\frac{1}{2}$ ins. long, several of them produced in May near the top of the shoot. Corolla yellowish-white, corrugated, pitcher-shaped, $\frac{1}{4}$ in. wide, contracted at the top to an orifice $\frac{1}{16}$ in. wide; stamens enclosed in the corolla, their stalks white, glabrous; anthers pink; ovary globose, glandular; style glabrous. Sepals five, lanceolate, pointed, $\frac{1}{8}$ in. long, pale at the margins, very hairy where they join the stalk.

Native of Japan, Alaska, Kamtschatka; described as a Menziesia as long ago as 1825 but always very rare in cultivation. Mr Reuthe re-introduced it to his nursery at Keston a few years ago. It is allied to P. cærulea, which has blue-purple flowers and to P. glanduliflora (*q.v.*). Suitable for a cool damp spot in the rock garden and a pretty plant, although scarcely equal in beauty to Breweri, cœrulea, or empetriformis. Mr Marchant had a plant in his nursery near Wimborne, Dorset, $2\frac{1}{2}$ ft. wide, when only five years old.

P. BREWERI, *A. A. Heller*

(Bot. Mag., t. 8146; Bryanthus Breweri, *A. Gray*)

A dwarf evergreen shrub, 6 to 12 ins. high, of tufted habit; young shoots erect, very leafy. Leaves almost stalkless, linear, blunt; $\frac{1}{2}$ to $\frac{3}{4}$ in. long (shorter immediately beneath the raceme), $\frac{1}{16}$ to $\frac{1}{12}$ in. wide; the margins decurved; dark glossy green. Flowers produced during May in a terminal raceme 2 to 4 ins. long, each flower on a slender, glandular stalk about $\frac{1}{2}$ in. long, from the axil of a short, leaflike bract. Corolla bright purplish rose, $\frac{1}{2}$ in. diameter, saucer-shaped, the five lobes ovate and rounded at the apex; stamens protruded. Calyx half as wide as the corolla, with five ovate, pointed, ciliate, but otherwise glabrous lobes. Seed-vessel globose, $\frac{1}{6}$ in. in diameter.

Native of California, and found on the Sierra Nevada at 9000 to 10,000 ft. altitude; first discovered by Mr W. H. Brewer about 1862. In some places it is said to cover extensive areas. It is a charming rock garden plant, delighting in a moist, peaty soil and a cool spot. The racemes vary considerably in length and in the density of the blossoms. The expanded corolla, elongated raceme, and protruded stamens distinguish it from the other three cultivated species, and bring it nearer than any to the true Bryanthus.

P. CÆRULEA, *Babington*

(Andromeda cærulea, *Linnæus*; Bryanthus taxifolius, *A. Gray*)

A dwarf, much-branched evergreen shrub about 6 ins. to 9 ins. high, of tufted habit. Leaves linear, blunt, much crowded; $\frac{1}{4}$ to $\frac{1}{2}$ in. long, $\frac{1}{16}$ in or less wide; not recurved at the margins, but minutely toothed there; dark glossy green. Flowers produced in June and July singly on a slender, glandular stalk up to 1½ ins. long, or in an umbel of three or four flowers. Corolla bluish purple, pitcher-shaped, nodding, five-toothed, $\frac{1}{3}$ in. long. Calyx with five lance-shaped, downy lobes; stamens ten, and, like the style, included within the corolla.

Native of high alpine summits and high latitudes in Europe, Asia, and N. America. It is found in Perthshire. Under cultivation it succeeds better in the north of England and in Scotland than in the south, where the summers are too dry and hot for it, and cause its foliage to drop prematurely. It is, consequently, uncommon. In the Botanic Garden of Edinburgh and in nurseries about that city it thrives very well. It should be planted in peat and sphagnum moss mixed, and have a surfacing of the latter also. One of the most interesting of British plants, and distinct in this genus because of its colour.

P. EMPETRIFORMIS, *Don*

(Bryanthus empetriformis, *A. Gray*; Menziesia empetriformis, *Smith*; Bot. Mag., t. 3176)

A low evergreen shrub, 6 to 9 ins high, of tufted habit, densely furnished with leaves. Leaves $\frac{1}{4}$ to $\frac{5}{8}$ in. long, $\frac{1}{16}$ to $\frac{1}{12}$ in. wide; linear, rounded at

PHYLLODOCE EMPETRIFORMIS

the tip, very shortly stalked, minutely toothed on the margin, dark glossy green. Flowers solitary, on slender, glandular-hairy stalks $\frac{1}{2}$ to $\frac{3}{4}$ in. long, produced during April from the leaf-axils near the end of the twigs. Corolla pitcher-shaped, bright reddish purple, $\frac{1}{4}$ in. long, scarcely so wide; with five rounded teeth at the orifice. Calyx-lobes five, ovate, $\frac{1}{8}$ in. long, glabrous; style exposed.

Native of western N. America; introduced in 1810. It is the most valuable of the members of this genus, being quite hardy and thriving in any position suitable for heaths. A group of plants well in bloom makes one of the daintiest of spring pictures. It is, of course, quite distinct from its neighbour, the racemed P. Breweri; and from P. cærulea and P. nipponica it differs in the colour of the corolla and the glabrous calyx.

P. GLANDULIFLORA, *Coville*

(Menziesia glanduliflora, *Hooker*; Bryanthus gland., *Gray*)

An evergreen shrub 4 to 8 ins. high (sometimes 12 ins.) with erect branchlets. Leaves numerous, covering the twig, linear, rounded at the end; $\frac{1}{4}$ to $\frac{1}{2}$ in. long, $\frac{1}{20}$ in. wide; minutely toothed, dark green with a white line beneath. Flowers produced several together in a cluster at the end of the shoot in April and May, each flower on a stalk $\frac{1}{2}$ to 1 in. long thickly furnished with glandular hairs, as are also the calyx and (to a lesser degree) the corolla. Corolla yellowish, pitcher-shaped, scarcely $\frac{1}{4}$ in. long, downy outside, narrowed at the top to a small orifice where are five tiny, glabrous, reflexed lobes. Stamens with downy stalks and purple anthers. Ovary downy; style longer than the stamens, glabrous. Sepals lanceolate, pointed, $\frac{1}{6}$ in. long, very glandular.

Native of western N. America, from Oregon to Alaska and on the Rocky Mountains, often just below the perpetual snow line. This species is rare in cultivation but used to be grown by Mr Murray Hornibrook at Knapton, Queen's Co., Ireland, who obtained it from Vancouver Island in 1912. Of the group of phyllodoces with the corolla contracted to a narrow orifice at the top (as distinct from those with an open bell-mouthed corolla) this is distinguished by its downy stamens and very glandular flower-stalks, sepals, and corolla. It is perhaps most closely akin to P. aleutica, but that has glabrous stamens—and corolla.

P. INTERMEDIA, *Rydberg*, is a hybrid between P. glanduliflora and P. empetriformis, two species which grow together in a wild state in British Columbia. Its flowers are pink, and they have the pointed sepals of P. glanduliflora. It has recently been introduced to this country.

P. NIPPONICA, *Makino*

(P. amabilis, *Stapf*; Bot. Mag., t. 8405)

An evergreen shrub about 4 to 8 ins. high, forming compact tufts of erect, stiff branches; young stems minutely downy, with erect, gland-tipped bristles interspersed. Leaves closely set on the branches (about twenty to the inch), linear, toothed, rounded at the end; $\frac{1}{4}$ to $\frac{3}{8}$ in. long, $\frac{1}{16}$ in. or less wide; glabrous and glossy dark green above, midrib white beneath with minute down. Flowers on slender, erect, glandular-downy stalks $\frac{1}{2}$ to 1 in. long, which are produced singly in from three to seven of the terminal leaf-axils in early May. Corolla open bell-shaped, about $\frac{1}{4}$ in. long, rather more wide, with shallow, rounded lobes; white tinged with pink on the lobes; sepals about $\frac{1}{12}$ in. long, pointed, ciliate. Stamens and style enclosed within the corolla. Seed-vessel globose, depressed at the top where it is roughened with short, hardened glandular hairs.

This delightful little shrub, one of the daintiest of the heath family, is a native of Japan. It flowered at Kew in 1911, but owing to some misplacement of labels its history was lost, and it was described as a new species by Dr Stapf.

PHYLLODOCE NIPPONICA

PHYLLOSTACHYS. GRAMINEÆ

For a general discussion of the bamboos belonging to this genus, see ARUNDINARIA. The distinctive characters of Phyllostachys are in the stems, which are always more or less zigzag and flattened on each side alternately above the joint; and in the two or three branches only at each joint, those at the base of the stem developing first. The dwarf P. ruscifolia may eventually prove to belong to a different genus.

P. AUREA, *Rivière*

(Bambusa aurea, *Hort.*)

Stems pale yellowish green, 10 to 15 ft. high in this country, stiffly erect, growing in tufts and spreading slowly, the joints often 5 or 6 ins. apart, except at the base, where they are crowded. Beneath each joint there is a curious swollen band, about $\frac{1}{4}$ in. wide, which distinguishes this from all other hardy bamboos. Leaves 2 to $4\frac{1}{2}$ ins. long, $\frac{1}{3}$ to $\frac{7}{8}$ in. wide, broadly tapered at the base, slenderly pointed, dark green above, glaucous beneath, glabrous on both surfaces, minutely toothed on the margins; secondary nerves four or five each side the midrib; stalk $\frac{1}{6}$ in. or less long; the leaf-sheath surmounted by two tufts of bristles at the summit.

Native of Japan, cultivated in Europe since the "seventies" of last century.

It flowered at Bitton in 1876 and again in various parts of the British Isles and overseas in 1904-5, 1919-21, and 1935-37, giving it a life cycle of about fifteen years. It is a pleasing bamboo if planted in a goodly sized mass, although not so graceful as the majority. It is only likely to be confused with P. mitis, which is, however, a taller bamboo without the crowded joints at the base of the stem, and without the swollen band beneath the joint, which is so distinctive a character in P. aurea.

P. Castillonis, *Mitford*. Kimmei-chiku

(P. bambusoides Castillonis, *Makino*)

Stems 8 to 10 ft. high (more no doubt in warmer climates), very hollow; bright yellow except on the flattened portion which extends from joint to joint either side alternately, and that is dark green. Leaves 2 to 5 ins. long as a rule, and ⅓ to ¾ in. wide; usually but not uniformly striped with creamy yellow lines; sometimes they are more yellow than green, sometimes wholly green; glaucous beneath; midrib and leaf-stalk downy; secondary veins four to eight each side the midrib; leaf-sheath furnished at the top with conspicuous bristles, sometimes nearly ½ in. long. Occasionally the leaves are much larger; I have seen them 8 or 9 ins. long, and 1½ ins. wide.

Native of Japan; introduced about 1890. This is the most beautifully coloured in its stems of all hardy bamboos. The curious alternation of green and yellow, together with the often variegated leaves, make it very distinct. It flowered in 1903 and 1904, and, according to the late Dr Stapf, there is nothing in its floral characters to distinguish it from P. nigra. In vegetative characters, however, it is near to P. Quilioi. Many plants died after flowering, and it is now uncommon.

P. flexuosa, *Rivière*

(Bambusa flexuosa, *Carrière*)

A bamboo of elegant but compact, rounded habit, and as far as I have seen, rarely exceeding 6 or 8 ft. in height, but up to 20 ft. on the French Riviera; stems at first bright green, becoming darker with age, sometimes almost black like those of P. nigra. Leaves 2 to 4 ins. long, ⅓ to ⅝ in. wide; dark green and glabrous above, glaucous beneath and downy at the base of the midrib, secondary nerves four to six each side the midrib; one margin toothed.

Native of China; introduced to France in 1864. In the characters of leaf and stem this bamboo bears much resemblance to P. viridi-glaucescens, but it is much dwarfer and more compact, and the change of the old culms to black does not, so far as I have observed, occur in that species. The stem sheaths also differ, as pointed out under P. viridi-glaucescens. P. flexuosa is a pleasing bamboo of the middle size, graceful and very hardy.

P. Henonis, *Mitford*

(Bambusa Henonis, *Hort.*, P. nigra Henonis, *Rendle*. Ha-chikw of the Japanese)

A very graceful and luxuriant bamboo, reaching in favourable situations 14 ft. in height, laden when in good health and well-established with heavy plumose masses of foliage, which make the outer stems arch outward; stems bright green at first, very hollow. Leaves rather uniform in size, and from 2 to 3½ ins. long and ⅓ to ⅝ in. wide, tapering at the base to a well-developed stalk $\frac{1}{8}$ in. long, slender-pointed; dark lustrous green above, glaucous and downy at the base of the midrib beneath; secondary veins four to seven.

Native of Japan; introduced about 1890. In the richness of its verdure combined with a remarkable elegance of form this bamboo is probably the loveliest of all its kind. From about 1894 to 1900 it made perhaps the most delightful feature of many gardens from October to January. In 1900 it commenced to flower all over the country, and by 1905 nearly every specimen was either dead or very severely crippled. A proportion of them recovered, and from these, as well as from plants imported afresh from Japan, it is now getting re-established in gardens. It has a long life cycle. In its floral characters P. Henonis differs but little from P. nigra. According to a Japanese botanist it is the same as Banbusa puberula, *Miquel*.

The bamboo known as P. BORYANA, *Mitford* (Bambusa Boryana, *Marliac*), which flowered in this country in 1905, is a near ally of P. Henonis, and of about equal beauty. Very few plants of it now exist.

P. FULVA, *Mitford*, appears also to belong to P. Henonis, differing chiefly in the yellow colour of the stems which is developed the second year.

P. MITIS, *Rivière*

(Bambusa mitis, *Hort.* Môsô-chiku of the Japanese)

Stems reaching sometimes nearly 20 ft. high in this country and bent somewhat stiffly, $1\frac{1}{2}$ ins. in diameter, deep yellow when mature. Leaves 2 to 5 ins. long, $\frac{1}{4}$ to $\frac{3}{4}$ in. wide, tapering or rounded at the base, slender-pointed, dark green above, glaucous beneath, glabrous except at the base of the midrib beneath, and toothed—especially on one margin; stalk $\frac{1}{8}$ in. or less long; leaf-sheath with a tuft of bristles at each side near the top; secondary nerves three to six each side the midrib.

Native of Japan; introduced about 1890. In foliage it resembles P. aurea, under which the distinctions are pointed out. It requires a sheltered spot and abundant sunshine to develop its best qualities, and does not recover from injury by cold so rapidly as P. aurea. The stems are never truly erect, but are bowed, with usually also an inclination to twist. The stems when young grow with great rapidity, sometimes nearly 1 foot in twenty-four hours in this country—more in hotter ones. They are the stoutest among our hardy bamboos. In Japan the young shoots are cooked and eaten; according to Lord Redesdale they are flavourless, but have a crisp and pleasant consistency.

The curious so-called "Tortoise-shell" bamboo—P. HETEROCYCLA, *Carrière*—is considered to be a variety of P. mitis. It is distinguished by the joints of the stems near the base not circling them in the ordinary way, but taking diagonal directions, the normal space between the joints being suppressed at each side alternately. Thus the scars join at opposite sides alternately for 1 or 2 ft. up the stem, when it assumes its normal form and the scars become horizontal rings. The plant is not well adapted for this country, and I have never seen a single characteristic stem produced here. The popular name—of Japanese origin—refers to the humped appearance of the space between the joints. This distortion is a freak of nature, and is not, as was once believed, due to the handiwork of Japanese gardeners. Introduced from Japan to France about 1877, and to England in 1893.

P. SULPHUREA, *Rivière*, has yellow stems scarcely so robust as typical P. mitis, but otherwise almost identical. In my experience it is more tender than P. mitis, but that is based on the behaviour of two plants only, and differs from the opinion of it held by others. At Trebah, Cornwall, there is a plant which, in June 1942, was 38 ft. high.

P. NIGRA, *Munro*. BLACK-STEMMED BAMBOO

(Bot. Mag., t. 7994; Bambusa nigra, *Hort.*)

Stems varying from 10 to 20 ft. high in different parts of the country, and from ½ to 1¼ ins. in diameter, very hollow; at first green, they become with age quite black; the branchlets usually mottled. Leaves in plume-like masses; usually 2 to 3½ ins. long, ¼ to ⅝ in. wide (sometimes larger); of thin texture, dark green above, rather glaucous beneath, glabrous on both surfaces, the margins roughened with minute teeth; secondary veins three to six each side the midrib. When quite young there is a slight downiness at the base of the midrib beneath. The leaf-sheath is terminated by a few erect bristles.

Native of China and Japan, and one of the most elegant of bamboos; very distinct because of its black sems. It is a quite hardy species when once established, although it grows much larger in hotter climates. It flowered in many parts of the world including Britain between 1931 and 1935 and has probably a very long life cycle. It is the oldest of Phyllostachys in English gardens and, according to Loudon, was 7 ft. high in the Horticultural Society's gardens in 1837.

Var. PUNCTATA.—A more robust form than the type, differing in the stems not becoming wholly black, but mottled. It flowered over Europe between 1900 and 1908, and many plants died in consequence.

P. QUILIOI, *Rivière*. MADAKE OF THE JAPANESE

(Bambusa Quilioi, *Carrière;* P. bambusoides, *Siebold*).

Stems 10 to 18 ft. high in this country, ¾ to 1¼ ins. thick at the base, deep green. Branches long; stem sheaths pinkish when young, conspicuously mottled with deep purple. Leaves among the largest in the hardy Phyllostachys group, varying from 2½ to 6 ins. long, ½ to 1¼ ins. wide (occasionally they are even larger); bright green above, glaucous beneath; glabrous except for some down at the base of the midrib beneath; one margin toothed; secondary veins five to seven each side the midrib; leaf-sheath with a conspicuous tuft of bristles at the top, ¼ to ½ in. long.

Native of Japan; introduced to France by Admiral Du Quilio in 1866. It is one of the finest of hardy bamboos, very hardy and free-growing. P. viridi-glaucescens is the only species with which, in the adult state, it is likely to be confused, and from that species it is distinguished by the mottled leaf-sheaths (in P. viridi-glaucescens they are simply striated or tinged with purple), by the larger leaves and longer branches.

Var. MARLIACEA (P. Marliacea, *Mitford*). Marliac's Bamboo.—A form of P. Quilioi, distinguished by the curious wrinkling of the stems especially towards the base. It does not appear to be so vigorous as P. Quilioi, and behaves more like P. mitis in regard to hardiness.

P. RUSCIFOLIA, *Nicholson*

(Shibatæa kumasasa, *Nakai*; Bambusa kumasasa, *Zoll*)

Stems erect, 1 to 2 ft. high but very zigzagged, very much flattened between the joints, ⅛ in. diameter, the central hollow only large enough to admit a horse hair; joints 1 to 3½ ins. apart. Branches three or four at each joint, 1 to 2½ ins. long, bearing one to three leaves. Leaves narrowly obovate, broadly tapered at the base, slenderly at the apex, 3 to 4 ins. long, ¾ to 1 in.

wide; glossy dark green and glabrous above, slightly glaucous and downy beneath, both margins toothed; secondary veins five to seven each side the midrib.

Native of Japan; cultivated by Messrs Veitch at Coombe Wood in the seventies of last century as "Bambusa viminalis" and probably introduced by John Gould Veitch during the previous decade. It is a pretty bamboo, suitable for a damp spot in the rock garden, being of neat, tufted habit. It is one of the most distinct of hardy bamboos, especially in its sturdy, zigzag stems, the great proportionate width of the leaves, their length of stalk and the uniformly short branches. The Japanese botanists separate it from Phyllostachys.

P. VIRIDI-GLAUCESCENS, *Rivière*

(Gardeners' Chronicle, 1894, i., fig. 53; Bambusa viridi-glaucescens, *Carrière*)

Stems 14 to 18 ft. long, about $\frac{3}{4}$ in. diameter, very hollow, yellowish green, except at the joints, which are purplish; the outer stems of vigorous plants growing in the open arch outwards and downwards to the ground. Stem-sheaths striped with close lines of purple and suffused with purple when young. Leaves 2 to 5 ins. long, $\frac{1}{3}$ to $\frac{7}{8}$ in. wide; abruptly tapered at the base, slender-pointed, bright green above, glaucous beneath, downy only at the base of the midrib beneath; toothed on one margin; secondary veins four to seven each side the midrib; leaf-sheath purplish, with two clusters of bristles at the top.

Native of China; introduced to France about 1846, and a very elegant, vigorous, and useful bamboo. It is liable to be confounded with P. Quilioi and with P. flexuosa, but the former is well distinguished by its mottled stem-sheaths, its stouter stems, and larger leaves, whilst P. flexuosa is altogether a smaller plant whose old stems are often almost black. There are also two little, fringed, ear-like projections at the top of the stem-sheath that are missing in P. flexuosa. P. virdi-glaucescens requires an isolated position, when it will in time form a graceful mass at least 25 ft. in diameter, with pendulous plumes of foliage. It spreads at the root with some freedom, and is easily propagated by offsets. It never appears to have flowered under cultivation.

P. VIOLASCENS, *Rivière*.—Allied to P. viridi-glaucescens, this is less hardy. It is very distinct in having the young stems of a deep violet, almost black, changing the second year to yellowish brown. The sheaths are also violet. Leaves from 2 to 7 ins long, by about one-fourth as wide; secondary veins three to eight; stalk purplish The best plant I have seen is at Shrublands, near Ipswich, about 12 ft. high; but frequently it is not a success, growing late, and having its summer growth cut back during the ensuing winter. Native of China or Japan.

PHYLLOTHAMNUS ERECTUS. *C. K. Schneider.*

ERICACEÆ

(Bryanthus erectus, *Lindley*; Phyllodoce erecta, *Drude*)

A dwarf evergreen bush, 6 to 10 ins. high, with numerous erect very leafy branches, minutely downy when young. Leaves alternate $\frac{1}{2}$ to $\frac{5}{8}$ in. long, linear, tapering towards each end, recurved slightly at the margins, finely toothed, deep glossy green, crowded on the branchlets Flowers solitary on slender, downy, glandular stalks $\frac{1}{2}$ to $\frac{3}{4}$ in. long produced in April in a cluster of four to ten at the end of each twig Corolla delicate rose, broadly funnel-shaped, $\frac{1}{2}$ in. across, with five triangular, pointed lobes. Calyx-lobes ovate, ⅛ in. long, glabrous; style protruded.

A hybrid raised about 1845 in the nursery of Messrs Cunningham & Fraser at Comely Bank, Edinburgh, between Rhodothamnus Chamæcistus and, so its raisers stated, Phyllodoce cærulea. The general belief is, however, that P. empetriformis was the other parent. It is a very pretty shrub, but requires considerable care to keep it in permanent health in the south, where the dry heats of July and August cause it to suffer. A cool, moist spot in the rock garden where the soil is peaty may be recommended for it. It is usually known in gardens as "Bryanthus," but being a bigeneric hybrid with neither of its parents a true Bryanthus, the name here adopted is to be preferred.

PICEA. SPRUCE. CONIFERÆ

A group of evergreen trees found in most of the cool temperate regions of the northern hemisphere, of pyramidal form, especially in a young state, with branches in tiers. Leaves linear or needle-like, mostly four-sided, arranged spirally on the shoots, but the undermost ones usually twisted at the base, so as to crowd them more on the upper side of the twig than on the lower. Each leaf is seated on a slight cushion which, if the leaf be gently pulled off downwards whilst fresh, it brings mostly away. When, however, the leaf falls naturally, or the twig is dried for herbarium purposes, it leaves at the base a peg-like stump. These leaf-stumps thickly studded on the shoot are extremely characteristic of the spruces, and well distinguish them from the firs (Abies). Flowers unisexual, both sexes produced on the same tree at or near the end of the twigs; the males solitary, stalked, composed of numerous anthers. Female cones nearly always pendulous, their scales persisting until they fall. Seeds winged.

There are two well-marked groups of Picea:—

1. PICEA proper.—Leaves quadrangular in section, with lines of stomata on all four sides.

2. OMORIKA group.—Leaves more flattened, with stomata usually on the dorsal surface only. By a twisting of the leaf-base this becomes usually the undermost or less exposed side. Of the species described in the following notes, those belonging to the Omorika group are:—*Breweriana*, *complanata*, *jezoensis var.*, *hondoensis*, *spinulosa*, *Omorika*, *sitchensis*.

The spruces have scarcely the garden value of the firs, but the following are handsome and effective: *Breweriana*, *jezoensis var.*, *hondoensis*, *Morinda*, *Omorika*, *orientalis*, *polita*, and *pungens*, and a well-grown isolated common spruce is scarcely inferior to any of them. Spruces are very frequently called "Abies" in British gardens, whilst the true silver-firs, or Abies, are called "Picea." This inversion of names seems to date from Loudon's time, but is nowhere in vogue except in this country. It is time the true designations were given to these genera, for they are easily distinguished:—

PICEA (Spruces).—Leaves as described above. Cones pendent, with the scales persistent on the central axis.

Abies (Silver-firs).—Leaves flatter, often notched at the apex, not falling away in drying, nor leaving the peg-like stumps of Picea; cones erect, with the scales falling away from the central axis. (See also under Abies.)

The spruces should always be raised from seeds; cuttings of some species take root, and grafting must be practised for forms coloured or abnormal in habit, but trees so raised are not so fine or long-lived as seedlings. They like abundant moisture at the root, most of them coming from regions with an abundant rainfall. If the rainfall be deficient it may be compensated for by planting in a deep moist soil. P. pungens is one of the best in a dry climate. Few conifers withstand town conditions worse than the spruces. Many of them produce a useful timber, especially P. excelsa in Europe. P. alba is cultivated in some of the northerly regions of Scandinavia too inclement for any other tree to live. Some of the species, P. excelsa in particular, are attacked by a gall-making insect (*Chermes*), the gall being a cone-like structure growing round the shoot. The best remedy is to spray with an emulsion of soft soap and paraffin in late March and April.

P. alba, *Link*. White Spruce

(P. canadensis, *Britton*; P. glauca, *Voss*)

A tree usually 60 to 100 ft. high; young specimens with much the habit of the common spruce, but of a greyer green; branchlets very pale brown, not downy; buds with ciliate scales. Leaves mostly on the upper side of the branches, evil-smelling when crushed; they are $\frac{1}{2}$ to $\frac{3}{4}$ in. long, pointed, but not prickly, four-angled, grey-green, with two to five lines of stomata on each face. Cones cylindrical, $1\frac{1}{2}$ to 2 ins. long, pale shining brown when mature; scales very thin and flexible, broad and rounded, nearly entire at the margins.

Native of N. America; introduced about the end of the seventeenth century. It is very widely spread in a wild state, reaching, according to Sargent, from Labrador to Alaska, extending southwards along the eastern side of the Rocky Mountains to Montana, and to New York, Michigan, etc. It reaches a higher latitude than any other evergreen tree, and nearly to the Arctic Sea, on ground which only thaws 3 or 4 ft. down in summer. It possesses little merit as an ornamental tree in Britain, especially in the south, but on the vast "Danish heaths and dunes of Jutland which are continually swept by the gales of the North Sea it has been extensively planted, especially as a shelter tree. It serves this purpose so well that no other known tree could take its place there" (Rafn). In the rank smell of its foliage it resembles P. Engelmannii, but that species has longer leaves and more tapered cone-scales, and it, as well as the more nearly allied P. nigra and P. rubens are further distinguished by their downy shoots.

Var. aurea has foliage of a yellowish tinge.

Var. cœrulea is more glaucous than the type. There are also dwarf forms such as compacta and echiniformis.

P. albertiana, *S. Brown*

Introduced by Mr H. J. Elwes in 1906, but little need be said of this spruce under cultivation. It is closely allied to, perhaps only a geographical form of, P. alba, differing in the slightly downy young shoots and resinous buds. It is a finer tree than P. alba, and is said to reach a stature of 160 ft. Native of western N. America.

Var. CONICA, *Bean* (P. glauca conica, *Rehder*).—This is a pygmy form and promises to be one of the most distinct and pleasing of dwarf spruces. It makes a slender cone-shaped bush, very closely and densely branched, resembling the old-fashioned candle extinguisher in shape. The young shoots are slightly downy, the leaves very slender, ¼ to ½ in. long, slenderly pointed, with one to three broken lines of stomata on each face.

This variety was found by Mr J. C. Jack near Laggan, Alberta, in 1904. He collected seedling plants of P. albertiana which he sent to the Arnold Arboretum and amongst them was one which proved to be this pigmy form. A plant was received at Kew in 1909 and in twenty years it got to be 6 ft. high and a perfect cone 3 ft. wide at the base. It can be increased by means of late summer cuttings.

P. ASPERATA, *Masters*

According to Wilson this spruce attains 100 ft. in height in Western China and closely resembles in general outline the common European spruce (P. excelsa) but is more glaucous in colour; young shoots pale, yellowish, changing to grey, and either glabrous or more or less downy. Leaves ½ to ¾ in. long, four-angled in cross section, stiff, pointed, with a few lines of stomata on all four surfaces; the uppermost ones of the twigs point forwards, those at the side and underneath standing out at right angles; the "pegs" or "cushions" left by the fallen leaves are very stiff, large and prominent. Cones cylindrical, up to 4 ins. long, 1¾ ins. wide, "fawn-grey when ripe, changing to chestnut-brown with age and retained on the tree six months after they mature" (Wilson); cone-scales variable in shape, obovate, rounded or truncate at the top.

Native of W. China; named from specimens collected by Wilson in 1903, but introduced to cultivation by seeds he sent home in 1910. He describes it as the common quadrangular-leaved spruce of N.W. Szechuen, old trees being very spire-like in appearance. Cultivated plants are growing more vigorously and succeeding better probably than any of the Chinese spruces. They vary a good deal in colour from grey-green to glaucous. The late Mr F. R. S. Balfour, who had two acres planted with this species at Dawyck in Peeblesshire, considered it the only Chinese spruce at present introduced likely to be of value in British forestry.

Var. NOTABILIS, *Rehder and Wilson*, differs in having the exposed part of the cone-scales broadly triangular and gradually or abruptly narrowed towards the tip.

Var. PONDEROSA, *Rehder and Wilson*.—Cones larger, 5 to 6 ins. long.

Dallimore and Jackson consider the following spruces closely related to, or identical with, P. asperata:—P. aurantiaca, *Masters*, P. gemmata, *Rehder and Wilson*, P. heterolepis, *Rehder and Wilson*, P. Meyeri, *Rehder and Wilson*, P. montigena, *Masters*, P. neo-Veitchii, *Masters*, and P. retroflexa, *Masters*. Of these P. montigena seems distinct in the often quite bristly shoots and the rhombic-ovate, truncate, or jagged cone-scales. But young plants are very puzzling and probably their identity will not be satisfactorily settled until they produce cones under cultivation.

P. BICOLOR, *Mayr*

(P. Alcockiana, *Carrière*)

A tree 80 ft. high in Japan; in cultivation a small pyramidal tree, with stiff branches; young shoots sparsely downy or glabrous, pale brown. Leaves very crowded, especially on the upper side of the shoots; ½ to ¾ in. long, blunt at the apex, quadrangular; glossy green, with usually two lines of stomata on the lower surfaces and four to seven lines on the upper ones. Cones 2 to 4 ins. long, 1 to 1½ ins. wide; tapered from the middle to the apex; scales slightly toothed on the margin.

Native of Japan, where it is a valuable timber tree; introduced by John Gould Veitch in 1861. At first, owing to a mixing of the seeds, it was much confused with P. jezoensis var. hondoensis—a more striking spruce with no stomata on the uppermost surfaces, and belonging to the Omorika or flat-leaved section. So far as I have seen, this spruce (named in honour of Sir Rutherford Alcock, British Minister at Yedo at the time of its introduction) has little to recommend it for British gardens generally.

P. BRACHYTYLA, *Pritzel*

(P. Sargentiana, *Rehder and Wilson*; P. pachyclada, *Patschke*)

A tree 40 to 80 ft. high, pyramidal when young but becoming widely conical or round-headed when grown in isolated positions; the main branches horizontal, the branchlets pendulous; young shoots either glabrous or downy, grey or yellowish. Leaves ½ to 1 in. long, $\frac{1}{20}$ to $\frac{1}{16}$ in. wide, with short rather spiny tips, bright green above, nearly covered with glaucous-white lines beneath. Cones 2½ to 5 ins. long, 1 to 1¾ ins. wide, tapering towards both ends but more abruptly towards the base; cone-scales dull brown, ¾ in. long, ⅝ in. wide at their largest, obovate, overlapping, the exposed part broadly rounded or tapering to a broadly triangular wavy apex.

Native of Central and W. China; discovered by the Abbé Delavay in 1889, introduced by Wilson in 1901. It is a variable species, as may be judged by the synonyms cited above, and it is now generally regarded as including the whole of the flat-leaved spruces of W. China. These, which constitute the Omorika section, are distinguished by the flatter leaves having as a rule no stomata on the upper surface. P. complanata, *Masters*, is still regarded as a species by some authorities, as are also P. ascendens and P. Sargentiana. But Dr Stapf came to the conclusion (Bot. Mag., *loc. cit. supra*), that there is no constant combination of characters that can be relied on to discriminate them. He distinguishes two forms by the shape of the cone-scales, viz., LATISQUAMEA, in which the exposed part is flatly rounded, and RHOMBISQUAMEA, in which it is triangular (P. ascendens belongs to the latter). P. brachytyla succeeds well under cultivation.

Var. COMPLANATA, *Cheng* (P. complanata, *Masters*).—A native of W. Szechuen, China, discovered and introduced by Wilson in 1903. Young shoots pale grey, usually glabrous. Leaves arranged mostly on and above the horizontal plane, a few standing out beneath, those on the top somewhat appressed to the branch and pointing forward; they are needle-like, ½ to 1⅛ ins. long, sharply bevelled off at the apex to a fine point; dark green on the exposed surface, blue-white with stomatic lines beneath. Cones 4 to 5 ins. long, 1¼ ins. wide; tapered towards the top and bottom; scales slightly jagged. (*Botanical Magazine*, t. 8969—as P. brachytyla.)

P. BREWERIANA, *S. Watson*. BREWER'S WEEPING SPRUCE

(Bot. Mag., t. 9543)

A tree up to 120 ft. high in a wild state, the trunk 2 to 3 ft. in diameter, the branches ultimately pendulous, with the final ramifications slender, whip-like, and often 7 to 8 or even 12 ft. long, but no thicker than a lead pencil, and hanging perpendicularly; pyramidal and stiffly branched when young.

Leaves pointing forwards, and arranged about equally all round the shoot, $\frac{1}{2}$ to 1 in. long, $\frac{1}{20}$ to $\frac{1}{12}$ in. wide, blunt at the apex, somewhat tapered at the base; one side dark glossy green without stomata, the other grey with stomatic lines. Cones cylindrical-oval, about 3 ins. long, purple, the scales rounded and entire at the margins.

Native of the Siskiyou Mountains of California and Oregon, where it occurs in comparatively small numbers in a few places at about 7000 ft. altitude; discovered by Mr W. H. Brewer, the Californian botanist. A single plant was sent by Prof. Sargent in 1897 to Kew, where it thrives very well but grows slowly in height. It first bore cones in 1920. It has an irregular mode of branching quite different from the flat, whorled arrangement seen in the branching of most spruces. The leaves are much more slender than in adult specimens. A very distinct and attractive spruce. A stock of seeds was imported in 1911.

P. ENGELMANNI, *Engelmann* (Plate 35)

A tree 80 to 100, occasionally 150 ft. high, assuming as a young tree in cultivation a pyramidal form, with slightly ascending branches; young shoots pale yellowish-brown, clothed with stiff, erect down. Leaves with an unpleasant odour when rubbed, arranged all round the twig, but thinly beneath; they are $\frac{3}{4}$ to $1\frac{1}{8}$ ins. long, quadrangular, bluntish at the tips, flexible, dull, slightly glaucous-green, with three or four lines of stomata on all four surfaces. Cones $1\frac{1}{2}$ to 3 ins. long, $\frac{3}{4}$ to 1 in. in diameter; tapered towards the top, pale shining brown when mature; scales with a truncate apex and jagged margins.

Native of the mountains of western N. America from Alberta and British Columbia (where it attains its greatest size), south to New Mexico and Arizona. This handsome spruce is very hardy, and thrives better in N. Continental Europe and New England, where the winters are severe, than it does in places with a mild winter and late spring frosts. It is comparatively rare in gardens, the tree grown under the name being frequently the glaucous form of P. pungens. The two species, although so much confused, are really very distinct. P. Engelmanni is easily recognised by its downy shoots; its unpleasant smelling leaves, soft and flexible to the touch and not spine-tipped; also by its shorter cones.

Var. GLAUCA has leaves of a more pronounced glaucous hue.

P. EXCELSA, *Link*. COMMON SPRUCE

(Abies Picea, *Miller*; Pinus Abies, *Linnæus*)

A tree 100 to 120, sometimes 150 ft. high, of tapering, pyramidal form, densely clothed with branches and leaves; bark thin and scaling; branchlets pale brown, usually more or less downy, sometimes glabrous. Leaves mostly arranged in two sets in or near the horizontal plane; $\frac{1}{3}$ to $\frac{3}{4}$ in. long; very deep glossy green, quadrangular, with a few faintly defined lines of stomata on each face. Cones cylindrical, tapered at the top, usually about 5 ins. long and $1\frac{1}{2}$ to 2 ins. wide; light shining brown; scales bluntly triangular at the apex, the end jagged as if bitten off.

Native of most of the mountainous parts of Central and Northern Europe, but not of Britain, where, however, it has been cultivated for at least three hundred years. Although handsome as an isolated tree and imposing in its height, it is known rather as a forest tree with us than in the garden. The best timber comes from places where growth is slowest, like Norway. It is often called "Norway Spruce," and is imported in large quantities from that country as "white deal." In the dry Thames valley it is not often found thriving well. Of a great number of garden varieties the following is a selection of the most distinct :—

Var. ARGENTEO-SPICA.—Young shoots of a clear creamy white, approaching afterwards the normal colour; very striking and ornamental. Var. FINEDONENSIS is of the same character.

Var. CLANBRASSILIANA.—An interesting variety of low, dense, rounded habit, usually wider than high. A plant thirty years old will be under 3 ft. in height. According to the late Earl Annesley, "it was named after Lord Clanbrassil, who first discovered it in his beautiful demesne of Tullymore, Co. Down, now the seat of the Earl of Roden, and the original plant is still to be seen there." Other dwarf forms are DUMOSA; GREGORYANA, a dense rounded bush, with crowded branchlets making growths ¼ to 1 in. long annually, the leaves standing out all round the twig; PYGMÆA, very close and dwarf; PUMILA GLAUCA, somewhat similar, but glaucous; GLOBOSA NANA, similar to Clanbrassiliana in leaf and shoot, but less spreading; REMONTII, shoots erect-growing.

Var. CRANSTONI, var. DENUDATA, and var. MONSTROSA are remarkable forms, with long snake-like branches, almost without branchlets; leaves rigid, stiff, thicker and longer (about 1 in.) than in the type. Of no beauty, and only worth growing as grotesque curiosities.

Var. INVERTA has stiff pendulous branches hanging close to the stem—a curiosity merely. First discovered by Mr R. S. Carrington, of the firm of Richard Smith & Co., of Worcester, in a plantation not far from Kinlet House, in Shropshire, about 1858. Var. PENDULA is not so strikingly pendulous.

Var. EREMITA, var. GIGANTEA, and var. DICKSONI have large stout leaves, the habit stiff and rather open.

Var. STRICTA, of slender, spire-like form, the branches erect; very distinct and striking.

Var. VIRGATA has thin, slender branchlets with the leaves appressed to the twig.

P. GLEHNII, *Masters*

(Bot. Mag., t. 9020)

A tree up to 130 ft. high; young shoots reddish, downy between the "cushions" on which the leaves are seated. Leaves ¼ to ½ in. long, quadrangular, abruptly and sharply pointed, with four stomatic lines on the upper side and two on the underside. Cones 1½ to 2½ ins. long, dark or bluish when young changing to brown; scales broadly rounded at the exposed part and more or less erose or entire.

Native of Japan, introduced from Yezo by Maries about 1877. It grows well in the soft moist climate of Ireland, and is very good in the Headfort pinetum in Co. Meath, occasionally cut by late spring frosts but not greatly injured.

P. JEZOENSIS, *Carrière*. YEDDO SPRUCE

(P. ajanenis, *Fischer*)

A tree from 100 to 150 ft. high with scaly, peeling bark; young shoots yellowish, without down; buds shining, resinous, broadly conical-ovoid. Leaves flattened, confined to the upper side of the shoots, the lower ones spreading horizontally; they are ½ to 1 in. long, shortly pointed, dark green and without stomata above, the ventral surface blue-white, almost covered with stomatic lines. Cones cylindric, 2 to 3 ins. long, about 1 in. wide, crimson when young; scales narrowly oblong with jaggedly toothed margins.

Native of Amurland, Manchuria, Korea and N. Japan, introduced by J. G. Veitch in 1861. Owing to a mixing up of seeds it was originally distributed as "P. Alcockiana," under which name it was to be found in gardens many years afterwards.

Var. HONDOËNSIS, *Rehder*.—A smaller tree found only in Japan. The shoots are pale reddish-brown, leaves shorter and more curved, blunt.

Neither of these trees have a good reputation as cultivated in Britain, but a good many years ago I saw a fine tree at Ochtertyre in Perthshire about 50 ft. high growing under this name. (P. hondoënsis, *Mayr*; *Botanical Magazine*, t. 6743.)

P. KOYAMAI, *Shirasawa*. KOYAMA'S SPRUCE

(Gardeners' Chronicle, 14th Aug. 1915, fig. 36; P. koraiensis, *Nakai*)

A tree 40 to 60 ft. high in Japan, with a slender trunk 10 to 18 ins. in diameter; of densely branched, pyramidal habit, the bark peeling off in paper-like flakes; the stronger leading young shoots glabrous, the lateral ones more or less minutely bristly; buds conical, bright brown, resinous. Leaves $\frac{1}{4}$ to $\frac{5}{8}$ in. long, four-sided, the underneath ones pectinately arranged, with stomata on all four surfaces. Cones cylindrical (smaller ones ovoid-cylindrical), 2 to 4 ins. long, $1\frac{1}{4}$ to $1\frac{1}{2}$ ins. wide, pale green changing to shining pale brown; scales broad and rounded with slightly jagged margins.

First discovered in the Shinano province of Central Japan by Mr Koyama on Mt. Yatsugatake at elevations of 5000 to 6000 ft.; afterwards found in Korea, where Wilson collected it in 1917; introduced to the Arnold Arborteum in 1914 and thence to Kew the following year. It is succeeding quite well under cultivation in Britain. According to Wilson, who visited its Japanese habitat in company with its discoverer in 1914, this spruce is only known to exist there in a grove of about one hundred trees. He describes it as shapely and decidedly ornamental. A Japanese specimen in the Kew Herbarium has the buds embedded in resin and Wilson's Korean specimen has the same character, but as yet there is little evidence of it in our cultivated trees. The stomatiferous lines are but faintly defined on the leaves, which are dark green above and below.

P. LIKIANGENSIS, *Pritzel*. LIKIANG SPRUCE

A tree usually 50 to 65 ft., but in favourable situations 100 ft. high, with a trunk 10 ft. in girth. Young shoots brown, more or less (sometimes very) bristly, the pegs left by the fallen leaves prominent, spreading outwards and often bristly too. Leaves quadrangular, those on the upper side pointing forward, $\frac{1}{3}$ to $\frac{3}{4}$ in. long, pointed. Cones ovoid, 2 to $2\frac{1}{2}$ ins. long, $1\frac{1}{2}$ to $1\frac{3}{4}$ ins. wide; cone-scales flexible, the upper part ovate, rounded, wavy, spreading outwards after ripening.

Var. PURPUREA, *Dallimore and Jackson* (P. purpurea, *Masters*).—Leaves $\frac{1}{3}$ to $\frac{3}{5}$ in. long. Cones described by Wilson as "small violet-purple in the young state, with the cone-scales abruptly contracted above the middle or merely rhombic, truncate or erose." He refers to it also as a handsome and remarkable spruce, pyramidal when young, but having wide spreading, thick, horizontal branches when old.

Both these spruces are natives of W. Szechuen, China. P. likiangensis was found by the Abbé Delavay in 1884, but introduced to cultivation by Wilson in

1908. He introduced the var. purpurea two years later. They come from elevations up to 12,000 ft. and are quite hardy; both are succeeding well in the National Pinetum at Bedgebury.

P. Balfouriana, named by Rehder and Wilson in honour of the late Mr F. R. S. Balfour of Dawyck, Peeblesshire, has been united with P. likiangensis by Dallimore and Jackson As with the spruces clustered round P. asperata, we shall probably have to wait until the forms of P. likiangensis bear cones under cultivation to define conclusively their taxonomic position. Wilson describes P. Balfouriana as one of the tallest Chinese spruces, its short branches giving it a spire-like appearance.

P. Maximowiczii, *Regel*

An unimportant spruce collected on Mount Fujiyama, Japan, in 1864. There are only small trees in cultivation, the largest mentioned by Henry being at Handcross Park in Sussex, and 32 ft. high; it does not appear to be very tall in nature. The young shoots are quite glabrous, the winter buds covered with resinous scales. Leaves averaging scarcely ½ in. in length, pointed, four-sided, with two to five stomatic lines on each face, dark glossy green. Cones 1¾ to 2 ins. long, cylindrical, tapered at both ends; scales rounded, not toothed, reddish-brown before maturity.

P. Morinda, *Link.* West Himalayan Spruce

(P. Smithiana, *Boissier*)

A tree 100 to 120, sometimes 200 ft. high, with horizontal branches, but perfectly pendulous branchlets; young shoots stiff, pale grey, shining, not downy; buds conical, often resinous, up to ½ in. long. Leaves arranged all round the twigs (rather more thinly beneath), standing out at an angle of about 60°; they are quadrangular, rigid, needle-like, with prickly points, 1½ ins. long, often slightly curved, green with a few stomatic lines on each of the four faces. Cones cylindrical, tapered towards the apex, 4 to 7 ins. long, 1½ to 2 ins. wide, brown when mature; scales broadly rounded and entire at the margin.

Native of the western Himalaya; introduced to Scotland in 1818 by cones sent to Lord Hopetoun. The specific name "Smithiana" refers to the gardener at Hopetoun who first raised this tree. It is distinct from the other spruces in the great length of leaf, and is also one of the most striking from the weeping character of its branchlets, which, perhaps, give it a somewhat funereal aspect. It is subject to injury by spring frost especially in the young state, and will thrive best in a situation shaded from early morning sun. It likes a moist, loamy soil.

P. morrisonicola, *Hayata*

A slender lofty tree, sometimes quite 150 ft. high, but usually under 100 ft., with a trunk girthing from 10 to 20 ft., bark grey, coming away in round thin scales. Young shoots glabrous, pale brown. Leaves very slender, ¼ to ⅔ in. long, quadrangular but flattish. Cones cylindrical or ovoid-cylindrical, 1½ to 2½ ins. long, 1 to 1½ ins. wide, tapering at top and bottom; cone-scales roundish obovate with slightly uneven margins.

Native of Formosa; discovered on Mt. Morrison in 1900; introduced to cultivation in 1918 by Wilson, who found that it constituted pure forests in precipitous country up to 9000 to 10,000 ft. The leaves are dark green and the aspect of the tree "decidedly sombre." Mr Hayata considers it to be related to P. Glehnii, but that species is easily distinguished by its downy shoots. It seems to resemble P. Watsoniana (*see under* P. Wilsonii) in its pale, slender, glabrous twigs, and more especially in the very slender leaves. It is growing in the Bedgebury pinetum, but is not particularly happy there, probably requiring, like most Formosan trees and shrubs, a somewhat warmer climate.

P. NIGRA, *Link*. BLACK SPRUCE

(P. mariana, *Britton*)

A tree 20 to 30 ft. (occasionally twice or thrice as) high, of close, pyramidal habit as seen in cultivation, branches densely twiggy; young shoots abundantly furnished with reddish down; terminal buds with a few downy awl-shaped scales at the base. Leaves arranged all round the twig, but thinly beneath, $\frac{1}{4}$ to about $\frac{5}{8}$ in. long, slightly curved, quadrangular, with a bluntish, bevelled point; more or less glaucous in hue, with two to five lines of stomata on each surface. Cones egg-shaped, $\frac{3}{4}$ to $1\frac{1}{4}$ ins. long, brownish-purple when young; scales rounded or somewhat bluntly triangular at the apex, and slightly jagged at the margin.

Native of N. America, where it covers an immense tract from Labrador and Alaska in the north to Virginia and Wisconsin in the south; introduced to the Fulham garden about 1700 by Bishop Compton. This is not one of the most ornamental of spruces, but is still pleasing in its dense furnishing of leaves and its large crops of rich purple young cones. It is nearly allied to P. rubra, but differs in its blue-green foliage and in the long persistence of its cones upon the branches—twenty to thirty years, according to Sargent.

Var. ERICOIDES, *Hort.*, is a pigmy form of the black spruce, and is a rounded bush with very slender leaves never more than $\frac{1}{3}$ in. long, almost heathlike; young shoots thin, much branched, downy the first two or three years. It has been known in gardens for fifty years, and is probably of garden origin. It grows extremely slowly. Intermediate between this and nigra itself is P. nigra var. DOUMETTII, which has longer leaves and is of less bushy habit than var. ericoides.

P. OBOVATA, *Ledebour*. SIBERIAN SPRUCE

In its general appearance this species bears a considerable resemblance to the common spruce, having similar leaves and very downy young shoots. It is, however, distinct in the cones, which are smaller (about 3 ins. long) and have the scales rounded and entire at the apex (not jagged as in P. excelsa). It is widely spread in Siberia and north-east Russia, and in places reaches a stature of more than 100 ft., valuable in supplying timber and fuel in cold, inclement regions. It has little garden value, being less to be preferred than the common spruce.

P. OMORIKA, *Purkyne*. SERBIAN SPRUCE

(Bot. Mag., t. 9163)

A narrow, short-branched tree, described as occasionally attaining over 100 ft. in height, with a remarkably slender trunk, 3 to 5 ft. in girth; juvenile trees assume a very slender, tapering, and elegant form; shoots covered with stiff down, persisting several years. Leaves mostly disposed in or above the horizontal plane, but with a few standing out beneath; those on the upper side appressed, pointing forwards and hiding the branch; they are $\frac{1}{2}$ to 1 in. long, $\frac{1}{16}$ to $\frac{1}{12}$ in. wide; abruptly and sharply pointed on young trees, rounded on old ones; dark glossy green, and without stomata on the uppermost side; greyish beneath, with stomatic lines. Cones egg-shaped, tapered at the top, 1¼ to 2 ins. long; scales broad and rounded, with jagged margins.

Native of Serbia and Bosnia, in the valley of the Drina River; discovered by Dr Pancic in 1875. According to Elwes, it grows on limestone. It was introduced to Kew in 1889 by means of seed from Belgrade, but may have been in cultivation a few years previously elsewhere. The plants raised from these seeds have grown very well, and the species is in my opinion one of the best spruces introduced. Near London it thrives better than any other, remaining well furnished with its dark green leaves, growing rapidly, and retaining a slender very elegant form. It deserves, I think, to be planted extensively.

P. ORIENTALIS, *Link*. ORIENTAL SPRUCE

A tree over 100 ft. high in nature, forming in a young state a densely branched, very leafy, pyramidal tree, with the shape of the common spruce, but smaller-leaved and more slenderly branched; branches stiffly horizontal; young shoots furnished with short, erect, bristle-like hairs. Leaves arranged mostly at and above the horizontal plane, the upper ones appressed to and hiding the twig; they are dark shining green, ¼ to ⅓ in. long, bluntish at the apex, quadrangular in section, with one to four lines of stomata on each surface. Cones of a beautiful purple when young, ultimately brown, 1½ to 3 ins. long, ¾ to 1 in. wide; cylindrical, slender, and pointed when young; scales entire at the margin.

Native of Caucasus and Asia Minor; introduced in 1839. This is undoubtedly one of the most attractive of all the spruces, its foliage being of a brilliant dark green, the habit neat and dense. It has the shortest leaves of all spruces, except, perhaps, some of the pigmy forms of other species. Near London, and in localities with a deficient rainfall, it is much to be preferred to P. excelsa, although slower-growing. In a small state it is one of the daintiest looking of spruces, and older, when bearing a crop of its richly coloured cones, it is very ornamental. It is over 70 ft. high in several places in England, and succeeds admirably also in Scotland.

Var. AUREA.—Young shoots golden-yellow, very handsome.

Var. GRACILIS.—A pigmy variety.

P. POLITA, *Carrière*. TIGER TAIL SPRUCE

A tree over 100 ft. high in Japan; in cultivation a small pyramidal tree of very stiff habit; branches rigid and densely clothed with leaves; young shoots not downy, pale and yellowish the first year; terminal buds conical, shining brown, with closely appressed scales. Leaves set all round the shoot except for an open V-shaped groove beneath; they are 1¾ ins. long, $\frac{1}{12}$ in. wide; diamond shaped in cross-section, very rigid, somewhat curved, spine-tipped; dark glossy green, with four to seven faint lines of stomata on all four surfaces. Cones 2½ to 4 ins. long, 1¼ to 1¾ ins. wide before opening; brown when mature; scales minutely toothed.

Native of Japan; introduced by J. G. Veitch in 1861. This spruce is decidedly one of the most distinct and striking in the genus, especially in the comparatively long, thick, rigid, spine-tipped leaves standing out at almost right angles to the shoot. It is also one of the handsomest, and in a young state forms a shapely tree suitable for an isolated position on a lawn; in the adult state the branches are said to become long and pendulous, but cultivated trees as yet show no indication of assuming that character. It is a very hardy spruce, but not quick-growing. The " pegs," or persisting bases of the leaves, left on the shoot are unusually large and prominent.

PICEA POLITA

P. PUNGENS, *Engelmann*

(P. Parryana, *Sargent*; P. commutata, *Hort.*)

A tree 80 to 100, occasionally 150 ft. high; pyramidal as a small tree in ultivation with stiff horizontal branches; young twigs not downy; buds rownish yellow. Leaves arranged all round the branchlets, more thinly eneath, the upper ones pointing forward; they are $\frac{3}{4}$ to $1\frac{1}{4}$ ins. long, stiff, uadrangular, spine-tipped, dark green in the type, with three or four lines of omata on all four faces. Cones cylindrical, shining, straw-coloured when pe; 3 or 4 ins. long, about $1\frac{1}{4}$ ins. wide; scales wavy, oval, blunt and jaggedly othed at the apex; seeds $\frac{1}{8}$ in. long, with a wing $\frac{1}{4}$ in. long.

Native of Colorado, Utah, and Wyoming; discovered by Dr Parry in 1862. The type is but little known in gardens, where the species is almost wholly represented by the glaucous forms. The green type nevertheless is very handsome—usually of slender, pyramidal form.

Var. GLAUCA, *Veitch*. Blue Spruce.—Forms of P. pungens vary much in the more or less glaucous hue of the foliage. In the variety glauca (known

PICEA PUNGENS

also as Annesleyana, Sargentii, Parryana glauca, and, erroneously, as Engelmannii glauca) the leaves are covered with a blue-white bloom. This is still more pronounced in the var. ARGENTEA and other selected forms. But it is all a matter of degree, and various shades may be selected in any batch of seedlings. To those who admire these silvery trees the "blue spruce" may be recommended as one of the most handsome. This applies to it more as a young specimen; with age it is apt to become rusty and thin of foliage at the bottom, especially those selected forms that have been grafted on common spruce.

Var. PENDULA, *Koster*.—A glaucous form with pendulous branches, very fine in the nursery of Messrs Koster & Co. at Boskoop.

P. RUBENS, *Sargent*. RED SPRUCE

(Bot. Mag., t. 9446; P. rubra, *Link*)

The red spruce is a close ally of P. nigra, but appears to be extremely uncommon in cultivation. It is, apparently, on the average a considerably larger tree than nigra, being usually 70 to 80 ft. high; it has similar although less persistently downy young shoots. The leaves are quadrangular, $\frac{1}{2}$ to $\frac{3}{4}$ in. long, with stomatic lines on all four surfaces; they differ from those of nigra in being of a dark yellowish, rather than glaucous, green, and somewhat more slender. Cones purple, up to 2 ins. long and thus larger than those of nigra; the scales, too, are entire, or only slightly toothed at the apex. But the most marked distinction between the two is in the duration of the cones on the branches. In P. rubens they begin to fall as soon as the scales open, but in P. nigra they persist sometimes twenty or thirty years. In a wild state P. rubens has a much more restricted distribution than nigra, being confined to eastern N. America, where it extends from Prince Edward Island southward to the mountains of N. Carolina. Introduced in 1755. It has not much to recommend it for gardens beyond its interest.

P. SCHRENKIANA, *Fischer and Meyer*

Although sometimes placed under P. obovata as a variety, this species is quite distinct. The branchlets are greyish white, glabrous or nearly so; the leaves arranged all round the twig, spine-tipped in young trees, blunter in adult ones, $\frac{3}{4}$ to $1\frac{1}{4}$ ins. long, quadrangular, dark green, with two to four very indistinct lines of stomata on all four surfaces. Cones 3 to 4 ins. long, cylindrical; scales rounded, and not toothed at the apex. Native of W. Central Asia in the region of the Thian Shan mountains; discovered in 1840. It is very distinct from P. obovata in the longer, more spreading leaves. It succeeds fairly well in cultivation.

P. SITCHENSIS, *Trautvetter and Meyer*. SITKA SPRUCE

(Abies Menziesii, *Lindley*)

A tree already over 100 ft. high in Great Britain, occasionally 200 ft. in its native state, bark scaling; young shoots very stiff, not downy, yellowish. Leaves standing out stiffly all round the branchlet, but thinnest underneath; $\frac{1}{2}$ to $1\frac{1}{4}$ ins. long, $\frac{1}{20}$ to $\frac{1}{12}$ in. wide; prickly pointed; green, mostly without stomata on the upper surface; silvery, with two bands of stomata beneath. Cones blunt, cylindrical, shortly stalked, $2\frac{1}{2}$ to 4 ins. long, about $1\frac{1}{4}$ ins. wide, pale brown; scales oval-oblong, $\frac{1}{2}$ to $\frac{5}{8}$ in. long, rounded and toothed towards the apex; seeds $\frac{1}{8}$ in. long, with a wing thrice as long.

Native of western N. America, near the coast, from Alaska to California; discovered in 1792 by Menzies; introduced by Douglas in 1831. The Sitka spruce is, above all, a moisture-loving tree, thriving best where the soil is permanently on the wet side. Planted in a moist gully near a stream in the late Mr Robinson's property at Gravetye, in Sussex, it is making growths 4 ft. long in a season. It also thrives admirably in the wet valleys of Scotland, forming in the open a broad pyramid. As an isolated tree it has, even in Scotland, the defect of retaining its inner branches and twigs after they are dead, and these the outer fringe of living growth is not dense enough to hide. In many places it is over 100 ft. high, with trunks $3\frac{1}{2}$ to 5 ft. in diameter. Planted closely it is one of the most promising of timber trees for moist places. Its wood is valued in the making of aeroplanes.

P. SPINULOSA, *Henry*

(P. morindoides, *Rehder*, Bot. Mag., t. 8169)

A tree of large size, over 200 ft. high, branches pendulous at the ends; young shoots pale, yellowish, without down. Leaves arranged all round the shoot most thinly underneath, the upper ones appressed to the branch and pointing forward; they are needle-like, $\frac{1}{2}$ to $1\frac{1}{3}$ ins. long, sharply pointed; green and without stomata on the uppermost side, glaucous, with stomatic lines beneath. Cones cylindric, $2\frac{1}{2}$ to $3\frac{1}{2}$ ins. long, 1 to $1\frac{1}{4}$ ins. wide; purple

PICEA SPINULOSA

when young, pale brown when mature; scales blunt at the apex, the margi jagged.

Native of the eastern Himalaya; date of introduction uncertain, beir first distinguished as a new species by Rehder, in 1902, by a cultivated tr in the garden of the late Mr Allard of Angers, France, who informed n that his tree bore infertile cones every year. A tree at Meñabilly, in Cornwa has produced fertile seeds. The best tree I have seen is at Leonardslee, ve graceful and well furnished. It belongs to the Omorika group and may be described as having the foliage and twigs of P. sitchensis with the habit of P. Morinda. It probably exists in some gardens under either of these names. From P. Morinda it is easily distinguished by its shorter leaves having stomata on one side of the leaf only.

P. WILSONII, *Masters*. WILSON'S SPRUCE

(Gardeners' Chronicle, 28th Feb. 1903, figs. 55, 56; P. Watsoniana, *Masters*)

A tree 70 to 80 ft. high of shapely pyramidal form, with short horizontally spreading branches. Young shoots quite glabrous, pale, greyish, becoming whitish the second year; "pegs" left by the fallen leaves quite small. Leaves stoutish, quadrangular, sharply pointed, up to ⅝ in. long, densely set and pointing forwards on the upper side, those beneath spreading laterally at right angles to the shoot in two sets. Cones ovoid to cylindrical, 1½ to 3 ins. long; cone-scales thin, broadly rounded, slightly jagged at the margin. Wilson observes that the cones are very freely produced and remain on the tree for a year or more after they are ripe.

Native of Central China; discovered by Wilson in 1901, introduced by him in 1908. Messrs Dallimore and Jackson have made P. Watsoniana, *Masters*, a synonym of P. Wilsonii. The two are undoubtedly closely related and probably conspecific, but the leaves of P. Watsoniana seem to be considerably more slender, and Wilson remarks that the cones are smaller and fall from the tree soon after they are ripe. As long ago as 1919 I had a cone from the Marquis of Headfort's pinetum, near Kells, Co. Meath. The pale, almost white, glabrous shoots with the small "pegs" or "cushions" do not seem to differ from those of P. Wilsonii.

PICRASMA AILANTHOIDES, *Planchon*. SIMARUBACEÆ

(P. quassioides, *Bennett*, in part)

A slender, deciduous tree, 20 to 40 ft. high, with very handsome young bark of a reddish brown, conspicuously marked with yellow spots. Leaves alternate, pinnate, 10 to 15 ins. long, glabrous, consisting of nine to thirteen leaflets, which are glossy green, 1 to 4 ins. long, ovate, unequal at the base, round or pointed at the apex, sharp-toothed at the margin, and with a very short stalk. Flowers green, ⅓ in. across, in a lax, branching corymb 6 to 8 ins. long, and often nearly as wide; stalks downy. Fruit a berry, about the size of a pea, red, rather obovoid, with the calyx still attached.

This tree, according to some authorities, is a form of P. quassioides, a species which, in that sense, is spread in a wild state from Japan and China through the Himalaya as far south as Java. This is no doubt extending the specific limits of P. quassioides too far. No tree from Java would be as perfectly hardy in our climate as is this. The above description is based on trees growing at Kew which were introduced from Japan in 1890. They have flowered and borne fruit several times, and young plants have been raised from the seed. They have no beauty of flower or fruit, but of the foliage in autumn Sargent observes, "few Japanese plants I saw are as beautiful as this small tree." The leaves turn first orange then scarlet. The whole tree is permeated by a singularly bitter principle. Its nearest ally among hardy trees is Ailanthus.

PIERIS. ERICACEÆ

A genus of about ten species, the hardy ones of which are found in N. America, Himalaya, Japan, and China. They are evergreen or deciduous shrubs, sometimes tree-like, with alternate leaves; flowers in terminal or axillary racemes or panicles, produced on the growth of the previous year. Corolla more or less pitcher-shaped, five-toothed; calyx five-lobed and persistent; stamens ten. Seed-vessel a globose capsule.

All the pierises are handsome shrubs of neat habit, and great freedom in blossoming. They need the same conditions and treatment as rhododendron; that is, either a peaty soil or a light lime-free loam improved by the addition of decayed leaves. They are also moisture-lovers at the root. Propagation is effected by seed, but more quickly by layering, for the purpose of which stools of P. japonica and P. floribunda are laid down in nurseries. These two species, as well as P. formosa, flower early in spring, and it is an advantage if they can be given a western exposure with shelter on the north and east sides.

P. FLORIBUNDA, *Bentham and Hooker*

(Andromeda floribunda, *Pursh*; Bot. Mag., t. 1566)

An evergreen shrub, from 3 to 6 ft. high, of bushy, rounded habit, and when in good condition furnished right to the ground, the branches rather stiff; shoots and leaf-stalks furnished with dark bristles appressed to the stem, and pointing forwards. Leaves ovate, 1½ to 3 ins. long, ½ to 1 in. wide; pointed, rounded or tapering at the base, slightly toothed, bristly at the edges; dark glossy green above, paler beneath, sprinkled with very short black hairs on both surfaces; stalk ¼ to ⅜ in. long. Flowers produced in March and April in erect terminal panicles 2 to 5 ins. high, each consisting of several slender, downy racemes; corolla pure white, pitcher-shaped, ¼ in. long calyx-lobes ovate; flower-stalk decurved so as to bring all the flowers to the lower side, and furnished with two linear bracts.

Native of the south-eastern United States; introduced in 1800. This is one of the most beautiful and hardy of flowering evergreens, slow-growing and of neat bushy habit, admirable for planting in groups. A fine specimen in the Wisley Gardens was some years ago 14 ft. wide and 6 ft. high.

Var. ELONGATA, *Marchant.*—A very fine form from Keeper's Hill nursery given an Award of Merit at Vincent Square, 5th April 1938. Some of the racemes were 8 ins. long.

P. FORMOSA, *D. Don*

(Bot. Mag., t. 8283; Andromeda formosa, *Wallich*)

A large evergreen shrub, 8 to 12, or sometimes 20 ft. high, spreading half as much more in diameter; young wood glabrous. Leaves lanceolate 3 to 7 ins. long, 1 to 2¼ ins. wide; pointed, tapering at the base, finely toothed glabrous, and dark glossy green, of firm, leathery texture. Flowers produced during May in a cluster of panicles, terminating the shoots of the previou year, and from 4 to 6 ins. long and wide. Corolla pendent, white, pitcher-shaped, $\frac{1}{4}$ to $\frac{3}{8}$ in. long, contracted at the mouth, where are five shallow, rounded teeth ; calyx-lobes $\frac{1}{8}$ in. long, green, narrowly ovate ; flower-stalk $\frac{1}{4}$ in. or less long, with a pair of bracts.

Native of the Himalaya at 6000 to 10,000 ft., from Nepal eastwards. This

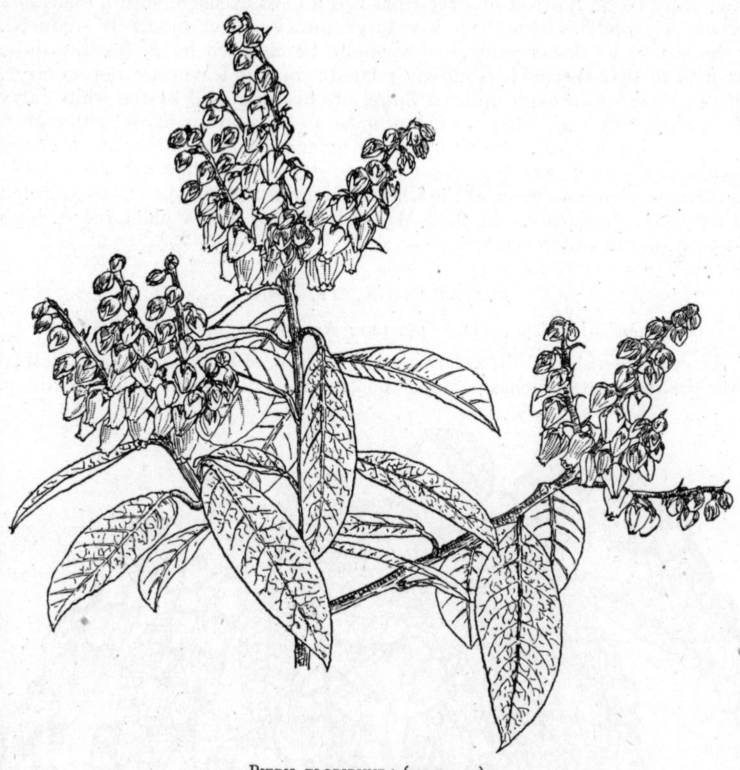

PIERIS FLORIBUNDA (see p. 454)

shrub is seen at its best in Cornwall, where it grows and blossoms to perfection. At Kew it is hardy in sheltered places, but does not grow more than 6 to 8 ft. high, flowering uncertainly. It is the most beautiful of this genus. The same shrub, or a slightly differing form of it, has been found in W. Hupeh, China, by Wilson.

P. FORRESTII, *Harrow*

(P. formosa Forrestii, *Airy-Shaw* ; Bot. Mag., t. 9371)

An evergreen shrub of erect growth 6 to 10 ft. high ; young shoots glabrous, often red. Leaves often crowded towards the end of the shoot, of a pale salmon shade when young, becoming dark green with age ; oblanceolate or oval lanceolate, finely and regularly toothed, tapered at both ends, 2 to $4\frac{1}{2}$ ins. long, $\frac{1}{2}$ to $1\frac{1}{2}$ ins. wide ; quite glabrous and slightly glossy on both surfaces. Panicles pyramidal, 4 to 6 ins. long, forming in autumn and showing well above the foliage. Flowers fragrant, closely set on the minutely downy flower-stalks, waxy white, pendulous, opening in April. Corolla urn-shaped, $\frac{3}{8}$ in. long, with five short erect lobes at the narrow mouth. Calyx-lobes linear-lanceolate, $\frac{3}{16}$ in. long, whitish. Anthers awned.

Native of Yunnan and N.E. Upper Burma; discovered in the former locality by Forrest when collecting for Bees, Ltd., who exhibited it showing flowers and the charmingly coloured, soft red young leaves at the Chelsea Show, May 1924. Forrest observes that it is a most excellent shrub, finer than any of its class he has seen, the flowers large, pure in colour and freely produced. In the size of its flower-panicles it seems to be equalled by P. formosa only, and it is to that species it is closely related; but its leaves are not so large, and the flowers, although quite as large, are distinguished by the white calyx (green in P. formosa). It does not promise to be quite so hardy, although it should succeed in most parts of southern England. The colouring of the young growths varies in depth in different plants; the richest coloured one (Forrest 8945) I have seen was shown at the Chelsea Show in May 1930. It was awarded a First-Class Certificate. In 1927 Mr A. K. Bulley had a plant $10\frac{1}{2}$ ft. high and 50 ft. in circumference.

P. JAPONICA, *D. Don*

(Gardeners' Chronicle, 1882, i., fig. 120; Andromeda japonica, *Thunberg*)

An evergreen shrub, ultimately 9 or 10 ft. high, of bushy habit, and clothed to the ground with branches; young shoots usually glabrous. Leaves leathery,

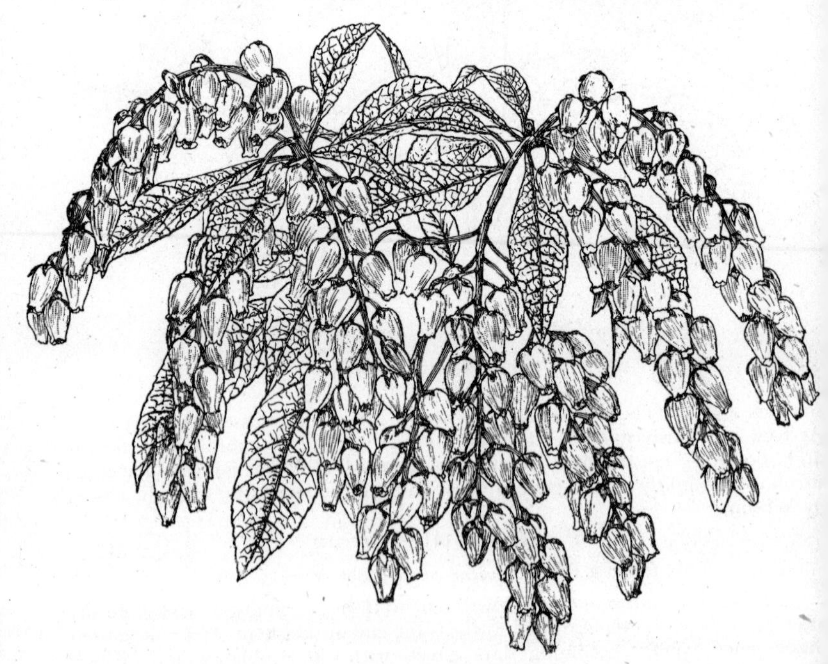

PIERIS JAPONICA

oblanceolate or narrowly oval, usually widest above the middle, tapering towards both ends; $1\frac{1}{4}$ to $3\frac{1}{2}$ ins. long, $\frac{1}{3}$ to $\frac{3}{4}$ in. wide; shallowly toothed, dark glossy green above, paler beneath, glabrous on both surfaces. Flowers in a terminal cluster of slender pendulous racemes each 3 to 6 ins. long; corolla pitcher-shaped, ¼ to ⅜ in. long, much narrowed towards the mouth, where are five shallow, rounded teeth; calyx-lobes lanceolate, scarcely half as long as the corolla; flower-stalk ⅛ in. long, glabrous.

Native of Japan. This shrub is not so hardy as P. floribunda, from which it is easily distinguished by the leaves being narrower and more tapering at the base, by the pendulous inflorescence, and by the absence of hairs on the young wood and flower-stalks. It flowers in March and April, and is often injured by frost. At its best it is a very beautiful shrub. It should be given a sheltered spot, with a western exposure.

Var. VARIEGATA has narrower leaves than the type, edged, especially towards the apex, with yellowish white. Well grown, it is one of the most attractive of variegated evergreens.

P. TAIWANENSIS, *Hayata* (Plate 36)

(Bot. Mag., t. 9016)

A compact evergreen shrub 6 to 10 ft. high, with yellowish-green, perfectly glabrous young shoots. Leaves oblanceolate or oval, tapered towards both ends, bluntish at the apex, shallowly toothed at the upper half only; 2 to 5 ins. long, ½ to 1 in. wide; stout and leathery, deep glossy green above, pale green beneath, quite glabrous. Flowers in a cluster of racemes or in panicles at the end of the shoot, each one of which is 3 to 6 ins. long, the stalks minutely downy, the flowers nodding. Corolla pure white, urn-shaped, ⅜ in. long, ¼ in. wide, with five small, slightly reflexed lobes at the much contracted mouth. Sepals normally five, but sometimes reduced apparently to three or four through one or two pairs being united, green, glabrous outside, tipped with down inside, ovate, ⅛ in. long. Stamens white, $\frac{1}{10}$ in. long, thickened towards the base, slightly downy except at the top; anthers brown, with two awns at the back; style ⅕ in. long. Flowers in April.

Native of Formosa up to elevations of 11,000 ft.; introduced by Wilson in 1918. Grown under glass, it flowered at Kew when only two years old, raised from seed. It promises to be genuinely hardy in the south and west as it has gone through several winters out-of-doors at Kew without suffering, and there is at Wisley a very healthy plant 3 ft. high. Wilson uses for it the epithet "lovely" which it well deserves. Lord Headfort was the first to give the public an opportunity of estimating its value by showing it beautifully in bloom at Westminster in March 1922. It is most nearly related to P. formosa, but has much smaller, differently shaped leaves. P. Forrestii differs in its leaves being toothed nearly all along the margins and in the more erect corolla lobes. Both resemble P. japonica in forming flower-buds in autumn, but are superior to that species in the more erect panicles which enable their flowers to be better displayed.

PILEOSTEGIA VIBURNOIDES. *Hooker fil. and Thomson.*

SAXIFRAGACEÆ

(Gardeners' Chronicle, 3rd Oct. 1914, fig. 95; Schizophragma viburnoides, *Stapf*, Bot. Mag., t. 9262)

An evergreen prostrate or climbing shrub described as from 10 to 20 ft. high, in a wild state growing over trees and cliffs; young leaves and shoots at first scurfy, afterwards quite glabrous. Leaves opposite, leathery, entire, narrowly oblong, obovate or oval, pointed, tapered at the base; $2\frac{1}{2}$ to 6 ins. long, $\frac{3}{4}$ to $2\frac{1}{2}$ ins. wide; dark, dullish green, strongly veined and minutely pitted beneath; stalk $\frac{1}{3}$ to 1 in. long. Flowers milky white, usually densely crowded in a terminal panicle 4 to 6 ins. wide and high, opening in September and October. Each flower is about $\frac{3}{8}$ in. wide, with four or five petals and twice as many stamens; the latter are $\frac{1}{4}$ in. long, white, and make the most conspicuous feature of the inflorescence. Calyx cup-shaped at the base with four or five short lobes. Fruit a small, dry, top-shaped capsule, rather like that of a hydrangea, to which genus Pileostegia is nearly akin.

Native of the Khasia Hills, India, also of China and Formosa. The plants in cultivation were introduced by Wilson, who sent seed to the Arnold Arboretum which he had collected in 1908. This, the only species of the genus as yet described, makes an excellent evergreen climber for a wall, covering it densely with its foliage and clinging of itself by aerial roots. Grown on a west wall at Kew, it has shown no sign of tenderness there. The late Hon. Vicary Gibbs first showed it at Westminster in bloom during September 1914, and sixteen years later Lord Wakehurst exhibited fine flowering sprays during the same month. It likes a good loamy soil and is easily propagated by cuttings. Dr Stapf has placed it in the genus Schizophragma (*loc. cit. supra*).

PINUS. PINE. CONIFERÆ

Among coniferous trees the pines constitute by far the most important group, regarded either from the point of view of number of species or that of economic value. As timber trees they easily predominate over any other genus in the northern hemisphere. They are evergreen, and range from trees over 200 ft. high to mere shrubs; very resinous, producing their branches in tiers.

The leaves of pines are nearly always produced in clusters or bundles of from two to five, occasionally there are six, and in one species—monophylla—they are solitary. The seedling leaves of all pines are solitary, the adult condition commencing to appear in the second and third years. The individual leaf or "needle" is long and narrow, mostly finely toothed at the margin, and always more or less conspicuously lined with rows of minute white, or whitish, dots called stomata. Where the leaves are in bundles of two the transverse section of each is semicircular, in the bundles of three to five they are three-sided. Each bundle of leaves, whatever their number, forms in the aggregate a slender cylinder. At the base of each bundle is a "sheath," whose varying length and duration give very useful indications of the identity of the species. The leaf-bearing shoots of each season are always to a greater or less extent naked at the base, being furnished there with "scale-leaves" only—small, thin, membranous bodies, often fringed, and usually falling away quickly. The terminal winter bud is an important differentiating character according to its shape and size, the character of the scales by which it is covered, and whether it be resinous or not, although in some species the last character is uncertain.

The flowers of pines are unisexual and borne in conical clusters, the males at the base, the females at the apex of the year's growth; the female inflorescence develops the second year into a woody fruit often of great size and weight, commonly known as a "cone," and of egg-shaped, cylindrical, or tapered form. These cones are composed of a number of woody scales which vary in length, in thickness, and in the character of the scar or boss at the end, and in the presence or absence of spines. When the cone is ripe (most frequently at the end of the second year), the scale opens and allows the two seeds at its base to escape; but some species take longer, and several appear never to release their seeds at all unless through some outside agency such as fire (in the West American forests), or squirrels, or birds. Some species have small seeds which are furnished with a large membranous wing whose object is to assist in their dispersion. The larger, edible seeds have only rudimentary wings or none at all.

As garden or park trees the pines are of varying merit, but the best of them are amongst the noblest of evergreens. They do not need a rich soil so much as an open, well-drained one. The hardier ones, like montana, sylvestris, and Banksiana, grow in some of the most inclement parts on the globe. On nearly all the mountains of the northern world it is some member of this genus that makes the highest timber line. On chalky soils, Brutia, halepensis, excelsa, Laricio, Pinea, and others succeed very well; whilst for spots exposed to sea-gales and in maritime situations generally, the Austrian pine, radiata, Pinaster, and Thunbergii are extremely useful in building up the first line of protection from sea-winds. The purely garden varieties have to be increased by grafting on the types to which they belong, but all other pines must be grown from seed. With few exceptions it is desirable to get them planted in their permanent places as young as possible.

As indicating broadly the affinities and leading distinctions of the species here dealt with, the following rough classification is given. Those marked * are most to be recommended for gardens:—

I. Leaves solitary

Monophylla.

II. Leaves in pairs

(a) *Buds cylindrical, resinous*

Banksiana. Leaves 1 to 1¾ ins. long; cones bent at the end.
**Muricata.* Leaves 3 to 5 ins. long; cones persisting for many years.
Virginiana. Leaves 1½ to 3 ins. long; young shoots purple-violet.
Pungens. Leaves stiff, sharply pointed; young shoots brown.
**Sylvestris.* Leaves glaucous; bark of trunk scaling, reddish.
Densiflora. Leaves green; bark of trunk scaling, reddish.
**Montana.* Leaf-sheath up to ⅝ in. long; bud-scales appressed.
Contorta. Leaf-sheath about ¼ in. long; bud-scales appressed.
Murrayana. Like contorta, but with scaling bark on trunk.

(b) *Buds broadly ovid, resinous*

**Laricio.* Leaf-sheath ½ in. long; leaf 4 to 7 ins. long.
**Thunbergii.* Leaf-sheath ½ in. long; leaf 2 to 4½ ins. long; bud resinous at base only.
Resinosa. Leaf-sheath ½ to ¾ in. long.

Leucodermis. Leaves stiff; young shoots shining brown, turning grey the second year.

(c) *Buds non-resinous*

**Pinaster.* Bud-scales with fringed margins and recurved points.
**Pinea.* Bud-scales as in Pinaster; leaves much shorter.
Halepensis. } Young shoots pale, and leaves more slender than in either of above.
Brutia. }
Echinata. Young shoots blue-white; leaves often in threes.
**Edulis.* Young shoots blue-white; leaves often in threes; leaf-sheath rosette-like.

III. LEAVES IN THREES

(a) *Leaf-sheath deciduous*

**Bungeana.* Leaf-sheath falling the first year.
Gerardiana. Leaf-sheath falling the second year.

(b) *Leaf-sheath rosette-like*

Cembroides. Leaves sometimes in pairs.

(c) *Leaf-sheath persistent; buds resinous*

**Coulteri.* Buds conical; leaf up to 1 ft. long. }
Sabiniana. Buds cylindrical; leaf up to 1 ft. long. } Young shoots orange-scented when cut.
**Ponderosa.* Shoots brown; leaf 5 to 10 ins. long. }
Jeffreyi. Shoots glaucous; leaf 5 to 10 ins. long. }
Rigida. Trunk furnished with small twigs.
**Radiata.* Cones persisting long; foliage grass green.
Tuberculata. Cones persisting long; leaf longer; grey-green.

IV. LEAVES IN FIVES

(a) *Leaf-sheaths persistent*

Hartwegi. Leaves 5 to 6 ins. long.
Montezumæ. Leaves 7 to 12 ins. long.

(b) *Leaf-sheaths rosette-like; leaves not toothed*

**Aristata.* Leaves resin-dotted; persisting twelve or fifteen years.
**Balfouriana.* Leaves not resin-dotted; persisting twelve to fifteen years.
Parryana. Leaves often in fours; persisting two or three years.

(c) *Leaf-sheaths deciduous; shoots downy*

Armandii. Shoots sometimes glabrous like excelsa, but cones stouter (see figures).
**Ayacahuite.* Basal scales of cone recurved.
Koraiensis. Bud-scales free at tips and spreading.
**Cembra.* Young shoots almost shaggy.
**Lambertiana.* Winter buds rounded or blunt.
Strobus. Shoots downy only at base of leaf-bundle as a rule.
**Monticola.* Shoots downy all over, otherwise similar to Strobus.
Parviflora. Leaves 1½ to 2½ ins. long, the shortest of this group.

(d) *Leaf-sheaths deciduous; shoots glabrous*

**Excelsa.* Leaves 5 to 7 ins. long.
Peuke. Leaves 3 to 4 ins. long.

(e) *Leaf-sheaths deciduous; leaf-margins not toothed*

Albicaulis. Cones short and thick.
**Flexilis.* Cones more slender.

P. ALBICAULIS, *Engelmann*. WHITE BARK PINE

A shrub 10 to 20 ft. high, rarely a tree twice as high; in the smaller state usually with two or three main stems. Young branchlets yellowish brown, minutely downy or glabrous, becoming grey the second or third year, finally whitish. Leaves in fives, persisting five to seven years, 1 to 2½ ins. long, green with whitish stomatic lines on all three surfaces, stiffly pointed; not toothed at the margins; leaf-sheaths ⅝ in. long, soon falling. Cones indehiscent, 1½ to 3 ins. long, and nearly as thick; scales very thick, with a spine-tipped boss. Seeds about ½ in. long, with little or no wing, sweet, edible.

Native of western N. America at high elevations, becoming in cold bleak sites reduced to dwarf scrub. It was introduced by Jeffrey in 1852, but subsequently disappeared from cultivation. Some years ago it was reintroduced to Kew, where small plants are quite healthy but slow-growing. They already show the characteristic tendency to form several leaders. Closely allied to P. flexilis, and with the same toothless leaves and nearly wingless seeds, but very different in the cones.

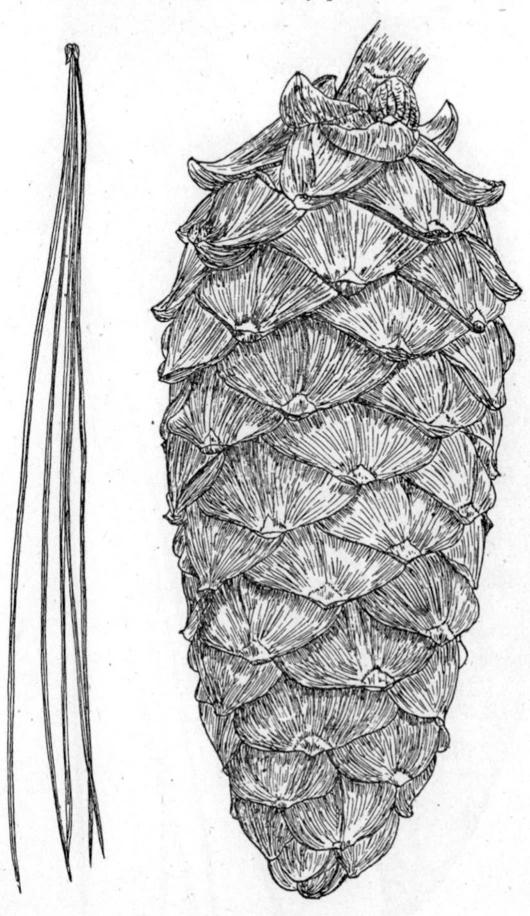

PINUS ARMANDII

P. ARMANDII, *Franchet*. ARMAND'S PINE

(Bot. Mag., t. 8347)

A tree described as becoming 60 ft. high in nature, with very much the aspect in a young state of P. excelsa; young shoots greyish-green, usually furnished with a minute, dark, often scattered glands. Leaves in fives, mostly falling the second year; 4 to 6 ins. long, white with stomata on two sides,

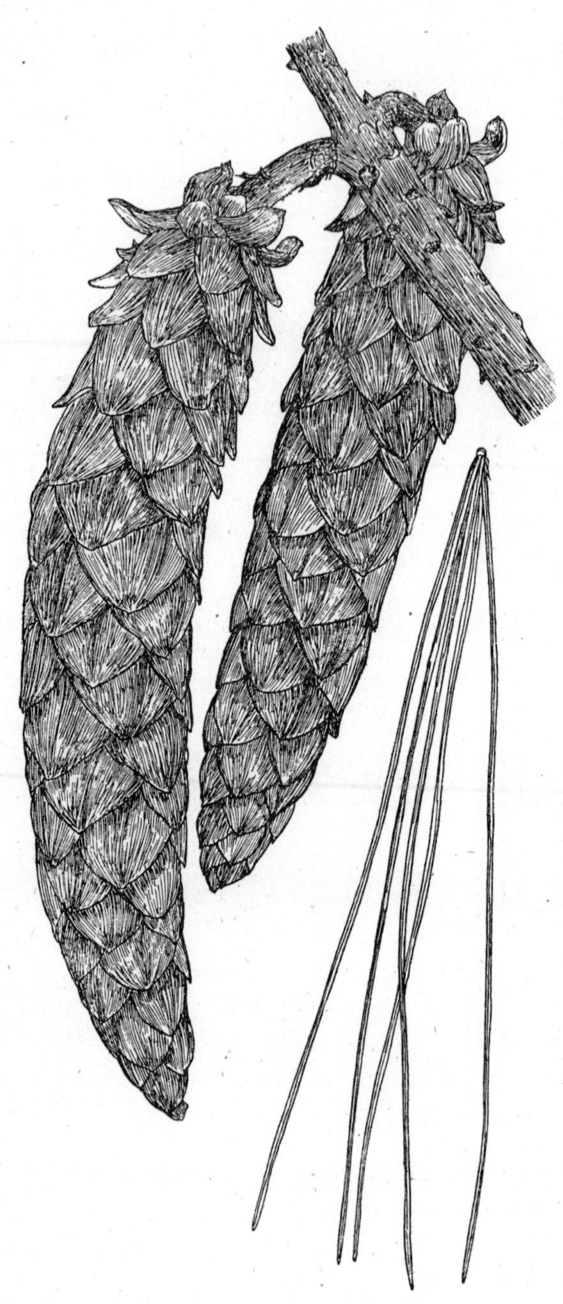

Pinus Ayacahuite

glossy green on the third; pointed, minutely toothed on the margin; leaf-sheath soon falling away. Cones 4 to 8 ins. long, $2\frac{1}{2}$ to 3 ins. thick before expanding, tapering slightly from the base. Scales thick, broadly triangular, about $1\frac{1}{4}$ ins. long.

Native of the mountains of W. China; first introduced to England by Henry, who sent seeds to Kew from Mengtse, Yunnan, in 1897. But two years previously seeds had reached Mr Maurice de Vilmorin from Père Farges. The trees raised from Henry's seed grew quickly when once established, and first bore cones (infertile) in 1909. In habit and foliage they scarcely differ from P. excelsa, and promise to have about the same garden value. The leaves often show the same kink towards the base as in excelsa. The cones, as may be seen from our figures, are very distinct. It has recently been found in Formosa and Korea.

P. Ayacahuite, *Ehrenberg*. Mexican White Pine

A tree said to be 100 ft. high in nature, and already between 60 and 70 ft. high in this country; in habit very similar to P. excelsa. Young shoots brownish, downy. Leaves in fives, very slender and pointed, falling the third year, 4 to 7 ins. long; three-sided, two surfaces with three or four white lines of stomata, the other bright green; margins toothed; leaf-sheaths ¾ in. long, soon falling completely away. Cones 6 to 12 ins. sometimes 18 ins. long, 1 to 2½ ins. wide before expanding, cylindrical, with a tapered slightly curved apex. Scales obovate, 2 ins. or more long, the edges thin. Seed with a narrow wing nearly 1 in. long. The scales at the base of the cone are always curled back almost or quite to the stalk, which they never are in P. excelsa.

A native of Mexico, where it is widely spread and very variable. Introduced by Hartweg for the Royal Horticultural Society in 1840, and afterwards under numerous names by Roezl. It varies in hardiness, but the shorter-coned form here figured is hardy at Kew.

Var. VEITCHII, *Shaw* (P. Veitchii, *Roezl*), is one of the more tender, larger-coned forms. Only hardy in Cornwall and similar places.

The cones of this pine are quite distinct from those of P. Armandii, but its shoots and foliage are very similar to the more downy states of the latter. But in P. Armandii the leaves fall usually a year earlier, the shoots are more slender, and the terminal buds have closer scales.

S. BALFOURIANA, *A. Murray*. FOX-TAIL PINE

(Gardeners' Chronicle, 1876, i., fig. 58)

A small tree, 20 to 40, rarely over 50 ft. high, forming in a small state a very densely branched, bushy tree; young shoots covered with minute but scarcely visible down, so closely packed are the leaf-bundles. Leaves mostly in fives, sometimes in fours, persisting as long as twelve or fifteen years, very stiff and sharply pointed, about 1½ ins. long, three-angled, two surfaces at first white with stomata, becoming nearly green like the third with age; margins not toothed. The scales of the leaf-sheath curl back and make a sort of rosette surrounding the base of the leaf cluster, and persist in that shape. Cones 2½ to 5 ins. long, each scale armed with a minute, incurved prickle.

Native of California; introduced in 1852 by Jeffrey. Still an uncommon pine, it is one of the most distinct and attractive for limited spaces. It grows very slowly, but its long retained, closely packed leaves give it a healthy, vigorous aspect. It and its close ally P. aristata (see below) are quite distinct in appearance, and differ from all other five-leaved pines in the rosette-like arrangement of the leaf-sheath.

P. ARISTATA, *Engelmann* (P. Balfouriana aristata, *Engelmann*), is very closely allied to the above, but is always distinguishable by conspicuous exudations of whitish resin on the leaves, giving them very much the appearance of being infested with some scale insect. The branches are more drooping, the young shoots more distinctly downy, and the cones of P. aristata are armed with considerably longer, slender prickles. Introduced in 1863 from Colorado, where it grows on the outer range of the Rocky Mountains, also in Nevada, Utah, and California.

P. BANKSIANA, *Lambert*. JACK PINE

(S. hudsonica, *Poiret*; P. divaricata, *Dumont de Courset*)

A tree varying in height from a scrubby bush to a tree 20 to 45 ft. high in this country, but said sometimes to become 70 to 90 ft. high in N. America; young shoots without down; terminal buds egg-shaped, ⅓ in. long, encased in resin. Leaves in pairs, persisting two to four years, 1 to 1¾ ins. long, flat on one side, convex on the other, dark green, much curved: leaf-sheaths about $\frac{1}{6}$ in. long. Cones pointing forward, slender, conical, but very much curved at the tapered point; about $1\frac{1}{2}$ ins. long, $\frac{3}{4}$ in. wide at the base before opening; yellow when ripe.

Native of eastern N. America, where it is the most northerly of pines, and is spread over a vast region, usually in poor soil; introduced early in the eighteenth century. It appears to be very well adapted for poor sandy soil, and has been planted in great numbers in Germany on that account. It has not much to recommend it for gardens. Among pines with short leaves in pairs and with resinous buds, this is to be distinguished by its slenderly tapered cones, curiously curved like a bent little finger at the apex.

P. BRUTIA, *Tenore*. CALABRIAN PINE

(P. pyrenaica, *David*; P. halepensis Brutia, *Henry*)

Although by some authorities regarded as nothing more than a form of P. halepensis, this seems to me to be a distinct species. The tree itself

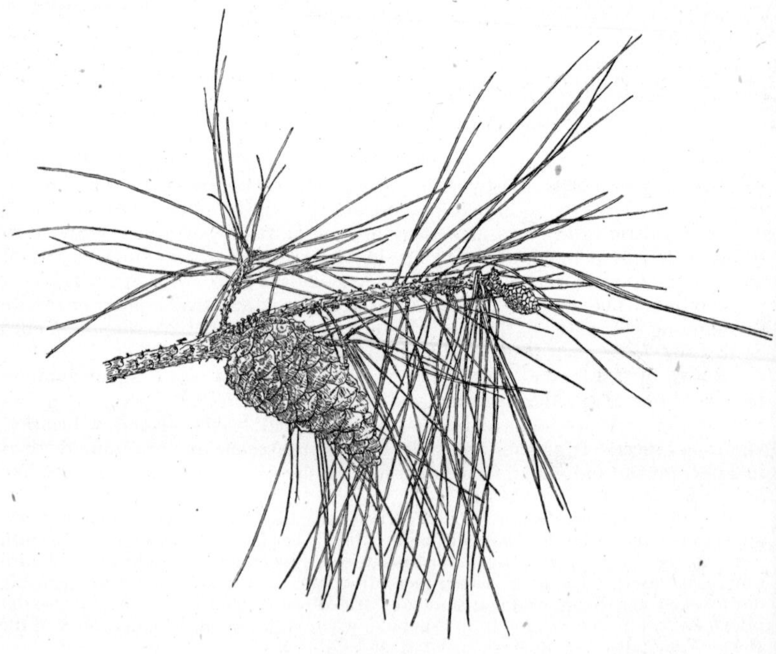

PINUS BRUTIA

is of thin, ungainly habit; its leaves (in pairs) are 4 to 6 ins. long, its young shoots are green, and more flexible than those of halepensis; finally, its cones point forwards instead of backwards, and are thicker (2 ins.) at the base. It is rather lacking in attractive qualities, being thin in branch and leaf and inferior in this respect to halepensis. It is said to grow 80 ft. high, and is a native of S.E. Europe (not of the Pyrenees, as a name under which it is frequently grown would imply), with much the same general distribution as P. halepensis, except that it reaches not farther west than Southern Italy.

P. Bungeana, *Zuccarini*. Bunge's Pine, Lace-bark Pine

(Bot. Mag., t. 8240)

A tree sometimes forming a rounded, bushy head, but frequently branching near the ground and forming several stems which grow erect to a height occasionally of 80 to 100 ft. The bark is smooth and peels off the trunk like that of a plane; in young specimens it is brown, but in old ones becomes quite white and gives to this pine its most remarkable character. Young shoots perfectly glabrous, shining, greyish green. Leaves in threes, persisting four or five years, about 3 ins. long, two-edged, stiff, sharply pointed, bright green, very minutely toothed, marked all round with faint stomatic lines; leaf-sheath ½ to ¾ in. long, soon falling. Cones 2 to 2½ ins. long, 1¼ to 1½ ins. wide, shortly stalked, the scales terminated by a decurved, triangular spine; seeds ⅓ in. long, with a short wing.

Native of China; first seen by Dr Bunge in 1831 in the environs of Pekin, where it has been largely planted for the sake of its remarkable white trunk; introduced by Fortune in 1848. It has been seen in quantity by Wilson in Central China. It is distinct from all other three-leaved pines, except P. Gerardiana, in the deciduous leaf-sheaths. It succeeds very well at Kew, where are trees approaching 30 ft. in height, only partially, however, showing the white bark. This is said not to appear, even in China, until the trees are fifty years old.

P. canariensis, *C. Smith*. Canary Island Pine

A tree upwards of 80 ft. high and 10 ft. in girth of trunk, of conical shape with somewhat pendulous branches; young shoots yellowish, not downy; winter buds ovoid, pointed, ¾ in. long, ½ in. wide; bud-scales reddish brown, free and reflexed at the top, but matted together lower down by a fringe of whitish bristles. Leaves in bundles of three, very slender, minutely toothed, averaging 8 or 9 ins. in length (sometimes 12 ins.) with two to four lines of stomata on each surface; basal sheath persistent, ½ to ¾ in. long. Cones solitary or several together, more or less deflexed, 5 to 8 ins. long, 3 ins. wide, the exposed part of the scales of rhomboid outline and pyramidal shape, altogether resembling those of P. Pinaster. Seeds with a wing over 1 in. long. The leaves remain on the shoots for two seasons.

Confined to the Canary Islands in a wild state and once very plentiful there, but now becoming restricted to the higher altitudes and less accessible places. It is most abundant on La Palma, Tenerife, and Grand Canary. At one time the islands contained many giant trees, most of which have been felled, but according to Dr Perez (*Kew Bulletin*, 1918, p. 1) there still exists in Tenerife, above the village of Vilaflor, a tree 160 ft. high and 36 ft. in girth of trunk. This pine is only hardy in our mildest localities; there is one at Heligan and another at Menehay in Cornwall. Probably no part of the British Isles except possibly Scilly is at once warm enough and sunny enough to bring out its better qualities. It makes a fine tree on the Riviera where it succeeds on calcareous soil. The timber is exceedingly durable and ranks with the best types of pine wood. Nearly related to this pine is

P. longifolia, *Roxburgh* (Himalayan Pine), one of the finest of Indian pines. It is described as attaining 150 to 180 ft. in height and a trunk-girth of 20 to 35 ft. The winter buds are ovoid, not resinous; the leaves in threes, 8 ins. to over 12 ins. long. Cones elongated, ovoid, 5 to 8 ins. long, 2½ to 3½ ins. wide. It is the chief resin-producing pine of India. Tender, although capable of being grown in Cornish gardens.

P. CEMBRA, *Linnæus*. AROLLA PINE (Plate 37)

A tree varying in height from 60 to over 100 ft. high, usually of pyramidal form, especially when young; young shoots clothed with a thick coat of brownish down. Leaves in fives, very densely packed on the shoots, persisting three to five years according to vigour; pointing forward, fragrant in summer, 1½ to 4½ ins. long, rich green; triangular, with three to five lines of stomata on two faces; margins toothed except near the point; leaf-sheaths ¾ or ⅞ in. long, soon falling away. Cones egg-shaped, 2 to 3 ins. long, scarcely as wide; the scales do not expand, and the seeds fall with the cones and are either released by birds or animals or by the decay of the scales.

Native of the Alps of Central Europe and Siberia; introduced in 1746. This well-known pine makes a very pretty small tree, pyramidal, densely branched and very leafy, especially from 8 to 20 ft. high. It does not appear to be long-lived nor produce cones freely in the south of England, although there are a few trees between 60 and 80 ft. high in old gardens. Young trees often die suddenly. It is, of course, a purely Alpine tree in Europe, its rugged line marking the highest frontier of tree growth on many of the mountain-sides of Switzerland, France, and the Tyrol. In the more sheltered upland valleys visitors to those parts will have noted picturesque old veterans that have braved the storms, doubtless for hundreds of years.

Var. SIBIRICA, *Loudon*.—A taller tree, but apparently less well adapted to our climate than the Central European form. Native of vast areas in European and Asiatic Russia. There is a garden variety—AUREA—with yellowish leaves.

In Japan, Manchuria, Siberia, and other cold regions of Eastern Asia grows P. PUMILA, *Regel*, botanically a close ally of P. Cembra, although of different aspect. It is a dwarf, mostly prostrate shrub never over 10 ft. high, the shoots covered with down and the five-clustered leaves 1½ to 2 ins. long. They differ from those of P. Cembra in being usually entire at the margins. Cones 1½ ins. long, orange-brown, similar to those of P. Cembra in never opening. It was in cultivation early last century, but appears to have been lost sight of until recently, when Admiral Clinton Baker, R.N., collected plants in Japan and sent them to the Bayfordbury collection. Prof. Sargent records that on Mt. Hakkoda, Japan, at 6000 ft., he saw impenetrable thickets of it a few feet high covering hundreds of acres.

P. CEMBROIDES, *Zuccarini*. THREE-LEAF NUT PINE

A bushy tree usually 15 to 20 ft. high, sometimes 40 or 50 ft., the young branches slender, glaucous. Leaves mostly in threes, sometimes in pairs, persisting for about three years; 1 to 2 ins. long, dark green; in each cluster the inner faces of the leaves are pressed together, especially when young; margins not toothed; leaf-sheath at first ¼ to ⅜ in. long, the scales afterwards becoming reflexed and forming a rosette round the base of each cluster. Cones roundish, egg-shaped, 1½ to 2 ins. long, 1 to 1½ ins. wide, with very few scales. Seeds ½ in. long, edible.

Native of Mexico, Arizona, and Lower California; introduced by Hartweg in 1839. The seeds are sold in Mexican markets as "piñones" along with those of P edulis, to which the present species is closely related. The leaves of that species, however, are chiefly in pairs instead of threes; the branches are stouter, and the leaves usually thicker. These two are the only pines with two or three leaves in a cluster that have rosette-like leaf-sheaths. (See also P. edulis and P. monophylla.)

P. CONTORTA, *Loudon*. BEACH PINE

A tree 20 to 30 ft. high in a wild state, but apparently likely to grow higher in cultivation; bark thick, roughly fissured; young shoots often curiously twisted, not downy; terminal buds narrowly cylindrical, $\frac{3}{4}$ to 1 in. long, resinous. Leaves in pairs, $1\frac{1}{2}$ to $2\frac{1}{4}$ ins. long, $\frac{1}{12}$ in. or less wide; dark green; persisting three, four, or more years; leaf-sheath $\frac{3}{16}$ in. long, persistent. Cones obliquely conical, up to 2 ins. long, $\frac{3}{4}$ in. wide at the base before expanding; the scales terminated by a slender spine which wears away in time. The cones remain on the tree for four or five years, or even longer, before shedding their seed.

Native of the coast region of western N. America, from Alaska to S. California; discovered by Douglas in 1825; introduced later at some uncertain date. (See also *P. Murrayana*.)

P. COULTERI, *D. Don*. COULTER'S PINE

A tree 50 to 80 ft. high, with a stout, erect trunk, 3 to 4 ft. in thickness, whose bark is divided into deep broad ridges. Young shoots very thick, often glaucous, not downy; the terminal part carrying a cluster of crowded leaves, the lower part furnished with fringed, slender-pointed scales, 1 in. long. The older portions of the branchlet are rough with the remains of these scales, and the prominences on which the leaf-bundles were seated. Buds conical, resinous, slender-pointed, $1\frac{1}{2}$ ins. long, $\frac{3}{4}$ in. wide. Leaves in threes, falling the fourth year; 10 to 14 ins. long, minutely toothed, grey-green, with lines of stomata on all three faces; leaf-sheaths persistent, 1 in. long. Cones 10 ins. to 12 ins. long, 5 to 7 ins. thick; the scales terminated by a stout triangular spine.

Native of California; discovered by Dr Coulter in 1832; introduced by Douglas the same year. The cones of this remarkable pine are the heaviest and most formidably armed among three-leaved pines, but are not often borne in this country. It resembles P. ponderosa in leaf and shoot, but is a shorter tree with more spreading branches. The cones are very different, and more like those of P. Sabiniana; which, however, has smoother, more slender shoots, and greyer leaves. Coulter's pine is not common in cultivation, but is very striking in its somewhat gaunt branching, its terminal bunches of leaves, spreading like a sweep's brush, and its immense cones.

P. DENSIFLORA, *Siebold and Zuccarini*. JAPANESE RED PINE

A tree 100 to 120 ft. high in Japan, with a trunk 3 to 4 ft. through; bark of trunk reddish, scaling; young shoots blue-white, glabrous; buds cylindrical, brown, resinous. Leaves in pairs, falling the third year, $2\frac{1}{2}$ to 4 ins. long, slender, dark green on both surfaces, margins very minutely toothed; leaf-sheath $\frac{1}{4}$ to $\frac{3}{8}$ in. long, persistent, terminated often by one or two slender threads. Cones $1\frac{1}{2}$ to 2 ins. long, $\frac{3}{4}$ to 1 in. wide before expansion, conical. pointed; seed $\frac{1}{4}$ in. long, with a wing about thrice as long.

Introduced by Siebold from Japan to Europe in 1854. It is a useful timber tree in its native country, filling much the same place in the flora there that the Scotch pine does in Europe. It is one of the favourite plants upon which the Japanese gardeners exercise their dwarfing arts. There is a group of trees at Kew, rather noticeable for their reddish crooked trunks. The species is not likely to have any timber value with us. It resembles P. sylvestris in the resinous buds and reddish trunk, but is very different in general appearance, the leaves being green (not grey) and the young shoots glaucous (not green). Both this pine and P. Thunbergii are found in gardens as "P. Massoniana," but the true P. MASSONIANA, *Lambert*, is a more southern tree, not, so far as I am aware, in cultivation, and probably too tender for our climate.

Var. AUREA behaves exactly like P. sylvestris aurea in the leaves turning yellow in autumn and winter, changing to green again in spring and summer.

P. ECHINATA, *Miller*. EASTERN YELLOW PINE

(P. mitis, *Michaux*)

A tree 30 to 50 ft. high in this country, over 100 ft. high in a wild state; young shoots quite glabrous, covered with blue-white bloom, slender, very brittle after they are one year old, the bark peeling the third year; terminal bud cylindrical, $\frac{1}{4}$ to $\frac{1}{3}$ in. long, not resinous, scales fringed. Leaves in pairs or in threes, mostly falling the second year; $1\frac{1}{2}$ to 4 ins. long, slender, dull green; leaf-sheath $\frac{1}{4}$ to $\frac{1}{2}$ in. long, persistent. Cones $1\frac{1}{2}$ to $2\frac{1}{2}$ ins. long, $\frac{3}{4}$ to 1 in. wide at the base before expanding; conical, with a short, distinct stalk.

Native of the eastern United States from New York State southwards; cultivated in this country since early in the eighteenth century. It is but little known, and has, indeed, no conspicuous qualities to recommend it for garden or park. It is distinct in its blue-white young shoots, occasionally three-leaved clusters, and brittle shoots covered with peeling bark after the second year. In N. America it is a very valuable timber tree.

P. EDULIS, *Engelmann*. TWO-LEAF NUT PINE

(P. cembroides edulis, *Voss*)

A small tree rarely more than 20 to 30 ft. high, often a mere bush in gardens; young shoots somewhat glaucous. Leaves in pairs, occasionally in threes, persisting three or four years; $\frac{3}{4}$ to $1\frac{1}{2}$ ins. long, stiff, pointed, without marginal teeth, dark green outside, inner faces glaucous with stomatic lines. The leaves in each bundle are inclined to remain with their inner faces close together; when they are in pairs they are semi-terete, when in threes triangular in section; leaf-sheath $\frac{1}{4}$ in. long at first, the scales afterwards reflexed, forming a rosette. Cones $\frac{3}{4}$ to 2 ins. long, composed of a few large woody scales, terminated by a small spine.

Native of the eastern foothills of the outer ranges of the Rocky Mountains from Colorado to New Mexico. The edible seeds are sold in the markets there. It is a pleasing small tree of neat dense habit, but very rare in gardens. It is not easy always to discriminate between this species and P. cembroides, both of which have rosette-like leaf-sheaths, but this appears to be sturdier in branch, and shorter and stiffer in leaf, and the leaves are more frequently in pairs than in threes.

P. EXCELSA, *Wallich*. BHOTAN PINE

(P. Wallichiana, *Jackson*; P. Griffithii, *McClelland*)

A tree reaching 150 ft. in height in a wild state, and already over 100 ft. high in cultivation; young shoots blue-green, perfectly free from down, slightly ridged below each bundle of leaves towards the apex. Leaves in fives, falling the second and third years, 5 to 7 ins. long, triangular in section, two faces white with stomatic lines, the third bright green; margins minutely toothed, sharply pointed ; leaf-sheath $\frac{5}{8}$ to $\frac{3}{4}$ in. long, soon falling wholly away. The leaves are often bent abruptly near the base, so that the greater part of the leaf is pendulous. Cones at first cylindrical, 6 to 10 ins. long, $1\frac{1}{2}$ to $1\frac{3}{4}$ ins. wide, before opening ; each on a stalk 1 to 2 ins. long ; scales $1\frac{1}{2}$ ins. long, 1 in. wide, with a small, pointed, thickened apex.

Native of the Himalaya ; introduced by A. B. Lambert in 1823. It is a handsome tree especially when of middle age, and grows with great rapidity when young, the leading shoot increasing by 2 to 3 ft. annually. It thrives best in a good sandy loam, and in a position sheltered from fierce gales, which give it a bedraggled appearance. Very hardy, and bearing cones early. It is only likely to be confused in gardens with P. Armandii, and P. Ayachahuite, both of which have more or less downy shoots and different cones. Its glabrous shoots, its five-clustered leaves and quickly falling leaf-sheath, distinguish it from all other pines except P. Peuce (*q.v.*).

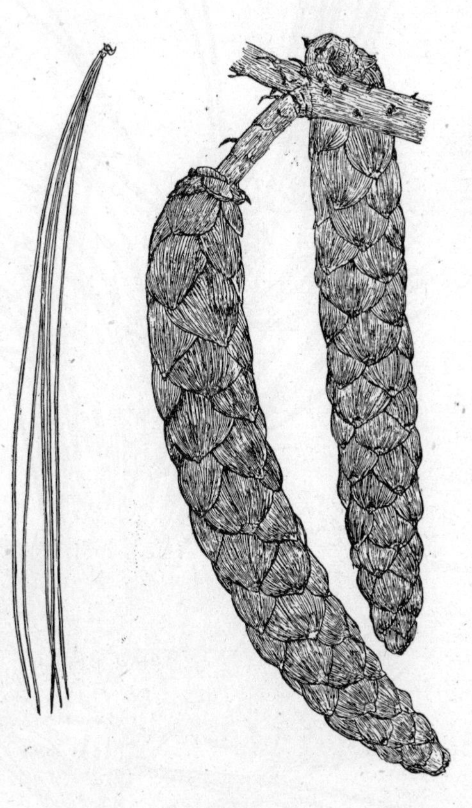

PINUS EXCELSA

P. FLEXILIS, *James*. LIMBER PINE

(Bot. Mag., t. 8467)

A tree 40 to 60, sometimes 80 ft. high ; branches long, slender ; the young parts so flexible that they can be bent double without breaking ; young shoots shining green, perfectly glabrous or with minute brownish down. Leaves in fives, persisting for about seven years, often pointing forwards, or the youngest ones even appressed to the branchlet ; $2\frac{1}{2}$ to $3\frac{1}{2}$ ins. long, triangular in section, all three sides marked with three or four white lines of stomata ; margins quite entire, apex finely pointed ; leaf-sheaths $\frac{1}{2}$ to $\frac{5}{8}$ in. long, soon falling away. Cones 3 to 5 ins. long, $1\frac{1}{2}$ ins. thick before the scales open.

Native of western N. America ; introduced by Jeffrey in 1851. Trees at Kew between 30 and 40 ft. high thrive well in gravelly soil, and bear cones most seasons. It is a very distinct pine, resembling P. Balfouriana in its long-persisting leaves, but very different in other respects. From all cultivated five-leaved pines, except P. albicaulis (*q.v.*), it is easily distinguished by the absence of teeth on the leaf-edges, combined with often glabrous branchlets and deciduous leaf-sheaths. Although a fairly lofty tree in favourable localities, it becomes at very high elevations reduced to mere prostrate scrub, barely 1 ft. high. In this state, according to Sargent, it holds in possession the bleak summits of the Cascade Mountains in California undisputed by any other tree.

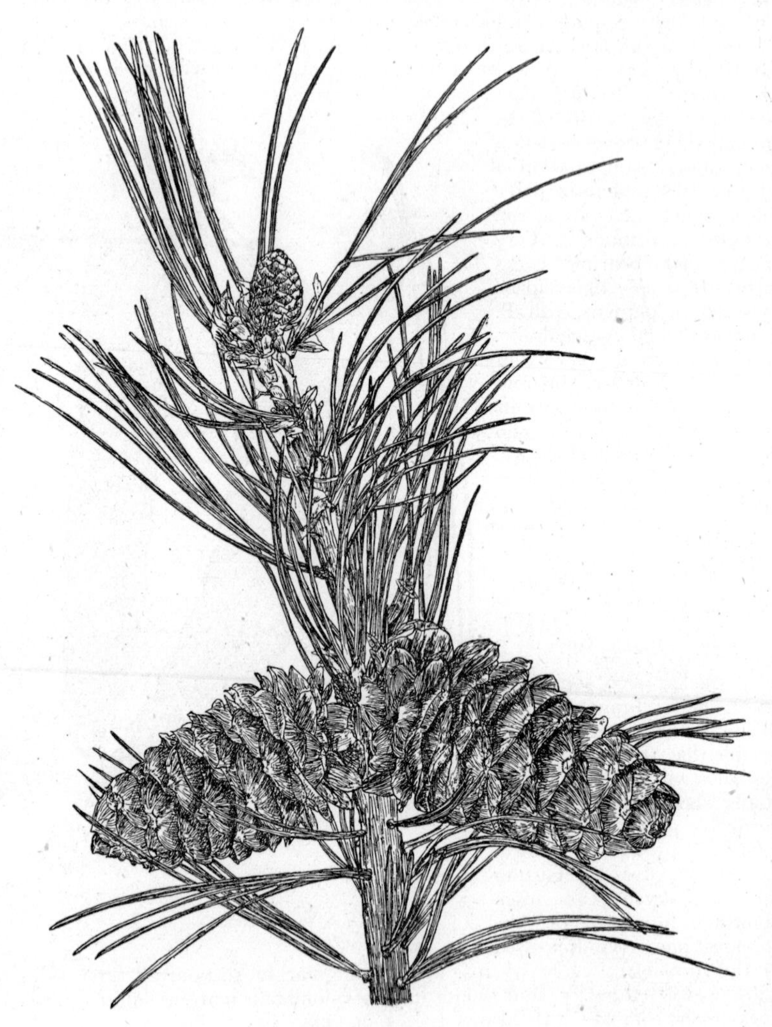

PINUS FLEXILIS

P. GERARDIANA, *Wallich*. GERARD'S PINE

One of the rarest of pines in cultivation, the only good specimen in England of which there is general knowledge being in the Cambridge Botanic Garden. This, when I saw it in February 1911, was a little under 15 ft. high, of shapely form and in perfect health. Small plants have from time to time been raised at Kew, but are spring tender and grow slowly. Except in the south-western gardens it has little interest to cultivators. In the Himalaya it is a tree 80 ft. high; its shoots are smooth, and its leaves three in a bundle. The leaves of the Cambridge tree are 2 to 4 ins. long, dark dullish green, sharply pointed; leaf-sheath ½ in. long, the scales becoming loose by winter and falling away the second year. In branch and leaf it is like P. Bungeana, and has a similar peeling bark; the trunk, however, does not become white in old trees like that of Bungeana, which differs also in its brighter leaves and quickly deciduous leaf-sheath. The cones of P. Gerardiana are described by Brandis as 6 to 9 ins. long, 4 to 5 ins. wide—thus many times larger than those of P. Bungeana.

P. HALEPENSIS, *Miller*. ALEPPO PINE

A tree rarely more than 30 to 50 ft. high in this country, but 70 to 80 ft. in favourable conditions; here it usually forms a rounded head of branches, but is more pyramidal in the south of Europe; young shoots pale grey, glabrous; buds slenderly conical, pointed, non-resinous, about ½ in. long, with the points of the scales slender, fringed, and recurved. Leaves in pairs (rarely in threes), falling the second and third years; 2½ to 4½ ins. long, very slender; leaf-sheath ¼ to ⅓ in. long. Cones pointing backwards, 2½ to 3½ ins. long, 1 to 1½ ins. wide at the base, tapering to a slender point; scales unarmed; stalk ¼ to ½ in. long; they are produced in pairs, threes, or singly and remain several years on the branches.

Native of S. Europe as far west as Spain and east to Asia Minor; introduced in the seventeenth century. Although tender in a young state it is hardy enough when once established; several examples at Kew have withstood 31° of frost, and are quite healthy. This species and P. Brutia are distinguished among two-leaved pines by the non-resinous buds having recurved scales. The newly cut or bruised young wood has a most pleasant aromatic odour. It is the commonest pine along the south coast of Europe, and reaches perhaps its finest development along the Dalmatian coast, where I have seen it 70 to 80 ft. high, remarkably handsome in its heavy plumose masses of foliage. It covers bleak rocky promontories near Ragusa. (See *P. Brutia* for differences between it and the present species.)

P. HARTWEGI, *Lindley*. HARTWEG'S PINE

(P. Montezumæ Hartwegi, *Engelmann*)

A very near relative of Montezuma's pine, but found in Mexico at higher levels and under colder conditions. It is, in consequence, a much hardier tree. There is a good specimen, perhaps 30 ft. high, in Windsor Forest, which is the nearest to London that I know of, of any size. I have had it also in cone from Luscombe Castle, Dawlish, and it is at Bayfordbury and Westonbirt. Leaves mostly in fives, but also in threes or fours; 5 to 6½ ins. long, crowded at the end of the shoot; stiff, grey-green, closely and minutely toothed on the margin, sharply pointed; leaf-sheaths quite persistent, ¾ to 1 in. long. Cones 3 or 4 ins. long, 1½ ins. wide; scales with a decurved spine-tipped boss. It differs chiefly from P. Montezumæ in its shorter leaves and much hardier constitution. It is a tree up to 70 ft. high, with stout young shoots.

Discovered and introduced by Hartweg in 1839.

P. HOLFORDIANA, *A. B. Jackson*

A natural hybrid pine of the five-leaved group between P. Ayacahuite and P. excelsa. It is similar in habit and general appearance to the former, from the famous example of which at Westonbirt the hybrid cone and seeds were gathered. The shoots differ from those of P. excelsa in usually being hairy and the cones are broader than in that species; from P. Ayacahuite it is distinguished by the apices of the cone-scales not being reflexed and by the smaller seeds which have a narrower, longer seed-wing. The difference between the cone of P. Ayacahuite and that of the hybrid are well shown by figures 68 and 69 in the *Gardeners' Chronicle*, 4th March 1933. Trees raised from seeds of the original hybrid now at Woburn and Bayfordbury have produced cones similar to it in character. It will perpetuate the memory of Sir George Holford, the late owner of Westonbirt and an enthusiastic cultivator of hardy trees and shrubs.

P. JEFFREYI, *A. Murray*. JEFFREY S PINE

(Bot. Mag., t. 8257)

So closely allied is this to P. ponderosa that it is very frequently regarded as a variety only of that species. It has the same lofty, columnar trunk (occasionally nearly 200 ft. high), stout branches with clusters of large spreading leaves in bundles of threes at the ends, and an orange-like odour when cut. It differs in the following respects: young shoots of a blue-white colour, leaves stiffer, and the cones much larger, 5 to 10 ins. long, 2 to 3 ins. wide. It is confined to California in a wild state, where, in the Shasta Valley, it was discovered in 1852 by Jeffrey, and introduced for the Oregon Association the same year. Jepson says it merges insensibly into P. ponderosa.

P. KORAIENSIS, *Siebold and Zuccarini*. KOREAN PINE

A tree reaching at its best 100 to 150 ft. in height; young shoots thickly clothed with short, reddish brown wool; winter buds ½ in. long, cylindrical, with a tapered point, resinous. Leaves in fives, persisting to the third year; 3½ to 4½ ins. long, dark glossy green, with white stomatal lines on two faces; margins toothed the whole length, the apex bluntish; leaf-sheaths about ½ in. long, soon falling. Cones about 5 ins. long, 2½ to 3 ins. wide at the base, tapering thence towards the apex. Scales 1¼ ins. wide, thick and woody. Seeds ⅝ in. long, not winged, edible.

Native of Korea, Japan, Manchuria, etc.; introduced by J. G. Veitch in 1861. It is, perhaps, most closely allied to P. Cembra, but the growth is more open, the leaves are much more spreading, blunter, and toothed quite to the apex. The cones, too, are twice as long. P. koraiensis is not a first-class pine in this country, growing slowly. The best example I have seen is in Mr Hunnewell's garden, at Wellesley, Mass., U.S.A., about 40 ft. high in 1910. There are good specimens at Kilmacurragh and Fota in Ireland, and at Segrez in France, all 35 to over 40 ft. high.

Var. VARIEGATA, *Hort.*, has some of the leaves yellow, others striped longitudinally in yellow and green, others wholly green—all sometimes in the same bundle.

P. LAMBERTIANA, *Douglas*. SUGAR PINE

A tree 70 to sometimes well over 200 ft. high, and with a trunk 3 to 8 ft. in diameter; young shoots minutely downy; winter buds ¼ in. long, usually round or blunt at the apex, the scales closely flattened. Leaves in fives, falling the third year; 3 to 4½ ins. long, minutely toothed at the margins, bluish green, often spirally twisted; leaf-sheaths ½ to ⅝ in. long, soon falling completely away. Cones borne at the ends of the uppermost branches; 12 to 20 ins. long, about 3 ins. thick before expanding; the woody scales 2 to 2½ ins. long, with a broadly pointed apex. Seeds ½ to ¾ in. long, nutty in flavour, the wing nearly twice as long.

Native of western N. America, in Oregon and California; introduced in 1827 by Douglas, who had also discovered it. It is probably the noblest of all pines. The popular name refers to a sugary exudation from the trunk. In this country it has rarely borne its remarkable cones. It is allied to, as well as a neighbour of, P. monticola, but besides the differences in cones, the buds are more rounded and the leaf is more sharply pointed in Lambertiana. From P. Strobus its uniformly downy shoots distinguish it. It likes a sheltered situation and a good loamy soil. Even then it grows but slowly, but is handsome nevertheless. Trees approaching 100 ft. exist in this country, perhaps the finest one being at Arley Castle, near Bewdley. A tree at Dropmore has borne cones at intervals since 1872.

P. LARICIO, *Poiret.* CORSICAN PINE

A tree from 100 to 150 ft. high, and 4 to 6 ft. in thickness of trunk, the bark dark grey and deeply fissured on old trees. Young shoots light brown, not downy; terminal buds resinous, ½ in. or more long, cylindrical at the base, narrowing abruptly at the apex to a slender point. Leaves in pairs, 4 to 7 ins. long, falling in their fourth year, semi-terete, very minutely toothed, dark green; leaf-sheath about ½ in. long. Cones often in pairs or in threes, 2 to 3 ins. long, 1¼ ins. wide before opening, conical, bright brown; the scales terminated sometimes by a minute prickle, but mostly unarmed.

This pine is a very variable one, and is found over a great range of country —from Spain in the West, to Greece, Asia Minor, and the Caucasus in the East; introduced in 1759. It reaches, perhaps, its finest development in Corsica, where it is sometimes 140 to 150 ft. high. Henry mentions a tree there with a short trunk 23 ft. in girth. In Britain it has been planted largely as a forest tree, and among introduced coniferous trees promises to be second in value only to the larch. It is bad to transplant if allowed to remain more than two years in one spot. The best results, perhaps, are obtained by planting trees not more than 1 ft. high. Rabbits are said not to touch it, although they eat the variety nigricans (Austrian pine), and it has the faculty of fighting its way through grass on all but the richest of land. As a garden tree it forms a handsome and stately specimen. It has a very involved nomenclature.

Var. NIGRICANS, *Parlatore* (P. austriaca, *Hoess*). Austrian Pine.—This well-known tree, introduced from S.E. Europe in 1835, is very distinct in general appearance from, and decidedly inferior to, the Corsican pine. It has a rougher, shorter trunk, with more numerous branches, and heavier masses of darker green leaves, which on the whole are shorter, stiffer, and straighter than those of P. Laricio. The whole tree has a coarser, heavier aspect. It is very useful for growing on poor chalky soil, and as a shelter tree in bleak situations, especially near the sea. Its value as a timber tree is much less than that of P. Laricio.

Var. PALLASIANA, *Endlicher.*—Distinct in habit, being more or less pyramidal, with the main branches growing erect; cones 3 to 4 ins. long. A handsome garden tree, native probably of the Crimea. The tree described by Loudon under the above name appears to be something quite different.

Var. TENUIFOLIA, *Parlatore* (P. pyrenaica). Pyrenean Pine.—A distinct variety with orange-coloured young bark, and very slender leaves 6 or 7 ins. long (in gardens); often a bushy tree. It is the most Western form of the Laricio pine, being found on the Spanish side of the Pyrenees, and in France in the Cevennes.

Of purely garden varieties are the following: AUREA, a form of Austrian pine whose young growths are tipped with gold; PUMILA (pygmæa), a dwarf, rounded bush, a specimen of which, at least forty years old, was only 8 ft. high at Kew.

Closely allied to P. Laricio is

P. LEUCODERMIS, *Antoine* (P. Laricio leucodermis, *Christ*).—A tree up to 90 ft. in height, young shoots light brown the first year, turning grey the second. Leaves in pairs, very rigid and erect, persisting five years, up to 4½ ins. long, dark green. Native of Bosnia, Herzegovina, and Montenegro; discovered in 1864, and introduced to Kew in 1890. A purely mountain tree, very hardy. It is, no doubt, very close to P. Laricio—perhaps only a geographical form. In young plants the chief distinctions are in the short, stiff leaves and glaucous young shoots. According to Elwes, it makes a much better root system than either the Austrian or Corsican pine, and therefore transplants better. It is worth looking after for forestry purposes.

P. MONOPHYLLA, *Torrey*. ONE-LEAF NUT PINE

(P. cembroides monophylla, *Voss*)

A tree usually 15 to 20 ft. high, pyramidal as represented by cultivated plants; young shoots grey, glabrous or nearly so. Leaves solitary and terete, or occasionally in pairs, and then semi-terete, not toothed at the margin; 1 to 1¾ ins. long, sharply pointed, curved; marked all round with stomatic lines, grey-green; leaf-sheaths at first about ¼ in. long, afterwards curled back round the base of the leaf like a rosette. Cones 1½ to 2 ins. long, with few thickened spoon-like scales; seeds ⅝ in. long.

Native of Utah, Nevada, Arizona, and Lower California; discovered in 1844, and introduced by Hartweg in 1848. This curious pine is distinct from all others in the mostly solitary leaves, although in the rosette-like sheath it clearly shows its affinity to the cembroides and edulis group. It is an interesting curiosity, but grows too slowly to have much value in the garden. The seeds, like those of its allies, are eaten by the Indian tribes of Nevada, and have a sweet, nutty flavour, improved by roasting. The healthiest tree I have seen was in Messrs Paul & Son's nursery at Cheshunt, 17 ft. high, and there was one about as large at Old Conna Hill, near Bray, Ireland.

P. MONTANA, *Miller*. MOUNTAIN PINE

(P. mugo, *Turra*)

This name is applied to a group of pines varying in stature from dwarf shrubs to trees 60 to 80 ft. high, yet in botanical characters almost identical; young shoots rough with scale leaves, not downy; terminal buds resinous, ¼ to ½ in. long. Leaves in pairs, persisting five or more years; 1½ to 3 ins. long, conspicuously curved and twisted, stiff, dark green, pointed; leaf-sheath ⅓ to ⅝ in. long. Cones 1 to 2½ ins. long; scales blunt-ended.

Native of S. and Central Europe, always in mountainous regions, where it is often the highest woody plant. The form most commonly cultivated in Britain is a dwarf one known as

P. PUMILIO, *Haenke*, or P. montana pumilio, *Willkomm*.—This grows 5 to 10 ft. high, forming not one leader but a cluster of several stems curving out from the bottom.

The cone is about 1½ ins. long. Native of Central and S.E. Europe, from the Jura Mountains of W. Switzerland to Montenegro. In gardens this pine is extremely useful as an evergreen covering for dry slopes and mounds, and thrives in the poorest soil. It transplants very well. Not often distinguished from this in gardens is P. MUGHUS, *Scopoli*, which is similar in habit, and differs in no important matter, but has a more Eastern distribution, reaching into Bulgaria and Serbia. It is also known as P. montana Mughus, *Willkomm*.

P. UNCINATA, *Ramond*, or P. montana uncinata, *Willkomm*. This is the largest form of P. montana, and becomes a tree 60 to 80 ft. high. It is also quite distinct in the cones, the scales of which are remarkably deflexed at their bluntly pyramidal apex. This is the Western form of P. montana, and occurs in Spain and France. So far as I have seen, it has little value as an ornamental tree in this country. Among two-leaved pines with resinous cylindric buds, the scales of which are appressed, all the forms of P. montana are distinguished by the greater length of the leaf-sheath.

P. MONTEZUMÆ, *Lambert*. MONTEZUMA PINE

A tree up to 70 ft. high, with very thick, reddish brown young branchlets that are rough with fringed scale-leaves, the scaly bases of the fallen leaf-bundles and the prominences on which they were seated; not downy. Winter buds 1 in. long, ⅓ in. thick, clothed with long, fringed scales. Leaves in fives, very crowded, persisting three years; from 7 to 12 ins. long, blue-green, minutely toothed on the margin; leaf-sheaths up to 2 ins. long, persistent. Cones very variable, usually from 4 to 8 ins. long, 2 to 3½ ins. wide at the base, tapering upwards.

Native of Mexico, where it is very widely spread and abundant; introduced by Hartweg in 1839. In some respects, especially in size of leaf (known sometimes to be 18 ins. long), this is the most remarkable of all pines, but it is only hardy in Cornwall, the south-west of Ireland, and such-like places. There are good specimens at Fota in Ireland, Bicton in Devon, Pencarrow, Menabilly, Tregothnan, and other places in Cornwall. It belongs to the small group of five-leaved pines, with persistent leaf-sheaths, the hardiest of which is P. Hartwegi. The pines known in the gardens of the south-west as P. RUSSELLIANA, DEVONIANA, and LINDLEYANA are forms of P. Montezumæ.

Nearly allied to it is P. PSEUDO-STROBUS, *Lindley*, which is, however, easily distinguished by its very glaucous, more slender shoots. It is as tender as P. Montezumæ, and appears only to exist in this country at Pencarrow and Tregothnan. The Pencarrow specimen (80 ft. high) has leaves 10 ins. long, more slender than in P. Montezumæ, but in other respects similar. Native of Mexico; introduced in 1839.

P. MONTICOLA, *Lambert*. WESTERN WHITE PINE

A tree up to 175 ft. high, with a trunk 4 ft. or more in diameter; young shoots downy; winter buds ovoid, with flattened scales. Leaves in fives, 3 to 4½ ins. long, rough at the margins (minutely toothed under the lens), glaucous green, with several lines of stomata on the inner sides; leaf-sheath about ⅝ in. long, soon falling. Cones 5 to 10 ins. long, 1¼ ins. wide before expanding, cylindrical, tapered, and curved towards the end; scales thin, smooth, rounded at the apex, terminated by a dark resinous scar (umbo).

Native of western N. America from British Columbia and Vancouver Island to California; introduced by Douglas in 1831. Although not so well known in this country as its eastern ally—P. Strobus, it is a handsome tree for gardens, assuming a shapely, slender, pyramidal shape. It is liable to be confused with P. Strobus, but the short down all over the shoot usually distinguishes it. Its leaves also are stiffer and stouter. It yields a useful timber in its native home, but in Europe is planted for ornament only. A tree at Murthly and another at Scone in Perthshire are both over 80 ft. high.

P. MURICATA, *Don*. BISHOP'S PINE (Plate 38)

(P. Edgariana, *Hartweg*)

A tree 50 to 90 ft. high, with a rough brown bark, often flat-topped and with wide-spreading branches; young shoots densely leafy, glabrous, brown; terminal buds cylindrical, pointed, $\frac{1}{2}$ to 1 in. long, coated with resin. Leaves in pairs, falling the third or fourth year, rigid, 3 to 5 (sometimes 7) ins. long, semi-terete, dark green; leaf-sheath persistent, $\frac{1}{2}$ to $\frac{5}{8}$ in. long. Cones obliquely egg-shaped, $2\frac{1}{2}$ to $3\frac{1}{2}$ ins. long, the boss on the scales terminated by a stiff, slightly hooked spine.

Native of California; originally discovered in 1832 at San Luis Obispo, from which it gets its popular name; introduced by Hartweg in 1846. This remarkable pine bears its cones in whorls of three to seven; they are deflexed, and the inner or less exposed side being less developed gives them their unsymmetrical shape. They remain on the tree and retain their seed for an indefinite period, at least twenty-five to thirty years, and often until the branch bearing them is 5 or 6 ins. in diameter. This enables the species to survive forest fires, which, although they destroy the old trees, only affect the cones sufficiently to expand the scales and allow the uninjured seed to escape. The tree grows on exposed bluffs and headlands in Monterey and other places along the coast of California, where it is at times drenched with ocean spray. I have a letter from a correspondent in Guernsey, who says that it withstands the salt winds of that island even better than P. radiata (insignis). In such places it will be chiefly valuable as a shelter tree, its timber being inferior; but it is also handsome, and worth growing for its interest. The finest tree I have seen is at Claremont; in 1910 this was between 70 and 75 ft. high. Among two-leaved pines with persistent leaf-sheaths this is distinguished by its cylindrical, resin-covered buds and long, deep green leaves.

P. MURRAYANA, *Balfour*. LODGE-POLE PINE

(P. contorta Murrayana, *Engelmann*)

By many authorities this is considered to be no more than a variety of P. contorta, but the aspect of the trees in cultivation is so distinct that the retention of the more convenient specific name seems desirable. P. Murrayana is most conveniently distinguished from contorta by the thin bark of its trunk (rarely more than $\frac{1}{4}$ in. thick), of a pale grey or brown, covered with thin scales, but comparatively smooth; also by its larger, broader leaves, 2 to 3 ins. long, about $\frac{1}{12}$ in. wide. The tree itself attains to a considerably larger size than P. contorta, and is usually 70 to 80 ft. high. On the Sierra Nevada it becomes 100 to 125 ft. high. Whilst P. contorta inhabits the coast region, this is found at elevations of 5000 to 11,000 ft. According to Elwes, there are trees at Westonbirt 59 ft. and 54 ft. high, and I saw one at Bayfordbury some years ago, 50 ft. high. Introduced in 1854, by Jeffrey. In a small state P. contorta, with its narrower, richer green leaves appears to be usually the handsomer tree.

These two trees belong to the group of two-leaved pines with persistent leaf-sheaths, and cylindrical, resinous winter buds. Branches alone would be most likely to be confused with the European P. montana, which has all the characters just mentioned, but whose leaf-sheath is twice or more than twice as long ($\frac{1}{3}$ to $\frac{3}{5}$ in.). The two are, of course, very different in habit.

P. Parryana, *Engelmann*

(P. quadrifolia, *Parry*)

A tree 20 to 40 ft. high; young shoots slightly downy. Leaves 1¼ to 1¾ ins. long, usually in fours, occasionally in fives or threes, mostly falling the third year, finely pointed, sharply triangular in section, white with stomata on the two inner sides, not toothed at the margin; scales of the leaf-sheath curled back in the form of a rosette. The first year each bundle of leaves keeps almost closed, showing little but the bright green outer side of each leaf. Cones roundish, 1½ to 2 ins. wide, with comparatively few scales. Seeds ⅝ in. long, edible.

Native of S. California and Lower California; discovered by Dr Parry, after whom it is named, in 1850. It is one of the cembroides group well marked by their entire-margined leaves and rosette-like leaf-sheaths. In this group monophylla has its leaves solitary; edulis has them in pairs; cembroides in threes; Parryana in fours; and Balfouriana and aristata in fives. This, however, is the general rule; all of them vary to some extent in this matter. The species is very rare and slow in growth.

P. parviflora, *Siebold and Zuccarini*. Japanese White Pine

A tree 30 to 40 ft. high at present in this country, but twice as high in Japan; young shoots minutely downy; winter buds ovoid, $\frac{3}{16}$ in. long, some of their scales free at the tips. Leaves in fives, falling the third year, 1½ to 2½ ins. long, very slightly toothed on the margins, with silvery lines of stomata on the inner surfaces; leaf-sheath ⅜ in. long, soon falling completely away. Cones egg-shaped, 2 to 4 ins. long, 1¼ to 1¾ ins. wide before expanding, usually produced in whorls of three or four, and in extraordinary profusion even when quite young.

Introduced from Japan in 1861, by John Gould Veitch, and frequent in gardens where its small size renders it easily accommodated, and where it is appreciated for its neat growth. Its cones open widely and persist six or seven years; a tree heavily laden with them has its aspect somewhat spoilt. There are two well-marked forms in cultivation; one with stiffer leaves, very glaucous inside, and quite pale shining shoots, distinguished as var. glauca; the other with softer, more grass-like foliage, and dark brown, more downy shoots. Many of the dwarfed pines so largely imported from Japan during the last two decades belong to this species. It likes a moist, well-drained, loamy soil.

P. pentaphylla, *Mayr*, is apparently a form of P. parviflora, with longer cones (3½ ins.) and thicker leaves. It has a more northerly habitat in Japan, whence it has recently been introduced.

P. patula, *Schlechtendal*. Mexican Pine

A tree ordinarily 40 to 50 ft., sometimes 80 ft. high, with rough old bark often branching low and acquiring a spreading round-topped shape when old. Young shoots glabrous, rather glaucous at first, becoming scaly and reddish brown. Winter buds not resinous, ½ to ¾ in. long, cylindrical; covered with awl-shaped, pointed, fringed, brown scales which are free except at the base and slightly spreading. Leaves pendulous, normally in threes (occasionally in fours or fives), 6 to 9 ins. long, very slender, and very minutely toothed on the margins, persisting two to four years; basal sheath persistent, about

1 in. long. Cones shortly stalked, often in clusters of two to five; $2\frac{1}{2}$ to 4 ins. long, $1\frac{1}{4}$ to $1\frac{1}{2}$ ins. wide at the base; tapering upwards, curved, unequally sided at the base, pale shining brown.

Native of Mexico; discovered in 1828 and introduced then or soon after as a plant 6 ft. high is recorded by Loudon to have been growing in the garden of A. B. Lambert in 1837. It must be accounted one of the rather tender pines, and it is found at its best in Cornwall and similar places. The finest tree I have seen is at Tregrehan, its wide-spreading, dome-like head of branches 50 ft. high, its trunk $7\frac{1}{2}$ ft. in girth. A taller but not so well-furnished a tree is at Carclew. This pine is unmistakable in its very slender, drooping leaves in bundles of threes with a persistent leaf-sheath. Very attractive and distinct for mild districts, it may also be tried in cooler places. In 1932 it was 20 ft. high at Wisley and about the same at Glasnevin.

P. GREGGII, *Engelmann*, is a pine from N.E. Mexico closely akin to P. patula. Leaves in threes, bright green, shorter and not so pendulous. Cones very like those of P. patula, but tawny yellow. A distinctive character is the smooth grey bark of P. Greggii. Were it not for this character, Shaw in *The Genus Pinus*, p. 86, remarks that it might be considered to be a north-eastern variety of P. patula with shorter, more erect leaves. It ought to be at least as hardy as that species and has in fact been grown out-of-doors at Leonardslee in Sussex for some years. (Syn. P. patula macrocarpa, *Masters*.)

P. PEUCE, *Grisebach*. MACEDONIAN PINE

A tree not yet more than 40 to 60 ft. high in this country, but twice as high in Bulgaria; densely branched, and slenderly pyramidal; young shoots glossy green, quite glabrous. Leaves in fives, mostly falling in their third year; 3 to 4 ins. long, very densely borne on the shoots, pointed forwards, three-sided; two of the sides have three or four lines of white stomata, the other one is bright green; margins roughened with tiny teeth; leaf-sheaths soon falling. Cones on stalks about $\frac{1}{3}$ in. long; themselves 4 or 5 ins. long, $1\frac{1}{4}$ to $1\frac{1}{2}$ ins. wide before expanding; scales in the middle about $1\frac{1}{2}$ ins. long, half as wide, thin at the margins.

Native of Macedonia, where it was first found by Dr Grisebach in 1839, also of Bulgaria and Montenegro; introduced in 1864. One of the smaller and slower growing pines, this is suitable for small gardens. Trees raised in 1864 are about 45 ft. high at Kew. It grows about 1 ft. in height yearly. It is considered to be very closely allied to P. excelsa, but the two are extremely distinct in general appearance. P. Peuke is much denser in leaf and branch; its leaves are shorter, greener, and never have the kink near the base seen in excelsa. The cones also are shorter and thicker. It resembles P. Cembra more as a young tree, but that species has very shaggy young shoots.

P. PINASTER, *Aiton*. CLUSTER PINE, MARITIME PINE

(S. maritima, *Durieu*)

A tree reaching 100 to 120 ft. in height, forming a tall, rugged, dark trunk. Young shoots not downy, pale brown; terminalwin ter buds, 1 to $1\frac{1}{4}$ ins. long, $\frac{1}{3}$ to $\frac{1}{2}$ in. wide, cylindrical with a conical apex, clothed with awl-shaped, outwardly curving scales conspicuously fringed with silvery threads. Leaves in pairs, 4 to 8 ins. long, $\frac{1}{12}$ in. wide, stiff and stout, dark green, falling the third and fourth years; slightly roughened at the margins; leaf-sheath $\frac{5}{8}$ to $\frac{3}{4}$ in. long, persistent. Cones usually borne in whorls, deflexed, 4 or 5 (sometimes 7) ins. long, 2 to $2\frac{1}{2}$ ins. wide at the base before opening, tapering to a point, bright brown, often persisting for many years.

Native of S. Europe, from W. France to Greece; cultivated since the sixteenth century. As an old tree it is singularly picturesque, its dark, deeply fissured trunk being naked for two-thirds of its height. As a young tree it grows with great rapidity—2 ft. per annum—and has a coarse, gaunt aspect. The leaves of this pine are the largest and stoutest of all hardy Old World pines and of all two-leaved pines, although they are of course exceeded in size by those of Californian and Mexican species. It is, as its common name implies, admirably adapted for maritime localities. The famous pine plantations of Bournemouth are largely composed of this tree. It is also one of the very best for light sandy soils. It yields a valuable product in its resin, but its timber is poor. Nowhere has its economic value been so efficiently demonstrated as in the Landes of France, south of Bordeaux. Here in 1904, mostly planted by man, it covered an area of about 1¾ million acres, yielding an annual revenue of £560,000, and this from land which previously was mainly desert. Among two-leaved pines it is distinguished by the size and length of leaf, and by the curly, fringed bud-scales.

P. PINEA, *Linnæus*. STONE PINE

A tree varying in height according to the position in which it grows, from 40 to 100 ft.; forming in the open a comparatively low tree with a short, deeply fissured trunk, supporting a broad spreading head of branches more in diameter than it is high. When the tree has been drawn up by others it becomes much taller, but develops the characteristically shaped head as soon as the opportunity comes. Young shoots not downy, pale yellowish brown, more or less devoid of leaves at the base. Buds very characteristic on account of the curly pointed scales edged with long silvery threads by which they are matted together; ¼ to ⅝ in. long. Leaves in pairs, occasionally in threes, 3 to 5 ins. long; cones 4 ins. wide, roundish egg-shaped, rounded at the top; glossy, pale brown. Seeds kidney-bean shaped, ¾ in. long.

Native of S. Europe from Spain and Portugal eastwards to Greece and Asia Minor; cultivated in England for probably four centuries at least. Its flat spreading head of branches is one of the most picturesque and characteristic objects of Italian scenery. A famous forest of this pine is that of Ravenna, near the coast of the Adriatic, about 16 miles long, and 1 mile wide, very much damaged in the great frost of 1879, when all the younger trees were killed. The tree has always been valued in Italy for its edible seeds, and as their husks have been found in the refuse heaps of Roman encampments in Britain, they would appear to have been sent over for the use of the army in occupation. Young plants are apt to be cut by severe frosts, and transplant badly if allowed to remain more than two or three years in one place. The solitary, very glaucous needles about 1 in. long, characteristic of seedling one- or two-year-old plants are frequently to be observed on scattered shoots over much older plants. Amongst two-leaved pines this is well distinguished by its habit, its large rounded cones, and by the fringed scales of the winter bud.

S. PONDEROSA, *Lawson*. WESTERN YELLOW PINE

A tree occasionally over 200 ft. high in nature, with a perfectly erect, columnar trunk sometimes 8 ft. thick, and comparatively short, often deflexed branches, forming a columnar or slenderly tapered head. Young shoots shining, reddish brown, not downy, smelling like an orange when cut, the older parts rough with remains of the fringed scale leaves. Buds cylindrical with a tapered apex, resinous, $\frac{3}{4}$ to 1 in. long, $\frac{1}{2}$ in. thick. Leaves in threes, falling the third or fourth year, 5 to 10 ins. long, three-sided (one side much broader and more rounded than the others), all with numerous stomatic lines; margins minutely toothed; leaf-sheath persistent, $\frac{5}{8}$ to $\frac{7}{8}$ in. long. Cones elongated oval, 3 to 6 ins. long, $1\frac{1}{2}$ to $2\frac{1}{2}$ ins. thick before opening; scales terminated by a short, decurved prickle.

Native of western N. America, from British Columbia to New Mexico. Introduced in 1827 by Douglas. This pine is very variable in the size of its leaves and cones, the former sometimes approaching those of P. Coulteri in dimensions. Thinly furnished with branches, it is, nevertheless, one of the most imposing and stately of all pines. There is a splendid example at Bayfordbury over 100 ft. high, with a trunk a yard thick. It likes a good loamy soil, but is very averse to redundant moisture.

Var. SCOPULORUM, *Engelmann*, has leaves frequently in pairs as well as in threes, and cones seldom exceeding 3 ins. in length. It has a more eastern distribution than the type, and is found in Nebraska, Texas, Colorado, etc. Only represented in cultivation by small plants.

P. PUNGENS, *Lambert*. PRICKLY PINE

A tree usually 20 to 40 ft. high; young shoots reddish brown, shining, not downy, very stiff and sturdy, with the crowded leaves of the lateral branches more or less erect; buds cylindrical, $\frac{3}{4}$ to 1 in. long, very resinous. Leaves in twos, falling the third year; very rigid and sharply pointed, deep green, 2 to 3 ins. long, somewhat spirally curved; leaf-sheath $\frac{1}{4}$ in. long, persistent. Cones usually in clusters of three or more, each cone 3 or $3\frac{1}{2}$ ins. long, 2 to $2\frac{1}{2}$ ins. wide at the base; the boss of each scale terminated by a broad, hooked spine.

Native of eastern N. America; introduced in 1804. This pine retains the cones on its branches frequently fifteen or twenty years. It is one of the least ornamental of pines in cultivation and its timber is of little value. It is allied to the Western American P. muricata, and, in the group of two-leaved pines with persistent leaf-sheaths and cylindrical resinous buds, is distinguished by its stiff, spine-tipped leaves and bright red-brown branchlets.

P. RADIATA, *Don*. MONTEREY PINE

(P. insignis, *Douglas*)

A tree up to 115 ft. high, with a trunk occasionally 6 ft. thick; bark very rugged, dark brown; young shoots glabrous, yellowish brown; buds resinous, cylindrical. Leaves in threes, falling the third year; 2 to 5 ins. long, soft and flexible, very dense on the branchlets, of a rich grassy green, convex on the outer face, faintly lined with stomata; margins minutely toothed; leaf-sheath persistent, $\frac{1}{4}$ to $\frac{1}{2}$ in. long. Cones obliquely conical, rich bright brown; 3 to 5 ins. long, 2 to 3 ins. wide near the base; shortly stalked and more or less deflexed, so that the inner side is close to the branch and is imperfectly developed; the boss of the scale is diamond-shaped, with a minute prickle in the centre. The cones are usually borne in whorls of two or three, and remain closed for years upon the branches.

Native of Monterey, California, where it is confined to a few hills near the sea; introduced in 1833 by Douglas. In maritime situations in the south and west of Britain this pine thrives splendidly, growing at the rate of 3 ft.

annually. The late Mr E. H. Pember, some years ago, showed me some trees in his grounds at Vicar's Hill, near Lymington, which, in twenty-one years from planting, had reached well over 60 ft. in height. But it is of no value in a climate like that of Kew, where the trees turn a sort of foxy-brown almost every winter, and are occasionally killed outright by cold. This tree, by its rich green leaves without any trace of the typical greyness of pines, by its persistent leaf-sheaths and long persisting cones, is unmistakable among three-leaved pines.

P. RESINOSA, *Aiton*. RED PINE

A tree 50 to 70 ft. high in this country, rarely twice as high in nature, with somewhat pendulous branches; young shoots deep yellowish brown, not downy; winter buds resinous, conical, $\frac{5}{8}$ in. long. Leaves in pairs, semi-terete; 5 to $6\frac{1}{2}$ ins. long, falling the fourth year, and leaving the branchlets rough with the remains of the prominences on which each bundle was seated; dark lustrous green, minutely toothed on the margin; densely crowded on the branchlets, so that each year's crop is continuous with the preceding one; leaf-sheaths $\frac{5}{8}$ to $\frac{7}{8}$ in. long, persistent. Cones egg-shaped, 2 to $2\frac{1}{4}$ ins. long, 1 to $1\frac{1}{4}$ ins. wide before opening; pale shining brown, scarcely stalked; scales unarmed.

Native of eastern N. America from Nova Scotia to Pennsylvania; introduced in 1756 by the Duke of Northumberland. It is a handsome pine as seen in its native country and yields a useful timber, but with us is inferior as a garden tree to both Thunbergii and Laricio, of which it may be said to be the American representative. It is only likely to be mistaken for Laricio, which has a denser, more horizontal branching. The best ready distinction between the two is in the leaf-sheath of P. Laricio being only two-thirds as long as that of P. resinosa. A tree at Bayfordbury is well over 50 ft. high. I saw this bearing cones in 1908.

P. RIGIDA, *Miller*. NORTHERN PITCH PINE

A tree reaching about 80 ft. in height, with a trunk 2 to 3 ft. thick, often sending out adventitious shoots from the trunk and older branches; young shoots glabrous, pale brown; buds cylindrical, resinous. Leaves in threes, falling the third year; 3 to $4\frac{1}{2}$ ins. long, rigid, twisted, dark green, margins minutely toothed; leaf-sheath $\frac{1}{3}$ to $\frac{1}{2}$ in. long. Cones very variable, ranging from conical to almost globose, and from 1 to $3\frac{1}{2}$ ins. long; occasionally small and numerous in clusters, long persisting; scales terminated by a short prickle.

Native of eastern N. America from New Brunswick to Georgia; introduced in the early eighteenth century. In a few places it has made a fine tree. At Arley Castle, near Bewdley, there are three fine specimens, the tallest of which is 79 ft. high; and according to Elwes, there is one at Dropmore 84 ft. high. As a rule it is rather a scrubby tree of little ornament, very well distinguished by the small branches springing directly from the trunk. Some trees produce these twigs so freely that the trunks are almost covered with foliage, but they never get very large, and mostly die after a few years.

P. SEROTINA, *Michaux*. Pond Pine.—This is closely allied to P. rigida, and seems to differ chiefly in its greater length of leaf (twice as long). It seems doubtful if it be in cultivation in this country, and in any case it is tender, and only likely to succeed in the south-western counties. Native of the south-eastern United States from N. Carolina to Florida.

P. Sabiniana, *Douglas*. Digger Pine

A tree 40 to 50, occasionally 90 ft. high, of curiously thin habit; young shoots blue-white, not downy, with the leaves clustered at the apex only, the major part naked except for the awl-shaped scale-leaves, ½ in. long. Leaves in threes, mostly falling the third year, 8 to 12 ins. long, of a pale greyish green, with two narrow flat faces, and one rounded broad one, all lined closely with stomata; extremely minutely toothed at the margin, slenderly and sharply pointed; leaf-sheath ¾ to 1 in. long, persistent. Cones produced on stout stalks about 2 ins. long, ovoid, 6 to 10 ins. long, 4 to 6 ins. thick, often remaining on the branch long after the seeds have fallen; scales terminated by a large, triangular, hooked spine.

Native of California, whence it was introduced by Douglas in 1832. Most nearly allied to P. Coulteri, and with similar large, heavy, spiny cones, it is very readily distinguished by its thin foliage, smoother and more slender young shoots, and narrow cylindrical winter buds. The young shoots when cut have the same orange-like odour as in Coulteri, ponderosa, and Jeffreyi. The seeds are large like those of P. Coulteri (but with much shorter wings), and were formerly much eaten by the Digger tribe of Indians. It is not a particularly ornamental tree, being thinly furnished with foliage, but is interesting in the curious contrast between the heavy trunk and the thin, light, shadeless head of branches.

P. sinensis, *Mayr*. Chinese Pine

(P. tabulaeformis, *Carrière*; P. Henryi, *Masters*; P. Wilsonii, *Shaw*)

A tree up to 80 ft. high; young shoots glaucous at first, afterwards dull yellow or brownish, not downy; bark of old trees described as reddish on the limbs, dark grey and fissured on the trunk; winter buds cylindrical, pointed, ½ to ¾ in. long, the scales closely appressed. Leaves thickly set on the shoots, mostly in pairs, sometimes in threes, 3 to 6 ins. long; basal sheath persistent, ¼ in. long. Cones solitary, ovoid, up to 2½ ins. long, persisting on the branches several years.

Native of N. and W. China. The specific name, sinensis, appears in Lambert's *Genus Pinus*, vol. i., t. 29 (1832), where the author observes that "all our knowledge of this species is derived from a Chinese drawing in the possession of the Horticultural Society, from which our figure was taken." This does not seem much on which to base a specific name and description, but the name is retained by G. R. Shaw, the leading authority in America, and by Dallimore and Jackson. It is difficult to say when it was first introduced; Lambert in 1832 wrote that seeds had been obtained from China, and Loudon gives the date of its introduction as 1829, but probably neither referred to what was the true thing, but more likely to P. Massoniana, which has never become established in cultivation. P. sinensis is widely spread in China and is closely related to P. yunnanensis, which has longer leaves that are usually three in a bundle. The latter is perfectly hardy at Kew.

Var. densata, *Shaw* (P. densata, *Masters*), is also from W. China. Its leaves are usually in twos and are the shortest and stiffest of this group. [*See also* P. yunnanensis, *Franchet*, which is regarded as a variety of sinensis by Shaw.]

P. Strobus, *Linnæus*. Weymouth Pine

A tree usually 60 to 80, rarely above 100 ft. high in this country, but known occasionally to have exceeded twice that height in the United States; bark of trunk shallowly fissured. Young shoots with a tuft of down extending downwards from each leaf-bundle, much of which soon falls away; winter buds ovoid, with closely flattened scales. Leaves in fives, mostly falling the third year, 3 to 5 ins. long, roughened on the margins, soft bluish green, with lines of white stomata on the inner sides; leaf-sheath about ½ in. long, soon falling completely away. Cones 5 to 8 ins. long, about 1 in. diameter before opening, cylindrical, tapering at the apex, curved; scales of cones thin, smooth, rounded, 1 to 1¼ ins. long, half as wide.

Native of eastern N. America; introduced in 1705. The common name of "Weymouth" pine does not refer to the town, but to a Lord Weymouth, who is recorded to have planted it largely at Longleat about two hundred years ago. In France, the name has been contracted to "Pin du Lord." This pine has at various times been largely planted both in England and on the Continent, and is, no doubt, a valuable timber tree, especially in sunnier climates than ours, producing a white, easily worked, light timber, very useful for many purposes, but not remarkable for strength. One hundred years ago this tree covered enormous areas in eastern N. America, and was one of the richest assets of the country. Now fine specimens are comparatively scarce there. It is an ornamental tree for gardens where the soil is not a heavy clay, especially up to its middle age, though its value is impaired through its being frequently infested on the lower side of the branches by a white chermes, very similar to the beech coccus in appearance. It is only likely to be confused with P. monticola, which differs in having young shoots wholly covered with down, thicker leaves, and cones of greater average length.

Var. NANA, *Knight.*—A dwarf form of dense, compact habit, and leaves less than half as long as the type. The forms known as COMPACTA, DENSA, and UMBRACULIFERA are of the same character.

Var. PROSTRATA is an absolutely prostrate form introduced from the United States about 1893. A plant in the rock garden at Kew hangs vertically over the face of a stone. Raised in the Arnold Arboretum.

P. SYLVESTRIS, *Linnæus.* SCOTCH PINE

A tree rarely more than 100 to 110 ft. high, with a trunk 3 ft., sometimes 5 ft. in thickness. The trunk has a beautiful red tinge, and is smooth, although in old trees it becomes fissured at the base; young shoots glabrous, green; winter buds resinous. Leaves in pairs, 2 to 3½ ins. long, falling in their third year, grey-green, twisted, stiff; leaf-sheath persistent, ¼ to ⅓ in. long. Cones 1 to 2½ ins. long, conical.

Native of nearly all Europe, including Britain, and extending across Siberia to the Amur River region. It has the widest distribution of any pine. In early ages it must have covered much of the poorer land in the British Isles, but primeval forests of it are now confined to a few places in the Scottish Highlands. It provides one of the most valuable timbers of its class, especially when grown in regions with a hot summer and cold winter. Much of it is imported from N. Europe as "Riga," "Dantzic," or "yellow" deal. For gardens there is scarcely any tree more picturesque than an old Scotch pine, or with a greater beauty of trunk, especially when lit up by the low rays of the winter sun. There are several forms that have been selected for their timber by continental foresters. An interesting series of these forms was planted, each in a large block, at Les Barres in France, by one of the de Vilmorins in the third and fourth decades of last century, which now clearly show certain differences in colour of trunk, character of bark, branching, etc. The best of them is considered to be var. RIGENSIS, or "Riga Pine." As purely garden varieties the following may be mentioned.

Var. ARGENTEA, *Steven*.—Foliage of a distinctly more glaucous or silvery hue. Native of the Caucasus.

Var. AUREA.—A curious variety whose leaves turn golden yellow in autumn, and remain so through the winter, changing in spring to green again. Each leaf must, of course, make both these changes twice or thrice before falling.

Var. BEAUVRONENSIS.—Very dwarf and slow-growing leaves ½ to 1 in. long, leaf-sheaths grey-white. Originated in Messrs Transon's nursery at Beauvron, near Orleans.

Var. ENGADENSIS, *Heer*.—A small slow-growing tree of pyramidal form. Leaves 1 to 1½ ins. long, cones oblique, 2 ins. long. Tyrol.

Var. FASTIGIATA, *Carrière*.—A tree of spire-like form ; branches erect.

Vars. GLOBOSA, NANA, PUMILA.—All dwarf rounded bushes of neat and interesting appearance. Leaves about 1 in. long ; cones ¾ in. long.

Var. VARIEGATA.—Leaves occasionally creamy white.

Of these varieties, aurea and fastigiata are best worth planting.

P. TEOCOTE, *Schlechtendal*. TWISTED-LEAVED PINE

A large tree up to 90 ft. high in a wild state ; young shoots brown, glabrous ; winter buds cylindrical, tapered at the top, clothed with fringed, awl-shaped, pointed resinous scales. Leaves normally in threes (sometimes in fours or fives), 5 to 8 ins. long, exceedingly finely toothed, sharply pointed, falling away in their third year ; basal sheath ½ in. or less long, persistent. Cones produced singly or in pairs, elongated-ovoid, 1½ to 2½ ins. long, ¾ to 1⅜ ins. wide, brown.

Native of Mexico and found in association with P. patula and other pines. Hartweg sent home seeds in 1839 which were distributed by the Horticultural Society. Most of the plants raised from them died, but there are (amongst a few others) two at Bicton which I have seen several times. The larger one when I measured it in 1920 was something over 60 ft. high and 7 ft. in girth of trunk. But this pine is very rare and only adapted for such localities as S. Devon and Cornwall.

P. THUNBERGII, *Parlatore*. BLACK PINE

(P. Massoniana of gardens, not of *Lambert*)

A tree 80 to 100 ft. (sometimes more) high, with a trunk 3 to 5 ft. through ; bark deeply fissured and darkly coloured ; young shoots light brown, not downy ; buds egg-shaped to almost globose, narrowing at the top to a short, slender point, not resinous, but with pale brown scales edged with conspicuous whitish threads. Leaves in pairs, 2½ to 4½ ins. long, persisting three to five years ; straight, stiff, sharply but abruptly pointed ; the margins are so minutely toothed as to be only just perceptible to the touch ; leaf-sheath ½ to ⅝ in. long, persistent, with two grey curly threads at the top. The lower part of each year's shoot is furnished with scale leaves only. Cones narrowly egg-shaped, 1½ to 2½ ins. long, about 1 in. wide ; scales unarmed ; although usually solitary or in pairs, the cones are sometimes clustered as many as fifty or sixty together, and then much smaller.

Native of Japan, and one of the chief timber-producing trees of that country ; introduced by John Gould Veitch in 1861. It is a very picturesque tree, with stiff, horizontal branches of often very unequal length, and although not likely ever to reach its natural dimensions in this country, well worth growing as an interesting and characteristic pine. The Japanese train it into many grotesque shapes. It is allied to Laricio, but besides the marked difference in habit is easily distinguished by its broad grey-white buds and shorter, stiffer leaves. It is promising as a seaside tree.

P. TUBERCULATA, *Gordon.* KNOB-CONE PINE

(P. attenuata, *Lemmon* ; P. californica, *Hartweg*)

A tree 20 to 50 ft. high in this country, occasionally twice as high in a wild state; young shoots glabrous, bright brown; buds cylindrical, $\frac{3}{4}$ to 1 in. long, $\frac{1}{8}$ to $\frac{1}{4}$ in. wide, resinous. Leaves in threes, falling the third or fourth year; 4 to $7\frac{1}{2}$ ins. long, slender, bright green, finely pointed, minutely toothed; leaf-sheath $\frac{1}{3}$ to $\frac{1}{2}$ in. long, persistent. Cones slenderly conical, usually 4 to 5 ins. long, 2 ins. wide at the oblique base; deflexed, with the scales near the base on the upper side developing the conical, spine-tipped knobs or prominences referred to in the popular name; the cones are produced in whorls of three or more, and persist on the branches for sometimes thirty or forty years, or until the death of the tree. At first they have a stalk $\frac{3}{4}$ in. long, which gradually becomes enclosed in the thickening branch.

Native of Oregon and California; discovered and introduced in 1847 by Hartweg. It has no special merits as an ornamental tree, although on account of its long persisting cones it is a very interesting one. On a piece of branch, 4 ft. long, from a tree grown at Bayfordbury and now preserved at Kew, there are over forty cones. It is botanically allied to P. radiata, but differs in the larger, stiffer, grey-green leaves and narrower cones. It is also a hardier tree, and, according to Jepson, inhabits the most desolate and inhospitable stations for tree growth in the Californian mountains. As may be judged from the life-history of its cones, it is admirably adapted to survive as a species on fire-swept zones. (See also *P. muricata.*)

P. VIRGINIANA, *Miller.* JERSEY PINE, SCRUB PINE

(P. inops, *Aiton*)

A tree 30 to 50 ft. high, but often of scrubby habit; young shoots covered with a vivid, pale, purplish bloom, smooth; winter buds very resinous. Leaves in pairs, falling the third year; $1\frac{1}{2}$ to 3 ins. long, twisted and curved; leaf-sheath persistent, $\frac{3}{16}$ in. long. Cones $1\frac{1}{2}$ to $2\frac{1}{2}$ ins. long, 1 to $1\frac{1}{4}$ ins. wide at the base, conical, prickly.

Native of eastern N. America; introduced early in the eighteenth century or perhaps before. Of all really hardy species this has, perhaps, less to be said in its favour as a tree for gardens than any. Apparently the best tree in the country is one at Bayfordbury, planted in 1842, now nearly 50 ft. high. The brightly coloured, slender young shoots of this species distinguish it among pines with short leaves in pairs. P. echinata, with slender, glaucous shoots, has its leaves often in threes.

P. YUNNANENSIS, *Franchet.* YUNNAN PINE

(Gardeners' Chronicle, 1905, ii., fig. 86)

A tree up to 100 ft. high in a wild state, with a trunk 8 to 12 ft. in girth; young shoots yellowish brown; buds cylindrical, brown, non-resinous, with a slender pointed apex, $\frac{3}{4}$ to $1\frac{1}{4}$ ins. long, and fringed, linear scales. Leaves in pairs or in threes, 4 to 9 ins. long, slender, much twisted and contorted in young specimens, toothed on the margins, finely pointed; sheath $\frac{3}{4}$ in. long. Cones shortly stalked, $2\frac{1}{2}$ to 4 ins. long, $1\frac{1}{2}$ to 2 ins. wide before expanding, brown, remaining on the branches four or five years.

Native of W. China and E. Tibet; introduced by Wilson about 1909, and only known in cultivation by quite young plants which appear very healthy at present, but whose capability of withstanding very severe frost has yet to be ascertained. Young plants already show the mixture of two-leaved and three-leaved bundles. (P. sinensis yunnanensis, *Shaw.*)

PIPTANTHUS. LEGUMINOSÆ

A genus of about half a dozen species of deciduous or partially evergreen, soft-wooded shrubs with trifoliolate leaves and entire, stalkless leaflets. Flowers always yellow, borne in erect terminal racemes. Provided they have a suitable climate—and they are not completely hardy—they are easily grown if put in a sunny spot and given a reasonably good loamy soil.

P. CONCOLOR, *Harrow*

A deciduous or partially evergreen bush up to 6 or 8 ft. high; young shoots clothed with white hairs, becoming glabrous and ultimately chestnut-brown. Leaves trifoliolate, the three leaflets on a common stalk 1 in. long. Leaflets narrowly oval to oblanceolate, tapered about equally towards both ends, entire; mostly 2¼ to 4 ins. long, ¾ to 1¼ ins. wide; rather glossy green above and but slightly paler green below; both sides very hairy when quite young, the upper one soon becoming glabrous, the lower one sparsely hairy. Racemes several inches long, with often three flowers at a joint, opening in May. Flowers pea-shaped, about 1 in. long, yellow, the standard petal stained with maroon. Calyx ½ in. long, glabrous inside, very hairy outside and on the margins; lobes slenderly pointed. Flower-stalk ¾ in. long, very hairy; ovary silky. Pod covered with appressed down, 2½ to 3½ ins. long, ⅜ in. wide.

Native of W. Szechuen, China; introduced in 1908 by Wilson. It was at first thought to be a form of P. laburnifolius, but in that species the leaves are glaucous beneath, in this they are green. P. concolor can be grown away from a wall at Kew, which is more than can be said of P. laburnifolius. But possibly a really hard winter would kill it.

Var. YUNNANENSIS, *Stapf*. Bot. Mag., t. 9234.—Shoots glabrous or only very slightly hairy when young; leaves glaucous beneath.

P. LABURNIFOLIUS, *Stapf*

(P. nepalensis, *Sweet*)

A shrub or low tree with very pithy young shoots; naturally 8 to 12 ft. high, but growing taller against walls, where it is generally placed in England. When grown at Kew it is deciduous, but in milder climates it retains more or less foliage during the winter. Leaves alternate, consisting of three lanceolate, stalkless leaflets, 3 to 6 ins. long, about one-third as wide, with a marginal nerve; glabrous except when quite young, dark green above, glacous beneath; the common leaf-stalk 1½ to 2 ins. long. Racemes stiff, erect, 2 to 3 ins. long, and as much broad, hairy, and set with hairy bracts. Flowers pea-shaped, 1½ ins. long, the stalk up to 1 in. long and, like the bell-shaped, deeply-lobed calyx, very hairy; petals bright yellow. Pod 3 to 5 ins. long, ¾ in. wide.

Native of the Himalaya; introduced to England in 1821. It thrives well against a wall, flowering in May, but is not permanently hardy in the open air at Kew. A shrub of exceptionally vigorous appearance, it is, nevertheless, not long-lived. It is easily propagated by seeds, which it ripens in quantity, and owing to its dislike of root disturbance should be grown in pots until planted in permanence. Its flowering sprays resemble those of the herbaceous genus THERMOPSIS.

Three species of Piptanthus have been introduced by Forrest from China, all with yellow flowers :—

P. BICOLOR, *Craib.*—A species resembling P. laburnifolius in the glaucous under-surface of the leaflets but differing in the narrower seed pod ($\frac{2}{5}$ in. wide) being covered with silky hairs. In P. laburnifolius it is $\frac{3}{4}$ in. wide and only slightly downy, or even glabrous.

P. FORRESTII, *Craib.*—In this species the leaflets are green, furnished with short, appressed hairs on both sides, and the young shoots are hairy. Flowers bright golden yellow. I saw a plant 6 ft. high fully in bloom in the Edinburgh Botanic Garden during early June 1931. So the species is evidently perfectly hardy.

P. TOMENTOSUS, *Franchet.*—As in P. Forrestii, the leaflets are hairy or even velvety on both sides, but more conspicuously so on the underside where the hairs are very dense; pod woolly, 2 to $3\frac{1}{2}$ in. long.

PISTACIA. MASTIC TREES. ANACARDIACEÆ

A genus of deciduous or evergreen trees of considerable economic importance in their native countries, but as a rule too tender to be of much garden value in this. Two species may be grown without protection in the open, viz., P. Terebinthus and P. chinensis, the latter, although still rare, appears to be especially well adapted for our climate. The leaves of Pistacia are either simple, trifoliolate or pinnate, and the pinnate leaves are either equally or unequally so. Flowers inconspicuous, and without petals; male and female flowers sometimes occur on separate trees. The nearest ally in gardens to this genus is Rhus, from which Pistacia differs in the absence of petals.

The two species mentioned above may be grown in the open ground, but for the rest it will be necessary to provide wall space. Any ordinary garden soil suffices for them.

The species of Pistacia may be arranged as follows :—

I. LEAVES EQUALLY PINNATE (without an odd terminal leaflet)

Chinensis. Deciduous.
Lentiscus. Evergreen.

II. LEAVES UNEQUALLY PINNATE

Vera. Leaflets three or five; large, downy.
Atlantica. } Leaflets five to nine; glabrous.
Terebinthus. }

P. ATLANTICA, *Desfontaines.* MT. ATLAS MASTIC

A deciduous tree up to 40 ft. high in N. Africa. Leaves pinnate, consisting of five to nine leaflets, the common stalk winged. Leaflets lanceolate, 1 to $1\frac{1}{2}$ ins. long, rounded at the apex, glabrous. Flowers in axillary pyramidal panicles 2 to 4 ins. long. Fruit obovoid, rather depressed at the end, $\frac{1}{8}$ in. long, dark blue when fully ripe.

Native of Algeria; producing a resin somewhat similar to that of P. Lentiscus, which is chewed by the Arabs as a dentifrice. It needs some protection in the ordinary climate of Great Britain, but will probably succeed in the south-western counties.

P. chinensis, *Bunge*. Chinese Pistachio

A large deciduous tree up to 80 ft. high in Central China. Leaves evenly pinnate, about 9 ins. long, composed of usually ten or twelve leaflets, generally but not invariably without the terminal odd one. Leaflets ovate-lanceolate, long-pointed, unequally divided by the midrib, 2½ to 3½ ins. long, ¾ in. wide; glabrous except when quite young. Flowers in a cluster of panicles near the end of the shoot, the male flowers crowded on an inflorescence 3 ins. long, the female ones on a much more open, lax panicle 7 to 9 ins. long. Fruit the size of large peppercorns, first red, then blue.

Native of Central and W. China, where the young shoots and leaves are eaten cooked as a vegetable by the Chinese. This is undoubtedly the best of the pistacias to cultivate in England. It was originally introduced to Kew by means of seed in 1897, and is apparently perfectly hardy, never having suffered in the least from cold up to now, although quite unprotected. It has no beauty of flower, but the foliage is of a glossy, cheerful green, and Mr Wilson (who sent home seeds during his 1908 and 1910 journeys in China) told me that it turns a gorgeous crimson before falling in autumn, rendering a large tree one of the most glorious pictures conceivable.

P. Lentiscus, *Linnæus*. Mastic

An evergreen bush or small tree, occasionally 15 or 20 ft. high; young shoots warted, not downy. The leaves are evenly pinnate, consisting of four to ten leaflets without a terminal odd one; the common stalk is winged. Leaflets ¾ to 1½ ins. long, ¼ to ½ in. wide; narrowly oblong to obovate, glabrous, with a very short, abrupt point. Flowers very densely packed in short axillary panicles 1 to 2 ins. long. Fruit first red, then black, about the size of large peppercorns.

Native of the Mediterranean region, especially of the Grecian Archipelago; introduced in 1664. In the islands of the Archipelago, especially Scios, it produces by incision of the bark the resinous substance known as "mastic." Mastic is chiefly used by the Greeks and Turks for chewing, to sweeten the breath and preserve the teeth. The tree is tender and needs the protection of a warm wall. There is a larger, broader-leaved variety with leaflets up to 2 ins. long and ¾ in. wide, known as LATIFOLIA.

P. Terebinthus, *Linnæus*. Chian Turpentine Tree

A deciduous tree 30 ft. or more high, sometimes a bush; with glabrous, pinnate leaves up to 6 or 8 ins. long. Leaflets usually seven or nine, ovate-lanceolate to oblong, 1½ to 2½ ins. long, entire, lustrous dark green, glabrous. Flowers in panicles 2 to 6 ins. long, small, greenish. Fruit roundish oval, ⅓ in. long, turning first red, finally purplish brown.

Native of Asia Minor and the shores and islands of the Mediterranean; introduced in 1656. The bark yields the valuable resinous juice known as Chian turpentine, from its being chiefly collected on the island of Scios; this has certain medicinal properties, and is also used as flavouring. The kernel of the nut yields a pleasant-smelling oil. The tree is hardy at Kew, and a few specimens have lived unprotected in the open there for at least twenty years, although their growth is very slow. The flowers have no beauty, but the leaves have a pleasant resinous odour.

P. VERA, *Linnæus*. PISTACHIO

A small deciduous tree, 20 ft. high, with long-stalked, pinnate leaves consisting usually of three or five leaflets, which are 1½ to 2½ ins. long, ovate or obovate, stalkless, entire, downy on both sides. Flowers in erect panicles 3 or 4 ins. long, small and of no beauty; the male panicles much denser than the female. Fruit reddish, oval, ¾ in. long.

Native of the Levant and W. Asia, long cultivated and naturalised over the Mediterranean region; introduced to England in 1770. This is the tree that produces the well-known pistachio-nuts, the kernels of which are eaten raw, or cooked, or made into confectionery. It has not much beyond its economic interest to recommend it, for it needs the protection of a warm wall, and even then is occasionally injured by cold; with us its fruits are never developed. In warm climates the leaflets are as much as 3½ ins. long by 2½ ins. wide.

PITTOSPORUM. PITTOSPORACEÆ

An interesting genus of evergreen shrubs and small trees whose head-quarters are in Australia and New Zealand, whence come most of the species cultivated in the open air in the British Isles. One well-known species is native of Japan, and others are found in the Canary Islands, Cape of Good Hope, and China. The genus is not represented in the New World. Leaves arranged alternately; flowers with five sepals, five petals, and five stamens; fruit many-seeded.

The pittosporums are essentially shrubs for the milder parts of the British Isles. At Kew they can only be grown against a wall. Several of the species are very handsome evergreens, and all here mentioned are charmingly fragrant when in flower. They are easily cultivated, and thrive in a light loamy soil. Cuttings taken from the half-ripened wood will root in gentle heat. Seeds ripen in favourable localities, and may also be used. Probably the best collection in this country is in the Rectory garden at Ludgvan in Cornwall assembled there by the late Canon Boscawen.

The generic name refers to the resinous or viscid substance by which the seeds are surrounded. The flowers in general must be regarded as more notable for their fragrance than their beauty.

P. BICOLOR, *Hooker fil.*

An evergreen shrub or even a small tree 30 to 40 ft. high, the younger shoots clothed with a pale brown, close felt. Leaves entire, linear, leathery, tapered at each end, pointed; 1 to 2½ ins. long, ⅛ to ⅓ in. wide but made to look narrower by the rolling under of the margins; upper surface dark green and glabrous; lower one felted, at first white then brown, like the young shoots; stalk ⅛ in. or less long. Flowers solitary or in small clusters, axillary, ⅜ in. long, fragrant, each on a downy stalk as long as itself; petals oblong, deep maroon crimson; sepals narrower and one-third the length of the petals; stamens yellow. Fruit nearly globose, ¼ to ⅓ in. wide.

Native of Tasmania. It requires winter protection at Kew but is hardy in the southern and western maritime counties. I saw some years ago a tree at Abbotsbury, Dorset, which was over 20 ft. high, and I have had a flowering specimen from Ventnor, Isle of Wight. Its flowering period extends from November to April. According to Hooker, the flowers in Tasmania are borne in corymbs in favourable situations, but are solitary or few together in Alpine places.

P. BUCHANANII, *Hooker fil.*

An evergreen shrub or small tree 10 to 20 ft. high; young shoots and leaves silky downy, becoming glabrous by late summer. Leaves alternate, of thinnish firm texture, oblong-lanceolate to oval, quite entire, tapered at both ends, pointed or rounded at the apex; 2 to 5 ins. long, ¾ to 2 ins. wide; dark glossy green above, pale and indistinctly net-veined beneath; margins not wavy; stalk ¼ to ⅝ in. long. Flowers ⅝ in. wide, produced singly or in pairs from the leaf-axils each on a stalk ⅓ to ½ in. long; petals dark purple, narrow oblong; sepals ¼ in. long, ⅛ in. wide, pointed; ovary covered with silky white hairs. Seed-vessel globose, ½ in. wide, downy at first.

Native of the North Island, New Zealand, where it is said to be rare and local. It has been cultivated at Kew for over fifty years in the Temperate House and flowers there in April. Major Johnstone grows it at Trewithen in Cornwall, where it flowers during the same month, and the late Mr H. W. Grigg had it in his garden at Cann House, S. Devon. It succeeds well also at Castlewellan, Co. Down, and with Col. Stern in his chalk garden on the South Downs, near Worthing. To P. Ralphii it has a certain superficial resemblance, but that species is amply distinguished by its permanently downy leaves and terminal inflorescence.

P. COLENSOI, *Hooker fil.*

(Bot. Mag., t. 8305)

An evergreen shrub or small tree ultimately 20 to 30 ft. high; young shoots stout, loosely silky when young. Leaves rather leathery, oval, oblong, or slightly obovate, pointed or bluntish, mostly tapered at the base; 1½ to 4 ins. long, ½ to 1¼ ins. wide; downy only when quite young, dark glossy green above with a yellowish midrib, pale and net-veined beneath; stalk ⅓ in. or less long. Flowers ⅝ in. wide, solitary or in threes, produced in April at and near the end of the shoots in the leaf-axils. Petals dark red, ⅔ in. long, oblong, much recurved; sepals broadly ovate, downy.

Native of the North and South Islands, New Zealand, up to 3500 ft. altitude. It is very closely akin to P. tenuifolium, which differs chiefly in its wavy-margined leaves, more slender shoots and, on the whole, smaller, paler green leaves. The two appear to be united by intermediate forms but are quite distinct in the typical states. It is cultivated and prized in many gardens in the south-west, Ireland, etc., but is not very hardy in our average climate. But there is a plant 10 ft. high in the Great Park, Windsor. It flowers with great freedom in the gardens of Tresco Abbey, Scilly.

P. CORNIFOLIUM, *A. Cunningham*

(Bot. Mag., t. 3161)

An evergreen shrub 2 to 5 ft. high of neat habit, with the slender young shoots glabrous (or downy only when quite young). Leaves leathery, clustered at the end of the twig only, oval-lanceolate or narrowly obovate, pointed, tapered at the base to a very short stalk; 1½ to 3¼ ins. long, ½ to 1¼ ins. wide; entire, quite glabrous. Flowers mostly unisexual, dull red, produced in

February and March two to five together at the end of the young twigs; each flower is $\frac{1}{3}$ in. wide, the males borne on very slender, thread-like, downy stalks $\frac{1}{2}$ to $\frac{3}{4}$ in. long, the females on shorter, stouter ones. Sepals and petals awl-shaped, the former much the shorter; anthers yellow. Seed-vessels egg-shaped, $\frac{1}{2}$ in. wide.

Native of the North Island of New Zealand up to 2000 ft. altitude; introduced by Allan Cunningham early in the nineteenth century. It is often found wild growing as an epiphyte on large forest trees or on rocks, rarely in pure earth. It is not hardy at Kew but can be grown in the open air in the south-west. In spite of its epiphytal character it succeeds well in ordinary soil. The flowers have a charming musk-like odour.

P. CRASSIFOLIUM, *Solander*

(Bot. Mag., t. 5978)

An evergreen shrub or small tree, 15 ft. or more high, of dense habit. Leaves $1\frac{1}{2}$ to 4 ins. long, obovate to oblong, always narrowed at the base to a stalk $\frac{1}{2}$ to 1 in. long; leathery, covered beneath with a pale brown or whitish felt, the margins recurved. Flowers unisexual in terminal clusters; males up to ten in each cluster, females up to five; petals strap-shaped, recurved, dark purple. Fruit roundish, dry, $\frac{2}{3}$ in. across, containing numerous black seeds.

Native of the N. Island of New Zealand; not hardy at Kew except on a wall, where it makes an interesting evergreen, but does not flower freely. It is suitable for the milder counties.

P. RALPHII, *Kirk*, another New Zealand species, is closely related to the above. It differs in its larger, oblong leaves more abruptly narrowed towards the stalk, in their margins not being recurved but flat, and in the smaller fruits.

P. DALLII, *Cheeseman*

A small evergreen tree 12 to 18 ft. high in a wild state, of rounded shape, with a trunk up to 8 ins. in diameter; older bark pale grey; young shoots glabrous, reddish. Leaves dark dull green, crowded towards the end of the shoot; oval-lanceolate, pointed, tapered about equally towards both ends, either coarsely or slightly toothed, or entire; $2\frac{1}{2}$ to $4\frac{1}{2}$ ins. long, $\frac{1}{2}$ to $1\frac{3}{4}$ ins. wide; of stiff leathery texture; soon quite glabrous; midrib raised above and beneath; stalk reddish, $\frac{1}{3}$ to $\frac{3}{4}$ in. long. Flowers white, fragrant, crowded numerously in a terminal cluster 1 to 2 ins. across; individually $\frac{1}{4}$ to $\frac{2}{3}$ in. long and $\frac{1}{2}$ in. wide when expanded; petals narrowly obovate; sepals awl-shaped; anthers bright yellow; flower-stalks downy. Seed-vessels woody, egg-shaped, $\frac{1}{2}$ in. long, with a short spine-like tip.

Native of the South Island, New Zealand. According to Cheeseman, "it appears to be rare in its only known habitat in the mountains near Collingwood, Nelson, and only a limited number of adult plants have been seen." It occurs at 3500 ft. altitude and is hardy enough to have survived five winters out-of-doors at Kew in a sheltered nook, quite uninjured. It is very distinct, especially in the foliage, and is the only species in New Zealand with regularly coarsely toothed leaves and white flowers. The young plants at Kew, however, which are very healthy, bear leaves that vary from being coarsely toothed to having no teeth at all. It should flower with us in June or July. Mr J. Dall, who first discovered it in 1905 in the rugged, mountainous country where it grows, obtained only imperfect fruiting specimens. He died in 1912, but it was found again by his friend, Mr F. G. Gibbs, in 1913, this time in bloom. Mr Gibbs, to whom Kew was indebted for seeds, describes the tree as "far more handsome than any of the other pittosporums I have seen." The seeds he sent to Kew laid dormant for a year. Cuttings appear difficult to root, but can be easily grafted on P. tenuifolium. There is a tree at Ludgvan, near Penzance, which was 15 ft. high and as much in diameter in 1930, and I saw one of similar size the following year in Mr M'Douall's garden at Logan in Wigtownshire.

P. DAPHNIPHYLLOIDES, *Hayata*

An evergreen shrub or sometimes a tree, up to 30 ft. high, slightly downy on the young shoots and beneath the young leaves. Leaves narrowly oblong to narrowly obovate, tapered towards both ends, but more gradually towards the base, dark green; 2½ to 8 ins. long, 1¼ to 3½ ins. wide; stalk ⅝ to 1¼ ins. long. Flowers ¼ in. long and wide, greenish yellow, crowded in several globose, umbellate clusters ¾ to 1½ ins. wide that form a terminal panicle; main and secondary flower-stalks downy; petals oblong, ¼ in. long, blunt; anthers yellow. Fruit globose, ¼ to ⅜ in. wide, wrinkled, red.

Native of W. Szechuen, China, whence it was introduced by Wilson in 1904. He describes it as a handsome species found in woods, thickets, and rocky places, and as having leaves sometimes 10 ins. long and 4 ins. wide without the stalk. As it occurs at low altitudes (3000 to 5000 ft.), it is probably best adapted for our milder localities. There is a healthy small tree at Caerhays, in Cornwall, very noticeable for the size of its leaves, which must be about the largest found on any pittosporum that can be grown in this country; another was bearing fine crops of berries at Warley, Essex, in November 1934. A closely related, perhaps identical, shrub grows in Formosa.

P. DIVARICATUM, *Cockayne*

A usually low, densely branched, evergreen shrub rarely more than a few feet high in Britain, but said to be up to 12 ft. high in a wild state; with the stiff, downy young twigs much divided, tortuous, and interlaced. Leaves glabrous and variously shaped; on young plants linear to obovate, ½ to ¾ in. long, ⅛ in. wide, pinnately lobed or merely toothed; on mature plants ¼ to ¾ in. long, linear-obovate, oblong or ovate, variously toothed or not at all; dark green and of leathery texture. Flowers small, ⅙ in. long, solitary, produced at the top of the twig; petals deep maroon, almost black, narrowly spoon-shaped. Seed-vessel nearly globose, ¼ in. wide.

Native of the North and South Islands of New Zealand. This is a curious shrub of little beauty, with a growth suggesting that of Corokia Cotoneaster. It flowers in December in New Zealand and I have seen it blossoming in the Vicarage garden at Bitton, Gloucestershire, in May. It was grown there as "P. rigidum," a species under which it was included by Hooker in his *Flora of New Zealand*. The true P. rigidum (*q.v.*) differs from the present species in the branches not interlacing and in the flowers being nearly always axillary.

P. EUGENIOIDES, *A. Cunningham*

An evergreen tree 20 to 40 ft. high, densely branched; young shoots glabrous, darkly coloured. Leaves clustered towards the end of each season's growth, narrowly oval or oblong, tapered at each end; 2 to 5 ins. long, ½ to 1¼ ins. wide; perfectly glabrous on both surfaces, dark glossy green above, paler beneath; margins often wavy; stalk ¼ to ¾ in. long. Flowers very fragrant, ⅙ in. wide, yellowish, densely and numerously packed in a cluster of short corymbs terminating the branch, each corymb 1 in. or less long; flower-stalks downy; petals strap-shaped, ⅛ in. long; sepals much smaller. Fruit ¼ in. long, egg-shaped.

Native of New Zealand, where it occurs on both islands up to 2500 ft. altitude. Requiring winter protection at Kew, it is perfectly hardy in the milder parts more to the south and west and makes a handsome evergreen tree there. It is the tallest of the New Zealand species and in Cornwall, at Heligan and the Rectory garden at Ludgvan, it is well over 30 ft. high.

Var. VARIEGATUM.—In this form the leaf has a creamy white margin of irregular width. Seen in Cornish gardens, usually as a small tree of columnar shape with its peculiarly clean, clear leaf-colouring, it strikes one as about the most attractive of all variegated shrubs grown in the open air.

The honey-like scent of the flowers of these two pittosporums is very charming and widely diffused. In earlier times the Maoris used to mix the flowers with fat and anoint their bodies therewith.

P. GLABRATUM, *Lindley*

An evergreen shrub, 4 to 6 ft. high, with quite glabrous young shoots, bearing the leaves in a cluster at the end. Leaves obovate to oblanceolate, tapered at both ends, but more gadually towards the base; 3 to 5 ins. long, ¾ to 1½ ins. wide; with entire, membranous margins; quite glabrous on both surfaces; dark green above, pale beneath; stalk ½ in. or less long. Flowers fragrant, dull yellow, produced singly or in few-flowered racemes in the leaf-axils of the young shoots in May; corolla ⅓ to ½ in. long, cylindrical at the base, dividing at the mouth in five oblong, recurved lobes, ⅙ in. long; flower-stalks usually ½ to ¾ in. long, glabrous. Fruit a glabrous, woody capsule, ⅝ in. long.

Native of China, introduced in 1908 from near Ichang to Kew. Wilson had previously found it at 10,000 ft. elevation in Hupeh. It is interesting as an apparently hardy pittosporum, but is not a shrub of much promise.

P. PATULUM, *Hooker fil.*

An evergreen shrub or small tree from 6 to 15 ft. high; young shoots and flower-stalks downy, glabrous elsewhere. Leaves always narrow in proportion to their length but otherwise variable; on young plants they are 1 to 2 ins. long, as little as ⅛ in. wide, and conspicuously lobed their whole length; as the plants reach maturity the leaves become wider (⅜ to ½ in.), more or less shallowly toothed, often almost or quite entire, and of lanceolate shape; they are of leathery texture. Flowers rather bell-shaped, four to eight together in a terminal cluster, each borne on a slender, downy stalk ½ in. long, very fragrant; petals nearly ½ in. long, oblong, blunt-ended, blackish crimson; sepals ovate-lanceolate, pointed, ciliate. Seed-vessels globose, ⅓ in. wide, woody.

Native of the South Island, New Zealand, at from 2000 to 4000 ft. altitude; very local in its distribution. Its flowers are said to be the most fragrant of all New Zealand pittosporums. There is a good plant in the garden at Ludgvan, near Penzance, 8 ft. or more high and of slender pyramidal habit. It also succeeds well at Bodnant, at Borde Hill in Sussex, and at Exbury, Hants. The best plant I have ever seen, however, grew at Rostrevor in the late Sir John Ross's garden; in 1922 it was 12 ft. high and flowered in May of that year.

P. REVOLUTUM, *Aiton*

(Bot. Reg., t. 186; P. fulvum, *Rudge*)

An evergreen shrub up to 10 or 12 ft. high, the young shoots felted with pale brown wool. Leaves lanceolate or narrowly oval, much tapered at both ends; 1½ to 4½ ins. long, ⅓ to 1¼ ins. wide; glabrous above, covered beneath with brown wool, especially on the midrib; stalk ¼ to ½ in. long, woolly. Flowers ⅓ to ½ in. long, produced in spring on a terminal, few-flowered umbel, sometimes solitary. Petals yellow, recurved; sepals awl-shaped, ¼ in. long; flower-stalks woolly.

Native of New South Wales; introduced according to Aiton in 1795. It is rather distinct on account of the dense covering of brown wool on the young shoots and leaves. It is not hardy near London and is adapted only for the south-western counties and places with a similar climate.

P. RIGIDUM, *Hooker fil.*

An evergreen shrub up to 10 ft. or more high (generally smaller), much branched but not interlacing; young shoots of juvenile plants densely clothed with reddish brown down. Leaves obovate or oval, round-ended, tapered at the base to a short stalk; entire and glabrous on old plants, often coarsely toothed and downy on young ones; ¼ to 1 in. long, ⅛ to ⅜ in. wide. Flowers small, dull purple, produced singly from the leaf-axils, very shortly stalked. Seed-vessel roundish ovoid, ¼ in. wide, ending in a spine-like tip.

Native of the North and South Islands, New Zealand, up to 4000 ft. altitude. It is of no great ornament, but is a curious, often dwarfish, small-leaved shrub which one might easily pass when in flower without noticing the blossom. A shrub sometimes grown under this name in British gardens is really P. divaricatum, a very nearly related and perhaps more interesting shrub on account of its dense interlacing habit of branching; its leaves are much less frequently entire on adult plants than in rigidum and its flowers are terminal. Of P. rigidum there is a healthy bush in the Edinburgh Botanic Garden.

P. TENUIFOLIUM, *Gaertner*

(P. Mayi, of gardens)

An evergreen tree up to 30 ft. in height, with a slender trunk and dark coloured, almost black young wood, and forming a dense mass of twiggy shoots. Leaves 1 to 2½ ins. long, oblong, obovate or elliptic, glabrous, of a pale shining green; the margins entire but wavy. The flowers come in the axils of the leaves, usually singly, but occasionally two or more together, and have dark chocolate-purple petals ¼ to ½ in. long. The fruit is a capsule ½ in. in diameter, wrinkled when old, the valves thin.

Native of both the North and South Islands of New Zealand, reaching up to 3000 ft. altitude. It is, perhaps, the hardiest of the Australasian pittosporums, and in several parts of Ireland is 20 to 30 ft. high. In the late Miss Willmott's garden at Warley it was 18 ft. high, a stately cone-shaped bush; and at Aldenham in Herts it has reached 8 or 9 ft. in height. The flowers are borne very abundantly where it thrives, but are not conspicuous; their chief attraction is an exquisite honey-like fragrance, strongest in the evening, and then apparent yards away from the tree. Often known in gardens as P. Mayi. The black young shoots and pale green leaves make a strong contrast.

In April 1930 I visited the Rectory garden at Ludgvan in Cornwall and was interested to note seedlings of variegated P. tenuifolium springing up in hundreds beneath the parent tree and most of them showing as much whiteness of leaf as it did.

P. TOBIRA, *Aiton*

(Bot. Mag., t. 1396)

An evergreen, bushy shrub of stiff habit, sometimes 20 or more ft. high. Leaves obovate, blunt or rounded at the apex, tapering at the base to a short stalk; 1½ to 4 ins. long, ¾ to 1½ ins. wide, leathery and glabrous, dark lustrous green, with a pale midrib. Flowers about 1 in. across, fragrant, produced at the end of the shoot in clusters 2 or 3 ins. across, the petals broadly oblong, creamy white, becoming yellowish with age. Fruit a pear-shaped capsule.

Native of Japan and China; first introduced to Kew in 1804. This shrub is not strictly hardy, and at Kew requires wall protection. In the south-western counties and at Castlewellan in Co. Down it succeeds admirably unprotected, being there a densely furnished, healthy-looking evergreen. In the gardens of the south of France, Italy, Dalmatia, etc., it is one of the commonest of evergreens, producing its flowers from April onwards. The largest examples I have seen are on the Isle of Lacroma, near Ragusa, in Dalmatia, picturesque, spreading bushes, 20 to 25 ft. high. The flowers have a scent like orange blossom.

P. UNDULATUM, *Ventenat*

An evergreen tree, 30 to 40 ft. high in this country; leaves large, laurel-like; 3 to 6 ins. long, 1 to 2 ins. wide, tapering towards both ends; glabrous, dark lustrous green above, pale beneath, quite entire, but wavy at the margins. Flowers in a terminal cluster of umbels 2 to 3 ins. diameter; each blossom creamy white, ½ to ¾ in. across.

Native of Australia, whence it was introduced in 1789. It is, of course, only hardy in the mildest counties; and probably the finest specimen in the British Isles is at Rossdohan, Co. Kerry, in the garden of Mr Herd. It flowers from May to July, and the blossoms are pleasantly fragrant. The leaves are bright and handsome, the undulations of the margin not more marked than in some other species.

PLAGIANTHUS. MALVACEÆ

A genus of trees and shrubs chiefly, but also containing a few herbs, confined in a wild state to Australia and New Zealand. There has been considerable confusion in gardens between this genus, Hoheria and Gaya. They are closely akin but, according to Cheeseman, Plagianthus is distinct in its "more or less unisexual" flowers and decurrent stigmas. Hoheria has "perfect" flowers, capitate stigmas and winged carpels. Gaya also has perfect flowers and capitate stigmas, but the carpels are not winged. Provided the climate is favourable—and they are rather tender—they are easily grown in a light loamy soil and propagated by cuttings.

P. BETULINUS, *A. Cunningham*

A deciduous tree, from 30 to 40 ft. high in New Zealand, with a trunk sometimes 3 ft. in diameter. In the milder parts of the British Isles it thrives very well, and there is a tree over 50 ft. high in the Earl of Ilchester's garden at Abbotsbury, in Dorset. In a young state its growth is remarkably elegant, consisting of a mass of slender, tortuous, interlacing branches, thinly furnished with foliage. At this stage the leaves are ½ to 1½ ins. long, narrowly or broadly ovate, deeply and irregularly toothed and lobed; they are borne on slender, downy stalks, nearly or quite as long as the blade. As the trees approach the adult state, the growth becomes less straggling, the leaves increase in size until they are 3 ins. long, and become less deeply lobed. Flowers produced very numerously on racemes at the end of the shoot and in the leaf-axils near, the whole forming a panicle as much as 9 ins. long; individually the flowers are unisexual; the male flowers yellowish white, the females greenish.

Native of the South Island of New Zealand; introduced about 1870. Besides the Abbotsbury tree there are fine ones in Ireland (at Castlewellan) and in other places. It is not hardy at Kew, and sometimes suffers in cold winters against a wall. There used to be a nice specimen at Warley Place, 12 ft. high.

P. DIVARICATUS. *Forster*

A much-branched shrub up to 8 ft. high, with long, slender, flexible, tough, dark coloured, pendulous branchlets bearing alternate leaves either singly or two to five clustered at each joint; both stem and leaves are glabrous. On young plants the leaves are linear, ½ to 1 in. long, $\frac{1}{12}$ in. or less wide, entire, bluntish; on adult plants they are smaller and often only ¼ in. or even less long. Flowers mostly unisexual, inconspicuous and of no beauty, yellowish white, $\frac{3}{16}$ in. wide, borne singly or a few together at the joints, very shortly stalked. Fruit globose, the size of a peppercorn, covered with very close pale down.

Native of New Zealand and the Chatham Islands; it was cultivated by the Vilmorins at Verrières, near Paris, and flowered there as long ago as May 1851. At Kew it was grown on a wall, for which it made a graceful and distinct covering, developing into a thick tangle of dark slender stems, many of them pendulous and unbranched for more than a foot of their length. They give the shrub an evergreen character. It belongs to an essentially New Zealand type of vegetation.

P. LYALLII, *Hooker fil.* (Plate 39)

(Bot. Mag., t. 5935; Gaya Lyallii, *Baker fil.*; Hoheria Lyallii, *Hook. f.*)

A deciduous shrub in this country, but attaining the dimensions of a small tree up to 30 ft. high in New Zealand, and said to be evergreen at the lower levels of its native habitat. Leaves 2 to 4½ ins. long, 1½ to 2 ins. wide; ovate, with a heart-shaped base, bright green above, paler or even whitish beneath, the margins jaggedly toothed; stalk half to fully as long as the blade. Sometimes the whole leaf is downy, sometimes nearly or quite glabrous. Flowers in clusters of from two to five (usually three) at the leaf-axils of the current season's growth; each flower 1½ ins. across, solitary on a slender, drooping stalk 1 to 1¼ ins. long. Petals overlapping, white, almost translucent; anthers yellow in the type, purple in var. glabrata; calyx with five triangular lobes. Fruit globose, ¾ to 1½ ins. across.

Native of New Zealand. This beautiful shrub, which flowers in late June and July, is not absolutely hardy. During the winter of 1908-9, a fine specimen at Kew, 10 ft. high and as much through, which had flowered profusely for several years previously, was killed down to the ground. It subsequently sprang up from the base again, but one has to be prepared for the same thing happening any winter. The species is represented in gardens by two forms, one of stiffer, sturdier habit and more downy in foliage than the other; flowers more cup-shaped; this is regarded as the type. The glabrous form is distinguished as var. GLABRATA. Both are beautiful, and when the branches are wreathed with the tissue-paper like flowers there is no shrub of its type more attractive at the time, and few at any other.

PLAGIANTHUS LYALLII

P. PULCHELLUS, *A. Gray*

An evergreen shrub or tree. Leaves ovate, with a heart-shaped base, $2\frac{1}{2}$ to $4\frac{1}{2}$ ins. long, green both sides, coarsely and irregularly toothed, often with two lateral lobes near the base; leaf-stalk slender, half as long as the blade. When young, the leaves and young wood are dotted with stellate hairs. Flowers produced on short racemes or singly, white, each $\frac{1}{4}$ in. across.

Native of S. Australia. Of the species of Plagianthus here dealt with, this has least merit in this country, whatever it may have in its own. It is a quick grower and flowers in July, but its blossoms have little beauty, nor has it shown the graceful and distinct growth of P. betulinus. It is also tender, and only hardy in mild districts.

P. LAMPENII is nearly allied to the above, but more ornamental, and distinguished by the greater hairiness of the younger parts. It has dullish white, fragrant flowers, about the size of those of P. pulchellus, but borne in longer racemes. It has flowered with Mr T. Smith of Newry, and, by him was described as hardy against a wall, and very free-flowering. Native of Tasmania.

PLANERA AQUATICA, *Walter*. WATER ELM. ULMACEÆ

A deciduous tree, 30 to 45 ft. high, with a trunk 15 to 20 ins. in diameter; young shoots thin, downy. Leaves alternately arranged in opposite ranks, ovate or oval, 1 to 3 ins. long, about half as wide, toothed (sometimes doubly so), scurfy downy beneath when young, ultimately harsh to the touch on both surfaces; veins about ten each side the midrib, forked near the margin; stalk $\frac{1}{8}$ to $\frac{1}{4}$ in. long. Flowers greenish, very small and inconspicuous, usually unisexual, sometimes bisexual, both sorts being found on the same tree. Males borne in few-flowered clusters, each one composed of a four-, sometimes five-lobed calyx with a corresponding number of stamens; females longer-stalked, borne one to three together in the leaf-axils of small lateral twigs. Fruit nut-like, $\frac{1}{2}$ in. in diameter, covered with elongated, wart-like excrescences, and containing one seed.

Native of the south-eastern United States, where it is frequently found in swamps. From its allies, Ulmus and Celtis (the former of which it resembles in foliage), it differs in the nut-like tubercled fruit. The tree is extremely rare in cultivation. What is found usually under the name of Zelkova crenata, a Caucasian tree. The genus is monotypic and is named after J. J. Planer, a German physician (1743-1789).

PLANTAGO CYNOPS, *Linnæus*. SHRUBBY PLANTAIN PLANTAGINACEÆ

An evergreen shrub 1 to 1$\frac{1}{2}$ ft. high, with erect branches that are downy when young. Leaves opposite, narrowly linear, 1 to 2$\frac{1}{2}$ ins. long, $\frac{1}{20}$ in. wide, grooved on the upper side, rough or bristly at the edges, rather triangular in cross section. The tiny flowers are produced from June onwards crowded in an ovoid head scarcely $\frac{1}{2}$ in. long, which is borne at the end of an erect, slender, downy stalk 1$\frac{1}{2}$ to 3$\frac{1}{2}$ ins. long. Corolla $\frac{1}{8}$ in. wide, four-lobed, yellowish white, the lobes lanceolate, just standing clear of a mass of broadly ovate bracts, which are green, pointed, and have a membranous, rather transparent margin.

Native of Central and Southern Europe; cultivated by Gerard at Holborn in 1596, under the name Psyllium sempervirens. It is of interest as a shrubby member of the same genus as the common lawn pests, but has not beauty. It was found by Mr Charles Baker flowering on Foxendown, Meopham, Kent, in August 1920, and Mr H. N. Ridley has a note on its existence there in the *Journal of Botany* for 1920, p. 271. It was growing on a dry bank of chalk where there is very little soil, and, as there are no houses near the spot, Mr Ridley considers it quite unlikely that a plant of so little attraction and so very rarely cultivated as this could have gained its footing there as an escape from gardens. He is, therefore, inclined to include it in the indigenous flora of England. But Mr C. E. Britton, at p. 294 of the same journal, thinks it had most probably been introduced with imported seeds. He had found it in 1902 on the slopes of a Kentish hill between Cobham and Luddesdown.

PLATANUS. PLANE. PLATANACEÆ

The planes are very distinct from any other group of trees and constitute in themselves a natural order. In foliage they bear some resemblance to the maples, but the leaves are alternate. The flowers are unisexual, both sexes occurring on the same tree. The most characteristic feature of the planes is the production of the seed-vessels (achenes) in spherical balls, which are sometimes solitary, but more often strung two to six together on a pendulous stalk. They persist on the tree more or less throughout the winter. The bark peels off in large flakes, and after a stormy spring day the ground beneath a large plane will frequently be seen strewn with pieces of bark torn off by wind.

Some of the noblest trees of the northern hemisphere belong to this genus. Specimens of the European P. orientalis are known to have trunks 40 ft. in circumference, and the American P. occidentalis growing in the Mississippi Valley has trunks about as large, and it occasionally reaches 170 ft. in height. They like a deep, moist, loamy soil, and thrive better in the south of England than in the north. They are essentially sun-lovers. Seeds ripen on P. acerifolia and orientalis, and germinate readily. Young plants may also be obtained from cuttings, which should be made at the fall of the leaf, of shoots 8 to 12 ins. long, with a "heel" of old wood at the base, and placed under a handlight in a sheltered spot. In nurseries they are usually propagated from stools by layers. Young plants are rather subject to being cut back by frost.

The plane trees of town streets and promenades are under suspicion of causing serious bronchial irritation by shedding the hairs from their leaves, and especially fruits. These break up into minute particles which, floating in the air, are inhaled. Although the alleged evil influences of these particles on the throat and lungs (and even on the eyes and ears as well) were suspected and written about by the ancients—among others by Galen and Dioscorides—they never appear to have deterred either them or later generations from planting the tree freely. There seems to be little doubt that on the Continent it produces, or helps to produce, a catarrhal affection analogous to hay fever. In Britain the crops of fruit are not so large, and probably our damper climate prevents the hairs travelling far from the tree; at anyrate, nothing has been proved against the tree to justify its wholesale condemnation.

P. ACERIFOLIA, *Willdenow*. LONDON PLANE

A deciduous tree of the largest size, frequently over 100 ft. high, with a smooth, erect trunk, whose bark peels off in flakes, and a huge, rounded head of branches, the terminal parts of which in large trees are pendulous; young shoots and leaves covered at first with a dense, pale brown wool much of which falls away by autumn. Leaves 5 to 10 ins. wide, usually rather less in length; five-lobed, the lobes triangular and extending from one-third to one-half the depth of the blade, more or less coarsely toothed; stalk 1 to 4 ins. long. Fruit-balls two to as many as six in a pendulous string, each 1 to 1½ ins. across, rendered burr like by the long, persistent remnant of the style at the apex of each fruit.

The origin of this plane is not known. Like the red horse-chestnut, it has never been found wild, and all the old historical planes of the Orient are P. orientalis. Now the commonest of planes, it first came into notice early in the eighteenth century. In London it is planted in greater numbers than all the other sorts of trees put together. It certainly has the power to withstand a smoke-laden city atmosphere better than any other tree at present known. Years ago some ingenious person suggested that this faculty was due to its habit of casting its bark, and this theory has been religiously repeated by nearly every writer since. There is no proof of this, for atmospheric influences do not affect branches large enough to shed their bark, but rather the leaves and other breathing parts of the tree. It is remarkable that a tree which, by descent at least, belongs to the sun-baked isles of Greece should be able to adapt itself so completely to the pavements and atmosphere of London.

In the original edition of this work (vol. ii., p. 202) I remarked that it had been suggested that the London plane (P. acerifolia) was of hybrid origin, its parents being P. occidentalis and P. orientalis. Since then, the late Professor A. Henry has devoted considerable research to its history, and in the *Proceedings of the Royal Irish Academy* for April 1919 records the results of his investigations. Reversing an opinion previously expressed in the *Trees of Great Britain and Ireland*, vol. iii., p. 620, he there supports the view that the London plane is a hybrid. He also endeavours to show that it probably originated at Oxford about 1670. Both at Oxford and in the British Museum specimens are preserved of the London plane, gathered from a tree growing apparently at or near Oxford, between 1680 and 1700. The famous tree at Ely, which I have never seen but which (following Elwes and Henry) I alluded to as P. orientalis in the first edition, now proves to be P. acerifolia.

Although usually propagated by cuttings or layers, the London plane produces plenty of fertile seeds. The plants raised from them show considerable variation in the characters of leaf and fruit. This is strong presumptive evidence of its being of hybrid origin. One of the finest of these seedlings from P. acerifolia is

P. HISPANICA.—Regarding the origin of this tree, Philip Miller, in the 7th edition of his *Dictionary*, published in 1759, says "there are two [planes] in English gardens which I suppose to be varieties that have accidentally risen from seed; one is titled the maple-leaved plane [*i.e.*, our London plane], the other is called the Spanish plane [P. hispanica]." The latter was in existence before 1731, because Miller records his planting it during that year. It is a quick-growing tree forming a tall, straight stem with larger leaves than any other of the London plane group; they are 10 to 12 ins. wide and, according to Henry, are "readily distinguished by the persistent down on the nerves and leaf-stalk and by five distinct, short, broadly triangular, toothed lobes." The fruit balls are nearly always reduced to one or two on each stalk, thus indicating a relationship to P. occidentalis, which has rarely more than one ball, whilst P. orientalis has two to seven on a stalk. P. hispanica is a fine tree with a noble carriage and graceful, pendulous branches, but it is unaccountably rare in gardens. It has, however, figured in nursery catalogues as "P. californica" and "P. macrophylla." Whilst its pendulous branching makes it less suitable for streets and thoroughfares, it is perhaps the best of all planes for ornamenting gardens and parks. There is a fine tree close to the Azalea Garden at Kew.

Var. SUTTNERI (P. occidentalis argenteo-variegata) is a handsome, variegated tree, its leaves being conspicuously blotched with creamy white; sometimes almost wholly of that colour. It is far from being as robust as the type.

P. PYRAMIDALIS, *Rivers*.—This, which is believed to be another seedling of the London plane group, originated in France about 1850. As its name implies, it is of slender pyramidal growth when young and never droops its branches even when old. For this reason it is very suitable for street planting. Its leaves are 6 to 8 ins. wide, three-lobed and bright green. The stiff habit and shallowly lobed leaves of this plane render it, in my opinion, inferior to P. acerifolia, P. hispanica, or P. orientalis for planting in gardens or parks.

P. CUNEATA, *Willdenow*

(P. orientalis cuneata, *Loudon*; P. nepalensis, *Hort.*)

By some writers this tree is considered to be a variety of the Oriental plane, and it is no doubt closely allied to it. It differs in the leaves being three-lobed as well as five-lobed, with the base wedge-shaped and tapering gradually to a stalk; they are also smaller, usually 3 to 6 ins. long and wide, occasionally half as long again. The tree is not so large, vigorous, or hardy as P. orientalis. Young plants raised at Kew from seed obtained from the north-western Himalaya (where it is probably only cultivated) are stunted, very slow-growing, and subject to injury by spring frosts; they have a narrow, pyramidal habit. The typical P. cuneata rarely bears fruit near London, and is scarcely worth a place in gardens, but there are forms intermediate between it and P. orientalis that make handsome small trees.

P. OCCIDENTALIS, *Linnæus*. BUTTONWOOD

One of the most widely spread and persistent of errors connected with the identity of trees has centred round this species. There is probably not a single specimen of the true thing in the British Isles with a trunk 3 ins. in diameter—yet scores of nurserymen still offer it in their catalogues. The tree they offer, and the tree discussed by Loudon and other writers under the name, is P. acerifolia, or the common London plane. The true P. occidentalis is a native of the southern and eastern United States, where, in the region of the Ohio and Mississippi rivers, it grows 140 to 170 ft. in height, with a trunk 30 ft. in girth. It differs from P. acerifolia in the leaves being only shallowly lobed, with a wide, roundish sinus between the lobes. Then the tree very rarely bears more than one ball of fruits on each stalk (the European ones have two to six), and the surface of the ball is smoother and less burr-like than in acerifolia or orientalis. From what has been said above, it will be gathered that the species has no value in British gardens. It has many times been raised from seed at Kew, and the young plants grow freely enough for a time, but owing to injury by spring frost and the attacks of parasitic fungi they rarely get beyond 6 ft. in height. In my experience at Kew only one plant ever reached the height of 12 ft. Our winter frosts will not harm it. The winter cold of Massachusetts is greater than we ever experience, but I remember seeing, near Lancaster in that State, a tree with a trunk 20 ft. in girth. In habit and in its tall trunk it resembles P. acerifolia.

P. ORIENTALIS, *Linnæus*. ORIENTAL PLANE

A deciduous tree of the largest size, in this country occasionally 80 to 100 ft. high, and 14 to 20 ft. in girth of trunk; in open situations it usually branches a few feet from the ground into several large spreading limbs; young shoots at first covered with pale brown hair-tufts, becoming glabrous later. Leaves palmate, 6 to 10 ins. wide, somewhat less in length, with five large lobes, and usually a smaller one on each side at the base; the lobes, which are half to two-thirds the depth of the blade, and lance-shaped, have each one to three large teeth or minor lobes at the sides. When they first unfold, the leaves are covered with a thick whitish brown felt composed of stellate hairs which later falls away, leaving the leaf glabrous except near the veins beneath, and glossy above; stalk 1½ to 3 ins. long. Fruit-balls two to six on each stalk, 1 in. wide, bristly.

Native of S.E. Europe and Asia Minor; cultivated in England in the middle of the sixteenth century. The true Oriental plane is comparatively rare in gardens, having been ousted by the more rapidly growing "London" plane, which is not so picturesque nor so pleasing as an isolated lawn tree. It is easily distinguished from acerifolia by its shorter, more rugged trunk, and its deeper, often doubly lobed leaves. Few trees are longer-lived than this. On the banks of the Bosporus there is a group of trees under which the knights of Godfrey de Bouillon on their way to the crusaders are said to have sheltered in 1069. Under a tree still living on the island of Cos in the Ægean Sea—its trunk 18 yards in circumference—tradition says that Hippocrates sat more than 2300 years ago. There is no direct evidence to support these stories, but they point to the perhaps unequalled longevity of the plane among European trees. In his account of fine British specimens Mr Elwes gives first place to one in the Palace Gardens at Ely, planted by Bishop Gunning between 1674 and 1684. This now proves, however, to be P. acerifolia. A fine specimen at Kew, near the sundial, and on the site of the famous seventeenth-century gardens of Sir Henry Capel of Kew House, has a trunk 15 ft. in girth.

P. RACEMOSA, *Nuttall*

A tree 40 to 100 ft. high in California, with a trunk 2 to 6 ft. in diameter; young shoots clothed with a thick wool which falls away during the summer. Leaves usually five- sometimes three-lobed; the lobes reaching half-way or more than half-way to the midrib, pointed and shallowly, often distantly, toothed, slightly heart-shaped at the base; thickly clothed below with pale, persistent down, especially along the midrib and veins; 6 to 12 ins. wide, rather more in length; stalks stout, downy, 1 to 3 ins. long. Flowers in ball-like clusters, two to seven of which occur on the pendulous stalk; by the time the fruits have developed the balls are ¾ in. across.

Native of California. It is doubtful if this plane be at present in cultivation, and it will probably prove tender. The young trees mentioned in early editions as existing at Kew proved to be wrongly named.

PLATYCARYA STROBILACEA, *Siebold and Zuccarini*
JUGLANDACEÆ

(Fortunæa chinensis, *Lindley*; Journ. Hort. Soc., i., p. 150)

A small or medium-sized, deciduous tree, with pinnate leaves, 6 to 12 ins. long. Leaflets five to fifteen, stalkless, ovate-lanceolate, obliquely wedge-shaped or rounded at the base, long and taper-pointed, sharply and often doubly toothed; 1½ to 4½ ins. long, ½ to 1¼ ins. wide; with at first scattered hairs above and along the midrib and veins beneath, becoming glabrous later. Flowers unisexual, both sexes borne on the same tree, but on separate inflorescences; sepals and petals absent. Male catkins slender, cylindrical, drooping, 2 to 3½ ins. long, ¼ in. wide; borne four to twelve together in a hairy raceme terminating the current year's growth; female inflorescence also terminal, surrounded by the male catkins, erect, usually solitary, 1¼ ins. long, 1 in. wide, resembling a cone. In both sexes the flowers are produced in the axils of small, lanceolate scales, followed in the female by tiny winged nutlets which, with the wings, are only ⅛ to ⅙ in. across.

Native of China; first discovered and introduced by Fortune in 1845; said also to be found in Japan. Allied to the walnuts and hickories, and resembling them in leaf and male catkins, it is very distinct in the female inflorescence and tiny nuts. It succeeds well in Central and S. France, but I am afraid is only adapted for the milder parts of Britain. It lives out-of-doors at Kew, but does not thrive.

PLATYCRATER ARGUTA, *Siebold and Zuccarini*

SAXIFRAGACEÆ

A low, deciduous, sometimes creeping shrub, with slender, glabrous stems. Leaves opposite, narrowly oval-lanceolate, the largest 5 to 8 ins. long and 1 to 2 ins. wide, tapering at both ends, the margins set with slender teeth, bristly hairy beneath; stalk ¼ in. long. Flowers of two kinds, viz. perfect and sterile, as in Hydrangea, produced in a lax terminal corymb. Perfect flowers 1 in. across, with four white, broadly ovate petals, two styles, very numerous yellow stamens, and a four-lobed calyx; the lobes ½ in. long, pointed, narrowly triangular. Fruit top-shaped, with the calyx-lobes persisting. Sterile flowers consist only of the united calyx-lobes, and form a white, flat, three- or four-sided disk, ¾ in. across, all the other parts of the flower being absent.

Native of Japan; introduced by way of St Petersburg about 1868. The plant is rather tender and apt to be cut to the ground in winter, or killed outright in severe frosts. I have never seen the sterile flowers above described on cultivated plants, usually there have been three perfect flowers produced in a corymb, the middle one opening first, each on a slender stalk 1 in. or less long. Both Siebold and Regel include sterile flowers in their figures (see *Flora Japonica*, t. 27, and *Gartenflora*, t. 516). Siebold says he found the plant growing on humid rocks with its branches flat on the ground. He mentions a curious use the Japanese made of the plant; this was to make an infusion of the leaves with which the images of Buddha were washed or baptized. But that was in 1835. The plant is easily increased by rather soft cuttings.

PLATYOSPRION PLATYCARPUM, *Makino*. LEGUMINOSÆ

(Sophora platycarpa, *Maximowicz*; Cladrastis platycarpa, *Makino*)

A deciduous tree, similar in habit and general appearance to Sophora japonica; branchlets glabrous, dark brown. Leaves pinnate, 8 to 10 ins. long; leaflets in five and a half to seven and a half pairs, obliquely ovate, pointed; $1\frac{1}{2}$ to 4 ins. long, 1 to $1\frac{1}{2}$ ins. wide; bright green above, downy on the midrib and stalk, otherwise glabrous at maturity. Flowers white, pea-flower-shaped, $\frac{5}{8}$ in. long, produced on slender, downy stalks about $\frac{1}{4}$ in. long, in panicles 4 to 6 ins. high, $2\frac{1}{2}$ to 4 ins. wide. Pod flat, 2 ins. long, $\frac{1}{2}$ in. wide, tapered to a point at both ends and winged on the seams; seeds three or four, often only one developing.

Native of Japan. This interesting tree was first placed in Sophora, from which its flat (not necklace-shaped) fruit distinguishes it. A Japanese botanist has placed it in Cladrastis, which it certainly resembles in the fruit. It is not common in cultivation, although offered by several continental dealers; Maackia amurensis is sometimes supplied for it. It has not yet flowered in this country, but will no doubt thrive wherever Sophora japonica does. In N. America it is said to have proved hardier.

PODOCARPUS. TAXACEÆ

There are some fifty or sixty species of Podocarpus known, which are found in Australasia, S. America, and E. Asia, only two or three of which can be regarded as hardy in our average climate, although a considerably larger number will thrive in Ireland, in Cornwall, and other mild counties. They are allied to the yews, and have rounded, or egg-shaped, plum-like fruits consisting of a single seed or nut with a fleshy covering. They require in cultivation a sheltered spot and a well-drained, loamy, or peaty soil. The generic name is derived from the Greek *podos*, foot, and *karpos*, fruit, and refers to the fleshy fruit-stalks characteristic of many of the species.

P. ALPINA, *R. Brown*

A low evergreen tree or shrub, forming a neat, dense, almost hemispherical mass of drooping branches at present 3 to 6 ft. high with us; branchlets produced in whorls, very slender and interlacing, glabrous and green when young. Leaves $\frac{1}{4}$ to $\frac{1}{2}$ in. long, $\frac{1}{16}$ to $\frac{1}{12}$ in. wide; linear, tapered at the base and either rounded at the apex or terminated by a small fine point; dark dull green above; slightly pale, with rows of stomata beneath. Fruit a small, bright red, plum-like body $\frac{1}{4}$ in. across, containing one seed.

Native of Tasmania and the mountains of Victoria, but quite hardy at Kew, where it has withstood 30° of frost without injury. It is a distinct shrub, and although quite healthy only attained 5 ft. in height in fifty years, or perhaps longer. A plant occasionally bears female flowers at Kew, and in 1892 one in the rock garden produced a few fruits. It leaves fall about their fourth year.

P. DACRYDIOIDES, *A. Richard.* NEW ZEALAND WHITE PINE

(Dacrydium excelsum, *A. Cunningham*)

An evergreen tree up to 100 ft. or more high, with a trunk 7 ft. to 16 ft. in girth, and drooping branches. Leaves of two kinds: (1) those of young trees which are arranged in two rows as in Taxodium distichum and are $\frac{1}{6}$ to $\frac{1}{3}$ in. long, $\frac{1}{24}$ in. wide, curved and pointed; (2) those of mature trees which are arranged all round the branch, are only $\frac{1}{16}$ to $\frac{1}{8}$ in. long, and, in their smallest state, scale-like, resembling the leaves of a juniper or cypress. There are intermediate types and often both forms of leaf occur on one branch. The trees are unisexual, the female bearing a black, egg-shaped fruit about $\frac{1}{6}$ in. long, the stalk of which is enlarged and becomes bright red and succulent.

Native of both Islands of New Zealand. It often occurs in swampy localities from sea level up to 2000 ft. and was originally discovered by Capt. Cook about 1774. Cheeseman describes it as probably the tallest of New Zealand trees, one specimen in the forests of Westland having measured 210 ft. in height. It is called "white pine" there. As a small tree it is thinly branched and very elegant. Only suitable for mild localities.

P. HALLII, *Kirk*

(P. Totara Hallii, *Pilger*)

Very nearly akin to P. Totara, this tree is of smaller stature and only from 25 to 60 ft. high; the bark, too, is thinner and always papery. As seen growing in a small state it is very distinct in the leafage, some of the largest leaves being $1\frac{3}{4}$ ins. long by $\frac{1}{4}$ in. wide, sharply pointed and of linear-lanceolate shape. On old fruit-bearing trees they become smaller and only $\frac{1}{2}$ to 1 in. long, $\frac{1}{8}$ in. wide, and more abruptly pointed. On young trees the leaves are mostly arranged distichously (*i.e.* in two opposite rows); on old ones all round the branches. The branching of young trees is also looser and weaker. The flowers apparently do not differ greatly from those of P. Totara, although the male flowers are more distinctly stalked; the leafage of old trees of both scarcely differs. Cheeseman observes, nevertheless, that the thin papery bark is always unmistakable.

Native of the North and South Islands of New Zealand, reaching up to 3500 ft. altitude. This is 1500 ft. higher than P. Totara attains and suggests that it should be hardier. It is perfectly hardy and in excellent health at Exbury, Hants., and is succeeding very well with Colonel Stern at Highdown, near Worthing, also at Tregrehan and Scorrier in Cornwall.

P. MACROPHYLLA, *D. Don*

An evergreen small tree, 25 to 50 ft. high, usually shrubby in this country, and forming a densely leafy, rounded bush. Leaves linear, tapering at both ends; 3 to 4 ins. long, $\frac{3}{16}$ to $\frac{1}{4}$ in. wide; of firm, rather leathery texture, perfectly glabrous, the midrib prominently raised above and below; margin thickened below; dark glossy green above, yellowish green beneath.

Native of China and Japan. According to Sargent it is a common hedge plant in Tokyo gardens, and is often clipped into fantastic shapes. It is fairly hardy in the south of England. It may be confused with P. chilina, but has larger, broader leaves of a yellower green, and they have not the sickle-like shape frequent in the Chilean species. In Japan the leaves are as much as 7 ins. long by $\frac{1}{2}$ in. wide.

In Cornwall and Ireland there may occasionally be seen P. NUBIGENA, *Lindley*, a Chilean species very distinct, but unfortunately only hardy in our mildest districts. The leaves (very closely set on the branchlet) are 1 to 1¾ ins. long, ⅛ to $\frac{3}{16}$ in. wide, tapering to a sharp point, of a rather pale, charmingly fresh green, with a broadish band of stomatic lines each side the midrib beneath. The young shoots are bright yellow. The best trees I have seen are two at Kilmacurragh, Co. Wicklow, about 25 ft. high, nearly as much through.

P. NAGEIA, *R. Brown*

(P. Nagi, *Pilger*)

An evergreen tree up to 80 ft. high in a wild state, with a trunk 8 ft. in girth; bark of large trees smooth and brownish purple, ultimately scaling off in large flakes. Leaves opposite, thick and leathery, varying in shape from roundish ovate to lanceolate, pointed, tapered at the base; 1 to 3 ins. long, ½ to 1¼ ins. wide; dark green, glabrous and glossy, with numerous veins running lengthwise. Male flowers in axillary, cylindrical, sometimes branched spikes ½ to 1 in. long, ⅙ in. wide. Females solitary or in pairs, developing a globose fruit about ½ in. wide, covered with plum-like bloom.

Native of Japan, Formosa, and China; introduced by Siebold to Ghent in 1830. Both Sargent and Wilson write enthusiastically of its beauty in Japan; the latter describes it as "one of the most strikingly beautiful of all evergreen trees." It has long been cultivated in the Temperate House at Kew, but is only likely to be hardy out-of-doors in the very mildest parts of our islands. It used to be grown in the open air at Pencarrow in Cornwall. This podocarpus is distinct from all those here mentioned in the wideness of its leaves as compared with their length. A variety even more marked in this respect than the type is

Var. ROTUNDIFOLIA, *Maximowicz*, which has still more rounded leaves. The Japanese cultivate another whose leaves are marked with broad, creamy-white stripes; it is known as var. VARIEGATA.

P. NIVALIS, *Hooker*. ALPINE TOTARA

An evergreen shrub of dense bushy habit up to 8 ft. high, its branches wide spreading in a wild state, the lower ones often taking root. Plants in cultivation are as yet small and of compact form, rather like one of the dwarf yews. Young shoots glabrous, carrying twenty to twenty-five leaves to the inch. Leaves set all round the twig, linear, abruptly contracted at the end to a small point, tapered but scarcely stalked at the base; ¼ to ½ in. long, $\frac{1}{16}$ to $\frac{1}{12}$ in. wide; dull green above; keeled and with two faintly defined, comparatively broad stripes of stomata beneath. Fruit (not yet seen in this country) described by Cheeseman as a small oblong-ovoid nut borne on a much enlarged, succulent, bright red stalk.

Native of both Islands of New Zealand, usually at from 2000 to 5000 ft. altitude. It was first described as long ago as 1843, but I have only seen it in cultivation during recent years and know of no full-sized plants in this country. It is said to be often prostrate in New Zealand and this habit, combined with the propensity of its branches to take root, makes it valuable as a soil-binder on mountain slopes. It promises to be the hardiest of all the podocarps and in its present state with us is an appropriate shrub for rock gardens, as is shown by one at Edinburgh which was 3½ ft. high and 5 ft. in diameter in June 1931.

P. SALIGNA, *D. Don*

(P. andina of gardens—not *Pœppig*; P. chilina, *Richard*)

A unisexual evergreen tree, 40 to 60 ft. high, but in this country a shrub except in the south and west; branchlets green, terete, quite glabrous. Leaves persisting two years, falling the third, linear, often sickle-shaped, tapered at the base, pointed at the apex; 2 to 4½ ins. long, ⅛ to $\frac{3}{16}$ in. wide; dark rather bluish green above, paler beneath, with numerous rows of minute stomata. Male flowers in a cluster of slender spikes 1 to 1½ ins. long. Fruits egg-shaped, ⅓ in. long, solitary or in pairs on a stalk ½ to ⅝ in. long and standing out at right angles from it.

Native of the Andes of Chile; introduced in 1853. At Kew it was killed during the frosts of February 1895, but survived in Messrs Paul's nursery at High Beech, on higher ground, whence a fresh stock was obtained which has also since been lost. Its chief value is in the south-western counties. There is a male tree in Mr Fox's garden, Penjerrick, Cornwall, 30 ft. high, which makes a very striking pyramidal mass of foliage.

P. SPICATA, *R. Brown*

(Prumnopitys spicata, *Kent*; Dacrydium taxifolium, *Banks and Solander*)

An evergreen tree 40 to 80 ft. high, with a rounded head of erect branches and a trunk 6 to 12 ft. in girth; bark bluish black, scaling off in large flakes. On young plants the branches are very slender and pendulous, forming a dense tangle, the leaves thinly disposed on them or only towards the tips in two opposite rows. On mature plants they are set thickly on the twigs in two opposite rows. Each leaf is ⅓ to ½ in. long, $\frac{1}{16}$ in. wide, slightly curved, blunt or with a short point, of leathery texture, green above, rather glaucous with faint stomatic lines beneath. The twigs and leaves in this adult state are not unlike those of one of the short-leaved garden varieties of yew. The trees are unisexual; the males producing their cylindrical flowers, each ¼ to ⅓ in. long, in spikes 1 to 2 ins. long to which they are attached at right angles; the females produce a black, globose, succulent fruit ¼ to ⅓ in. wide.

Native of both Islands of New Zealand from sea level up to 2000 ft. altitude, originally discovered by Sir Joseph Banks about 1770. It is distinct amongst the podocarps of New Zealand in the male flowers being produced in spikes and in the fruit *not* having the usual enlarged, succulent stalk. It is a free-growing tree only suitable for mild districts.

P. TOTARA, *D. Don*. TOTARA

(Hooker's London Journal of Botany, vol. i., t. 19)

A fine evergreen tree in a wild state, 40 to 80 ft., sometimes 100 ft. high, with a trunk 6 to 18 ft. in girth, clothed with thick, furrowed, stringy and papery bark which can be removed in sheets; young shoots glabrous, furrowed. Leaves leathery, stiff, linear with a sharp hard point, quite glabrous, dull green; ½ to 1¼ ins. long, $\frac{1}{12}$ to ⅛ in. wide; not stalked. Male and female flowers are borne on separate trees. Male flowers cylindrical, ½ to ¾ in. long, axillary, solitary or two or three together at the top of a very short stalk. Female flowers axillary, solitary or in pairs. Fruit ovoid-oblong, rounded at the tip, the stalk usually much enlarged, red, succulent, swelling out as large as a cherry and bearing one or two of the small seeds at the top.

Native of the North and South Islands of New Zealand, up to 2000 ft. altitude; hardy in the southern and western parts of the British Isles. There are healthy trees 30 ft. high at Ludgvan and Tregrehan, and several smaller ones in other Cornish gardens. It succeeds well at Craignish Castle, Argyllshire, and Messrs Hillier state that a plant has grown in the open air in their nursery at Winchester for many years. At Kew it has to be grown in the Temperate House. In New Zealand its timber is extremely valuable, being straight grained, very durable and reddish; it is much used for house building, piles of wharves, etc. I do not know that the totara has ever shown any fertility in this country, but the comparatively small fruits, solitary or twin, are very interesting, being borne on the top of a swollen, fleshy, globose stalk much larger than they are. Nearly related to P. Totara is

P. ACUTIFOLIA, *Kirk*, but it is shrubby, and its normal height is given as 5 to 10 ft., its leaves are narrower and thinner, and in the adult stage more finely pointed. It was discovered at the source of the Buller river by T. Kirk on the South Island in 1874. It should be as hardy, if not hardier, than the totara. (*See also* P. Hallii.)

POLIOTHYRSIS SINENSIS, *Oliver*. BIXACEÆ

(Hooker's Icones Plantarum, t. 1885)

A deciduous tree, up to 30 or 40 ft. high, with ovate, slenderly pointed leaves 4¼ to 6 ins. long and 2½ to 5 ins. wide; rounded or sometimes heart-shaped at the base, very downy beneath, becoming glabrous as the season advances; stalk slender, downy, ¾ to 1¾ ins. long. Flowers in a terminal inflorescence, each flower ⅓ in. across, white, soon changing to yellow; they are unisexual, with both sexes on the same inflorescence; calyx-lobes ovate, pointed; styles three. Fruit an ellipsoid capsule ½ to ¾ in. long, many-seeded, seeds winged.

Native of China; discovered by Henry in the province of Hupeh about 1889. It did not reach English gardens until 1908, when Wilson sent seeds to the Arnold Arboretum, some of which were distributed in Europe. Some of the young seedlings raised at Kew perished in the severe winter of 1908-9, but others survived, and there is every probability that established plants will be hardy. It is the only known member of its genus, and is nearly allied to Idesia polycarpa, but differs in having a dry capsular fruit instead of a berry. Of its merits as a garden tree little can yet be said. Wilson observes that the bark in adult trees is grey and deeply furrowed, and that the leaves vary in toothing and pubescence.

POLYGALA. MILKWORT. POLYGALACEÆ

A large genus spread over both hemispheres and comprising herbaceous plants, shrubs and a few trees. Leaves alternate, simple, entire; flowers in racemes or spikes; sepals five, three of which are small; petals usually three, united to one another to some extent and forming a keel; stamens eight, united to form a tube. The name is derived from the Greek *polys-gala*, meaning much milk, some species being supposed to increase the flow of milk.

P. CHAMÆBUXUS, *Linnæus*

(Bot. Mag., t. 316)

A dwarf, creeping, evergreen shrub, from 6 to 12 ins. high, with glabrous, alternate, box-like, dull green leaves, ½ to 1 in. long, oval or narrow oblong, not toothed, but with a small pointed tip. Flowers ½ in. long, produced from the leaf-axils near the end of the shoot, singly or in pairs; they rather resemble the flowers of the pea family, and are creamy white, with the end of the keel bright yellow. The fruit is a flat, two-seeded capsule; seeds downy.

This charming little shrub is a native of the mountainous regions of Central Europe, where it occurs most abundantly on calcareous formations. It succeeds in cool, moist positions, forming neat tufts covered with the delightful flowers in April and May. Under cultivation it seems to thrive very well in a peaty soil or in a sandy loam. In positions where it thrives (and the Thames Valley with its dry, hot spells is not the most suitable) it is readily propagated by taking off the sucker growths with roots attached.

Var. GRANDIFLORA (syn. var. purpurea).—Wing-petals purple, the keel yellowish at the apex.

P. VAYREDÆ, *Costa*

(Bot. Mag., t. 9009)

A dwarf, procumbent, evergreen shrub rarely more than 4 ins. above the ground; twigs wiry, glabrous or slightly downy. Leaves alternate, linear, pointed; ½ to 1 in, long, $\frac{1}{12}$ in. wide; of rather leathery texture, glabrous except for the ciliate margins when young; very shortly stalked. Flowers produced during May from the leaf-axils of the previous season's shoots, singly or in twos or threes. Outer sepals pale green or purplish, quite small; the two inner sepals ⅝ in. long, half as much wide, obovate, tapering to a narrow claw, bright rose-purple like the side petals; the keel is ½ in. long and terminates in a kind of hood which is yellow with a curious seven-lobed protuberance at the end.

Native of Spain on the Eastern Pyrenees of Catalonia, confined to a small area. Discovered originally in the early part of last century, but apparently lost sight of until 1877, when it was re-discovered by Senor Vayreda. It is related to P. Chamæbuxus, but is well distinguished by the narrow leaves and the seven-lobed crest terminating the keel. It is an equally charming tiny shrub, especially for the rock garden, where, given the same treatment as its ally, it will form good tufts.

P. MYRTIFOLIA, *Linnæus* (Bot. Mag., t. 3616) is a native of S. Africa and was once a rather popular greenhouse shrub. It grows and flowers well in the open air at Rosehill, Falmouth. The flowers are purple of various depths of shade, and carry a curiously marked resemblance to the Leguminosæ with a keeled petal.

POLYGONUM BALDSCHUANICUM, *Regel.* POLYGONACEÆ

(Bot. Mag., t. 7544)

A vigorous, deciduous twining climber, its shoots growing as much as 20 ft. in one season, ultimately 40 or more ft. high; stems slender, glabrous, grey. Leaves alternate, broadly ovate, heart-shaped or spear-shaped at the base, pointed or rounded at the apex; 1½ to 4 ins. long, 1 to 2½ ins. wide; glabrous, pale green. Panicles produced in summer and autumn in such abundance as to envelop the plant in a cloud of blossom; they are terminal on lateral shoots, much branched, 8 to 16 ins. long. Flowers pale pink or almost white; each $\frac{1}{3}$ in. across, with transparent ovate sepals in two whorls, the three in the outer whorl winged at the back, the wing passing downwards to the flower-stalk. As these wings persist on the pinkish young seed-vessel, they give it the characteristic three-angled shape.

Native of Bokhara; discovered by Dr A. Regel in 1883; introduced to gardens by way of the St Petersburg Botanic Garden about 1894. No more beautiful climber has been introduced for many years, and its value is enhanced by the late date of its blossoming and the beauty of its young fruits. The best way to cultivate it is to give up to it some worn-

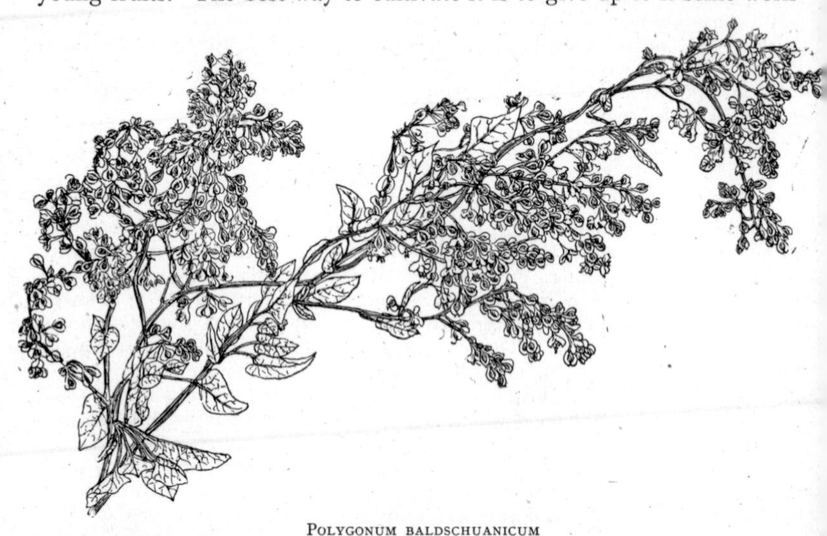

POLYGONUM BALDSCHUANICUM

out tree which it may be allowed to ramble over or envelop at will. Failing that, a stout spruce pole with the side branches left several feet long, or some such support, may be given it. Few climbers give so charming an effect in so short a time. It likes a rich loamy soil and a fully exposed position. Seeds rarely or never set with us, and the plant is best propagated by cuttings. These should be made in summer of pieces of the current year's growth, with a " heel " of older wood attached, and placed in gentle heat. Cuttings of leafless wood, made in February with a heel, will also take root.

P. AUBERTII, *L. Henry*, is a new species from W. China, closely allied to baldschuanicum. Flowers smaller, greenish white tinged with rose; not so desirable according to my experience.

P. EQUISETIFORME, *Sibthorp*, from the Mediterranean region, is well worth growing for its distinct growth and abundant milky white flowers produced in autumn. The plant consists of a dense mass of slender, mare's tail-like stems about as thick as a knitting needle and 2 or 3 ft. high. It needs a warm sunny corner, and even then is often cut back by winter cold.

POPULUS. Poplar. SALICACEÆ

A group of large, usually quick-growing, deciduous trees, with alternate leaves pinnately veined or three-nerved at the base, those on vigorous leading shoots larger, and often different in shape and character from those on lateral twigs. Flowers produced in catkins on the naked shoots in spring, the sexes nearly always on separate trees. Male catkins more densely flowered than the female, the flowers composed of usually numerous stamens attached to a disk, and springing from the axil of a toothed or fringed scale, which soon falls away. Anthers red or purple. Female catkins lengthening until mature, the egg-shaped or rounded ovary seated in a cuplike disk, and crowned by two to four stigmas. The seed is surrounded by a conspicuous tuft of white, cottony hairs which enables it to be carried long distances by wind. Poplars occur in most parts of the northern hemisphere, from subarctic regions to subtropical ones, some inhabiting arid places, others always found in association with moisture.

There are four well-marked groups of poplars :—

I. Balsam Poplars.—These burst into leaf the first, and are distinguished by very gummy winter leaf-buds and leaves, which emit a pleasant balsamic odour, especially when just expanding in spring. Leaves usually whitish, but not woolly beneath ; leaf-stalk not compressed. This group includes *angustifolia*, *balsamifera*, *candicans*, *laurifolia*, *Simoni*, *suaveolens*, *trichocarpa*, *tristis*. Most of these can be increased by cuttings of leafless shoots in the open ground or by suckers.

II. White Poplars.—Leaves woolly, and white or grey beneath, coarsely toothed or lobed, the younger trunks and main branches at first pale and smooth, then pitted with numerous diamond-shaped holes. It includes *alba* and *canescens*. Increased by leafless cuttings in the open ground.

III. Aspens.—Leaves with long, laterally flattened stalks, and noted for their restless movement. It includes *grandidentata*, *tremula*, *tremuloides*, none of which root readily from branch cuttings.

IV. Black Poplars.—The latest group to break into leaf. Leaves green on both sides and with compressed, slender stalks, nearly always in motion ; margins cartilaginous. Trunks with a corrugated bark like an oak. This group includes *angulata*, *Eugenei*, *Fremontii*, *marilandica*, *monilifera*, *nigra*, *regenerata*, *robusta*, *serotina*, *Wislizenii*. All the black poplars except some forms of angulata are easily increased by cuttings of leafless shoots 1 ft. or more long, placed in the open ground in November. Many of the male black poplars in spring are handsome on account of their richly coloured catkins.

The production of hybrids on the Continent, where the poplars seed freely, has produced much confusion in the nomenclature of the black poplar group. Students are much indebted to Prof. A. Henry for a laborious investigation into the tangled identity of these hybrids, the results of which have been recently published. Several hybrids of the balsam poplar group are not of sufficient importance or merit to be given detailed description, such as Petrowskyana, *Schroeder* ;

RASUMOWSKYANA, *Schroeder*; and WOBSTII, *Schroder*—all of Russian origin. The two first are hybrids between some black poplar and laurifolia and suaveolens respectively; Wobstii is thought to be between tristis and laurifolia.

Poplars do not produce good seed freely as a rule, and one does not often see seedling plants of the majority. All of those worth cultivating thrive best in a good moist loam, but many (of the black poplar group especially) also succeed well in heavy, wet ground, and are valuable on that account.

A few notes are here appended to a few species of little importance:—

P. SIEBOLDII, *Miquel*, is the Japanese ally of P. tremula, from which it is well distinguished by the whitish down on the young shoots and the well-developed glands at the base of the leaf-blade. A tree 60 to 70 ft. high in Japan. It has been in cultivation for over fifty years, often under the name "rotundifolia," but is not common.

P. PSEUDO-GRANDIDENTATA, *Dode*, has been in cultivation since 1869 but is of unknown origin. It is perhaps a hybrid between grandidentata and tremula. There are good trees at Abbotsbury and Glasnevin. The young shoots are covered with a whitish wool at first and the leaves are similar in shape and toothing to those of P. tremula, but they are stouter in texture, 3 to 4½ ins. wide, not quite so long.

P. HICKELIANA, *Dode*, is a white poplar wild in N. Africa and Andalusia. On young plants at Kew, received from Mr Hickel in 1923, the leaves are ovate, 1 to 2 ins. long, mostly tapered but sometimes rounded or slightly heart-shaped at the base, three-lobed and irregularly toothed, thinly downy above, covered with white wool beneath. Mr Dode observes that the habit of the tree recalls that of the common beech. It is popularly known in France as "peuplier de Saragosse" and must be nearly related to P. alba, differing in its smaller, narrower leaves. Flowers and fruit unknown to me.

P. TOMENTOSA, *Carrière*, the Chinese White Poplar, is closely related to the "abele" (P. alba), differing from it in the leaves of the vigorous shoots not being lobed but only coarsely and irregularly toothed and white-woolly beneath; whilst on fertile shoots and on old trees the leaves are merely wavy on the margins and become glabrous beneath. Syns. P. alba var. tomentosa, *Wesmael*; P. pekinensis, *L. Henry*.

P. ACUMINATA, *Rydberg*

(P. coloradensis, *Dode*)

A deciduous tree up to 60 ft. high in a wild state; young shoots quite free from down, ordinarily round, but angled when very vigorous; buds slender-pointed, glutinous. Leaves ovate to somewhat diamond-shaped, wedge-shaped to rounded at the base, slenderly pointed, finely round-toothed; 2 to 4 ins. long (larger on vigorous shoots), half as much wide; shining green on both sides and but little paler beneath; leaf-stalks 1 to 2½ ins. long, slender. Catkins slender, not downy, up to 2¾ ins. long.

Native of western N. America; a balsam poplar discovered by Mr Rydberg in Nebraska, in 1891. Plants introduced from the Arnold Arboretum to Kew in 1913 are succeeding well. It is a loose-habited tree with slender, lax shoots with us, vividly green in leaf. Most closely related to P. angustifolia, it is a sturdier, more compact tree which ordinarily has a much shorter leaf-stalk than angustifolia.

P. ADENOPODA, *Maximowicz*. CHINESE ASPEN

(P. Silvestrii, *Pampanini*)

This is a Chinese ally of the aspen, differing from ordinary P. tremula in the long drawn-out apex of the leaves of mature trees and in the shallower undulations of the margin. There are also two conspicuously large glands where the blade joins the stalk which are distinctive. The species is a native of Central and W. China and first appeared in cultivation about 1906 as "P. Silvestrii." These early plants were more persistently downy in leaf and young shoot than later ones. Wilson observed that wild trees varied in this character but that on old trees the leaves were always glabrous at maturity.

P. ALBA, *Linnæus*. WHITE POPLAR

A tree said to be 90 to 100 ft. high, but I have seen none much more than half that size in this country; bark of trunk smooth; young shoots and lower surface of the leaves covered with a thick, vividly white wool, which on the lobed leaves persists and keeps white until the fall of the leaf. Leaves variable; rounded to slightly heart-shaped at the base, blunt-pointed; on short twigs they are broadly ovate or almost round, irregularly wavy at the margins, 1 to 2 ins. long; on vigorous shoots and young trees they are much larger, usually of maple-like form, being deeply three- or five-lobed and from 1½ to 5 ins. long, each lobe with a few large teeth. When the leaves first expand they are covered above with a loose white floss which falls away during the summer, leaving the upper surface very dark green and glabrous; stalk ½ to 1½ ins. long, woolly. Male catkins about 3 ins. long; females 2 ins. long.

Native of Europe, but not, as is usually believed, of Britain, where it is much confused with P. canescens. The true white poplar is not particularly common, and all the trees I have seen are comparatively small. Large trees so called are invariably P. canescens. In gardens it is called "P. alba nivea," and "P. Arembergiana," to distinguish it from P. canescens figuring as P. alba. The true P. alba is easily recognised by the leaves, especially the lobed ones, remaining white and woolly beneath until they fall, and by their being palmately lobed on vigorous shoots. The foliage sometimes turns a fiery red in autumn.

Var. GLOBOSA, *Späth*.—A dwarf form making a rounded, bushy head. Leaves of the rounded form, with slightly lobed or undulated margins. Very slow-growing.

Var. PYRAMIDALIS, *Bunge* (P. Bolleana, *Carrière*). Bolle's Poplar.—A slender pyramidal tree of great beauty, resembling the Lombardy poplar in habit, but wider in proportion to its height, and distinguishable in winter by its pale smooth trunk. There is a fine specimen about 70 ft. high near the Fern House at Kew. Seen in a breeze, this tree has an enlivening effect, caused by swift flashes of white when the under-surface of the leaf is revealed. According to a statement in the *Garden* for 10th Dec. 1887, p. 543, it was originally found in September 1841 forming a little grove on the north side of the Karataw mountains, between Bokhara and Samarcand, and apparently wild. It was introduced to W. Europe between 1875 and 1878. It produces sucker growths from the roots freely.

Var. RICHARDII.—In this form the upper surface of the leaf is golden yellow, the under-side and the young shoots felted with white wool as in the type. First shown at the International Exhibition, Chelsea, 1912.

P. ANGULATA, *Aiton*. CAROLINA POPLAR

A large tree whose angular or ribbed young shoots are without down, but marked by long, narrow, pale lenticels. Leaves heart-shaped (sometimes truncate at the base), with short or slender points; 4 to 7 ins. long, 3 to 5 ins. wide; the cartilaginous margins regularly set with comparatively small, rounded, incurved, gland-tipped teeth, and minutely hairy; both surfaces glabrous, except when just unfolding, and glossy green; there are one or two pairs of glands at the base of the leaf on the upper side; stalk glabrous, flattened. Female catkins 2 to 4 ins. long; flower-scales not fringed, but only slightly lobed at the margins; stigmas three or four.

Var. CORDATA.—Messrs Simon-Louis have in their nursery at Plantières, near Metz, a fine form of P. angulata which they call var. cordata. Mr Jouin informed me that it is hardier than the type. It produces very fine foliage; many of its heart-shaped leaves being 6 or 8 ins. long, and 5 or 6 ins. wide. Crossed with P. Eugenei, this variety has produced a very vigorous hybrid—P. ROBUSTA, *C. K. Schneider* (known in nurseries as "P. angulata cordata robusta" (*q.v.*).

P. angulata is believed to be a native of the south-eastern United States, but if really wild there, its habitat does not appear at present to be known. It has been cultivated in England since early in the eighteenth century. It is allied to P. monilifera, but is a more striking tree, especially in its foliage, differing from that species in its angled or ribbed young shoots, and its larger, but comparatively narrower, smaller-toothed leaves and shallowly lobed (not fringed or laciniated) catkin scales. There is a male tree in the Syon Gardens 111 ft. high.

P. ANGUSTIFOLIA, *James*. WILLOW-LEAVED POPLAR

(P. balsamifera angustifolia, *S. Watson*)

A tree 50 to 60 ft. high in a wild state (Sargent), but, as seen in cultivation here at present, a low bushy-headed tree with short, much-forked, crooked branches; young shoots round, glabrous or minutely downy, especially towards the apex; winter buds sticky, slender-pointed. Leaves lanceolate or ovate-lanceolate; 2 to 5 ins. long, ½ to 1½ ins. wide; wedge-shaped at the base, tapering gradually to a point at the apex, minutely and evenly round-toothed, green on both sides, although paler beneath, glabrous except sometimes for minute down beneath; stalk ordinarily about ½ in. long. Catkins not seen in this country, but the male ones described by Sargent as 1½ to 2½ ins. long, densely flowered; the female catkins are 2 to 4 ins. long when mature.

Native of western N. America, but not of the Pacific side of the Rocky Mountains. It is one of the balsam group with the characteristic odour, and is distinguished by its willow-like leaves, not white beneath. In foliage it most resembles P. laurifolia, but that species has angular, more downy young shoots, and leaves pale beneath.

P. BALSAMIFERA, *Linnæus*. BALSAM POPLAR

A tree 100 ft. high in a wild state, but rarely more than half as high in this country, producing suckers freely; young shoots smooth, round; winter buds thickly covered with a balsamic, very fragrant, viscid, yellowish resin, often 1 in. long, long-pointed. Leaves broadly ovate, rounded or slightly heart-shaped at the base, slender-pointed, very variable in size, round-toothed, ordinarily 2 to 5 ins. long, 1½ to 3 ins. wide; dark shining green above glabrous or slightly downy beneath, the pale or whitish ground conspicuously net-veined; stalk ⅔ to 2 ins. long. Male catkins 3 ins. long; female ones 4 or 5 ins. long.

Native of N. America, where it is widely spread and abundant in the northern latitudes. It was introduced sometime in the seventeenth century. The true balsam poplar is an erect-branched tree now rarely seen in this country, where nearly all poplars so-called are the closely allied, broader-topped P. candicans. It produces suckers freely, which afford the best means of increase. The great charm of this tree is the balsamic odour of its unfolding leaves in spring which fills the air around. It is the type of a group of poplars with the same quality more or less developed, but it is not so valuable a tree as its W. American ally, P. trichocarpa. The leaves on vigorous suckers are occasionally of enormous size. I have measured one 13 ins. long, and 10 ins. wide. Only the male plant appears to be in cultivation.

P. BEROLINENSIS, *Dippel*. BERLIN POPLAR

(P. certinensis, *Dieck*)

A supposed hybrid between P. laurifolia (female) and the Lombardy poplar, said by Koch (*Dendrologie*, ii., p. 497) to have first appeared in the Botanic Garden of Berlin. Although described nearly fifty years ago, it has spread but little in cultivation, although a handsome tree of slender columnar shape. Its young shoots are downy, slightly angled. Leaves broadly ovate and rounded at the base, or somewhat diamond-shaped and wedge-shaped at the base, slender-pointed, finely toothed like P. laurifolia; 1½ to 4 ins. long; upper surface bight green, lower one pale, scarcely whitish; both sides soon quite glabrous; stalk slender, downy at first, ¾ to 1½ ins. long. This tree thrives remarkably well in the vicinity of Berlin, where it originated. Some years ago I saw some particularly handsome examples in Mr Späth's nursery near that city. It is strongly recommended by him for street-planting, and as being well adapted for the cold winters and hot summers of middle Europe. The larger of two trees planted at Kew in 1880 is now over 60 ft. high; these trees are males (generally known as "P. certinensis"), and for this country appear to be preferable to the female.

P. CANDICANS, *Aiton*. BALM OF GILEAD, ONTARIO POPLAR

(P. ontariensis, *Desfontaines*)

This is the tree generally called balsam poplar in Britain, and much more common in gardens than the true P. balsamifera (*q.v.*). It is, no doubt, very nearly allied to that tree, and Sargent (*Trees of N. America*, p. 159) only admits it as a form. Most other authorities now regard it as a species, as did Aiton and Loudon. It has the general character of P. balsamifera, the same sucker-producing habit, balsamic resin-covered buds, and odoriferous young foliage; also the whitish under-surface of the leaf conspicuously netted over with veins. But it differs in the following respects: its branches are more spreading than in P. balsamifera, and it thus forms a broader, more open crown; its leaves are broader and more generally heart-shaped, more downy beneath, and ciliate; and its leaf-stalks and young shoots are downy. It has been in cultivation since 1773, but there is considerable doubt as to its origin, the general opinion being that it is N. American, where, however, there appears to be some difficulty in distinguishing between escapes from cultivation and genuinely indigenous specimens. The authors of the last edition of

Gray's Manual of Botany put it down as "introduced, perhaps of Asiatic origin." (In this, possibly, they have in mind P. tristis—see p. 527.) For cultivation in this country P. candicans is a better tree than P. balsamifera, but not so good as P. trichocarpa. It may often be seen in out of the way places in London suburbs producing a swarm of suckers, and scenting the air around on moist spring days.

P. CANESCENS, *Smith*. GREY POPLAR (Plate 40)

A tree 100 ft. high, with a trunk 12 ft. or more in girth; bark of the young trunk and branches yellowish grey, with horizontal, angular scars, becoming furrowed like an oak or ash with age. Both the terminal part of the young shoots and the under side of the terminal leaves are covered with white or grey felt, but much of this disappears by the fall of the leaf, and it is never abundant on the short twigs or on the lower leaves of the strong shoots, which become usually green and glabrous by the end of the season. Leaves roundish on lateral twigs, much larger and ovate on strong leading shoots, the smaller ones 1 to 2 ins. long, the larger ones 3 to 4 ins. long; all with large, blunt, rounded teeth, and rounded or slightly heart-shaped at the base; stalk flattened, ½ to 3 ins. long, carrying about the same amount of wool as that part of the shoot to which it is attached.

Native of W. Europe, including the south of Britain, where the tree usually called "abele," or "white poplar," is really this species. It differs from P. alba in the leaves being grey rather than white beneath, except when quite young, and in those at the base of the shoot becoming glabrous or almost glabrous by autumn; the leaf-stalks are generally much longer and more naked, and the catkins are longer. The leaves are never maple-like in form, as in P. alba. This is a very vigorous and handsome poplar which produces suckers freely. It affords a useful timber. Some authorities regard it as a hybrid between P. alba and P. tremula, but this is extremely doubtful, seeing that it is a native of Britain, and P. alba is not.

Var. AUREO-VARIEGATA.—Leaves usually smaller than in the type, and marbled with yellow; poor, and apt to revert to the green type.

Var. MACROPHYLLA. Picart's Poplar.—An exceptionally vigorous form of P. canescens, the leaves being often 6 ins. long on vigorous shoots. It is usually sold in nurseries as "P. alba macrophylla" and "P. Picartii."

Var. PENDULA.—Branches slender and gracefully arching or pendulous.

All the forms are easily increased by leafless cuttings.

P. EUGENEI, *Simon-Louis*

A tree of the largest size, believed to be a hybrid between the Lombardy poplar and P. marilandica or P. regenerata, but its origin is not definitely known. It is a tree of columnar habit, producing short, comparatively weak but spreading side branches; young shoots glabrous, somewhat angular. Leaves on ordinary branches 2 or 3 ins. across (considerably larger on vigorous leading shoots), broadly triangular, widely tapered to nearly straight across at the base, slender pointed; the margins set with rather coarse, incurved gland-tipped teeth, and furnished more or less with minute hairs. It is a male tree; catkins 2½ to 3½ ins. long; anthers red.

This fine tree originated in the nursery of Messrs Simon-Louis near Metz about 1832, as a seedling. The original tree still stands where it was planted in 1837, and is now one of the most remarkable objects in that famous establishment. I saw it in July 1904, and Mr Jouin gave me its dimensions as follows: Height, 150 ft.; girth of trunk at base, 38 ft.; girth at 4 ft. up, 23 ft. The extraordinary vigour indicated by these figures seems to show that this tree should be tried as a timber-producing tree in this country in places where there is a demand for soft wood suitable for packing-cases, toys, etc. Even in poor soil at Kew a tree planted in 1888 got to be over 80 ft. high and 5 ft. in girth of trunk in a little over twenty years. It produces remarkably little brushwood in proportion to its trunk.

P. FREMONTII, *S. Watson.* FREMONT'S COTTONWOOD

This is the common cottonwood of California, and of other W. United States, which does not appear to have been introduced to Britain previous to 1904. It is one of the black poplars with the characteristic compressed leaf-stalk of that group. Leaves broadly diamond-shaped, triangular, or somewhat kidney-shaped; $1\frac{1}{2}$ to 4 ins. wide, usually less in length; the margin coarsely round-toothed, except at the short, abrupt point, and at the straight, broadly wedge-shaped or slightly heart-shaped base; stalk $1\frac{1}{2}$ to 3 ins. long, and, like the young shoots and leaves, soon quite glabrous. Catkins 2 to 4 ins. long. From the black poplars of eastern N. America (P. monilifera and P. angulata) this appears to differ in its proportionately broader leaves without glands at the base. According to Jepson it is 40 to 90 ft. high in California, having a round-topped, massive head of branches. It appears to be quite hardy, but so far as is known has no particular value for the garden.

P. WISLIZENII, *Sargent*, differs from P. Fremontii in having the stalks of the female flowers conspicuously longer; they are $\frac{1}{2}$ in. long, but only $\frac{1}{12}$ to $\frac{1}{8}$ in. long in P. Fremontii. Its habitat in Texas, New Mexico, etc., is south and east of that of P. Fremontii.

P. GENEROSA, *A. Henry*

This hybrid poplar was first raised at Kew in 1912 by crossing a female tree of P. angulata, the Carolina poplar, with pollen from P. trichocarpa. The seed was ripe by the end of June and, being sown immediately, germinated the following October. The cross was repeated in 1914. The plants so raised made extraordinary growth and in seven years from sowing the seed were up to 37 ft. high and 22 ins. in girth of trunk. Enormous vigour is a characteristic of nearly all young hybrid poplars but none of them appears to be quite so vigorous as P. generosa. Growths over 12 ft. long have been made in one season. It is too early yet to estimate what value it may have as a timber tree, but the trunks have already been used as pit props.

The young shoots are glabrous, shining grey-green, and angled (but by no means so markedly as those of P. angulata); winter buds, awl-shaped, about 1 in. long, freely supplied inside with yellowish, viscid, balsamic resin. Leaves deciduous, triangular-ovate, truncate or slightly heart-shaped at the base, pointed, the translucent margin set with regular, incurved, gland-tipped teeth; rather pale green above, greyish beneath but not so pale as in P. trichocarpa; they vary much in size, the largest 12 or 13 ins. long, 9 or 10 ins. wide, the smaller ones one-third those dimensions; leaf-stalk 3 to 4 ins. long, more or less flattened, with two or three conspicuous glands where it joins the midrib. Many of the leaves turn a good yellow in autumn. Male catkins 4 to 5 ins. long; stamens with reddish anthers and long white stalks; female catkins rather longer, ovary glabrous, stigmas usually three. The flowers open in April. This poplar is interesting as uniting by its parentage the black poplars and the balsam poplars.

P. GRANDIDENTATA, *Michaux*. LARGE-TOOTHED ASPEN

A tree up to 60 or 70 ft. high in a wild state, but never so high in this country; young shoots at first downy, becoming glabrous and glossy later; winter buds coated with fine down. Leaves roundish ovate, the smallest sometimes oval; 1½ to 5 ins. long, mostly short-pointed, and with a broadly tapered or rounded base, the margin set with large broad teeth; at first they are covered with a loose grey wool which soon falls away, leaving them dark green above; stalk 1 to 2½ ins. long, slender, compressed towards the top. Catkins 1½ to 2½ ins. long, the female ones becoming twice the length at maturity.

Native of eastern N. America; introduced in 1772, according to Loudon. The tree is exceedingly rare in Britain at the present time, and does not appear to thrive well. It appears to be most closely related to P. tremula, from which it differs in the downy young shoots and more downy winter buds. Its deep toothing distinguishes it from P. tremuloides. It appears to be difficult to increase by cuttings, and is usually grafted on P. canescens.

P. HETEROPHYLLA, *Linnæus*. SWAMP COTTONWOOD

A tree 40 to 100 ft. high, young branches clothed at first with a thick felt as in P. alba, much of which falls away by late summer; winter buds slightly gummy, bright red-brown. Leaves heart-shaped, up to 7 or 8 ins. long and nearly as wide, rounded at the apex, shallowly and rather evenly toothed, covered on both surfaces when they unfold with a thick whitish down, which soon falls away from the upper surface, leaving it dark green, but remains longer on the lower surface, especially on the midrib and veins. The leaves hang laxly on their stalks, which are round, felted at first like the shoot, 1½ to 3½ ins. long. Male catkins 2 to 2½ ins. long; female catkins longer.

Native of the eastern United States; introduced in 1765. Until the introduction of several new Chinese species this poplar had the largest leaves of any in cultivation, but unfortunately it does not thrive well with us. Loudon observes that he had not seen plants more than 5 or 6 ft. high, and to-day I know of no tree any bigger. P. angulata, which has leaves almost as large, is distinguished by its compressed leaf-stalks, leaves green on both sides, and glabrous, angular shoots.

P. KOREANA, *Rehder*. KOREAN POPLAR

A deciduous tree up to 80 ft. high in a wild state; young shoots shiny with viscid fragrant gum, not angular or downy. Leaves ovate or oval, pointed, broadly wedge-shaped to slightly heart-shaped at the base, closely, evenly, and minutely toothed; 3 to 6 ins. long, 1½ to 3 ins. wide; dark green, glabrous and very wrinkled above, midrib reddish; whitish and glabrous beneath; stalk stout, ⅕ in. or occasionally more long. These characters are taken from vigorous shoots on a young tree at Kew received from the Arnold Arboretum. Rehder observes that on short shoots the leaves are narrower, more tapered at the base and sometimes minutely hairy on the veins beneath, also on the stalks, which may be up to ⅗ in. long. Flowers and fruit not seen.

Native of Korea; introduced by Wilson in 1918 to the Arnold Arboretum, thence to Kew in 1923. It is one of the balsam poplars, resembling and being closely related to P. Maximowiczii, which differs in its downy young shoots and brighter green leaves that are curiously twisted at the apex; it inhabits the more southern part of Korea. It should make a handsome, well-grown tree in this country if it proves immune from injury by spring frosts. The young shoots and leaves have a pleasant balsamic odour.

P. LASIOCARPA, *Oliver*

(Bot. Mag., t. 8625)

A tree 40 to 60 ft. high; young shoots very stout, downy. Leaves on adult trees 6 to 10 ins. long, 4 to 8 ins. wide; heart-shaped, with a deep notch where the stalk joins the base, pointed, the margin regularly set with shallow, rounded, incurved, gland-tipped teeth; both surfaces are at first downy but the upper one soon becomes quite glabrous, the midrib and chief veins of a rich red; the lower surface remains downy until the fall, especially on the veins; stalk 2 to 4 ins. long, round, red like the midrib. Male catkins about 4 ins. long, ¾ in. thick, with numerous stamens; female catkins about 4 ins. long, ¾ in. thick, with numerous stamens; female catkins 6 or 8 ins. long when mature.

Native of Central China; discovered by Henry in 1888, and introduced for Messrs Veitch by Wilson in 1900. In regard to its foliage this is the most remarkable and striking of all cultivated poplars. I gathered a leaf on a small tree in the Coombe Wood nursery in October 1908, 14 ins. long by 9 ins. wide (without the stalk). The leaves do not decrease much in size as the tree grows older. The beauty of the leaf is also increased by the rich rhubarb-like red of the stalk and midrib. Wilson describes it as a shapely tree inhabiting moist woods. I doubt if the tree will succeed as well grafted as on its own roots; after a while there ought to be no difficulty in getting cuttings to take root. Mr Wilson told me that on one of his journeys he came to a little Chinese farm where the farmer had made an enclosure for his animals by driving stakes in the ground. These were of Populus lasiocarpa, and they had taken root and grown freely.

P. LAURIFOLIA, *Ledebour*

(P. balsamifera viminalis, *Loudon*)

A tree 40 to 70 ft. high, of spreading, lax growth, branches ultimately pendulous, with conspicuously angular, grey young shoots, downy chiefly in the grooves; winter buds covered with balsamic gum. Leaves lanceolate, narrowly oval or obovate, rounded or tapering at the base, taper-pointed, minutely and evenly toothed, the teeth gland-tipped; 1 to 5 ins. long, ⅓ to 2 ins. wide; dark green and glabrous above; slightly downy and conspicuously net-veined on a greyish ground beneath; stalk very variable in length even with leaves of the same size on the same shoot, ¼ to 1¼ ins. long, downy. Male catkins 1½ to 2 ins. long, at first erect, then drooping; stamens very numerous.

Native of the Altai Mountains; introduced about 1830. This tree has never become common, and has not much to recommend it for English gardens, although a tree at Kew growing in damp clayey soil is a rather elegant pendulous-branched tree 50 ft. high. It is evidently very hardy, and belongs to the group of balsam poplars, with narrow leaves and angular branches.

P. MARILANDICA, *Bosc*

A large tree of spreading habit, with a corrugated, not burred, trunk; young shoots glabrous. Leaves glabrous, triangular-ovate, inclined to diamond shape, nearly always widely tapering at the base, and with a long, slender point ; 3 to 6 ins. long, three-fourths as wide ; shallowly round-toothed, teeth incurved ; glands at base none to two ; stalks 1½ to 3 ins. long, compressed. Catkins always female, ultimately 4 to 6 ins. long ; stigmas two to four.

A female hybrid between nigra and probably monilifera, bearing some resemblance to P. serotina, but with longer points and more wedge-shaped bases to the leaves, and not so erect and straight-growing a tree—the sex also is different. There is a fine tree on the lawn near the Water-lily House at Kew, 80-90 ft. high and 10 ft. 8 ins. in girth, no doubt planted there about 1843. Although handsome and imposing, it is not a perfect lawn tree, owing to the litter its cottony seeds make on the ground at seeding-time. It is one of the trees commonly known as "Canadian poplar," coming earlier into leaf than P. serotina. The ordinary young shoots are round or very slightly angled ; the vigorous ones ribbed.

P. MAXIMOWICZII, *Henry* (Plate 41)

I only know this species from a plant received at Kew from the Arnold Arboretum in 1916, which agrees pretty well with Rehder's description in his *Manual of Cultivated Trees and Shrubs*, p. 89. This is very different from the figure in the *Gardeners' Chronicle* for 29th March 1913, p. 198. The leaves of some poplars, however, vary very much according to whether they are borne on strong shoots of vigorous young plants or on the shoots of adult, seed-bearing trees. The differences are evident in shape, amount of down, and length of leaf-stalk.

A tree at Kew, which died in 1945, had hairy shoots, not angled nor viscid, and roundish ovate to oval leaves tapered or rounded at the base, abruptly pointed, finely and evenly toothed ; 3 to 5 ins. long, 2½ to 3 ins. wide ; dark green and wrinkled above, whitish beneath and more or less downy, especially when young ; stalk stout, ¼ in. long. The apex of the leaf, as noted by Rehder, is curiously twisted.

The P. Maximowiczii figured by Henry in the *Gardeners' Chronicle* (*loc. cit. supra*) and represented by numerous specimens in Kew Herbarium is in the adult state and has more rounded leaves with often a heart-shaped base and is especially different in the slender downy leaf-stalk 1 to 2 ins. long. Male catkins 2 to 4 ins. long ; female ones up to 10 ins. long ; seed-vessel glabrous.

Native of N.E. Asia, including Korea and Japan, long known as P. suaveolens until distinguished by A. Henry in 1913. A handsome vigorous tree. P. suaveolens has glabrous leaves and only slightly downy shoots.

P. MONILIFERA, *Aiton*. NECKLACE POPLAR

(P. canadensis, *Michaux* ; P. deltoides, *Marshall* (in part))

A tree up to 100 ft. high ; young shoots rounded or slightly angled, green, marked with long, light-coloured lenticels ; glabrous. Leaves broadly heart-shaped with a long, slenderly tapered apex, the cartilaginous margins set with coarse, incurved, gland-tipped teeth, except at the base and apex ; 3 to 5 ins. long and wide, glabrous and bright green on both surfaces, but darker above ; margins densely set with hairs ; there are one or two pairs of glands at the base ; stalk slender, smooth, 2½ to 3½ ins. long, flattened. Male catkins densely flowered, 3 to 4 ins. long ; females twice as long, stigmas three or four.

Native of eastern N. America ; introduced in 1772. This tree with P. angulata (*q.v.*) forms, in the opinion of some botanists, one species known as P. deltoides. In a broad sense this may be so, but the tree cultivated as P. angulata is so distinct, that for garden purposes at least it is better to keep it apart. The true P. monilifera is now exceedingly uncommon in Britain

It hybridised many years ago with the Old World P. nigra, and has been ousted from gardens by its more vigorous progeny. Its distinguishing marks among black poplars are the ciliate margins and basal glands of the leaf, which distinguish it from P. nigra; and the round or only slightly angled young shoots and coarse teeth of the proportionately broader leaf, which distinguish it from P. angulata.

P. NIGRA, *Linnæus*. BLACK POPLAR

A tree 100 ft. or more high, with a rugged trunk 5 or 6 ft. in diameter, often forming large burrs on the surface; young shoots glabrous and round; buds glutinous. Leaves variable, broadly diamond-shaped, triangular or ovate; 2 to 4½ ins. long; some are wider than they are long, others twice as long as they are wide; usually broadly tapered, sometimes straight across at the base; broad or slender pointed; both surfaces green, quite glabrous, the cartilaginous margins regularly and shallowly round-toothed; the teeth gland-tipped; stalk ¾ to 2¼ ins. long, compressed to a knife-like form. Catkins 2 to 3 ins. long; anthers deep red; stigmas two in female flowers.

Native of Europe. The true black poplar is not very frequently seen now, being supplanted to a great extent by hybrids which have sprung up between it and P. monilifera or P. angulata; possessing a superior vigour, the latter are favoured by planters. It is not easy to distinguish it always from its hybrid progeny, but from the two American species just mentioned it is to be recognised by the absence of marginal hairs and basal glands on the leaves. The hybrids also have these characters in a greater or less degree. As a timber-producing tree, P. nigra is not equal to P. serotina and P. marilandica, which are discussed in their place, but as a tree for parks and gardens it has advantages. It is more leafy, has a more compact and shapely habit, branches more freely and finely, and it does not grow so rampantly.

Var. BETULIFOLIA, *Torrey* (P. hudsonica, *Michaux*). Downy Black Poplar (Bot. Mag., t. 8298).—A variety differing from the type in the young shoots, leaf-stalks, midrib, and main flower-stalk being downy. The tree, or rather its naming, has a curious history. It was first recognised by Michaux early in the nineteenth century growing on the banks of the Hudson River, near Albany, in New York State; he thereupon named it P. hudsonica. There is no doubt, however, that it is of European origin, and trees are known to have existed in England in the eighteenth century. Indeed black poplars with downy shoots, collected in England, are common in the older herbaria. This variety, like the type, produces great burrs on the trunk, and up to its middle age at least is a neat, densely branched, leafy tree, very much superior to the gaunt rampant hybrids now almost exclusively planted.

Var. ITALICA, *Duroi* (var. pyramidalis, *Spach*; P. fastigiata, *Desfontaines*). Lombardy Poplar.—This well known and beautiful tree, the most valuable of all fastigiate trees, differs only from the type in its slender tapering form and quite erect branches. Nearly all the Lombardy poplars in cultivation are male, but a few female ones are known. There is one near Kew Palace over 50 ft. high, but it is not so slender as the common male tree. For this reason, and still more because it litters the ground near with its cottony tufts at seeding-time, it is much less desirable. As the Lombardy poplar is propagated only by cuttings, the female tree must be of independent origin. The male, which is occasionally 100 to 125 ft. high, is recorded to have been brought to England from Turin by Lord Rochford in 1758, and according to Loudon, one of the first importation existed at Purser's Cross in 1838.

Var. PLANTIERENSIS, *C. K. Schneider* (P. plantierensis, *Simon-Louis*).—Very similar in habit to the Lombardy poplar (scarcely so slender), this differs from it in having slightly downy twigs and leaf-stalks. For this reason it is considered to have sprung from var. betulifolia, perhaps crossed with the Lombardy. It originated at Plantières, near Metz, in the nursery of Messrs Simon-Louis, who offer it in both sexes. It grows very well, but so far as I can see has nothing to recommend it before the ordinary Lombardy poplar.

Var. THEVESTINA (P. thevestina, *Dode*).—This appears to be a form of Lombardy poplar with a white bark, very striking as seen in Algeria, where it has been abundantly planted on the outskirts of towns, to keep back the drifting sand. Female specimens collected in Algeria show the catkins to be 1 to 1½ ins. long, the leaves triangular-ovate, with a broadly wedge-shaped base, without glands; the leaf-stalks and young shoots downy. It has been introduced to Kew, and shows the fastigiate habit, but owing perhaps to reasons of climate or insufficient age, the bark does not yet show the vivid whiteness of Algerian trees.

Var. VIADRI (P. viadri, *Ruediger*).—A slender, rather erect form of nigra (not so much so as the Lombardy poplar). Introduced to Kew in 1893.

P. ROBUSTA, *C. K. Schneider*

(P. angulata cordata robusta, *Hort. Simon-Louis*)

A very vigorous deciduous tree, with ascending branches; young shoots ribbed and minutely downy; winter-buds sticky, pointed, reddish brown. Leaves reddish when young, triangular-ovate, pointed, truncate or nearly so at the base, the margins set with even, rounded teeth which become wide apart towards the base; 2 to 5 ins. long, 1½ to 4 ins. wide; stalk 1 to 2 ins. long. The glands where the stalk joins the blade are either two, one, or absent altogether. This is a male tree and its catkins are 2½ ins. long.

Briefly mentioned in previous editions, this fine poplar deserves fuller notice. It is a hybrid raised in 1895 in the nursery of Messrs Simon-Louis at Plantières, near Metz, of which the seed parent was P. angulata. The male parent was believed to be P. Eugenei, but Henry considered this as improbable, owing to the shoots of P. robusta being minutely downy. Those of P. Eugenei and P. angulata are perfectly glabrous. He suggested P. nigra var. plantierensis as the pollen parent. Mr E. Jouin of the Plantières Nurseries believed it to be capable of surpassing P. Eugenei in size. In a letter he also says it is preferred to that tree both by planters and joiners because it grows more quickly and its timber is easier to work. In view of the interest now being taken in poplars and the various uses to which their timber is being put, P. robusta would seem to be worth a thorough trial as a profitable timber tree in this country.

The minute down on the young shoots of this hybrid will serve to distinguish it from others of its class like Eugenei, serotina, regenerata, and marylandica, but it requires a lens to detect it.

P. SARGENTII, *Dode*

This is one of the black poplars and is common on river banks in N. America, east of the Rocky Mountains from Saskatchewan to New Mexico. It is related to P. monilifera, the common black poplar or cottonwood of the E. United States, differing from it, according to Sargent, by its pale yellow branches, downy buds, much shorter stalk of the female flower, and by the larger, fewer teeth of the leaves. Judging by plants received from the Arnold Arboretum in 1919, it has nothing to recommend it for this country before the numerous black poplars already in cultivation. It is known in America as the "Great Plains Cottonwood."

P. SEROTINA, *Hartig*. BLACK ITALIAN POPLAR

A large tree, always male, frequently over 100 ft. high, with an open, rather gaunt habit, and extremely vigorous; young shoots glabrous, green, slightly angled. Leaves ovate-triangular, with a broad, straight base, and a short, abrupt, slender apex; 2 to 6 ins. wide and long, regularly round-toothed, the margin cartilaginous and at first minutely hairy; one or more glands occur at the base near the stalk, which is 1½ to 2½ ins. long, glabrous, compressed. Catkins 3 to 4 ins. long; flower-stalks glabrous; anthers rich red.

A hybrid between P. nigra and probably P. monilifera, which was introduced to Britain about the middle of the eighteenth century. It appears to have originated earlier in the century in France, where it is known as the Swiss poplar (*peuplier suisse*), and is now the commonest of poplars in that country—also in this, where it is often known as the "Canadian poplar." It is one of the quickest growing of all trees in Great Britain that attain large size, and produces a given bulk of timber in a shorter time than most. Starting late in growth and very hardy, it is never injured by late frosts, and it possesses great value as a timber tree in localities where its wood can be disposed of, or readily converted into planks. Although too soft to be of much use for permanent work, it is valuable for the many temporary uses for which wood is needed nowadays, such as cotton reels, packing-boxes, toys, domestic utensils, etc. It is propagated very readily from cuttings not less than 1 ft. long, put in the open ground after the leaves have fallen.

Var. AUREA, *Henry* (P. canadensis aurea, *Van Geert*).—A form with leaves very yellow in spring and early summer, becoming yellowish green later. It originated in the nursery of Van Geert at Ghent, in 1871, as a sport.

Var. ERECTA, *Henry* (P. monilifera erecta, *Selys*; P. canadensis erecta, *Dippel*).—A columnar or semi-fastigiate tree, resembling in other respects P. serotina, being also a male. It originated in Belgium about 1820.

P. REGENERATA, *Henry* (P. grandifolia, and the *peuplier régénéré* of the French), is another hybrid of the black poplar group, probably between nigra and monilifera. It originated in a nursery near Paris, in 1814, and is a female tree with the shoots and foliage of P. serotina. The catkins are about 3 ins. long, lengthening out by June to 6 or 8 ins.; stigmas usually two. Leaves often broader than long, triangular, with short points and a straight cut base. It is sold in nurseries as "P. canadensis grandis."

P. SIMONI, *Carrière*

A medium-sized tree with pendulous branches and elegant habit, bursting into leaf early; young shoots glabrous, prominently angled. Leaves diamond-shaped or obovate, tapering about equally to both ends, sometimes more abruptly towards the apex; minutely and regularly blunt-toothed; 2 to 5 ins. long, 1¼ to 3½ ins. wide; dark green above, very pale beneath; glabrous on both sides; stalk often very short, even on the leaves of vigorous shoots, and only ⅛ to ½ in. long.

Native of N. China; introduced to the Simon-Louis nursery at Metz in 1862. As represented at Kew it is one of the balsam group breaking into leaf early, and fragrant then. Its distinguishing characters are its angular young shoots devoid of down, and the variable but often very short leaf-stalk. The original tree at Plantières, near Metz, has a trunk white almost as a birch.

P. SUAVEOLENS, *Fischer*

One of the balsam poplars with a balsamic odour, especially noticeable when the young leaves are developing. It has glabrous, ovate, or ovate-lanceolate leaves, rounded or broadly tapered at the base, 1½ to 4½ ins. long, two-thirds as wide, finely and bluntly toothed; margins and leaf-stalk downy. Young shoots round, slightly downy. A tree up to 50 ft. high.

Native of Siberia, Manchuria, etc. It was mentioned by Loudon in 1838 as "the new sweet-scented poplar of the nurseries," and was stated to have been offered in Loddiges' catalogue of 1836; but if the tree he mentioned was the true P. suaveolens it has not made any progress in this country. It is now rarely seen, although it succeeds well in the Arnold Arboretum, and in continental European nurseries.

P. SZECHUANICA, *C. K. Schneider*

A deciduous tree over 100 ft. high in a wild state, with a trunk 4 ft. or more in diameter; young shoots downy at first, distinctly angled; buds viscid. Leaves heart-shaped, slender-pointed, finely toothed, the teeth incurved and gland-tipped; 4 to 9 ins. long, 2 to 5 ins. wide; reddish when quite young, becoming dark lustrous green and glabrous above; pale, greyish, and downy beneath when young; stalks 1 to 3 ins. long, reddish, at first downy. Female catkins 6 ins. long; ovary glabrous.

Native of Western China; discovered and introduced by Wilson. The description given above is made from plants growing at Kew which were originally obtained in 1916 from the Arnold Arboretum. From the amount of pubescence on the leaves and young shoots, they may be Schneider's var. TIBETICA, of which there is a specimen in Kew Herbarium collected by Wilson in W. Szechuen in June 1904 (Veitch Expedition No. 4527). Schneider describes typical P. szechuanica as glabrous on leaf and branchlet. Young shoots of the plants at Kew much resemble those of P. lasiocarpa, especially in the downiness and red colour of the young leaves, but in lasiocarpa the adult leaves are pure green beneath and much larger. P. szechuanica is a fine balsam poplar, a good grower and a worthy associate of P. lasiocarpa and Wilsonii, both of which differ from it in their downy ovaries (see P. Wilsonii).

P. TREMULA, *Linnæus*. ASPEN

A tree rarely more than 50 ft. high in this country; winter buds bright brown; young shoots glabrous. Leaves greyish green, roundish to broadly ovate; from ½ to 2 ins. wide on the short lateral twigs, as much as 4 ins. wide on vigorous long shoots; apex pointed, base rounded or straight; prominently toothed, the teeth being few, large (often ⅛ to ⅙ in. deep), blunt, and somewhat incurved; margin thickened; more or less woolly when young, becoming quite glabrous by autumn, or with remains of the down beneath towards the base near the leaf-stalk; stalk very slender, usually smooth, ½ to 2½ ins. long, two-edged. On the leaves of vigorous shoots there is a pair of glands where it joins the blade. Male catkins grey, 2 to 4 ins. long, produced in February.

Native of Europe (including Britain), eastward to Asia Minor and the Caucasus. It is more common in the north of Britain than the south. The best known attribute to the aspen is the perpetual quiver of the leaf. "To tremble like an aspen leaf" is a phrase whose use goes back to Spenser's time, perhaps long before. This movement is seen in other poplars with compressed leaf-stalks, but is never so marked as in this. In the south of England the aspen does not succeed as well as in the north, but is worth planting for its interest. A curious superstition prevailed in the Scottish Highlands (perhaps does so now) that the cross on which the Saviour was crucified was made of the wood of this tree, and it was, in consequence, held in abhorrence. In the north of England it is (or was, sixty years ago) regarded by peasant women and children with a feeling of dislike akin to fear, probably owing to some similar legend.

The aspen is only likely to be confounded with two other poplars—the

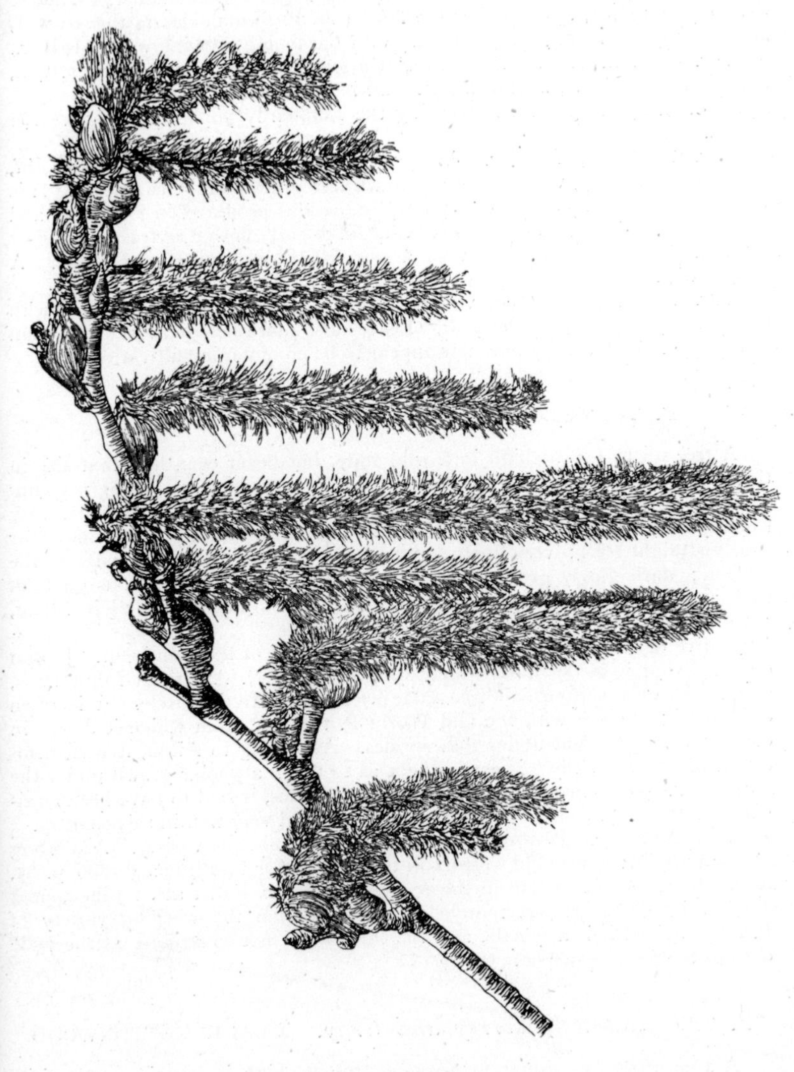

Populus tremula

one, P. tremuloides, an American species distinguished by the pale yellowish bark of young trunks and main branches, and by the smaller type of leaf, being very finely and evenly toothed, and furnished with hairs on the margin when young, but otherwise glabrous; the other, P. canescens, is easily distinguished by the whitish wool on the under-surface of the leaf, and also pale bark of the young trunk.

Var. DAVIDIANA, *C. K. Schneider* (Chinese Aspen), was introduced by Wilson in 1907. It differs from the common aspen in the smaller, shallower teeth of the leaves, approaching the American P. tremuloides in this respect, also in its looser, more graceful habit. Very hardy and growing well in Britain.

Var. ERECTA. In the *Gardeners' Chronicle* of 12th June 1926, p. 414, there is mentioned as having been found in the woods of Svalof, Sweden, an aspen of fastigiate growth resembling the Lombardy poplar, but I have not seen it.

Var. PENDULA, *Loudon*. Weeping Aspen.—A male form with stiff, pendulous branches, well known as a lawn tree grafted on P. canescens. It is valued for its great wealth of grey purplish catkins produced in February, and is one of the most conspicuous and beautiful of early-flowering trees.

Var. PURPUREA.—Leaves with a purplish tinge, not very marked. A female tree.

Var. VILLOSA, *Syme* (P. villosa, *Lang*). Downy Aspen.—A form with shoots hairy until the second year. Leaves also more persistently downy than in the type. The variety does not appear to be common in cultivation.

P. TREMULOIDES, *Michaux*. AMERICAN ASPEN

A tree up to 100 ft. high in a wild state, but never even half that size in this country; trunk slender, paler than in P. tremula when young; young shoots reddish brown, glabrous. Leaves 1 to 2½ ins. long and wide, very broadly ovate or roundish, with a short, abrupt apex, and a broad, rounded or nearly straight base; very finely toothed, and furnished with fine hairs on the margin; dark glossy green above, pale and dull beneath, glabrous on both sides; stalk slender, two-edged, 1 to 2½ ins. long. Catkins 2 to 2½ ins. long, more slender than in P. tremula.

Native of N. America, and found on both sides of the Continent. Jepson observes that it is the most widely distributed of N. American forest trees, and is the only Californian tree that reaches the Arctic Circle. It is often confused in gardens with the Old World P. tremula, from which it differs in characters pointed out under that species. According to Aiton, it was introduced in 1812, but there is some doubt as to this; a poplar grown under the name of P. græca, but identical with P. tremuloides, is said to have been cultivated in 1779. P. tremuloides has never succeeded very well in this country.

Var. PENDULA. Parasol de St Julien.—A pendulous variety. According to a note by M. Ferdinand Cayeux in the *Garden* for 21st January 1886, p. 65, it was found by a foreman in the employ of Messrs Baltet at St Julien, near Troyes, in 1865. It has more slender twigs than the weeping variety of P. tremula, but it is a female, and the catkins are not so striking as the male ones of the weeping aspen.

P. TRICHOCARPA, *Torrey and Gray*. BLACK COTTONWOOD

A tree often (according to Sargent) 200 ft. high in certain parts of its habitat; young trees marked by a slender, pyramidal habit, and by peeling, ultimately smooth, yellow-grey bark; winter buds coated with fragrant balsamic gum, brown and slender; young shoots slightly angled, furnished at first with a slight down, soon nearly or quite glabrous. Leaves ovate, slightly heart-shaped at the base or broadly wedge-shaped, slender-pointed, finely and shallowly toothed, very variable in size; as much as 8 or 10 ins.

long, and half as wide on very vigorous leading shoots, down to 2 ins. long, and 1 in. wide on lateral twigs; dark lustrous green above, very white and conspicuously net-veined beneath, soon quite smooth on both surfaces; stalk 1 to 2 ins. long. Male catkins 2 to 2½ ins. long, female ones twice as long at maturity.

Native of western N. America, and undoubtedly the finest of the balsam poplars, if not of all poplars. It is remarkable that although distinguished sixty years ago, it was introduced to this country only about fifty years since. A tree planted on the banks of the ha-ha between Kew Gardens and the Thames, became in thirteen years 55 ft. high, and about 4 ft. in girth. A fine tree in the Dresden Botanic Garden was in 1908 about 70 ft. high and 5 ft. 10 ins. in girth. In the early stages of its growth in spring, this tree fills the air around with its balsamic odour. It is the quickest grower of the balsam group, amongst which its peeling young bark distinguishes it. Easily increased by cuttings, and worth trying extensively as a timber-producing tree.

P. TRISTIS, *Fischer*

This is a balsam poplar with downy shoots and leaf-stalks; the ovate or ovate-lanceolate leaves are also slightly downy beneath, but narrower in proportion to their length; 2 to 5 ins. long, 1½ to 3 ins. wide. Brandis, alluding to it as P. balsamifera, says it occurs in arid valleys of the inner north-western Himalaya. Probably our climate is too moist and dull for it. Although introduced in 1896, from Späth's nursery at Berlin, it has never succeeded; and although it makes vigorous growths during the summer they are frequently cut back in winter, and it has never got beyond a few feet high. Easily increased by cuttings. The leaves of this poplar have a curious habit of hanging on the branches after they are dead.

P. VANCOUVERIANA, *Trelease*

(P. tremuloides vancouveriana, *Sargent*)

This species, a native of British Columbia, etc. (including Vancouver Island), represents in that region P. tremuloides. It differs from it in the young shoots being downy and in the leaves being woolly when young. Trelease, who describes it as a tree 15 to 35 ft. high, says it is easily distinguished from P. tremuloides by the peculiar toothing of the leaves. "The teeth are much larger than in any of its immediate allies and besides being crenulate are depressed so that each tooth viewed from the edge forms a double curve." It is flourishing at Dawyck in Peeblesshire.

P. WILSONII, *C. K. Schneider*. WILSON'S POPLAR

A deciduous tree up to 80 ft. high in a wild state, of pyramidal shape, with a trunk 2 ft. in diameter; young shoots soon glabrous, stout, not angled, olive-brown, becoming brown or purplish the second year; buds shining, slightly viscid. Leaves heart-shaped, bluntish at the apex, minutely toothed; from 3 to 9 ins. long, 2½ to 7 ins. wide; dull pale green above, pale greyish beneath and soon quite glabrous on both surfaces; stalk up to 6 ins. long. Female catkins slender, downy, 3 to 6 ins. long; ovary very woolly in the young state; male catkins not seen.

Native of Central and Western China; discovered and introduced by Wilson in 1907. This poplar is related to P. lasiocarpa, which is easily distinguished by its downy shoots and bright green leaves with red midrib and stalk. Another big-leaved poplar, P. szechuanica, differs in its angled young shoots, bright green leaves, and glabrous ovary. P. Wilsonii is a fine poplar with leaves of notable size; it is succeeding very well under cultivation and seems more amenable to artificial conditions than P. lasiocarpa. Mr P. D. Williams, in May 1931, sent me a flowering spray from a female tree at Lanarth, in Cornwall; the young ovaries were like little balls of white wool.

P. YUNNANENSIS, *Dode*. YUNNAN POPLAR

A deciduous tree with strongly angled, glabrous, pale green (afterwards brown) young shoots; buds not downy, viscid. Leaves obovate-lanceolate to oval-lanceolate, much tapered to the base, more abruptly to the apex; marginal teeth rounded, glandular; bright vivid green above, pale and greyish beneath, glabrous on both surfaces; up to 6 ins. long by 3 ins. wide; stalk ¼ to ½ in. long. Leaves of this size, shape, etc., are as they occur on vigorous young trees at Kew; on older plants and as figured by Dode they are of ovate shape and often truncate at the base. Female catkins 4 to 6 ins. long; seed-vessels glabrous.

Native of Yunnan, China. A living plant was sent to Mr L. A. Dode, of Paris, by Père Ducloux some time previous to 1905, and from this the present stock of plants in cultivation was derived. It appears to belong to the same section of the genus as P. laurifolia and szechuanica and is, therefore, one of the balsam poplars which are distinguished by their viscid buds and whitish undersurface of the leaf. But very little really is known about it. The fact that the leaves are usually broadest above the middle and have such short stalks seems distinctive, at least on young plants.

POTENTILLA. CINQUEFOIL. ROSACEÆ

Of this large genus the vast majority are hardy herbaceous plants, but three species are shrubby, and quite hardy in Britain. They have compound leaves, and white or yellow flowers resembling a small single rose in form. From all other hardy trees and shrubs at all allied to them these potentillas are distinguished by the bracteolate calyx; *i.e.*, alternating with and outside the ordinary lobes of the calyx are five bracts, narrower and shorter than they are. The cinquefoils are nearly allied to the strawberries, but differ in having the tiny fruits (achenes) crowded on a dry, not fleshy or succulent, receptacle.

The following species like a good loamy soil with plenty of moisture. Propagation is best effected by seeds, but cuttings of late summer wood will take root, even of Salesoviana, which, however, does not root readily. All three species are useful in flowering after most shrubs are out of bloom.

P. DAVURICA, *Nestler*. DWARF SHRUBBY CINQUEFOIL

(P. glabra, *Loddiges*, Bot. Mag., t. 3676)

A very dwarf, compact, deciduous shrub, usually below 1½ ft. in height, with erect stems and drooping twigs. Leaves glabrous, 1 in. or less long, composed of five leaflets which are stalkless, oblong-obovate, ⅜ to ½ in. long, the three terminal ones united at the base. Flowers white, ¾ to 1¼ ins. across, usually solitary on a slender downy stalk 1 in. long; petals roundish, calyx-lobes lanceolate; bracts green, obovate, or ovate.

Native of China and Siberia; introduced by way of St Petersburg in 1822. This charming little shrub from its dense close habit and very slow growth, is well adapted for the rock garden. It is much confused with white-flowered forms of P. fruticosa, but the combination of a dwarf habit with white flowers and glabrous leaves distinguishes it well enough. The late Mr Greshoff found that the leaves yielded a principle very similar in odour to attar of roses.

P. FRUTICOSA, *Linnæus*. SHRUBBY CINQUEFOIL

A deciduous shrub of varying height and habit, usually a rounded bush 2 to 5 ft. high, and more in diameter, with erect branches, and a bright brown,

POTENTILLA FRUTICOSA VEITCHII

ultimately peeling bark, largely covered when young by the stipules. Leaves pinnate, 1 to 1½ ins. long, composed generally of five leaflets, occasionally three or seven. Leaflets ½ to 1 in. long, ⅛ to ¼ in. wide; lanceolate, pointed, entire; downy beneath, stalkless; the three terminal ones sometimes united at the base. Flowers bright butter-cup yellow, each 1 to 1½ ins. across, solitary or a few together. Calyx green, with five broad triangular lobes alternating with five narrow linear bracts, all hairy like the flower-stalk.

Native of the north of England and of the west of Ireland, and scattered over many parts of the northern hemisphere, both in the New and Old Worlds. With such an extensive habitat it naturally varies a great deal, and the following varieties may be briefly distinguished :—

Var. FRIEDRICHSENII, *Rehder*.—A reputed hybrid between P. fruticosa and P. davurica sent out by Späth of Berlin in 1897. It is a vigorous bush with large downy leaflets and flowers from early June to September, the blossoms being pale yellow. I have seen it 6 ft. high. (P. Friedrichsenii, *Späth*.)

Var. GRANDIFLORA, *Willdenow*.—Leaves and flowers larger than ordinary, the latter averaging 1¼ ins. across, yellow.

Var. LEUCANTHA, *Späth*.—Flowers white.

Var. MICRANDRA, *Koehne*.—Differs from the type in its low-spreading habit, its broader leaflets, and shorter stamens. Flowers yellow.

Var. OCHROLEUCA, *Späth*.—Flowers of a soft sulphur-yellow.

Var. PYRENAICA, *Willdenow* (P. prostrata, *Lapeyrouse*).—A dwarf mountain form, 6 to 18 ins. high, of close habit. Flowers yellow.

Var. TENUIFOLIA, *Lehmann*.—Native of western N. America, with narrower leaflets than ordinary, also distinguished by being more hairy, and of a greyer aspect.

Var. VEITCHII (P. Veitchii, *Wilson*).—Leaves silky-hairy, grey-green, not silvery above, glaucous beneath ; flowers white. A very fine form from Hupeh, China. Syn. P. davurica Veitchii, *Jesson* (Bot. Mag., t. 8637).

Var. VILMORINIANA.—Leaves of a marked silvery hue ; flowers creamy white. The most striking of the white-flowered sorts.

In all its forms P. fruticosa is welcome, because it flowers after the great bulk of hardy shrubs are past, and remains for many weeks in beauty. It commences to bloom in July, and continues until the end of September.

P. SALESOVIANA, *Stephan*

(Bot. Mag., t. 7258)

A deciduous shrub of lax habit, 3 to 4 ft. high, making coarse, erect, reddish growths, but little branched, silky, half covered with the large silvery stipules. Leaves pinnate, 2 to 4 ins. long ; leaflets five to nine, shortly stalked, oblong, ¾ to 1½ ins. long, ¼ to ⅝ in. wide, increasing in size towards the end of the leaf, with broad angular teeth ; dark green and glabrous above, grey-woolly beneath. Flowers rosy-tinted white, produced in June and July at the summit of a long-stalked corymb 4 to 6 ins. high, each of the three to seven flowers 1½ ins. across ; petals obovate ; calyx-lobes lanceolate, and as long as the petals, the five bracts smaller, linear, and about half as long, very downy.

Native of Siberia ; introduced in 1823. This species is very distinct from the other shrubby species in its larger, more numerous, toothed leaflets, and in its coarser growths, which are hollow and die back considerably in winter.

PRINSEPIA. ROSACEÆ

A genus of three or four species of deciduous shrubs ; the shoots have axillary spines and the pith is lamellate, *i.e.*, reduced to thin transverse disks ; leaves alternate ; fruit a drupe. It is closely akin to Prunus, which is easily distinguished by its continuous pith. Named after James Prinsep, one-time Secretary to the Asiatic Society of Bengal, a meteorologist and a friend of Royle, the author of the name (1800-1840).

P. SINENSIS, *Oliver*. ROSACEÆ

(Plagiospermum sinense, *Oliver*; Hooker's Icon. Plant., t. 1526)

A deciduous shrub of rather lax, spreading habit, about 6 ft. high; stems armed with solitary, stiff, short spines, from beneath which spring the leaves; pith chambered (divided into thin plates). Leaves alternate on the shoots of the year, oblong lanceolate, finely ciliate; 1½ to 3 ins. long, about ½ in. wide; produced in clusters on the year-old shoots. Flowers borne singly in the leaf-axils on slender stalks ½ in. long; they are solitary, or clustered two to four together; each flower ½ to ¾ in. diameter, petals five, bright yellow, roundish, tapered to a short claw. Fruit red and juicy, ⅗ in. long, ripening in August.

Native of Manchuria; first described from dried material and in the absence of fruit in 1886 as Plagiospermum, but afterwards, when fruit became available, it was found to belong to Prinsepia, a small North Asiatic genus allied to Prunus. It was introduced from France in 1908 and is quite hardy. In February 1916 I had a spray from Glasnevin very prettily in flower.

PRINSEPIA SINENSIS

P. UNIFLORA, *Batalin*

A deciduous shrub of lax, spreading habit and free growth, 5 or 6 ft. high; young shoots glabrous, pale shining grey, armed at each joint, with a sharp slender spine ¼ to ½ in. long. Leaves linear, 1 to 2¼ ins. long, ⅙ to ⅓ in. wide, pointed, the lower two-thirds toothed (sometimes sparsely), dark glossy green, glabrous. Flowers white, ⅗ in. wide, borne in early spring one to three together along with a cluster of leaves from the joints of the previous summer's growth, each flower on a glabrous stalk ⅙ in. long. Petals five, obovate, ⅕ in. wide; stamens ten; anthers yellow. Fruit globose, ⅓ in. wide, purple with a slight bloom when ripe.

Native of Shensi, China; introduced to the Arnold Arboretum by W. Purdom in 1911, thence to England a few years later. It is closely akin to P. sinensis, but that species has yellow flowers, longer flower-stalks, and mostly toothless leaves, P. uniflora grows very freely at Kew, making long, slender, very leafy shoots annually. But, flowering as it does early in the year, it is apt to suffer from inclement weather. For the same reason it rarely develops fruit. Farrer under his number 278 describes the fruits as "glowing pendulous drops of crimson"; personally I have never seen living fruits but they appear in the dried state to be black-purple, and Batalin, the author of the name, describes them as "schwarz, bereift."

P. UTILIS, *Royle*

A deciduous, very spiny shrub of exceedingly vigorous habit; young shoots slightly downy at first, soon glabrous. Spines stout, produced in every leaf-axil, eventually becoming 1 to 2 ins. long and some bearing leaves. Leaves lanceolate, slender-pointed, tapered at the base, toothed, up to 4 ins. long and 1¼ ins. wide, dull green and quite glabrous. Flowers creamy white, fragrant, ¼ in. wide, produced from between the spine and the leaf in racemes 1 to 2 ins. long, or sometimes few or even solitary. Fruit purple, cylindric, ½ to ¾ in. long.

Native of the Himalaya, where it is sometimes used for hedges, also of W. China. Although Hooker gives its height as 3 to 5 ft., a plant growing at Kew in a corner outside the Temperate House, facing north-east, is 9 ft. high and 12 ft. in diameter, a rampant grower. It is distinguished from the other two species by its usually racemose inflorescence, numerous stamens, and by flowering on the leafy shoots of the current season. Judging by dried specimens it often flowers in India with great freedom from the terminal leaf-axils in late autumn and winter, transforming the end of each shoot into a cylindrical wand of blossom, the fruits from such flowers being developed in April and May. To get it to flower well in this country it requires no doubt the sunniest spot obtainable and a lightish, not very fertile soil.

PROSTRANTHERA ROTUNDIFOLIA, *R. Brown*. MINT BUSH. LABIATÆ

(Bot. Mag., t. 9061)

An evergreen shrub of bushy habit, usually, as found wild, from 4 to 12 ft. high; young branchlets very slender, clothed with a dense, short, greyish white down; both they and the leaves are aromatically scented when rubbed. Leaves opposite, either roundish, obovate, or oval; entire or with a few comparatively large teeth; from ⅙ to ⅓ in. long, usually about ¼ in. wide; dark, rather glossy green above, paler and dull beneath, both surfaces sprinkled thickly with tiny pitted glands; stalk $\frac{1}{12}$ to ⅛ in. long. Flowers rich blue-purple or deep lilac, produced during April and May in short terminal racemes of five or more. Corolla ⅜ in. wide, somewhat bell-shaped, but rather pouched on the lower side, with five rounded lobes, the lower lobes projecting more than the upper ones. Stamens four, purple, very short, attached to the base of the corolla. Calyx ⅛ in. wide, helmet-shaped, with two unequal rounded lobes, scaly outside, purplish. Style purple, as long as the corolla.

Native of Tasmania, especially near Launceston, whence it was introduced in 1824. This is one of the most beautiful of all cultivated Tasmanian shrubs, but is unfortunately too tender for all but the milder counties. Even there it is usually grown on a wall. In a climate like that of Kew it might, if given a sheltered place on some warm south wall, survive through a series of mild winters, but I am aware that even under most favourable conditions its tenure would be insecure. It is quite frequently seen in the gardens of Cornwall and S. Devon, always beautiful in the spring time. Nowhere have I seen it so fine as in the Rectory garden at Ludgvan, near Penzance. A plant on a wall there was, when I saw it, some 10 ft. high, one gorgeous mass of blue-purple. I believe it is not a long-lived shrub, but it takes root very readily from soft cuttings in early summer.

P. LASIANTHOS, *Labillardière*, is another Tasmanian species with fine pyramidal panicles of larger white or pale blue flowers, but more tender. It bloomed at Trewidden, Cornwall, in 1928. (*Bot. Mag.*, t. 2434.)

PRUMNOPITYS ELEGANS, *Philippi*. TAXACEÆ

(Podocarpus andina, *Poeppig*)

An evergreen tree, 40 to 50 ft. high in a wild state, but in gardens as yet usually a pyramidal or rounded bush less than half as high; very dense in habit; young shoots green, quite glabrous. Leaves linear, $\frac{1}{3}$ to $1\frac{1}{8}$ ins. long, $\frac{1}{16}$ to $\frac{1}{8}$ in. wide; tapered to a short stalk at the base, bluntish or abruptly pointed at the apex; dark green above, with a dull glaucous strip each side the midrib beneath; they are densely and spirally set on the shoot (ten to fifteen to the inch), falling the third year. Male flowers in axillary and terminal panicles about 1 in. long. Fruit yellowish white, plum-like, $\frac{3}{4}$ in. long, consisting of a stone surrounded by a thin layer of flesh. The seed has no resinous odour, and is eaten by the Chileans. Flowers of both sexes appear on the same plant.

Native of Chile; introduced in 1860 by Pearce, for Messrs Veitch. It is very closely allied to, perhaps scarcely generically distinct from, Podocarpus. It requires a sheltered spot, especially one shielded from north and east winds, and in such a position will be found quite hardy in most gardens. It thrives in either a loamy or peaty soil, enriched with a plentiful mixture of decayed leaves. Increased by cuttings made of late summer wood with a "heel." It bore large crops of fruit at Kew in 1922. The name, "Podocarpus andina," originally given to this plant, is often erroneously applied to Podocarpus chilina.

PRUNUS. ROSACEÆ

There is no genus of flowering trees which contributes so much to the beauty of English gardens in March, April, and early May as Prunus. Following the now generally accepted signification of the word, not only the plums (or PRUNUS proper) are dealt with under this heading, but the almonds and peaches (AMYGDALUS), apricots (ARMENIACA), cherries (CERASUS), bird cherries (PADUS), and the cherry laurels (LAUROCERASUS) also. With even this extended interpretation the genus is well distinguished by its fruit, which is always a one-celled, one-seeded drupe.

The leaves are alternate, either deciduous or evergreen; the flowers white or rose-coloured, rarely yellowish; petals five, calyx five-lobed, stamens numerous.

In order to facilitate recognition of the species it will be necessary to denote the characters roughly distinguishing each section. It should be said, however, that some species (perhaps hybrids) are of uncertain position.

AMYGDALUS. ALMONDS AND PEACHES

Leaves conduplicate in bud (*i.e.* the two halves of the leaves are folded together lengthwise like a sheet of notepaper). Flowers and fruit very shortly stalked; fruit covered with velvety down (nectarine an exception, see *P. Persica*): *Amygdalus, Davidiana, nana, argentea, Persica, triloba.*

CERASUS. CHERRIES

Leaves conduplicate in bud. Flowers in clusters, racemes, or short corymbs, produced from the previous year's wood; fruit smooth, usually without bloom: *acida, Avium, Besseyi, canescens, Cerasus, emarginata, eminens, fruticosa, Fontanesiana, humilis, incana, Jacquemontii, glandulosa, Mahaleb, Maximowiczii, microcarpa, pennyslvanica, prostrata, cantabrigiensis, pumila, rufa, Sargentii, serrulata, subhirtella, tomentosa.*

PRUNUS. PLUMS

Leaves convolute in bud (*i.e.* each half of the leaf is rolled inwards). Flowers solitary or in clusters of one to four (sometimes six or seven); fruit smooth, rarely downy, but often covered with a blue or purplish bloom. The American species, with the exception of *P. subcordata*, are connecting links between plums and cherries, having leaves conduplicate in bud. but plum fruits: *alleghaniensis, americana, angustifolia, cerasifera, Cocomilia, communis, curdica, divaricata, hortulana, insititia, maritima, monticola, nigra, orthosepala, spinosa, subcordata, salicina, Watsoni.* (*Simoni* may be a hybrid between this group and Amygdalus or Armeniaca.)

ARMENIACA. APRICOTS

Leaves convolute in bud. Flowers and fruit very shortly stalked, fruit velvety: *Armeniaca, brigantiaca, Mume, sibirica.* (*P. dasycarpa* may be a hybrid between this group and Prunus.)

PADUS. BIRD CHERRIES

Leaves conduplicate in bud. Flowers in racemes produced on the young branches of the year: *cornuta, Cuthbertii, demissa, Grayana, nepaulensis, Padus, serotina, Ssiori, virginiana.* (*P. Maackii* is intermediate between this group and Laurocerasus, its racemes being axillary, but its leaves deciduous.)

LAUROCERASUS. CHERRY LAURELS

Evergreen. Flowers in racemes like those of the bird cherries, but produced from the axils of the still persisting leaves of the previous year: *caroliniana, ilicifolia, Laurocerasus, lusitanica.*

The cultivation of Prunus generally is somewhat varied owing to the wide variety of the species composing it. Generally they are very hardy; where they are not, the fact is noted. All the deciduous species enjoy full exposure to sunlight; it is on this more than anything else that the flower crop depends. They all thrive on loamy soil, and most of them, the plums especially, are at home on limestone formations.

Many of the species, or most, can be increased by cuttings. This method of propagation is well worth trying for those that are found to be short-lived when grafted or budded. The cuttings should be made of young wood getting firm, with a "heel" attached, and put in gentle heat. Peaches and almonds are usually grafted or budded on plum stocks because of the greater hardiness of the plum. The various cherries may be worked on P. Avium, and the bird cherries on P. Padus. The laurels may be increased by cuttings.

To this large genus of trees and shrubs, which includes the almonds; peaches, plums, cherries, bird-cherries, and cherry-laurels, the additions most important from the gardening point of view, made since the first edition of this work have been to the cherries.

JAPANESE CHERRIES especially have come very much into public notice and many varieties have been imported which have already added immensely to the beauty of English gardens in spring. They are almost entirely of garden origin and, according to Wilson, they belong chiefly to two species, P. SERRULATA, *Lindley*, and P. LANNESIANA, *Wilson.* So numerous are they, and so minute are the differences between many of them that, were it even necessary, it would be useless to attempt to distinguish them on paper, but E. H. Wilson's *Cherries of Japan*, published in 1916, and Collingwood Ingram's paper in the *Journal of the Royal Horticultural Society* for 1925 (vol. 50) should be consulted. Mr Ingram describes over thirty species and varieties, but these are only a part of the collection he grows at Benenden, in Kent—a collection more extensive than any other in Britain. A Japanese botanist named Miyoshi published a work on the Japanese cherries almost simultaneously with Wilson's. These three authorities are far from being in unison with regard to names and all I can do here is to recommend a few of what I consider to be good representative varieties under names about which there is some measure of agreement; varieties, moreover, that can be obtained from English nurseries. I must confess that I am unable to say whether some of the varieties belong to P. serrulata or to P. Lannesiana as defined by Wilson; and as Mr Ingram ignores the latter name and uses "serrulata" only, I assume he is in the same uncertainty.

ALBO-ROSEA (Shirofugen) flowers pink in bud, white later; young leaves brownish; two leaf-like carpels are in the centre of the flower; one of the later blossoming varieties.

AMANOGAWA, a variety of strictly fastigiate growth, more so even than a Lombardy poplar; flowers pink, fragrant, semi-double, often developing the small black fruits.

FUGENZO, a later flowering variety described in earlier editions as P. serrulata Veitchiana.

GRANDIFLORA is the proper name of the variety with greenish yellow flowers appearing in early editions as "flore luteo pleno." GIOIKI has also yellowish flowers, but they are streaked with green and tinged with pink.

HOKUSAI, *Ingram* (Ojochin, *Wilson*), has been longer in cultivation, perhaps, than any of the Japanese garden cherries except P. serrulata itself; young leaves bronzy, flowers 2 ins. across, light pink, semi-double. Mr Ingram has a tree at Benenden Grange about 40 ft. in diameter, probably the finest Japanese cherry in the country; and Lord Digby has a beautiful avenue of it at Minterne in Dorset.

KIRIN, similar to Sekiyama in colour of young leaf and flower but flowering rather earlier, of much more spreading habit and with more compact flower clusters.

MIYAKO (P. serrulata longipes, *Miyoshi*), a late-flowering variety with long-stalked, drooping clusters of double, white, fragrant flowers.

ROSEA PENDULA, a weeping variety with long, slender, perfectly pendent branches; flowers deep pink, very double; it does not appear to be of Japanese origin and is probably Chinese; also known as "lidera nova," "Shidara-sakura" and "Cheal's weeping cherry."

SEKIYAMA or KANZAN, young foliage coppery red, flowers double, rich rosy pink; habit rather erect. This variety is the best for street planting and where there is not a wide lateral space available. Also known as "hisa-kura," but wrongly, according to Wilson.

SENRIKO, of sturdy, vigorous growth, flowers single, pink to white, nearly 2 ins. wide.

SIROTAE, of spreading, vigorous habit; flowers double or semi-double, fragrant, of the purest snowy white; Wilson describes it as the finest of all double white cherries. It is also known as "Mount Fuji."

TEMARI, of semi-erect habit, flowers single or semi-double, 2 ins. or more across, produced in compact clusters, white flushed with pink.

An unfortunate thing with regard to some of the older Japanese or Chinese cherries is that the specific names were originally given to plants of garden origin. Thus it came about that the wild types from which they sprang, and which became known later, had to be given varietal names, thereby following botanical rules but reversing the natural order of things. The wild form of P. Lannesiana is known as var. ALBIDA, *Wilson*. P. serrulata SPONTANEA, *Wilson*, which is a common tree in woods and thickets on mountain sides in various parts of Japan, is probably the wild type of the species; its flowers are single, white flushed with pink, about 1 in. wide, produced in clusters of two to four. Wilson mentions an avenue near Tokyo, three miles long, planted almost wholly with this tree in 1735. It flowers at Kew from mid- to late April, and is a pretty, early-blossoming cherry, following on the subhirtellas. Leaves glabrous.

P. SERRULATA PUBESCENS, *Wilson*, is another of the cherries native of Japan which has shared in the origin of the now popular garden varieties of Japanese cherries. Wilson describes it as having leaves pale green below, more or less sparsely pubescent; leaf-stalk bearded, often on the upper side only; flower-stalks normally more or less pubescent; otherwise as in var. spontanea. According to Wilson's *Cherries of Japan*, p. 33, the cherries in cultivation under the name P. tenuiflora, *Koehne*, and under Wilson's numbers 3[a], 13, 20, 51, 51[a], all from W. China, belong to this variety of serrulata. And as other cherries collected by Wilson in China and named tenuiflora have been found to belong to the var. spontanea, the name tenuiflora has no standing.

P. SERRULATA SACHALINENSIS, the name given by Wilson to the cherry described in this work as "P. Sargentii," is regarded by him as the parent of some of the finest Japanese garden cherries.

P. ACIDA, *Ehrhart*

(Cerasus acida, *Borkhausen*)

A deciduous rounded bush, rarely more than 8 to 10 ft. high, with sturdy, erect branches, and glabrous branchlets. Leaves oval, 1½ to 3 ins. long, glabrous, doubly toothed, and shining. Flowers white, ¾ in. across, produced in early May in crowded clusters. Fruit dark red, sour.

The origin of this cherry is doubtful, but it is probably East European, either cultivated or wild. It is very nearly allied to P. Cerasus (*q.v.*), and by some authorities is not separated from it.

Var. DUMOSA.—When budded or grafted on low standards, this makes a dwarf, round-headed tree, profuse in flower, and of very slow growth. A charming tree for a small lawn, where it may stand for many years and cause no inconvenience by over-growing.

Var. SEMPERFLORENS (Cerasus semperflorens, *De Candolle*). All Saints Cherry.—This remarkable variety has been cultivated in gardens since the eighteenth century, but its origin is not known. It is usually grafted on standards of cherry, and thus makes a small, very elegant round-headed tree, with pendent, slender branches and curiously clustered twigs, which in the leafless state render it easily distinguishable. The most interesting and attractive thing about it is its method of flowering. It bears a small crop of blossom in April when in ordinary leafless condition, and in ordinary clusters; it then goes out of flower until the new shoots are a few inches long (early June), when it commences to blossom again, and continues to do so until September. These second flowers, however, are produced singly from the leaf-axils, and from the ends of the young leaf-bearing shoots. This variety in reality produces during the growing season the flowers which ought normally to be (and are in other cherries) produced simultaneously the following spring. By the time the later flowers are open the earlier ones have developed fruit, which is acid, but pleasantly flavoured. An interesting and attractive lawn tree.

P. EMINENS, *Beck*, a pretty small tree similar to P. acida in flower, but of more open growth; is described as a hybrid between it and P. fruticosa.

P. ALLEGHANIENSIS, *Porter*. AMERICAN SLOE

(Garden and Forest, 1890, fig. 53)

A small deciduous tree, sometimes up to 20 ft. high, but often a shrub a few feet high; branches erect, rigid, glabrous except when quite young, ultimately almost black, the spur-like growths sometimes terminating in a spine. Leaves ovate or oval-lanceolate, pointed, finely and sharply toothed; 2 to $3\frac{1}{2}$ ins. long, $\frac{3}{4}$ to $1\frac{1}{4}$ ins. wide; downy on the midrib beneath; stalk $\frac{1}{3}$ in. long, downy, without glands. Flowers $\frac{1}{2}$ in. across, produced in April in stalkless umbel-like clusters of two to five, each flower on a slender stalk $\frac{1}{4}$ to $\frac{1}{2}$ in. long; petals rather dull white, turning pink with age; calyx funnel-shaped at the base, with ovate-oblong lobes, downy. Fruit globose or slightly elongated, $\frac{1}{2}$ to $\frac{2}{3}$ in. diameter, reddish purple, covered with blue bloom.

Native of the Allegheny Mts. in Pennsylvania, where its fruits are known as sloes, and used for preserving, etc. It does not appear to have been recognised in the United States as a distinct species until 1877, when it was named as above. First introduced in 1892 from the Arnold Arboretum to Kew, where for a time it grew and flowered very well, but did not fruit. This tree, however, has since died. It is allied to P. americana, but differs in its blue fruits.

P. AMERICANA, *Marshall*. AMERICAN RED PLUM

A deciduous tree, 12 to 20, occasionally over 30 ft. high, of graceful habit, with the trunk dividing low down; branches pendulous towards the ends; young shoots glabrous or slightly downy. Leaves oval or obovate, tapering abruptly to a drawn-out point; 3 to 4 ins. long, $1\frac{1}{4}$ to $1\frac{3}{4}$ ins. wide; sharply and often doubly toothed, glabrous except for tufts of down along the midrib in the axils of the veins; stalk $\frac{1}{3}$ to $\frac{3}{4}$ in. long; downy and without glands. Flowers 1 in. across, pure white, produced two to five together in stalkless umbels, each flower on a slender glabrous stalk $\frac{2}{3}$ to 1 in. long; calyx reddish, lobes entire, hairy within. Fruit round or nearly so, 1 in. or less in diameter, first yellow, finally bright red; flesh yellow.

Native of the United States, where it is widely spread, reaching as far west as the eastern slopes of the Rocky Mountains. It and varieties derived from it are now largely grown in the eastern United States for the fruits. It has not yet borne fruit freely in Britain, although it flowers very well. The flowers have a faint and rather unpleasant odour. It is said to be extremely handsome when loaded with its red and yellow fruits. It may be distinguished from P. hortulana and P. nigra by the non-glandular leaf-stalks, and from P. alleghaniensis by the colour of its fruits and more graceful habit.

P. AMYGDALUS, *Batsch*. ALMOND

(Amygdalus communis, *Linnæus*)

A deciduous tree, 20 to 30 ft. high, erect branching when young, of bushy habit when old; branchlets quite glabrous. Leaves glabrous, lanceolate, 3 to 5 ins. long, $\frac{3}{4}$ to $1\frac{1}{2}$ ins. wide; long-pointed, margins finely toothed; stalk glandular, up to 1 in. long. Flowers 1 to 2 ins. across, borne in March and April, singly or in pairs from the buds of the previous summer's twigs, each on a short stalk scarcely longer than the bud-scales. Calyx bell-shaped at the base, the five lobes $\frac{1}{6}$ in. long, oblong, rounded, downy towards the edges; petals rosy or nearly white. Fruit $1\frac{1}{2}$ to $2\frac{1}{2}$ ins. long, not quite so much wide, covered with a velvety down; flesh rather dry, enclosing a smooth nut with a pitted shell.

The almond is naturalised in many countries of S. Europe and W. Asia, and it is now, perhaps, impossible to determine the original limits of its distribution; but it has been found undoubtedly wild in Algeria. The dimensions of flower and leaf in wild specimens are about half those given above. It was cultivated in Britain early in the sixteenth century, perhaps long before. Of the earliest blossoming trees it is the most beautiful, flowering in early spring when almost all other deciduous trees and shrubs are merely showing signs of reawakening growth, and providing then a delightful feast of softest colouring, which gives, perhaps, a deeper pleasure than any of the great Prunus tribe. To see the almond at its best it should be given some sunny bay with evergreens like holly or holm oak as a background. With no other backing than the cold March sky, almond flowers lose half their charm. In Britain it is propagated chiefly by budding on the plum stock, and thrives very well. Seeds or seedlings can be obtained at very cheap rates from continental nurseries, but on its own roots it is said to be less hardy and more fastidious as to soil than it is when worked on the plum. The soil need not be particularly rich, but it should be warm and well drained. Although the almond occasionally produces good eatable nuts in England, it is never likely to be valued in gardens on that account. It is for its beauty of flower alone that it is cultivated. We can therefore ignore the numerous varieties that are grown in the south of Europe for their nuts. The following named varieties are obtainable in this country:—

Var. AMARA. Bitter Almond.—Flowers larger than ordinary, darkest in the centre, almost white towards the tips of the petals. Leaves broadest about the middle. This variety produces the nuts used so largely in confectionery, for macaroons, etc.

Var. DULCIS. Sweet Almond.—The flowers do not differ materially from those of the bitter almond, except that the style stands well out beyond the stamens. Leaves rather glaucous green, broadest close to the base. This tree produces dessert almonds.

Var. MACROCARPA.—Notable for its large fruits, 3 ins. in length; flowers up to 2 ins. across.

Var. PENDULA.—Branches pendulous.

Var. PRÆCOX.—Flowers produced a fortnight earlier than in the type, frequently in February (also grown as var. persicoides).

P. ANGUSTIFOLIA, *Marshall*. CHICKASAW PLUM

(P. chicasa, *Michaux*)

A deciduous tree, 15 to 20 ft. high, with glabrous, lustrous, reddish young branchlets. Leaves 1 to 2 ins. long, one-third as wide; oval-lanceolate, pointed, sharply toothed, tapering at the base to a reddish stalk ¼ to ½ in. long. Flowers white, ½ in. across, in clusters of two to four; calyx glabrous outside. Fruit bright red and shining, ½ in. across, round or nearly so.

The native country of this plum, according to Sargent, is still uncertain, but it is either native or widely naturalised in the south-eastern United States. It is the source of several varieties of plums cultivated in the Southern States. Several times introduced to Kew, it never thrives, and it is probably only adapted for the warmest parts of the British Isles, and unless it bears fruits it is scarcely ornamental enough to be worthy of cultivation there. Its close ally, P. Watsoni, is better worth growing. The P. chicasa of Michaux, usually regarded as synonymous with P. augustifolia, is said by Mr Hedrick to be different.

P. APETALA, *Franchet and Savatier*

(P. Tschonoskii, *Koehne*)

A small deciduous tree or (more often) a bush up to 16 ft. high; young shoots hairy, slender. Leaves mostly obovate, with a slender, tail-like apex, tapering and often rounded at the base, conspicuously doubly-toothed; 2 to 4 ins. long, 1 to 1½ ins. wide; hairy on both sides, especially below; stalk ¼ to ½ in. long, very hairy. Flowers produced during May singly or in pairs, each on its slender hairy stalk ½ to ¾ in. long. The small white or pink petals very soon fall, and such little beauty as the flower possesses is in the calyx and stamens, which become purplish red. The calyx-tube is cylindrical, downy, ⅜ in. long, the lobes ovate, ⅛ in. long. Fruit roundish-oval, black, ⅜ in. long, the stalk elongated to 1 or 1⅜ ins.

Native of Japan; introduced by Wilson in 1914. The leaves of this cherry are rather handsome and distinct in the long, tail-like point and in their hairiness. The most marked character of the species, however, is the persistent, coloured calyx and stamen stalks. It will rank in gardens chiefly as a curiosity. In the style of the toothing of the leaves it has some resemblance to P. incisa and nipponica. A plant at Benenden was 10 ft. high in May 1931.

P. ARGENTEA, *Rehder*

(P. orientalis, *Koehne*; Amygdalus orientalis, *Miller*)

A deciduous shrub or small tree with whitish, downy twigs. Leaves elliptical or ovate, short-stalked, ¾ to 1½ ins. long, covered with a close silvery down. Flowers solitary or in pairs, ¾ in across; petals rose-coloured, thin, and of short duration. Fruit egg-shaped, ⅝ in. long, pointed, rather compressed, covered with a close, white down.

Native of Asia Minor, chiefly Kurdistan; introduced in 1756. This almond is easily distinguished from all others of this genus in cultivation by the silvery leaves. It is not hardy in the open, and on a wall should be given a sunny place. In a shady position the leaves lose their whiteness, and suggest mildew rather than silveriness. It flowers very shyly in this country, and is only worth growing for the unusual aspect of its foliage.

P. ARMENIACA, *Linnæus*. APRICOT

(Armeniaca vulgaris, *Lamarck*)

A round-headed, deciduous tree, 20 to 30 ft. high, with sturdy, tortuous branches; branchlets glabrous. Leaves broadly ovate to roundish, 2½ to 3½ ins. long, 1½ to 2 ins. wide; abruptly pointed, deep lustrous green, glabrous or with axil tufts beneath, evenly set with rounded teeth; stalk up to 1 in. long. Flowers white or pinkish, 1 in. across, produced singly on very short stalks from the previous year's wood, often crowded on short spur-like twigs. Fruit round, 1¼ ins. wide in a wild state, larger under cultivation, yellow tinged with red, the nut having a thickened furrowed margin.

Native of N. China, where it was found genuinely wild by Dr Bretschneider, and raised at Kew from seeds sent by him. It is, of course, best known as a fruit tree on walls, but is quite hardy in the open, where, however, it does not bear fruit satisfactorily. The fruiting apricot is believed to have been cultivated by the Chinese many centuries anterior to the Christian era, gradually spreading westwards to Europe. It existed in English gardens early in the sixteenth century, probably long before. Flowering in March and early April, the apricot has something to recommend it, but it must be regarded as an inferior flowering tree, not in the same class as the almond and peach. The specific name refers to its supposed Armenian origin.

Var. ANSU, *Maximowicz*.—An apricot cultivated in Japan and Korea; leaves broadly cuneate to truncate; flowers pink, mostly in pairs, red, downy.

P. AVIUM, *Linnæus*. GEAN, MAZZARD

(Cerasus sylvestris, *Loudon*)

A deciduous tree up to 60 ft. or more high, with a trunk occasionally 2 ft. and upwards in diameter, the bark shining and peeling horizontally; young twigs glabrous. Leaves ovate to oval with a drawn-out point; 3 to 5 ins. long, 1½ to 2 ins. wide (sometimes considerably larger on vigorous young trees); rather coarsely and irregularly toothed, hairy along the veins and midrib beneath; leaf-stalk 1 to 1¾ ins. long, with reddish glands near the blade. Flowers pure white, about 1 in. across, produced on stalks from 1 to 1¾ ins. long, in stalkless clusters from the previous year's shoots, and from spur-like branches of earlier date. Fruit round, blackish red, ¾ in. diameter, sweet or bitter but not acid.

Native of Europe, including Britain, and one of the parents of cultivated fruiting cherries, especially the black ones. In the woodland the gean is very desirable, and in suitable places makes a big tree; in plantations separated from the house by a valley it might be planted in numbers for its effect in April and early May, but in the garden itself it should give place to the improved varieties. There is a good deal of confusion in botanical works between this species and P. Cerasus and P. acida. But P. Avium differs from the other two in the following respects: it is a tree sometimes of full middle size (the others are more or less dwarf or shrubby); the leaves are more coarsely toothed and hairy beneath; the fruit is not acid. The following varieties are the most notable of those in cultivation:—

Var. ASPLENIFOLIA.—Leaves deeply and irregularly toothed. Var. LACINIATA is the same or very similar.

Var. DECUMANA, *Koch* (P. macrophylla, *Poiret*).—A remarkable variety with large single flowers and enormous leaves, often 8 to 10 ins. long, and broad in proportion.

Var. PLENA.—This, the most beautiful of gean cherries, and one of the most beautiful of all flowering trees, has been known perhaps for two centuries. Healthy trees never fail to flower in the utmost profusion, every branch and twig being wreathed from end to end with thick pendulous masses of the purest white blossom. Each flower is about 1½ ins. across, and consists of, perhaps, thirty to forty petals lasting long in beauty; fruits are rarely or never formed.

Var. NANA.—A dwarf stunted form with single flowers. Useful to represent the species where space is limited.

Var. PENDULA.—Branches pendulous, but too stiffly so to be attractive.

Var. PRÆMORSA.—Leaves of curious shape, with the appearance of the ends having been bitten off.

P. BESSEYI, *Bailey*. ROCKY MOUNTAIN CHERRY

(Bot. Mag., t. 8156)

A dwarf deciduous shrub, 2 to 4 ft. high, with glabrous branchlets. Leaves grey-green, oval or oval-lanceolate, sometimes obovate, 1 to 2½ ins. long shallowly toothed on the upper two-thirds, glabrous. Flowers in stalkless clusters of two to four from the buds of the previous year's shoots; each flower pure white, ⅝ in. across, on a stalk ⅓ in. long; calyx green, with ovate, slightly toothed lobes. Fruit on more or less pendent stalks, oblong or nearly round, ¾ in. long, covered with a purplish bloom at first, finally black.

PRUNUS BESSEYI

Native of the hot, dry plains east of the Rocky Mountains in Colorado, Nebraska, Kansas, etc., where it promises to be a valuable fruit-bearing shrub. It is remarkably prolific there, and in Colorado sixteen quarts of fruit have been gathered from a bush three years old, and eighty fruits from a branch 1 ft. long. It was introduced to Kew in 1900, and has proved to be an ornamental little shrub, flowering so freely in late April or early May as to make each twig a cylindrical mass of blossom. Its fruits are only sparingly borne in England, but the species is worth the notice of fruit-growers in S. Africa,

Australia, and other colonies with a dry sunny climate. P. UTAHENSIS, *Koehne*, is believed to be a hybrid between P. Besseyi and P. Watsoni; it originated as an accidental cross in the grounds of Mr J. E. Johnson, at Red River, Nebraska. Fruits blue-black. (See also P. pumila.)

P. BLIREIANA, *Andrè*

Referred to in earlier editions of this work as the best variety of P. cerasifera, this is now regarded as a hybrid between the var. Pissardii of that species and a double-flowered P. Mume. It is still the best of the purple-leaved plums, the flowers being bright rose, very double and equal in beauty to a double-pink peach. It is a tree for every garden that can find room for it. A dark-leaved form of Pissard's plum is var. NIGRA; the best of all, perhaps, is one known as the "Hazeldene Variety."

P. BRIGANTIACA, *Villars*. BRIANÇON APRICOT

(Armeniaca brigantiaca, *Persoon*)

A small, deciduous, bushy tree, 10 to 20 ft. high, with a short trunk. Leaves ovate or oval, often slightly heart-shaped at the base, shortly and abruptly pointed, the margins doubly and rather jaggedly toothed; 1½ to 3 ins. long, 1 to 2½ ins. wide; hairy beneath, especially on the veins and midrib; stalk ⅓ to ⅔ in. long. Flowers white or pinkish, ¾ in. or so across, two or more together. Fruit like a small apricot, of a rather clear yellow, smooth.

This tree grows spontaneously in the neighbourhood of Briançon, and it is said also to occur wild in Piedmont. From the seeds the Briançonnais express an inflammable, agreeably perfumed oil, known as *huile de Marmotte*. This apricot has little to recommend it for gardens.

P. CAMPANULATA, *Maximowicz*. BELL-FLOWERED CHERRY

(Bot. Mag., t. 9575)

A deciduous cherry tree up to 30 ft. high, of graceful habit, free from down in all its parts; year-old shoots freely marked with warts. Leaves ovate, oval or slightly obovate, slender-pointed, broadly wedge-shaped to slightly heart-shaped at the base; margins regularly set with fine forward-pointing or incurved teeth; 2½ to 4 ins. long, 1 to 1¾ ins. wide; nerves in six to eight pairs; stalks ½ to ¾ in. long. Flowers ¾ in. wide, produced in March and April, two to six together on main-stalks 1 to 1½ ins. long that bear usually a couple of leaf-like bracts; individual flower-stalks ½ to ¾ in. long. Petals of a beautiful deep rose, roundish ovate, notched at the apex, ¼ in. wide. Calyx-tube rose-coloured except at the base, the reflexed, sparsely toothed lobes also rosy; stamens deep rose, anthers yellow. Fruit described as red, conical, ⅝ in. long, scarcely ½ in. wide.

Native of Formosa and thought to be wild also in the Liukiu Islands of Japan. The bell shape of the flowers to which the specific name refers seems to be characteristic of them in a young state only. It appears to have been introduced by Messrs Sander of St Albans in 1899, but owing to its tenderness was lost and not seen again until Wilson took plants from Japan to the Arnold Arboretum in 1915. Its flowers are, perhaps, the most highly coloured of all the genuinely wild types. Unfortunately it is only likely to succeed in our mildest counties. It succeeds admirably on the Riviera and a tree at Trewithen, Cornwall, is 40 ft. high. It flowers quite freely in the Temperate House at Kew in March.

P. CANESCENS, *D. Bois.* GREY-LEAVED CHERRY

A deciduous shrub of dense, rounded, bushy form, probably 6 to 8 ft. high eventually; branchlets more or less hairy. Leaves lanceolate or narrowly ovate, 1½ to 2½ ins. long, ½ to 1 in. wide; coarsely and doubly toothed, the base rounded or tapering, the apex long-pointed; both surfaces, especially the lower one, furnished with persistent, soft, greyish hairs; stalk ¼ to ⅓ in. long, hairy, issuing from between two leaf-like, deeply toothed, hairy stipules ¼ in. long. Flowers rosy white, scarcely ½ in. wide, produced (each on a sparsely hairy stalk ⅓ in. long) in clusters of three to five; calyx tubular, with five triangular lobes half as long as the tube; petals soon falling. Fruit round to oblong, ½ in. diameter, glabrous, red, with a pleasant cherry-like taste.

Native of China; obtained in 1898 from the province of Szechuen by Mr Maurice de Vilmorin, and flowered at Les Barres in 1901. Introduced in 1905 to Kew, where it flowers about mid-April. It is a very distinct cherry because of the thick coat of soft hairs which covers the leaves and other younger parts of the plant, but is reduced in value as an ornamental plant by the fleeting nature of the petals. Mr Bois, the author of the name, assumes a relationship between it and P. Maximowiczii. The latter species, however, is very distinct in its stalked racemes several inches long furnished with leaf-like bracts. P. canescens is abundant in Wilson's later collectings.

P. CANTABRIGIENSIS, *Stapf.* CAMBRIDGE CHERRY

(Bot. Mag., t. 9129; P. pseudocerasus, *Koidzumi*)

In a previous edition under the heading of P. pseudocerasus, I gave a short description of a cherry, based on a specimen labelled by that name, which is preserved in the Lindley herbarium at Cambridge University. I there observed that the true P. pseudocerasus was probably not then in cultivation and that the trees grown under the name in gardens were mostly forms of P. serrulata. In February 1917 there flowered in the Cambridge Botanic Garden a cherry which, after being critically examined by the late Mr R. I. Lynch, the Curator, and compared with Lindley's specimen, was considered by him to be the true thing (see *Gardeners' Chronicle*, 4th August 1917, p. 47). I was afterwards furnished with flowering and leaf-bearing shoots and concurred with Mr Lynch's verdict. The flowers are pink, ¾ to 1 in. wide, produced on shortly stalked racemes three to six together; petals scoop-shaped, ⅜ in. long, scarcely as wide, notched at the apex; anthers yellow; style and ovary glabrous. Calyx-tube $\frac{3}{16}$ in. long and, like the flower-stalks, slightly hairy. The fruit is bright red, rather larger than the British wild cherry. The Cambridge tree is reputed to date back to Lindley's time and as the specimen in the herbarium is labelled " P. pseudocerasus " in Lindley's own handwriting, it was by most people concluded that the mystery of the cherry of that name was solved.

A flowering spray from the Cambridge tree has lately been figured in the *Botanical Magazine*, t. 9129, and Dr Stapf, the editor, whilst agreeing in the accompanying text that it matches Lindley's specimen, refused to agree that the latter is the true P. pseudocerasus, although it is labelled by Lindley himself. He pointed out that it does not match the *Botanical Register* plate (t. 800) which, in the absence of a co-related specimen, constitutes the only available evidence of what P. pseudocerasus really is. (It may be pointed out that although the *Botanical Register* picture is legended as " Prunus paniculata, *Thunberg*," the plant so called by Thunberg is really the Symplocos cratægoides described in our earlier vol. ii, p. 564, and not a prunus at all. It was to replace this erroneous name that Lindley substituted " P. pseudocerasus " for it. The figure, therefore, constitutes the standard on which the identity of the species is based.) Dr Stapf calls the Cambridge tree P. cantabrigiensis, and, if he is right, P. pseudocerasus remains as forlorn a mystery as ever, having appeared in the year 1819 as an introduction from China by a nurseryman called Samuel Brooks of Ball's Pond, Newington Green, London; flowered in the spring of 1824 in the Horticultural Society's Garden at Chiswick; been figured in the *Botanical Register* under a wrong name; and never been recognised since, either wild or cultivated.

P. cantabrigiensis is very hardy and flowers often in February at Cambridge. In the milder parts of the country where it had a chance to develop its flowers uninjured by frost it should be a handsome tree valuable for the exceptional earliness of its blossom.

P. CERASIFERA, *Ehrhart*. CHERRY PLUM, MYROBALAN

(Bot. Mag., t. 5934)

A deciduous, round-headed tree up to 30 ft. in height; young bark glabrous. Leaves ovate, oval or obovate, 1½ to 2½ ins. long, 1 to 1¼ ins. wide; toothed, downy along the midrib and veins beneath. Flowers ¾ to 1 in. across, pure white, produced usually singly, sometimes two or three together, at each bud of the previous year's shoots, but often crowded on short spur-like twigs so as to form dense clusters. Fruit smooth, red, 1 to 1¼ ins. in diameter, round, indented at the junction with the stalk.

Of doubtful origin, but thought to be a native of the Caucasus. The cherry plum is now a well-known tree in gardens, and is sometimes used as a stock for grafting. As flowering trees it and its near ally P. divaricata are the most beauitful of the true plums, being almost covered with pure white blossom in March. The fruits are developed not infrequently at Kew, but never in great quantity. They are occasionally to be seen in considerable quantities in July in the fruit shops of southern watering-places, having been imported from the Continent. They are used for tarts, etc., like ordinary plums. A considerable number of varieties have been put upon the market by French and German nurserymen, some of which are absolutely worthless. The best known is

Var. PISSARDI (var. atropurpurea, *Dippel*; P. Pissardi, *Carrière*).—In spring this tree, like the type, is laden with blossom, which is of a delicate rose. Its foliage, however, is its most distinctive feature; when it first expands it is of a tender ruby-red, changing later to claret colour, finally to a dull heavy purple. Its fruits, too, are purple. This variety was first noted in Persia by Mr Pissard, gardener to the Shah, and by him was sent to France in 1880, whence it rapidly spread in cultivation, and is now a very common tree.

Var. ELEGANS (syn. " Louis Asselin ").—Leaves narrower and edged with white.

P. CERASUS, *Linnæus*. WILD DWARF CHERRY

(Cerasus vulgaris, *Miller*)

A deciduous bush or small rounded tree, suckering at the root and often making thickets in a wild state, but 10 to 20 ft. high under cultivation. Leaves oval or ovate, abruptly short-pointed, 1½ to 3 ins. long, half to two-thirds as wide; glabrous on both surfaces, rather lustrous above, the margins set with double gland-tipped teeth; stalk ½ to ¾ in. long, usually glanded. Flowers pure white, ¾ to 1 in. across, produced in clusters, each flower on a stalk ¾ in. long. Fruit red to blackish, roundish and depressed, with soft, juicy, acid flesh.

Native of Europe, including Britain, and one of the parents of the cultivated fruit-bearing cherries—including the morellos. Some authorities have united it with P. acida and P. Avium as a species, but P. Cerasus produces suckers from the roots, and never makes a tall quick-growing tree like P. Avium, with its clean leader and pyramidal form when young; the leaves of P. Cerasus are nearly or entirely without down; and, perhaps more important than all, the fruit is not sweet nor bitter, but acid, the stone round. It is much more difficult to provide distinctions between P. Cerasus and P. acida, and the latter may have been derived from P. Cerasus in cultivation. It is considered to be distinguishable by its still dwarfer, more bushy form, its smaller leaves and more elongated stone.

Var. PLENA.—The typical P. Cerasus is scarcely worth a place in gardens, and its flowers are neither so beautiful nor so durable as this double-flowered variety (often known also as "Rhexii" or "ranunculiflora"). The flowers are pure white, 1½ ins. across, very "double," with stalks almost twice as long as in the type. A worthy rival of P. Avium plena.

Vars. GLOBOSA and HUMILIS are dwarfed forms very useful on small areas; flowers single.

Var. MARASCA.—A vigorous tree whose fruits are employed in the manufacture of the famous Maraschino liqueur in Dalmatia, especially about the town of Zara.

Var. MULTICARPA.—A strong-growing, large-leaved form, with long-stalked single flowers, which derives its name from often having two fruits united.

Var. SALICIFOLIA.—Leaves long and narrow, 4 to 6 ins. long, about one-fourth as wide, coarsely and doubly toothed. A distinct variety with single flowers.

P. COCOMILIA, *Tenore*. NAPLES PLUM

A deciduous thorny bush or small tree, with glabrous shoots and oval or obovate leaves 1½ to 2 ins. long, ½ to ¾ in. wide, finely toothed, nearly or quite glabrous. Flowers white, scarcely ½ in. wide, appearing towards the end of April on short stalks, mostly in pairs. Fruit yellow, well-flavoured, of an oval or oblong form, 1½ ins. long, scarcely 1 in. wide, tapered at the apex. But little is known of this plum in this country. It was first described early in the nineteenth century by Tenore, an Italian botanist who made a special study of the flora about Naples, where the species grows wild in hedges, etc. The specific name has been variously spelled. The tree has little to recommend it for gardens; it rarely bears fruit in this country.

P. COMMUNIS, *Hudson*. WILD PLUM

(P. domestica, *Linnæus* (in part))

A deciduous tree up to 15 or 20 ft. high, or a shrub, of suckering habit, with brown, glabrous, unarmed branches. Leaves elliptical or obovate, downy beneath on the midrib and veins, 1½ to 3 ins. long, of a dull greyish green, margins set with rounded even teeth; stalk downy, glandular, about ½ in. long. Flowers produced in April singly or in pairs, from the buds of the previous year's shoots, white, ¾ to 1 in. across; stalks ¼ in. long, glabrous. Fruit black with blue bloom, egg-shaped, 1 to 1½ ins. long. (See also P. insititia.)

The wild plum, although occasionally met with in hedgerows, etc., as an escape from cultivation, is not a true native of Britain. It is even doubtful if it be a native of Europe, although found in many places apparently naturalised. The plum is largely used as a stock for almonds, peaches, etc., being very hardy. It is not worth growing for ornament in gardens, at least in its typical form. An old tree in blossom is pretty, but not more so than the fruit-bearing plums commonly grown, of which it is one of the parents.

Var. PLENA has double flowers, and is more ornamental than the type. The double-flowered plum, P. PLANTIERENSIS, is of a similar character.

P. CONCINNA, *Koehne*

A deciduous shrubby cherry up to 6 or 8 ft. high; young shoots soon glabrous. Leaves purplish when young, narrowly oval to obovate, sharply and finely toothed, long-pointed, rounded to tapered at the base; 1½ to 3 ins. long; dull green above, greyish beneath, and slightly hairy on both surfaces especially when young; stalk ¼ in. long. Flowers white or pale pink, about 1 in. wide, produced either singly or up to four in a cluster; flower-stalk ½ in. long. Petals obovate, mostly notched; calyx-tube glabrous, tubular, tapered to the base; the lobes ovate-triangular, not toothed. Fruit roundish, ½ in. long, black.

Native of W. Hupeh, China; introduced by Wilson in 1907. This shrubby cherry is very rare in cultivation although offered in catalogues. It produces its flowers during March or April in great profusion in advance of the leaves and is then a very pretty shrub.

P. CONRADINÆ, *Koehne*

A deciduous tree of graceful habit up to 35 ft. high; young shoots glabrous. Leaves oval to oval-lanceolate, or inclined to obovate; slender-pointed, mostly rounded at the base, toothed, often doubly so; 2 to 4½ ins. long, 1 to 2¼ ins. wide; glabrous or with sprinkled hairs above, more or less hairy on the veins beneath; stalk ½ in. long. Flowers produced on the leafless shoots during early spring in very shortly stalked clusters of two to five, each on a glabrous stalk ¼ to ⅝ in. long; white or pale pink, 1 in. wide. Calyx quite glabrous, the tube bell-shaped, the lobes triangular. Fruit red, ovoid, ⅖ in. long.

Native of W. Hupeh, China; introduced in 1907 by means of seeds sent to Kew from the Arnold Arboretum, Mass., which had been collected that season by Wilson, who first discovered the species. It is the best of the early flowering wild cherries and is usually in bloom during normal seasons in February or early March. In the warmest counties it will flower in January. The petals are always notched at the end, occasionally lobed in addition, and the flowers frequently show a tendency to "double." Mr Collingwood Ingram of Benenden, Kent, found in his collection a tree with this "doubleness" unusually developed, which he named var. SEMI-PLENA. This lasts longer in bloom than the single type. The flowers are pleasantly fragrant. If possible, it should be planted where it has an evergreen background to the north and east; this will give shelter to the early blossoms and bring out their beauty more definitely.

P. CONSOCIIFLORA, *C. K. Schneider*

A small deciduous tree; young shoots glabrous, brown. Leaves oblanceolate to obovate, narrowed at the apex to a longish point, tapered at the base; minutely toothed, the teeth glandular; 1½ to 3 ins. long, ¾ to 1¼ ins. wide;

undersurface with tufts of down in the vein-axils. Flowers ½ in. wide, white, fragrant, produced in April before the leaves, usually in twos or threes and often crowded on short twigs to make a cluster 1 in. across; calyx and flower-stalk quite glabrous, the former funnel-shaped with narrowly triangular lobes, the latter slender, about ¼ in. long; ovary glabrous.

Native of China; introduced by Wilson in 1900 when collecting for Messrs Veitch. Although it is a plum, its leaves are conduplicate in the bud state; that is, the two halves are folded together lengthwise like a sheet of notepaper, whereas in most plums they are convolute in bud, which means that each half of the leaf is rolled inwards. Judging by the trees at Kew, this plum is very similar to P. salicina *Lindley* (P. triflora) with the same immense quantities of small white flowers which are quite pleasantly scented. P. salicina has always convolute leaves.

P. CORNUTA, *Wallich*. HIMALAYAN BIRD CHERRY

(Bot. Mag., t. 9423; Padus cornuta, *Carrière*)

A deciduous tree, 50 to 60 ft. high in a wild state; young shoots either finely downy or quite glabrous. Leaves ovate-oblong, or somewhat obovate; 3 to 6 ins. long, 1½ to 2 ins. wide; the base varying from heart-shaped to tapering, the apex slender-pointed, the margins finely toothed; downy along the midrib and veins beneath when young, deep dull green above, paler beneath; stalk ½ to 1¼ ins. long, mostly with glands at the top. Flowers white, densely set on cylindrical, quite glabrous, or finely downy racemes, 3 to 6 ins. long, ¾ to 1 in. wide; each flower is ¼ to ⅓ in. across. Fruit round, ⅓ in. in diameter, red, changing to dark brown purple. Flowers in May.

Native of the Himalaya, where it is widely spread up to 10,000 ft., and represents in that region P. Padus. So nearly are they allied that many botanists regard them as forms of one species. According to travellers in the Himalaya, P. cornuta grows to considerably larger size than does P. Padus as we know it in England. The name cornuta (horned) refers to the shape of the fruits as often seen in the Himalaya. An insect deposits its eggs in the young fruit, and as the larvæ develop they set up irritation and cause a curious growth, which is from 1 to 2 ins. long and curled like a horn. It is analogous to the many galls that occur on our own trees—notably oaks.

In the Botanic Garden at Trinity College, Dublin, there is a very interesting downy form of P. cornuta—or it may be P. NAPAULENSIS, *Steudel*. This tree, now over 30 ft. high, was raised from Himalayan seed in 1881. The late Mr F. W. Burbidge described the young foliage to me as looking as if made of copper or bronze. The leaf-stalks are without glands, and, like the main and secondary flower-stalks, thickly covered with close down. Flowers very fragrant, and densely packed on the raceme. The glandless leaf-stalk seems to point to this tree being P. napaulensis rather than cornuta, but the latter is very variable in a wild state.

P. CUTHBERTII, *Small*

(Padus Cuthbertii, *Small*)

A deciduous tree up to 20 ft. high, with a trunk sometimes 6 ins. in diameter in a wild state, but shrubby in cultivation here; young shoots downy. Leaves almost glabrous except for greyish hairs along the midrib beneath, obovate or oval, 1½ to 3½ ins. long, more than half as wide; usually rounded or even notched at the apex, tapering at the base to a downy stalk ¼ in. long; margins very shallowly toothed, lower teeth glandular. Flowers very small, white, produced on leafy racemes 2 to 3 ins. long, flower-stalks downy. Fruit red, roundish, ¼ in. in diameter.

Native of Central Georgia, U.S.A., where it inhabits woods. It was introduced to this country in 1901, and, although slow-growing, has proved hardy so far. Allied to P. serotina, it differs very markedly in its round-ended leaves and downy shoots and flower-stalks. It is never likely, I think, to become so handsome a tree. Its flowers, which come in June, are not showy, but its foliage is handsome and distinct among bird cherries, and falls late.

P. DASYCARPA, *Ehrhart*. BLACK APRICOT

(Armeniaca dasycarpa, *Persoon*)

A deciduous tree, 12 to 20 ft. high, with purplish, glabrous twigs. Leaves oval to ovate, with a rather abrupt tapering point, finely toothed, 1½ to 2½ ins. long, two-thirds as wide, downy beneath on the midrib and main veins; leaf-stalk ¾ to 1 in. long, often glanded. Flower ¾ in. across, pure white, produced on the naked wood in March, each on a downy stalk. Fruit round, 1½ ins. across, black, with purple bloom, minutely downy.

The origin of this tree is not known, but it may be a hybrid between the plum and apricot. It bears fruit only sparsely in this country, but is offered in German catalogues of fruit trees as "plum-apricot." The fruit is described as ripening in August, purple-black, covered with fine down, the flesh red, juicy, sweet, and of an apricot flavour. It would probably need wall treatment in this country to develop its fruit properly. It is worth cultivation as an early free-flowering tree.

P. DAVIDIANA, *Franchet*. DAVID'S PEACH

(Persica Davidiana, *Carrière*)

A deciduous tree, 20 to 30 ft. high, with glabrous branchlets. Leaves 3 to 5 ins. long, 1 to 1½ ins. wide; tapering to a long fine point like the almond, finely and sharply toothed, stalk ½ to ¾ in. long, with one or two glands. Flowers white, 1 in. across, produced singly on very short stalks from the buds of the previous year's shoots. Calyx glabrous, with five rounded, oblong lobes. Fruit spherical, 1¼ ins. across, yellowish, downy; flesh thin; nut pitted. The twigs become grey by autumn.

Native of China; introduced to Paris in 1865, by means of seeds sent by the Abbé David, who stated that the tree made a beautiful and conspicuous feature in the vicinity of Pekin. In English gardens this species is chiefly valuable for the earliness of its blossoms, which expand at any time between January and March, according to the weather, the normal time, perhaps, being about mid-February. Owing to their earliness, they are liable to injury (I have frequently seen snow resting on trees in bloom), and should be given a sheltered spot—the south-western side of a plantation of evergreens for preference. In such a position, given favourable weather the slender twigs, 1 to 2 ft. long, wreathed with white or, in var. RUBRA, rosy blossom, have a charming effect. Propagated by budding on almond or plum stocks.

P. DAWYCKENSIS, *Sealy*

(Bot. Mag., t. 9519)

A deciduous cherry up to about 16 ft. high; young shoots hairy, grey to purplish, becoming shining, glabrous and warty later. Leaves broadly oval to obovate, 2 to 5 ins. long, 1½ to 2½ ins. wide (those of the flowering shoots smaller), more or less slenderly pointed, coarsely round-toothed, slightly hairy above, glaucous-green and more or less hairy beneath. Flowers in shortly stalked downy umbels of two or three blossoms, each $\frac{5}{8}$ in. across, petals roundish, overlapping, pale pink; style glabrous. Fruit a globose, scarlet-crimson cherry, $\frac{1}{2}$ in. wide, stalk about 1 in. long.

Origin not definitely known, but most probably introduced from W. China early in the present century by E. H. Wilson. It is near enough to P. Dielsiana and P. canescens to have suggested its being a hybrid between them. The original plant is in the late Mr F. R. S. Balfour's garden at Dawyck in Peeblesshire.

P. DEMISSA, *D. Dietrich*. WESTERN CHOKE CHERRY

(Padus demissa, *Roemer*)

A deciduous tree, rarely 30 or more ft. high, more often a shrub; young bark glabrous, strongly scented. Leaves broadly oval, 2 to 5 ins. long, half as wide, rounded or slightly heart-shaped at the base, dark green above, paler beneath, glabrous on both surfaces except for a few hairs on the midrib and veins when young; stalk glandular, $\frac{1}{2}$ to $\frac{3}{4}$ in. long. Flowers in cylindrical racemes terminating short leafy shoots, 3 to 6 ins. long, each flower $\frac{1}{3}$ in. across and white. Fruit globose, shining, very dark purple or nearly black, $\frac{1}{3}$ in. diameter.

Native of western N. America, where its fruits are made into a very palatable preserve, having a cherry flavour. It is closely allied to the East American P. virginiana, which differs in its thinner leaves and red fruits.

P. DIELSIANA, *C. K. Schneider*

A deciduous cherry up to 30 ft. high; young shoots glabrous. Leaves oval, obovate, or inclined to oblong, abruptly narrowed at the apex to a short slender point, rounded or slightly heart-shaped at the base, sharply and often doubly toothed; 3 to 7 ins. long, $1\frac{1}{4}$ to 3 ins. wide; glabrous above, distinctly downy beneath, especially on the midrib and veins; stalk $\frac{1}{4}$ to $\frac{5}{8}$ in. long, usually downy and furnished with one to three large glands. Flowers 1 in. wide, pink or white, produced before the leaves, three to six in a cluster, each on a hairy stalk $\frac{1}{2}$ to $1\frac{1}{4}$ ins. long. Calyx-tube bell-shaped, hairy, its reflexed awl-shaped lobes longer than the tube; petals narrowly oval, deeply notched at the end. Fruit globose, $\frac{1}{3}$ in. wide, red. The flowers spring from the axis of an involucre of conspicuously glandular-fringed bracts.

Native of W. Hupeh, China; introduced in 1907 by Wilson. It has about the same degree of beauty as the other wild cherries introduced by Wilson at the same time, but is rather distinct on account of the downy undersurface of its large leaves, the hairy flower-stalks, and the very glandular-edged bracts. Nearly related to it is

P. CYCLAMINA. *Koehne*, also introduced from the same region by Wilson in 1907. This differs from P. Dielsiana in the leaves being nearly or quite glabrous below, and in the glabrous leaf-stalk and calyx-tube. It flowered first in this country, I believe, with Mr Woodward at Arley Castle, near Bewdley, in February 1919. The flowers are a charming pink and a little over 1 in. wide, the oblong petals deeply notched at the end. The lobes of the calyx are longer than the tube and are much reflexed as in P. Dielsiana; their resemblance to the recurved petals of a cyclamen suggested the specific name. Both species have very linear stipules about $\frac{1}{2}$ in. long, conspicuously fringed with stalked glands.

P. DIVARICATA, *Ledebour*

(Bot. Mag., t. 6519; P. cerasifera divaricata)

A deciduous tree with the same habit and general aspect as P. cerasifera; neither does it appear to differ in the flowers or foliage. The fruit, however, is smaller (about ¾ in. across), yellow, and not indented at the junction with the stalk. Probably this tree and P. cerasifera are only varieties of one species. They flower at the same time, and are not distinguishable then. There was an old specimen near the Cactus house at Kew which was probably one of the largest in the country. It was 25 ft. high, 27 ft. through, and its trunk was 3 ft. 8 ins. in girth. Quite possibly trees may be growing in various gardens as P. cerasifera. The trees at Kew have rarely borne fruits, but these are quite distinct from cherry plums. The species is said to be a native of the Caucasus, Persia, Macedonia, etc., and to have been introduced in 1822.

P. EMARGINATA, *Walpers*

A deciduous tree, sometimes 30 to 40 ft. high, with a trunk 1 ft. or more in diameter, often a shrub; branches downy when young becoming glabrous with age; bark exceedingly bitter. Leaves obovate-oblong, usually rounded or blunt at the apex, tapering towards the base; 1½ to 2½ ins. long scarcely half as wide; finely and bluntly toothed, downy beneath; stalk about ¼ in. long. Flowers dullish white, not ½ in. across, produced six to twleve together in May on corymbose clusters 1½ ins. long; each flower on a downy stalk ¼ to ½ in. long; petals notched at the apex; calyx downy, lobes rounded. Fruit ¼ to ½ in. diameter, red, finally almost black.

Native of western N. America; introduced to Britain in 1865 by the British Columbia Association, and afterwards becoming known in gardens as Cerasus Pattoniana. It is a handsome tree of healthy aspect and of neat habit, but its flowers are not sufficiently pure white to be really effective. The bark, leaves, and fruit are permeated by an intensely bitter principle.

P. FONTANESIANA, *C. K. Schneider*

(P. græca, *Desfontaines*; Cerasus Fontanesiana, *Spach*)

A deciduous, quick-growing tree, 40 ft. or more high; young shoots covered with shaggy down. Leaves ovate to oval, sometimes heart-shaped, 3 to 5 ins. long, 1½ to 2½ ins. wide; doubly round-toothed, somewhat hairy on the midrib and veins; leaf-stalk ¾ to 1¼ ins. long, very downy, glandular. Flowers 1 in. across, white, produced during May on short, broad racemes of about five to seven, sometimes ten, flowers from the buds of the previous year's wood, each flower on a stalk ½ to ¾ in. long, the common stalk ¾ to 1 in. long, downy. Fruit, globular, the size of a small cherry, nearly black; very sparingly borne.

This tree was originally introduced to Paris from Greece, where it is supposed to be a natural hybrid between P. Avium and P. Mahaleb. The form of the inflorescence is certainly intermediate, and the very downy shoots show P. Mahaleb. The tree has much the habit of P. Avium, and when in flower it is quite as beautiful as the typical form of that species, or even more so.

P. FRUTICOSA, *Pallas*. GROUND CHERRY

(P. Chamæcerasus, *Jacquin*)

A deciduous shrub, 1 to 3 ft. high, of low, spreading habit, with glabrous round twigs. Leaves obovate to narrowly oval, tapering to both ends, from ¾ to 2 ins. long, ¼ to ¾ in. wide; with shallow, rounded teeth, dark glossy green, and quite glabrous; stalk ⅛ to ¼ in. long. Flowers white, ¾ in. across, produced in usually stalkless umbels of about four from buds on the previous year's shoots, each flower on a slender stalk ½ to 1 in. long. Fruits about the size of a large pea, very deep reddish purple.

Native of continental Europe and parts of Siberia; cultivated in England for more than three centuries. It is a shrub of neat and pleasing habit, forming naturally a low, mound-like mass of slender branches, and wearing a very healthy aspect because of the deep shining green of its foliage. In gardens it is rarely seen except grafted standard high on a cherry stock. In this way its branches form a mop-headed mass with the lower branches pendent of their own weight, and it is called "pendula." The fruits have a cherry flavour, but are too harsh and acid to be palatable. It blossoms in early May.

Var. VARIEGATA, has the leaves stained more or less with yellowish white, sometimes half the leaf being of this colour, the other half green.

P. REFLEXA, *Hort.* (not *Gardner*), is a cherry allied to P. fruticosa, and perhaps a hybrid between it and some form of P. Cerasus. It differs from P. fruticosa in its more robust habit and sturdier branches, its more deeply and irregularly toothed leaves (of the same shining dark green), and its shorter stalked flowers. A very pretty small tree with pendulous branches.

P. GLANDULOSA, *Thunberg*

(P. japonica, not *Thunberg*; Bot. Mag., t. 8260)

A dwarf bush of neat, rounded habit, up to 4 or 5 ft. high, with glabrous branches. Leaves ovate-lanceolate, 1 to 2½ ins. long, ¾ to 1 in. wide; more or less drawn out at the apex, finely toothed, almost or quite glabrous; stalk ¼ in. or less long; stipules linear, with gland-tipped teeth. Flowers white or rosy, scarcely ½ in. across, on stalks ¼ in. long, produced in April. Fruits scarcely ½ in. in diameter, red, making a bright display when freely borne.

Var. PLENA.—The double varieties of P. glandulosa, of which there are two—ALBO (white) and ROSEO (pink)—provide a remarkable illustration of how much the flowers of a plant can be improved by cultivation. The typical plant in flower is a pretty but by no means striking shrub, whereas the double varieties are amongst the very élite of their class. The flowers carry numerous petals, and are 1 to 1¼ ins. in diameter, and their stalks become ¾ in. or more long. The foliage too, is finer, the leaves measuring 3 to 4 ins. in length by 1 in. in width. They flower in early May, later than the type. The double varieties have been cultivated, and brought to their present perfection in China and Japan. The rosy-coloured one was growing in Lee's nursery at Hammersmith in 1774.

PRUNUS GLANDULOSA PLENA

The single-flowered type appears to have been cultivated in England in Loudon's time as Cerasus japonica, but it disappeared from gardens and was not reintroduced until late in the nineteenth century. It is allied to P. humilis (*q.v.*). The double-flowered varieties are now very largely used for forcing early into bloom under glass. Out-of-doors they are seen to best advantage planted against a south wall, where the flowering shoots should be pruned back almost to the older wood as soon as ever the flowers are faded. But they are also very delightful in the open ground. They can be propagated by cuttings, but layers prove more satisfactory as a rule.

P. GRAYANA, *Maximowicz*. GRAY'S BIRD CHERRY

(Padus Grayana, *C. K. Schneider*)

A native of Japan, where it is a small tree 20 to 30 ft. high, with a slender trunk. This species is very closely allied to our common bird cherry (P. Padus), differing chiefly in the leaves, which have no glands on the very short stalks (almost invariably present in P. Padus), and in the teeth being finer and more hair-like. The white flowers are borne in erect racemes up to 4 ins. long. Fruit black, about the size of peas, narrowing towards the apex. The species inhabits the mountain forests of the main island of Japan, and the southern parts of Yezo. The true plant is very uncommon in cultivation.

P. HORTULANA, *Bailey*. WAYLAND PLUM

A deciduous tree, 20 to 30 ft. high, sometimes a shrub. Leaves ovate-lanceolate, 4 to 6 ins. long, one-quarter as much wide, hairy below along the midrib and in the axils of the veins; margins set with glandular teeth. Flowers white, ¾ to 1 in. across, produced on the year-old wood in April and May in stalkless clusters of two to six; calyx-lobes glandular, toothed. Fruit roundish, ¾ to 1 in. in diameter, with a thick red or yellow skin.

Native of the southern and central United States; founded as a species in 1892, but known long before. It has been regarded as a hybrid between P. americana and P. angustifolia, but the fact that it comes true from seed is adverse to that theory. Many varieties of it are cultivated for fruits in the United States, which are especially well adpated for the Mississippi Valley and the southern States. It is unlikely that it will have any economic value in Britain.

P. HUMILIS, *Bunge*. CHINESE DWARF CHERRY

(Bot. Mag., t. 7335; P. Bungei, *Walpers*)

A low-growing, deciduous shrub 4 to 5 ft. high, with downy young branchlets. Leaves oval or obovate with a tapering base, 1 to 2 ins. long, half as wide, almost glabrous except when quite young, finely and doubly toothed; stalk ⅛ in. long; stipules ¼ in. long, linear, very glandular. Flowers pale pink, ½ in. across; produced singly, in pairs, or in threes from the buds of the previous year's wood, each on a stalk ⅓ in. long. Fruit bright red, very acid in this country, but not unpalatable, about ½ in diameter.

Native of N. China; introduced to Kew in 1881 by the late Dr Bretschneider. This pretty dwarf cherry, which is cultivated in North China for its fruits, is perfectly hardy. Nearly allied to P. glandulosa, it may be roughly distinguished by its downy shoots and its leaves being widest above the middle. From P. Jacquemontii, with which it has been confused, its downy shoots also distinguish it. P. Jacquemontii, besides, has laciniated stipules.

P. ILICIFOLIA, *Walpers*

(Laurocerasus ilicifolia, *Roemer*)

An evergreen shrub of compact habit; branchlets glabrous. Leaves ovate, 1 to 2 ins. long, ¾ to 1¼ ins. wide; rounded or slightly heart-shaped at the base, sharply toothed, the hollows between the teeth wide and rounded, dark glossy green, glabrous on both surfaces. Flowers in racemes 1½ to 3 ins. long, produced in summer; each flower ⅓ in. across, white, on a stalk ⅙ in. long. Fruit roundish, but slightly pointed at the end, ½ in. diameter, changing to red, then black-purple.

Native of California, and too tender to be of much value in any but the mildest parts of the British Isles. It has borne flowers at Kew on a wall, but even there is killed or injured by our hardest winters.

Another N. American cherry laurel, but from the east side—P. CAROLINIANA, *Aiton*—is equally tender. Loudon states that in 1833 there was a bush 10 ft. high at Swallowfield in Hampshire, but this is very doubtful. It was probably some form of common cherry laurel, wrongly named. P. caroliniana has entire leaves 3 to 4½ ins. long, oblong-lanceolate; flowers creamy white, in short racemes; and black, shining, oblong fruit, ½ in. long. A native of S.E. United States, where it is used, much as the common laurel is here, to make hedges. Originally introduced in 1759, and many times since, it has never long survived, unless it be in some of the south-western counties.

P. INCANA, *Batsch.* WILLOW CHERRY

(Bot. Reg. 25 t. 58; Amygdalus incana, *Pallas*; Cerasus incana, *Spach*)

A deciduous shrub, 4 to 8 ft. high, of rather open, loose habit; shoots minutely downy. Leaves oval-lanceolate or obovate, pointed, 1½ to 3 ins. long, ⅓ to ⅞ in. wide; regularly, finely, and sharply toothed, tapering towards both ends, dark green and glabrous above, covered with a close white wool beneath. Flowers ½ in. across, borne singly from the buds of the previous year's shoots; petals deep rosy red; calyx ¼ in. long, tubular, with five short, rounded, downy lobes. Fruit glabrous, red, ⅓ in. across.

Native of S.E. Europe and Asia Minor; introduced in 1815. Its flowers appear in April along with the young leaves, and it is then very pretty. Sometimes confused with P. nana, it is easily distinguished from that and most other species by the close white felt on the under-surface of the willow-like leaves. The fruit is quite different from that of P. nana, being cherry-like.

P. INCISA, *Thunberg.* CUT-LEAVED CHERRY (Plate 42)

(Bot. Mag., t. 8958; Wilson's Cherries of Japan, t. 5; Cerasus incisa, *Loiseleur*)

A small, elegant, deciduous tree 20 to 30 ft. high, more often a bush 6 to 18 ft. high; young shoots slender, glabrous, and finally grey. Leaves reddish at first, obovate to ovate, slenderly pointed, sharply and doubly or trebly toothed; 1 to 2½ ins. long, ⅔ to 1¼ ins. wide; downy above and on the veins beneath; stalk ¼ to ½ in. long, hairy, slender, with two purple glands near the blade. Flowers ½ to ¾ in. wide, two to four borne on a main-stalk ⅛ to 1 in. long, each flower slenderly stalked and springing from the axil of a leaf-like deeply toothed bract; petals notched or jagged at the end, white or pale pink. Calyx-tube glabrous, tubular, wine-red, the lobes minutely ciliate; stamens thirty, their stalks reddish and the anthers yellow; style slightly hairy; ovary glabrous. Fruit roundish egg-shaped, ¼ in. long, purplish black.

Native of Japan; discovered by Thunberg as long ago as 1776. It was sent to Kew in 1916 from the Arnold Arboretum, and flowered annually there in early April, but has since been lost. It had, however, been introduced to Ireland in 1913. Wilson describes it in Japan as very ornamental, and although the petals do not remain on the flower for any great length of time, the calyx and stamens persist and heighten in colour. According to the same authority the main flower-stalk is very variable in length, although in our cultivated plants it is usually very short. He observes that it is the only Japanese cherry that can be fashioned into dwarf trees which will live and flower freely in small pots. It may, therefore, have come over from Japan with the large shipments of dwarfed trees sent previous to 1914. It is undoubtedly one of the most beautiful of the wild cherries, profuse in blossom, and very distinct on account of the deep double toothing and long, drawn-out point of the leaf.

Var. SERRATA, *Koidzumi*, is distinguished from the type by the leaves not being so markedly doubly toothed, often simply toothed, each tooth ending in a bristle-like point. A charming bush. There are also several varieties offered in Japanese catalogues that have native names.

P. INSITITIA, *Linnæus*. BULLACE

A small deciduous tree with foliage similar to that of P. communis, but with some of its branches spiny. Fruit globular, ¾ in. diameter, black or yellow; several white-fruited varieties are grown in orchards. The bullace is a native of Britain and other parts of Europe. Being found in many hedgerows, the typical form scarcely deserves a place in the arboretum, but the double-flowered variety is more ornamental. P. spinosa, insititia, and communis are by some authorities considered as all forms of one species. It is easy enough to distinguish P. spinosa by its black bark, its small, sharply toothed leaves, and small, round, black fruits. But P. insititia and communis are more closely allied; they both have brown bark, larger and more bluntly toothed leaves, but the fruit of the bullace is round, and often white or yellow, whilst the plum is black and oval. Intermediate forms occur, of which the damson is one, having an oval, purple, sour fruit. (The damsons take their name from Damascus, where they have been cultivated since before the Christian era.) The Mirabelle group of plums, with round, yellow fruits, acid and sweet, belongs to P. insititia.

P. JACQUEMONTII, *Hooker fil.* AFGHAN CHERRY

(Bot. Mag., t. 6976; Amygdalus humilis, *Edgeworth*)

A deciduous bush up to 12 ft. high, with glabrous, slender, grey branchlets. Leaves ovate to obovate, pointed at both ends, up to 2½ ins. long, by 1 in. wide; glabrous, sharply and regularly toothed; stalk ¼ in. long. Flowers one to three at each joint, very short-stalked, bright rosy pink, ⅓ to ½ in. diameter; calyx funnel-shaped, ⅕ in. long, with short, pointed lobes. Fruit roundish, ⅝ in. long, red, juicy, containing a roundish stone ¼ in. or rather more long.

Native of the north-western Himalaya, Tibet, and Afghanistan; introduced to Kew in 1879 by Dr Aitchison from the Kurrum Valley, where it occurs at altitudes of about 6000 ft. It has been confused with P. humilis, under the notice of which the distinctions have been pointed out. P. Jacquemontii is a pretty cherry, perfectly hardy, and makes shoots over 1 ft. long during a season, which are well furnished with flowers towards the end of the following April. Propagated by layers. There used to be bushes at Kew 12 ft. high and 12 ft. through.

P. KANSUENSIS, *Rehder*

(Amygdalus kansuensis, *Skeels*)

A tall, deciduous shrub or a small tree up to 20 ft. high with lanceolate, slender-pointed leaves, 2 to 4 ins. long, $\frac{3}{8}$ to $1\frac{1}{4}$ ins. wide, finely toothed, hairy along the midrib; stalk $\frac{1}{8}$ to $\frac{3}{16}$ in. long. Flowers crowded on the naked glabrous shoots, mostly in pairs and making cylindrical spikes 1 to $1\frac{1}{2}$ ft. long; they are white, $\frac{3}{4}$ in. wide, pink in bud; petals roundish ovate, $\frac{3}{8}$ in. long; calyx grey, hairy outside, ciliate, the lobes oblong-ovate, $\frac{1}{8}$ in. long; stamens white, anthers and style yellow.

Native of N.W. China, introduced to California by Meyer in 1914. It will be welcomed in gardens for its early blossoms which (regulated by the weather) may appear any time in late January or February. It is closely related to the common peach, the stone being widely, shallowly grooved but not pitted.

P. LANNESIANA, *Wilson* (Plate 46)

(Cerasus Lannesiana, *Carrière*, Garden, vol. iv., p. 275; Bot. Mag., t. 8012, as P. pseudocerasus)

This cherry and its varieties have been grown in many gardens as "P. serrulata" and even as "P. pseudocerasus." With the latter of these (see under cantabrigiensis) it has nothing to do; but it is so closely related to the former that several authors have united the two. The typical P. Lannesiana as distinguished by Wilson is of garden origin; the wild form from which it sprung is called by Wilson

P. LANNESIANA ALBIDA.—This is a deciduous tree up to 30 ft. high, without down on leaf or stem, the young shoots becoming pale shining grey by autumn. Leaves ovate or obovate, with long slender points and long bristle-like teeth, green but "often having a more or less brownish metallic lustre" as they open (Wilson). Flowers single, fragrant, 1 to $1\frac{1}{2}$ ins. wide, glabrous, white, produced during May in corymbose racemes whose main-stalk is 1 to 3 ins. long. The individual flowers are on stalks about 1 in. long springing from the axils of conspicuous, obovate, fringed bracts about $\frac{1}{2}$ in. long. Fruit egg-shaped, black, shining, about the size of a pea. Very commonly planted in Japan, this cherry is said by botanists of that country to be indigenous on the Oshima or De Vries Island at the entrance to the Sagami Sea. It is cultivated in some European gardens as "yoshino cherry," a name which properly belongs to P. yedoensis.

The typical P. Lannesiana has pink flowers, single as in the var. albida and not differing from it in any other respect. It has produced in Japanese gardens many varieties, which differ from each other in habit, in the single or more or less double flowers, and in the colour of the petals, which varies from pure white to various shades of pink and yellow. Wilson, in his *Cherries of Japan*, enumerates nearly fifty forms; they are in fact much more numerous than those he puts under P. serrulata, and they include the majority of the best double-flowered Japanese cherries. They are too numerous and too difficult to distinguish in words to be enumerated here, but in the introductory notes to this genus I have mentioned a dozen good varieties; of these the following are placed under P. Lannesiana by Wilson: *Amanogawa*, *grandiflora*, *Hokusai*, *miyako*, *senriko*, *sirotae*, and *temari*.

The following are the distinctions between P. Lannesiana and P. serrulata as set out by Wilson:—

P. Lannesiana.—Leaves unfolding green or slightly reddish, pale green beneath, the marginal teeth like long bristles; bark pale grey; flowers fragrant.

P. serrulata.—Leaves more or less glaucous beneath, marginal teeth shorter; bark dark chestnut brown; flowers not fragrant.

But there are some cherries so intermediate between the two that it appears impossible to determine to which they belong.

P. LAUROCERASUS, *Linnæus*. CHERRY LAUREL

(Laurocerasus officinalis, *Roemer*)

An evergreen shrub of quick growth and wide-spreading habit, attaining a height of over 20 ft., twice as much in width; young shoots pale green and, like all other parts of the plant, devoid of hairs or down. Leaves of leathery texture, dark shining green, of various shapes and sizes, usually oblong, but sometimes oblanceolate; averaging from 4 to 6 ins. in length by rather less than one-third as much wide; margin obscurely toothed; stalk about ½ in. long. The blade always bears on its lower surface near the base two or more glands. Flowers in axillary and terminal racemes, 3 to 5 ins. long, ¾ in. through; each flower on a stalk ⅙ in. long, itself dull white, ⅓ in. across. Fruit black-purple, about ½ in. long, conical, and containing a similarly shaped stone.

Native of E. Europe and Asia Minor; introduced, according to Aiton, in 1629. It flowers in April, nearly two months in advance of the Portugal laurel, but is not so ornamental. For some strange reason the cherry laurel is rarely seen at its best, which is when it is grown as an isolated specimen unmolested by the pruner. It then makes a vigorous evergreen of exceptional size and elegance. It bears pruning well, however, and is, in consequence, often used to form a low covering for banks and slopes by keeping it severely cropped. This may have been necessary in earlier times when dwarf evergreens were scarcer, but there are several now that may be made to serve such a purpose without having to undergo the periodical mutilation to which laurels are subjected. Still less is it adapted for planting in ordinary shrubberies, where its vigorous self-assertion and hungry roots give little chance for things near it.

The cherry laurel does not appear to be quite so hardy as the Portugal laurel, although on dry soil it is not much injured by any temperature above 5° F. It is admirably adapted for planting as undergrowth in thin woodland, where there is room for its full development. All the forms are easily increased by late summer cuttings placed in gentle heat. A considerable number of varieties are now offered by nurserymen, some of garden origin, some natural. Only the most distinct of these can be mentioned, and of these very few have been authoritatively described.

Var. ANGUSTIFOLIA.—Leaves usually about 3 ins. long by 1 in. wide.

Var. CAMELLIÆFOLIA.—Leaves of ordinary size, but curled and twisted. Curious, but not ornamental.

Var. CAUCASICA.—Leaves up to 7 ins. long, about 3 ins. wide, deep green; one of the finest.

Var. COLCHICA.—Leaves up to 7 ins. long, about 2 ins. wide, tapering to the stalk.

Var. COMPACTA.—Leaves about the ordinary size, but the habit dwarf and close.

Var. MAGNOLIÆFOLIA.—The finest of all the varieties in foliage, the largest leaves 10 to 12 ins. long, 3 to $4\frac{1}{2}$ ins. wide. A strong grower, it may, if desired, be trained into tree form by tying up a lead and gradually removing the lower branches.

Var. OTINII.—Leaves large and broad, but not remarkable for size so much as for their dark, almost black, lustrous green; the plant is of more compact habit than most varieties.

Var. PARVIFOLIA.—A dwarf, narrow-leaved form, the smallest leaves 1 in. long by $\frac{1}{4}$ in. wide only, and the plant $1\frac{1}{2}$ to 2 ft. high. It may occasionally be seen reverting back to the typical form. Known in gardens as "Hartogia capensis."

Var. ROTUNDIFOLIA.—Leaves about half as broad as long.

Var. SCHIPKÆNSIS.—Originally found wild near the Shipka Pass, and brought into cultivation about 1886. It has narrow, entire leaves, 2 to $4\frac{1}{2}$ ins. long, $\frac{3}{4}$ to $1\frac{1}{2}$ ins. wide, and a certain elegance of habit, but is not so ornamental as some of the larger-leaved varieties. Racemes $2\frac{1}{2}$ to 3 ins. high. Its great value is its extreme hardiness. It will withstand winters where no cherry laurel has been known to do so before, such as N. Germany and parts of N. America.

Var. ZABELIANA is another of the same type as schipkænsis, and is equally hardy. Leaves also entire, narrow, and almost willow-like, the branches growing rather stiffly and obliquely upwards. Put into cultivation in 1898.

P. LITIGIOSA, *C. K. Schneider*

(P. pilosiuscula media, *Koehne*; P. Rehderiana, *Koehne*)

A deciduous cherry up to 20 ft. or more high; young shoots glabrous. Leaves ovate to oblong with a rounded base and a slender drawn-out apex, finely toothed, often doubly so; $1\frac{1}{2}$ to 3 ins. long, half as much wide; downy on the midrib above and in the vein-axils beneath; stalk $\frac{1}{4}$ to $\frac{1}{3}$ in. long. Flowers opening in April with the young leaves in pendulous clusters of two or three on a main-stalk $\frac{1}{4}$ in. or less long; each flower on a glabrous stalk $\frac{3}{4}$ to 1 in. long, white, $\frac{3}{4}$ in. wide. Calyx tube shortly cylindrical or funnel-shaped, the lobes triangular and ultimately reflexed; both reddish and quite glabrous. Stamens numerous, $\frac{1}{3}$ in. long, white or pinkish; anthers yellow; style furnished with long hairs towards the base; ovary glabrous.

Native of Hupeh, China; first discovered by Henry; introduced by Wilson in 1907 and distributed as "P. pilosiuscula media." P. litigiosa is a very attractive tree when in bloom, with its profusely borne flowers hanging down more or less in a stiff row alone the branches; they are, however, soon over. Its most closely related species is P. pilosiuscula, which has coarsely toothed leaves rough to the touch, with small stiff hairs on both sides but especially beneath; the main-stalk of the inflorescence is longer (up to 1 in.), both it and the individual stalks usually more hairy, sometimes very much more so.

P. LUSITANICA, *Linnæus*. PORTUGAL LAUREL

(Laurocerasus lusitanica, *Roemer*)

An evergreen shrub of wide, bushy form, usually 10 to 20 ft., but occasionally 40 to 50 ft. high, more in diameter; young branches quite glabrous and very dark. Leaves ovate or oval, $2\frac{1}{2}$ to 5 ins. long, $1\frac{1}{4}$ to 2 ins. wide; quite glabrous on both surfaces; very dark, glossy green above, paler below, shallowly roundish toothed. Racemes produced in June from the ends of the previous summer's shoots, and from the axils of their leaves; 6 to 10 ins. long, 1 to 1¼ ins. through, more or less erect. Flowers white, ⅓ to ½ in. across, calyx cup-shaped, with shallow, rounded lobes; stalk ⅓ in. long. Fruit dark purple, ⅓ in. long, cone-shaped, pointed.

Native of Spain and Portugal; introduced in 1648 (Aiton). In all but the coldest parts of Great Britain the Portugal laurel is one of the handsomest and most effective of evergreens. It should be grown as isolated specimens, especially in thinly wooded parts of the grounds. Although it is chiefly valued for the luxuriance of its rich green lustrous foliage, it has some merit as a flowering shrub, for in June it produces an extraordinary profusion of long, slender racemes, whose only defect is that the flowers are rather dull. It is hardier than the cherry laurel, and on warm, well-drained soil withstands thirty-two degrees of frost without being in the least affected.

Var. AZORICA.—The largest leaved of all the forms of Portugal laurel, the leaves being sometimes over 5 ins. long and 2½ ins. wide. In the Canary Islands and the Azores it becomes 60 to 70 ft. high. Introduced about 1860 by Osborn's, once famous nurserymen of Fulham.

Var. MYRTIFOLIA.—A shrub of neat, rounded habit, and of stiffer, closer growth than the type. Leaves much smaller, usually 1½ to 2 ins. long.

Var. ORMSTONIENSIS.—Leaves dark green and leathery, of the ordinary size; habit compact.

Var. VARIEGATA.—Leaves margined with white; more tender than the green forms.

All the forms of Portugal laurel are easily increased by late summer cuttings; the type also by seeds.

P. MAACKII, *Ruprecht*

(Laurocerasus Maackii, *C. K. Schneider*)

A Manchurian bird cherry up to 40 or more ft. high in a wild state, very distinct through the bark of the trunk being smooth and of a striking brownish yellow colour, and peeling like that of a birch; young wood downy. The leaves are ovate, rounded at the base, pointed, very finely toothed; 3 or 4 ins. long, by about half as wide; they are hairy on the midrib and veins, and are rendered very distinct by being covered with glandular dots on the lower surface. Raceme 2 to 3 ins. long, springing from the previous season's wood, downy; calyx-tube cylindrical, bell-shaped, the lobes glandular-toothed; petals white, not so long as the stamens.

Introduced to cultivation by way of St Petersburg in 1910; the cultivated plants already show the distinct, smooth, yellowish trunk. It is different from ordinary bird cherries in the racemes coming on the year-old wood and from the laurels in being deciduous. In July 1939 I saw a tree at Borde Hill, Sussex, its trunk charmingly coloured.

S. MAHALEB, *Linnæus*. ST LUCIE CHERRY (Plate 43)

(Cerasus Mahaleb, *Miller*)

A free-growing, deciduous tree up to 30 or 40 ft. high in gardens, with a loose, spreading head of branches; young twigs downy. Leaves broadly ovate or roundish, with a short, abrupt, often blunt apex, the base rounded or slightly heart-shaped, shallowly toothed; 1 to 2½ ins. long, ¾ to 2 ins. wide; almost or quite glabrous above, more or less hairy on each side of the midrib beneath, glossy green; stalk ½ in. long, with a pair of glands. Racemes 1¼ to 2 ins. long, carrying six to ten flowers, which are pure white, ½ to ¾ in. across, very fragrant, each on a stalk about ½ in. long. The racemes spring from the wood of the previous year, and are furnished towards the base with small leaf-like bracts. Fruit about $\frac{1}{4}$ in. long, somewhat egg-shaped, black.

Native of Central and S. Europe; introduced in 1714. It flowers in the last week of April and early May, and is then one of the most beautiful of flowering trees, filling the air with fragrance for yards around. It is fast-growing, and if planted in very rich soil is apt to become rank and ungainly. In the sandy soil of Kew it thrives and blossoms remarkably well. Both the true Mahaleb and its varieties may be increased by cuttings made of moderately firm young wood, and placed in gentle bottom heat, also by layers. The type, raised from seed, is used as a stock for grafting cherries on.

Var. BOMMII.—A variety of pendulous habit, much more marked than that of var. pendula itself.

Var. CHRYSOCARPA (fructu-flavo).—Fruits yellow (Syn. xanthocarpe).

Var. GLOBOSA.—A dwarf, bushy form of rounded habit and slow growth, (" compacta " is the same).

Var. PENDULA.—A very beautiful tree, more graceful than the type, yet not strikingly pendulous.

There are also coloured forms, such as AUREA, with leaves more or less yellow; and VARIEGATA, which is a better tree of its class than most variegated forms of this genus, the leaves having a broad, unequal margin of yellowish white (syn. albo-marginata).

P. MARITIMA, *Wangenheim*. SAND PLUM, BEACH PLUM

(Bot. Mag., t. 8289)

A deciduous shrub of low, compact habit, 4 to 8 ft. high and more in diameter, with grey, downy young branchlets, becoming dark with age. Leaves oval or obovate, $1\frac{1}{2}$ to 3 ins. long, $\frac{3}{4}$ to $1\frac{1}{4}$ ins. wide; saw-toothed, covered beneath when young with down, which becomes reduced to the midrib and veins towards the end of the season; leaf-stalk $\frac{1}{3}$ in. long, downy. Flowers white, $\frac{1}{2}$ in. across, produced in May usually in pairs or in threes at each bud on last year's shoots; on the short side spurs the flowers appear to be in clusters, owing to the crowded buds; flower-stalks $\frac{1}{3}$ in. long, downy. Calyx downy, funnel-shaped, with five rounded, oblong lobes. Fruit red or purple, round or oblong, $\frac{1}{2}$ to 1 in. in diameter. A yellow-fruited variety (FLAVA) is also cultivated.

Native of the eastern United States, frequently inhabiting sandy or gravelly places near the coast. Its fruits are gathered for preserving there, but they appear to vary in quality and sweetness. The flowers are borne profusely in this country, and the species is one of the most attractive of dwarf plums. Judging by its hardy, robust constitution, and by its natural habitats, it ought to succeed in exposed maritime localities in Britain.

P. MAXIMOWICZII, *Ruprecht*

(Bot. Mag., t. 8641; Garden and Forest, vi., p. 195)

A deciduous tree up to 20 or 50 ft. high, with a slender trunk; branchlets downy, the down persisting through the first winter. Leaves ovate or oval, pointed, rounded to cuneate at the base; $1\frac{1}{2}$ to 3 ins. long, $\frac{3}{4}$ to $1\frac{1}{4}$ ins. wide; doubly toothed, downy on the midrib and veins beneath, and with scattered hairs above; stalk $\frac{1}{3}$ to $\frac{1}{2}$ in. long, downy. Flowers rather dull yellowish white, about $\frac{5}{8}$ in. across, produced in mid-May on stalked racemes 2 to $3\frac{1}{2}$ ins. long, remarkable for the large leaf-like bracts with which they are furnished; from six to ten flowers occur on a raceme, each flower on a downy stalk $\frac{1}{2}$ to

¾ in. long; calyx hairy, with pointed, toothed lobes. Fruit globose, ⅙ in. wide, shining, at first red, then black; ripe in August.

Native of Korea, Manchuria, and Japan; introduced by Sargent to the United States in 1892, and by him sent to Kew in 1895. The tree is interesting and very distinct among cherries because of the conspicuous bracts on the inflorescence, which remain until the fruit is ripe; but neither in flower nor fruit is it particularly attractive as cherries go. For its autumn colouring it may prove valuable, as it turns a brilliant scarlet both in Japan and N. America. It is very hardy.

P. MICROCARPA, *C. A. Meyer*

(Bot. Mag., t. 8360; Cerasus tortuosa, *Boissier and Haussknecht*)

A deciduous bush, 3 or 4 ft. high, of sturdy habit, with stiff, short-jointed branches and downy branchlets. Leaves broadly ovate, with a rounded base and acute apex, ½ to 1 in. long, nearly as much wide, coarsely and sharply toothed, with a few scattered hairs when young beneath; stalk ⅙ to ¼ in. long. Flowers produced in spring in clusters of two or three, from buds and spurs of older branches, each on a downy stalk ⅓ in. long; the petals are rosy pink, the calyx cylindrical and glabrous. Fruit ovoid, nearly ½ in. long, red or yellow.

Native of Asia Minor; introduced to Kew in 1890. It is a pretty little shrub (a cherry) requiring the sunniest position available. In a wild state it is rather variable in the amount of down on the younger parts, in stature, and in the rigidity or otherwise of its habit. The most downy form has been distinguished under the name TORTUOSA, the pubescence being associated with a tortuous growth. Both these characters are believed to depend on climate and environment.

P. MIRA, *Koehne*

(Bot. Mag., t. 9548)

A deciduous almond up to 30 to 35 ft. high; shoots glabrous, smooth at first, becoming warty with age. Leaves lanceolate, 2 to 5 ins. long, ¾ to 1½ ins. wide, dark green and glabrous above, rather glaucous and more or less grey-hairy along the midrib beneath. Flowers solitary or in pairs, axillary on the leafless shoots, opening in March and April, 1 to 1¼ ins. wide; petals roundish-obovate, white, prettily tinged with pink, margins wavy; stamens with red stalks and yellow anthers. Fruit nearly globose, 1¾ ins. long, velvety, the flesh edible but bitter, the stone smooth.

Native of W. Szechuen, China, up to 8000 ft. altitude, discovered and introduced by E. H. Wilson in 1910. It is of great botanical interest in being the only almond known to have a smooth stone. It is evidently quite hardy and flowers and bears fruit freely. It has succeeded particularly well at Kemsing in Kent growing on one foot of loam on chalk.

P. MONTICOLA, *C. Koch.* MOUNTAIN PLUM

A spreading, deciduous shrub, 5 to 8 ft. high, usually more in width. Leaves oval or ovate, 1½ to 2 ins. long, ¾ to 1 in. wide, glabrous or nearly so, coarsely toothed; stalk ¼ in. long. Flowers white, ½ in. across, borne usually in pairs from the crowded buds of short, spur-like branches; stalk glabrous, slender, ½ to ¾ in. long. Fruit a globose plum, ¾ to 1 in. across, red with an acid yellow flesh; stone ovate, compressed, over ½ in. long.

Native of the mountains of Asia Minor and Armenia; discovered and introduced to Europe by Koch in 1843. It is an interesting, shrubby plum, allied to P. cerasifera, and flowers profusely about the middle of April.

P. MUME, *Siebold and Zuccarini*. JAPANESE APRICOT

(Armeniaca Mume, *Siebold*)

A deciduous tree of rounded habit, 20 to 30 ft. high, with glabrous, lustrous twigs. Leaves 2½ to 4 ins. long, roundish or broadly ovate, contracted at the end into a long tapering point, sharply and often doubly toothed, with scattered hairs on both sides, becoming glabrous except about the midrib beneath; leaf-stalk ½ to ¾ in. long. Flowers pale rose, 1 to 1¼ ins. across, produced singly or in pairs (each on a very short stalk) from the joints of the previous year's wood; petals broadly obovate; calyx ½ in. across, with oblong rounded lobes. Fruit described as yellowish, globose, 1 to 1¼ ins. wide, scarcely edible; shell of nut perforated.

Native of Korea and perhaps China. It is much cultivated in Japan for ornament, and the double-flowered form was originally introduced to Europe from that country, by Messrs Baltet of Troyes, in 1878. It was first distributed as "P. Myrobalana fl. pleno"—a name which still clings to it in many places. It is a true apricot, not a plum. In late years it has been imported from Japanese nurseries in quantity, and in various forms, of these the following are now in our gardens: ALBA (white), ALBA PLENA (double white), PLENA (double rose), PENDULA (weeping). The flowers are delicately perfumed. This apricot is valuable in gardens, especially the double-flowered forms, for its early, profuse flowering, being in bloom generally about the same time as the almond, and at its best almost as beautiful. It should be given a sheltered place. It can be distinguished from the common apricot by the longer, more slender apex to the leaf.

P. NANA, *Stokes*. DWARF RUSSIAN ALMOND

(P. tenella, *Batsch*; Amygdalus nana, *Linnæus*; Bot. Mag., t. 161)

A low, deciduous shrub of bushy form, 2 to 5 ft. high; twigs glabrous. Leaves obovate or oblong, 1½ to 3½ ins. long, ½ to 1 in. wide; saw-toothed, dark glossy green above, pale beneath, glabrous on both surfaces. Flowers one to three on each bud of the previous year's shoots, rosy red, ½ in. long, ½ in. or more in diameter. Fruit like a small almond, 1 in. long, covered with velvety down; not often produced in England.

Native of S. Russia and the other parts of S.E. Europe; long cultivated in this country (Aiton says since 1683). It is a very pretty shrub, flowering abundantly in April, growing well on its own roots, and easily increased by layering. In spite of this it is frequently grafted on plum, and is short-lived in consequence.

Var. ALBA.—Flowers white.

Var. GEORGICA.—A taller shrub, with smaller, more glossy, and not such deeply toothed leaves.

Var. GESSLERIANA.—Flower large, ¾ in. across; the finest form of this species.

P. NIGRA, *Aiton*. CANADIAN PLUM

(Bot. Mag., t. 1117)

A deciduous tree, 20 to 30 ft. high, branches erect, forming a narrow head. Leaves broadly elliptical or obovate with a long, abrupt apex, the base rounded or often slightly heart-shaped; 3 or 4 ins. long, more than half as wide; doubly round-toothed, downy all over or only on the midrib and veins beneath; leaf-stalks ½ in. to 1 in. long, with two dark glands near the top.

Flowers pure white, 1¼ ins. across, produced three or four together in stalkless clusters, each flower on a reddish, glabrous stalk ½ in. or more long; calyx usually glabrous, reddish, with narrow-pointed glandular lobes. Fruit oval, 1 to 1¼ ins. long, red or yellowish red, with a compressed stone ¾ in. long.

Native of Canada and the eastern United States; introduced in 1773. Flowers fragrant, produced towards the end of April, turning reddish with age. This plum has been much confused with P. americana, from which it differs in the broader, round-toothed, more downy leaves, in the glandular leaf-stalks, larger and more fragrant flowers, and stiffer habit. It was cultivated at Kew in the eighteenth century, but has never been common.

P. NIPPONICA, *Matsumura*. JAPANESE ALPINE CHERRY

(P. iwagiensis, *Koehne*; P. nikkoensis, *Koehne*)

A deciduous bush 8 to 16 ft. high, or occasionally a bushy-headed tree up to 20 ft. high; young shoots glabrous, grey by autumn, ultimately chestnut brown. Leaves ovate, sometimes obovate, with a long, tail-like point, and a usually rounded base, sharply and doubly toothed; thinly hairy when young, chiefly on the veins; 1½ to 3½ ins. long, 1 to 1¾ ins. wide; stalk ½ to ¾ in. long, glabrous. Flowers opening in May, solitary or in twos or threes, each on a glabrous or thinly hairy stalk ½ to 1¼ ins. long; they are ¾ to 1 in. wide, white or pale pink. Calyx-tube glabrous, funnel-shaped to bell-shaped; petals rounded and entire or notched at the end. Fruit black, globose, ⅓ in. wide.

Var. KURILENSIS, *Wilson*, differs in having larger flowers and a downy leaf-stalk, calyx-tube and flower-stalk.

Native of Japan; the type was introduced to the Arnold Arboretum in 1915, the variety (which is found in the Kurile Islands as well as Japan proper) ten years earlier. There has been considerable confusion between this species, P. incisa, and P. apetala, all three distinguished by having black fruits and a leaf with a long tail-like apex and a conspicuous double toothing. It is distinct enough in other respects from P. apetala (*q.v.*), a cherry very downy or hairy in many of its parts. P. incisa is also more or less downy on the young shoots, leaf-stalk and calyx, the leaves are smaller, the branchlets never become bright brown as in P. nipponica, and the flowers are normally smaller.

P. ORTHOSEPALA, *Koehne*. TEXAN PLUM

A deciduous shrub or small tree, with glabrous, slightly zigzag, ultimately dark brown branchlets. Leaves oval or ovate, long-pointed, sharply saw-toothed; 2½ to 3 ins. long, about 1 to 1½ ins. wide; glabrous and glossy green at maturity; leaf-stalk ½ to ¾ in. long with a pair of glands towards the top, remaining downy longer than the blade. Flowers white, ⅝ in. across, produced during the second week of May in clusters of three or four; petals narrowly obovate; calyx-lobes downy on the inner surface and margins, not toothed; flower-stalk ⅓ in. long, glabrous. Fruit round, 1 in. across, nearly black covered with a blue bloom; flesh juicy, palatable.

Native of Texas; discovered by Engelmann in 1880, and introduced to cultivation by him through the Arnold Arboretum. It succeeds very well at Kew, where there used to be a small tree 11 ft. high, obtained in 1896 from Späth's nursery, near Berlin. Three years previously it had been given the above name by Dr Koehne. The American plums are not particularly effective in English gardens, but this promises to be one of the best. It is allied to P. hortulana, differing in its darker coloured fruit and in the absence of glands on the calyx-lobes.

P. PADUS, *Linnæus*. BIRD CHERRY

(Padus racemosa, *Lamarck*)

A deciduous tree, with strong, rather acrid smelling bark, from 30 to over 50 ft. high, of open, rather gaunt habit when young; the branchlets usually covered at first with a fine down, sometimes quite glabrous. Leaves oval or obovate, 3 to 5 ins. long, 1½ to 2½ ins. wide; pointed at the end, mostly rounded or slightly heart-shaped at the base, finely toothed, dull dark green above, glabrous beneath or with tufts of down in the vein-axils beneath; stalk glabrous with two or more glands, ½ to ¾ in. long. Flowers fragrant, white, ⅓ to ½ in. wide, borne on drooping or spreading racemes 3 to 6 ins. long, and from ¾ to 1¼ ins. through, which terminate short leafy shoots; calyx with five shallow, rounded, often glandular lobes. Fruit round, ¼ in. to ⅓ in. diameter, black, harsh and bitter to the taste.

Var. AUCUBÆFOLIA.—Leaves spotted after the manner of Aucuba japonica; of little value.

Var. AUREA.—Young leaves yellowish. This form is of no particular value in regard to its leaves, which soon turn green, but it has good robust foliage and its flowers are of larger size than ordinary.

Var. COMMUTATA, *Dippel*.—A wild variety from Manchuria, remarkable for flowering about three weeks in advance of any other bird cherry, being usually in bloom by the middle of April. Its flowers are fully ½ in. across. Sometimes cut by late frosts. (*Garden and Forrest*, vol. i., fig. 47.)

Var. PLENA.—Flowers large and "double." This is the most attractive of all the varieties, and remains longer in flower than any.

Var. LEUCOCARPA.—Fruits white.

Var. PENDULA.—Branches pendulous.

Var. ROTUNDIFOLIA (P. Laucheana, *Bolle*).—Leaves almost as wide as long. It has been suggested that this is a hybrid between Padus and virginiana and this is probably correct.

Var. STRICTA.—Racemes quite erect.

Var. WATERERI.—The best of the single-flowered varieties, the racemes being up to 8 ins. long; leaves with conspicuous tufts of down in the axils of the veins.

The bird cherry is widely spread over the northern part of the Old World, extending in one or other of its forms from the British Isles to Japan. It is a very hardy tree, and not particular as to soil. Whilst the typical form may give place in gardens to such varieties as plena and Watereri, it is itself very charming when planted in thin woodland. The named varieties are best propagated by budding on seedlings of the type in July. The tree has little economic value, although the timber, when available, is valued by cabinet-makers, and the fruit (according to Loudon) has been used to flavour brandy and home-made wines. It flowers in May.

P. PENNSYLVANICA, *Linnæus fil*. WILD RED CHERRY

(Bot. Mag., t. 8486; Cerasus pennsylvanica, *Loiseleur*)

A deciduous tree reaching 30 to 40 ft. in height, with a trunk 1½ ft. in diameter; bark bitter, aromatic, reddish and shining on the young shoots. Leaves ovate, long-pointed; 3 to 4½ ins. long, ¾ to 1¼ ins. wide; glabrous, bright green, finely toothed, the teeth much incurved and gland-tipped; stalk glabrous, ½ in. long, with one or two glands at the top. Flowers ½ in. across, white, produced four to ten together in umbellate clusters or short racemes, each flower on a slender glabrous stalk ¾ in. long; petals round, downy outside at the base; calyx glabrous, with rounded lobes. Fruit round, ¼ in. diameter, red.

Native of N. America, where it is very widely spread; introduced to England in 1773. It flowers very freely in this country at the end of April and in May when the leaves are half-grown, and is very beautiful then. According to Sargent it is a short-lived tree, but plays an important part in the preservation and reproduction of N. American forests. Its abundant seed is freely distributed by birds, and the rapidly growing young trees give valuable shelter to the other trees longer-lived than they are, which ultimately suppress them. It might be planted in thin woodland, in places where our native P. Avium thrives. Var. SAXIMONTANA.—Shrubby. Rocky Mts.

P. PERSICA, *Batsch*. PEACH

(Persica vulgaris, *Miller*; Amygdalus Persica, *Linnæus*)

A deciduous tree, 20 ft. high, of bushy habit; branchlets glabrous. Leaves lanceolate, 3 to 6 ins. long, ¾ to 1½ ins. wide; long-pointed, finely toothed, glabrous; stalk glandular, ½ in. long. Flowers usually solitary, sometimes in pairs, produced in early April from the buds of the previous season's growth, pale rose, 1 to 1½ ins. across, with stalks scarcely longer than the bud-scales. Fruit fleshy, globose, clothed with velvety down, 2 to 3 ins. across, yellowish suffused with red on the sunny side, enclosing a grooved stone.

The peach is one of those fruits which have been cultivated for so long, and over so wide an area, that its place of origin is doubtful. It is generally believed to be a native of China; it was certainly cultivated there hundreds, doubtless thousands, of years before it was known in W. Europe. Closely allied to the almond, but less robust, it differs chiefly in its fleshy, juicy fruit with a wrinkled stone; also in the thinner, shorter-stalked leaves, smaller flowers, and in flowering two or three weeks later. The flowering peaches are some of the loveliest of all trees, especially the double red varieties. They are usually propagated by budding on plum stocks, but trees so raised rarely attain to great age. Quite possibly the peach is not in any case a long-lived tree, but worked on the plum it is very subject to canker and premature decay, owing to an imperfect adaptation of stock to scion. Yet it is difficult to suggest a better. On its own roots the peach succeeds in the south, but is too tender for the colder localities, and the fine double and richly coloured varieties now so popular can only be conveniently propagated by budding or grafting. Of varieties grown for fruit there are many, but with them we are not here concerned. The following, with the exception of vars. compressa and lævis, are "flowering" peaches; the double-flowered ones often bear fruit:—

Var. COMPRESSA. Flat Peach.—Remarkable for the flattened or compressed fruits. This was known in gardens eighty years ago, and after being lost to cultivation for many years was reintroduced from China in 1906.

Var. ALBA.—Flowers white, single.

Var. ALBA PLENA.—Flowers white, double.

Var. ROSA PLENA.—Flowers rose-coloured, double.

Var. SANGUINEA PLENA.—Flowers crimson, double. Introduced from China by Fortune.

Var. FOLIIS RUBRIS.—Leaves and fruits purplish red.

Var. LÆVIS. Nectarine.—Fruit glabrous (Syn. var. nucipersica).

Var. MAGNIFICA.—Flowers crimson, double, up to 1¾ ins. across; habit rather spreading and lax. (*Garden*, pl. 1255, Dec. 30, 1899.)

Var. PENDULA.—Branches pendulous.

Var. PYRAMIDALIS.—Branches quite erect.

Double-flowered peaches have been known in European gardens for three centuries, and several others besides those mentioned are offered by nurserymen, such as "Clara Meyer," dianthiflora, camelliæflora, etc. They represent only minor variations. All the varieties like a warm soil and sheltered position, and their effect in bloom is enhanced by a background of evergreens.

P. PILOSIUSCULA, *Koehne*

(Bot. Mag., t. 9192; P. tatsiensis pilosiuscula, *C. K. Schneider*; P. venusta, *Koehne*)

A deciduous shrub or a small tree sometimes 40 ft. high, with a trunk over 1 ft. in diameter; young shoots sparingly hairy or glabrous. Leaves oval or obovate, the base wedge-shaped to rounded or slightly heart-shaped, the apex contracted to a slender point, conspicuously (often doubly) toothed; 1½ to 4 ins. long, about half as much wide; sprinkled with, and roughened by, short bristles above, more thickly on the midrib and veins beneath; stalk about ½ in. long. Flowers produced with the young leaves in April two to four on a main-stalk ¼ to 1 in. long, the individual stalks up to 1⅛ ins. long or sometimes solitary; they are white, ¾ in. wide; calyx-tube cylindrical to funnel-shaped with narrowly triangular more or less glandular lobes; style hairy towards the base; ovary glabrous. Fruit narrowly ovoid, ⅓ in. long, red, ripe in June.

Native of W. Hupeh, China; originally discovered by Henry about 1888; introduced by Wilson in 1907. It belongs to the same group of cherries as P. litigiosa, which has only axil-tufts of hairs beneath the leaves and a much shorter main flower-stalk. P. pilosiuscula varies a good deal in regard to pubescence and in the var. SUBVESTITA, *Koehne* (Wilson No. 41), the flower-stalks, young shoots, and both sides of the leaves are downy or hairy. P. POLYTRICHA, *Koehne*, appears to be merely a still more downy or even shaggy variety of this species, the downiness extending to the calyx. All these are pretty but their blossom is somewhat evanescent.

P. POLLARDII, *Hort*

Probably the finest of the Amygdalus (*i.e.* peach and almond) group is P. Pollardii, which has large, bright pink flowers 2 ins. across and leaves very like those of the common almond but more sharply toothed, the shell of the nut being pitted as well as furrowed. It is believed to be a hybrid between the peach and the almond, and the form now in cultivation was raised about 1904 by Mr Pollard of Ballarat, Victoria, Australia. Dr Rehder considers its origin probably the same as that of P. persicoides, which he dates as "before the sixteenth century" (see Prunus Amygdalus praecox "as var. persicoides"). Where there is only space available for one almond tree, as in so many town gardens, this should be the one selected.

P. PROSTRATA, *Labillardière*. MOUNTAIN CHERRY

(Cerasus prostrata, *Loiseleur*)

A deciduous shrub, 2 to 3 ft. high, of low, spreading habit, and measuring much more in width than it does in height. Branches slender, arching outwards and downwards, the young ones covered with a minute dark-coloured down. Leaves ovate or obovate, pointed, from 1 to 1½ ins. long, sharply toothed, and downy beneath (less markedly so in cultivation). Flowers ½ to ¾ in. across, produced singly or in pairs with the young leaf-clusters from the previous season's shoots in April; very short-stalked; petals of a lively rose colour; calyx tubular. Fruit almost stalkless, red, $\frac{1}{3}$ in. long, tapering towards the end.

Native of the mountains of the Levant, where it usually makes a close, stunted bush, very unlike the rather free-growing plant seen in this country. It needs a sunny position, and is admirably suited on some roomy shelf in the rock garden fully exposed to the sun. In such a position, following a hot summer, it flowers profusely enough almost to hide its branches. It is perfectly hardy at Kew, and it is rather remarkable that it remains so rare and little known, seeing that it was introduced (from Mt. Lebanon) in 1802.

P. PUMILA, *Linnæus*. DWARF AMERICAN CHERRY

A deciduous shrub of variable stature, often a low bush about 2 ft. high, but sometimes a slender shrub 6 to 8 ft. high, with erect, dark branches; branchlets glabrous. Leaves narrowly obovate, $1\frac{1}{2}$ to 2 ins. long, about one-third as wide; slightly toothed towards the apex, entire at the narrowed base, greyish green. Flowers white (sometimes rather dull) about $\frac{1}{2}$ in. across, produced in stalkless umbels of two to four, each flower on a stalk $\frac{1}{3}$ to $\frac{1}{2}$ in. long. Fruit black or purplish, $\frac{1}{3}$ to $\frac{1}{2}$ in. diameter, without bloom, bitter.

Var. DEPRESSA (P. depressa, *Pursh*).—A prostrate form growing flat on the ground and scarcely rising more than 12 ins. from it.

Native of the north-eastern United States; cultivated in England in 1756. Its flowers appear in mid-May, and although small, so profusely are they borne that it is very pretty then, especially if grown in a mass, and if the whitest flowered forms are obtained, for some are much purer than others. Propagated by cuttings and layers. This species may be regarded as the type of a small, but very distinct group of dwarf American cherries including Besseyi, cuneata, and utahensis. P. pumila is distinguished by its leaves being broadest above the middle, and by the fruit having no bloom. It has also a more northern distribution than the others.

P. RUFA, *Hooker fil.* HIMALAYAN CHERRY

(Cerasus rufa, *Wallich*)

A deciduous tree, 15 to 20 ft. high; young branches thickly covered with reddish brown down. Leaves from 2 to 4 ins. long; narrowly oval or oblong-lanceolate, with a long drawn-out apex, toothed, each tooth tipped with an egg-shaped gland; downy on the midrib and veins only when young; stalk $\frac{1}{2}$ in. long. Flowers pink, $\frac{1}{2}$ in. across, produced singly or a few together in clusters from the buds of the previous year's growth; calyx $\frac{1}{3}$ in. long, funnel-shaped, with triangular, toothed lobes, hairy or glabrous; flower-stalk $\frac{1}{3}$ to 1 in. long, slightly downy. Fruit longer than wide, red, fleshy.

Native of Nepal and Sikkim, reaching to elevations of 12,000 ft. It was introduced to Kew about 1897, and proved quite hardy there, flowering in early May. This tree, however, died in 1950. It is distinct on account of the rusty-coloured down and the very glandular teeth of the leaves, but it is not one of the most ornamental of cherries. There are two distinct forms in cultivation, one of which has a close bark on the trunk, a glabrous or nearly glabrous calyx, and short flower-stalk; the other has a peeling bark, shaggy calyx, and flower-stalk occasionally over 1 in. long.

P. SALICINA, *Lindley*. JAPANESE PLUM

(P. triflora, *Roxburgh*)

A deciduous tree, 20 to 30 ft. high, with glabrous, dark young wood. Leaves obovate or oval, 3 to 4½ ins. long, nearly half as wide; downy in the axils of the veins beneath, doubly round-toothed. Flowers white, ¾ in. across, produced in early April, each on a slender glabrous stalk ½ in. long, normally in threes from each bud of the previous year's shoots, but sometimes in pairs or singly; calyx with five rounded oblong lobes, glabrous, often slightly toothed. Fruit heart-shaped, 2 to 2¾ ins. deep, nearly as wide, or globular with a deep depression where the stalk is attached; the colour in cultivated varieties varies considerably, being of different shades or combinations of red, orange, and yellow.

This tree is presumably a native of China, but does not appear to be known in a wild state. The name triflora was given by Roxburgh to a plant growing in Calcutta Botanic Garden early last century. It has long been cultivated by the Japanese, and in 1870 was introduced to California, where its cultivation has developed into an important industry. In this country its ornamental value is about equal to that of P. cerasifera, from which it differs in the shape of the fruits, the more numerous flowers at each node, and in the longer leaves. Whether it will prove worthy of cultivation for its fruit is very doubtful. Probably it requires a hotter summer than ours to develop its best qualities. Californian fruits are sometimes offered in London shops.

P. SARGENTII, *Rehder*. SARGENT'S CHERRY

(Bot. Mag., t. 8411; P. serrulata sachalinensis, *Wilson*)

A deciduous tree, 40 to 80 ft. high, with a trunk sometimes 3 ft. in diameter;

PRUNUS SARGENTII

young shoots glabrous. Leaves obovate to oval, drawn out at the apex into a long, slender point; rounded, sometimes slightly heart-shaped at the base, sharply toothed; 2 to 4 ins. long, about half as wide; quite glabrous on both surfaces, often reddish when young; stalk glabrous, ½ to 1 in. long, with a pair of glands near the blade. Bracts red, oblong, ½ in. long, edged with small glandular teeth. Flowers 1¼ to 1½ ins. across, of a lovely deep blush colour, produced two to six together in short-stalked umbels, each flower with a stalk 1 to 1¼ ins. long; petals obovate, notched at the broad apex; calyx tubular, with five ovate, pointed lobes ¼ in. long, glabrous and entire; stamens deep rose. Fruit a small black cherry, ⅓ in. wide.

Native of Japan; introduced by Sargent to Kew in 1893. This splendid cherry, probably the finest of the true cherries as a timber tree, is also one of the most beautiful in its autumnal colour and blossom. It flowers in April. In June 1910 I saw the trees first introduced to America in the Arnold Arboretum; they were then laden with an extraordinary profusion of small black cherries. The seeds germinate freely after lying dormant a year.

P. SEROTINA, *Ehrhart*. RUM CHERRY

(Padus serotina, *Agardh*)

A large deciduous tree, reaching in its most favoured situations a height of 80 to 100 ft., and occasionally found with trunks 16 ft. in circumference. In England it is usually 30 to 50 ft. high, the young bark glabrous, bitter, aromatic, not unpleasant to the taste. Leaves oval-lanceolate, sometimes narrowly obovate, tapering towards both ends; 2 to 5½ ins. long, and from 1 to 1¾ ins. wide; glabrous and shining above, paler beneath, and usually hairy along the midrib; margins set with shallow incurved teeth; stalk ¼ to 1 in. long. Flowers white, ⅓ in. in diameter, produced during late May and June in cylindrical racemes 4 to 6 ins. long, ¾ in. in diameter. Fruit black, ⅓ in. across, round, but rather flattened like an orange.

Native of N. America, where it is widely spread, reaching from Nova Scotia to Florida, and westwards to Dakota, Texas, Arizona, etc. At its finest, which is in the Allegheny mountains of Virginia, it is probably the largest of all the Prunus tribe. In Great Britain it thrives very well, and makes a handsome middle-sized tree of graceful habit, whose dark glittering foliage in summer very much resembles that of a Portugal laurel, but it is of course deciduous, and dies off a pleasing yellow. Whilst the flowers are borne profusely, the fruits come but sparingly; in the United States the latter are used for flavouring rum and brandy, and for that purpose are said to be equal to the Morello cherry. I am not aware that this tree has been tried under forest conditions here, but its timber is much valued by cabinet-makers, and judging by its behaviour at Kew it will thrive better than many trees on sandy ground. The largest specimen there is 45 ft. high, with a trunk 5 ft. 3 ins. in girth.

Var. ASPLENIFOLIA.—Leaves deeply and irregularly cut at the margins.

Var. PENDULA.—A pretty tree with weeping branches, usually budded on tall stems of P. Padus.

Var. SALICIFOLIA, *Nicholson*.—Under this name a very distinct form of P. serotina is grown at Kew. It is a tree 25 ft. high, with pendulous branches, and leaves of a dark glossy green like those of the type, but narrow, and hanging loose and pendent like those of a willow. It is perfectly hardy, and occasionally bears good crops of fruit.

The rum cherry is widely spread in N. America, and one of its allies reaches through Mexico across the Isthmus of Panama as far south as the mountains of Peru. Near Quito in Ecuador, where this tree grows on the equator, it appears to be in fruit the whole year round. This is P. SALICIFOLIA, *Kunth*, distinct from the variety of P. serotina so named.

P. SERRULA, *Franchet*

A deciduous tree 30 to 50 ft. high; bark of trunk shining brown, ultimately peeling; shoots finely downy when quite young. Leaves lance-shaped, rounded or wedge-shaped at the base, long and slenderly pointed, finely and regularly toothed; 2 to 4 ins. long, ½ to 1¼ ins. wide; downy along the midrib beneath and in the chief vein-axils, sometimes glabrous or soon becoming so; there are several large glands at the base near the stalk, which is ¼ to ½ in. long. Flowers white, ⅔ in. wide, produced usually in twos or threes (sometimes solitary or in fours) during April, each on its stalk ½ in. long. Calyx-lobes ovate-triangular, toothed; style finely downy towards the base. Fruit oval, ½ in. long, red.

Native of W. China. Two characters make this cherry distinct; one is the narrowness and fine toothing of the leaves which are rather willow-like; the other is the beautiful bright brown peeling bark, at least of young trees. This feature alone makes the tree worth cultivating, for it is not more striking in any tree of similar character. So far as I have seen its flower beauty is not great.

The typical P. serrula was introduced by Forrest in 1913 who found it at 10,000 ft. altitude "N.E. of the Yangtze Bend." He describes the fruits as "deep crimson, edible." Var. THIBETICA, *Koehne*, was introduced by Wilson in 1908; it also has shining brown bark.

S. SERRULATA, *Lindley*. JAPANESE CHERRY (Plates 44-45)

A deciduous tree sparsely branched; shoots quite glabrous. Leaves ovate to ovate-lanceolate, 3 to 5 ins. long, 1¼ to 2½ ins. wide, long and taper-pointed, toothed (sometimes doubly), quite glabrous on both surfaces, rather glaucous beneath. Flowers in short-stalked racemose clusters of two to five, white or tinged with rose, 1 to 1¾ ins. across, double, not scented, individual stalks up to 1½ ins. long; they open in April and early May along with the young leaves. Fruit a small black cherry.

The well-known flat-topped, widely spreading, double-flowered cherry of our gardens, which is to be considered the type, was introduced early in the nineteenth century. The real wild type found in Japan, Korea and China was named by E. H. Wilson as var. SPONTANEA. Its leaves are tinged with brown whilst opening, becoming glaucous beneath afterwards; flowers single, white or pink, about ¾ in. wide. It is a tree 60 to 80 ft. high.

The following garden varieties are placed under this species by Wilson: albo-rosea, fugenzo, hisakura, Kirin, sekiyama, horinji. Rehder adds amanogawa, sirotæ, Ojochin, shirofugen—all beautiful.

P. SIEBOLDII, *Wittmack* (syn. P. Watereri), mentioned under P. pseudocerasus in previous editions, is a beautiful cherry related to P. serrulata, but very distinct in the leaves being soft with down, especially beneath. It has not yet been found in a wild state. On cultivated plants the flowers are about 2 ins. wide, "double," pinkish white or rose coloured. Usually the tree is not so vigorous as P. serrulata.

P. SIBIRICA, *Linnæus*. SIBERIAN APRICOT

(Armeniaca sibirica, *Persoon*)

A deciduous bush or small tree; leaves ovate, the apex long drawn-out; 2 to 3½ ins. long, half as wide, reddish at first, then bright green and glabrous above, with axil tufts of down beneath; stalk ½ to 1 in. long. Flowers mostly solitary, white or pink. Fruits scarcely stalked, about 1 in. long, yellow except on the sunny side, covered with a velvety skin; the flesh scanty, dry, harsh and scarcely edible; kernel of nut with an almond-like, bitter taste.

Native of the mountains of S. Siberia, where, according to Pallas the Russian botanist, some mountain-sides are covered with its pink blossoms in May, when the northern sides are purple with Rhododendron dauricum. Although an old tree in gardens (it was cultivated at Kew one hundred years ago), and still offered for sale by continental dealers, it is scarcely known in England nowadays. So far as I have seen, it has very little to recommend it for gardens, being of about the same value as the wild apricot, to which it is very closely akin. Its leaves have usually much more elongated points.

P. SIMONI, *Carrière*. APRICOT PLUM

A small deciduous tree of slender, pyramidal habit, the branches erect, young shoots glabrous. Leaves oval-lanceolate, finely toothed, 3 to 4 ins. long, 1 to 1¼ ins. wide; resembling those of the peach; stalk short, glanded. Flowers white, solitary or in pairs, up to 1 in. across, opening in March and April; petals obovate. Fruit 2 ins. wide, 1½ ins. deep, tomato-shaped, very shortly stalked, uniform brick-red, smooth like a nectarine, the flesh apricot-yellow and pleasantly fragrant, aromatic, and very palatable.

There seems to be some doubt as to the origin of this tree, and although it is believed to be a native of north China, its wild habitat is unknown. It is cultivated about Pekin, and was introduced originally to the Jardin des Plantes at Paris in 1867 by M. Eugene Simon, after whom it is named, and was put in commerce by Messrs Thibaut & Keteleer of Sceaux, near Paris, in 1872. It has borne fruits in the gardens of Aldenham House, Elstree, but this happens rarely, owing to flowers being so liable to damage by frost. Although called "Apricot" plum, its affinities are doubtful. Some authors regard it as a plum, but it appears rather to be intermediate between that and the nectarine. It is a useful fruit tree in California, and has been hybridised with P. salicina—the Japanese plum. Very distinct in its almost fastigiate habit.

P. SPINOSA, *Linnæus*. SLOE, BLACKTHORN

A deciduous, suckering shrub, 10 or 15 ft. high, or in gardens a small tree; bark of young shoots downy, many short branches terminated by a spine. Leaves varying from obovate to oval and ovate, ¾ to 1¾ ins. long, ½ to ¾ in. wide; sharp-toothed, downy beneath on the midrib and veins, becoming sometimes quite glabrous with age. Flowers produced in March or early April usually on the naked wood, singly, sometimes in pairs, from the previous year's buds, each ½ to ¾ in. across, pure white, and borne on a glabrous stalk ⅕ in. long. Fruit round, ½ in. in diameter, at first blue, then shining black, very harsh to the taste.

Var. PLENA.—Flowers not so wide as the single-flowered type, but pure white and very double. A very delightful spring-flowering shrub.

Var. PURPUREA.—Leaves a beautiful red when young, becoming purple, flowers pink, sent out by Barbier & Co., Orleans, in 1903.

The sloe is found wild in Britain and other parts of Europe as well as in north Asia. It occurs in hedgerows and in woods, where it is occasionally a tree over 20 ft. high. It is oftenest seen in wild places or poor soils as a scrubby bush. If introduced to the garden or park for ornament, it should be trained up into tree form. The double-flowered variety is neglected but is most attractive, the flowers being crowded on short spiny branches whose blackness enhances their purity. Its slow growth makes it suitable for small gardens. It seems first to have appeared spontaneously at Tarascon. It is propagated by budding on the wild plum, whose suckers, if produced, are more easily detected than those of the wild sloe. The wood of this species is very hard, and prized in rural districts for making hay-rake teeth.

P. CURDICA, *Fenzl and Fritsch*, is intermediate between spinosa and insititia, of spreading habit, less thorny; leaves downy on both sides when young; flowers white, ¾ in. across; flower-stalks downy; fruit blue-black. S. Armenia.

P. SSIORI, *F. Schmidt*

(Padus Ssiori, *C. K. Schneider*)

Although, according to Sargent, this bird cherry is a common tree in Yezo, and in the mountain forests of Hondo, Japan, it was not brought into cultivation until 1915. The same author (*Forest Flora of Japan*, p. 38) observes that it is always easily distinguished by its pale, nearly white bark. Young shoots glabrous. Leaves 3 to 6 ins. long, oblong, often inclined to obovate, the apex drawn out into a long slender point, the base more or less heart-shaped, the margins closely set with fine almost bristle-like teeth; thin, membranous, glabrous above and the same beneath except for the tufts of brownish down in the vein-axils; stalk slender, 1 to 1½ ins. long, with one or two glands near the blade. Flowers small, white, produced in slender, glabrous cylindrical racemes 4 to 6 ins. long, about 1 in. wide. The species has been found in Manchuria and Saghalin. "The wood is very hard and close-grained, and is used by the Ainos for numerous domestic purposes" (Sargent).

P. SUBCORDATA, *Bentham*. OREGON PLUM

A deciduous tree up to 20 or 25 ft. high in a wild state, but often shrubby and forming thickets; branchlets reddish. Leaves broadly ovate or broadly oval, usually rounded or sometimes slightly heart-shaped at the base, 2 to 3 ins. long, 1 to 2 ins. wide; sharply sometimes doubly toothed, downy at first, becoming nearly or quite glabrous; leaf-stalk ½ to ¾ in. long, glandular. Flowers white, ⅔ in. across, produced in stalkless umbels of two to four blossoms, each on a stalk ¼ to ½ in. long. Fruit oblong, dark red or sometimes yellow, ½ to 1¼ ins. long.

Native of Oregon and California, and although discovered by Hartweg in 1847, not introduced to Europe until about forty years later. In its native country its leaves turn a brilliant red before falling. It differs from most other American plums in having the young leaves rolled up from the sides ("convolute" in bud), as are the Old World species, whereas the N.E. American species are "conduplicate" in bud, *i.e.* the halves of the leaf fold up in bud like a sheet of note-paper. It succeeds at Kew, where there used to be a tree nearly 20 ft. high.

P. SUBHIRTELLA, *Miquel*

(Bot. Mag., t. 7508)

A small deciduous tree, with twiggy, erect branches, 20 to 30 ft. high; branchlets hairy, especially when young. Leaves 1½ to 3 ins. long, scarcely half as wide; ovate, taper-pointed, sharply, unequally, often doubly toothed; downy on the midrib and veins beneath; leaf-stalk ¼ in. long, hairy. Flowers in short-stalked clusters of two to five, each flower ¾ in. across, soft rose-coloured, becoming paler with age, and borne on a sparsely hairy stalk ⅓ in. long;

calyx cylindrical, with short lobes; petals notched at the end. Fruit not seen by me, but described as round, shining black when ripe, ⅓ in. across.

Native of Japan; introduced to Kew in 1895, and since proved to be one of the most beautiful of the cherries. It flowers from the end of March until

PRUNUS SUBHIRTELLA

mid-April, before the leaves appear. It is easily propagated by cuttings put in about the middle of June, when the shoots are half woody.

Var. *autumnalis*.—Of lax habit; flowers semi-double, appearing from October onwards. A small tree.

Var. *pendula*.—Of weeping habit, spring-flowering.

Var. *ascendens*.—This was found 50 to 60 ft. high in Japan by Wilson, and is there twice as high as the type, which is not known in a wild state.

Mr Ingram has in cultivation at Benenden a beautiful double form of var. pendula, the flowers very full of petals.

P. TANGUTICA, *Koehne*

(P. dehiscens, *Koehne*; Amygdalus tangutica, *Korshinsky*; Bot. Mag., t. 9239)

A large deciduous bush up to 15 ft. or more high, of dense habit; young shoots very minutely downy or glabrous, grey, becoming brown later, often spine-tipped. Leaves, except on the young shoots, mostly clustered on short spurs or at the nodes, oblanceolate or oblong, pointed or bluntish, tapered at the base, shallowly round-toothed; 1 to 2 ins. long, ¼ to ½ in. wide; stalk slender, ½ in. or less long. Flowers solitary, stalkless, 1 in. wide, of a beautiful rosy pink, opening in March. Petals roundish-obovate; calyx-lobes fringed with pale hairs, otherwise glabrous; stamens white, with yellow anthers. Fruit described as ⅘ in. wide, covered with velvety down, the fleshy part merely a thin layer; according to Wilson it dehisces (splits), on which character one of its specific names is based.

The plants of this almond now in cultivation, notably in Col. Stern's garden at Highdown, near Worthing, and at Glasnevin, were raised from seeds collected by Wilson in W. Szechuen, China, in 1910 (No. 4029). The shrub flowers profusely and over a long season at Highdown every spring, and is a beautiful addition to the flowering almonds in cultivation, very distinct in its bushy twiggy mode of growth; it is still rare although offered in the trade. The Highdown bush in June 1930 was 10 ft. high and 15 ft. in diameter. There is also a fine example at Bodnant in N. Wales of similar size. Coming from Kansu it should be very hardy.

P. TOMENTOSA, *Thunberg*. DOWNY CHERRY

(Bot. Mag., t. 8196)

A deciduous shrub of spreading habit, 4 to 8 ft. high and twice as wide; branchlets covered densely with a close, pale down. Leaves obovate or oblong, with an abrupt point, 2 to 3 ins. long, ¾ to 1½ ins. wide; toothed, dark dull green, and furnished with scattered hairs above, paler and densely woolly beneath. Flowers ¾ in. across, white, tinted with rose, produced singly or in pairs at the joints of the previous year's growth, each on a stalk ⅙ in. long. Fruit bright red, about the size of a small cherry, slightly hairy, ripe in July.

Native of N. and W. China, but introduced from Japan over seventy years ago. It usually flowers about the fourth week in March, and is then an object of great beauty and charm. Shoots from 1 to 2 ft. long are made in one season, and these the following spring are furnished from end to end with the delicately tinted flowers. It must be said, however, that its beauty is short-lived. The petals are fragile and easily fall, so that if sharp rain-storms or harsh winds are prevalent (as often happens when they are expanding), their full beauty is never displayed. Some sheltered nook should be chosen for it, a consideration to which its early blossoms entitle it. The fruits are not freely produced with us, although about Pekin the shrub is cultivated for their sake. Propagated by layers and cuttings of half-ripened wood.

P TRILOBA, *Lindley* (Plate 47)

(Bot. Mag., t. 8061; Amygdalopsis Lindleyi, *Carrière*)

A deciduous shrub or small tree, 12 to 15 ft. high, young shoots usually glabrous. Leaves ovate or obovate, 1 to 2½ ins. long, ¾ to 1¼ ins. wide; tapering at both ends, irregularly, doubly, and rather coarsely toothed; slightly hairy beneath. Flowers pinkish white, ¾ to 1 in. across, produced singly or in pairs (sometimes more) from each bud of the previous year's shoots; calyx glabrous, ⅕ in. long, with shallow, rounded lobes. Fruit covered with pale down when quite young; not seen mature by me, but said to be red, ½ in. wide, globose and downy.

Var. PLENA.—Flowers 1½ ins. across, of a delicate rose, very "double." Leaves more obovate than in the type, often more or less three-lobed towards the apex.

Prunus triloba is a native of China, and the double-flowered variety was introduced by Fortune in 1855; it was upon this that Lindley founded the name. It is the most popular and beautiful form of the species, flowering in the greatest profusion about the end of March or early in April. It is seen at its best against a south wall, where it should be pruned once a year as soon as ever the flowers are faded, cutting the blossoming twigs close back. Shoots 1 to 2½ ft. long are then made, which flower the following year. It may be grown in the open ground, but does not flower so profusely there; it is also very extensively used for forcing early into bloom for greenhouse decoration. The single-flowered, type plant was of later introduction, but is by no means so exquisite a shrub as the other, neither do the flowers last as long. The form known in gardens as PETZOLDII is very much the same as the type, but has ovate, not trilobed leaves. Propagated by cuttings of firm wood or by layers. Plants worked on the plum stock are often troublesome because of suckers.

P. VIRGINIANA, *Linnæus*. VIRGINIAN BIRD CHERRY

(Padus virginiana, *Roemer*)

Usually a shrub in a wild state, 2 to 15 ft. high, occasionally a tree, deciduous, with grey, glabrous branchlets. Leaves varying from broadly oval to broadly obovate, with a short abrupt point, finely toothed; 1½ to 5 ins. long, two-thirds as wide; glabrous, shining, and dark green above, paler beneath, with tufts of down in the vein-axils beneath; stalk ½ to ¾ in. long, with two or more glands. Flowers white, ⅓ in. or rather more across, produced in racemes 3 to 6 ins. long, 1 in. wide, terminating short leafy shoots. Fruit dark red, round, ⅓ in. across, very harsh to the taste.

Native of the eastern and central United States and Canada; introduced to England in 1724, but not often seen now. It is much rarer in gardens than its near ally, P. serotina, which has a black rather than a red fruit and proportionately narrower leaves. The western N. American P. demissa is perhaps a variety of this, with thicker leaves and fruits not so harsh to the palate. P. virginiana flowers well during May in England, and is pretty then, but does not bear fruit so freely as our native bird cherry.

Var. NANA.—A dwarf form.

P. WATSONI, *Sargent*. SAND PLUM

(Garden and Forest, 1894, fig. 25)

A deciduous shrub or small tree, 6 to 12 ft. high, with glabrous, reddish branchlets. Leaves ovate, pointed, decurved, 1 to 1¾ ins. long, ½ to ¾ in. wide; shallowly round-toothed, dark shining green above, paler below, quite glabrous on both surfaces; stalk ¼ to ⅓ in. long, grooved, with two glands near the base of the blade. Flowers white, ½ in. diameter, produced in clusters of three or four, each on a slender stalk ¼ in. long. Fruit round, orange-red, ¾ in. diameter, the stone deeply pitted.

Native of the central United States, where it is said to form thickets in low, sandy soils near streams. It was first recognised as a distinct species by Sargent in 1894, having previously been confused with P. angustifolia, from which it differs in its "thicker leaves, thicker skinned fruit, and smaller more deeply pitted stone." It is very distinct from angustifolia in its behaviour under cultivation, thriving well where that species is a total failure. Introduced to Kew in 1897, but unfortunately it is no longer represented there. It flowers in late April and May, but is not one of the most effective plums in this country.

P. YEDOENSIS, *Matsumura*. TOKYO CHERRY

(Bot. Mag., t. 9062; P. paracerasus, *Koehne*)

A deciduous tree up to 40 or 50 ft. high, of rounded, spreading habit, shortly trunked, usually wider than high; young shoots thinly clothed with soft hairs. Leaves oval, broadly ovate or obovate, rounded or broadly wedge-shaped at the base, rather abruptly narrowed to a slender point, sharply toothed; $2\frac{1}{2}$ to $4\frac{1}{2}$ ins. long, $1\frac{1}{2}$ to $2\frac{1}{2}$ ins. wide, dark green and glabrous above, downy on the midrib and veins beneath. Flowers slightly fragrant, white or pink, produced in racemes of four or more, usually before (but sometimes with) the leaves; flower-stalks and calyx dull red, usually densely downy, but less so on young trees; calyx-tube cylindrical, lobes sharply toothed. Style either very downy or nearly glabrous. Fruit shining black, globose, $\frac{2}{5}$ in. wide, bitter. According to Wilson, the origin of this cherry is doubtful. It is planted abundantly in Tokyo and Yokohama, where it is known as the "Yoshino Cherry," but has not yet been found wild. It may be a hybrid between P. Lannesiana and P. subhirtella. Wilson describes it as "remarkably distinct from all other Japanese or Chinese cherries and one of the most floriferous and beautiful of them." It is perfectly hardy and grows vigorously—in its young state at least.

About 1910 it was obtained from Germany and was grown as "P. paracerasus" at Kew, but it has always been rare until lately, when large numbers of it have been imported or raised in this country. It is likely in the near future to fill a notable place among spring-flowering trees. It is remarkable that a tree so beautiful should have been comparatively overlooked so long. At Kew it flowers in late March and April. It varies in the amount of pubescence on the undersurface of the leaf; sometimes the midrib and veins are densely covered with tawny down. In regard to habit, too, some trees are more erect and less spreading than others. If the tree is truly of hybrid origin, the fact that some of the stock now in nurseries has been raised from seed might account for this diversity.

PSEUDOLARIX AMABILIS, *Rehder*. GOLDEN LARCH. CONIFERÆ

(P. Fortunei, *Mayr*; Bot. Mag., t. 8176; Larix Kæmpferi, *Carrière*)

A deciduous tree, occasionally 100 to 130 ft. high, with a trunk 2 to 3 ft. thick; branches spreading horizontally; young shoots glabrous Leaves linear, $1\frac{1}{2}$ to $2\frac{1}{2}$ ins. long, $\frac{1}{12}$ to $\frac{1}{8}$ in. wide; produced in a radiating cluster from the end of short, spur-like branches, or on terminal shoots singly and spirally arranged. Their arrangement and general aspect are similar to those of larch, but the leaves are stouter and larger than those of any true larch. In spring they are of a tender yellowish shade of green, and in autumn they turn a rich golden yellow before falling. Male flowers yellow, produced in densely clustered catkins about 1 in. across at the end of the short, spur-like branchlets. Cones about 2 ins. long, nearly as wide; the scales thick, woody, triangular, blunt, often notched at the tip, $\frac{3}{4}$ to $1\frac{1}{4}$ ins. long, ultimately spreading and falling away with the seeds.

Native of China, where it was discovered in the Chekiang province and introduced by Fortune in 1853. This beautiful tree, the only one of its genus, whilst it bears a marked resemblance to the larches in foliage and branching, is remarkably distinct in its clustered male catkins (solitary in Larix), and in the large woody scales of the cone, which falls to pieces when ripe (remaining intact in Larix). Slow growing, but perfectly hardy, it is one of the most beautiful as well as one of the most interesting of trees. It has not, so far as I know, produced fertile seed in this country, and is not so much grown as it deserves to be. The finest tree I have seen was in Messrs Rovelli's nursery at Pallanza, on Lake Maggiore. This was nearly 70 ft. high,

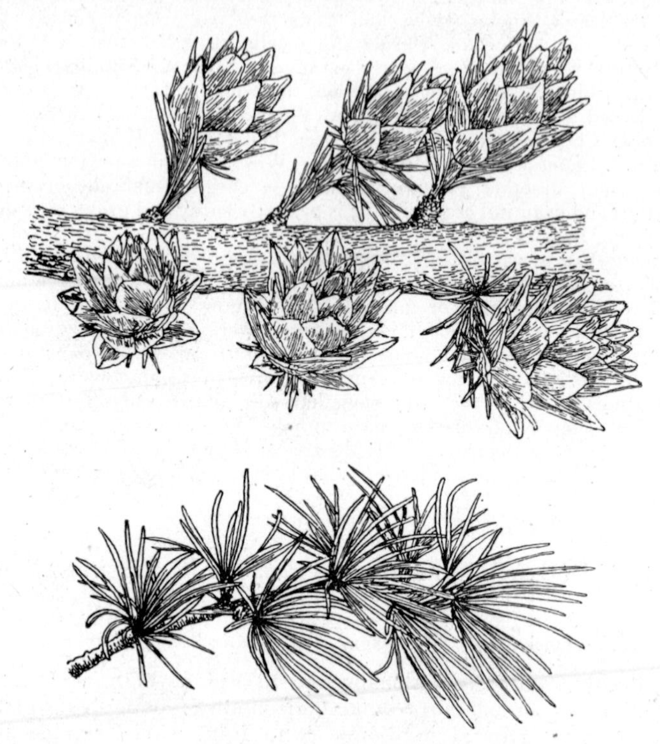

CONES AND LEAFY SPRAY OF PSEUDOLARIX AMABILIS

and very fertile; when I saw it in 1912 there were beneath its boughs hundreds of young trees that had sprouted from its fallen seeds, varying from a few inches to 2 or 3 ft. high. It dislikes limy soil.

PSEUDOPANAX CRASSIFOLIUM, *C. Koch.* ARALIACEÆ

(Aralia crassif., *Solander*; Panax crassif., *Decaisne*; Panax longissimum, *Hooker fil.*)

This remarkable New Zealand tree is only hardy in the maritime counties of the south and west. It is evergreen and in a wild state grows 20 to 50 ft. high. The leaves are extraordinarily variable according to the age and development of the tree, and Cheeseman describes them in four distinct stages. At the first or seedling stage they are 1 to 2 ins. long, diamond-shaped or ovate-lanceolate, tapered at the base, coarsely toothed or lobed. At the second and most remarkable stage the plant is a straight, erect, unbranched, slender stem, bearing the leaves on the upper part; they are then sword-shaped, very stiff, deflexed, often

1½ to 3 ft. long but only 1 to 2 ins. wide, of very leathery texture, the margins armed with large sharp teeth. At the third stage, when the tree begins to branch, the leaves are erect or spreading, some of them divided into three or five stalkless leaflets, whilst others retain the No. 2 shape but are only one-third as long. At the fourth or mature stage they become simple leaves again, 3 to 8 ins. long, 1 to 1½ ins. wide, linear to linear-obovate, either without teeth or toothed towards the apex and tapered at the base to a stout stalk ½ to 1 in. long. Sometimes the third stage is omitted and the tree never bears compound leaves. It is at that stage trees commence to flower, the sexes on different ones. The blossoms are small, of no beauty, produced in terminal compound umbels 3 or 4 ins. across. Fruit globose black, ⅕ in. wide.

There is a good specimen of this araliad at the second stage and about 20 ft. high at Tregrehan, Cornwall, its leaves being 2 ft. long, 1 to 2 ins. wide, the midrib bright yellow. It is also hardy at Exbury, Hants. Trees with two or more distinct types of leaves are very characteristic of the New Zealand flora, but in none is the diversity more remarkably developed than in this. The species was originally discovered during Cook's first voyage (1769-1770). The only other tree with which it can be confused is

P. FEROX, *T. Kirk*, whose always undivided leaves are, at the stage equivalent to the second one in crassifolium, equally deflexed, but with the whole of the margins coarsely and continuously jagged, with large unequal hooked teeth, not remotely set apart as in crassifolium. The leaves are 1 to 1½ ft. long, ½ to 1 in. wide, and more closely set together on the stem. At the adult stage they are only 4 to 8 ins. long and sparingly toothed to almost entire.

Native of New Zealand. As it occurs on the North Island only, it should be less hardy than P. crassifolium which reaches as far south as Stewart Island. Nevertheless, according to Thurston, there is a plant 12 ft. high at Rosehill, Falmouth, and others at Tregothnan and Ludgvan.

PSEUDOTSUGA. CONIFERÆ

A genus of five species of large evergreen trees found in western N. America and N.E. Asia. Leaves set spirally, but spreading and crowded into two opposite rows, linear, grooved above, with two bands of stomata beneath. Cones pendulous and with persistent scales, thus differing from the Abies, which have erect cones with deciduous scales.

P. DOUGLASII, *Carrière*. DOUGLAS FIR (Plate 48)

(P. taxifolia, *Britton*; Abies Douglasii, *Lindley*)

A tree 200 to 300 ft. high, with a trunk 8 to 12 ft. in diameter; main branches horizontal, secondary ones pendulous; young shoots usually more or less downy, with terminal buds that are ovate, pointed, ¼ to ½ in. long, brown, shining; also occasional axillary buds along the shoot. Leaves disposed either all round the shoot or (especially on weak shoots) in two opposite ranks crowded, linear, $\frac{3}{4}$ to $1\frac{1}{2}$ ins. long, $\frac{1}{16}$ to $\frac{1}{12}$ in. wide; rounded or blunt (never notched) at the apex, of various shades of green (from grass green to more or less glaucous), and with several lines of stomata each side the midrib beneath. Cones pendulous, shortly stalked, averaging $2\frac{1}{2}$ to 4 ins. long and 1 to $1\frac{1}{2}$ ins. wide at the base, slenderly egg-shaped, pointed, very distinct on account of the conspicuously obtruded bracts. Male flowers axillary, composed of a cylindrical cluster of orange-red stamens.

Native of western N. America from British Columbia to Mexico; discovered by Menzies in 1793, and introduced by Douglas in 1827. As might be expected from its extended habitat, it shows much variation. In any large group of trees more or less distinct shades are discernible. The most distinct of the varieties is

Var. GLAUCA, often called "Colorado Douglas fir," which not only differs in general appearance, but has its own habitat. The common and finest type of Douglas fir occurs near the Pacific coast, in British Columbia and Washington. The var. glauca is of inland and mountain distribution, and is hardy in places where the other will not live. It differs chiefly in being a smaller tree, in the leaves being stouter and often very glaucous, and in their having a turpentine-like odour. As an ornamental tree it is worth growing, especially the bluest forms (it varies much in that respect), but for timber it is by no means so promising as the coast type.

Var. PENDULA has the pendulous character of the branchlets exceptionally developed. On a tree at Bayfordbury they are 2 to 3 ft. long, and of practically the same thickness throughout, scarcely branched.

Var. STAIRII.—Foliage of a pale greenish yellow. It originated at Castle Kennedy, in Wigtownshire. The best tree I have seen is at Ochtertyre, near Crieff, in Perthshire, about 50 ft. high.

In 1905 Messrs Koster & Sons of Boskoop sent to me some shoots of a remarkable form raised in their nursery in Holland. Its leaves are only $\frac{1}{3}$ to $\frac{1}{2}$ in. long, and are either pointed or rounded at the apex. The raisers thought it might be a hybrid with Tsuga Sieboldii, which the foliage resembled in shape and colour. It was subsequently named var. FRETSII by Beissner.

No foreign tree except the larch and Corsican pine has aroused so much interest among foresters as the Douglas fir. In favourable situations it grows with extreme rapidity, and has already reached in many places a stature of over 100 ft. But in its adaptability to the various soils and climates available for forestry it is far inferior to either of the other two. To get it at its best it requires a climate where the rainfall is abundant, and at least a moderately good soil. On dry, hungry soil, and in bleak spots, it is a failure. To see this tree in its finest condition and in its greatest numbers one must visit the Perthshire properties—especially those of Murthly and Taymouth. Solitary trees are magnificent, the enormous trunks supporting a mass of large plume-like branches.

Several varieties of the Douglas fir, P. Douglasii (or P. taxifolia as there is now an attempt to call it), have to be mentioned: CÆSIA, *Schwerin*, leaves stiffer and grey-green, young shoots smooth or slightly downy, cones smaller, $2\frac{1}{2}$ ins. long, intermediate between those of the type and P. glauca and native of the N. Rocky Mountain region; FASTIGIATA, *Carrière*, of slender pyramidal form, branches erect; FLETCHERI, a dwarf form of compact growth reaching only a few feet high, suitable for the rock garden, leaves glaucous-green, raised by Messrs Fletcher Bros. of the Ottershaw Nurseries, Chertsey; NANA, *Hort.*, a dwarf rounded bush with short leaves (the names *compacta*, *globosa*, and *pumila* have been given to similar forms); MOERHEIMII, leaves glaucous-blue, branches pendulous; REVOLUTA, leaves curled; STANDISHII, leaves silvery below.

The Colorado Douglas fir is now generally regarded as a good species, P. GLAUCA, *Mayr*, and not merely a glaucous variety of P. Douglasii.

P. FORRESTII, *Craib*. FORREST'S DOUGLAS FIR

An evergreen tree 60 to 80 ft. high, with more or less downy young shoots. Leaves 1 to nearly 2 ins. long, $\frac{1}{12}$ in. wide, notched at the tips, grooved on the upper surface, marked with a whitish band of stomata at each side of the prominent midrib beneath. Cones 2 to 2½ ins. long, 1¼ to 1½ ins. wide, egg-shaped, distinctly stalked. The exposed, three-lobed part of the bracts is bent sharply back over the scales, the central lobe awl-shaped, the side ones triangular.

Native of Yunnan, China; discovered in 1914 by Forrest in mixed woods in the Mekong Valley at 10,000 ft. altitude. I have only seen this as a small tree at Caerhays, where it is grown under Forrest's number 13,003. In this the winter buds are ½ to ⅝ in. long, the bud-scales pale brown; the young shoots are only sparsely downy, brown the first year, greyish the second. The slender leaves are nearly always notched at the tip, but occasionally taper to a fine undivided point. The affinity of the species is closest with P. sinensis, which it resembles in the notch-ended leaves and downy shoots; but the leaves, cones, and reflexed bracts of the cones are distinctly shorter in P. sinensis.

P. JAPONICA, *Beissner*

(Abies japonica, *Rovelli*; Tsuga japonica, *Beissner*)

A tree up to 100 ft. high in Japan, only known in this country by a few plants. The young shoots appear to be always without down, and the leaves, except on quite young plants, to be notched at the apex; both these characters afford good distinctions between this and the West American species. The leaves are ¾ to 1¼ ins. long, and have two broad stomatic strips beneath. Cones only 1½ to 1¾ ins. long, 1 in. wide. This tree was discovered in 1893 by the Japanese botanist Shirasawa, and is a native of the provinces of Yamanto and Kii; first introduced to the botanic garden at Hamburg, and to Ansorge's nursery at Flottbeck. Mr Ansorge in 1907 sent me some twigs off young plants, the leaves of which were rounded at the apex. This can be characteristic of young plants only. Older ones exhibited at the British-Japanese Exhibition of 1910 had decidedly notched leaves.

P. MACROCARPA, *Mayr*

This is a close ally of the Douglas fir, but according to Jepson is only from 30 to 90 ft. high. It differs from P. Douglasii in its leaves being incurved instead of straight, and taper-pointed instead of usually rounded at the apex. Cones larger, occasionally 6½ to 7½ ins. long, with the bracts not protruded so much beyond the scales. Native of S. California and Lower California.

Although very distinct because of its large cones, it has not much value either as a timber producer or as an ornamental tree. It was introduced to cultivation in 1910 by Mr H. Clinton Baker, who found it susceptible to injury by spring frost.

P. SINENSIS, *Dode*. CHINESE DOUGLAS FIR

An evergreen tree described by its discoverer as "grand et superbe" in a wild state; young shoots brown, minutely downy. Leaves mostly in two opposite rows, notched at the end, ¾ to 1¼ ins. long, $\frac{1}{16}$ to $\frac{1}{12}$ in. wide, furrowed above, with two whitish bands of stomata beneath. Cones 1¾ to 2¼ ins. long, 1 to 1¼ ins. wide; the bracts reflexed, three-lobed, the middle lobe ⅛ to ¼ in. long, the side ones shorter.

Native of Yunnan, China; discovered by Père Maire, the French missionary, growing on limestone at 8500 ft. elevation; described and named in 1912; seeds introduced and plants raised the same year by Mr Chenault of Orleans. P. sinensis and P. Forrestii (*q.v.*) are closely allied and according to Prof. Craib "form a geographical and systematically distinct sub-genus." The other Asiatic species in cultivation, P. japonica, is distinguished by its glabrous young shoots.

A fine Douglas fir found in Formosa about 1908 was at first thought to be the same as P. japonica. It has since been found to be more nearly akin to P. sinensis and been named P. WILSONIANA, *Hayata*. It has downy young shoots like P. sinensis, but the leaves of adult trees are scarcely 1 in. long. It was found by Wilson in Formosa during 1918 to be a "loosely pyramidal" tree 90 ft. high and 12 ft. in girth, in the province of Shinchiku. I do not know that it is in cultivation and it is probably rather tender.

PTELEA. RUTACEÆ

A genus of some eight or nine species of deciduous small trees or shrubs most fully represented in North America, but occurring also in Mexico. The leaves are usually trifoliolate but are sometimes made up of four or five leaflets, aromatic and (with a lens) seen to be covered with pellucid dots. Flowers small. The most distinctive feature of this genus is provided by the fruits, which are thin, flat and broadly winged, rather like hops or elm seed.

P. BALDWINII, *Torrey*. WESTERN HOP TREE

A deciduous shrub up to 20 ft. high with trifoliolate leaves much smaller than those of P. trifoliata. Leaflets 1¼ to 2½ ins. long, narrowly ovate or obovate, the terminal one the longest; very downy beneath. Flowers in small terminal corymbs. Fruit winged, ½ in. across. It differs from P. trifoliata in its narrower leaves, larger flowers, and narrow wing to the fruit. Native of N. California; introduced to Kew in 1893. Not so notable a plant as its Eastern ally.

P. LUTESCENS, *Greene*

A deciduous small tree with slender young shoots of a pale yellowish grey at first, becoming shining pale grey with age, thickly covered with small warts, not downy. Leaves trifoliolate, the leaflets of lanceolate shape, faintly round-toothed, stalkless, slenderly pointed or bluntish, the side ones oblique at the base; 1¾ to 3½ ins. long, ⅜ to ⅞ in. wide; shining green above, dull beneath, quite glabrous on both surfaces; main-stalk 1 to 2 ins. long. Fruit elm-like, but occasionally two- or even three-winged, ¾ to 1 in. wide, wrinkled, notched at the top, glandular in the centre; seed flattish, oval.

Native of the Grand Canyon, Arizona. There was a small tree at Kew about 10 ft. high which was raised from seed received from the Arnold Arboretum in 1914 as "P. angustifolia," which I believe to be P. lutescens. Dr Rehder collected this species on the Bright Angel Trail of the Grand Canyon in 1914 and it is probably from the seed he gathered then that this tree was raised.

Another site for the species in the Grand Canyon is the Red Canyon Trail, where it was collected by Lester F. Ward in 1901 and distributed as "P. angustifolia." The name angustifolia has been dropped in connection with this tree; as used by Bentham it appears to have been made to cover several species. P. lutescens has the same odour as the well-known P. trifoliata and the leaves are thickly sprinkled with oil glands that show transparently when the leaf is held up to the light and examined through a lens. It is very distinct from the older species in its narrow lanceolate leaves.

P. TRIFOLIATA, *Linnæus*. HOP TREE

A low deciduous tree, usually under 25 ft. high, often of greater breadth than height, with a short, comparatively thick trunk, often inclined. Leaves trifoliolate, the leaflets lanceolate, ovate or oblong, finely toothed or entire, downy beneath when young, the middle one the largest, and from 2 to 6 ins. long, with a short stalk, the lateral leaflets unequal-sided, stalkless; the common leaf-stalk is 2 to 4 ins. long. Held against the light and seen through a lens the blade is found to be dotted with oil-glands. Flowers borne on slender, downy stalks in corymbs 2 or 3 ins. across during June and July, dull greenish white, $\frac{1}{3}$ to $\frac{1}{2}$ in. across. They are unisexual, the males soon falling away. Fruit in dense clusters, each a flat, thin disk from $\frac{2}{3}$ to 1 in. across, consisting of an almost circular wing, with prominent netted veins surrounding one seed in the centre. Occasionally the fruit has more than one wing.

Var. AUREA.—Leaves yellow.

Var. FASTIGIATA.—Branches erect.

Var. GLAUCA.—Leaves blue-green instead of the ordinary rich dark green.

Var. HETEROPHYLLA.—Leaves mostly trifoliolate as in the type, but others have four, some five leaflets; they are also narrower in proportion to their length. (Syn. var. pentaphylla.)

Var. MOLLIS, *Torrey* (P. mollis, *Curtis*).—Leaflets broader than in the type, but its chief distinguishing characteristic is the dense permanent covering of greyish down on the lower surface.

Native of S. Canada and the eastern United States; introduced to England in 1704. Ptelea trifoliata is one of the most distinct of hardy trees, and it is interesting for its large crops of curious elm-like fruits which often strew the ground in its neighbourhood throughout the winter, the fleshy part of the wing having decayed and left the netted veins. Very little of the seed is fertile in this country, but the tree is easily increased by cuttings. The bark, leaves, and young fruits emit a strong and aromatic scent when bruised, and the last have been suggested as a substitute for hops because of their intense bitterness. The tree is of picturesque habit, perfectly hardy, and appears to thrive in any well-drained soil. The leaves die off yellow in autumn.

PTEROCARYA. WING-NUT. JUGLANDACEÆ

At present six of the seven species of Pterocarya known are in cultivation. They are deciduous trees with large, alternate, pinnate leaves and pithy young wood, the pith lamellate; leaflets varying from five to twenty-seven, toothed, more or less oblong. Flowers unisexual, both sexes borne on the same tree but on different catkins; male catkins about one-third the length of the female ones. The fruit is a small nut, large numbers of which are strung on slender spikes 8 to 20 ins. long. From its allies in the same natural order—the walnuts and hickories—Pterocarya differs in the curiously winged nuts, and from the latter in the chambered pith.

In gardens the only species well known is the Caucasian one (of the rest five come from China, one from Japan), and no handsomer pinnate-leaved tree can be grown in our climate. The others also are handsome, but they have not yet shown their qualities as ornamental trees in Britain. All of them are moisture-lovers, and for their best development should be planted in deep loam. Young plants making vigorous succulent shoots are sometimes cut by winter cold, and even old trees are liable to injury by late spring frosts. Seeds afford the best means of propagation; some species produce suckers, and cuttings of the shoots may also be employed.

P. FRAXINIFOLIA, *Spach*. CAUCASIAN WING-NUT (Plate 49)

(P. caucasica, *C. A. Meyer*)

A large deciduous tree, ultimately 80 to 100 ft. high, usually much less in this country, and branching low down, forming a wide-spreading head; trunk of large trees 10 to 12 ft. in girth, with deeply furrowed bark; ends of young shoots minutely scurfy. Leaves 8 to 18 ins. (sometimes over 2 ft.) long, composed of from three and a half to thirteen and a half pairs of leaflets; these are stalkless, oblong, obliquely rounded at the base, pointed, toothed, normally 2 to 4½ ins. long by ¾ to 1¾ ins. wide (occasionally, on vigorous shoots, 8 or 9 ins. long); dark green, glabrous and glossy above, tufted with stellate hairs along the midrib beneath; common stalk round. Male catkins 3 to 5 ins. long, cylindrical, the flowers closely packed; female catkins 12 to 20 ins. long, with the flowers scattered; both pendulous; afterwards developing nuts which, with the wings, are ¾ in. in diameter, roundish, oblique, horned at the top.

Native of the Caucasus and Persia, inhabiting moist places. It was introduced to France by the elder Michaux, who took back seeds from Persia in 1782. According to Elwes, the finest specimen in Britain is at Melbury, in Dorset, which is 90 ft. high and 12 ft. in girth of trunk. There is a beautiful specimen at Claremont, Surrey, which, when I saw it in 1910, measured 19 ft. round its short, rugged trunk. This tree likes a rich loamy soil and abundant moisture, and whilst the fine specimens mentioned above show that it will thrive very well in the south of England, it loves more sunshine than our climate affords. The lover of trees will find nothing more interesting in and around Vienna than the magnificent examples of Pterocarya fraxinifolia. There, of course, the summers are much hotter, and the winters colder than ours; the tree bears fruit freely, and is very attractive in late summer when hung with the long slender catkins.

Var. DUMOSA, *C. K. Schneider* (P. dumosa, *Lavallée*).—A shrubby variety of dwarf habit, with small leaflets 2 or 3 ins. long. Although first noticed in the Arboretum of the late Mr Lavallée at Segrez, in France, this is apparently a truly wild form, judging by the following statement of the late Jean Van Volxem :—

"The country around Lagodechi (in the Caucasus) is very interesting. Near the river are extensive swamps, where I saw P. caucasica growing sometimes as an enormous tree, sometimes as a large shrubby bush. The two forms are intermixed with each other, so that no condition of soil or exposure can explain the fact, and there is, as far as I saw, no intermediate form, and I could detect no difference between the two forms except as to habit and size." (*Gardeners' Chronicle*, 1877, I. p. 72.)

P. HUPEHENSIS, *Skan.* HUPEH WING-NUT

A tree 70 ft. or more high, with glabrous, minutely glandular young shoots. Leaves 7 to 12 ins. long, composed of five, seven, or nine leaflets, which are oval-lanceolate, oblong, or slightly obovate, pointed, obliquely rounded at the base, toothed; 1½ to 5 ins. long, ¾ to 2 ins. wide; glabrous except for tufts of brownish down in the vein-axils beneath; common stalk glabrous, roundish, not winged. The fruiting catkin is 12 to 18 ins. long, each nut with a pair of roundish wings, the whole rather more than 1 in. across.

Native of the mountains of Hupeh, China; discovered by Henry in 1888, and introduced by Wilson for Messrs Veitch in 1901. The young trees appear to be quite hardy. The species is closely allied to P. fraxinifolia; so far as we know at present it has not so many leaflets on each leaf, and they are slightly stalked. The base of the blade of the leaflet does not overlap the main-stalk as it usually does in P. fraxinifolia. It is growing well with Mr J. B. Stevenson at Tower Court, near Ascot.

P. PALIURUS, *Batalin*

A tree 50 or more feet high, the young shoots downy, glandular. Leaves 8 to 12 ins. long, composed usually of seven or nine leaflets, which are oblong or oval, very obliquely tapered or rounded at the base, pointed or blunt at the apex, finely toothed; 2½ to 5 ins. long, 1 to 2½ ins. wide; dark glossy green, and glabrous except for fine down on the midrib on both surfaces; common stalk not winged, downy. Male catkins slender, 2½ to 4 ins. long, frequently in pairs. Fruiting catkin 8 to 10 ins. long, each nut surrounded by a wing, the whole forming a circular disk 1½ to 2½ ins. diameter.

Native of the mountains of Central China; discovered by Henry in 1888, and introduced by Wilson for Messrs Veitch in 1901. The fruits of this species are very remarkable, suggesting miniature cymbals; in having the wing continuous all round the nut, they distinguish it from all other species. Henry says it ought to be hardier than P. stenoptera, as coming from higher elevations. Seeds were again sent by Wilson during his later journeys.

P. REHDERIANA, *C. K. Schneider*

A hybrid between P. fraxinifolia and P. stenoptera, raised in the Arnold Arboretum, near Boston, Mass., from seeds received in 1879 from the late M. Lavallée's collection of Segrez, where the cross had no doubt been effected by wind on trees growing together. As the seeds were received as P. stenoptera, that species was no doubt the mother plant. I saw the original hybrid in the Arnold Arboretum in June 1910, which was then 40 ft. high and, owing to the faculty of producing sucker-growths from the root, forming by itself quite a grove. At least one of the parent species has the same faculty—rarely developed, however, unless the main stem is cut down. P. Rehderiana is intermediate between the parents. The common stalk of the leaf has wings, but they are not so much developed as in P. stenoptera, and never toothed as they often are in that species. The wings of the fruit are shorter and rounder. In the Arnold Arboretum this hybrid has proved hardier and a better grower than either of its parents. Living plants were introduced to Kew in 1908 and have grown extremely well.

P. RHOIFOLIA, *Siebold and Zuccarini*. JAPANESE WING-NUT

A tree 80 to 100 ft. high, trunk 8 to 10 ft. in girth; young shoots nearly glabrous. Leaves 8 to over 12 ins. long, composed of eleven to twenty-one leaflets, which are rounded at the base, pointed at the apex, oblong, finely and evenly toothed, 2½ to 4 ins. long, 1 to 1½ ins. wide; common stalk not winged. The stalk and leaves vary in regard to pubescence, but the plants which grew at Kew were glabrous except for tufts of stellate down about the midrib and axils of the veins beneath; but in Japan a form is commonly much more downy on the leaves and leaf-stalks. Male catkins 3 ins. long; females 8 to 10 in. long; wings of the nut horizontal, broadly crescent-shaped, the whole fruit ¾ to 1 in. across.

Native of Japan; introduced in 1888. It is quite hardy, and in a moist loam would apparently grow well. Professor Sargent found it abundant on Mt. Hakkoda at 2500 to 4000 ft. above sea-level, and almost the largest deciduous tree in that part of Japan.

P. STENOPTERA, *De Candolle*

A tree 50 to 80 ft. high, with a fissured trunk 6 to 8 ft. in girth; young shoots and common stalk of the leaf of some plants furnished with pale hairs persisting through the first winter, but in others both are quite glabrous. Leaves 8 to 15 ins. long, composed of eleven to twenty-one (sometimes twenty-five) leaflets, which are oblong or narrowly oval, tapered at both ends, finely and regularly toothed, 2 to 5 ins. long, ⅓ to 2 ins. wide; the common stalk winged in the spaces between each pair of leaflets, the wings sparsely toothed. Male catkins 2½ ins. long; female ones 8 ins. long. Nut roundish oval with a short beak, the two wings erect, narrow, tapering, ¾ in. long, ⅕ in. wide at the base, forming a V.

Native of China, whence specimens were sent to France by a missionary named Calery in 1844, on which Mr Casimir de Candolle founded the species. It appears to have been introduced to Europe about 1860. It will, no doubt, thrive best in moist loam like P. fraxinifolia, but very few plants appear to be in cultivation. The best I have seen was in the late Mr Cory's collection at Duffryn, over 30 ft. high and 4 ft. 2 ins. in girth. I saw a tree fruiting freely at Segrez, in France, in July 1904. Its winged leaf-stalks and the erect narrow wings of the nuts distinguish it from P. fraxinifolia.

PTEROCELTIS TATARINOWII, *Maximowicz*. ULMACEÆ

A deciduous tree with the habit and general aspect of a Celtis; young shoots slender and, like the leaves, at first clothed with small appressed hairs which mostly soon fall away. Leaves alternate, toothed, ovate lance-shaped; 2 to 4 ins. long, ¾ to 2 ins. wide; the apex with a long tapered point, the base three-nerved and broadly wedge-shaped; upper surface harsh to the touch, with innumerable minute warts, lower surface with tufts of down in the vein-axils; stalks ¼ to ⅓ in long. Flowers unisexual, the males in stalkless clusters, the females solitary in the leaf-axils; neither of any beauty. Fruit a globose nut about ⅛ in. wide, surrounded by a circular wing notched at the top, the whole ½ to ¾ in. wide, borne on a slender stalk about ½ in. long.

Native of Central China; introduced to France in 1894 by Mr Maurice de Vilmorin, who raised the first plants at Les Barres from seed. One of these I saw bearing fruit in July 1904, but none of its seeds had up to then proved fertile. It was introduced to Kew in 1897. Interesting botanically, it will probably only appeal to connoisseurs and lovers of curiosities, for the flowers are quite inconspicuous. Closely allied to Celtis, it is very distinct in its winged fruits, which more resemble those of Ulmus, but their arrangement singly in the leaf-axils of the shoots of the year make the tree very distinct from the elms. This is the only species of the genus known.

PTEROSTYRAX. STYRACACEÆ

Bentham and Hooker united this genus to Halesia, apparently on insufficient grounds, for most botanists now concur in keeping the two separate. They are really very distinct. Pterostyrax is exclusively Chinese and Japanese (Halesia is East N. American); the inflorescence is paniculate and many-flowered; the parts of the flowers are in fives (fours in Halesia); the stamens are protruded in Pterostyrax (enclosed in Halesia); the pith is continuous (chambered in Halesia).

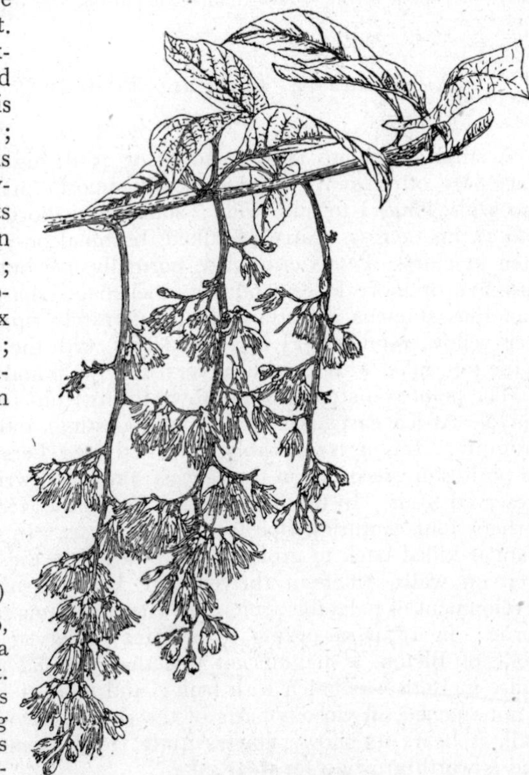

Pterostyrax hispidum

P. HISPIDUM, *Siebold and Zuccarini*

(Bot. Mag., t. 8329; Halesia hispida, *Masters*)

A deciduous shrub, 15 to 20 ft. high, or a tree up to 30 or 40 ft. high, of coarse, vigorous growth and spreading habit; young shoots glabrous. Leaves alternate, 3 to 8 ins. long, 1½ to 4 ins. wide; oval or obovate, wedge-shaped at the base, pointed, toothed, covered beneath with fine whitish down or nearly glabrous; stalk ½ to 1 in. long. Flowers white, fragrant, produced during June and July on axillary, downy, pendulous panicles, 4 to 9 ins. long, 2 to 3 ins. wide, with often two or three leaves at the base. Corolla of five oval lobes, divided almost to the base, finely downy on both sides, $\frac{1}{3}$ in. long. Stamens, flower-stalks, and calyx downy. Fruit spindle-shaped, $\frac{1}{2}$ in. long, terminated by the persistent calyx-lobes and style, the whole densely clothed with pale brown hairs $\frac{1}{12}$ in. long.

Native of Japan and China; introduced in 1875. This beautiful and distinct tree is very hardy and flowers almost every year, but most profusely when the preceding summer and autumn have been hot. It needs a good loamy soil and a sunny position. Seed is ripened occasionally, and this affords the simplest and best means of propagation. The finest trees I have seen are in the neighbourhood of Queenstown, Ireland, 30 to 40 ft. high, and as much in diameter.

So far as I am aware, P. hispidum is at present the only species in cultivation, although it is often found under the name of "P. corymbosum." The true species of that name is very clearly distinguished from hispidum by the fruit, which is $\frac{1}{2}$ in. long, $\frac{1}{3}$ in. wide, five-winged (not merely ribbed as in hispidum), and covered with a very close down (not hairy). The panicles are also broader. Native of Japan, farther south than P. hispidum, and probably not so hardy.

PUNICA GRANATUM, *Linnæus*. POMEGRANATE. LYTHRACEÆ

(Bot. Mag., t. 1832)

A small deciduous tree, up to 15 or 25 ft. high, free from down in every part, often spiny. Leaves mostly opposite, narrow oblong, entire; 1 to 3 ins. long, $\frac{1}{3}$ to 1 in. wide; stalks very short. Flower scarlet-red, 1 to $1\frac{1}{2}$ ins. across, scarcely stalked, terminal on short side twigs, and often in pairs. Petals crumpled, normally five but often more; calyx with five or more lobes, and a funnel-shaped base to which the very numerous stamens are attached. Fruit rarely ripened in this country, deep yellow, roundish, $2\frac{1}{2}$ to 3 ins. across, with the calyx-lobes adhering at the top, filled with a reddish, very juicy pulp and numerous seeds.

The pomegranate has been grown for its fruits in the south of Europe and N. Africa eastwards to Persia, Palestine, and India from remote antiquity. But it is probably only native of Persia and Afghanistan. Its praises are recorded in the earliest songs and writings that have been preserved to us. In the British Isles, where the tree has been grown for perhaps four centuries, ripe fruit is denied us. In the open ground the plant is killed back to ground-level in any but the mildest winters, and even on walls, where it thrives well, lack of sunshine precludes the development of palatable fruits. At the same time fruits are occasionally borne: in 1874, according to a letter preserved at Kew from Lady Rolle of Bicton, a magnificent tree that covered the whole front of a house in Bath was laden with fruit; and in 1911 fruits were produced, if not ripened, in various parts of the south. Grown on a sunny south wall, it bears its showy flowers quite freely from June to September, and is worth growing for their sake.

Var. ALBESCENS.—Flowers white or yellowish.

Var. PLENA.—Flowers double red; the showiest form.

Var. NANA (P. nana, *Linnæus*).—Shrubby, with linear leaves. It is often cultivated as a flowering plant on the Continent.

The pomegranate can be raised from seeds, cuttings, or by grafting; the varieties by either of the two last methods; if grafted, seedling stocks of the type should be used. In the gardens of Versailles, visitors will have noticed growing in tubs many remarkable, very old pomegranate trees, with gnarled, crooked trunks which to all appearances are as old as the chateau itself.

PURSHIA TRIDENTATA, *De Candolle*. ROSACEÆ

(Bot. Reg., t. 1446)

A deciduous grey shrub, 3 to 6 ft. high in cultivation, but occasionally 10 ft. in a wild state; young branchlets downy. Leaves wedge-shaped or obovate, $\frac{1}{4}$ to $\frac{5}{8}$ in. long, $\frac{1}{8}$ to $\frac{1}{4}$ in. wide towards the apex, where it is cut into three large, rounded teeth, tapering gradually towards the base; covered with white down beneath; grey-green and downy above. Flowers yellow, almost stalkless, produced in May, usually singly from buds on twigs of the previous year's wood; calyx covered with grey down, intermixed with gland-tipped hairs, funnel-shaped, five-lobed; stamens numerous, arranged in a ring. Each flower in about $\frac{1}{3}$ in. wide. Fruit $\frac{1}{2}$ in. long, downy, crowned with the persistent style.

Native of western N. America, from British Columbia to California; introduced by Douglas in 1826, first flowered in the Horticultural Society's Garden in 1830. According to Loudon, all the plants about London were killed during the winter of 1837-8, but plants grew unsheltered in a border at Kew for over twenty years. Unfortunately these have now been lost. It is not a very attractive shrub, although curious and interesting. It prefers a rather light soil, and can be propagated by layers. The genus, of which two species are known, was named in honour of Fred. Pursh, author of a flora of N. America (1814).

PYRACANTHA. ROSACEÆ

The species whose descriptions are given below have been by various authors placed in Cotoneaster, Mespilus, and Cratægus. They are, no doubt, most closely allied to the last, differing chiefly in having leafy thorns, in being evergreen, and in the leaves being either entire or merely toothed, never lobed. There are also differences in the ovules. From Cotoneaster they are equally distinct in having thorny branches and toothed leaves. For the rest they may be described as evergreen shrubs with alternate leaves and white flowers; stamens about twenty; styles five. Fruits globose or orange-shaped, yellow, or scarlet. They are easily satisfied as regards soil, thriving in any that is warm and not very heavy. P. coccinea is the hardiest species and is excellent in the open ground; in cold districts the others may need wall protection to enable them to develop really fine crops of berries. Propagation is by seeds, or by cuttings made of firm leafy twigs in late summer.

P. ANGUSTIFOLIA, *C. K. Schneider*

(Bot. Mag., t. 8345; Cotoneaster angustifolia, *Franchet*)

An evergreen shrub probably 10 or 12 ft. high, of dense, spreading, bushy habit; branches rather rigid, horizontal, often spine-tipped, covered the first year with a thick, grey down. Leaves narrow oblong or slightly obovate, rounded or tapered at the base, rounded at the apex with a minute tip or slight notch there; the larger leaves have a few minute dark stiff teeth near the apex, the smaller ones mostly entire; they are $\frac{1}{2}$ to $2\frac{1}{4}$ ins. long, $\frac{1}{8}$ to $\frac{1}{2}$ in. wide, glabrous, dark green above, covered beneath with a grey felt; stalk $\frac{1}{12}$ to $\frac{1}{4}$ in. long. Flowers white, $\frac{1}{4}$ in. across, in corymbs 2 ins. wide, of little beauty; calyx and flower-stalk felted. Fruit brilliant orange-yellow when ripe, covered with grey down when young, $\frac{1}{4}$ to $\frac{3}{8}$ in. in diameter, much flattened at the top; seeds five.

Native of W. China; introduced to Kew by Lieut. Jones in 1899, and again a few years later through Mr de Vilmorin. I saw it in great beauty at Les Barres in 1908, loaded with fruit, and the whole plant much more woolly than it is in Great Britain. After the hot summer of 1911, a plant on a wall at Kew bore fruit very freely. The later introductions of this species are proving hardier than the first ones and they can be grown in the open. Its round-ended, nearly or quite entire leaves, and dense woolliness readily distinguish it from the two other species. It is valuable in retaining its berries in full beauty until March, long after those of P. coccinea have fallen.

P. ATALANTIOIDES, *Stapf*

(Bot. Mag., t. 9099; P. Gibbsii, *A. B. Jackson*; Sportella atalantioides, *Hance*)

An evergreen shrub 15 to 20 ft. high, of erect habit, frequently destitute of spines; young shoots at first clothed with down but becoming glabrous and bright olive-brown by autumn. Leaves oblong, oval, or inclined to obovate, tapered either equally towards both ends or (more usually) abruptly tapered to a point; sometimes rounded at the apex, sometimes entire, sometimes finely toothed except towards the stalk; 1 to 3 ins. long, $\frac{1}{2}$ to $1\frac{1}{3}$ ins. wide; dark glossy green above, pale and dull beneath, glabrous except when quite young; stalk $\frac{1}{8}$ to $\frac{1}{3}$ in. long. Flowers $\frac{1}{3}$ to $\frac{1}{2}$ in. wide, white, produced in May or early June in corymbs $1\frac{1}{2}$ to 2 ins. wide which terminate short, leafy twigs that spring from the previous season's growths. Fruit rather flattened-globose, $\frac{3}{16}$ to $\frac{1}{4}$ in. wide, scarlet, topped by the shrivelled calyx-lobes, and persisting until March.

Native of Szechuen and Hupeh, China; discovered by General Mesny about 1880, and introduced by Wilson in 1907. This fine pyracanth promises to be the strongest grower in the genus. It was named after the late Hon. Vicary Gibbs, in whose garden at Aldenham was a magnificent pyramidal specimen 20 ft. high. But at the time it was figured in the *Botanical Magazine* it was found, unfortunately, that it had been given the specific name atalantioides by Hance in 1877. Although the fruits are smaller than those of P. coccinea, they ripen later and remain for several months longer on the bushes. In all really essential botanical characters it does not differ much from the Himalayan P. crenulata, but is very distinct as a garden shrub. It is perfectly hardy, its leaves and flowers are larger, its growth much stronger, and it is often quite spineless. By training up a leading shoot and gradually removing the lower branches it can be made into a small tree, as has been done at Aldenham.

P. COCCINEA, *Roemer*. PYRACANTH, BUISSON ARDENT

(Cratægus Pyracantha, *Medicus*)

An evergreen shrub or small tree, up to 15 ft. high, of very dense, leafy habit; young shoots covered with grey down, the slender thorns $\frac{1}{2}$ to $\frac{3}{4}$ in. long; branches often thorn-tipped. Leaves narrowly obovate or oval, tapered at both ends, blunt-toothed; 1 to $2\frac{1}{2}$ ins. long on the barren shoots, $\frac{1}{2}$ to $1\frac{1}{2}$ ins. long on the flowering ones, varying from $\frac{1}{4}$ to $\frac{3}{4}$ in. wide; dark glossy green above, paler beneath, glabrous except at the margins near the base; stalk $\frac{1}{3}$ in. or less long, downy. Flowers white, $\frac{1}{3}$ in. across, very numerously borne in early June in corymbs terminating short twigs which, springing from the shoots of the previous year, form one large panicle; flower-stalks and calyx slightly downy; calyx-lobes broadly triangular. Fruit brilliant coral-red, orange-shaped, about $\frac{1}{4}$ in. across.

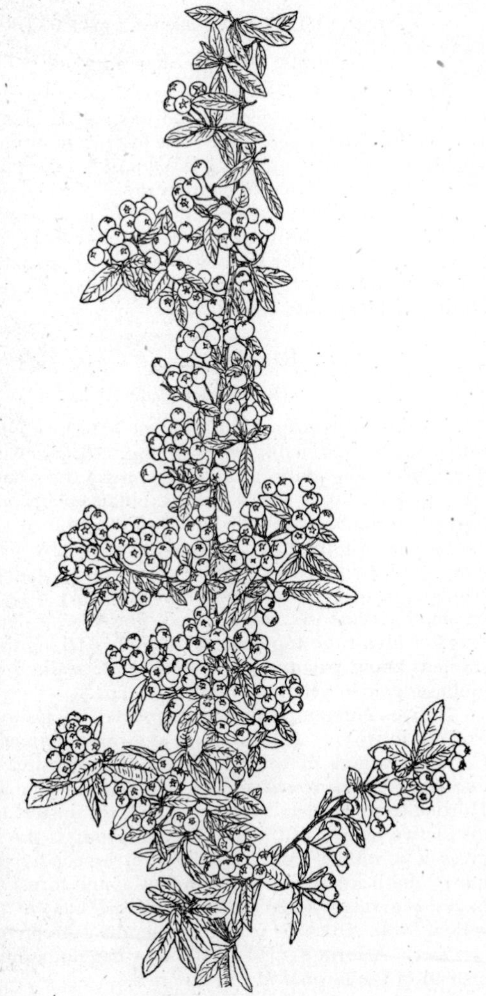

PYRACANTHA COCCINEA

Native of S. Europe and Asia Minor; introduced in 1629. This well-known evergreen is more often seen growing against a wall than in the open, and no doubt bears fruit more abundantly there. It is, in fact, one of the most desirable of evergreen wall shrubs. But when once established it is quite hardy in the open; at Kew there are specimens 15 ft. high that bear fruit profusely. The shrubs have to be netted, as birds (blackbirds especially) are very greedy for the fruits. The pyracanth should be used more than it is as an evergreen shrub. It bears pruning well, and its only defect is that it transplants badly except when young.

Var. LALANDEI, *Dippel*.—A variety raised from seed by M. Lalande of

Angers about 1874. It is of more vigorous, upright growth than the type, and has leaves of proportionately greater width on the average, as well as larger fruits of a more yellowish red, or orange. There is a white-fruited form (FRUCTU-ALBO); and one described as dwarf and of spreading, close-branched habit, bearing fruit sparsely (PAUCIFLORA, *Dippel*). I have not seen the former.

P. CRENULATA, *Roemer*. NEPALESE WHITE THORN

(Cratægus crenulata, *Roxburgh*, Bot. Reg., vol. 30, t. 52)

Nearly allied to the common pyracanth (P. coccinea), this differs chiefly in the leaves being rounded instead of tapered and pointed at the apex, and in the smaller flowers and fruit. The leaves are ultimately quite glabrous, narrow-oblong or obovate, up to 2½ ins. long, ⅝ in. wide, rounded, but with a short bristle-tip. The styles differ from those of P. coccinea in being more separated at the base. Fruit orange-yellow. It is a large, more or less thorny bush, and can scarcely be regarded as more than a variety of P. coccinea. It is, however, much slower in growth and more tender. Being quite inferior to the European pyracanth, it is rarely seen in cultivation. It needs a south wall. Native of Temperate Himalaya.

P. ROGERSIANA, *Chittenden* (Plate 50)

(P. crenulata Rogersiana, *A. B. Jackson*)

A spiny evergreen shrub of erect habit probably 8 to 10 ft. high, of dense rather pyramidal habit when young. Branchlets clothed with a short pale down, becoming glabrous and pale brown the second season. Leaves glabrous, set ¼ to ½ in. apart on the shoots, oblanceolate or narrowly obovate, slenderly tapered to the base, rounded or abruptly tapered at the apex, shallowly toothed except towards the base, each tooth tipped by a blackish gland; ½ to 1½ ins. long, ⅛ to ½ in. wide; bright green above, paler dull green beneath; stalk slender, up to ⅓ in. long. Flowers white, ¼ to $\frac{5}{16}$ in. wide, produced in June on small corymbose racemes, each flower on a slender glabrous stalk ½ to ¾ in. long. Calyx-tube top-shaped, the lobes triangular, glabrous; petals round; stamens about twenty with smooth white stalks; styles five. Fruit ¼ in. wide, globose, golden yellow to reddish orange.

Native Yunnan, China; discovered by Delavay in 1889; introduced by Forrest in 1911. A charming pyracanth named in honour of the late Mr Coltman-Rogers of Stanage Park, Radnorshire, and the author of *Conifers and their Characteristics*, who first showed young plants at one of the Royal Horticultural Society's Shows at Westminster in March 1913. The most distinctive feature of this shrub in its group is the smallness of its leaves, which gives it a rather dainty appearance, especially in a small state. It is very hardy and bears fruit very abundantly, and forms with variously coloured fruits have been raised at Wisley; the name FLAVA has been given to the bright yellow form, AURANTIACA to the reddish orange one. They are in beauty by October. A form named SEMIPLENA has numerous petals in two or more rows instead of the normal five in one row.

P. YUNNANENSIS, *Chittenden*

(Bot. Mag. t. 9099; P. crenato-serrata, *Rehder*.)

An evergreen shrub up to 12 or 18 ft. high, related to P. atalantioides, but more spiny and less downy in a young state. It can best be distinguished from the two pyracanths just described by the shape of the leaves, whose oblanceolate shape and broad rounded ends are only to be seen occasionally in them; the leaves are from 1 to 3 ins. long, $\frac{1}{3}$ to 1 in. wide, and are often broadest close to the end. The red fruits are rather smaller than those of P. atalantioides, of a lighter shade and later maturing, although the two are connected by intermediate forms.

Native of Yunnan; introduced to France in 1906 by Père Ducloux and raised and distributed by the late Maurice de Vilmorin from his garden at Les Barres. It is useful in retaining its fruits well on into spring.

There is another pyracanth in cultivation going by the name of "P. crenulata taliensis" which no doubt belongs to the same group as the three species just described; it appears to be most closely related to P. yunnanensis or intermediate between it and P. Rogersiana. It has leaves similar in their obovate or obovate-lanceolate shape to those of P. yunnanensis but they are distinct in their smaller size and are finely toothed almost to the base. The young shoots are slightly downy, the leaves quite glabrous. It is very handsome in fruit, the berries being shining yellow, orange-shaped, $\frac{1}{4}$ in. wide, but falling much sooner than those of P. yunnanensis and in colour by October. It was obtained for Kew from Messrs Chenault of Orleans in 1924, and from its name should be a native of the Tali Range, N.W. Yunnan.

PYRACOMELES VILMORINII, *Rehder*. ROSACEÆ

(Gardeners' Chronicle, Feb. 19, 1938, fig. 49)

An evergreen shrub up to 6 ft. high; young shoots slender, at first greyish-downy, soon glabrous. Leaves pinnate at the base, pinnately lobed towards the apex, 1 to $1\frac{1}{2}$ ins. long; leaflets or lobes five to nine, oval, rounded and toothed at the apex, glabrous or nearly so. Flowers white, $\frac{2}{5}$ in. wide, numerous in terminal corymbs; stamens twelve to fifteen. Fruit $\frac{1}{6}$ in. wide, globose, coral-red.

A natural hybrid between Pyracantha atalantioides and Osteomeles subrotunda, which appeared in Mr Chenault's nursery at Orleans sometime previous to 1922, when it had been obtained for, and was in cultivation in, the de Vilmorins' garden at Verrières. It develops numerous fruits and is very handsome when they are ripe in autumn. Said to come true from seed.

PYRETHRUM ARGENTEUM, *Willdenow*. COMPOSITÆ

(Chrysanthemum argenteum, *Willdenow*; Tanacetum argenteum, *Willenow*; Achillea argenteum, *Lamarck*—not *Visiani*)

A low, spreading, "evergreen" shrub from 8 to 15 ins. high and up to 3 ft. or more in diameter; young shoots clothed with a dense white felt. Leaves closely set on the stem, about $1\frac{1}{2}$ ins. long (of which half is stalk), 1 in. wide, ovate in main outline, doubly pinnate, the final divisions linear, $\frac{1}{8}$ to $\frac{1}{4}$ in. long, $\frac{1}{16}$ in. wide, the whole covered with a silvery white coat of hairs and down. Flowers produced during June in a close cluster of about twenty heads at the top of an erect, slender stalk 6 to 12 ins. high, carrying a few greenish leaves towards the base; each flower head is $\frac{1}{4}$ in. wide, somewhat top shaped, consisting of twelve to twenty yellow disk-florets; there are no ray-florets. The involucral scales are closely appressed and covered with white wool.

Native of S.E. Europe, Asia Minor, Syria; cultivated by Philip Miller at Chelsea in 1731. The foliage when crushed has a strong, rather oily, but not wholly unpleasant aromatic odour. It is suitable for a well-drained ledge in the rock garden, fully exposed to the sun, where it is attractive in its silvery white foliage; it has no particular beauty of blossom. It is sometimes grown in gardens as "Chrysanthemum densum," a quite different plant; nor must it be confused with Achillea argentea, *Visiani*, which has more ornamental flower-heads with white ray-florets and is figured by Farrer in his *Rock Garden*, vol. i., p. 8.

P. PRÆTERITUM (Chrysanthemum præteritum, *Horwood*) is an evergreen shrub of flat spreading habit, 1 to 2 ft. high, more in width; the bark on old stems shredding off. Young shoots terete, covered with a close white felt which persists two or more seasons. Leaves alternate, regularly pinnate, 2 to 3 ins. long (including the main-stalk), ½ to ¾ in. wide. Leaflets so closely set together on the main-stalk that they touch, linear, ¼ to ⅜ in. long, $\frac{1}{16}$ in. wide, grooved along the centre, the margins set from end to end with even, regular, rounded teeth, the whole covered with a down which at first is white, becomes grey, and finally wears mostly away, leaving the surface dull green. Flower-heads solitary at the top of a slender, leafy, erect stalk, 3 to 6 ins. high; ray-petals about sixteen, ¼ to ⅜ in. long, creamy white; disk yellow, ⅜ in. wide.

Native probably of S.E. Europe or Asia Minor, but no wild specimen is in the Kew Herbarium and no record of its introduction has been found. It has been grown in gardens as "Chrysanthemum densum" and "C. Aucherianum," from both of which it is very distinct. This shrub is suitable for the rock garden, its habit being close and neat and its foliage and young shoots noticeably white. It flowers in June and is perfectly hardy, having grown without any protection at Kew for over twenty years. It can be propagated by cuttings. The leaves when rubbed give off a rather sour or acrid but not altogether unpleasant odour. It is well distinguished from P. argenteum by its simply pinnate leaves and linear closely packed leaflets.

PYRUS. PEAR

Deciduous trees, rarely shrubs, with simple, toothed, but seldom lobed leaves and top-shaped or globose fruits rarely indented at the junction with the stalk, grit-cells abundant; styles two to five, free; stamens twenty to thirty.

The true pears include some of the tallest and bulkiest trees in its group of genera, but the species as a whole have not such striking attributes for the garden as some of the other sections. Their flowers are often beautiful, but they have little attractive colouring in fruit, and the leaves frequently die off black. Some, like P. salicifolia and P. nivalis, are particularly effective in their young expanding foliage, being covered with a snowy white, thick down. The pears, although represented in N.E. Asia, are more particularly identified with Europe—especially S. and E. Europe—Asia Minor, and N. Africa. In that region there is a strong group, of which P. amygdaliformis, nivalis, salicifolia, and glabra are leading types. No species is a genuine native of the New World Seeds ripen freely, but owing to the hybrid origin of some it is safer to graft the various sorts on their own or nearly allied seedlings—especially as many cultivated trees are of selected forms that could not be relied on to come true from seed.

(See also Malus and Aronia.)

P. AMYGDALIFORMIS, *Villars*

A small tree occasionally 20 ft. or more high, or a large rounded shrub; branches sometimes terminated by a spine; young shoots slightly woolly at first. Leaves very variable in shape and size; oval, ovate, or obovate; 1½ to 2½ ins. long, ½ to ¾ in. wide; wedge-shaped or rounded at the base, the margins very slightly round-toothed; covered with silky hairs when young, but becoming glabrous and lustrous above, and almost or quite glabrous beneath; stalks slender, ½ to 1½ ins. long. Flowers white, 1 in. across, produced in April in corymbs 1½ to 2 ins. across, carrying eight to twelve flowers; calyx white, woolly. Fruit rather orange-shaped, ¾ in. long, 1 in. wide, yellowish brown, produced on a short, thick stalk.

PYRUS AMYGDALIFORMIS

Native of S. Europe, especially in the countries bordering the northern shores of the Mediterranean. It has no particular merit in the garden except that in age it makes a quaint and picturesque tree; from its ally, P. salicifolia, it differs in its nearly glabrous leaves.

Var. CUNEIFOLIA is a name sometimes given to the form with small narrow leaves whose base is slender and tapering.

Var. OBLONGIFOLIA (P. oblongifolia, *Spach*).—This represents another extreme, with oblong or oval leaves, rounded at the base, the stalk 1 to 1½ ins. long. Fruit yellowish, tinged with red on the sunny side, considerably larger than in P. amygdaliformis. It is common in Provence, and known there as the "Gros Perrussier." Perhaps a hybrid between P. amygdaliformis and P. nivalis.

P. SINAICA, *Dumont de Courset*, is allied to P. amygdaliformis, but has larger leaves and longer-stalked fruits, which are round and rather flattened. It is not a native of Sinai, in spite of its name, but is believed to originate from Asia Minor or the islands of the Grecian Archipelago. Its leaves, as in the rest of this group, are white with down in spring, becoming glabrous and shining later.

P. BETULIFOLIA, *Bunge*

A slender, quick-growing, graceful tree, 20 to 30 ft. high; young shoots covered thickly with a grey felt which persists the whole of the year. Leaves ovate or roundish ovate, 2 to 3 ins. long, 1¼ to 1½ ins. wide; long-pointed, tapered or rounded at the base, regularly and sometimes rather coarsely toothed, downy on both surfaces at first, remaining so on the veins beneath throughout the season; dark green, glabrous and lustrous above; stalk 1 to 1¼ ins. long, grey-felted like the shoot. Flowers eight to ten together in a corymb, white, each about ¾ in. across, on a downy stalk ¾ to 1 in. long; calyx downy, its short triangular teeth falling away from the small roundish fruit, which is about the size of a large pea, greyish brown with white dots.

Native of N. China; introduced to Kew in 1882 through seeds sent by the late Dr Bretschneider. The chief characteristics of the tree are its quick graceful growth, and small fruits not crowned by calyx teeth. Its fruit would appear to be of no value, but the tree is used by the Chinese as a stock on which they graft fruiting pears.

P. COMMUNIS, *Linnæus*. WILD PEAR

A deciduous tree, usually 30 to 40, occasionally as much as 60 ft. high, with a trunk 3 ft. through; branches forming short stiff spurs, sometimes spiny. Leaves variable, from ovate, heart-shaped and oval, to almost round; from 1 in. to 4 ins. long, up to 2 ins. wide, very finely round-toothed or entire; stalk slender, 1 to 2 ins. long; the leaves are variable in their downiness, but are either glabrous from the beginning or become nearly or quite so later, and glossy green. Flowers white, 1 to 1½ ins. across, produced in corymbs 2 to 3 ins. across, each flower on a more or less woolly stalk ½ to 1½ ins. long. Fruit top-shaped or rounded, with a tapering or rounded base.

Native of Europe and W. Asia, and found wild in Britain, but doubtfully indigenous. Some authorities have professed to find two sub-species, viz., P. ACHRAS, with elongated fruits and slightly downy mature leaves; and P. PYRASTER, with rounded fruits and glabrous mature leaves; but these characters do not prove constant. The wild pear, as the parent of a multitude of varieties of one of the most delicious of northern fruits, is a tree of interest. It is found scattered in the forests of Central and E. Europe, usually as individuals, never, it is said, in large groups. It produces a most excellent timber, heavy, tough and durable, which, however, is not plentiful enough to be of much importance in commerce. In gardens the wild pear has not much claim to notice. Its graceful, often pendulous branches and large crops of flowers in April are beautiful, but the garden varieties are just as much so, and give useful fruits as well.

P. CORDATA, *Desvaux*, often regarded as a species, is really nothing more than a from of P. communis, smaller in all its parts. The leaves, sometimes heart-shaped, but often rounded or broadly wedge-shaped at the base, are usually less than 1½ ins. long, finely and evenly round-toothed. Flowers smaller, in distinct racemes. Fruits globular, ⅜ to ½ in. diameter, brown spotted with white, smooth. These small rounded fruits afford the best distinction between this pear and P. communis. Long known as a native of France, Spain, and Portugal, it was, in 1865, also discovered wild in the south-west of England by Mr T. R. Archer-Briggs. (It is sometimes called P. communis Briggsii, *Syme*.)

P. LONGIPES, *Cosson and Durieu.*—Also of the communis group and very nearly allied to P. cordata, this pear is a native of Algeria, especially in the mountain gorges above Batna. It is a small tree or shrub, with glabrous branchlets. Leaves roundish oval or broadly ovate, 1 to 2 ins. long, ¼ to 1½ ins. wide; the base sometimes slightly heart-shaped, more especially tapering; very finely and evenly round-toothed, quite glabrous on both sides. lustrous above; stalk slender, 1 to 2 ins. long. Flowers white, 1 to 1¼ ins. across, produced in corymbs 2 to 3 ins. in diameter. Fruit about the size and shape of a small cherry, produced on a slender stalk 1 to 1½ ins. long, turning from green to brown as it ripens, the calyx-lobes falling away. Introduced to Kew from France in 1875.

P. GLABRA, *Boissier.* PERSIAN PEAR

A tree 15 to 20 ft. high, with often spine-tipped branches; young shoots at first covered with grey wool, becoming glabrous by summer. Leaves 1½ to 4 ins. long, ⅓ to ¾ in. wide; linear-lanceolate, long-pointed, slightly round-toothed or quite entire, green on both sides and quite glabrous almost from the very first on both sides; stalk ⅓ to 1½ ins. long. Flowers 1 in. across, white, produced in a cluster of five to eight; flower-stalks and the inner face of sepals more or less woolly. Fruit roundish.

Native of Persia. In Decaisne's observations on this species (*Jardin Fruitier*, vol. i., t. 11), it is stated on the authority of a Mr Haussknecht that the pips of this pear are pickled in brine by the Persians and eaten. The tree is rare in gardens, where, indeed, it has little to recommend it.

P. MICHAUXII, *Bosc*

A small tree with unarmed branches forming a rounded head. Leaves entire, ovate or oval-oblong, blunt at the apex, or with a short, abrupt point; up to 3 ins. long, 1 to 1½ ins. wide; covered when young with white, cottony down, which afterwards falls away and leaves them shining and glabrous above. Flowers white, in very short corymbs. Fruit globose or top-shaped, greenish yellow when ripe, spotted with brown. By some curious error this tree was long regarded as a native of N. America; but no true pear is indigenous to the New World. It is probably from the Levant, and no doubt a hybrid between P. amygdaliformis and P. nivalis. It differs from the former in its entire leaves.

P. NIVALIS, *Jacquin*

A small tree, sturdy in habit; young shoots thickly covered with a white wool. Leaves oval or obovate, 2 to 3 ins. long, ¾ to 1¼ ins. wide, entire, covered when young on both sides, but especially beneath, with a white wool much of which falls away later. Flowers pure white, 1½ ins. across, produced in April in conspicuous clusters. Fruit roundish, 1½ ins. or more wide, yellowish green, borne on a stalk as long or longer than itself.

Native of E. Europe and Asia Minor, where it is sometimes over 50 ft. high; introduced early in the nineteenth century. It is a very beautiful tree early in the season, owing to the pure white leaves and abundant flowers. The tree is cultivated in France for the sake of its fruits, which are not eaten until bletted. It and P. KOTSCHYANA, *Boissier*, are the parents of a race of pears known as "poirier sangers."

Pyrus nivalis may be considered the type of a group of European pears. The following are sometimes regarded as varieties of it, sometimes as species:—

P. CANESCENS, *Spach.*—Probably a hybrid between nivalis and salicifolia. In regard to it Decaisne wrote that it "is intermediate between P. nivalis and P. salicifolia;

its leaves are of the same size as those of nivalis, and often twisted as in salicifolia. They are lanceolate or narrowly oval, finely round-toothed, very white when young, shining dark green above when mature. Fruit pale green, much shorter stalked than P. nivalis. A handsome tree in spring. P. KOTSCHYANA, *Boissier*.—Fruits smaller and harder than in P. nivalis. P. ELEAGRIFOLIA, *Pallas*, differs from Kotschyana in its spiny branches—a character on which no reliance can be placed in cultivation. Native of E. Europe and Asia Minor.

P. PASHIA, *Hamilton*, KUMAONI, *Stapf*

(Bot. Mag., t. 8256)

A tree 25 to 35 ft. high, branches glabrous. Leaves ovate, 2 to 4 ins. long, 1¼ to 2 ins. wide; rounded at the base, the apex varying from long taper-

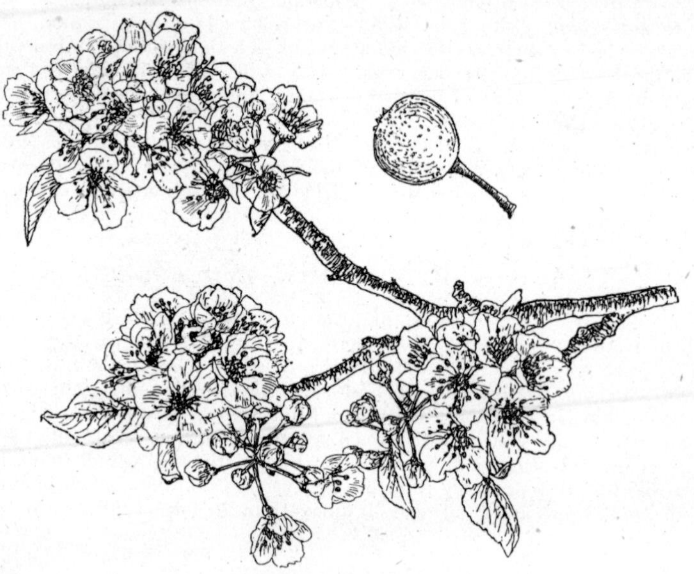

PYRUS PASHIA KUMAONI

pointed to blunt, both surfaces quite glabrous, the margins set with fine, rounded teeth; stalk 1 to 1½ ins. long. Flowers at first rose-tinted, finally white, ¾ in. across, closely packed in rounded corymbs 2 ins. across, each flower on a stalk ½ to ¾ in. long; calyx glabrous outside, woolly inside the lobes; stamens numerous, red. Fruit nearly globular, but narrowed towards the stalk, brown with pale specks, ¾ to 1 in. diameter.

Native of the Himalaya; introduced in 1825. This variety from Kumaon, which appears to be the only representative of the species in cultivation, differs only from the typical P. Pashia in the absence of down from the younger parts. There is a tree 35 ft. high at Kew, with a broad, rounded head, which gives every year a pretty display. It is quite distinct among pears by the compact flower clusters, the rounded overlapping petals, and especially for the pretty effect made by the cluster of deep red stamens in the centre of each flower. The leaves on sucker shoots or on the vigorous shoots of cut-back trees are frequently deeply three-lobed. In N. India the fruit is eaten after having " bletted," like a medlar.

P. REGELII, *Rehder*

(P. heterophylla, *Regel*—not *Steudel*)

A small tree, ultimately 20 to 30 ft. high, whose young branches are covered with a close grey down which persists over the first winter. Leaves exceedingly variable in shape, the two extreme types of which are: (1) ovate with a rounded base and pointed apex, 2 to 3½ ins. long, ¾ to 1½ ins. wide; bluntly, unequally, and rather coarsely toothed; (2) cut back to the midrib into three to seven narrow, linear lobes, which are ¾ to 2 ins. long, ⅛ to ¼ in. wide, finely toothed (see figure). Between these two forms of leaf, which may occur on the same plant, there are many intermediate ones. For the rest, the leaves are of firm, rather leathery texture, and very downy when young, remaining more or less so until they fall; the pinnatifid form, however, appears to be less downy than the undivided one. Flowers white, ¾ to 1 in. across, produced a few together in small clusters. Fruit like a small ordinary pear.

PYRUS REGELII

This extraordinary pear was originally discovered in E. Turkestan by the late Albert Regel, and was raised and distributed (about 1891) by Dr Dieck of Zoeschen, Germany. The two forms of leaf described above would never be regarded as belonging to the same species, but I have seen both, as well as intermediate ones, on the same plant.

P. SALICIFOLIA, *Pallas*. WILLOW-LEAVED PEAR

A tree 15 to 25 ft. high, branchlets covered with down which is quite white when young. Leaves 1½ to 3½ ins. long, ⅓ to ⅔ in. wide; narrowly lanceolate, tapering gradually towards both ends, covered when young on both sides with a beautiful silvery grey down; later in the year this falls away from the upper surface, leaving it shining green; margins quite entire; stalk ½ in. long or less, sometimes scarcely noticeable. Flowers pure white, about ¾ in. across, produced in April, closely packed in small rounded corymbs, the calyx and flower-stalk covered with white wool. Fruit of the typical pear-shape, 1 to 1¼ ins. long and wide.

Native of S.E. Europe and Asia Minor; introduced in 1780. It is the most ornamental of all true pears. Its leaves and flowers often open simultaneously, and it then presents a very charming picture, the willow-like leaves being of a conspicuous silky white. After the flowers fade, the leaves remain silvery for some weeks, gradually, however, becoming greener on the upper surface. The fruit is harsh to the palate, and of no value.

Var. PENDULA is a very elegant tree, with the branches more drooping than ordinary; but in the type they are more or less pendulous.

P. USSURIENSIS, *Maximowicz*

(P. sinensis, *Decaisne*—not of *Lindley*)

A deciduous tree, 40 to 50 ft. high; young shoots warted, nearly or quite glabrous, turning purplish brown the second year, often long and unbranched especially in var. ovoidea. Leaves roundish ovate to obovate-oblong, 2 to 4 ins. long, rounded or slightly cordate at the base, abruptly narrowed to a short, slender point; margin beautifully, finely and regularly bristle-toothed; glabrous or nearly so; stalk slender, 1 to 2¼ ins. long. Fruit globose on a very stout stalk, greenish yellow, 1 to 1½ ins. across, hard and inedible.

Native of N. China and Korea; introduced about 1865. This pear flowers very freely at Kew in late April and is then a very distinct and handsome tree.

Var. HONDOENSIS is wild in Japan. Its leaves are more strictly ovate, with fine, more appressed toothing; very handsome in blossom.

Var. OVOIDEA, *Rehder*.—Remarkable for its curiously gaunt habit, the branches few and scarcely forked. Fruit conical, juicy, pale yellow, 1½ ins. long and wide.

QUERCUS. OAK. FAGACEÆ

A large genus of evergreen and deciduous trees and shrubs, of which nearly three hundred species are known. Sixty to seventy are in cultivation. Leaves alternate, a spiral of five making one circuit of the branchlet, frequently lobed somewhat deeply, but occasionally merely toothed or even entire. The down on the leaves, etc., is mostly stellate. Male and female flowers occur on the same trees, but on separate inflorescences. The males are numerous on pendulous (rarely erect) catkins, small, green or greenish, forming sometimes tassel-like clusters; females few and quite inconspicuous. The most distinctive feature of the oak is its fruit, which consists of a usually egg-shaped or rounded nut (acorn), the lower part of which is more or less enclosed by a cup covered with woody, sometimes fringe-like scales. The acorn frequently takes two seasons to mature. The nearest allies of the oaks are the sweet chestnuts, beeches, and hazels. One group—PASANIA—to which densiflora and cuspidata belong, is sometimes kept apart as a distinct genus.

The oaks are amongst the finest of the large trees of temperate regions. The two native of Britain, Q. pedunculata and Q. sessiliflora, are the largest and longest lived of our deciduous trees, and produce the most valuable timber. Nor are they surpassed in rugged beauty and strength. Their maximum duration of life is probably not less than one thousand years. For some reason the planting of oaks in parks and gardens has fallen into desuetude in recent times. Beyond a few coloured or variegated sorts they are now stocked by very few nurserymen, who cannot, of course, be expected to keep up supplies for which there is no demand. Few firms appear now to grow oaks in such number and variety as did Lee of Isleworth, Smith of Worcester, or Booth of Hamburg, sixty to eighty years ago. The finest collections to-day, after that at Kew, are Lord Ducie's at Tortworth, and the one at Aldenham got together by Mr Vicary Gibbs. To those who contemplate planting oaks I would recommend the following as a selection of twenty of the best, apart from our British species and their varieties :—

DECIDUOUS.—**Castaneæfolia*, *Cerris*, **coccinea* **conferta*, *imbricaria*, **Leana*, *Libani*, *Lucombeana*, **macranthera*, **Mirbeckii*, *palustris*, *Phellos*, **rubra*, *Toza*, **velutina*.

EVERGREEN.—*Acuta*, *coccifera*, *densiflora*, *Ilex*, *phillyræoides*.

Some of the deciduous species, like those marked *, are amongst the handsomest and most striking in foliage of all our big trees, and would impart distinction to any demesne, whilst coccinea and palustris give the richest touches of crimson to our autumn landscape. Q. Ilex forms a class by itself among evergreen trees hardy with us. Oaks, as a whole, thrive best on good deep loams. The old conception that the value of a soil for agriculture was indicated by the size and quality of the oaks upon it has many times been verified, not only in this country but in others, especially by the early settlers in both the east and west coast regions of N. America. Oaks should always if possible be raised from acorns, which should be kept from getting dry after gathering until sown. Grafting has, perforce, to be resorted to for special varieties and rare species ; but although one may see occasionally fine grafted specimens, the practice should only be adopted where absolutely necessary, for it tends to shorten the life of the tree, and in the end retard its growth. I strongly advocate getting all oaks into their permanent places as soon as possible. If I could, I would sow all acorns *in situ*, for thereby the tap-root is preserved and the plant never checked, but for many reasons that is not often possible except in pure forestry. Few trees in nurseries need transplanting with greater regularity every two or three years than oaks do if their final removal is to be accomplished safely, and few suffer more through shifting if their roots have been allowed to wander at will for a longer term. Evergreen species especially are liable to die. They should never be transplanted until after they show signs of growth in late May or early June, or else in September.

Some of the deciduous oaks are infested with an extraordinary variety of gall-producing insects, the best known of which are those that produce oak-apples and flat, circular, disk-like galls, sometimes so dense on the leaf as to partially overlay each other. Although frequently a disfigurement, and inducing a premature yellowing of the leaf, the production of galls does not seem to have noticeable effects on the health of trees. There is no generally practicable means of preventing them.

Q. ACUTA, *Thunberg*

An evergreen tree up to 30 or 40 ft. high in Japan, often shrubby in this country ; young shoots and leaves covered at first with a brown floss, then quite glabrous. Leaves stout and leathery, oval, sometimes inclined to ovate ; tapering or (especially in young plants) rounded at the base and with slenderly tapered, often bluntish points; $2\frac{1}{2}$ to $5\frac{1}{2}$ ins. long, $\frac{7}{8}$ to $2\frac{1}{4}$ ins. wide; the margins entire and undulated; stalk up to 1 in. long, at first downy like the young wood. The upper surface is dark glossy green; lower one dull, yellowish; veins eight to ten each side the midrib. Acorns crowded on a spike; cup downy.

Introduced from Japan by Maries about 1878 to the Coombe Wood nursery, where one of his original plants became a bushy tree over 20 ft. high. It has proved to be perfectly hardy and is a useful evergreen of slow growth. It is only likely to be confused with edulis (*q.v.*)

Q. ÆGILOPS, *Linnæus*. VALONIA OAK

This famous oak, which is widely spread in the eastern Mediterranean region, is but little known in this country, although specimens are to be found in the south and west. Its acorn cups are of remarkable size—up to 1 in. deep and 2 ins. in diameter, covered with long, flattish, downy scales—and were at one time an important article of commerce owing to the remarkable amount of tannin they contain. Young shoots and leaves downy, the latter oval or oblong, 2 to 4 ins. long, $1\frac{1}{2}$ to $2\frac{1}{2}$ ins. wide, with four to six angular bristle-tipped lobes down each margin; the base usually rounded or heart-shaped. There is a good specimen at Abbotsbury, near Weymouth, which has for many years past borne acorns. At Kew the tree is quite hardy and thriving, but although its acorns form, they never ripen. No other cultivated oak produces acorns so large as Q. Ægilops, they are sometimes $2\frac{1}{2}$ ins. by 1 in. It is, however, allied to Q. Cerris.

Var. PYRAMI, *Boissier* (Q. Pyrami, *Kotschy*).—Two specimens of this oak at Kew, 20 to 25 ft. high, are interesting and neat-habited trees of close, rather pyramidal habit. Leaves up to 3 ins. long, obovate, coarsely toothed, often fiddle-shaped through a deep cutting below the middle, glossy green above; dull grey and stellately downy beneath. Trunk rugged, with deep squarish scales.

Q. AGRIFOLIA, *Née*. ENCINA

An evergreen tree up to 80 ft. or more high in California; young shoots densely covered with starry down. Leaves hard in texture, oval or roundish, heart-shaped to tapered at the base, margined with slender, spiny teeth; 1 to 2 ins. long, $\frac{3}{4}$ to $1\frac{1}{2}$ ins. wide; dark shining green and glabrous above; paler, not so glossy beneath, and glabrous except for tufts of down in the vein-axils; stalk $\frac{1}{4}$ to $\frac{1}{2}$ in. long, stellately downy. Acorns cone-shaped, solitary or in pairs, stalkless, about 1 in. long, $\frac{5}{8}$ in. wide near the base, tapered gradually to a point, the lower third enclosed in a cup which is silvery within, and covered with close, flattened scales without.

Native of California; introduced for the Horticultural Society by Hartweg, in 1849; now very rare. A tree at Kew about 35 ft. high, occasionally bears fruit and is quite hardy. According to Elwes the best tree in the country is at Killerton, and now 45 ft. high. Among cultivated evergreen oaks with spiny toothed leaves it is distinct by reason of the tufts of down in the vein-axils and the tapered, conical acorns. It is an interesting oak, but of no particular merit.

Q. ALBA, *Linnæus*. WHITE OAK

The white oak of the eastern and southern United States has no more than a sentimental interest for us in this country, for although, according to Aiton, introduced in 1724, it has after many trials proved a complete failure.

There does not appear at present to be a tree 25 ft. high in the British Isles. Yet it is one of the most magnificent trees of its native country, reaching in places 100 to 150 ft. in height, with a trunk 3 to 6 ft. in diameter, producing a splendid timber with much the same qualities of durability, etc., as our native species. Its young shoots are soon glabrous; its leaves obovate, five- to nine-lobed, 5 to 9 ins. long, scarcely half as wide, the upper surface dark glossy green and glabrous, the lower one pale or glaucous, and at first downy. Acorn ¾ in. long, with about one-fourth enclosed in the cup. This is the type species of the American white oaks, whose acorns mature in one season.

Q. ALIENA, *Blume*

A deciduous tree 60 ft. or more high; young shoots bright yellowish green, not downy, but slightly warted. Leaves obovate to oblong-lanceolate, pointed or rounded at the apex, always tapered at the base, very coarsely wavily toothed with ten to fifteen often bluntish teeth on each margin; veins conspicuous, parallel, running from the midrib to the point of each tooth; 4 to 8 ins. long, 2 to 4½ ins. wide; dark lustrous green and glabrous above, pale or even semi-glaucous and covered with a fine close felt beneath; stalk ½ to 1¼ ins. long. Acorn stalkless or nearly so, mostly solitary but occasionally developing in twos or threes, ½ to 1 in. long, downy at the top, the cup enclosing one-third to one-half of the acorn, the scales appressed, downy.

Native of Japan, Korea, and China; introduced in 1908 to Kew, where trees 25 to 30 ft. high are succeeding very well. They are notable for the fine dark green leaves which strongly resemble those of the American chestnut oak, Q. Prinus in their large size, obovate shape and prominent parallel ribs. That species is, however, well distinguished, in the adult state at any rate, by the distinctly stalked acorns and somewhat smaller leaves.

Var. ACUTESERRATA, *Maximowicz*, has the teeth of the leaf more pointed and often terminated by a distinct mucro. Both are promising oaks.

Q. ALNIFOLIA, *Poech*. GOLDEN OAK OF CYPRUS

An evergreen small tree or shrub; young shoots clothed with grey down. Leaves stiff and hard in texture, roundish or broadly obovate, the terminal part toothed, the margins of the older leaves deflexed so that the inverted leaf has very much the shape of a shallow scoop; 1 to 2¼ ins. long, and about the same or rather less wide; upper surface dark glossy green, lower one yellow or greyish yellow, covered with a dense close felt; stalk downy like the young wood, ¼ to ⅝ in. long. There are five to eight prominent veins each side the midrib. Acorns 1 to 1½ ins. long, ⅓ to ½ in. wide; broadening from the base upwards, and thus somewhat truncheon-shaped, but ending in a short point; cup about ½ in. deep, with downy scales.

Native of Cyprus; introduced to Kew in 1885, where it has proved perfectly hardy, but slow-growing. The peculiar attraction of this oak is the yellow under-surface of its leaves, but out-of-doors in England this colour is only slightly developed, and the under-surface is really greyish. But on the young leaves of a plant grown in a cool greenhouse at Kew the yellow was as markedly developed as in Castanopsis chrysophylla. Very rare in cultivation, and worth reintroducing.

Q. AQUIFOLIOIDES, *Rehder and Wilson*

An evergreen bush or small tree up to 30 ft. high; young shoots thickly furnished with dark, clustered hairs. Leaves leathery, oval, or occasionally obovate, rounded at the apex, and either rounded or broadly wedge-shaped at the base; in young plants the margin is conspicuously spiny-toothed, the teeth $\frac{1}{10}$ in. long; 1 to 2 ins. long, $\frac{3}{4}$ to $1\frac{1}{2}$ ins. wide; dark shining green and rough to the touch above, clothed at first beneath with yellow-brown down; stalk $\frac{1}{12}$ in. long. The midrib is very prominent beneath and branching from it at obtuse angles are five to eight pairs of equally prominent veins which fork towards the decurved margins and terminate in the spiny teeth. Lower surface very corrugated. The acorns (not yet seen on cultivated plants) are described as being produced as many as five together in erect spikes, each acorn about $\frac{1}{2}$ in. long, not so wide, the cup $\frac{2}{5}$ in. wide, half as deep and silky inside. They take two seasons to develop.

Native of W. Szechuen; introduced by Wilson in 1908. According to him this is a scrub oak found over large areas on wind-swept uplands, only developing into a tree in sheltered spots. Small plants in cultivation at Kew grow slowly, but are quite hardy. The spiny character of the leaves, so constant in young plants, apparently is less marked in adult trees, as Wilson records that spineless ones occur. But it is quite usual in evergreens of this type, such as hollies and osmanthuses, for the leaves to become less spiny or even entire as the trees increase in age and size. This oak is probably a dwarf or bushy form of the Himalayan Q. semecarpifolia.

Var. RUFESCENS, *Rehder and Wilson* (Q. Ilex var. rufescens, *Franchet*), differs from the type in its matted down on the lower surface of the leaves and young shoots which is pale grey.

Q. ARKANSANA, *Sargent*. ARKANSAS OAK

A deciduous tree 20 to 30 ft. high; young shoots clothed with short, clustered hairs, which mostly fall away by autumn. Leaves obovate or broadly wedge-shaped, often lobed towards the apex, the midrib always, and the lobes often, terminated by a short bristle (mucro); base mostly tapered, sometimes rounded; 2 to $3\frac{1}{2}$ ins. long, $1\frac{1}{2}$ to $2\frac{1}{2}$ ins. wide; on first expanding they are covered with clustered hairs which soon fall away, leaving the upper surface glabrous and of a clear pleasant green; the lower surface is glabrous also, except for tufts of down in the vein-axils; midrib and veins pale coloured and prominent beneath; leaf-stalks $\frac{1}{2}$ in. or rather more long. Acorns described as solitary or in pairs borne on a short stalk, roundish egg-shaped, $\frac{1}{2}$ in. wide; cup shallow.

Native of Arkansas, where it is rare and local; introduced from the Arnold Arbortetum to Kew, where it has succeeded well and is now a bushy-headed tree 20 ft. high. It is related to Q. marilandica, but the leaves are not so firm and leathery nor ordinarily so deeply lobed.

Q. BARONII, *Skan*. BARON'S OAK

(Q. Dielsiana, *Seemen*)

An evergreen (or it may be, in cold climates, sub-evergreen) shrub 6 ft. or more high; young shoots very slender, furnished with starry down at first, becoming nearly or quite glabrous by late autumn. Leaves ovate-lanceolate to oblong, pointed, rounded to wedge-shaped at the base, the margins set with triangular spine-tipped teeth; $\frac{3}{4}$ to $2\frac{1}{2}$ ins. long, $\frac{3}{8}$ to $1\frac{1}{8}$ ins. wide; dark green and at first starry downy on both surfaces, becoming nearly glabrous by autumn except on the midrib and especially at the base beneath; stalk $\frac{1}{12}$ to $\frac{1}{4}$ in. long. Acorn short-stalked, solitary, roundish egg-shaped, $\frac{1}{3}$ to $\frac{1}{2}$ in. wide, silky at the top; cup $\frac{1}{2}$ to $\frac{3}{4}$ in. wide, with reflexed, awl-shaped downy scales.

Native of W. China; originally discovered by the Italian missionary Giraldi, in Shensi, in 1895; introduced in 1914, probably by F. N. Meyer. It was sent to Kew from the Arnold Arboretum in 1927 and seems to be quite hardy. It is an interesting addition to shrubby evergreen oaks, but has not yet shown any outstanding qualities. Wilson found it common in warm, semi-arid regions of the Min River in W. Szechuen.

Q. BICOLOR, *Willdenow*. SWAMP WHITE OAK

(Q. platanoides, *Sudworth*)

A deciduous tree, 60 to 70 ft. (occasionally more) high, with loose, scaly bark; young shoots slightly downy at first, becoming glabrous. Leaves obovate, 3 to 7 ins. long, 1½ to 4 ins. wide; tapered at the base, the six to eight shallow, rounded lobes at each side often reduced to mere undulations towards the top; upper surface dark polished green, soon becoming glabrous; lower surface pale grey, clothed with a close, soft felt; midrib and stalk yellowish, the latter ½ to ¾ in. long, more or less downy. Acorns about 1 in. long, borne usually in pairs on a more or less downy stalk 2 to 3 ins. long, about one-third enclosed in the cup.

Native of eastern N. America; introduced in 1800. Although the best of the white oaks for this country it is not a first-rate tree, nor has it attained to any great size, although Elwes mentions two or three that are between 50 and 60 ft. high. At Kew it is quite healthy, and has reached 40 ft. in height, the trunk very shaggy through the bark being attached in loose scales. The under-surface of the leaf does not become so silvery white as in N. America, but even here the soft felt beneath renders it distinct. Its acorns are occasionally formed with us, but rarely ripen, although in nature they mature in one season.

Q. CALLIPRINOS, *Webb*. SINDIAN OR PALESTINE OAK

(Q. coccifera palæstina, *Boissier*; Q. coccifera pseudococcifera, *Boissier*)

Brief mention is made of this oak in previous editions, where, following Boissier, Hooker, and other botanists, I regarded it as a variety of the Kermes oak, Q. coccifera. Since then Dr Stapf has studied the Palestine oaks (*Kew Bulletin*, 1920, p. 258) and has come to the conclusion that they represent one type which may be regarded as a good species distinct from Q. coccifera, and to which the name Q. Calliprinos belongs. This name was given by Webb in 1838. Other authors have made several species and several varieties.

Q. Calliprinos differs from Q. coccifera in the large size it attains; it is occasionally a large tree with a trunk 3 ft. and upwards in diameter; its leaves are larger and more oblong in outline; the acorns have larger cups (sometimes over 1 in. deep) the scales of which are linear or lanceolate-oblong, free from the middle upwards and covered with close grey down.

During the campaign against the Turks in the first Great War, acorns of this oak were occasionally gathered by soldiers and sent home. Some were sent to Kew by Major M. Portal, D.S.O., from which plants were raised.

A sentimental and historic interest is attached to Q. Calliprinos because it is the species to which belongs the famous tree known as "Abraham's Oak," or the "Oak of Mamre." This tree grows at Hebron, just below the Russian convent which overlooks the Plain of Mamre, and it is the largest and oldest specimen of its kind known. It is popularly regarded as marking the spot where grew the tree under which Abraham pitched his tent, and on this account is held sacred by Christian, Jew, and Mahommedan alike. In its prime the trunk was 23 ft. in girth. Dr Stapf, basing his calculations on the annual rings of a branch preserved at Kew, considered Abraham's oak to have started its career about 1150 A.D., the time of the Second Crusade. Four hundred years later, when Belon the naturalist visited Hebron, he made no mention of this tree, although it must by then have been of goodly size. But apart from the circumstance that fine trees of Q. Calliprinos were no doubt much commoner then than now in Palestine, the explanation of the omission of Belon to mention this oak is due rather to the fact that, at that time, the legend of Abraham was attached not to an oak but to a species of Pistacia or Terebinth.

Abraham's oak was much damaged during the winter of 1856-7 when a great snowstorm occurred. In the streets of Jerusalem the snow lay deep for many days. The accumulation on this oak was so great that it broke down one of its finest branches, and it was from this that the piece now preserved at Kew was cut. Sir Joseph Hooker records that owing to the superstition that anyone who should cut or maim the tree would lose his first-born son, it was difficult to get anyone to cut up this branch for transportation.

Q. CASTANEÆFOLIA, *C. A. Meyer*. CHESTNUT-LEAVED OAK (Plate 51)

A wide-spreading, deciduous tree reaching 100 ft. in height in a wild state; young branches downy. Leaves narrowly oval or oblong, tapered at both ends, margined with coarse triangular teeth, each terminated by a small, slender, abrupt point; 3 to 7½ ins. long, 1¼ to 3 ins. wide; dark glossy green above and glabrous except when quite young; dull greyish beneath, and clothed with minute down; stalk ½ to 1 in. long, downy. The larger leaves have ten to twelve pairs of parallel veins, prominent beneath, which run out and furnish the short mucronate tip of the tooth. Acorn ¾ to 1¼ ins. long, flattened at the top, and half enclosed in a cup with reflexed downy scales.

Native of the Caucasus and Persia; introduced in the first half of the nineteenth century. A very handsome and striking tree, with a leaf resembling that of a Spanish chestnut in form; it is still very rare. There is a fine tree at Kew over 60 ft. high, and about 10 ft. in girth of trunk, with a wide-spreading head of branches. Akin to the Turkey oak; introduced about 1840.

Var. ALGERIENSIS.—Whilst what may be regarded as the type is found in the Caucasus, an almost identical tree occurs in great numbers in Algeria. This differs from the Caucasian form in its erect pyramidal habit and deeply furrowed bark. Two trees are in the Kew collection raised from acorns sent from Algeria in 1869. The leaves of these trees are much smaller than in the type (the largest 4 to 5 ins. by 1¾ ins.), and the young shoots are more downy. Pomel, who regarded the Algerian form as a distinct species and called it Q. AFARES, says that it also differs in having the acorns clustered four or five together. As in the type, they ripen the second year.

Q. CATESBÆI, *Michaux*. CATESBY'S OAK

(Q. lævis, *Walter*)

A deciduous tree usually 20 to 30 ft., but occasionally twice as much high, with a narrow, round-topped head of more or less contorted branches; winter-buds coated towards the point with rust-coloured down; young shoots reddish, soon becoming nearly glabrous. Leaves of the typical "red" oak shape, being obovate to triangular in main outline, wedge-shaped at the base, but very deeply cut into three, five, or seven lobes which reach to within ½ in. of the midrib; the lobes vary from roughly rectangular to roughly triangular and are themselves toothed, each having a long bristly tip; 4 to 8 ins. long, rather less wide; both surfaces are shining green at maturity and quite glabrous except for tufts of reddish down in the axils of the veins; stalk ¼ to ¾ in. long.

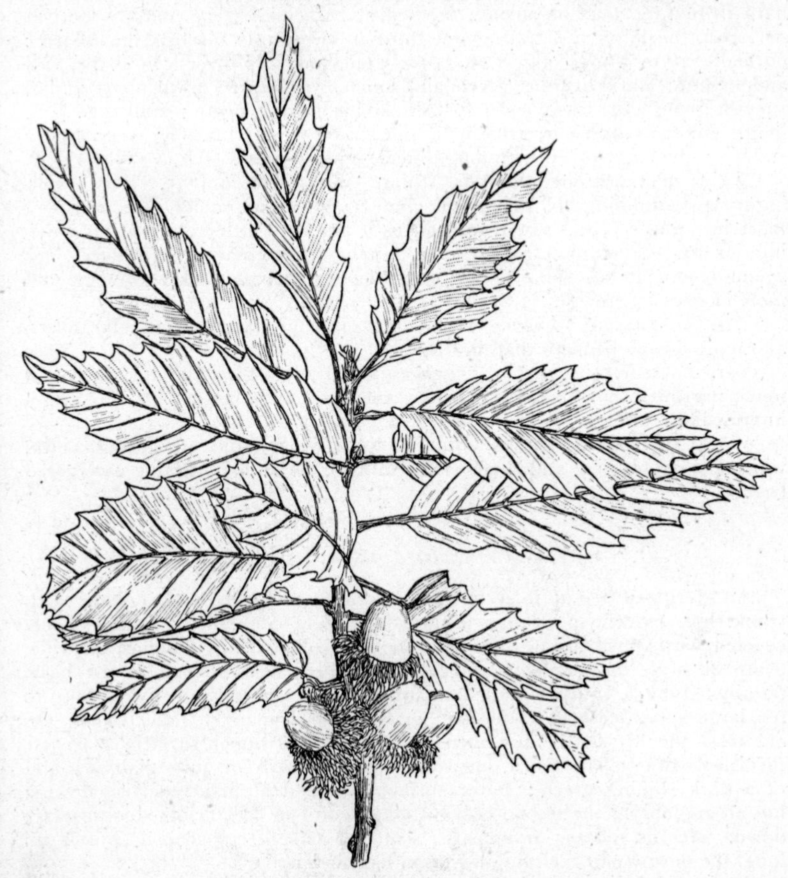

QUERCUS CASTANEÆFOLIA

Acorns usually solitary on a very short stalk, egg-shaped to roundish oval, ¾ in. long, with a ring of white scurf surrounding the conspicuous mucro at the summit; cup thin, enclosing one-third of the acorn, its scales extending down one-third of the inner surface as well as over the entire outer one.

Native of the S.E. United States; introduced in 1823, but now, and perhaps always, very rare in cultivation. Loudon, writing of the tree in 1837, did not know of any tree near London. Certainly it is far from thriving as well as most of the "red" oaks. Plants at Kew only reached about 8 ft. in height in fifteen years. According to Sargent the leaves are sometimes 12 ins. long by 10 ins. wide. It is distinct among the "red" oaks by reason of its very short leaf-stalks. The leaves turn reddish brown before falling.

Q. CERRIS, *Linnæus*. TURKEY OAK

A noble deciduous tree over 120 ft. high, with a trunk occasionally more than 6 ft. in diameter; winter buds all furnished with long, linear, downy scales; young shoots covered with a close, greyish down. Leaves thin and hard in texture, oval or oblong, tapered at both ends, very coarsely toothed or lobed, the lobes penetrating one-third to two-thirds towards the midrib; normally 2½ to 5 ins. long, 1 to 3 ins. wide, but very diverse in shape, size and lobing; dark lustrous green and harsh, with starry down above; dull greyish green and closely covered with similar down beneath; stalk ½ to ¾ in. long. Acorns solitary, in pairs or in fours, each 1 to 1¼ ins. long, very shortly stalked; the cup clothed with long, linear, downy scales.

Native of S. Europe and Asia Minor; introduced in 1735. It is a very hardy tree attaining to dimensions under cultivation nobler than those of most introduced trees. As a timber tree it has very little value, being much inferior to the common oak. As a purely ornamental tree, however, for avenues, etc., it has some points in its favour, being quicker-growing and more elegant in growth.

Var. AUSTRIACA.—Leaves with comparatively shallow triangular lobes, and more downy beneath than in the type.

Var. LACINIATA (dissecta).—Leaves lobed almost to the midrib, often much narrower than in the type, between which and this variety are several intermediate forms.

Var. VARIEGATA.—Leaves bordered by a white band of varying width, which penetrates here and there to the midrib. A rather effective variegated tree.

Q. CHRYSOLEPIS, *Liebmann*. MAUL OAK

An evergreen tree up to 40 to 60 ft. high in a wild state, with a short, thick trunk, but scarcely more than a shrub as yet in cultivation; young shoots covered with starry down. Leaves 1 to 3½ ins. long, half to almost as wide, ovate or oval, the smaller ones often roundish, heart-shaped at the base, terminated by a spiny tooth, also furnished on young plants with four to ten large spiny teeth at each side, terminating as many parallel veins. On old trees the leaves are described as entire. The upper surface is at first furnished with stellate down, but soon becomes nearly or quite glabrous, and of a dark shining green; lower surface dull and at first yellowish downy, but often glabrous the second year; stalks $\frac{1}{12}$ to $\frac{1}{6}$ in. long, clothed with starry down. Acorns solitary or in pairs, scarcely stalked, egg-shaped, ¾ to 1 in. long, the downy cup enclosing less than half its length.

Native of California; introduced by Sargent in 1877, but apparently lost to cultivation afterwards, as none but young trees are at present in gardens. It is distinguished among evergreen oaks with foliage of the same character, by the yellowish appressed down beneath the leaves, which, however, is not so thick on plants cultivated in this country as it is in W. America. Of this tree Sargent observes that, in its native state, it is surpassed in majestic dignity and massive strength by no other American species except Q. virginiana of the southern Atlantic States. Trees exist with heads of branches fifty yards across.

Q. VACCINIFOLIA, *Kellogg*.—This is sometimes associated with the above as a variety, but is probably a quite distinct species. It is a prostrate shrub up to 4 ft. high, with small, oval, mostly entire leaves, covered beneath with a pale grey scurf. Introduced in 1909, not much is known of its behaviour. Wild on rocky hillsides in Oregon and California.

Q. CLEISTOCARPA, *Seemen*

(Q. Wilsonii, *Seemen*; Lithocarpus cleistocarpa, *Rehder and Wilson*)

An evergreen tree from 30 to 50 ft. high; young shoots glabrous. Leaves oblong or narrowly oval, long and slenderly pointed, tapered at the base, quite toothless; 3 to 8 ins. long, 1 to 2½ ins. wide; but on vigorous young plants as much as 1 ft. long and 3 or 4 ins. wide; greyish green, quite glabrous; midrib and veins yellowish, the latter in nine to twelve pairs; stalk ¼ to ¾ in. long. Acorn-cups ¾ to 1 in. wide, densely clustered on a stiff spike 2 to 3 ins. long, the acorns almost enclosed.

Native of W. Hupeh and Szechuen, China; introduced for Messrs Veitch by Wilson in 1901. In regard to the individual leaf this is probably the finest of the newer Chinese oaks. But it needs rather warmer conditions than our average climate affords to develop its best qualities. The finest plant in this country grows in the woods at Caerhays, in Cornwall, where it is of erect habit and vigorous growth, a most attractive evergreen bearing leaves over 1 ft. long. It should have shelter from wind. It is hardy at Kew but grows very slowly. Wilson describes old trees as having a much-branched, wide-spreading, flattened crown. The acorns take two years to reach maturity.

Q. COCCIFERA, *Linnæus*. KERMES OAK, GRAIN TREE

An evergreen shrub up to 10 or 12 ft. high, of sturdy, dense, neat habit, sometimes a small tree; young shoots clothed with starry down. Leaves stiff and hard, broadly oval, oblong, or ovate, rounded or heart-shaped at the base, ending in a stiff, sharp spine similar to the three to five with which each margin is armed; ½ to 1½ ins. long, half to three-fourths as wide; dark green above, slightly paler below, shining and glabrous on both surfaces; stalk about ⅛ in. long, downy like the young shoot. Acorns usually solitary on a short stalk about ½ in. long in cultivated specimens, and more than half enclosed in the cup, which is covered with reflexed spiny scales.

Native of the Mediterranean region from Spain eastwards to Syria; cultivated in England in the seventeenth century. Of the dwarf evergreen oaks, this is, perhaps, the most pleasing in the glitter of its foliage and neat bushy habit. It is as prickly-leaved and well-armed as a small-leaved holly. It is variable in its foliage.

Quercus coccifera obtains its popular name of "Kermes oak" from being the host plant on which the kermes insect (*Chermes ilicis*) breeds. This insect, after certain treatment, produces a beautiful scarlet dye remarkable for its richness and lasting quality, once much employed and known in commerce as "grain" or "scarlet grain," but now, owing to cheaper substitutes, fallen into disuse. Three sprigs of Quercus coccifera or "grain tree" still form the crest of the Dyers' Company, whose arms were granted to them between 1420 and 1450. From this one may gather how high was the estimation in which "Kermes" was held in the Middle Ages; but so much has this dye disappeared from modern use that until the matter was investigated at Kew a few years ago, the Company itself did not know to what tree the sprigs were supposed to belong. For an interesting account of this oak in regard to its connection with the dye, and various allusions to the latter quoted from Chaucer and Shakespeare, see *Kew Bulletin*, 1910, p. 167.

Q. AUZANDRI, *Grenier*, is a hybrid between Q. coccifera and Q. Ilex, found wild in S. France, etc. Its leaves are felted beneath, and its acorns are borne two or three together on a stalk up to 1 in. long. It used to be cultivated in the Heatherside nursery, near Bagshot.

The largest tree of Q. coccifera I have noted in this country is or was in the Vicarage garden at Bitton—about 20 ft. high.

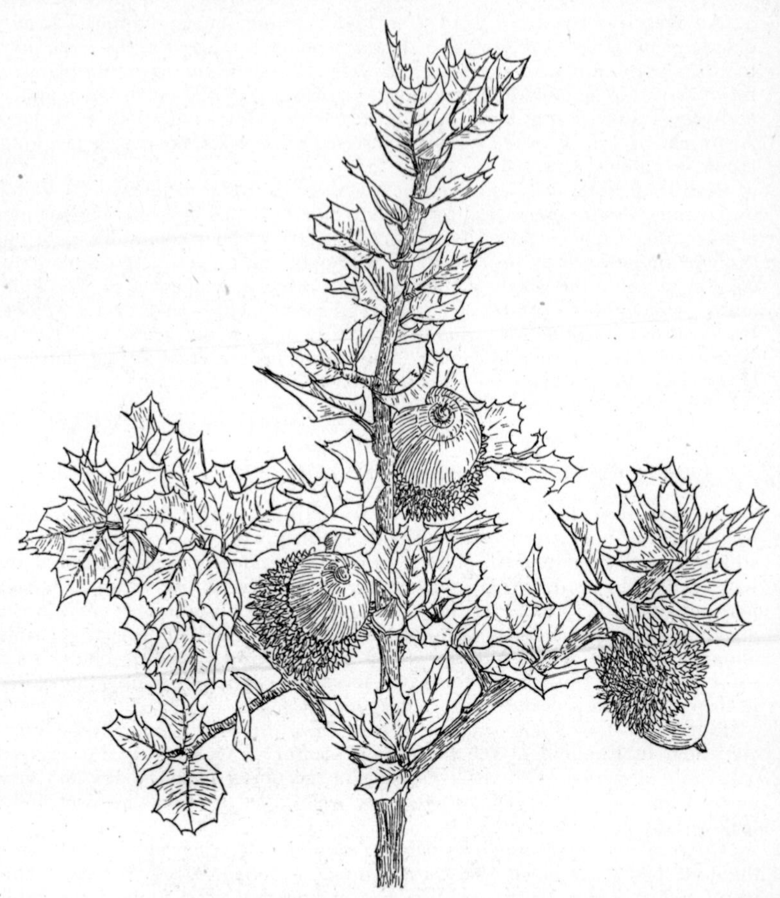

QUERCUS COCCIFERA

Q. COCCINEA, *Muenchhausen*. SCARLET OAK

A deciduous tree up to 70 or 80 ft. high; young shoots warted, not downy; winter buds downy towards the points. Leaves 3 to 6 ins. long, $2\frac{1}{2}$ to $4\frac{1}{2}$ ins. wide (in young trees as much as 6 ins. wide); obovate or oval, tapered at the base, deeply seven- sometimes nine-lobed, the lobes oblong or triangular, coarsely and unequally toothed at the apex; dark green above, paler beneath, both sides lustrous and glabrous, except that there are sometimes tufts of brownish down in the vein-axils beneath; stalk $1\frac{1}{2}$ to $2\frac{1}{2}$ ins. long, glabrous, yellow. Acorns $\frac{1}{2}$ to 1 in. long, two-thirds as wide, one-third to one-half enclosed in a deep, thin-edged cup.

Native of eastern N. America; introduced about the end of the seventeenth century. The true scarlet oak retains its leaves until November or December, and for the last six or eight weeks they are of a brilliant red, and make one of the richest of autumnal effects. The tree frequently known in gardens as "Q. americana splendens" represents the best form of Q. coccinea in cultivation. Q. coccinea differs from Q. rubra in the leaves being lustrous beneath, usually smaller, and with one pair less lobes; also in the acorn cup being hemispherical rather than saucer-shaped. (See also Q. palustris.)

Q. CONFERTA, *Kitaibel.* HUNGARIAN OAK

(Q. Farnetto, *Tenore*)

A deciduous tree of stately habit, up to 100 ft. high in a wild state; young shoots slightly downy, glabrous and grey the second year. Leaves obovate, but deeply cut into six to ten oblong lobes at each side, the largest of which are 2 ins. deep, and penetrate from half to three-fourths of the distance towards the midrib; they frequently have two to five rounded teeth on one or both sides. The largest leaves are 6 to 8 ins. long, and 3 to 4½ ins. wide; the smallest about half those dimensions, all tapering at the base to a short stalk ⅓ in. or less long, the blade usually prolonged at each side into a pair of short auricles. The upper surface is dark green and soon becomes glabrous, the lower one downy, and greyish green. Acorns ½ to ¾ in. long, scarcely stalked, produced two to four together, the lower half enclosed by the cup, which is clothed outside with flattened downy scales.

Native of S.E. Europe; probably introduced about 1837. It is one of the handsomest of all oaks of the sessile-flowered group, and thrives well in cultivation. It is only likely to be confused with Q. macranthera, a species very distinct, nevertheless, in its woolly shoots. Occasional crops of acorns are produced on cultivated trees.

Q. CUSPIDATA, *Thunberg*

(Castanopsis cuspidata, *Schottky*)

In cultivation in Britain this evergreen oak has never got beyond the dimensoins of a bushy shrub, but in Japan it is described as a large tree with elegant drooping branches; young shoots not downy. Leaves oval, broadly tapered at the base, the apex drawn out into a slender blunt tip, leathery; 2 to 3½ ins. long, ¾ to 1½ ins. wide; either entire, wavy, or shallowly toothed towards the apex; stalk ⅛ to ½ in. long. The upper surface is dark shining green, the lower one grey and with a slight metallic sheen. Acorns ⅝ to ¾ in. long, ⅜ in. wide, tapering to a fine point, six to ten borne on an erect stalk. This oak has borne acorns in the late Mr R. Cory's garden, Duffryn, near Cardiff.

Native of China and Japan; introduced by Maries for Messrs Veitch in 1879. According to Siebold, acorns were successfully transported by him to Europe in 1830 by encasing them in clay. Although apparently quite hardy near London, it gives no promise of attaining its natural dimensions here, and probably needs a somewhat warmer climate to be seen at its best, but even in its present state it makes an elegant evergreen shrub. It is distinct from all other evergreen oaks with entire or nearly entire leaves of the same size, in the long drawn-out apex and roundish tip of the leaf, and in the absence of down from the shoots.

Var. VARIEGATA has smaller leaves than the type; they are rarely more than 2 to 2½ ins. long, and have a broad regular margin of creamy yellow; sometimes the whole of one side of the midrib is of that colour. It is not so hardy as the green type, but is occasionally used in greenhouse decoration.

Q. DENSIFLORA, *Hooker and Arnott*. TANBARK OAK

(Bot. Mag., t. 8695; Pasania densiflora, *Oersted*)

An evergreen tree, 70 ft. or more high, in a young state pyramidal; young shoots clothed with a thick pale wool which persists through the second season. Leaves stiff and leathery, oval or oblong, rounded or broadly tapered at the base, pointed, twelve to fourteen parallel ribs on either side the midrib, each rib ending in a sharp tooth; 2 to 4 (occasionally 6) ins. long, ⅞ to 2¼ ins. wide; upper surface at first covered with loose, stellate down which falls away by the end of the season, leaving it dark glossy green; lower surface with a thick down, at first pure white, becoming tawny and ultimately falling away, leaving it grey, glaucous, and nearly glabrous; stalk ⅓ to ¾ in. long. The leaves remain on the tree for two or three years. Male flowers in erect, slender spikes, 2 to 4 ins. long. Acorn solitary or in pairs, ¾ to 1 in. long; the cup shallow, covered with slender, downy, reflexed scales.

Native of California and Oregon; introduced in 1874 to Kew, where it has proved a perfectly hardy and very striking oak. The milk-white down which covers the young leaves of the new shoots is very effective, and with the strong parallel ribs renders the species quite distinct from all other evergreen oaks. It is at present rare, but young plants have recently been raised from acorns introduced by the late Mr F. R. S. Balfour of Dawyck. This is fortunate, as it is becoming rare in a wild state through being cut down for its bark, which is exceedingly rich in tannin.

Q. DENTATA, *Thunberg*. DAIMYO OAK

(Q. Daimio, *Koch*)

A deciduous round-headed tree, 60 or more feet high, described as being of ungainly, unpicturesque habit—only known in a small state in cultivation; young shoots stout, densely covered with greyish soft hairs. Leaves amongst the largest of all hardy oaks; occasionally over 1 ft. long and 6 or 7 ins. wide; the smallest one-third those dimensions; obovate, tapered at the base, blunt or rounded at the apex, the margin with five to nine rounded lobes or deep undulations at each side. When quite young the upper surface is covered with minute down, the under-surface with a whitish felt; but, as the season advances, the down falls away from the upper surface, the lower one remaining sparsely downy. Acorns ½ to ¾ in. long, rounded, produced in clusters; the cup covered with long narrow, downy scales.

Native of Japan and Korea; introduced to Europe in 1830. It is a remarkable oak on account of its enormous leaves, but has never been really a success in this country, and is usually short-lived. Its habit is thin and gaunt. The under-surface of its leaves sometimes presents an extraordinary appearance because of an infestation of disk-like galls, so thickly placed as to overlap each other.

Q. EDULIS, *Makino*

(Q. glabra, *Siebold and Zuccarini*)

An evergreen small tree up to 30 ft. high, usually a shrub in this country, of spreading habit; young shoots glabrous. Leaves glabrous, narrowly oval or oblanceolate, tapered at both ends, blunt-pointed, entire, of hard, leathery texture; 3½ to 6 ins. long, 1 to 2¼ ins. wide; glossy yellowish green above, dull and greyish beneath, nine to eleven veins on either side the midrib; stalk ⅓ to 1 in. long. Acorns produced in triplets on spikes 2 to 3 ins. long, but only an occasional acorn attains to full size, for which it requires two seasons; it is then about 1 in. long, ⅓ in. wide, pointed at the apex, and in shape very like the modern bullet. The cup is about ¼ in. deep.

Native of Japan; introduced in the first half of the nineteenth century, but still somewhat rare. It is a distinct and handsome evergreen, most nearly resembling Q. acuta, but differing in the more tapered base of its leaves and in its glabrous character. When very young the leaves have a scaly covering, but in Q. acuta they are distinctly woolly. It is best adapted for the milder parts of the country, but has produced perfect acorns at Kew.

Q. ENGLERIANA, *Seemen*. ENGLER'S OAK

(Q. obscura, *Seemen*; Q. sutchuenensis, *Franchet*)

A small evergreen tree 20 to 30 ft. high, the young shoots clothed at first with a close, dense, grey down. Leaves leathery, narrowly ovate to oblong, mostly rounded at the base, slenderly pointed; ribs in nine to thirteen pairs, very prominent beneath, each one running out at the margin to a sharp tooth up to 1/12 in. long; 3 to 7 ins. long, 1 to 2 ins. wide; dark shining green and glabrous above, paler and covered with a brown wool beneath; stalk ¼ to ⅝ in. long, clothed with brown wool. Stipules awl-shaped, up to ½ in. long, silky-hairy. The acorns, which ripen the first year, are solitary or two or three together, egg-shaped, about ½ in. long, the cup ⅜ in. wide, ¼ in. deep, the scales grey-downy, appressed.

Native of Hupeh and Szechuen, China; introduced to the Coombe Wood Nursery by Wilson in 1900. He observes that this is always a small tree and is common in rocky places at from 3000 to 6000 ft. altitude. The old leaves fall in spring as the new ones unfold. The leaves as above described are such as are produced by examples at Kew where the tree is hardy, the largest nearly 8 ft. high in 1950. Wilson observes that the leaves are sometimes quite un-toothed. As regards foliage this is undoubtedly one of the finest of hardy evergreen oaks and in the milder counties should make a very handsome tree. Named after Prof. A. Engler (1844-1930), for long Director of the Dahlem Botanic Garden, Berlin.

Q. FALCATA, *Michaux*. SPANISH OAK

(Q. cuneata, not of *Wangenheim*, but of various authors)

A deciduous tree up to 70 or 80 ft. high in nature; young shoots and leaves covered with stellate scurf. Leaves obovate, three-lobed with a wedge-shaped base, or more ovate and five- or seven-lobed; 4 to 7 ins. long, 3½ to 5 ins. wide; the terminal lobe mostly oblong, 2 to 3½ ins. long, the side ones shorter, triangular, or scythe-shaped—often furnished with a few bristle-teeth. The upper surface is dark glossy green, the lower one dull grey and more persistently scurfy; stalk ¾ to 1½ ins. long, slender. Acorns very shortly stalked, about ½ in. wide and long, the cup shallow or saucer-shaped.

Native of the eastern and south central United States; introduced in 1763, but extremely rare. It is hardy and quite healthy at Kew, but slow-growing. According to Sargent, the two forms of leaves occur sometimes on the same, sometimes on separate trees; but I have only seen the three-lobed ones (with the lobes at the terminal part of the leaf) in this country. In this state they are very distinct in the tapered base, and in the scurfy starry down on the various parts. (See Q. marilandica.) It does not colour well in autumn; usually brown.

Q. FRUTICOSA, *Brotero*

(Q. humilis, *Lamarck*)

A semi-evergreen shrub often forming matted scrub about 1 ft. high, but in good soil and other conditions it is to be found 3 to 6 ft. (rarely 12 ft.) high. Leaves almost sessile, 1 to 2 ins. long, oval, rounded or sub-cordate at the base, spiny-toothed, more or less matted at first with grey, stellate down beneath; veins and marginal teeth in four to seven pairs, the latter triangular and spiny-pointed. Acorn about 1 in. long, ovoid, about two-thirds enclosed by the cup which is on a stalk ½ in. long.

Native of Spain and Portugal, reaching as far east as Gibraltar. Near Lisbon it is, or used to be, abundant as matted scrub about 1 ft. high. It was cultivated in the Milford Nurseries, near Godalming, as long ago as 1827, and an acorn-bearing shoot was figured in the *Gardeners' Chronicle*, 24th June 1874, p. 113. The late Sir Oscar Warburg of Boidier, near Epsom, and Mr Collingwood Ingram of Benenden, Kent, re-introduced this oak a few years ago, and I believe it is growing well in both places. It is apparently quite hardy.

Q. GAMBELII, *Nuttall*. SHIN OAK

Little is known in cultivation of this West American oak, which has recently been introduced to this country. It is described by Sargent as a tree 20 to 25 ft. high, whose young shoots are clothed at first with a pale rusty down; often a shrub spreading by underground suckers. Leaves of firm texture, 3 to 5 ins. long, 2 to 3 ins. wide; obovate, tapered at the base, with three to six deepish lobes at each side; the lobes oblong, often with two or three undulations or minor lobes near the apex; upper surface dark glossy green, covered (at least when young) with starry down; pale, dull, and more conspicuously downy beneath; stalk slightly downy, ¼ to ½ in. long. Acorns stalkless or short-stalked, ¾ in. long, half enclosed by the cup.

Native of the eastern slopes of the Rocky Mountains in Colorado, Utah, Nevada, etc., up to 7000 ft. elevation.

Q. GARRYANA, *Douglas*. GARRY OAK. OREGON OAK

A deciduous tree often 60 to 80 ft. high, with a broad compact head of tortuous branches; buds ⅜ in. long and, like the young shoots, densely clothed with reddish brown down. Leaves obovate in main outline but with two or three deep, rounded or blunt lobes at each side, the base usually wedge-shaped; 2 to 5 ins. long, not so wide; dark shining green and glabrous above, more or less downy and conspicuously veined beneath; stalk downy, ½ to 1 in. long. Acorns stalkless, usually solitary, oval or obovoid, about 1 in. long, the base enclosed in a shallow, downy cup.

Native of western N. America, especially of Vancouver Island, of which it is the only native oak. This tree bears considerable resemblance to our native oak in shape of leaf and acorn, but is very distinct in the hairy shoots and large downy winter buds. It has many times been introduced to this country, but I have never seen other than quite small trees, and it is evidently not well adapted to our climate. Douglas named it after his friend, Mr Garry of the Hudson's Bay Company, who greatly assisted him in his early journeys.

Q. GILLIANA, *Rehder and Wilson.* GILL'S OAK

A small evergreen tree up to 25 ft. high, or a bushy shrub; young shoots brown, clothed at first with loose starry down. Leaves leathery, oval, or slightly obovate, rounded or slightly heart-shaped at the base, rounded at the apex, margins stiffly toothed on young plants, becoming largely entire on adult ones; 1 to 2½ ins. long, ½ to 1⅓ ins. wide; dark glossy green, sprinkled beneath when young with starry down; stalk ⅛ in. or less long. Acorns (which ripen the first year) egg-shaped, ½ in. wide, borne two to four together on a short, stiff stalk, themselves scarcely stalked; acorn-cup hemispherical, enclosing about half the acorn, downy inside, the outside scales appressed, triangular, clothed with yellowish grey down.

Native of W. Szechuen, China; introduced by Wilson in 1910. This oak, which has some resemblance in leaf-shape to Q. Ilex Gramuntia but belongs to the cork oak group, requires, like most of the recent Chinese oaks, rather warmer conditions than exist in places like Kew.

Q. GLANDULIFERA, *Blume*

A deciduous tree up to 30 or 45 ft. high, of elegant habit; young shoots with silky, appressed, and forward-pointing hairs. Leaves obovate or narrowly oval, 2 to 7 ins. long, 1 to 2½ ins. wide; tapered at both ends, with six to twelve incurved, gland-tipped teeth at each side, and eight to fourteen pairs of parallel veins running out to the apex of the teeth; dark green above, greyish beneath, both surfaces white with appressed silvery hairs when quite young, much of which falls away from the upper one; stalk ¼ to ½ in. long. Acorns small, solitary, or several on a short stalk; cup shallow.

Native of Japan, Korea, and China; introduced in 1893 by Prof. Sargent. It varies in size and shape of leaf on different trees; the leaves of one form at Kew are only ½ to 1½ ins. wide. All the forms promise to make shapely specimens. The species thrives remarkably well in the vicinity of Boston, Mass.

Q. GROSSESERRATA, *Blume*

(Q. mongolica grosseserrata, *Rehder and Wilson*)

A large deciduous tree, 80 to 100 ft. high; young shoots irregularly furnished with pale warts, but not downy. Leaves obovate, 4 to 9 ins. long, 2½ to 5½ ins. wide; tapered to a pair of auricles at the base, pointed at the apex, ten to fifteen teeth on each margin, the largest from ½ to ¾ in. deep, triangular, and again toothed; dark, rather glossy green above, pale beneath, glabrous except on the midrib and veins, which are more or less downy on both surfaces; stalk ⅛ to ⅓ in. long, glabrous. Acorns one to three on a short stalk, about one-third enclosed in the hemispherical cup (not yet produced in this country).

Native of Japan; introduced to Kew by Prof. Sargent in 1893. Although it appears to be quite hardy in this country, this oak does not thrive so well with us as it does in the eastern United States. In the suburbs of Boston, Mass., and in the Arnold Arboretum trees of the same generation as those at Kew are already remarkably striking for their size, rude vigour, and splendid foliage. Even on young trees in this country I have measured leaves 12 ins. by 7 ins., but on adult trees no doubt they are much smaller.

Q. CRISPULA, *Blume*, is closely allied to and may be specifically the same as Q. grosseserrata. So far as leaf, bark, and habit were concerned, Sargent was unable to distinguish between the two when he was in Japan. But according to Miyabe, the Japanese botanist, the acorn cup of Q. crispula is deeper, embracing about half the cylindrical acorn, both falling off together when ripe; whilst in Q. grosseserrata the cup is hemispherical, enclosing only one-third of the acorn, which falls away free when ripe. (*Forest Flora of Japan*, pp. 67-68.) Introduced from Japan in 1893.

Q. Henryi, *Seemen*. Henry's Oak

(Lithocarpus Henryi, *Rehder and Wilson*)

An evergreen tree up to 50 ft. high, forming a neat, oval, or rounded crown of branches as seen in a wild state; leaves and shoots glabrous except for a thin down when quite young. Leaves quite toothless, narrowly oblong, tapered at both ends, more slenderly to the point; 4 to 9 ins. long, 1½ to 2 ins. wide; leathery, pale green, shining; stalk up to 1 in. long. Acorns (which take two years to mature closely packed on a stout spike 4 to 8 ins. long at or near the end of the shoot; they are globose, flattened at the top, ¾ in. wide. Acorn-cup shallow, thin, ⅛ in. deep.

Native of W. Hupeh and E. Szechuen, China; introduced to the Coombe Wood Nursery by Wilson in 1901. This oak is hardy at Kew but is very slow in growth. Like Q. cleistocarpa, which it much resembles, it will succeed much better in the warmer counties and make a handsome evergreen tree with probably larger leaves than those described above. It is quite distinct from that species in the longer spikes of acorns and especially in the shallow thin cup; but in foliage it is not so easy to distinguish the two. Q. Henryi has leaves greener beneath, with more pairs of veins on the average, and longer stalks.

Q. Ilex, *Linnæus*. Holm Oak

An evergreen tree of large size, attaining in favourable places a height of 70 to 90 ft., and developing in open situations a huge head of densely leafy branches as much across, the terminal portions of the branches usually pendulous in old trees; trunk sometimes over 20 ft. in girth; young shoots clothed with a close grey felt. Leaves very variable in shape, most frequently narrowly oval or ovate-lanceolate; 1½ to 3 ins. long, ½ to 1 in. broad; rounded or broadly tapered at the base, pointed, sometimes entire, sometimes (especially on young trees) more or less remotely toothed. When quite young both surfaces are clothed with whitish down, which soon falls away entirely from the upper surface leaving it a dark glossy green; on the lower surface it turns grey or tawny, and persists until the fall of the leaf; stalk ⅛ to ⅝ in. long. Acorns usually ½ to ¾ in. long in this country, produced one to three together on a short downy stalk.

Native of the Mediterranean region; cultivated in England since the sixteenth century. The holm oak is in many respects the finest of all evergreen trees, apart from conifers, cultivated in the British Isles. Its foliage is most abundant, and the branches form heavy dark masses on the tree. The habit of young trees is curiously diverse, some being of distinctly pendulous habit, others rigidly pyramidal. The leaves, too, vary very much in size, shape, and toothing. On strong sucker shoots I have gathered them 5 ins. long and 2¼ ins. wide, but that is very unusual. This oak likes a warm, rather light soil, and is perfectly hardy in the south and west of England, and near the coast. In very severe winters it is occasionally denuded of foliage. It thrives well near the sea, and is much planted on the sea-front of some of the southern watering-places, where it is seen as a dense, flat-headed bush, stunted, but otherwise quite healthy. It has one defect as a tree in trim gardens, due to shedding the leaves of the previous year during May and June, and making an unsightly litter day after day. One way of avoiding this nuisance is to plant the ground underneath the branches with ivy, amongst which the leaves fall and automatically disappear. Grown in woods under

Quercus Ilex (in flower)

semi-forest conditions, the holm oak makes a tall slender trunk of rather picturesque appearance, due to the corrugation of the bark. It may also, if so desired, be clipped into rounded or pyramidal shapes and kept permanently dwarf. It should only be propagated by acorns, which it produces in quantity in dry hot seasons. They ripen the first autumn.

Var. BALLOTA, *De Candolle*.—A Spanish and North African form sometimes kept up as a distinct species (Q. Ballota, *Desfontaines*). It has large edible acorns, to which it owes such distinctness as it possesses. The leaves are oblong, mostly rounded at both ends, with a mucronate tip; ½ to 2 ins. long; grey beneath as in Q. Ilex.

Var. CRISPA.—A curious form with small, orbicular leaves, averaging about ½ in. in length, the margins decurved. Very slow-growing, and a curiosity merely; known in gardens since the early nineteenth century.

Var. FORDII.—Leaves of a peculiarly dark glossy green, narrow; 1 to 2 ins. long, ⅓ to ⅝ in. wide; the margins wavy and more or less toothed. Said to have first appeared in Lucombe & Pince's nursery at Exeter.

Var. GENABII.—Leaves very large and leathery, as much as 5 ins. long by 2½ ins. wide, coarsely toothed towards the apex.

Var. GRAMUNTIA, *Loudon* (Q. Gramuntia, *Linnæus*).—Leaves oval to roundish, with slender, spiny teeth, often heart-shaped at the base, up to 2 ins. long, short-stalked. It is more stunted in habit. The name is derived from the Grammont estate, near Montpelier, on which the tree originally described by Linnæus grew.

Var. LATIFOLIA.—A large-leaved form like Genabii, the leaves of about the same size, but not so thick and rigid; toothed towards the apex.

Other names such as longifolia, macrophylla, rotundifolia, serratifolia, have been given to supposed forms; but they show no more differences than might be detected in an ordinary batch of seedlings.

Q. ILICIFOLIA, *Wangenheim*. BEAR OAK

(Q. nana, *Sargent*; Q. Banisteri, *Michaux*)

A small deciduous tree up to 20 or 30 ft. high, more frequently a rounded shrub; young shoots hoary with short down. Leaves 2 to 4 ins. long, 1 to 2½ ins. wide; obovate or oval in the main, but deeply three- five- or seven-lobed, the apex and the lobes narrowly triangular, pointed, and terminated by a bristle-like tip; the base wedge-shaped; dark glossy green and glabrous (or soon becoming so) above, clothed beneath with a close whitish felt; stalk ¼ to ⅝ in. long, slender. Acorns solitary or in pairs, ½ in. long, roundish, ripening the second season, the lower half enclosed in a short-stalked cup with thin, flattened, downy scales.

Native of the eastern United States; introduced in 1800. A neat-habited and interesting oak, distinguished among the species with similar leaf shape by its small stature and the felted under-surface of its leaves. The freedom with which it bears acorns has led to the suggestion that it may make good pheasant covert. In Messrs Barbier's nursery at Orleans and at Les Barres I have seen it bearing great crops, but it does not produce them so freely in Britain. Its leaves die off scarlet and yellow in America, but are rarely highly coloured with us.

Q. IMBRICARIA, *Michaux*. SHINGLE OAK

A deciduous tree, 50 to 60 ft. high; young shoots soon glabrous, angled. Leaves narrowly oval or oblong-ovate, 4 to 7 ins. long, 1 to 3 ins. wide; tapered at both ends, often blunt at the apex, nearly always entire (rarely three-lobed near the apex); dark polished green and glabrous above, covered all the season beneath with a short grey starry down; stalk ¼ to ⅝ in. long. Acorns solitary, seldom in pairs, ½ to ⅔ in. long, nearly as broad, the shortly-stalked, shallow cup about half covered with thin flattened scales.

Native of the south-eastern and central United States; introduced by

John Fraser in 1786. This handsome and striking oak is uncommon in cultivation in spite of its early introduction, but Elwes mentions a tree at Milford, near Godalming, 60 ft. high. It is quite distinct from all other cultivated deciduous oaks in the long, narrow, entire leaves, downy beneath.

Q. INCANA, *Roxburgh*

An evergreen tree up to 80 ft. high, whose bark peels off the trunk in large flakes; young shoots clothed with close grey felt. Leaves oblong-lanceolate or narrowly oval, wedge-shaped at the base, tapered to a fine slender point; margins conspicuously toothed except towards the base; 2½ to 6 ins. long, 1 to 2 ins. wide; upper surface dark green soon becoming glabrous, lower one clothed with a pure white close felt which persists until the leaf falls; the veins are prominent beneath and number eight to twelve each side the midrib; stalk ⅓ to ⅝ in. long. Acorns solitary, or sometimes two or three together on a very short, felted stalk, egg-shaped to conical, 1 in. long; acorn-cups ½ in. wide, enclosing about half the acorn.

Native of the Himalaya, up to elevations of 8000 ft. The oak is interesting as the almost inseparable companion in a wild state of Rhododendron arboreum, and it was no doubt introduced to this country about the same time—1815. It just misses being hardy at Kew. During a series of mild winters it will grow 7 or 8 ft. high, but a fairly hard winter will cut it back to ground level and a really hard one kill it outright. It is remarkable that so distinct and beautiful a tree—for the felt beneath the leaves is perhaps the whitest seen in cultivated oaks—should have been so long neglected in the gardens of the south and west. Wherever Rhododendron arboreum succeeds it should be perfectly at home. The largest tree I have seen was in the Himalayan House at Kew. The whiteness of the leaves as seen from the ground and the flaking bark are very noticeable.

Q. KELLOGGII, *Newberry*. CALIFORNIAN BLACK OAK

(Q. californica, *Cooper*; Q. sonomensis, *A. De Candolle*)

A deciduous tree up to 80 ft. or more high in a wild state, the bark very dark coloured in age, smooth and grey on young trees; young shoots downy at first. Leaves oval in the main, but cut up into deep lobes after the fashion of Q. coccinea; the lobes (usually seven or nine) being oblong and furnished with two to four bristle-tipped teeth, the space between the lobes rounded at the base. The leaves are 3 to 6 ins. long, two-thirds as wide; dark shining green and glabrous above, paler beneath, and either downy or becoming almost or quite glabrous; stalk yellowish like the midrib, at first slightly downy, 1 to 1½ ins. long. Acorns solitary or a few on a stalk, 1 to 1¼ ins. long, downy at the top, one-third to two-thirds enclosed in a cup which has ovate-lanceolate scales, and is borne on a short, thick stalk.

Native of California and Oregon; very rare in cultivation, but a handsome tree with the red oak type of foliage. It is quite hardy, and occasionally produces fertile acorns at Kew; they take two seasons to mature, and at the end of the first are almost entirely enclosed in the cup. It is the only oak west of the Rocky Mountains which possesses the red or black oak character of leaf. It may be said to represent there the Q. velutina of the eastern States.

Q. KEWENSIS, *Osborn*. KEW OAK

(Gardeners' Chronicle, 26th Dec. 1931, fig. 209)

This remarkable evergreen hybrid oak was raised at Kew in 1914 from acorns gathered from Q. Wislizenii, an evergreen species from California.

Three plants were raised and it was soon evident from their foliage and rate of growth they were not of pure parentage. The leaves are 1½ to 3½ ins. long, ¾ to 1¾ ins. wide, oblong-ovate in main outline, but with the margins cut into five or six triangular lobes ⅛ to ½ in. deep, each lobe and the apex having a mucronate tip, the base subcordate or truncate; dull green and glabrous above; shining green with loose stellate hairs on the midrib and stalk beneath, the latter ¼ to ½ in. long. Young shoots slightly furnished at first with stellate hairs, bright brown. The tree is evergreen, its branching slender, dense and erect; the largest example in 1932 was about 28 ft. high and growing vigorously. Acorns ¾ to 1 in. long, ½ in. wide, taking two years to reach maturity like those of Q. Wislizenii.

The mother tree is standing in the oak collection at Kew and it is fairly certain that its female flowers were fertilised by wind-blown pollen from a large Turkey oak (Q. Cerris) growing some forty yards away. The angular lobing of the leaves of Q. kewensis is very suggestive of the Turkey oak and so is its fine network of veins on the under surface. But the dull grey-green beneath the leaves of the Turkey oak and the very characteristic thread-like stipules that surround its buds disappear in the hybrid, which is also quite evergreen.

Q. LAMELLOSA, *Smith*

An evergreen tree of large size (up to 120 ft. high with a trunk girthing 15 ft.); scales of buds round and downy; young shoots furnished at first with tawny down. Leaves variable in size and shape, mostly narrowly oval or oblong, rounded or broadly tapered at the base, pointed, the margins usually conspicuously and sharply toothed except towards the stalk; dark glossy green above, glaucous and at first downy beneath; ordinarily 6 to 10 ins. long, 2½ to 4 ins. wide; stalk 1 to 1¾ ins. long; ribs sunken above, very prominent beneath, in usually twenty to twenty-five pairs. Acorns stalkless, solitary to as many as four on a short stout spike, the flattish nut 1 in. or more across, almost enclosed by the cup which is twice as wide and made up of about ten thin, concentric, downy rings set one above the other.

Native of Nepal, Sikkim, Bhotan; discovered in Nepal by Buchanan-Hamilton in 1802. Of all the Asiatic oaks that are likely to grow outside in any part of this country this is the finest alike in the size of the leaves and that of the acorn cups. Sir Jospeh Hooker described it as the noblest of all oaks. A leaf collected by him in Sikkim about 1850 and preserved at Kew is 15 ins. long and 9 ins. wide; another is 18 ins. long by 6 ins. wide, and has thirty-five pairs of veins. It is found up to 9000 ft. altitude in Sikkim, at about the same elevation as Rhododendron grande, and they ought to be of similar hardiness. There are young plants in Cornish gardens and there was a very healthy young tree, 9 ft. high, in Col. Stephenson-Clarke's garden at Binstead, Isle of Wight.

Q. LEANA, *Nuttall*. LEA'S HYBRID OAK

A natural hybrid between Q. imbricaria and Q. velutina, of which there are several fine trees in this country. The leaves in shape approach those of imbricaria, being oblong and tapered at both ends; they are, however, rarely entire as in that species, but are more or less irregularly, and either deeply or shallowly lobed; 3 to 7 ins. long, 1 to 2½ ins. wide; dark green and glossy above, furnished with a scurfy down beneath, but not so thickly as in Q. imbricaria. Young shoots more or less scurfy with starry down. This oak is named in honour of Mr T. G. Lea, who discovered it about 1830, near

Cincinnati, Ohio. According to Sargent, it is scattered widely as solitary individuals over the south-eastern United States. From the variable character of trees given this name, especially in shape and pubescence of leaf, it is probable that it represents trees of different origin, although Q. imbricaria is undoubtedly one parent. In 1910 I saw trees in the Arnold Arboretum with leaves 3 to 5 ins. wide. It is always a vigorous, handsome oak. Of somewhat similar character and origin is

Q. HETEROPHYLLA, *Michaux*, supposed to be a hybrid between Q. Phellos and Q. velutina or Q. rubra. It has glabrous shoots, and the leaves are also glabrous except for tufts of down in the leaf-axils. The leaves are 3 to 6 ins. long, 1 to 2½ ins. wide, varying from almost entire to having three to five deep, bristle-tipped lobes at each side. The origin of this tree is doubtful, and possibly more than one oak goes under the name. The heterophylla we cultivate now has leaf-stalks up to 1 in. or more long, but an oak of this name grown at Kew sixty to seventy years ago had all its leaf-stalks about ⅛ in. long. Originally discovered in the early part of the eighteenth century near Philadelphia in a field belonging to John Bartram.

Q. LIBANI, *Olivier*. LEBANON OAK

A deciduous tree of elegant growth not apparently attaining to a great size; young shoots clothed at first with minute down. Leaves oblong-

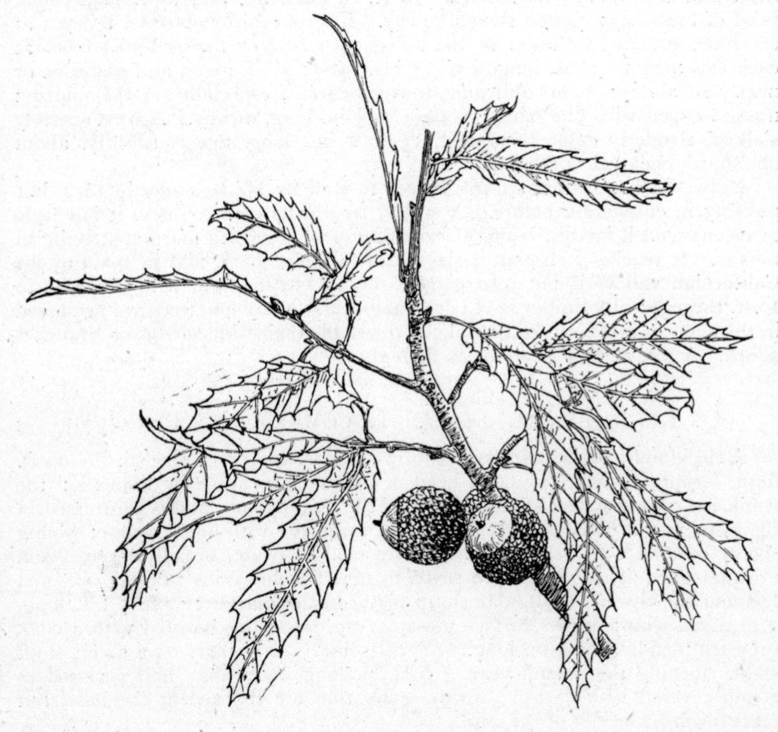

QUERCUS LIBANI

lanceolate, rounded at the base, tapered to a fine point; 2 to 4 ins. long, ½ to 1 in. wide; dark glossy green above, paler green beneath; stalk about

$\frac{1}{2}$ in. long. On our cultivated trees the leaves soon become glabrous on both surfaces except for a few hairs on the midrib and veins, but on wild specimens the under-surface is frequently thickly covered with down. Springing from each side of the midrib at an angle of 45°, and running out to the margin, where each forms the bristle-like point to a triangular tooth, are nine to twelve parallel veins. Acorns solitary or in pairs on a thick woody stalk $\frac{1}{2}$ in. or more long, on which they ripen the second year; they are about 1 in. long on cultivated trees and more than half enclosed in a large cup.

Native of the mountains of Syria, including Mt. Lebanon, and of Asia Minor; introduced to Paris about 1855. Although the branches are slender and elegant they are scarcely pendulous on young trees. Acorns are frequently produced, but they do not become so large as those of some native trees. Among cultivated oaks this is most nearly allied to Q. macedonica (*q.v.*). It is sometimes met with in nurseries as "Q. serrata pendula."

Q. LOBATA, *Née*. VALLEY OAK

(Q. Hindsii, *Bentham*)

A deciduous tree of the largest size, often over 100 ft. high in a wild state, the trunk occasionally as much as 10 ft. in diameter, and forming a broad head of branches; young shoots downy. Leaves oval or obovate, tapered at the base, rounded or blunt at the apex, with four or five rounded lobes at each side; $1\frac{1}{2}$ to 3 ins. long, $\frac{5}{8}$ to $1\frac{3}{4}$ ins. wide; dark green and glabrous or nearly so above; pale, dull and downy beneath, especially on the midrib; margin edged with fine hairs; stalk $\frac{1}{8}$ to $\frac{1}{2}$ in. long, downy. Acorns scarcely stalked, slenderly conical, pointed, $1\frac{1}{4}$ to 2 ins. long, mostly solitary, about one-fourth enclosed in the cup.

Native of W. California; introduced to Kew by Mr Bolander in 1874, but possibly in cultivation before. A stately tree in its own country, it has little to recommend it in this, being of exceedingly slow growth and not striking in foliage. It reaches its greatest size on deep moist loam, and in some of the Californian valleys is not infrequently 100 to 150 ft. high, with trunks 8 to 10 ft. through. Its timber is of poor quality, but many fine trees are preserved in the fields of the West for the sake of the shade their wide-spreading branches afford. A tree at Kew is about 40 ft. high.

Q. LUCOMBEANA, *Sweet*. LUCOMBE OAK (Plate 52)

A deciduous, or, in some of its forms, almost evergreen tree up to 100 ft. high, forming a large, rounded head of branches as much in diameter; the trunk has a corrugated bark like that of the Turkey oak, and is buttressed in the same way at the base; terminal bud furnished with linear scales; young shoots covered with grey down. Leaves oval or ovate, broadly tapered and unequal-sided at the base, with seven to nine parallel veins running out, and forming the tips of, triangular sharp teeth on the margin; 2 to 5 ins. long, 1 to 2 ins. wide; upper surface glossy green, lower one covered with a close grey felt; stalk $\frac{1}{4}$ to $\frac{1}{2}$ in. long. Acorns solitary or in pairs on a short, stout stalk, ripening the second year, $\frac{3}{4}$ to 1 in. long, more than half enclosed in a cup covered with narrow, downy scales that are reflexed at the base, but erect towards the rim of the cup.

A hybrid between the cork oak and the Turkey oak, raised about 1765 from seed borne on a tree of the latter, by Lucombe, a gardener and nurseryman of Exeter. It is a handsome and stately oak, producing fertile acorns in plenty. From these many trees have been raised which show considerable variation within the limits set by the two parent species. It is not necessary, nor indeed easy, satisfactorily to define all these variations on paper, although they are palpable enough when the trees grow together. When seedlings of Q. Lucombeana deviate towards the Turkey oak, the bark shows little or no corkiness, and the foliage is strictly deciduous. When, on the other hand, the influence of the cork oak predominates, it is evident in corky bark and nearly or quite evergreen leaves. The practice of calling the Lucombe oak and its progeny varieties of Q. Cerris is unsatisfactory, and I here follow the more logical one adopted by Elwes and Henry of keeping it distinct, and treating its seedling forms as varieties.

Var. CANA MAJOR.—Leaves often three-lobed.

Var. CRISPA, *Loudon.*—A corky barked, nearly evergreen form; leaves brilliant dark green above, white beneath. Habit more compact than ordinary Lucombe oak. A reversion towards Q. Suber, raised in 1792.

Var. DIVERSIFOLIA.—Leaves of extraordinary shapes; usually the middle part of the blade is reduced to a narrow strip about ⅛ in. wide each side the midrib, widening at the apex like the bowl of a spoon, sometimes entire, sometimes three- or five-lobed; the base with from one to five shallow or deep, rounded or pointed lobes. The leading types of leaves may be described as fiddle-shaped and spoon-shaped. Bark corky; habit very erect; evergreen. A small tree.

Var. FULHAMENSIS. Fulham Oak.—As represented at Kew by old trees, this is a tall oak with a round head of branches more slender and graceful than those of Lucombeana or the other varieties. Shoots and under-surface of leaves grey, as in Lucombeana, the latter more coarsely toothed. This variety got its name from a tree that grew for many years in Osborne's nursery at Fulham—now built over—and originally no doubt a seedling of Lucombe oak, although this particular tree was grafted.

Q. PSEUDOSUBER, *Santi*, found in Italy and Provence, is a probable hybrid between Q. Suber and Q. Cerris. The leaves have much the character of some seedlings of Lucombe oak, reverting to Q. Suber.

Q. LUSITANICA, *Lamarck*

A deciduous tree of middle size, or sometimes shrubby, with a rough thick bark cut up into square scales; young shoots densely downy. Leaves extremely variable; commonly oval or obovate, 2 to 3 ins. long, about half as wide; rounded or unequal at the base, blunt or pointed at the apex, with five to nine coarse triangular teeth at each side; upper surface dullish grey-green, scurfy downy at first, but ultimately nearly glabrous except on the midrib; lower surface clothed with a close, grey felt; stalk ¼ to 1 in. long. Acorns ¾ in. long, clustered two or three together; cup hemispherical.

Native of Spain and Portugal; introduced, according to Loudon, in 1824; still uncommon in gardens. A tree on a lawn near the Cactus House at Kew is a spreading, low tree, slow-growing, and of no particular merit. Closely allied to Q. lusitanica and with similar acorns is

Q. INFECTORIA, *Olivier.*—It is a more Eastern tree, being found in S.E. Europe and Asia Minor, differing from its Western relative in the glabrous or nearly glabrous leaves and young shoots. As represented at Kew, it is a rather elegant small tree with grey foliage, hard in texture, and not falling till late in autumn. Leaf-stalk glabrous, up to 1 in. long, slender. Var. BOISSIERI, *De Candolle.*—Leaves larger and more numerously toothed, often over 3 ins. long; young shoots and leaf-stalks downy. Perhaps intermediate between the two species. Var. PETIOLARIS, *De Candolle.*—Leaf-stalk up to 1 in. long. Leaves almost entire or toothed towards the apex, and often of large size.

Q. MACEDONICA, *A. De Candolle*. MACEDONIAN OAK

(Q. trojana, *Webb*)

A small deciduous tree of slender, pyramidal habit when young; branchlets dull and grey, furnished at first with stellate scurf. Leaves ovate-oblong, slightly heart-shaped at the base, taper-pointed, with nine to twelve parallel veins either side the midrib, each terminating at the apex of a comparatively large, incurved, triangular tooth; 1¼ to 2¾ ins. long, ½ to 1¼ ins. wide; shining with a rather metallic lustre above, duller beneath; both surfaces quite glabrous by the time the leaf is fully grown; stalk ⅛ in. or less long. Acorn usually solitary, scarcely stalked, ¾ to 1¼ ins. long.

Native of S.E. Europe; introduced about 1890. A very distinct oak, rather stiff in habit and (in a young state at least) retaining its leaves until December. It is very hardy, and I have never seen it injured by frost. As described, this oak resembles Q. Libani, but it is really a much stiffer tree, the leaves are shorter and greyer green, and both they and the acorns are much shorter stalked.

Q. MACRANTHERA, *Fischer and Meyer*

A deciduous tree up to 60 ft. high, with very stout young shoots and leaf-stalks covered with a thick, soft, greyish down that becomes dark, and persists through the second season; buds clothed with slender, hairy scales ¾ in. long. Leaves broadly obovate, tapered at the base, the margin conspicuously cut into seven to eleven rounded lobes down either side, each lobe ½ to 1 in. deep, sometimes with one to three teeth on its lower side. The largest leaves are 6 ins. long and 4 ins. wide, the smallest half as large; green, with minute hairs above; pale beneath, and clothed with soft down; stalk ½ to ⅝ in. long. Acorns scarcely stalked, about 1 in. long, the lower half enclosed by a cup which is covered outside with erect, lanceolate, downy scales.

Native of the Caucasus and Persia; introduced about 1895. This is one of the most distinct of European oaks with large leaves, equalling conferta and Mirbeckii in that respect, but distinct from them in the densely downy shoots and under-surface of the leaves. It is quite hardy, and young trees have already been raised from acorns of introduced trees.

Q. MACROCARPA, *Michaux*. BURR OAK

A deciduous tree, rarely more than 60 ft. high in this country, but 80 to 170 ft. high in nature; bark scaling; young shoots and buds downy. Leaves obovate, 4 to 10 ins. (sometimes 1 ft.) long, about half as wide, wedge-shaped at the base, five- or seven-lobed, the terminal lobe often large (consisting of about half the leaf), ovate, and itself wavy-lobed; the lower lobes often reach almost to the midrib; dark green, glabrous and glossy above, covered beneath with a pale, dull, minute felt; stalk up to 1¼ ins. long, downy. Acorn ¾ to 1½ ins. long, usually solitary, about half enclosed in a cup distinguished by having the scales near the rim almost thread-like and forming a fringe, on account of which this tree is often known as the "mossy-cup oak."

Native of eastern N. America; introduced in 1811. It is very similar to bicolor, but is distinguished by the more deeply lobed leaves, and especially by the acorn cup. Like all the white oaks of America, it is not very happy in our climate, but there are a few healthy small trees up to 40 ft. high at Kew and elsewhere.

Q. LYRATA, *Walter.* Overcup Oak.—This is sometimes though rarely seen in gardens, and is not suited to our climate. It is allied to Q. macrocarpa, but its acorn is distinguished by being almost or entirely enclosed in the cup. The leaves are obovate, deeply five- to nine-lobed, the largest 7 to 9 ins. long, nearly half as wide, dark green and glabrous above, pale and downy beneath; stalk up to ¾ in. long. Native of the southern United States, where it is occasionally 100 ft. high; introduced in 1786.

Q. MARILANDICA, *Muenchhausen.* BLACK JACK OAK

(Q. nigra, *Wangenheim*)

A deciduous tree, 20 to 40 ft. high, forming a low, spreading head of rugged branches; young shoots covered with scurfy stellate down, becoming shining grey the second year. Leaves broadly obovate, tapered to a narrow, rounded or wedge-shaped base; broad and three-lobed at the apex; the lobes sometimes shallow and little more than undulations, sometimes broad, deep oblong, each with subsidiary lobes or teeth terminated by a bristle. The leaves vary from 2 to 7 ins. long, and are nearly or quite as much wide; upper surface dark polished green, at first covered with stellate scurf; lower surface paler, with conspicuous lines and tufts of down along the midrib and veins; stalk ¼ to ½ in. long. Acorns ¾ in. long, solitary or in pairs, on a short, thick, downy stalk; cup one-third to two-thirds the length of the acorn.

Native of the eastern United States; introduced early in the eighteenth century. Occasionally its leaves turn rich red in autumn, but more often brown. It is a slow-growing and comparatively dwarf oak, but its foliage is striking. The three-lobed form of leaf in Q. falcata is rather like the above, but has a slender stalk twice or more than twice as long.

Q. MIRBECKII, *Durieu*

A deciduous tree of stately habit, 60 to 80 ft. high in England, up to 120 ft. in Algeria; young shoots ribbed, not downy, brown the second year. Leaves oval or obovate, coarsely toothed or lobed, the base rounded to heart-shaped, or frequently lobed each side the stalk (auricled). In young trees the leaves are 3 to 7 ins. long, 1¾ to 3½ ins. wide; in adult trees they are smaller generally; dark green and glabrous above, rather glaucous beneath and also glabrous except for some loose brown floss on the midrib, especially towards the base and on the stalk, which is ½ to 1 in. long; ribs in eight to fourteen pairs. Acorns scarcely stalked, produced two or three together, about 1 in. long; the cup encloses the lowest third, and is itself clothed outside with flattened downy scales.

Native of N. Africa and S.W. Europe; perfectly hardy, and one of the handsomest of all oaks, being a vigorous grower and notable for the rich green and large size of its leaves, which remain on the branches until Christmas, sometimes a month or two later. It is of the same type as conferta and macranthera, but differs from both in the glabrous, less deeply lobed leaves. From pontica it is distinguished by the leaves having much fewer ribs. It was introduced from Algeria to France by General Pelissier, about 1845, by acorns, some of which were at the time sent by Louis Philippe to Queen Victoria. A tree at Hawkwood, near Chiselhurst, has a trunk girthing 12 ft. In E. Algeria, according to Henry, it is an important timber tree, the forests of that region yielding about three and a half million cubic feet of timber annually.

Q. MYRSINÆFOLIA, *Blume*

(Q. bambusæfolia, *Fortune* ; Q. Vibrayeana, *Franchet*)

An evergreen tree, said to be 30 to 50 ft. high in nature, but usually a bush in cultivation; young shoots glabrous, slender, warted the second year. Leaves lanceolate, broadly tapered or rounded at the base, and with long slender points, the upper half toothed; 2½ to 4 ins. long, ⅝ to 1¼ ins. wide; pale shining green above, somewhat glaucous beneath, glabrous on both surfaces; stalk ½ in. long. When young the leaves are of a rich purplish red, very striking against the green of the older foliage. The acorns are produced two to four on a spike, but have not yet been developed in this country.

Native of China and Japan; introduced from China in 1854, by Fortune. As a garden oak it is chiefly notable for the colour of its narrow graceful foliage when young.

Q. NIGRA, *Linnæus*. WATER OAK

(Q. aquatica, *Walter*)

A deciduous tree up to 80 ft. high in a wild state; young shoots glabrous, Leaves often crowded at the end of short twigs, extremely variable in shape. mostly obovate, tapered at the base and rounded or bluntish at the apex; some, however, are narrow-oblong, liket hose of Q. Phellos, and entire; others have several shallow or deep lobes towards the apex; they vary from 1½ to 4 ins. long, and from ½ to 2 ins. wide, and are of a pale green and glabrous on both surfaces except for tufts of down in the vein-axils beneath; stalk $\frac{1}{10}$ to ¼ in. long. Acorns usually solitary, ½ in. broad and long, one-third enclosed in a broad, shallow, short-stalked cup with appressed scales.

Native of the southern United States; introduced in 1723. The water oak is not common, but a few good specimens are scattered about the country chiefly in old-established gardens. The best at Kew is near the chief entrance, and about 50 ft. high. It retains its leaves quite fresh until about the New Year. Its affinities are with Q. Phellos, which, however, never has the broad, obovate or lobed leaves. In the southern United States it is popular as a shade tree for streets, etc. This oak must not be confounded with the "Black Jack oak"—the Q. nigra of *Wangenheim*—a very different tree. (See Q. marilandica.)

Q. OXYODON, *Miquel*

(Q. lineata oxyodon, *Wenzig*)

A low-growing evergreen tree up to 30 ft. high, with wide-spreading branches forming a flattened crown; young shoots soon becoming glabrous. Leaves hard and leathery, narrowly oblong, long and slenderly pointed, rounded to tapered at the base, conspicuously toothed, teeth incurved; 3 to 8 ins. long, 1 to 3 ins. wide; dark glossy green and glabrous above; glaucous and covered with close felt beneath; midrib yellowish beneath and, like the twelve to twenty pairs of veins, conspicuously raised on the under surface. Acorns (which ripen in one year) not stalked but clustered on a spike 1 to 1½ ins. long near the end of the shoot; they are about ½ in. wide, the cup basin-shaped, concentrically ringed.

Native of W. Hupeh and E. Szechuen, China, where it is common in woods up to 4000 ft. altitude; introduced to the Coombe Wood Nursery by Wilson in

1900. The same or a nearly related oak is found in Assam. It is scarcely hardy enough to succeed at Kew, but in more southern and western localities should make a handsome evergreen. Among the newer Chinese oaks it bears most resemblance in leaf to Q. Engleriana, but that species has fewer veins to each leaf and in the earlier part of the season is readily distinguished by the brown wool on the stalk, midrib, and lower vein-axils.

Q. PALUSTRIS, *Muenchhausen*. PIN OAK

A deciduous tree, 70 to 100 ft. high, forming a dense head of slender branches pendulous at the ends; young shoots not downy, warted. Leaves 3 to 6 ins. long, nearly as wide, obovate, tapered or cut nearly straight across at the base, five- or seven-lobed; the lobes reaching three-fourths of the way to the midrib, oblong or triangular, unequally toothed near the apex; both surfaces are glossy green and glabrous, except that, in the vein-axils beneath, there are large conspicuous tufts of greyish down; stalk very slender, up to 2 ins. long. Acorn about ½ in. long and broad, flattish at the base, where it is enclosed by a shallow saucer-shaped cup.

Native of the eastern United States; introduced to England in 1800. It occasionally bears crops of acorns, which require two seasons to mature. It is one of the very best growers among American oaks cultivated in this country, and is very elegant in its slender branches, especially whilst young or of the middle size. The leaves often turn deep scarlet in autumn, but I do not think it is so effective and reliable in this respect as Q. coccinea; on the dry soil at Kew it is, at any rate, much inferior. It is frequently confused with Q. coccinea, but Q. palustris is distinguished by its more densely branched graceful head, by the invariable and conspicuous tufts of down beneath the leaf, by the shallower acorn-cup, and by the glabrous winter buds. From rubra it differs in the more deeply divided leaves, polished green on both sides.

Var. PENDULA.—Branches much more drooping than in the type.

Q. PEDUNCULATA, *Ehrhart*. COMMON OAK

(Q. robur, *Linnæus* (in part))

A deciduous tree which develops in the open ground a broad, spreading head of rugged branches wider than the tree is high. In such positions, fully grown trees are 60 to 80 ft. high, but where they are growing close together they reach 100 ft. or more in height; young shoots glabrous. Leaves stalkless or shortly stalked, obovate or oblong, ordinarily 2 to 4 ins. long, ¾ to 2½ ins. wide; the margins cut into three to six rounded lobes; tapered towards the base, where are two small lobes; upper surface dark green, lower one greyish, glabrous. Acorns ¾ to 1¼ ins. long, ovoid, one to several on a slender stalk 2 to 5 ins. long, one-third enclosed in the cup. The common oak has produced many varieties, of which the following are a selection:—

Var. CONCORDIA, *Lemaire*. Golden Oak.—Leaves of a bright yellow lasting during the summer, but liable to scorch; not of a strong constitution. It appeared in Van Geert's nursery at Ghent about 1843-4. Var. AUREA LEUCOCARPA is somewhat similar.

Var. CRISPA.—Leaves small, very wrinkled.

Var. FASTIGIATA, *De Candolle*. Cypress Oak.—A form with leaves and acorns like those of the common oak, but having the habit of a Lombardy poplar. It has been found wild in various parts of Europe. As a picturesque tree of slower growth but longer life than the Lombardy poplar, it is worthy of more notice from planters than it has yet received. Sub-varieties of it are

GRANGEI, of broadly pyramidal rather than columnar growth; and TORTUOSA branches contorted; neither is of any importance.

Var. FILICIFOLIA, *Lemaire* (Q. asplenifolia; Q. pectinata; Q. taraxacifolia). Fern-leaved Oak.—Leaves downy beneath, long-stalked, cut almost or quite to the midrib into narrow, slender, pointed lobes about ¼ in. wide; base of leaf tapered. The leaves are occasionally 6 or 7 ins. long. The stalked, downy leaves would seem to point to an affinity with Q. sessiliflora, but the acorns are stalked.

Var. HAAS, *De Candolle* (Q. Haas, *Kotschy*).—This, by some regarded as a distinct species, has downy shoots, leaf-stalks, and under-surface of leaves. Acorns and leaves very large, the latter up to 7¼ ins. long by 4½ ins. wide, and the acorn-stalks up to 3 ins. long; young shoots very stout. Wild in Asia Minor.

Var. HETEROPHYLLA, *Loudon* (var. Trinessii).—Leaves very variously shaped, some long and narrow, scarcely or not at all lobed, often hooded; others deeply and raggedly cut, never so regularly as in filicifolia. They usually hang loosely from the branches, and are 3 to 9 ins. long, ½ to 2 ins. wide. This must not be confused with the American Q. heterophylla described under Q. leana (*q.v.*).

Var. HOLOPHYLLA.—I first saw this remarkable variety in the Arnold Arboretum. Its leaves are stalked, oval or slightly obovate, perfectly entire, blunt at the apex, and with the ordinary pair of auricles at the base; 1 to 3½ ins. long, ½ to 1½ ins. wide; stalk ¼ to ½ in. long. Acorn stalk 3 ins. or more long.

Var. PENDULA, *Loudon*. Weeping Oak.—Branches pendulous. A slender tree as I have seen it, but probably variable in this respect, as there are many specimens of independent origin.

Var. PURPURASCENS, *A. De Candolle*.—Leaves, young shoots, and young acorn-cups purple. This occurs in several forms, the most striking of which is NIGRA (or "nigricans"), with very deep purple foliage which keeps its colour late. Var. GRANBYANA is of the same group.

Var. VARIEGATA.—There are several forms of variegated common oak, but very few, so far as I have seen, of much value in the garden. The leaves are variously marked with white or yellow, either on the margins or over the blade generally. A curious form at Kew is green on the first growth of the season, variegated on the second.

The common oak of Britain is well known as one of the longest-lived and most valuable timber trees of the world. It is spread pretty generally over Europe, the Caucasus, and Asia Minor. Although its timber is in less demand now than it was before iron and steel came into use for ship-building, it is still the best that can be used in house-building—floors, panelling, and the like. None other lasts so well, has so much beauty, or satisfies one's sentiment so completely in an English house.

It is only likely to be confused with Q. sessiliflora, the durmast oak, which differs in having comparatively long-stalked leaves, but stalkless or nearly stalkless acorns; its leaves, too, are always more or less downy beneath, and have not the little lobes or auricles at the base common to pedunculata. Intermediate or hybrid forms occur.

Q. PHELLOS, *Linnæus*. WILLOW OAK

A deciduous tree from 70 to 100 ft. high, forming a rounded or columnar head of branches; bark glabrous, grey; young shoots and leaves at first downy, then glabrous. Leaves pale green, thin, oblong-lanceolate, tapered at the base, mostly pointed at the apex, entire, or slightly wavy on each margin;

2 to 5½ ins. long, ⅓ to 1 in. wide; stalk ⅛ to ¼ in. long, minutely downy or glabrous. Acorns (rarely seen on introduced trees) scarcely bigger than a large red currant, and produced in a shallow, saucer-shaped cup.

Native of the eastern United States; introduced early in the eighteenth century. It is quite distinct from all other cultivated deciduous oaks in its glabrous, narrow, normally untoothed leaves. In a young state it is a very elegant tree. There are several examples from 70 to 100 ft. high in England.

Q. PHILLYRÆOIDES, *A. Gray*

A large evergreen shrub of rounded, bushy habit, or a small tree 20 to 30 ft. high; young shoots clothed with starry scurf. Leaves leathery, obovate or oval, heart-shaped or rounded at the base, tapering at the apex to a blunt or rounded tip, shallowly and usually bluntly toothed at the upper half; 1¼ to 2½ ins. long, ¾ to 1¼ ins. wide, bright dark green above and glabrous except on the midrib; paler and also glossy beneath; stalk ¼ in. or less long, clothed with stellate scurfy down, which extends along the lower part of the midrib. Acorn ½ to ¾ in. long, formed but rarely developed in this country.

Native of China and Japan; introduced in 1861 by Richard Oldham when collecting for Kew. The largest specimen at Kew is about 16 ft. high and through—a handsome cheerful bush, well clothed to the ground with shining foliage. It is remarkable that this oak is not better known in gardens. From the rest of the evergreen oaks it can be distinguished by the bright green, nearly glabrous surfaces of its leaves, combined with an absence of spine-tipped teeth.

Q. PONTICA, *Koch*. ARMENIAN OAK

A low deciduous tree or shrub, probably under 20 ft. high; young shoots glabrous, stout, strongly ribbed. Leaves oval or obovate, broadly tapered at the base, rather abruptly pointed; sharply, coarsely, and unequally toothed; 4 to 6½ ins. long, 1¾ to 3½ ins. wide; slightly glossy, glabrous, green with a yellow midrib above; glaucous beneath and hairy along the midrib and chief veins. When young there are also appressed hairs over the whole lower surface. The leaf is strongly marked by (usually) sixteen or seventeen ribs running out from the midrib to the points of the teeth at an angle of about 45°; stalk ¼ to ½ in. long, at first slightly hairy, yellow.

Native of N.E. Armenia and the Caucasus; introduced to Germany by Dr Dieck of Zoeschen, about 1885, but not to England until considerably later; there appears to be none but comparatively small plants in the country at present. It is a very striking oak, its strongly ribbed leaves sometimes as much as 8 ins. long by 4 ins. wide. The shoots form conspicuously large terminal buds, whose slender scales are clothed with silky hairs. Very well worth planting.

Q. PRINOIDES, *Willdenow*. CHINQUAPIN, SCRUB OAK

A deciduous shrub, spreading by means of root-suckers, and forming dense thickets; young shoots ribbed, not downy. Leaves obovate, tapered at the base, pointed, with four to seven coarse, triangular teeth at each side; 3 to 6 ins. long, about two-thirds as wide; dark glossy green and glabrous above, grey and minutely downy beneath; stalk ¼ to ½ in. long. Acorns scarcely stalked, up to ¾ in. long, nearly half enclosed by the cup.

Native of the eastern and central United States; introduced in 1828. It is interesting and curious as a suckering oak, but has little to recommend it for ornament. It is said not to exceed 15 ft. in height in a wild state, but I have only seen it one-third that height in cultivation, and never bearing acorns.

Q. Prinus, *Linnæus*. Basket Oak

A deciduous tree, 60 to 100 ft. high in a wild state; young shoots stout, glabrous. Leaves obovate, 3 to 7 ins. long, 1½ to 3½ ins. wide; tapered at the base, more abruptly so to the blunt apex; from each side of the midrib there spring ten to fifteen prominent parallel veins, each of which, except one or two at the base, runs out to the apex of an oblique rounded tooth. The upper surface is dark glossy green and glabrous, midrib bright yellow; lower surface dull pale grey, and covered with a minute down; stalk yellow, ½ to 1¼ ins. long, glabrous. Acorns oval, 1¼ ins. long, solitary or in pairs, borne on a stout stalk about ½ in. long; usually less than half enclosed in the thin, warted cup.

Native of the eastern United States; introduced about the end of the seventeenth century, but still an uncommon tree. Young specimens at Kew, where it thrives well, show it to be a handsome and striking oak. It resembles Q. Mirbeckii, but that species is downy only along the midrib beneath and on the stalk, and its acorns are scarcely stalked.

Q. Muehlenbergii, *Engelmann* (Q. acuminata, *Sargent*). Yellow Oak.—This is very nearly allied to Q. Prinus, but differs in having little or no stalk to the acorn; the teeth of the usually narrower leaves also are sharper and are tipped by a glandular mucro. It scarcely exists in cultivation in Britain, and does not seem likely to succeed as well as Q. Prinus. Native of the eastern and central United States, reaching southern Ontario.

Q. pubescens, *Willdenow*

(Q. lanuginosa, *Thuillier*)

A medium-sized or small deciduous tree; young shoots covered with dense greyish down. Leaves very wavy at the margins, mostly obovate, 1½ to 4 ins. long, half as wide; with usually four to eight rounded or pointed lobes on either side; upper surface at first covered with grey down, most or all of which falls away before the end of the summer; lower surface permanently and usually very thickly covered with down; stalk ¼ to ¾ in. long. Acorns either very shortly stalked or stalkless, solitary or as many as four together, each about half enclosed in the downy cup.

Native of S. Europe, and allied most closely to Q. sessiliflora, but with greyer and much more downy leaves. It is also a smaller tree with more scaly bark. To the Californian Q. lobata it bears a resemblance, but has longer leaf-stalks.

Var. dissecta.—Leaves smaller, lobes deeper, much undulated.

Q. rubra, *Duroi* (not *Linnæus*). Red Oak

(Q. borealis, *Michaux*)

A deciduous tree from 60 to 80 ft. high, with a trunk 3 to 6 ft. in diameter; young shoots warted, not downy. Leaves oval or obovate, usually tapered, sometimes rounded at the base, with three to five lobes at each side, the lobes obliquely triangular or ovate, pointed, and with a few unequal teeth; the blade is 4 to 9 ins. long, 4 to 6 ins. broad, dark green and glabrous above, pale dull green or greyish beneath, usually with tufts of brownish hairs in the vein-axils; stalks yellowish, glabrous, 1 to 2 ins. long. Acorns ¾ to 1¼ ins. long nearly as wide, flat at the bottom, which is set in a shallow, almost saucer-shaped cup covered with closely appressed, short broad scales; they take two seasons to mature.

Native of eastern N. America; introduced early in the eighteenth century. The red oak is undoubtedly the best grower among the American species introduced to Britain. In a young state it grows vigorously, and its fine, boldly cut foliage makes it one of the handsomest of deciduous trees. It frequently ripens acorns at Kew, from which young trees are raised. Its leaves change in autumn to a dull reddish or yellowish brown. The largest tree noted in England by Elwes is at Pains Hill—80 ft. high, its trunk 19 ft. in girth. The red oak is much confused with Q. coccinea and palustris, but it has larger leaves than either, usually not so deeply lobed, dull beneath. and not so bright above. The shallow acorn cup distinguishes it also from Q. coccinea. The Q. borealis maxima of *Sargent* has larger acorns.

Var. AUREA.—In spring the leaves of this form of red oak are of a beautiful clear yellow, giving quite as bright an effect from a distance as flowers. To those who admire trees of this character it may be recommended as one of the best. It needs a sheltered spot with an evergreen background, and is nothing like so vigorous as the green-leaved type.

In the grounds of Arley Castle (largely planted by Lord Mountnorris about 1820) I saw in autumn some years ago a number of trees which, in foliage, did not appear to differ from ordinary Q. rubra, except that they were making a very fine display of rich red, which Q. rubra does not make as a rule. Henry (*Trees of Great Britain and Ireland*, p. 1248) believed these trees to be hybrids between Q. rubra and Q. coccinea, deriving their rich autumnal colouring from the latter.

Q. SEMECARPIFOLIA, *Smith*

An evergreen or sub-evergreen tree naturally of very large size (100 ft. high and 18 ft. in girth of trunk); young shoots furnished with soft, rust-coloured down. Leaves leathery, oval or oblong, usually rounded at the apex and more or less heart-shaped at the base; on young trees they are spiny-toothed at the margins but on old ones become entire; 2 to 4 ins. long, two-thirds as much wide; dark green above and soon glabrous except on the midrib; paler and covered with reddish brown down beneath; veins eight to twelve each side the midrib, forking before they reach the margin; stalk $\frac{1}{12}$ to $\frac{1}{8}$ in. long. Acorns solitary or in pairs on a short downy stalk, globose to egg-shaped, $\frac{1}{2}$ to 1 in. wide, the base enclosed in a thin, shallow cup with triangular, erect, ciliate scales. The acorns take fifteen months to reach maturity.

Native of the Himalaya up to 12,000 ft. altitude, also found by Henry and Wilson in Yunnan and Szechuen, China. Wilson observes that on the uplands round Tachien-lu it is a common gregarious shrub associated with Juniperus squamata and small-leaved rhododendrons, helping there to constitute the highest limit of woody vegetation. Plants originating from this region, if the species has been correctly identified, ought to be perfectly hardy. A tree now over 25 ft. high was raised from Himalayan seed by the late Mr J. S. Gamble at East Liss, Hants, which has never been injured by cold. There are two trees in the milder climate of Tregrehan, Cornwall, the larger, according to Thurston, 35 ft. high and 2½ ft. in girth of trunk in 1927.

Q. SEMISERRATA, *Roxburgh*

An evergreen tree of the middle size, the young shoots clothed at first with a soft white down, becoming almost glabrous by autumn. Leaves oblong or narrowly oval, leathery, wedge-shaped at the base, slenderly pointed, toothed (often shallowly) towards the apex, entire below; 5 to 10 ins. long, 1¼ to 3½ ins. wide; dark green and glabrous above, paler and rather glaucous beneath; midrib yellowish; chief veins parallel in fifteen to twenty pairs; stalk up to 1 in. long. Acorns solitary or in pairs (sometimes in threes) scarcely stalked, the cup up to 1¼ ins. wide, more than half enclosing the broad flattish acorn, the rim thick and woolly, subtended by several concentric downy rings.

Native of Assam, Khasya, Burma, etc. The only place where I have seen this oak growing out-of-doors is Abbotsbury, near Weymouth. It has been there many years. The size and conspicuous parallel ribbing of the leaves make it a handsome tree. I do not think it would have any chance of surviving in the average climate of England.

Q. SERRATA, *Siebold*

(Q. acutissima, *Carruthers*)

A deciduous tree up to 50 ft. high, with a slender trunk; young shoots at first downy, soon becoming glabrous. Leaves oblong or narrowly oval, rounded or broadly tapered at the base, terminated by a slender bristle-tipped point; each of the twelve to sixteen parallel veins at either side the midrib running out into a bristle-like tooth ⅙ in. long; the leaves are 3 to 7 ins. long, 1 to 2¼ ins. wide; the stalk slender, ⅝ to 1¼ ins. long; upper surface glabrous and shining, lower surface not so bright and of a paler green, with tufts of down in the vein-axils. Acorns (not seen in this country) small, and half embedded in cups which are covered with long, slender, pointed, downy scales.

Native of China, Japan, and the Himalaya; introduced from Japan to Kew by Richard Oldham about 1862. It is a neat and cheerful-looking tree suitable for a limited space. Sargent says that in Japan it springs up on waste land in great numbers, but is only valued as fuel. Silkworms feed on its leaves. Nearly allied to it is Q. variabilis, with a corky bark, the leaves grey-felted beneath, and with shorter teeth. The only other oak with which it is likely to be confused is Q. castanæfolia algeriensis, but that may be easily distinguished by its shoots being downy throughout the first season or longer, by the thicker, shorter, quite downy leaf-stalk, and by the absence of the bristly termination to its coarser teeth.

Q. SESSILIFLORA, *Salisbury*. DURMAST OAK

(Q. petræa, *Leiblin*)

A deciduous tree, 60 to 80 ft. or more high, closely allied to and resembling Q. pedunculata, but with a head of branches less rugged and open; young shoots downy. Leaves 3 to 5 ins. long, with stalks up to 1 in. long; oval or obovate, deeply lobed, usually larger than in Q. pedunculata; dark glossy green and glabrous above, greyish and more or less downy beneath. Acorns ¾ to 1¼ ins. long, solitary or clustered (two, three, or more together) close to the twig, or on a quite short stalk. The durmast oak has not been so prolific of varieties as Q. pedunculata, but the following are worth notice:—

Var. AFGHANISTANENSIS, *Booth*.—Leaves oval or obovate, with shallower lobes than the type. Acorn with a distinct stalk as much as ½ in. long.

Var. COCHLEATA, *Petzold*.—Leaves decurved at the margin so that the centre is humped or hooded.

Var. FALKENBERGENSIS.—Leaves short and broad, with large lobes; very downy beneath.

Var. GIESLERI, *Späth*.—Leaves long, deeply and unequally lobed, as in Q. pedunculata heterophylla.

Var. IBERICA.—Lobes of leaf pointed.

Var. MESPILIFOLIA, *Wallroth*.—Leaves long, narrow, 4 to 8 ins. long, ½ to 2 ins. wide; entire, or shallowly lobed, tapered at both ends. A remarkably distinct variety, often grown as "Q. Louettii."

Var. MUSCOVIENSIS, *Koehne*.—Leaves of first growth often nearly or quite entire, those of the second or July growth nearer the type, and lobed.

Var. RUBICUNDA (purpurea).—Young leaves reddish purple.

The durmast oak, a native of Europe and Asia Minor, is found wild in the British Isles, generally in elevated districts. Although it is considered by some planters to be better adapted to dry situations than Q. pedunculata, it is most abundant in some of the wettest parts of the country, as for instance on the hills between Kenmare and Killarney, where all the oaks seem to be sessiliflora. On the south-western coast of Scotland, too, it succeeds admirably. Generally it appears to be the quicker grower, and is capable of attaining to a great height. Mr Elwes mentions one in Whitefield Park, Herefordshire, 130 ft. high. But, generally, the trees with huge trunks and the famous oaks of history appear to be Q. pedunculata. There appears to be little difference in the quality of the timber of the two; if any, the consensus of opinion is in favour of Q. pedunculata. I have never seen the Durmast oak attacked by the Tortrix moth, which disfigures the foliage of Q. pedunculata so much or almost clears it off.

There are oaks intermediate in various ways between Q. sessiliflora and Q. pedunculata, sometimes uniting stalked acorns with downy leaves, or sessile acorns with auricled leaves, and so on; but generally they are easily determinable.

Q. SHUMARDII SCHNECKII, *Sargent*

(Q. Schneckii, *Britton*)

According to American writers, this deciduous oak, a native of the southern and central United States, attains a maximum height of 200 ft., with a trunk 8 ft. in diameter. It must, therefore, be about the tallest of all oaks. The leaves are of the typical "red" oak shape, up to 6 or 8 ins. long, obovate, with five to nine sharply pointed, narrowly triangular, sparsely toothed lobes; dark glossy green and glabrous above, at first covered with loose, stellate down beneath, which soon falls away, leaving the surface shining green and glabrous except for conspicuous tufts of down in the vein-axils, as seen in Q. palustris. From that species it differs chiefly in the acorns being much longer proportionately to their width, egg-shaped, and up to 1 in. long. In 1908 some small trees of this oak were introduced to Kew from the Arnold Arboretum, but what is the same tree had been obtained in 1901 from Meehan's nursery as Q. texana. These trees which succeeded very well, turn a beautiful golden brown or rich red in autumn, but they are no longer represented at Kew.

The true Q. TEXANA, *Buckley*, is a small tree or even shrub found in dry or rocky soil in S. and W. Texas, not in cultivation.

Q. STELLATA, *Wangenheim*. POST OAK

(Q. obtusiloba, *Michaux*; Q. minor, *Sargent*)

A deciduous tree 50 to 60 ft. high in a wild state; young shoots covered with short, close, brownish down which persists until the fall of the leaf. Leaves obovate or almost obversely triangular in main outline, but with usually three large lobes towards the end and often two to four smaller ones lower down; lobes rounded; base tapered; 4 to 8 ins. long, 3 to 5 ins. wide;

upper surface dark, brightish green, rough to the touch; lower surface pale, dull, and sprinkled thickly with stellate hairs; stalk $\frac{1}{3}$ to $\frac{3}{4}$ in. long. Acorn solitary or in pairs, $\frac{3}{4}$ to 1 in. long, broadly egg-shaped, downy at the top; the cup, which encloses about one-third, is covered with pointed, downy, appressed scales.

Native of the United States, where it is widely spread, extending from Massachusetts southwards to Florida and westwards to Nebraska and Texas. Although, according to Aiton, it was introduced in 1800, it has always been uncommon. Sargent remarks that its rounded head of foliage is so dark as to appear nearly black in the landscape and that it is always a beautiful tree. It is akin to Q. alba and Q. utahensis, but the rough upper surface of the leaf distinguishes it. At Kew it is healthy but grows slowly.

Q. SUBER, *Linnæus*. CORK OAK

An evergreen tree up to 60 ft. high, with a trunk 5 ft. in diameter, whose bark is remarkably thick and corky; young shoots covered with a close, grey down. Leaves oval, ovate or oblong, 1 to $2\frac{1}{2}$ ins. long, $\frac{5}{8}$ to $1\frac{1}{2}$ ins. wide; rounded or abruptly tapered at both ends, toothed except near the base; upper surface dark glossy green, glabrous except when quite young; lower surface clothed with a minute grey felt; stalk $\frac{1}{4}$ to $\frac{1}{2}$ in. long, minutely downy. Acorns ripening the first year, $\frac{3}{4}$ in. long, about half enclosed in the cup, and borne singly or in pairs on a short, downy stalk.

Var. OCCIDENTALIS, *Henry* (Q. occidentalis, *Gay*).—The French botanist Gay was the first to distinguish this from the type about 1855. Its chief distinction is in the fruits taking two seasons to mature. It has also a distinct habitat, being found on the west or Atlantic side of Europe, whilst the true Q. Suber occurs north and south of the Mediterranean. Q. occidentalis is hardier, and no doubt many of the cork oaks in Britain are of this form.

The bark of this tree (which affords the best distinction between it and other evergreen oaks) produces the common cork of everyday use. It is stripped from the trunk and chief branches every eight or ten years. Portugal is the great centre of the cork industry. As a tree for gardens, the cork oak is only adapted for the southern and milder parts of Britain. The finest trees are in the south-western counties, where there are several 50 to 60 ft. high. The largest I know of near London is in the grounds at Claremont; this has a trunk about 14 ft. in girth, but is past its best. The species is supposed to have been introduced about the end of the seventeenth century.

Q. TOZA, *De Candolle*. PYRENEAN OAK

(Q. pyrenaica, *Willdenow*; Q. Tauzin, *Persoon*)

A deciduous tree up to 70 ft. high, with slender, often pendulous branches; young shoots densely clothed with grey down. Leaves very variable in size, from 3 to 9 ins. long, $1\frac{1}{2}$ to $4\frac{1}{2}$ ins. wide, conspicuously and deeply lobed; the lobes four to seven on each side, oblong, rounded or pointed, the larger ones often coarsely round-toothed; dark glossy green, and with sparse, minute, starry down above; grey and felted beneath; stalk downy, $\frac{1}{4}$ to $\frac{3}{4}$ in. long. Acorns about $\frac{3}{4}$ in. long, produced two to four together on a downy, erect stalk $\frac{1}{2}$ to $1\frac{1}{2}$ ins. long, about half enclosed by a cup with appressed downy scales.

Native of S.W. Europe; introduced, according to Loudon, in 1822. It is a very distinct and elegant oak, well marked by the deeply and pinnately lobed leaves, and by their dense, close felt beneath. The leaves, however, show much variation in size and character of lobing. In its velvety downiness it resembles Q. macranthera, which has more but shallower lobes. Q. Toza produces long pendulous shoots under cultivation, and in a young state is extremely liable to be broken by autumnal gales. According to Elwes, there is a tree 66 ft. high at Clonmannon, Co. Wicklow, with a trunk 9 ft. in girth. The so-called var. SPLENDENS is merely a big-leaved form. There is at Tortworth an interesting hybrid between Toza and pedunculata, the leaves much more minutely felted beneath, and the fruit-stalks much longer.

Q. TURNERI, *Willdenow*. TURNER'S OAK

A supposed hybrid between Q. Ilex and Q. pedunculata, said to have been raised in the nursery of Mr Spencer Turner, Holloway Down, Essex, in the latter half of the eighteenth century. It is a tree of spreading habit, growing sometimes over 50 ft. in height, with foliage which persists through the winter until February or March, according to the mildness or otherwise of the season. But even after the mildest winters the tree, so far as I have seen, is always destitute of foliage for some weeks. The young shoots are clothed with a dense pale down. Leaves leathery, oblong-obovate, mostly rounded but unequal at the base, bluntish at the apex, and with four to six rounded lobes on each margin; 2½ to 4½ ins. long, ¾ to 1¾ ins. wide; dark green and glabrous above, paler beneath and downy at the base, also on the midrib and veins. Acorns borne usually one or two on a stalk 1 to 2 ins. long; they are each about ¾ in. long, the lower half enclosed in a cup with downy, erect, appressed scales.

The above is a description of Turner's oak as usually represented in gardens, but it does not appear to be quite the same as the tree originally raised by Turner, which has shorter, broader leaves, the teeth of which are smaller and terminate in a minute, abrupt (mucronate) tip. This hybrid produces fertile seed, and as nearly always happens with hybrids, the seedlings vary in their affinity to one or other of the parents. Several forms of Turner's oak have been named, such as "austriaca," and "austriaca splendens." The form with long narrow leaves described above has been called Q. PSEUDO-TURNERI. A seedling raised from it at Kew produces both the short broad (or typical Turneri) leaves and the longer narrower ones. It seems unnecessary therefore to multiply names.

Q. UNDULATA, *Torrey*

A small deciduous tree up to 25 or 30 ft. high, more often a shrub; young shoots slender, covered with a greyish down which persists into the second season. Leaves (on plants cultivated in this country) oblong or narrowly oval in main outline, but deeply, pinnately, seven- to eleven-lobed after the fashion of the American "red" oaks, the lobes penetrating half to three-quarters of the way to the midrib; 1½ to 3 ins. long, 1 to 1½ ins. wide; when the leaves unfold they are covered with stellate down, much of which falls away by autumn. Upper surface bright green, lower surface quite dull; stalk about ¼ in. long.

Native of Colorado, Arizona, Texas, and New Mexico. Sargent says the acorns are eaten by Indians and Mexicans and furnish pigs with excellent food. As figured by him (*Silva of N. America*, vol. viii., t. 385) the leaves vary very much in size and shape in wild plants. On the dry hills of the S.W. United States, whilst some are of the type described above, others are only 1 in. long and quite entire; and there are numerous intermediate shapes. In Central Arizona, Sargent observes that it covers low mountain ranges with vast thickets 6 to 8 ft. high. Although originally discovered in 1820, it was only brought into cultivation in 1917 at the Arnold Arboretum and thence to Kew in 1922. Small trees are now 4 or 5 ft. high. The plant has the appearance of a miniature form of "red" oak, but its affinities are with the "white" oaks of N. America.

Q. UTAHENSIS, *Rydberg*. UTAH OAK

(Q. submollis, *Rydberg*)

A deciduous tree 30 to 50 ft. high; young shoots densely covered with yellowish-grey down, which on young plants persists until the end of the season. Leaves obovate in main outline, but deeply three- to five-lobed on each side, the lobes penetrating from half-way almost up to the midrib, and the larger middle lobes again lobed; the apex of the lobes may be either rounded or pointed; 3 to 5 ins. long, 1¼ to 3 ins. wide (in young vigorous plants larger); dark shining green and almost glabrous above; dull, pale, and persistently downy beneath; stalk ¼ to ⅝ in. long. Acorns solitary or in pairs, ½ to ¾ in. long, broadly egg-shaped, the cup, which encloses the lower one-third, is covered with short, appressed, downy scales.

Native of the S.W. United States; introduced to Kew in 1912. Among other places it is wild in the Grand Canyon, Arizona. This oak is growing promisingly at Kew and the lustrous dark green of its leaves gives it a handsome appearance. The dense soft down, especially of the shoots and undersurface of the leaves, is a marked character. It is one of the "white" oaks of N. America.

Q. VARIABILIS, *Blume*

(Q. Bungeana, *Forbes*; Q. chinensis, *Bunge*)

A deciduous tree up to 80 ft. high, with a thick, corky bark; young shoots slightly hairy. Leaves oblong or narrowly oval, 3 to 7 ins. long, 1 to 2 ins. wide; broadly tapered or somewhat rounded at the base, pointed, the margins set with bristle-like teeth $\frac{1}{10}$ in. long, which terminate the nine to sixteen pairs of parallel veins; upper surface dark dullish green, glabrous; lower one pale grey and covered with a minute close felt.

Native of China, Japan, and Korea; introduced by Fortune in 1861, and in 1882 by the late Dr Bretschneider; in both instances from the neighbourhood of Pekin, where it is a common tree. Although a finer tree than its near ally, Q. serrata, its foliage is not so bright. It differs from that species most noticeably in the whitish under-surface and smaller teeth of the leaves. The acorn also is smaller and almost hidden in the cup, which has long curly scales. The bark has some economic value as a source of cork. On young trees it is blackish at first, and is not long before it shows its corky nature.

Q. VELUTINA, *Lamarck*. BLACK OAK

(Q. tinctoria, *Bartram*)

A deciduous tree, 70, 80, or more ft. high; young shoots at first covered with brownish starry down; buds very downy. Leaves oval or obovate, 5 to 12 ins. long, half to two-thirds as wide; more or less deeply five- or seven-lobed; the lobes ovate or triangular, toothed or nearly entire; upper surface dark green and shining, glabrous or becoming so, lower surface paler, covered with a thin, scattered down, and with tufts of down in the vein-axils; stalk 1 to 2½ ins. long. Acorns usually solitary, scarcely stalked, ½ to ¾ in. long, half enclosed in the cup.

Native of the eastern and central United States; introduced in 1800. The finest form of this oak in cultivation (and one of the most remarkable of all oaks) is known as "Champion's Oak" or var. RUBRIFOLIA, the leaves of which on young trees are often 12 to 15 ins. long, somewhat hooded, and hang laxly on the shoots. The bark and acorns of this species are permeated by a yellow principle, and from the former a yellow dye, "quercitron," is obtained. Among the oaks of its group (rubra, coccinea, etc.) this species is distinguished by its yellow inner bark, the large downy buds, and the stellate down on young leaf and shoot.

Q. WISLIZENI, *De Candolle*

An evergreen oak, varying in a wild state from a mere shrub to a tree 70 or more ft. high; young shoots furnished with a loose, scattered, starry down. Leaves oblong to ovate, rounded or slightly heart-shaped at the base, terminated and edged with slender, spiny teeth; 1 to 2¾ ins. long, ½ to 1¾ ins. wide; often entire on adult native trees; both sides shining green and quite glabrous; stalk ⅛ to ¼ in. long, downy, the stellate down often continued down the midrib. Acorn ¾ to over 1 in. long, about ⅓ in. wide; two-thirds enclosed in a cup with thin, downy, flattened scales.

Native of California; introduced to Kew in 1874, where it has proved hardy but slow-growing. It has also borne acorns there. In its glossy green leaves, glabrous on both surfaces, it resembles only Q. coccifera, but the tree is of much more open habit, and the leaves are larger. Henry has also pointed out differences in the shape of the buds; in Wislizeni they are conical, pointed, and longer than the rounded blunt ones of coccifera.

METASEQUOIA GLYPTOSTROBOIDES, *Hu and Cheng*. METASEQUOIACEÆ

In 1945 a Chinese botanist, Mr T. Wang, discovered growing in China living representatives of the genus Metasequoia, previously known only from fossil specimens. The following year additional material was collected from Szechuan, China, and named by Drs Hsen-Hsu Hu and Wan-Chun Cheng *Metasequoia glyptostroboides*.

A tree up to 115 ft. in height in the wild state with a trunk about 6½-9½ ft. in diameter at the base. Bark fissured, dark grey in colour, peeling off in old trees. Branches opposite, glabrous, green in the young state, turning brown later and becoming brownish-grey in the second or third year. Lateral shoots deciduous in winter, glabrous, opposite, up to 2¼ ins. long, arranged distichously, persistent buds at the base. Winter buds ovoid or obtuse, ⅙ in. long, ⅛ in. wide, glabrous. Bracts decussate, broadly ovate, yellowish-brown, paler and thinner on the margins. Leaves deciduous, opposite, arranged in two ranks, linear, ⅓ to ½ in. long, $\frac{1}{24}$ to $\frac{1}{12}$ in. wide, sessile or nearly sessile, blue-green above, light green below. Flowers monoecious, solitary; staminate flowers axillary and terminal about ⅕ in. long, in a raceme or panicle; bracts decussate, triangular-ovate or obovate. Pedicels about ⅛ in. long, Stamens 20, filaments short. Pistillate flowers solitary, about ⅓ in. long; bracts decussate, both sides glabrous, the lower ones triangular-ovate. Peduncles $\frac{1}{8}$ in. long, leafy. Cones ripening in the first year, pendulous, subquadrangular-globose or shortly cylindric, $\frac{3}{4}$ to 1 in. long, $\frac{2}{3}$ to $\frac{9}{10}$ in. wide, dark brown in colour. Seeds 5 to 9 under each scale, winged, compressed, obovate, the apex notched, $\frac{1}{5}$ in. long, $\frac{1}{6}$ in. wide.

There are a number of young plants of this species now growing in this country. Specimens at Kew, Wisley znd Bedgebury grown from seed distributed by the Arnold Arboretum in 1948 had reached a height of 3 to 4 ft. in their second season. The plants show promise of being hardy.

The above description is based on that published in the *Bulletin of the Fan Memorial Institute of Biology*, New Series, vol. i, No. 2, p. 153, 1948.

PHILADELPHUS LEWISII, *Pursh*

A shrub up to 12 ft. high, of graceful, pendulous habit; year-old branches with greyish-brown, non-peeling bark. Leaves broadly ovate to ovate-lanceolate; $1\frac{1}{2}$ to 4 ins. long, 1 to $2\frac{1}{2}$ ins. wide; coarsely and distinctly toothed or, especially on the flowering twigs, entire; with scattered hairs beneath, still fewer above. Flowers five to nine, in racemes, scentless, white, $1\frac{1}{3}$ in. across; petals oval; calyx smooth outside like the flower-stalk, downy at the margins, and near the apex of the lobes inside; styles divided half-way down.

Native of western N. America from British Columbia to California; introduced about 1823. It is one of the most elegant and floriferous of all the taller species.

END OF VOL II.

PRINTED IN GREAT BRITAIN BY OLIVER AND BOYD LTD., EDINBURGH

PLATE 3.—FORSYTHIA INTERMEDIA var. SPECTABILIS (Flowers rich yellow)

PLATE 4.—FRAXINUS ORNUS, Manna Ash, at Kew

PLATE 7.—GORDONIA AXILLARIS (Flowers creamy-white)

PLATE 8.—HALESIA CAROLINA, Snowdrop Tree, at Kew

PLATE 9.—HALESIA MONTICOLA (Flowers pure white)

PLATE 10.—HYDRANGEA BRETSCHNEIDERI

PLATE 11.—HYDRANGEA PETIOLARIS at Kew

PLATE 12.—ILEX CRENATA

Plate 13.—Itea virginica

PLATE 14.—JASMINUM PRIMULINUM

PLATE 15.—JUNIPERUS RECURVA at Claremont

PLATE 16.—LABURNUM ALPINUM, Scotch Laburnum, at Kew

Plate 17.—Lagerstrœmia indica

PLATE 18.—LIBOCEDRUS DECURRENS at Orton Longueville

PLATE 19.—LIGUSTRUM SINENSE, Chinese Privet, at Kew

PLATE 20.—LONICERA TELLMANNIANA (Flowers yellow, flushed with red)

PLATE 21.—MAGNOLIA SINENSIS (Flowers white with crimson stamens)

PLATE 22.—MAGNOLIA SOULANGEANA at Kew

PLATE 23.—MAGNOLIA STELLATA

PLATE 24.—MALUS BACCATA, Siberian Crab

PLATE 25.—MALUS ELEYI (Fruits purplish-red)

PLATE 26.—MALUS FLORIBUNDA, Japanese Crab, at Kew

PLATE 27.—MALUS PURPUREA (Flowers ruby red)

PLATE 28.—MELIOSMA OLDHAMII at Kew

PLATE 29.—MELIOSMA VEITCHIORUM at Kew

PLATE 30.—MORUS NIGRA, Mulberry, in Syon Park

PLATE 31.—NEILLIA BRACTEATA (Flowers white)

PLATE 32.—NOTHOFAGUS OBLIQUA at Kew

PLATE 33.—PERNETTYA MUCRONATA

PLATE 34.—PHILADELPHUS CORONARIUS, Mock Orange

PLATE 35.—PICEA ENGELMANNI, in the Arnold Arboretum, U.S.A.

PLATE 36.—PIERIS TAIWANENSIS (Flowers pure white)

PLATE 37.—PINUS CEMBRA, Arollar Pine, at Claremont, Esher

PLATE 38.—PINUS MURICATA, Bishop's Pine, at Claremont

PLATE 39.—PLAGIANTHUS LYALLII

PLATE 40.—POPULUS CANESCENS, Grey Poplar

PLATE 41.—POPULUS MAXIMOWICZII, in Japan

PLATE 42.—PRUNUS INCISA SERRATA (Flowers white or tinged with pink)

PLATE 43.—PRUNUS MAHALEB, St Lucie Cherry, at Kew

PLATE 44.—PRUNUS SERRULATA, Japanese Cherry

PLATE 45.—PRUNUS SERRULATA var., Japanese Cherry, "Fugenzo"

PLATE 46.—PRUNUS LANNESIANA, " Hokusai "   *Photo by Country Lif*

Plate 47.—Prunus triloba (Double-flowered), at Kew

PLATE 48.—PSEUDOTSUGA DOUGLASII, Douglas Fir, at Murthly Castle, Perth

PLATE 49.—PTEROCARYA FRAXINIFOLIA at Claremont

PLATE 50.—PYRACANTHA ROGERSIANA (Fruits orange-red)

PLATE 51.—QUERCUS CASTANEÆFOLIA at Kew

Plate 52.—Quercus Lucombeana, Lucombe Oak, at Kew